Citizenship
PASSING THE TEST

CIVICS & LITERACY

THIRD EDITION

Lynne Weintraub

New Readers Press

Citizenship: Passing the Test 3rd Edition
Civics & Literacy
ISBN 978-1-56420-888-0

Copyright © 2009 New Readers Press
Photos updated January 2022
New Readers Press
ProLiteracy's Publishing Division
101 Wyoming Street, Syracuse, New York 13204
www.newreaderspress.com

Printed in the United States of America
24

Proceeds from the sale of New Readers Press materials support professional development, training, and technical assistance programs of ProLiteracy that benefit local literacy programs in the U.S. and around the globe.

Developmental Editor: Paula L. Schlusberg, Mesa Crest Consulting
Creative Director: Andrea Woodbury
Art and Design Supervisor: James P. Wallace
Production Specialist: Maryellen Casey
Cover Design: Carolyn Wallace

Contents

How to Use This Book 4

1. **Welcome to America** 5

2. **American Places** 23

3. **13 Colonies** 36

4. **The New United States** 50

5. **The Civil War** 71

6. **Later History** 85

   U.S. History: Putting It All Together.........................99

7. **The Constitution** 106

8. **Congress** 124

9. **The President** 138

10. **A Country of Laws** 153

   U.S. Government: Putting It All Together 171

   More Practice...176

   Answer Key 179

How to Use This Book

The citizenship test has 4 parts:
1. speaking
2. history and government
3. reading
4. writing

When you answer questions about your citizenship application, the examiner will hear you speak English. That will be your speaking test.

This book helps you study for the history and government test by showing you all of the questions on the USCIS 100 questions list. Look for the Test Question boxes in each chapter:

• Why does the flag have 50 stars? **because there are 50 states**

If you know the answers to these questions, you can pass the history and government test.

You will see some words in dark letters like this: **government.** These words are important to understand and remember. You will hear or say these words on the test.

On many pages you will also see spelling words like this:

 SPELLING: capital _____

These words are on the writing test. Practice writing these words. Try to remember the letters to spell them all.

Say it words look like this:

 SAY IT: country
                     kun tree

These are words you will say in your answers. You will have to say them to answer the history and government questions. You will also read them aloud for your reading test. Practice saying these words clearly.

1. Welcome to America

There are many countries in the world.

Which **country** are you from? _____

 SAY IT: country
                    kun tree

Every country has a **flag.**
Can you find your home country's flag?

 SPELLING: flag   _flag_

 SAY IT: flag

There are 50 **stars** on the U.S. flag. Why?
Because the U.S. has 50 **states.**

Which is your state? _____

 WHAT DOES IT MEAN: U.S. = United States

stars =

SAY IT: stars   why
         starz   wiy

• Why does the flag have 50 stars? **because there are 50 states**

U.S. Holiday

JUNE						
S	M	T	W	T	F	S
1	2	3	4	5	6	7
8	9	10	11	12	13	14
15	16	17	18	19	20	21
22	23	24	25	26	27	28
29	30					

Flag Day is in June.

The **colors** of the flag are red, white, and blue.
The flag has red and white **stripes.**

 WHAT DOES IT MEAN: stripes=

 SPELLING: colors _____

blue   _____

June   _____

SAY IT: stripes   colors
striypz   **cuh** lerz

"Oh, say can you see..."

Every country has a song.
That song is the country's **national anthem.**
The name of our national anthem is "**The Star-Spangled Banner.**"

 WHAT DOES IT MEAN: national = of our country
anthem = song
banner = flag

SAY IT: Star-Spangled Banner
star **span** gild **ban** ner

• What is the name of the national anthem? **The Star-Spangled Banner**

"I pledge allegiance to the flag..."

Sometimes we say the **Pledge of Allegiance** together.
This is a way to say: I love America.
We show **loyalty** to the United States when we say the Pledge of Allegiance.

? **WHAT DOES IT MEAN:** pledge=promise
allegiance = loyalty = love

- What do we show loyalty to when we say the Pledge of Allegiance?
the United States

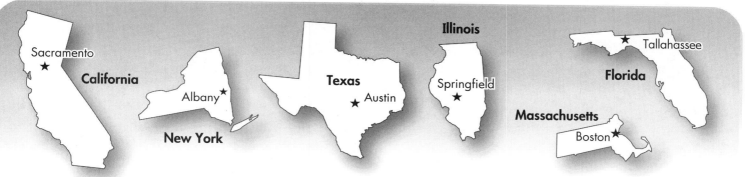

United States
Washington D.C. ★
France ★ Paris
Taipei ★ Taiwan
New Delhi ★
India
Beijing ★
China
Japan
Rabat ━★
Morocco
England
Mexico ★
London ━★
Mexico City ★
Tokyo ★

Every country has a **government.**
A country's government is in its **capital.**
The capital of the U.S. is **Washington, D.C.**

California
Sacramento ★
New York
Albany ★
Texas
Austin ★
Illinois
Springfield ★
Massachusetts
Boston ★
Florida
Tallahassee ★

Every state in the U.S. has a capital too.

What is the capital of your state? _____

? **WHAT DOES IT MEAN:** government = people who are in charge
capital = city where the government is

abc **SPELLING:** capital _____

SAY IT: capital   what
cap ih tul   wuht

- What is the capital of the United States? **Washington, D.C.**
- What is the capital of your state? _____

South Africa

United States

Saudi Arabia

United Kingdom

China

Japan

New Zealand

Bangladesh

Every country has a **leader.**
The leader of the United States is the **president.**

What is the name of the president of the U.S. now? _____

? **WHAT DOES IT MEAN:** leader = number 1 man or woman in the government

• What is the name of the president of the U.S. now? _____

Michigan

Hawaii

Oklahoma

California

The leader of a U.S. state is a **governor.**

Who is the governor of your state? _____

• Who is the governor of your state? _____

The United States is a **democracy.**
In a democracy, we pick our own leaders.
We choose our leaders by **voting** in **elections.**

 SAY IT: choose   United States
                 chewz   u **niyh** tid staytz

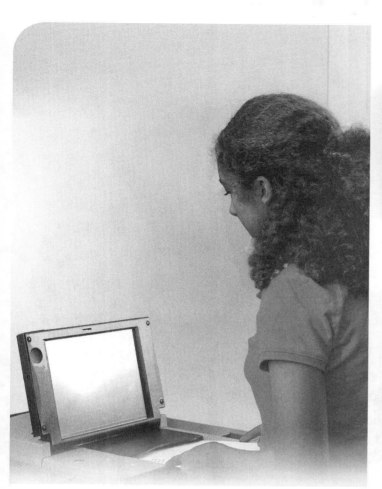

Americans can **participate** in their democracy.
For example, we participate by voting in elections.
Writing to a **newspaper** is another way to participate.

?   **WHAT DOES IT MEAN:**   participate = join in

SAY IT: newspaper
         nooz pay pir

• What are 2 ways that Americans can participate in their democracy?
voting and writing to a newspaper*

U.S. leaders belong to groups.
These groups are called **political parties.**
There are 2 major political parties in the U.S.: the **Democratic** Party and the **Republican** Party.

What is the political party of the President now? _____

? **WHAT DOES IT MEAN:**   major = big

SAY IT: Democratic   Republican
              dem uh **krah** dik   ree **pub** lik in

- What are the 2 major political parties in the United States? **Democratic and Republican**
- What is the political party of the President now? _____

In every country, people buy things and sell things.
The government makes rules about money.
Our country's rules are our **economic system.**
The U.S. economic system is called a **market economy.**

 WHAT DOES IT MEAN: money =

 SAY IT: market   economy
             mar kit   ee **kah** nuh mee

• What is the economic system in the United States? **market economy**

Match

Find the words that go with the pictures.
Copy the words on the lines.

flag

United States

1. _____

4. _____ stars _____

states

2. _____ newspaper _____

stars

5. _____ flag _____

voting

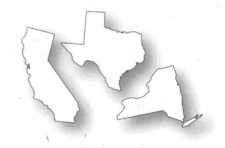

3. _____ United States _____

newspaper

6. _____ states _____

What does it mean?

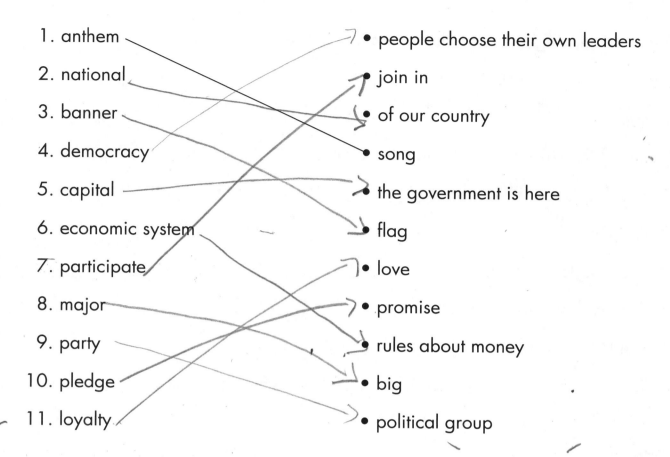

1. anthem
2. national
3. banner
4. democracy
5. capital
6. economic system
7. participate
8. major
9. party
10. pledge
11. loyalty

- people choose their own leaders
- join in
- of our country
- song
- the government is here
- flag
- love
- promise
- rules about money
- big
- political group

Yes or No?

1. There are 50 states.   Yes   No
2. The flag has 52 stars.   Yes   (No)
3. Every state has a capital.   (Yes)   No
4. The capital of the United States is Washington, D.C.   (Yes)   No
5. The colors of the flag are red, white, and blue.   (Yes)   No
6. Flag Day is in May.   Yes   (No)
7. The flag has blue and white stripes.   Yes   (No)
8. The United State is a democracy.   (Yes)   No
9. The U.S. has a market economy.   (Yes)   No

Spelling

A. Fill in the missing letters for the words in this lesson.

1. Wash_i_ngton, D.C.

2. capi__tal

3. blu_e_

4. _J_une

5. strip_e_s

6. colo_r_s

B. Now use the same words to fill in the blanks.

1. The flag is red, white, and ___blue___.

2. Flag Day is in ___June___.

3. Washington, D.C. is the ___capital___.

4. The flag has red and white ___stripes___.

5. The U.S. government is in ___washington D.C___.

6. The ___colors___ of the flag are red, white, and blue.

Say the answer.

Remember: This is a <u>listening</u> and <u>speaking</u> test. The best way to practice the questions is to listen to the CD or ask someone to read the questions to you.

1. Why does the flag have 50 stars? → one for each state.

2. What is the name of the national anthem? The start.Spangled Banner

3. What do we show loyalty to when we say the Pledge of Allegiance? flag united

4. What is the capital of the United States? whashington D.C.

5. Who is the governor of your state? Bell.Lee.

6. What is the capital of your state? Nashville

7. What are the 2 major political parties in the United States? Democratic/Rep.

8. What are 2 ways that Americans can participate in their democracy? voting, wv

9. What is the economic system in the United States? market economyor

10. What is the name of the president of the U.S. now? Joe Biden.

11. What is the political party of the president now? Democratic

Read and Write

Read each question aloud. Copy the answer on the line.
Then write the answer five times in your notebook.

1. How many states are in the United States? _The United States has 50 states._

The United States has 50 states.

2. What is the capital of the United States? _Washington, D.C. is the capital._

3. What are the colors of the flag? _The flag is red, white, and blue._

4. What is on the American flag? _The flag has red and white stripes._

5. When is Flag Day? _Flag Day is in June._

Test Hint #1

Key Words

Sometimes people feel nervous about taking a test.
It's hard to remember things when you are nervous.
Here is a trick to make it easier:

Listen for key words in the questions.

Even if you do not understand every word in the question, you can answer it!
If you hear a key word in the question, there is only one possible answer.

For example, *national anthem* is a key .
There is only one question about the *national anthem*.
If you hear *national anthem* in a question, there is only one answer.
The answer is *Star Spangled Banner*.

If you hear:	say:
national anthem	Star-Spangled Banner
50 stars	because there are 50 states
governor	(name of your state's governor)
democracy	vote and write to a newspaper
economic system	market economy

Look for the key words in each chapter of this book.

2. American Places

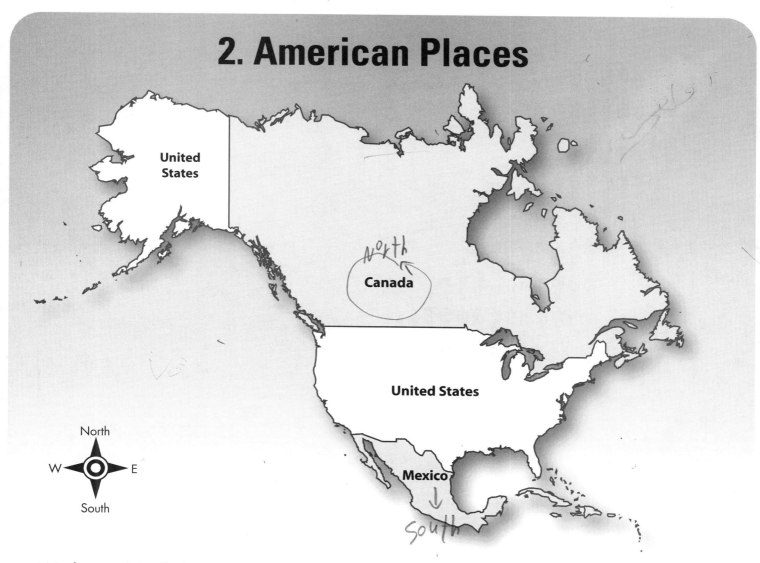

We live in North America.
The U.S. is in the middle of North America.
Canada is **north** of the U.S.
Mexico is **south** of the U.S.

 SPELLING: Canada _____

Mexico _____

SAY IT: north   south
              north   sowth

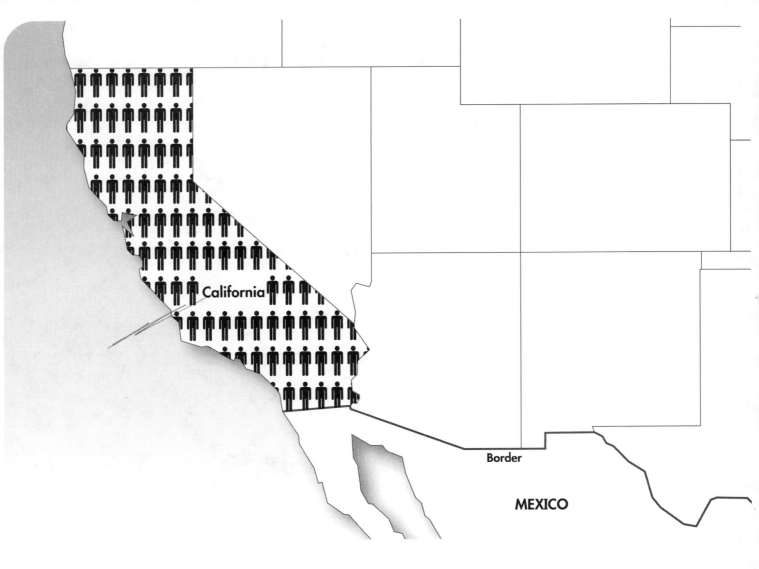

The state of **California** is near Mexico.
California **borders** Mexico.
California is the state with the most people.

SPELLING: California _____

most _____

SAY IT: California people
Cal ih **forn** yuh **pee** pul

• Name one state that borders Mexico. **California***

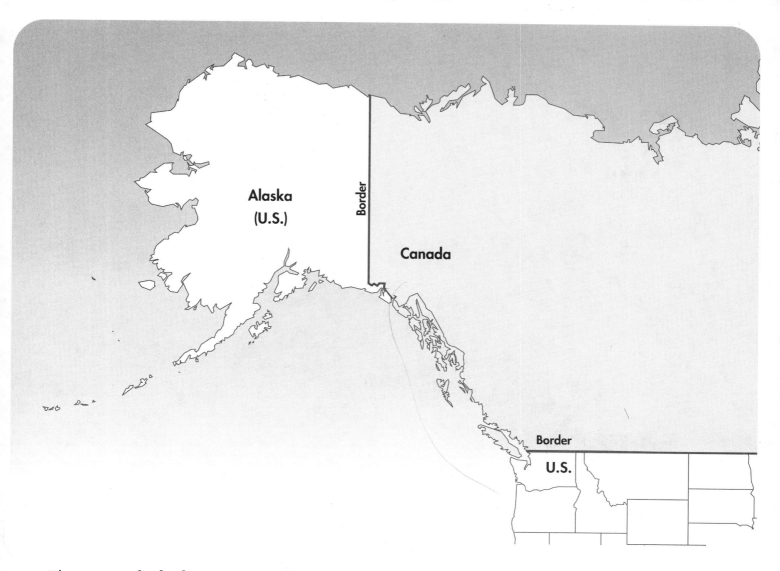

The state of **Alaska** is near Canada.
Alaska borders Canada.
Alaska is the **largest** state.

? **WHAT DOES IT MEAN:** largest = biggest

abc **SPELLING:** Alaska _____

largest _____

SAY IT: largest
lahr jist

• Name one state that borders Canada. **Alaska***

The **Statue of Liberty** is in New York City.
New York City was the **first** U.S. capital.
Later on, the capital moved to Washington, D.C.

SPELLING: New York City _____

first _____

SAY IT: New York
noo **york**

• Where is the Statue of Liberty? **New York City**

Mississippi
River →

The U.S. has many **rivers.**
One of the **longest** rivers is the **Mississippi.**

? **WHAT DOES IT MEAN:** river =

SAY IT: Mississippi
Mis sis **sip** pee

• Name 1 of the 2 longest rivers in the United States. **the Mississippi***

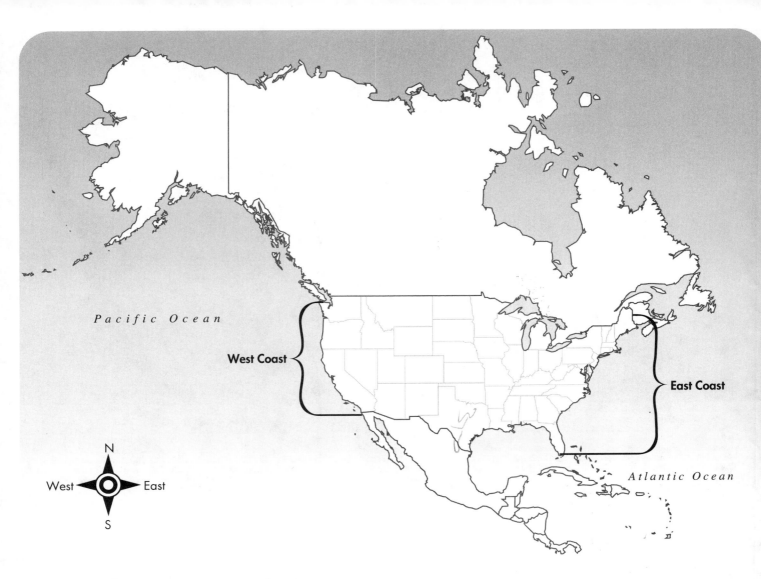

The **Atlantic Ocean** is on the **East Coast**.
The **Pacific Ocean** is on the **West Coast**.

? **WHAT DOES IT MEAN:** ocean =

coast = where the land meets the ocean

SAY IT: Atlantic   Pacific
             at **lan** tik   puh **sif** ik

• What ocean is on the East Coast of the United States? **the Atlantic**
• What ocean is on the West Coast of the United States? **the Pacific**

U.S. Territories

Mariana Islands

Guam

Samoa

Puerto Rico

U.S. Virgin Islands

The island of **Guam** is in the Pacific Ocean.
Guam belongs to the United States, but it is not one of the 50 states.
It is a U.S. **territory.**

? **WHAT DOES IT MEAN:** island =

🫦 **SAY IT:** Guam
gwahm

• Name one U.S. territory. **Guam***

There are many **American Indian** tribes in the U.S.
For example, the name of one Indian **tribe** is "Hopi."

SPELLING: American _____

Indians _____

SAY IT: Hopi
ho pee

• Name one American Indian tribe in the United States. **Hopi***

Where is it?

Write the place names on the map.

2. Alaska
3. Canada
4. California
7. Mississippi River
1. Guam
6. Mexico
5. Pacific ocean
8. New York
9. Atlantic ocean

Canada	Mexico	California
New York	Alaska	Atlantic Ocean
Pacific Ocean	Mississippi River	Guam

Which way?

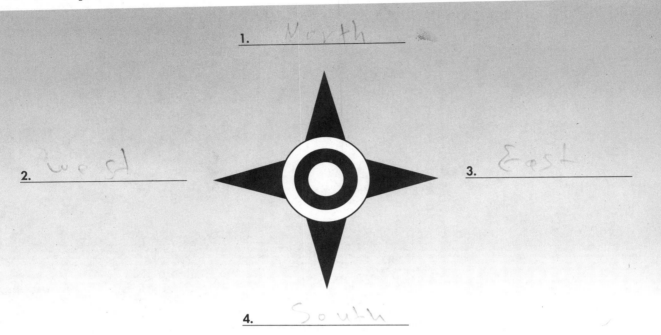

1. _North_
2. _West_
3. _East_
4. _South_

North	East	South	West

Yes or No?

1. California has the most people.   Yes   No
2. Guam is a U.S. state.   Yes   No
3. The Statue of Liberty is in New York City.   Yes   No
4. Canada is south of the United States.   Yes   No
5. Mexico is south of the United States.   Yes   No
6. California is the largest state.   Yes   No
7. The Pacific Ocean is on the West Coast.   Yes   No
8. Mississippi is the name of a long river.   Yes   No
9. The Atlantic Ocean is on the East Coast.   Yes   No
10. California borders Canada.   Yes   No
11. Alaska borders Canada.   Yes   No

Spelling

A. Fill in the missing letters for the words in this lesson.

1. N_e_w York Cit_y_   4. Canad_a_   6. larg_e_st

2. firs_t_   5. Me_x_ico   7. Ind_i_an

3. C_a_lifor_n_ia

B. Now use the same words to fill in the blanks.

1. New York City was the _____first_____ capital.

2. The Statue of Liberty is in __new york city__

3. Alaska borders on __Canada__ .

4. California borders on __mex___ .

5. Alaska is the _____largest_____ state.

6. _____ has the most people.

7. "Hopi" is the name of an American ____Indians____ tribe.

Say the answer.

1. Name one of the 2 largest rivers in the United States.

2. What ocean is on the West Coast of the United States?

3. What ocean is on the East Coast of the United States?

4. Name one U.S. territory.

5. Name one state that borders Canada. Alaska

6. Name one state that borders Mexico. California

7. Where is the Statue of Liberty? N

8. Name one American Indian tribe. Hopi

Read and Write

Read each question aloud. Copy the answer on the line.
Then write the answer five times in your notebook.

1. What was the first U.S. capital? _New York City was the first capital._

_____

2. What state has the most people? _California has the most people._

_____

3. What country is north of the United States? _Canada is north of the United States._

_____

4. What is the largest state? _Alaska is the largest state._

_____

5. What country is south of the United States? _Mexico is south of the United States._

_____

Key Words

If you hear:	say:
rivers	Mississippi
Canada	Alaska
Mexico	California
Statue of Liberty	New York
Indian	Hopi

Test Hint #2

Taking the Test

Nobody is perfect.
You may forget a few answers.
But you can still pass the test.

What will you do if you can't remember an answer?
Don't get upset.
It's OK to say, "I don't remember."
The examiner will ask you another question.

The examiner will ask 10 questions.
You only need 6 answers to pass the test.

If you remember one part of the answer, tell the examiner the part you remember.

For example:

Examiner

What are the two major political parties in the United States?

Applicant

Democratic and . . .
I can't remember the other one.

The examiner will know that you tried hard to study for the test.

3. 13 Colonies

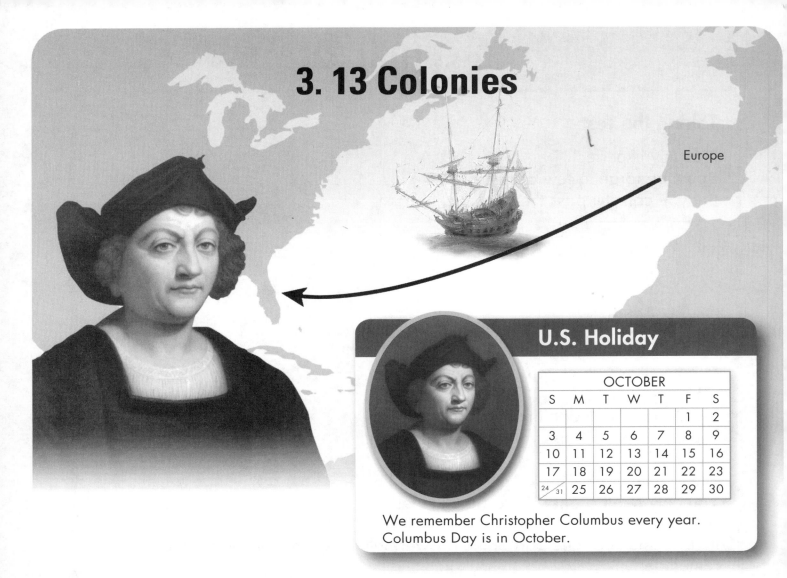

Europe

U.S. Holiday

OCTOBER

S	M	T	W	T	F	S
					1	2
3	4	5	6	7	8	9
10	11	12	13	14	15	16
17	18	19	20	21	22	23
24/31	25	26	27	28	29	30

We remember Christopher Columbus every year. Columbus Day is in October.

Christopher **Columbus** came to America in 1492.
He came here from **Europe.**

? **WHAT DOES IT MEAN:** Europe = countries on the other side of the Atlantic Ocean

abc **SPELLING:** Columbus _____

October _____

SAY IT: Columbus
kuh **lum** bus

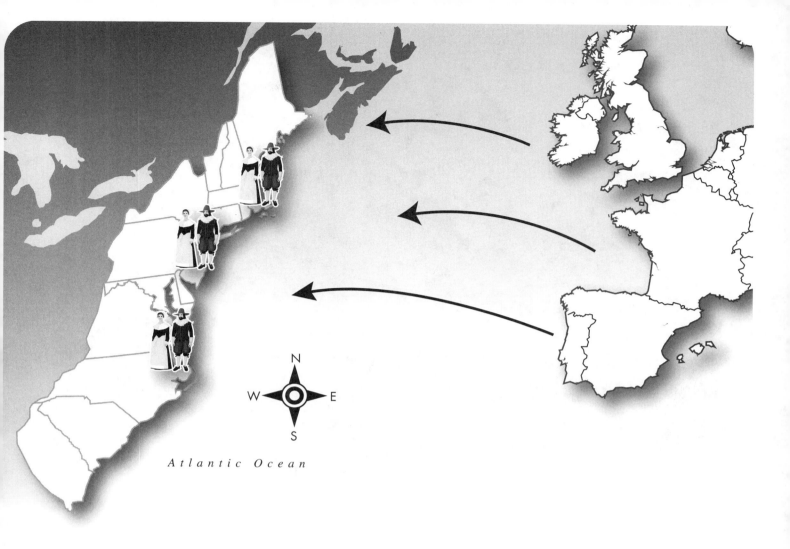

Atlantic Ocean

Later, more people from Europe came to America.
Many **Europeans** arrived in America in the 1600s.

? **WHAT DOES IT MEAN:**   Europeans = people from Europe

Who lived in America before the Europeans arrived?
American Indians lived here first.

SPELLING: here _____

SAY IT: who   American   Indians
         hoo   uh **mer** i kin   **in** dee inz

- Who lived in America before the Europeans arrived? **American Indians**

Sometimes the Indians and Europeans lived in peace.
At other times, there were problems.

SPELLING: live _____

lived _____

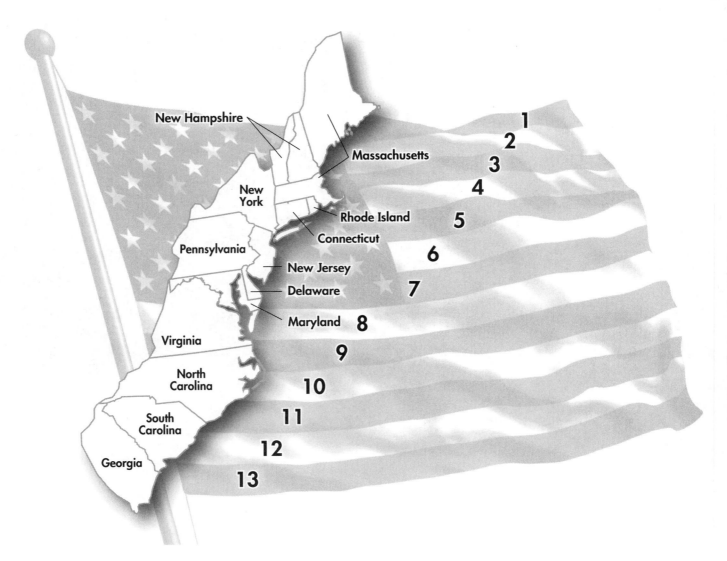

The Europeans lived in places called **colonies.**
Before there were 50 states, there were 13 colonies.
Why does the flag have 13 **stripes?**
Because there were 13 **original** colonies.

? **WHAT DOES IT MEAN:** original = from the beginning

SAY IT:

colonies	because	original	13
kah luh neez	bee **cawz**	uh **rid** jin uhl	thir **teen**

• Why does the flag have 13 stripes? **because there were 13 original colonies**

Europe

Why did the colonists leave their homes in Europe?
Why did people come to America?
Here is one reason: For freedom. They came here to be free.
They wanted to live in a free country.

? **WHAT DOES IT MEAN:**   reason = answer why
colonists = people who lived in the 13 colonies

abc **SPELLING:**   come _____

live _____

SAY IT: freedom
free dum

• What is one reason colonists came to America? **for freedom***

U.S. Holiday

		NOVEMBER				
S	M	T	W	T	F	S
	1	2	3	4	5	6
7	8	9	10	11	12	13
14	15	16	17	18	19	20
21	22	23	24	25	26	27
28	29	30				

We celebrate Thanksgiving every year in November.

The American colonists **celebrated** the first **Thanksgiving.**
We celebrate Thanksgiving every year in **November.**

?   **WHAT DOES IT MEAN:**   celebrate = get together on a special day

abc   **SPELLING:**   Thanksgiving _____

🗣   **SAY IT:**   Thanksgiving   November
               thanks **giv** ing   no **vem** ber

Some of the people in the colonies were not free.
Slave traders took people from their homes in **Africa.**
Men and women were taken to America.
They were sold as slaves.

? **WHAT DOES IT MEAN:**   slaves = people who are not free
traders = people who buy and sell

SAY IT: Africa
af rih kah

• What group of people was taken to America and sold as slaves?
people from Africa

Who was the leader of the 13 colonies?
The King of England.
The **British** king made the rules for the 13 colonies.

? **WHAT DOES IT MEAN:** British = from England

Match

Find the words that go with the pictures.
Copy the words on the lines.

American Indians

colonists

1. _____

4. _____

slaves

2. _____

Africa

5. _____

Columbus

3. _____

6. _____

Thanksgiving

Spelling

A. Fill in the missing letters for the words in this lesson.

1. liv__

2. __ere

3. Colum__us

4. Oct__ber

5. c__me

6. fre__

7. l__ved

8. Thank__giving

B. Now use the same words to fill in the blanks.

1. Europeans _____ to America for freedom.

2. People wanted to _____ in a free country.

3. Slaves are people who are not _____.

4. Columbus Day is in _____.

5. Indians _____ here before the Europeans arrived.

6. _____ came to America in 1492.

7. People came _____ to be free.

8. American colonists celebrated the first _____.

Yes or No?

1. The Indians were the first people to live in America.   Yes   No
2. There are 15 stripes on the U.S. flag.   Yes   No
3. The British king was the leader of the 13 colonies.   Yes   No
4. There were slaves in the 13 colonies.   Yes   No
5. The slaves came from Europe.   Yes   No
6. Many Europeans came to America for freedom.   Yes   No
7. Columbus Day is in September.   Yes   No
8. Thanksgiving is in November.   Yes   No

Say the answer.

1. Why does the flag have 13 stripes?
2. What is one reason colonists came to America?
3. Who lived in America before the Europeans arrived?
4. What group of people was taken to America and sold as slaves?

Read and Write

Read each question aloud. Copy the answer on the line.
Then write the answer five times in your notebook.

1. Who lived here first? _American Indians lived here first._

2. Why do people want to be citizens? _They want to live in a free country._

3. Why do people come to America? _People come here to be free._

4. When is Columbus Day? _Columbus Day is in October._

5. When is Thanksgiving? _Thanksgiving is in November._

Key Words

If you hear:	say:
stripes	because there were 13 original colonies
slaves	people from Africa
reason	freedom

Test Hint #3

Asking for Help

It's OK to ask the examiner to repeat a question.

If you don't understand a question, you can ask the examiner to say it again.

Say:
Excuse me, could you repeat the question?

Fill in the missing words:

Excuse me, _____ you repeat the _____?

Excuse ____, could you _____ the question?

_____ ____, could you _____ _____ _____?

Now, practice asking the question.

If you can't hear the questions, it's OK to ask the examiner to speak louder.

Say:
Excuse me, what did you say?

Fill in the missing words:

Excuse ____, what did you _____?

_____ me, _____ did you say?

Excuse me, what _____ _____ _____?

Now, practice asking the question.

4. The New United States

In the 1770s, the colonists were angry at the British king.
They said, "The British laws are not fair."
The colonists fought a war against the British army.

? **WHAT DOES IT MEAN:** war = fight between 2 countries

army =

Why did the colonists fight the British?
They did not want the king to choose their leaders anymore.
The colonists wanted to choose their own leaders.

 SAY IT: choose   wanted
                  chooz   **wun** tid

• Why did the colonists fight the British? **They wanted to choose their own leaders.***

During the war, the colonists put their ideas on paper.
The paper was called **The Declaration of Independence.**
The Declaration told everyone, "Now the United States is free."

? **WHAT DOES IT MEAN:**   independence = freedom
declaration = a letter for everyone to read

SAY IT: Independence
in dee **pen** dints

• What did the Declaration of Independence do? **It said the United States is free.**

The Declaration of Independence said: All people have **rights.**
We have the right to live our lives in freedom.
We have the right to **life** and **liberty.**

? **WHAT DOES IT MEAN:** liberty = freedom
rights = things the government lets you do

abc **SPELLING:** Independence _____

👄 **SAY IT:** life liberty
liyf **lib**-er-tee

• What are 2 rights in the Declaration of Independence? **life and liberty***

YES!

U.S. Holiday

			JULY			
S	M	T	W	T	F	S
				1	2	3
4	5	6	7	8	9	10
11	12	13	14	15	16	17
18	19	20	21	22	23	24
25	26	27	28	29	30	31

We celebrate Independence Day on July 4th every year.

The leaders of the 13 colonies agreed with the ideas in the Declaration.
They voted "yes" on the Declaration.
The Declaration of Independence was **adopted** on **July 4th, 1776.**

? **WHAT DOES IT MEAN:**   agree = said "yes"
adopted = leaders voted "yes"

abc **SPELLING:** July _____

SAY IT: July   4th,   1776
          ju **lahy**   forth   **sev** en teen sev en **tee** six

- When was the Declaration of Independence adopted? **July 4th, 1776**
- When do we celebrate Independence Day? **July 4th**

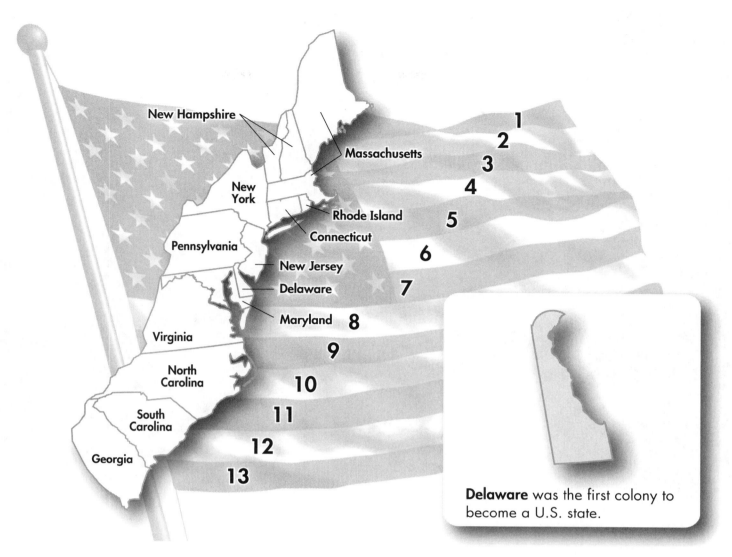

New Hampshire
Massachusetts
New York
Rhode Island
Connecticut
Pennsylvania
New Jersey
Delaware
Maryland
Virginia
North Carolina
South Carolina
Georgia

1
2
3
4
5
6
7
8
9
10
11
12
13

Delaware was the first colony to become a U.S. state.

The Americans won the war.
The 13 colonies became the United States of America.
The 13 colonies became the 13 original states.
New York, New Jersey, and **New Hampshire** were 3 of the new states.

 SPELLING: Delaware _____

 SAY IT: New York   New Jersey   New Hampshire
                 noo **york**   noo **jer** see   noo **hamp** shir

- There were 13 original states. Name 3. **New York, New Jersey, New Hampshire***

The U.S. leaders needed to make the rules for the country.
They needed to **set up** a government.
In **1787,** the leaders met together to write the U.S. **Constitution.**

? **WHAT DOES IT MEAN:**   Constitution = rules about the country's government

SAY IT: government   1787
                gov er mint   **sev** en teen **ay** tee **sev**in

---

- What does the Constitution do? **It sets up the government.**
- When was the Constitution written? **1787**

The meeting in 1787 was called the **Constitutional Convention.**
What happened at the Constitutional Convention?
The Constitution was written.

? **WHAT DOES IT MEAN:** convention = meeting

SAY IT: Constitution written
con stih **too** shun **rit** in

• What happened at the Constitutional Convention? **The Constitution was written.**

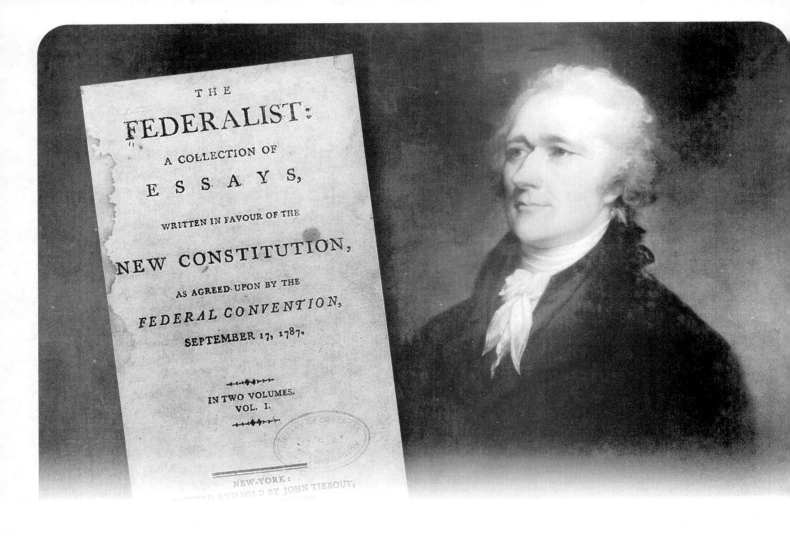

Some of the leaders wanted everyone to understand the new Constitution.
They wanted everyone to say "yes" to the Constitution.
They wrote their ideas in **The Federalist Papers.**

? **WHAT DOES IT MEAN:** wrote =

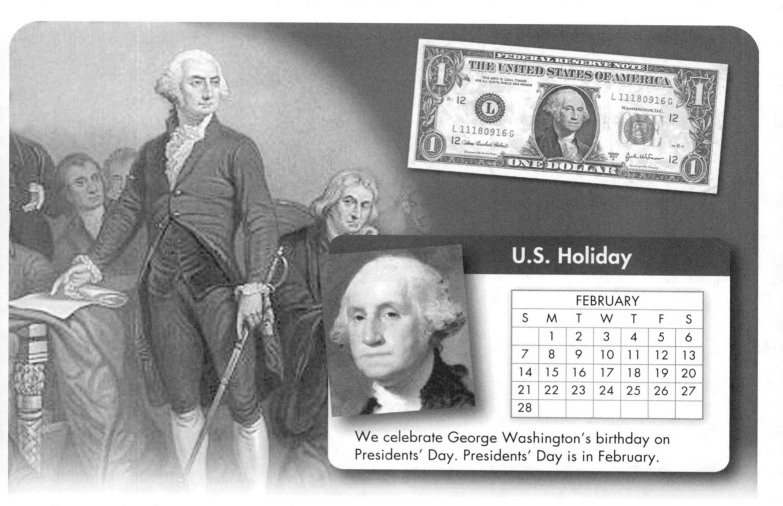

U.S. Holiday

FEBRUARY						
S	M	T	W	T	F	S
	1	2	3	4	5	6
7	8	9	10	11	12	13
14	15	16	17	18	19	20
21	22	23	24	25	26	27
28						

We celebrate George Washington's birthday on Presidents' Day. Presidents' Day is in February.

George Washington was the first U.S. president.
We call him "the father of our country."
Today, you can see George Washington on every **dollar bill.**

?   **WHAT DOES IT MEAN:**   dollar bill =

president = top leader of a country

   SPELLING: Washington _____

father _____

dollar bill _____

   SAY IT: father   George   dollar
               fah thir   jorj   **dah** lir

- Who is the father of our country? **Washington**
- Who was the first president? **Washington**

Here are some more **famous** leaders.
They helped the new United States in many ways.

Thomas **Jefferson**
wrote the Declaration of Independence

Benjamin **Franklin**
started the first free **libraries**

? WHAT DOES IT MEAN: famous = important
free library = a place with books for everyone

ābc SPELLING: free _____

SAY IT:
| started | libraries | Jefferson |
| **star** did | **lahy** brer reez | **jef** fer sun |

- What is one thing Benjamin Franklin is famous for? **He started the first free libraries.***
- Who wrote the Declaration of Independence? **Jefferson**

John **Adams**
was the second U.S. president

Alexander **Hamilton**
wrote the Federalist Papers

? **WHAT DOES IT MEAN:** second = number 2

`abc` **SPELLING:** second _____

Adams _____

👄 **SAY IT:** Hamilton   Adams   second   president
ham uhl tin   **ah** dumz   **sek** und   **preh** zuh dent

• The Federalist Papers supported the passage of the U.S. Constitution.
Name one of the writers. **Hamilton***

Match

Find the words that go with the pictures.
Copy the words on the lines.

wrote

1. _____ _____

library

4. _____

_____

fight

British

2. _____

5. _____

Declaration of
Independence

3. _____ _____

Independence Day

6. _____

Famous People

Draw a line to show what each man was famous for.

1. Jefferson

• started the first free libraries

2. Hamilton

• the second president

3. Adams

• wrote the Declaration of Independence

4. Franklin

• the father of our country

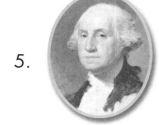

5. Washington

• wrote the Federalist Papers

What does it mean?

1. independence

2. declaration

3. liberty

4. rights

5. adopted

6. famous

7. second

8. president

- leaders voted "yes"

- things the government lets you do

- important

- not first; #2

- top leader of the country

- a letter to all the people

- freedom

- freedom

Yes or No?

1. The colonists wanted the British king to be their leader.   Yes   No
2. The colonists wanted to choose their own leaders.   Yes   No
3. The colonists fought against the British.   Yes   No
4. The Declaration of Independence was adopted in 1876.   Yes   No
5. Washington wrote the Declaration of Independence.   Yes   No
6. Washington was the first president.   Yes   No
7. We celebrate Independence Day in July.   Yes   No
8. Delaware was the first U.S. state.   Yes   No
9. Benjamin Franklin is the father of our country.   Yes   No
10. Washington is on the dollar bill.   Yes   No
11. Adams was the first president.   Yes   No
12. Hamilton wrote the Federalist Papers.   Yes   No
13. The Constitution sets up the government.   Yes   No
14. The Constitution was written in 1776.   Yes   No

Spelling

A. Fill in the missing letters for the words in this lesson.

1. Indep__ndence   3. Dela__are   5. dolla__ b__ll   7. Ad__ms

2. __uly   4. fath__r   6. sec__nd

B. Now use the same words to fill in the blanks.

1. _____ was the _____ president.

2. Washington is on the _____ _____.

3. Washington is the _____ of our country.

4. _____ was the first state.

5. _____ Day is in _____.

Say the answers.

1. Why did the colonists fight the British?

2. When was the Declaration of Independence adopted?

3. What did the Declaration of Independence do?

4. What are 2 rights in the Declaration of Independence?

5. When do we celebrate Independence Day?

6. There were 13 original states. Name 3.

7. Who is the father of our country?

8. Who was the first president?

9. Who wrote the Declaration of Independence?

10. What does the Constitution do?

11. What happened at the Constitutional Convention?

12. When was the Constitution written?

13. What is one thing Benjamin Franklin is famous for?

14. The Federalist Papers supported the passage of the U.S. Constitution.
    Name one of the writers.

Read and Write

Read each question aloud. Copy the answer on the line.
Then write the answer five times in your notebook.

1. What was the first U.S. state? _Delaware was the first state._

2. Who is the father of our country? _Washington is the father of our country._

3. Who was the first president? _Washington was the first president._

4. What president is on the dollar bill? _Washington is on the dollar bill._

5. Who was the second president? _Adams was the second president._

6. Who was George Washington? _Washington was the first president._

7. When is Independence Day? _Independence Day is in July._

Key Words

If you hear:	say:
Independence Day	July 4th
original states	New York, New Jersey, and New Hampshire
father	Washington
Convention	the Constitution was written
Federalist Papers	Hamilton

Writing Cards—Directions

Study the Words

Read each sentence.

Copy each sentence two times on the lines.

Try to remember the letters in each word.

Make Writing Cards

Make Writing Cards to help you practice these sentences.

There are two ways to make the cards.

1. Make a copy of page 69 on a copy machine. Use strong paper!
   Use scissors to cut on the lines.

   OR

2. Get index cards. Copy each sentence three times on one index card.

Practice Listening and Writing

After you make your Writing Cards, give them to a helper.

Ask your helper to read the directions on page 68.

Listen to your helper read each sentence three times.

Write the words that you hear on a paper.

When you're finished, use the Writing Cards to check your paper.

If you see a mistake, copy the Writing Card three times to help you remember.

Then get a new paper and ask your helper to read the card to you again.

When You Take the Writing Test

There are seven pages with Writing Cards in this book. When you take your citizenship test, you will write a sentence like the ones on these pages. Practice writing these sentences so that you will be ready for your writing test.

Writing Cards—Instructions for Helpers

The sentences in the Writing Cards sets in each lesson are for practicing the writing (dictation) part of the U.S. citizenship test. Sentences like the ones in the Writing Cards sets will be used in the test.

Read each sentence slowly and clearly, three (3) times, while the learner writes it.

When you have finished reading all the cards in the set, help the learner check the sentences. If there is a mistake in a sentence, the learner will copy the sentence three times. Then read that card to the learner again, three (3) times, while the learner writes the sentence again.

Writing Cards

1. People come here to be free.

_____

_____

2. Columbus Day is in October.

_____

_____

3. Thanksgiving is in November.

_____

_____

4. Delaware was the first state.

_____

_____

5. Independence Day is in July.

_____

_____

Test Hint #4

Getting Time to Think

Sometimes you need time to remember an answer.

But if you are slow to speak, the examiner might think that you don't know the answer.

Here are some words you can use to ask for some time to think:

- let me see . . .
- let me think . . .
- let's see . . .

Examiner:

Who wrote the Declaration of Independence?

Applicant:

Uh . . . let's see . . . Jefferson.

You can also repeat some words from the question.

For example:

Who was the first president?

The first president? . . . uh . . . Washington.

You can do these two things together:

There were 13 original states. Name 3.

Original states? . . . um . . . let me think . . . New York . . . New Jersey, and uh . . . New Hampshire.

5. The Civil War

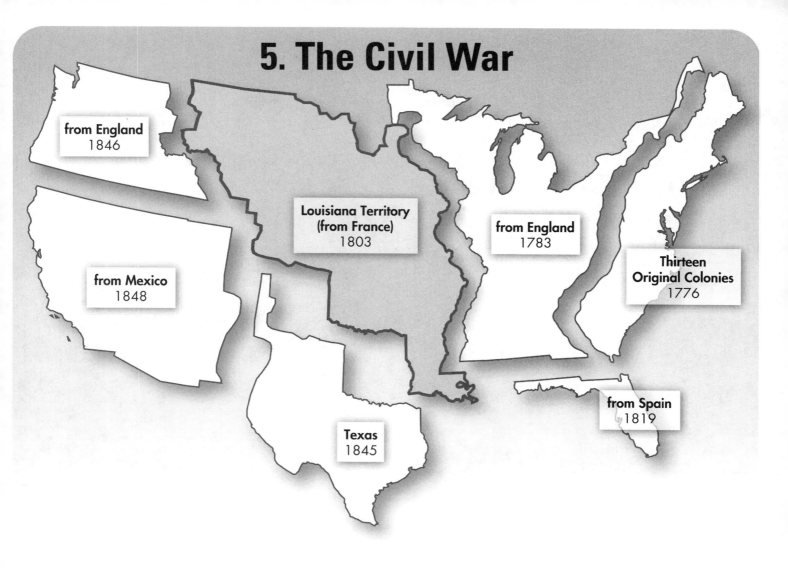

from England
1846

from Mexico
1848

Louisiana Territory
(from France)
1803

from England
1783

Thirteen
Original Colonies
1776

from Spain
1819

Texas
1845

The new United States grew quickly.
The U.S. got new lands from other countries.
For example, the U.S. bought the **Louisiana Territory** from France in 1803.

?   **WHAT DOES IT MEAN:**   grew = got bigger
France = a country in Europe

SAY IT: Louisiana
loo ee zee **ah** nuh

• What territory did the United States buy from France in 1803? **Louisiana**

For many years, slaves worked on American farms and in homes.
In the 1860s, Americans in the North said, "People should not be slaves."
They wanted to end **slavery** in the U.S.

? **WHAT DOES IT MEAN:**   slavery = owning slaves

abc **SPELLING:**   North _____

But Americans in the South did not want to free their slaves.
The problem of slavery led to the **Civil War.**

? **WHAT DOES IT MEAN:**   free = let go of
                                     led to = was a reason for

`abc` **SPELLING:** Civil War _____

👄 **SAY IT:**   slavery   civil war
                     slay ver ee   **siv** uhl war

- Name one war fought by the United States in the 1800s. **the Civil War***
- Name one problem that led to the Civil War. **slavery***

States in the South tried to leave the United States.
They wanted to become a new country.
The Civil War was a terrible fight between the North and the South.

? WHAT DOES IT MEAN: terrible = very bad

ᵃᵇᶜ SPELLING: South _____

• Name the U.S. war between the North and the South. **the Civil War**

Abraham Lincoln was president during the Civil War.
He wanted to keep the North and South together.

? **WHAT DOES IT MEAN:**   during = at the time of

ăbč **SPELLING:** during _____

👄 **SAY IT:**   Abraham   Lincoln
                ay bruh ham   **link** in

Lincoln signed a paper called the **Emancipation Proclamation.**
The paper said, "The slaves are free."
The Emancipation Proclamation **freed** the slaves.

?   **WHAT DOES IT MEAN:**   signed = put his name on
freed = made them free
emancipation = freedom
proclamation = paper for everyone to read

abc   **SPELLING:**   Lincoln _____

👄   **SAY IT:**   freed

- What was one important thing that Abraham Lincoln did? **freed the slaves***
- What did the Emancipation Proclamation do? **freed the slaves**

U.S. Holiday

On Juneteenth, we celebrate the end of slavery in the U.S. Juneteenth is a national holiday.

June						
S	M	T	W	T	F	S
	1	2	3	4	5	6
7	8	9	10	11	12	13
14	15	16	17	18	19	20
21	22	23	24	25	26	27
28	29	30				

The North won the war in 1865. The United States stayed together.

U.S. Holiday

FEBRUARY						
S	M	T	W	T	F	S
	1	2	3	4	5	6
7	8	9	10	11	12	13
14	15	16	17	18	19	20
21	22	23	24	25	26	27
28						

We celebrate Lincoln's birthday with Washington's birthday. The holiday is called Presidents' Day. Presidents' Day is in February.

An angry man killed Lincoln at the end of the war.
Americans remember Lincoln because he helped the U.S. at a hard time.

 SPELLING: February _____

• Name two national U.S. holidays. **Presidents' Day and Juneteenth**

Here is another famous American from the 1800s.

Susan B. Anthony
- worked to end slavery
- worked for women's rights

 SAY IT: women's   rights
              wim inz   riytz

• What did Susan B. Anthony do? **She worked for women's rights.**

What does it mean?

1. signed

2. freed

3. led to

4. territory

5. The Civil War

6. Emancipation Proclamation

- was the reason for

- a fight between the North and South

- made people free

- a paper that ended slavery

- put his name on

- area of land

Yes or No?

1. The U.S. bought Louisiana from France.   Yes   No
2. The U.S. fought the Civil War in the 1900s.   Yes   No
3. The Emancipation Proclamation freed the slaves.   Yes   No
4. Susan B. Anthony signed the Emancipation Proclamation.   Yes   No
5. The problem of slavery led to the Civil War.   Yes   No
6. Abraham Lincoln was president during the Civil War.   Yes   No
7. George Washington freed the slaves.   Yes   No
8. Susan B. Anthony worked for women's rights.   Yes   No
9. Presidents' Day is in October.   Yes   No
10. Presidents' Day and Juneteenth are national holidays.   Yes   No

Spelling

A. Fill in the missing letters for the words in this lesson.

1. Linc__ln

2. Februa__y

3. Civ__l W__r

4. d__ring

5. No__th

6. Sout__

B. Now use the same words to fill in the blanks.

1. Presidents' Day is in _____.

2. The _____ won the Civil War.

3. The states in the _____ tried to leave the U.S.

4. _____ freed the slaves.

5. The problem of slavery led to the _____ _____.

6. Lincoln was president _____ the Civil War.

Say the answers.

1. Name one war fought by the United States in the 1800s.
2. Name the U.S. war between the North and the South.
3. Name one problem that led to the Civil War.
4. What was one important thing that Abraham Lincoln did?
5. What did the Emancipation Proclamation do?
6. Name two national U.S. holidays.
7. What territory did the United States buy from France in 1803?
8. What did Susan B. Anthony do?

Read and Write

Read each question aloud. Copy the answer on the line.
Then write the answer five times in your notebook.

1. Who was Abraham Lincoln? <u>Lincoln was the president during the Civil War.</u>

_____

2. When is Presidents' Day? <u>Presidents' Day is in February.</u>

_____

Key Words

If you hear:	say:
France	Louisiana
North and South	Civil War
Civil War	slavery
Abraham Lincoln	freed the slaves
Emancipation	freed the slaves
Susan B. Anthony	worked for women's rights
1800s	Civil War

Writing Cards

1. Washington is the father of our country.

_____

_____

2. Washington was the first president.

_____

_____

3. Washington is on the dollar bill.

_____

_____

4. Adams was the second president.

_____

_____

5. Lincoln was the president during the Civil War.

_____

_____

Test Hint #5

The Writing Test

The examiner will read a sentence to you.
Say the sentence slowly to yourself.
Then write the words that you hear.
You don't have to write the sentence perfectly.
If <u>most</u> of the sentence is OK, you can pass the writing test.

What will you do if you can't spell a word?
Try to write <u>most</u> of the letters in the word—even if it's not correct.
Finish the sentence anyway.
If you write <u>most</u> of the sentence correctly, you can still pass.

What if you don't understand the sentence?
Ask the examiner to say it again.
Or ask the examiner to explain what it means.

If you still can't write the sentence, don't get upset!
The examiner will read you a different sentence. Try again.
What if you can't write the second sentence?
The examiner will give you a third sentence.

<u>You have 3 chances to write a sentence correctly. You only need to get one right.</u>

If you practice all of the sentences in this book, you can pass the writing test.

6. Later History

In 1917, the U.S. fought against Germany in **World War 1.**
President **Wilson** was the leader of the U.S. during the war.

In 1929, the **Great Depression** began.
Many people lost their jobs.
Some people had no money or food.
President **Roosevelt** helped Americans during the Depression.

? **WHAT DOES IT MEAN:**   work = jobs for earning money

abc **SPELLING:**   people _____

👄 **SAY IT:**   Wilson   Roosevelt
                  wil sin   **Roh** seh velt

• Who was President during World War 1? **Wilson**

In the 1940s, the U.S. fought **World War 2.**
We fought **Japan, Germany, and Italy.**

 SAY IT: World War 2   **Ja**pan   **Ger**many   **Italy**
werld wor **too**   Ji **pan**   **Jer** min ee   **Id** a lee

- Name one war fought by the United States in the 1900s. **World War 2.***
- Who did the United States fight in World War 2? **Japan, Germany, and Italy**

More Famous Americans

President **Roosevelt**

General **Eisenhower**

President Roosevelt was the leader of the U.S. during the Great Depression and World War 2.
General Eisenhower helped the U.S. to win World War 2.
Later, General Eisenhower became president.

 **WHAT DOES IT MEAN:** general = leader of the army

SAY IT: Roosevelt
Roh seh velt

- Who was President during the Great Depression and World War 2? **Roosevelt**
- Before he was President, Eisenhower was a general. What war was he in?
World War 2

In the 1950s and 1960s, the U.S. fought against **Communism.**
This was called the **Cold War.**
Communism was the **main concern** of the U.S. during the Cold War.

? **WHAT DOES IT MEAN:** Communism =

main concern = biggest problem to fight

abc **SPELLING:** United States _____

SAY IT: Communism
Com yu nizm

• During the Cold War, what was the main concern of the United States?
Communism

U.S. Holiday

MAY						
S	M	T	W	T	F	S
1	2	3	4	5	6	7
8	9	10	11	12	13	14
15	16	17	18	19	20	21
22	23	24	25	26	27	28
29	30	31				

Memorial Day is in May.

Every year, we remember Americans who died fighting in U.S. wars.
Memorial Day is in **May.**

?   **WHAT DOES IT MEAN:**   Memorial = remembering

abc   **SPELLING:**   May   _____

                 Memorial   _____

  SAY IT: Memorial Day
            mem **mor** ree uhl   day

In the 1960s, some people wanted to change laws that were not fair to
African Americans.
They wanted to make the laws fair for all people.
These people tried to end **racial discrimination.**
This was called the **Civil Rights Movement.**

? WHAT DOES IT MEAN: racial discrimination = treating people differently
because of their skin color

👄 SAY IT:

civil	rights	movement
siv uhl	riytz	**moov** mint

• What movement tried to end racial discrimination? **the Civil Rights Movement**

U.S. Holiday

JANUARY

S	M	T	W	T	F	S
					1	2
3	4	5	6	7	8	9
10	11	12	13	14	15	16
17	18	19	20	21	22	23
24/31	25	26	27	28	29	30

Martin Luther King's birthday is a national holiday.
Martin Luther King, Jr. Day is in January.

Martin Luther King, Jr. was a leader in the Civil Rights Movement.
He worked for civil rights for all American people.

? **WHAT DOES IT MEAN:** Jr. = Junior

 SPELLING: rights _____

American _____

• What did Martin Luther King, Jr. do? **He worked for civil rights.***

On **September 11, 2001,** a terrible thing happened here.
Terrorists attacked the United States.
Many Americans died.
It was a **major event** in American history.

? **WHAT DOES IT MEAN:** terrorists = killers
attacked = hurt
event = thing that happened

SAY IT: terrorists   attacked
ter er ists   uh **takt**

• What major event happened on September 11, 2001 in the United States?
Terrorists attacked the United States.

Famous People

Draw a line to show what each man was famous for.

 1.   Wilson   • president during the Great Depression

 2.   Roosevelt   • worked for civil rights

 3.   Roosevelt   • general in World War 2

 4.   Eisenhower   • president during World War 1

 5.   Martin Luther King   • president during World War 2

What does it mean?

1. World War 2

2. The Great Depression

3. general

4. Cold War

5. racial discrimination

6. Civil Rights Movement

7. terrorists

8. attacked

- working to make the laws fair for everybody
- killers
- hurt
- a fight against Germany, Italy, and Japan
- leader in the army
- a time when many people did not have work
- treating people differently because of skin color
- a fight against Communism

Yes or No?

1. Wilson was president during World War 2.   Yes   No

2. Roosevelt was president during the Great Depression.   Yes   No

3. The U.S. fought England and France in World War 2.   Yes   No

4. Eisenhower was a general in World War 2.   Yes   No

5. Martin Luther King worked for Civil Rights.   Yes   No

6. Terrorists attacked the U.S. on September 11, 2001.   Yes   No

Spelling

A. Fill in the missing letters for the words in this lesson.

1. Mem__rial

2. R__ghts

3. peop__e

4. Un__ted St__tes

5. Ma__

6. Am__ricans

B. Use the words in the box to fill in the blanks.

1. Martin Luther King was a leader in the Civil _____ movement.

2. On _____ Day, we remember Americans who died in U.S. wars.

3. Memorial Day is in _____.

4. During the Great Depression, many _____ did not have work.

5. President Roosevelt was the leader of the _____

    _____ in World War 2.

6. Civil rights leaders wanted the laws to be fair to all _____.

Say the answers.

1. Who was president during World War 1?
2. Name one war fought by the United States in the 1900s.
3. Who was president during the Great Depression and World War 2?
4. Who did the United States fight in World War 2?
5. Before he was president, Eisenhower was a general. What war was he in?
6. During the Cold War, what was the main concern of the United States?
7. What movement tried to end racial discrimination?
8. What did Martin Luther King, Jr. do?
9. What major event happened on September 11, 2001 in the United States?

Read and Write

Read the question aloud. Copy the answer on the line.
Then write the answer five times in your notebook.

1. When is Memorial Day? _Memorial Day is in May._

_____

Key Words

If you hear:

If you hear:	say:
World War 1	Wilson
1900s	World War 2
Depression	Roosevelt
World War 2	Japan, Germany, and Italy
Eisenhower	World War 2
Cold War	Communism
movement	Civil Rights Movement
Martin Luther King	worked for civil rights
September 11	terrorists attacked the United States

Writing Cards

1. Memorial Day is in May.

_____

_____

2. The flag has red and white stripes.

_____

_____

3. Washington, D.C. is the capital.

_____

_____

4. The flag is red, white, and blue.

_____

_____

5. Flag Day is in June.

_____

_____

Test Hint #6

The Reading and Writing Tests

The examiner will give you a paper with a question on it.
You don't have to <u>answer</u> the question!
Just <u>read the question aloud</u>.
Next, the examiner will tell you the answer and ask you to write it down.
This is the writing test.

For example:

Examiner: I'm going to give you a reading test. Please read to me what you see on this page.

Maria: When is Memorial Day?

Examiner: OK. Now I'm going to read a sentence to you. Write the words that you hear.

Examiner: Memorial . . . Day . . . is . . . in . . . May.

U.S. History: Putting It All Together

When is the holiday?

Find the right holiday. Then finish the sentences and copy them.

- Independence Day
- Flag Day
- Columbus Day
- Thanksgiving
- Presidents' Day
- Memorial Day

1. _____ is in November.

_____

2. _____ is in July.

_____

3. _____ is in February.

_____

4. _____ is in _____.

_____

5. _____

_____

6. _____

_____

People to Remember

Christopher Columbus

George Washington

Thomas Jefferson

Alexander Hamilton

Benjamin Franklin

John Adams

Abraham Lincoln

Susan B. Anthony

Woodrow Wilson

Franklin D. Roosevelt

Dwight D. Eisenhower

Martin Luther King, Jr.

American Indians

Pilgrims

Slaves

Terrorists

1. He was president during World War 1. _____

2. He came to America in 1492. _____

3. He worked for civil rights for all Americans. _____

4. He freed the slaves. _____

5. He helped the U.S. during the Great Depression. _____

6. He was a general in World War 2 and a president. _____

7. He is the father of our country. _____

8. He wrote the Declaration of Independence. _____

9. He started the first free libraries. _____

10. He was the second president. _____

11. He wrote the Federalist Papers. _____

12. She worked for women's rights. _____

13. They lived here first. _____

14. They were brought from Africa and sold in America. _____

15. They came to America from Europe. _____

16. They attacked the United States on September 11, 2001. _____

When did it happen?

Here are some important things that happened in U.S. history.
Put them on the right date on the time line.
Use the time line on page 103.

- The U.S. fought against Japan, Italy, and Germany.

- Martin Luther King, Jr. worked for civil rights.

- The Constitution was written.

- The U.S. bought Louisiana from France.

- Terrorists attacked the United States.

- The U.S. fought in World War 1.

- Abraham Lincoln freed the slaves.

- Columbus came to America.

- The 13 colonies became the United States.

- Roosevelt helped the U.S. during the Great Depression.

- People from Europe came to live in the 13 colonies.

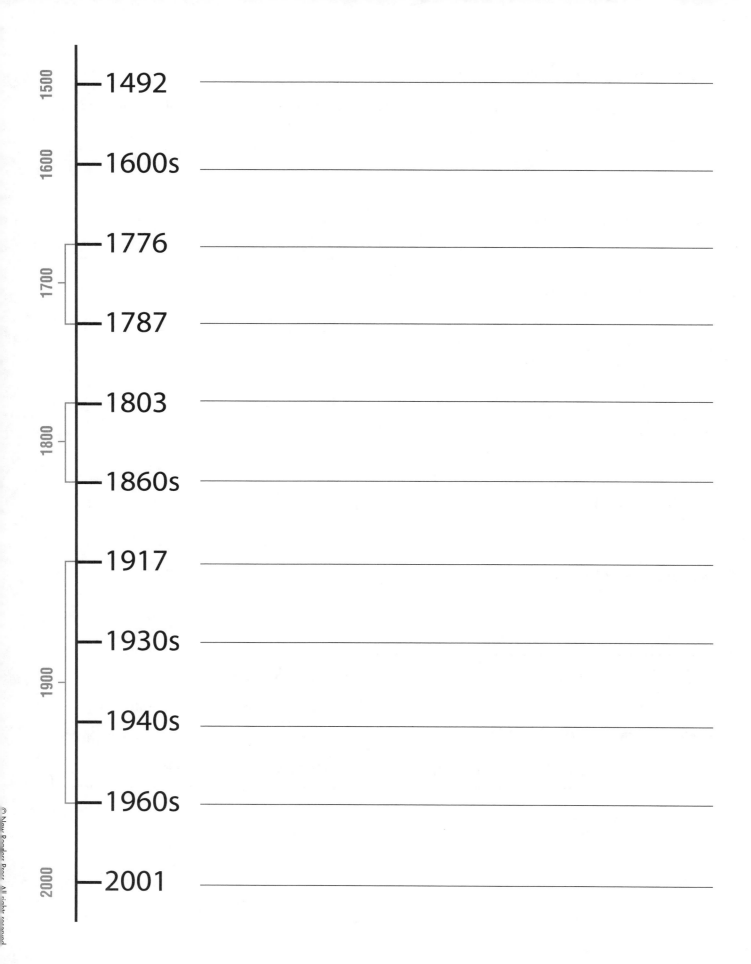

1500

1492 _____

1600

1600s _____

1700

1776 _____

1787 _____

1800

1803 _____

1860s _____

1917 _____

1930s _____

1900

1940s _____

1960s _____

2000

2001 _____

U.S. History: Find the Answers

Read each question aloud. Find the answer in the box, and copy it below the question.

1. Who lived here first?

_____

2. What was the first U.S. state?

_____

3. Who is the father of our country?

_____

4. Who was the first president?

_____

5. What president is on the dollar bill?

_____

6. Who was the second president?

_____

7. Who was Abraham Lincoln?

_____

Lincoln was the president during the Civil War.	American Indians lived here first.
Washington is on the dollar bill.	Adams was the second president.
	Washington is the father of our country.
Washington was the first president.	Delaware was the first state.

About the United States: Find the Answers

Read each question aloud. Find the answer in the box, and copy it below the question.

1. What was the first U.S. capital?

_____

2. What state has the most people?

_____

3. What country is north of the United States?

_____

4. What is the largest state?

_____

5. What country is south of the United States?

_____

6. How many states are in the United States?

_____

7. What is the capital of the United States?

_____

8. What are the colors of the flag?

_____

9. What is on the American flag?

_____

California has the most people.   Mexico is south of the United States.

The flag has red and white stripes.   Washington, D.C. is the capital.

The United States has 50 states.   The flag is red, white, and blue.

Alaska is the largest state.   Canada is north of the United States.

New York City was the first capital.

7. The Constitution

The Constitution tells us how the U.S. government works.
It tells us our most important laws.
The Constitution is the **supreme** law of the land.

? **WHAT DOES IT MEAN:**   supreme = number 1

• What is the supreme law of the land? **the Constitution**

These are the first 3 words of the Constitution: **"We the People."**
We, the people, make our own government.
This is the **idea** of **self-government.**

?   **WHAT DOES IT MEAN:**   idea = thinking

- The idea of self-government is in the first three words of the Constitution.
  What are these words? **We the People**

U.S. Government

Congress

The President

The Courts

The Constitution sets up a U.S. government with 3 parts.
Each part is called a **branch.**

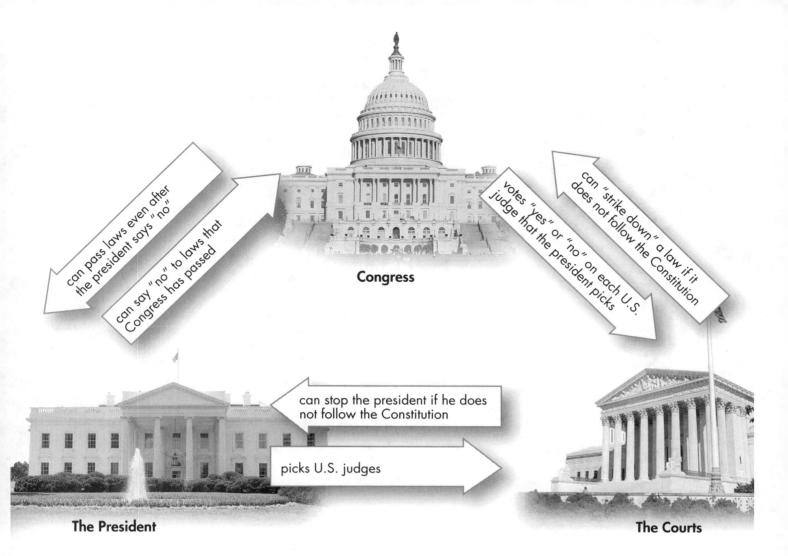

Congress

can pass laws even after the president says "no"

can say "no" to laws that Congress has passed

votes "yes" or "no" on each U.S. judge that the president picks

can "strike down" a law if it does not follow the Constitution

can stop the president if he does not follow the Constitution

picks U.S. judges

The President

The Courts

Each branch has some **powers.** Each branch can do some things.
But no branch can control everything.
This is called the **separation of powers.**

? **WHAT DOES IT MEAN:**   power = things it can do
separation = not all together

🗣 **SAY IT:**   separation   powers
       sep er **ay** shun   **pow** erz

• What stops one branch of government from becoming too powerful?
separation of powers*

The Constitution gives some government powers to the states. For example, each state gives its own **driver's license.**

 SAY IT: driver's   license
                    dri verz   **lie** sens

• Under our Constitution, some powers belong to the states. What is one power of the states? **to give a driver's license***

The Constitution says that only the federal government has some powers.
For example, only the U.S. government can **print money.**

 SAY IT: money
                muh ney

- Under our Constitution, some powers belong to the federal government.
  What is one power of the federal government? **to print money**

We can make changes to the Constitution.
We can add things or take things out.
A change is called an **amendment.**

• What is an amendment? **a change**

BILL OF RIGHTS

1 · 2 · 3 · 4 · 5 · 6 · 7 · 8 · 9 · 10

1791

Americans added 10 amendments to the Constitution when it was new. These first 10 amendments are called the **Bill of Rights.**

 SAY IT: rights
                                        riytz

• What do we call the first 10 amendments to the Constitution? **the Bill of Rights**

The Constitution tells what the government can and cannot do.
The Bill of Rights tells what the people can do.
We all have rights that the government cannot take away.

SPELLING: have _____

SAY IT: government   have
               guh ver mint   hav

Everyone living in the U.S. has **rights.**
The First Amendment tells about some of these rights.
We have freedom of **speech.**
We can speak freely.

 **SPELLING:** freedom _____

speech _____

• What is one right or freedom from the First Amendment? **freedom of speech***

We also have freedom of religion.
We can **practice** any **religion** we like.
Or we can choose no religion.

? **WHAT DOES IT MEAN:**   practice = follow
religion = ways that people think about God

- What are two rights of everyone living in the United States?
  freedom of speech and freedom of religion*
- What is freedom of religion? **We can practice any religion, or no religion.**

Over the years, we have added other amendments to the Constitution.
Four of the amendments tell about who can vote.
For example, the 26th Amendment says that **18-year-old** citizens can vote.

 **SPELLING:** vote _____

citizens _____

SAY IT: 18
ay **teen**

- There are 4 amendments to the Constitution about who can vote.
  Describe one of them. **18-year-old citizens can vote.***
- How old do citizens have to be to vote for President? **18**

BILL OF RIGHTS

1 · 2 · 3 · 4 · 5 · 6 · 7 · 8 · 9 · 10
1791

AMENDMENTS

11 · 12 · 13 · 14 · 15 · 16 · 17 · 18 · 19 · 20
1795 · 1795 · 1865 · 1868 · 1870 · 1870 · 1913 · 1919 · 1920 · 1933

21 · 22 · 23 · 24 · 25 · 26 · 27
1933 · 1951 · 1961 · 1964 · 1967 · 1971 · 1992

Today the Constitution has 27 amendments.

• How many amendments does the Constitution have? **27**

What does it mean?

1. supreme • what someone can do

2. branch • the supreme law

3. powers • a First Amendment right

4. amendment • most important

5. religion • part of government

6. Bill of Rights • change

7. the Constitution • ways that people think about God

8. freedom of speech • the first 10 amendments in the Constitution

Yes or No?

1. The Constitution is the supreme law of the land.   Yes   No
2. State governments have the power to print money.   Yes   No
3. The U.S. government can give you a driver's license.   Yes   No
4. An amendment is a change to the Constitution.   Yes   No
5. Freedom of speech is in the First Amendment.   Yes   No
6. The First Amendment is in the Bill of Rights.   Yes   No
7. All Americans must practice a religion.   Yes   No
8. You can practice any religion you like.   Yes   No
9. The Constitution has 72 amendments today.   Yes   No
10. 18-year-old citizens can vote.   Yes   No

Spelling

A. Fill in the missing letters for the words in this lesson.

   1. freed__m   2. spe__ch   3. hav__   4. citi__ens   5. v__te

B. Now use the same words to fill in the blanks.

   1. Freedom of _____ is a right.

   2. We _____ for president in November.

   3. All Americans _____ rights.

   4. _____ of speech is in the First Amendment.

   5. American _____ can vote.

Say the answers.

   1. What is the supreme law of the land?

   2. The idea of self-government is in the first three words of the Constitution. What are these words?

   3. What stops one branch of government from becoming too powerful?

   4. Under our Constitution, some powers belong to the states. What is one power of the states?

   5. Under our Constitution, some powers belong to the federal government. What is one power of the federal government?

   6. What do we call the first ten amendments to the Constitution?

   7. What is one right or freedom from the First Amendment?

   8. What are two rights of everyone living in the United States?

   9. What is freedom of religion?

  10. There are four amendments to the Constitution about who can vote. Describe one of them.

  11. How old do citizens have to be to vote for President?

  12. How many amendments does the Constitution have?

Read and Write

Read each question aloud. Copy the answer on the line.
Then write the answer five times in your notebook.

1. Name one right in the Bill of Rights. _Freedom of speech is a right._

   _____

2. Who can vote? _Citizens can vote._

   _____

3. Why do people want to be citizens? _They want to vote._

   _____

Key Words

If you hear:	say:
supreme law	Constitution
first three words	We the People
too powerful	separation of powers
First Amendment	speech
religion	you can practice any religion, or no religion.
How old	18

Writing Cards

1. Citizens can vote.

_____

_____

2. Freedom of speech is a right.

_____

_____

3. They want to vote.

_____

_____

4. New York City was the first capital.

_____

_____

5. California has the most people.

_____

_____

Test Hint #7

The Reading Test

What will you do if you don't know how to say a word in the question?

Try to sound it out—even if your pronunciation is not correct.

Read the question as well as you can.

If you read <u>most</u> of the question correctly, you can still pass.

If you have trouble reading the question aloud, don't get upset!

The examiner will give you a different read-aloud question. You can try again.

What if you can't read the second question?

The examiner will give you a third read-aloud question.

<u>You have 3 chances to read a question aloud. You only need to get one right.</u>

If you practice all of the read-aloud questions in this book, you can pass the reading test.

8. Congress

The American people elect leaders to go to Washington, D.C.
This group is called **Congress.**
Congress is one of the 3 branches of government.

 SPELLING: Washington, D.C. _____

Senate

House of Representatives

There are 2 parts of Congress, the **Senate,** and the **House of Representatives.**

 SPELLING: Congress _____

 SAY IT: senate   representatives
                 seh nit   rep ree **zen** tuh tivz

• What are the two parts of the U.S. Congress? **the Senate and the House**

U.S. Senate, 2010

Senators work in the Senate.
We elect a U.S. senator for 6 years.

 SPELLING: elect _____

 SAY IT: senators
                sen id erz

• We elect a U.S. Senator for how many years? **6**

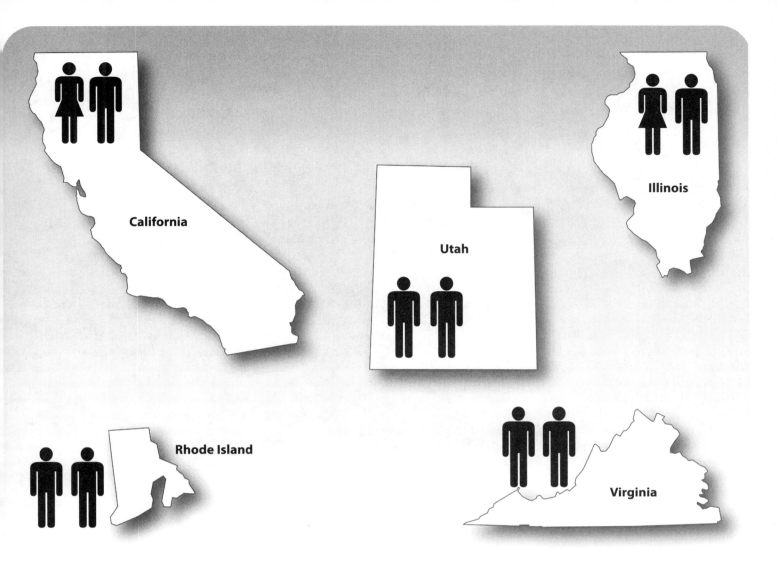

California

Utah

Illinois

Rhode Island

Virginia

We have 100 senators.
There are 2 senators from each state.

Can you name one of the senators from your state? _____

 SPELLING: name _____

 SAY IT: 100 / one hundred
wun **hun** drid

• How many U.S. Senators are there? **100**
• Who is one of your state's U.S. Senators? _____

Who do senators work for?

Senators **represent** all of the people living in their state.

 SPELLING: people _____

Representatives work in the House of Representatives.
We elect a U.S. representative for 2 years.

 SPELLING: elect _____

 SAY IT: representatives
rep ree **zen** tuh tivz

• We elect a U.S. representative for how many years? **2**

There are **435** U.S. representatives.
The House of Representatives has 435 **voting members.**

Can you name your U.S. representative? _____

| ? | **WHAT DOES IT MEAN:**   voting members = leaders |

| 👄 | **SAY IT:** | 435 / four hundred and thirty-five
for **hun** drid and **thir** tee fiyv |

• The House of Representatives has how many voting members? **435**
• Name your U.S. representative. _____

Some states have many people.
These states have a lot of representatives.

New York
20,201,249

Florida
21,538,187

California
39,538,223

Some states do not have many people.
These states have only a few representatives.

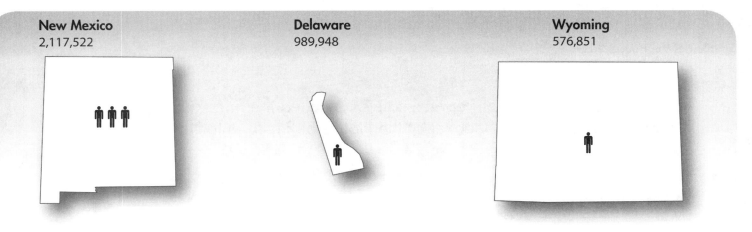

New Mexico
2,117,522

Delaware
989,948

Wyoming
576,851

• Why do some states have more representatives than other states?
Some states have more people.

Speaker of the House, 2021

The leader of the House of Representatives is called the **Speaker.**
What is the name of the Speaker of the House of Representatives now?

_____

• What is the name of the Speaker of the House of Representatives now?

_____

What does it mean?

1. voting members   • work for

2. Speaker   • representatives

3. represent   • the Senate and the House

4. 2 parts of Congress   • leader of the House

Yes or No?

1. Each state elects leaders for Congress.   Yes   No
2. There are 3 parts of Congress.   Yes   No
3. We have 100 senators.   Yes   No
4. We elect a U.S. Senator for 2 years.   Yes   No
5. We elect a U.S. Representative for 6 years.   Yes   No
6. Senators represent all people living in their state.   Yes   No
7. The leader of the House is called the president.   Yes   No
8. The House has 435 voting members.   Yes   No
9. All states have the same number of senators.   Yes   No
10. All states have the same number of representatives.   Yes   No

Spelling

A. Fill in the missing letters for the words in this lesson.

1. el__cts

2. peop__e

3. Congre__ __

4. sen__tors

5. W__shingt__n, D.C.

B. Now use the same words to fill in the blanks.

1. Congress meets in _____.

2. We have 100 _____.

3. The people elect _____.

4. Some states have more _____.

5. Each state _____ leaders to meet in Washington, D.C.

Say the answers.

1. What are the two parts of the U.S. Congress?
2. How many U.S. senators are there?
3. We elect a U.S. senator for how many years?
4. Who is one of your state's U.S. senators?
5. Who does a U.S. senator represent?
6. The House of Representatives has how many voting members?
7. We elect a U.S. representative for how many years?
8. Name your U.S. representative.
9. Why do some states have more representatives than other states?
10. What is the name of the Speaker of the House of Representatives?

Read and Write

Read each question aloud. Copy the answer on the line.
Then write the answer five times in your notebook.

1. Who elects Congress? _The people elect Congress._

_____

2. How many senators do we have? _We have 100 senators._

_____

3. Where does Congress meet? _Congress meets in Washington, D.C._

_____

Key Words

If you hear:	say:
voting members	435
Speaker of the House	(name of current Speaker: _____)

Writing Cards

1. The people elect Congress.

2. We have 100 senators.

3. Congress meets in Washington, D.C.

4. Canada is north of the United States.

5. Alaska is the largest state.

Test Hint #8

Studying for the Test

After you send in your citizenship application, you will go to a fingerprint appointment.

At this appointment, they may give you a book about U.S. history and government.

This book may be hard to read.

If you do not understand the book, don't worry! You do not need the USCIS book to pass the test.

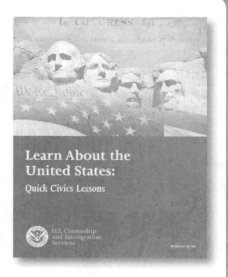

Learn About the United States: Quick Civics Lessons

U.S. Citizenship and Immigration Services

You only need to study the 100 questions and answers in this book.

The 100 questions and answers are all in this book. Look for the Test Question boxes, like this one:

• Who signs bills to become laws? **the president**

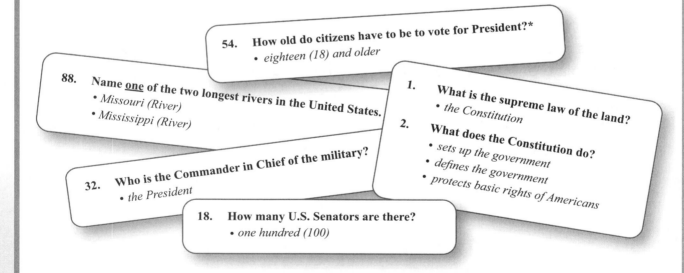

54. How old do citizens have to be to vote for President?*
 • *eighteen (18) and older*

88. Name <u>one</u> of the two longest rivers in the United States.
 • *Missouri (River)*
 • *Mississippi (River)*

1. What is the supreme law of the land?
 • *the Constitution*

2. What does the Constitution do?
 • *sets up the government*
 • *defines the government*
 • *protects basic rights of Americans*

32. Who is the Commander in Chief of the military?
 • *the President*

18. How many U.S. Senators are there?
 • *one hundred (100)*

9. The President

The **executive branch** is one of the 3 branches of the U.S. government. Who is in charge of the executive branch? The president.

? **WHAT DOES IT MEAN:** in charge of = the leader of

👄 **SAY IT:** president
preh zi dent

- Name one branch or part of the government. **the president***
- Who is in charge of the executive branch? **the president**

The president lives in the White House.
Where is the White House? In Washington, D.C.

 SPELLING: White House _____

 SAY IT: White House
                  wite hous

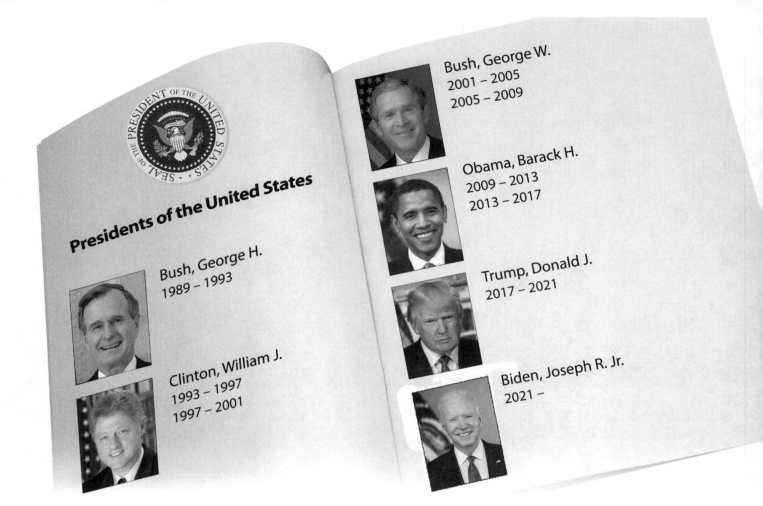

Presidents of the United States

Bush, George H.
1989 – 1993

Clinton, William J.
1993 – 1997
1997 – 2001

Bush, George W.
2001 – 2005
2005 – 2009

Obama, Barack H.
2009 – 2013
2013 – 2017

Trump, Donald J.
2017 – 2021

Biden, Joseph R. Jr.
2021 –

We elect a president for 4 years.
We vote for president every 4 years.

 SPELLING: vote _____

• We elect a president for how many years? **4**

We vote for president in November.
We elect the president in November.

 SPELLING: November _____

• In what month do we vote for President? **November**

The **vice president** helps the president.
If something happens to the president, who will be our leader?
If the president can no longer **serve,** the vice president becomes the new president.

What is the name of the vice president of the United States now? _____

? **WHAT DOES IT MEAN:**   can no longer serve = cannot do the job

👄 **SAY IT:**   vice president
                    vise **preh** si dent

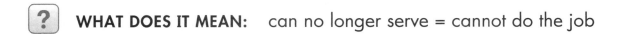

- What is the name of the vice president of the United States now? _____
- If the president can no longer serve, who becomes president?
  the vice president

But what if something happens to the president <u>and</u> the vice president?
If both the president and the vice president can no longer serve, the Speaker of the House becomes the new president.

 SPELLING: president _____

 SAY IT:　　　speaker
　　　　　　　　　spee ker

• If both the president and the vice president can no longer serve, who becomes President? **the Speaker of the House**

The president is the leader of the U.S. Army.
The president is the **Commander in Chief** of the **military.**

? **WHAT DOES IT MEAN:** military = army, navy, air force, marines

• Who is the Commander in Chief of the military? **the president**

The Biden Cabinet, 2021

The president has a group of people who help to run the government.
This group is called the **cabinet.**
The cabinet **advises** the president.

? **WHAT DOES IT MEAN:**   advises = helps

SAY IT: advises
                 ad **viy** sez

> • What does the president's cabinet do? **It advises the president.**

Secretary of State, 2021

There are 15 people in the president's cabinet.
One of the 15 **cabinet-level positions** is **Secretary of State.**
The Secretary of State is the president's number 1 advisor.

? **WHAT DOES IT MEAN:**   position = job
secretary = cabinet member

SAY IT: Secretary of State
sek rih ter ee of stayt

Secretary of Labor, 2021

U.S. Holiday

		SEPTEMBER				
S	M	T	W	T	F	S
					1	2	3
4	5	6	7	8	9	10
11	12	13	14	15	16	17
18	19	20	21	22	23	24
25	26	27	28	29	30	

We remember American workers on Labor Day.
Labor Day is in September.

Another cabinet-level position is Secretary of Labor.
The Secretary of Labor advises the president about American workers and jobs.

? **WHAT DOES IT MEAN:**   labor = work

abc **SPELLING:**   September _____

Labor _____

SAY IT: Secretary of Labor
sek rih ter ee of **lay** bir

• What are 2 cabinet-level positions? **Secretary of State and Secretary of Labor***

What does it mean?

1. president   • the president's home

2. cabinet   • work

3. advise   • cannot work

4. military   • cabinet member

5. White House   • group that helps the president

6. Secretary   • help

7. Labor   • army, navy

8. can no longer serve   • Commander in Chief of the military

Yes or No?

1. The president is in charge of the executive branch.   Yes   No
2. The president lives in the White House.   Yes   No
3. We elect a president for 6 years.   Yes   No
4. We vote for president in September.   Yes   No
5. The president is Commander in Chief of the military.   Yes   No
6. The cabinet advises the president.   Yes   No
7. Secretary of State is a cabinet-level position.   Yes   No
8. The Secretary of Labor advises the president about jobs.   Yes   No

Spelling

A. Fill in the missing letters for the words in this lesson.

1. Lab__r   3. Nov__mber   5. Whit__ Hou__e

2. pres__dent   4. Septe__ber   6. v__te

B. Now use the same words to fill in the blanks.

1. The Secretary of _____ helps the president.

2. The president lives in the _____ _____.

3. We _____ for president every 4 years.

4. Labor Day is in _____.

5. The leader of the U.S. is the _____.

6. We vote for president in _____.

Say the answers.

1. Who is in charge of the executive branch?
2. What is the political party of the president now?
3. We elect a president for how many years?
4. In what month do we vote for president?
5. What is the name of the vice president of the United States now?
6. If the president can no longer serve, who becomes president?
7. If both the president and the vice president can no longer serve, who becomes president?
8. Who is the Commander in Chief of the military?
9. What does the president's cabinet do?
10. What are two cabinet-level positions?

Read and Write

Read each question aloud. Copy the answer on the line.
Then write the answer five times in your notebook.

1. When do we vote for president? _We vote for president in November._

2. Where does the president live? _The president lives in the White House._

3. Where is the White House? _The White House is in Washington, D.C._

4. Who lives in the White House? _The President lives in the White House._

5. When is Labor Day? _Labor Day is in September._

Key Words

If you hear:	say:
executive branch	the President
military	the President
positions	Secretary of State and Secretary of Labor

Writing Cards

1. We vote for president in November.

   _____

   _____

2. The president lives in the White House.

   _____

   _____

3. The White House is in Washington, D.C.

   _____

   _____

4. Presidents' Day is in February.

   _____

   _____

5. Labor Day is in September.

   _____

   _____

Test Hint #9

Questions with More than One Answer

36. **What are <u>two</u> Cabinet-level positions?**
    - *Secretary of Agriculture*
    - *Secretary of Commerce*
    - *Secretary of Defense*
    - *Secretary of Education*
    - *Secretary of Energy*
    - *Secretary of Health and Human Services*
    - *Secretary of Homeland Security*
    - *Secretary of Housing and Urban Development*
    - *Secretary of Interior*
    - *Secretary of State*
    - *Secretary of Transportation*
    - *Secretary of Treasury*
    - *Secretary of Veterans' Affairs*
    - *Secretary of Labor*
    - *Attorney General*

If you have a USCIS question list, you will see that some questions have many answers.

You do not need to know every answer to pass the test!

For example, look at question #36 in the box.

There are 15 answers.

They are all correct.

But you only need <u>2</u> to get the question right.

This book gives you easy answers for each question.

You will not see a long list of answers here.

You do not need to study every answer on the USCIS list.

10. A Country of Laws

Photo courtesy: City of Louisville

When you become a citizen, you make a **promise.**
You promise to **obey the laws** of the United States.

? **WHAT DOES IT MEAN:** promise = agree
obey the laws = follow the rules

SPELLING: laws _____

SAY IT: obey   laws
oh **bey**   lawz

• What is one promise you make when you become a United
States citizen? **to obey the laws**

The United States is a country of laws. Everyone must obey the laws.
The people must obey the laws. The police must obey the laws.
Our leaders must obey the laws too.
This is the **"rule of law."**

? **WHAT DOES IT MEAN:**   police =

abc **SPELLING:**   country _____

• What is the "rule of law"? **Everyone must obey the law.**

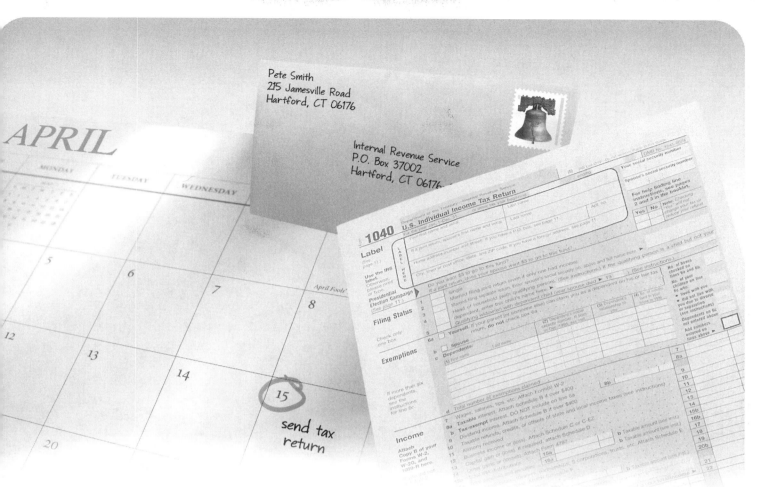

Here is an example of a U.S. law:

Everyone must pay taxes.

The law says that you must send in your U.S. income tax papers each year by April 15th.

April 15th is the last day you can send in **federal income tax forms.**

? **WHAT DOES IT MEAN:**   income tax = money we pay the government

forms = papers

abc **SPELLING:**   pay _____

taxes _____

SAY IT: April   15th

ay pril   fif **teenth**

• When is the last day you can send in federal income tax forms? **April 15th**

Another law says that young men must give their names to the government.
This is the **Selective Service law.**
Selective Service helps the U.S. to stay ready for emergencies.
All **males** must **register** for Selective Service when they turn 18.

? **WHAT DOES IT MEAN:**   males = men
                           register = put your name on a list

• When must all males register for the Selective Service? **at age 18**

Vote

Travel with a U.S. Passport

U.S. law gives special rights to citizens:
Only citizens can carry a U.S. **passport.**
Only citizens can vote.
U.S. citizens also have a **responsibility** to vote.

? **WHAT DOES IT MEAN:** responsibility = something your country needs you to do
passport = travel papers

SAY IT: passport
pass port

- What is one responsibility that is only for United States citizens? **to vote***
- Name one right only for United States citizens? **to vote in a federal election***

Senate

House of Representatives

Congress makes federal laws.
Congress makes laws for our country.

 SPELLING: makes _____

• Who makes federal laws? **Congress**

An idea for a new law is called a **bill.**
First, Congress votes to pass a bill.
Next, the president signs it. Then the bill is a law.
The president signs bills to become laws.

 **?** **WHAT DOES IT MEAN:** signs = puts his name on

abc **SPELLING:** signs _____

bills _____

• Who signs bills to become laws? **the president**

If the president does not like a bill, he can say "no."
This is called a **veto.**

 SAY IT: does
                        duz

• Who vetoes bills? **the president**

Sometimes, after a law is passed, someone needs to study the law and decide what it means.
This is the job of the **judicial branch.**
The judicial branch **explains** laws.

 WHAT DOES IT MEAN: judicial = judges =

explain = help people to understand something

 SAY IT: explains
                    ex **playnz**

• What does the judicial branch do? **It explains laws.**

The judicial branch is the U.S. courts.
The most important court is the **Supreme Court.**
The Supreme Court is the **highest** court.

? **WHAT DOES IT MEAN:** supreme = highest = number 1

SAY IT: supreme court
suh **preem** cort

• What is the highest court in the United States? **the Supreme Court**

The Supreme Court, 2021

There are 9 **justices** on the Supreme Court.
The leader of the Supreme Court is the **Chief Justice.**

Who is the Chief Justice today? _____

? **WHAT DOES IT MEAN:** justice = judge =

- How many justices are on the Supreme Court? **9**
- Who is the Chief Justice of the United States? _____

What does it mean?

1. males   • say you will do something

2. veto   • the last day to send tax forms

3. explain   • men

4. register   • law makers

5. forms   • judicial branch

6. April 15th   • everyone must obey the law

7. responsibility   • the president says "no" to a law

8. taxes   • help people understand something

9. promise   • put your name on a list

10. Congress   • Supreme Court leader

11. bill   • something your country needs you to do

12. rule of law   • papers

13. U.S. courts   • money we pay to the government

14. Chief Justice   • idea for a law

Whose responsibility is it?

Find the words that tell what each person or group does.
Copy the words on the lines.

1. The president

_____

explains laws

pays taxes

2. Congress _____

_____

makes laws

vote

3. The judicial branch

_____

signs bills

obeys the laws

4. Everyone _____

_____

5. Everyone _____

_____

6. Only citizens _____

_____

Yes or No?

1. Citizens promise to obey the laws.   Yes   No
2. People must send in their tax forms by June 15th.   Yes   No
3. Males must register for Selective Service.   Yes   No
4. The president makes the laws.   Yes   No
5. Congress makes the laws.   Yes   No
6. The president signs bills.   Yes   No
7. The president can say "no" to a bill.   Yes   No
8. Congress can veto a bill.   Yes   No
9. The judicial branch explains laws.   Yes   No
10. Justices and presidents must obey the laws.   Yes   No
11. The Supreme Court is the highest court.   Yes   No
12. There are 15 justices on the Supreme Court.   Yes   No
13. Voting is a responsibility that is only for citizens.   Yes   No
14. Only citizens can carry a U.S. passport.   Yes   No

Spelling

A. Fill in the missing letters for the words in this lesson.

1. count__y   3. tax__s   5. m__kes

2. p__y   4. l__ws

B. Now use the same words to fill in the blanks.

1. We _____ taxes to the government.

2. Congress _____ laws.

3. Everyone must obey the _____.

4. We live in a free _____.

5. Everyone pays _____.

Say the answers.

1. What is one promise you make when you become a United States citizen?

2. When is the last day you can send in federal income tax forms?

3. When must all males register for the Selective Service?

4. Who makes federal laws?

5. Who signs bills to become laws?

6. Who vetoes bills?

7. What does the judicial branch do?

8. What is the "rule of law"?

9. What is the highest court in the United States?

10. How many justices are on the Supreme Court?

11. Who is the Chief Justice of the United States?

12. What is one responsibility that is only for United States citizens?

13. Name one right only for United States citizens?

Read and Write

Read each question aloud. Copy the answer on the line.
Then write the answer five times in your notebook.

1. What do we have to pay to the government? _We have to pay taxes._

_____

2. What does Congress do? _Congress makes laws._

_____

Key Words

If you hear:	say:
judicial branch	explains laws
highest court	the Supreme Court
Supreme Court	9
Chief Justice	(name of current Chief Justice) _____
rule of law	everyone must follow the law
promise	obey the laws
income tax	April 15th
Selective Service	18
responsibility	vote
vetoes	the President
signs	the President

Writing Cards

1. Congress makes laws.

   _____

   _____

2. We have to pay taxes.

   _____

   _____

3. Mexico is south of the United States.

   _____

   _____

4. American Indians lived here first.

   _____

   _____

5. They want to live in a free country.

   _____

   _____

Test Hint #10

Question Words

Each read-aloud question starts with a question word.
It's important to know how to say these words.
Make sure you can read them.

Practice saying the question words clearly.

word	sounds like:	rhymes with:
Who	hu	new
What	wuht	but
Where	wayr	air
When	wen	ten
Why	wiy	hi
How many	how men-ee	now penny
Name	naym	same

U.S. Government: Putting It All Together

Match

Find the words that go with the pictures.
Copy the words on the lines.

a justice

the cabinet

1. _____

4. _____

the Supreme Court

the U.S. military

2. _____

5. _____

Congress

3. _____

the White House

6. _____

Which branch are they in?

Put the government leaders in the right branch.

Executive Branch

president

_____

_____

Legislative Branch

_____

_____

_____

Judical Branch

_____

Important Numbers

Here are some important numbers in American history and government. Can you remember which numbers go with the words below?

50	2	18	13	✓9	4	6
435	10	13	27	3	2	100

__9__   1. Supreme Court justices

_____   2. years a president is elected for

_____   3. stripes on the flag

_____   4. amendments to the Constitution

_____   5. U.S. senators

_____   6. years a senator is elected for

_____   7. U.S. representatives

_____   8. states in the U.S.

_____   9. amendments in the Bill of Rights

_____   10. years a representative is elected for

_____   11. original colonies

_____   12. parts of Congress

_____   13. branches of government

_____   14. age for men to register for Selective Service

Which is it?

Declaration of Independence   **The Federalist Papers**   **Constitution**   **Bill of Rights**   **Emancipation Proclamation**

Write **D** for the Declaration of Independence
Write **F** for the Federalist Papers
Write **C** for the Constitution
Write **B** for the Bill of Rights
Write **E** for the Emancipation Proclamation

_____ 1. Thomas Jefferson wrote it.

_____ 2. Abraham Lincoln signed it.

_____ 3. It promises free speech to all Americans.

_____ 4. It said, "The United States is free."

_____ 5. It freed slaves.

_____ 6. Alexander Hamilton wrote it.

_____ 7. It is the supreme law of the land.

_____ 8. It sets up the government.

_____ 9. It was adopted on July 4th, 1776.

_____ 10. It is the first 10 amendments to the Constitution.

_____ 11. The first 3 words are "We the People."

_____ 12. It was written at the Constitutional Convention.

_____ 13. It was written in 1787.

_____ 14. It supported the passage of the U.S. Constitution.

Current Leaders

The president of the U.S. is _____.

The vice president of the U.S. is _____.

The Chief Justice of the Supreme Court is _____.

The Speaker of the House of Representatives is _____.

My U.S. representative is _____.

One of my state's U.S. senators is _____.

The capital of my state is _____.

The governor of my state is _____.

More Practice

Read Aloud Practice

Practice reading these questions aloud. You do <u>not</u> need to say the answer.
For extra practice, find the writing card that matches each question.

1. How many states are in the United States?
2. What is the capital of the United States?
3. What are the colors of the flag?
4. What is on the American flag?
5. When is Flag Day?
6. What was the first U.S. capital?
7. What state has the most people?
8. What country is north of the United States?
9. What is the largest state?
10. What country is south of the United States?
11. Who lived here first?
12. Why do people want to be citizens?
13. Why do people come to America?
14. When is Columbus Day?
15. When is Thanksgiving?
16. What was the first U.S. state?
17. Who is the father of our country?
18. Who was the first president?
19. What president is on the dollar bill?
20. Who was the second president?
21. Who was George Washington?
22. Who was Abraham Lincoln?
23. When is Presidents' Day?
24. When is Memorial Day?
25. Name one right in the Bill of Rights.
26. Who elects Congress?
27. How many senators do we have?
28. Where does Congress meet?
29. When do we vote for president?
30. Where does the president live?
31. Where is the White House?
32. Who lives in the White House?
33. When is Labor Day?
34. What do we have to pay to the government?
35. What does Congress do?
36. Who can vote?
37. Why do people want to be citizens?
38. When is Independence Day?

Sentences for Writing Practice

Write each sentence ten times in your notebook.

1. The United States has 50 states.
2. Washington, D.C. is the capital.
3. The flag is red, white, and blue.
4. The flag has red and white stripes.
5. Flag Day is in June.
6. New York City was the first capital.
7. California has the most people.
8. Canada is north of the United States.
9. Alaska is the largest state.
10. Mexico is south of the United States.
11. American Indians lived here first.
12. They want to live in a free country.
13. People come here to be free.
14. Columbus Day is in October.
15. Thanksgiving is in November.
16. Delaware was the first state.
17. Washington is the father of our country.
18. Washington was the first president.
19. Washington is on the dollar bill.
20. Adams was the second president.
21. Lincoln was the president during the Civil War.
22. Presidents' Day is in February.
23. Memorial Day is in May.
24. Freedom of speech is a right.
25. The people elect Congress.
26. We have 100 senators.
27. Congress meets in Washington, D.C.
28. We vote for president in November.
29. The president lives in the White House.
30. The White House is in Washington, D.C.
31. Labor Day is in September.
32. We have to pay taxes.
33. Congress makes laws.
34. Citizens can vote.
35. They want to vote.
36. Independence Day is in July.

Months of the Year

Spell the months.

| January |
| M_ _ |

| F_ _ _ _ _ _ _ |

| March |

| April |

| M_ _ |

| J_ _ _ |

| J_ _ _ |

| August |

| S_ _ _ _ _ _ _ _ |

| O_ _ _ _ _ _ |

| N_ _ _ _ _ _ _ |

| December |

Answer Key

1. Welcome to America

Match (page 18)

1. voting
2. newspaper
3. United States
4. stars
5. flag
6. states

What does it mean? (page 19)

1. anthem = song
2. national = of our country
3. banner = flag
4. democracy = people choose their own leaders
5. capital = the government is here
6. economic system = rules about money
7. participate = join in
8. major = big
9. party = political group
10. pledge = promise
11. loyalty = love

Yes or No? (page 19)

1. yes
2. no
3. yes
4. yes
5. yes
6. no
7. no
8. yes
9. yes

Spelling (page 20)

A.
1. Washington, D.C.
2. capital
3. blue
4. June
5. stripes
6. colors

B.
1. blue
2. June
3. capital
4. stripes
5. Washington, D.C.
6. colors

2. American Places

Where is it? (page 31)

1. Guam
2. Alaska
3. Canada
4. California
5. Pacific Ocean
6. Mexico
7. Mississippi River
8. New York
9. Atlantic Ocean

Which way? (page 32)

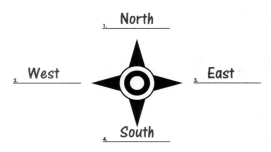

Yes or No? (page 32)

1. yes
2. no
3. yes
4. no
5. yes
6. no
7. yes
8. yes
9. yes
10. no
11. yes

Spelling (page 33)

A. 1. N<u>e</u>w York Cit<u>y</u>
2. firs<u>t</u>
3. C<u>a</u>lifor<u>ni</u>a
4. Canad<u>a</u>
5. Me<u>x</u>ico
6. larg<u>e</u>st
7. Ind<u>i</u>an

B. 1. first
2. New York City
3. Canada
4. Mexico
5. largest
6. California
7. Indian

3. 13 Colonies

Match (page 45)

1. colonists
2. American Indians
3. Thanksgiving
4. Africa
5. slaves
6. Columbus

Spelling (page 46)

A. 1. liv<u>e</u>
2. <u>h</u>ere
3. Colum<u>b</u>us
4. Oct<u>o</u>ber
5. c<u>a</u>me
6. fre<u>e</u>
7. l<u>i</u>ved
8. Thank<u>s</u>giving

B. 1. came
2. live
3. free
4. October
5. lived
6. Columbus
7. here
8. Thanksgiving

Yes or No? (page 47)

1. yes
2. no
3. yes
4. yes
5. no
6. yes
7. no
8. yes

4. The New United States

Match (page 62)

1. Declaration of Independence
2. British
3. Independence Day
4. wrote
5. fight
6. library

Famous People (page 63)

1. Jefferson – wrote the Declaration of Independence
2. Hamilton – wrote the Federalist Papers
3. Adams – the second president
4. Franklin – started the first free libraries
5. Washington – the father of our country

What does it mean? (page 64)

1. independence = freedom
2. declaration = a letter to all the people
3. liberty = freedom

4. rights = things the government lets you do
5. adopted = leaders voted "yes"
6. famous = important
7. second = not first; #2
8. president = top leader of the country

Yes or No? (page 64)

1. no	8. yes
2. yes	9. no
3. yes	10. yes
4. no	11. no
5. no	12. yes
6. yes	13. yes
7. yes	14. no

Spelling (page 65)

A.
1. Independence
2. July
3. Delaware
4. father
5. dollar bill
6. second
7. Adams

B.
1. Adams, second
2. dollar bill
3. father
4. Delaware
5. Independence, July

5. The Civil War

What does it mean? (page 80)

1. signed = put his name on
2. freed = made people free
3. led to = was the reason for
4. territory = area of land
5. The Civil War = a fight between the North and South
6. Emancipation Proclamation = a paper that ended slavery

Yes or No? (page 80)

1. yes	6. yes
2. no	7. no
3. yes	8. yes
4. no	9. no
5. yes	10. yes

Spelling (page 81)

A.
1. Lincoln
2. February
3. Civil War
4. during
5. North
6. South

B.
1. February
2. North
3. South
4. Lincoln
5. Civil War
6. during

6. Later History

Famous People (page 93)

1. Wilson – president during World War 1
2. Roosevelt – president during the Great Depression
3. Roosevelt – president during World War 2
4. Eisenhower – general in World War 2

5. Martin Luther King – worked for civil rights

What does it mean? (page 94)

1. World War 2 = a fight against Germany, Italy, and Japan
2. The Great Depression = a time when many people did not have work
3. general = leader in the army
4. Cold War = a fight against Communism
5. racial discrimination = treating people differently because of skin color
6. Civil Rights Movement = working to make the laws fair for everybody
7. terrorists = killers
8. attacked = hurt

Yes or No? (page 94)

1. no
2. yes
3. no
4. yes
5. yes
6. yes

Spelling (page 95)

A. 1. Memorial
2. Rights
3. people
4. United States
5. May
6. American

B. 1. Rights
2. Memorial
3. May
4. people
5. United States
6. Americans

U. S. History: Putting It All Together

When is the holiday? (page 99)

1. Thanksgiving
2. Independence Day
3. Presidents' Day
4. Flag Day
5. Columbus Day
6. Memorial Day

People to Remember (page 101)

1. Wilson
2. Columbus
3. Martin Luther King, Jr.
4. Lincoln
5. Roosevelt
6. Eisenhower
7. Washington
8. Jefferson
9. Franklin
10. Adams
11. Hamilton
12. Susan B. Anthony
13. American Indians
14. slaves
15. colonists
16. terrorists

When did it happen? (page 103)

1492	Columbus came to America.
1600s	People from Europe came to live in the 13 colonies.
1776	The 13 colonies became the United States.
1787	The Constitution was written.

1803	The U.S. bought Louisiana from France.
1860s	Abraham Lincoln freed the slaves.
1917	The U.S. fought in World War 1.
1930s	Roosevelt helped the U.S. during the Great Depression.
1940s	The U.S. fought against Japan, Italy, and Germany.
1960s	Martin Luther King, Jr. worked for civil rights.
2001	Terrorists attacked the United States.

U.S. History: Find the Answers (page 104)

1. American Indians lived here first.
2. Delaware was the first state.
3. Washington is the father of our country.
4. Washington was the first president.
5. Washington is on the dollar bill.
6. Adams was the second president.
7. Lincoln was the president during the Civil War.

About the United States: Find the Answers (page 105)

1. New York City was the first capital.
2. California has the most people.
3. Canada is north of the United States.
4. Alaska is the largest state.
5. Mexico is south of the United States.
6. The United States has 50 states.
7. Washington, D.C. is the capital.

8. The flag is red, white, and blue.
9. The flag has red and white stripes.

7. The Constitution

What does it mean? (page 119)

1. supreme = most important
2. branch = part of government
3. powers = what someone can do
4. amendment = change
5. religion = ways that people think about God
6. Bill of Rights = the first 10 amendments in the Constitution
7. the Constitution = the supreme law
8. freedom of speech = a First Amendment right

Yes or No? (page 119)

1.	yes	6.	yes
2.	no	7.	no
3.	no	8.	yes
4.	yes	9.	no
5.	yes	10.	yes

Spelling (page 120)

A.
1. freedom
2. speech
3. have
4. citizens
5. vote

B.
1. speech
2. vote
3. have
4. Freedom
5. citizens

8. Congress

What does it mean? (page 133)
1. voting members = representatives
2. Speaker = leader of the House
3. represent = work for
4. 2 parts of Congress = the Senate and the House

Yes or No? (page 133)
1. yes
2. no
3. yes
4. no
5. no
6. yes
7. no
8. yes
9. yes
10. no

Spelling (page 134)
A. 1. elects
   2. people
   3. Congress
   4. senators
   5. Washington, D.C.
B. 1. Washington, D.C.
   2. senators
   3. Congress
   4. people
   5. elects

9. The President

What does it mean? (page 148)
1. president = Commander in Chief of the military
2. cabinet = group that helps the president
3. advise = help
4. military = army, navy
5. White House = the president's home
6. Secretary = cabinet member
7. Labor = work
8. can no longer serve = cannot work

Yes or No? (page 148)
1. yes
2. yes
3. no
4. no
5. yes
6. yes
7. yes
8. yes

Spelling (page 149)
A. 1. Labor
   2. president
   3. November
   4. September
   5. White House
   6. vote
B. 1. Labor
   2. White House
   3. vote
   4. September
   5. president
   6. November

10. A Country of Laws

What does it mean? (page 164)
1. males = men
2. veto = the president says "no" to a law
3. explain = help people understand something
4. register = put your name on a list
5. forms = papers
6. April 15th = the last day to send tax forms
7. responsibility = something your country needs you to do

8. taxes = money we pay to the government
9. promise = say you will do something
10. Congress = law makers
11. bill = idea for a law
12. rule of law = everyone must obey the law
13. U.S. courts = judicial branch
14. Chief Justice = Supreme Court leader

Whose responsibility is it? (page 165)

1. President – sign bills
2. Congress – make laws
3. The judicial branch – explain laws
4, 5. Everyone – obeys the laws, pays taxes
6. Only citizens – vote

Yes or No? (page 166)

1. yes	8. no
2. no	9. yes
3. yes	10. yes
4. no	11. yes
5. yes	12. no
6. yes	13. yes
7. yes	14. yes

Spelling (page 167)

A. 1. country
2. pay
3. taxes
4. laws
5. makes

B. 1. pay
2. makes
3. laws

4. country
5. taxes

U.S. Government: Putting It All Together

Match (p. 171)

1. the cabinet
2. Congress
3. the White House
4. the Supreme Court
5. the U.S. military
6. a justice

Which branch are they in? (p. 172)

Executive Branch: president, vice president, cabinet

Legislative Branch: senators, representatives, Speaker of the House

Judicial Branch: justices

Important Numbers (page 173)

1. 9	8. 50
2. 4	9. 10
3. 13	10. 2
4. 27	11. 13
5. 100	12. 2
6. 6	13. 3
7. 435	14. 18

Which is it? (p. 174)

1. D	8. C
2. E	9. D
3. B	10. B
4. D	11. C
5. E	12. C
6. F	13. C
7. C	14. F

HUMAN HEREDITY

PRINCIPLES AND ISSUES

FOURTH EDITION

MICHAEL R. CUMMINGS

University of Illinois at Chicago
Department of Biological Sciences
and Department of Genetics

WEST/WADSWORTH
I(T)P® an International Thomson Publishing Company

Belmont, CA • Albany, NY • Bonn • Boston • Cincinnati • Detroit • Johannesburg
London • Los Angeles • Madrid • Melbourne • Mexico City • Minneapolis/St. Paul
New York • Paris • Singapore • Tokyo • Toronto • Washington

PRODUCTION CREDITS

Production Editor
Matthew Thurber

Copyeditor
Chris Thillen

Interior and Cover Design
Diane Beasley

Interior Electronic Page Layout
Diane Beasley

Artwork
Precision Graphics, Carlyn Iverson

Index
Schroeder Indexing Services

Cover Image
Dr. Michael Speicher, Yale University

Composition
Carlisle Communications, Ltd.

Production, Prepress, Printing, and Binding
West Publishing Company

ABOUT THE COVER   The colored chromosomes were produced using a newly-developed technique called multiplex-fluorescence *in situ* hybridization (MFISH). This method, developed by Dr. Michael Speicher and colleagues at Yale University, uses fluorescent dyes individually and in combination to produce a different color for each human chromosome. MFISH can be used to detect chromosome rearrangements associated with cancer (see Chapter 6). The MFISH technique was named as one of the most important scientific discoveries of 1996 by *Discover* magazine.

COPYRIGHT ©1988, 1991, 1994 BY WEST PUBLISHING COMPANY
COPYRIGHT ©1997 BY WADSWORTH PUBLISHING COMPANY
A Division of International Thomson Publishing Inc.
I(T)P® The ITP logo is a registered trademark under license.

Printed in the United States of America
1   2   3   4   5   6   7   8   9   10

For more information contact Wadsworth Publishing Company, 10 Davis Drive, Belmont, CA 94002, or electronically at http://www.thomson.com/wadsworth.html

International Thomson Publishing Europe
Berkshire House 168-173
High Holborn
London, WCIV7AA, England

Thomas Nelson Australia
102 Dodds Street
South Melbourne 3205
Victoria, Australia

Nelson Canada
1120 Birchmount Road
Scarborough, Ontario
Canada M1K5G4

International Thomson Publishing GmgH
Konigswinterer Strase +18
53227 Bonn, Germany

International Thomson Editores
Campos Eliseos 385, Piso 7
Col. Polanco
11560 Mexico D.F. Mexico

International Thomson Publishing Asia
221 Henderson Road
#05-10 Henderson Building
Singapore 0315

International Thomson Publishing Japan
Hirakawacho Kyowa Building, 3F
2-2-1 Hirakawacho
Chiyoda-ku, Tokyo 102, Japan

International Thomson Publishing Southern Africa
Building 19, Constantia Park
240 Old Pretoria Road
Halfway House, 1685 South Africa

Library of Congress Cataloging-in-Publication Data

Cummings, Michael R.
    Human heredity: principles and issues/Michael R. Cummings.– –
    4th ed.
        p.   cm.
    Includes bibliographical references and index.
    ISBN 0-314-09578-0
    1. Human genetics.   2. Heredity, Human.   I. Title.
QH431.C897   1997
    599.93'5––dc21   97-999
                                                                                              CIP

To those who mean the most,

Lee Ann,

Brendan and Shelly,

Kerry, Terry, Colin, and Maggie.

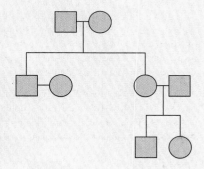

ABOUT THE AUTHOR

MICHAEL R. CUMMINGS received his Ph.D. in Biological Sciences from Northwestern University in 1968. His doctoral work, conducted in the laboratory of Dr. R. C. King, centered on ovarian development in *Drosophila melanogaster*. After a year on the faculty at Northwestern, he moved to a teaching and research position at the University of Illinois at Chicago. Here, he established a research program on the developmental genetics of *Drosophila* and began teaching courses in genetics, developmental genetics, and evolution. Currently an associate professor in the Department of Biological Sciences and in the Department of Genetics, he has also taught at Florida State University.

About ten years ago, Dr. Cummings developed a strong interest in scientific literacy. In addition to teaching genetics to biology majors, he organized and currently teaches a course in human genetics for non-majors, and participates in teaching general biology. He is now working to integrate the use of electronic resources such as the Internet and World Wide Web into the undergraduate teaching of genetics and general biology. His current research interests involve the role of the short arm/centromere region of human chromosome 21 in chromosomal aberrations. His laboratory is engaged in a collaborative effort to construct a physical map of this region of chromosome 21 to explore molecular mechanisms of chromosome interactions.

Dr. Cummings is the author and co-author of a number of widely used college textbooks, including *Biology: Science and Life, Concepts of Genetics,* and *Essentials of Genetics.* He has also written sections on genetics for the *McGraw-Hill Encyclopedia of Science and Technology,* and has published a newsletter on advances in human genetics for instructors and students.

He and his wife, Lee Ann, are parents of two adult children, Brendan and Kerry, and have two grandchildren, Colin and Maggie. He is an avid sailor, enjoys reading and collecting books (biography, history), music (baroque, opera, and urban electric blues), eating the fine cuisine at Al's Beef, and is a long-suffering Cubs fan.

TABLE OF CONTENTS

Preface xix

 Chapter 1

GENETICS AS A HUMAN ENDEAVOR   1

The Domestication of Plants and Animals 1
Ancient Concepts about Genetics 2
Ideas about Heredity Changed in the 18th and 19th Century 3
    Ancient Theories Remained Influential 4
    New Theories Revolutionized Biology 4
    Darwin and Wallace Developed the Theory of Natural Selection 4
    Mendel Changed Ideas about Inheritance 5
Natural Selection and Eugenics 6
    The Eugenics Movement in the United States 6
        Eugenics and Immigration Laws 7
CONCEPTS AND CONTROVERSIES   Genetics, Eugenics, and Nazi Germany 8
        Eugenics and Reproductive Rights 8
    Eugenics and the Nazi Movement 9
The Emergence of Human Genetics as a Distinct Branch of Genetics 9
GUEST ESSAY   Genomic Research by J. Craig Venter 10
The Future of Human Genetics 11
CONCEPTS AND CONTROVERSIES   Genetic Disorders in Society, History, and Art 12
For Further Reading 13

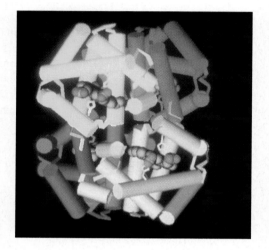

 Chapter 2

CELLS, CHROMOSOMES, AND CELL DIVISION   14

There Are Two Main Types of Cells: Prokaryotic and Eukaryotic 15
Cell Structures and Functions 15
    There is a Wide Range of Cell Sizes 16
    The Plasma Membrane and the Cytoplasm 17
    Organelles Are Specialized Structures in the Cytoplasm 18
SIDEBAR   A Fatal Membrane Flaw 19
        Endoplasmic Reticulum 19
        Golgi Apparatus 19
        Lysosomes 20
        Mitochondria 20
        Nucleus 20
Identification and Classification of Chromosomes 22
The Cell Cycle Describes the Life History of a Cell 23
SIDEBAR   Cell Division and Spinal Cord Injuries 24
    Interphase Has Three Stages 24
CONCEPTS AND CONTROVERSIES   HeLa Cells: The Ultimate Growth Industry 25
    Cell Division by Mitosis Occurs in Four Stages 25
        Prophase 28
        Metaphase 28

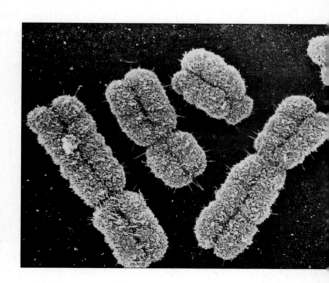

Anaphase 29
Telophase 29
Cytokinesis Begins during Telophase 29
Significance of Mitosis 30
The Human Chromosome Set 31
Cell Division by Mitosis: The Basis of Sex 33
CONCEPTS AND CONTROVERSIES Making a Karyotype 34
Meiosis I Reduces the Chromosome Number 36
GUEST ESSAY Nothing in Biology Makes Sense without Evolution
by Michael Rose 37
Meiosis II Begins with Haploid Cells 38
Meiosis Produces New Combinations of Genes in Two Ways 40
Formation of Gametes: Spermatogenesis and Oogenesis 43
Summary 46
Questions and Problems 46
Science and Society 48
Internet Activities 48
For Further Reading 48

 Chapter 3

TRANSMISSION OF GENES FROM GENERATION TO GENERATION 49

SIDEBAR Mendel and Test Anxiety 50
Heredity: How Does it Work? 50
Mendel's Experimental Approach Resolved Many Unanswered Questions 51
Crossing Pea Plants: The Principle of Segregation 52
Results and Conclusions from Mendel's First Series of Crosses 53
SIDEBAR Why Wrinkled Peas Are Wrinkled 53
CONCEPTS AND CONTROVERSIES Ockham's Razor 54
Inheritance of a Single Trait: The Principle of Segregation 56
More Crosses with Pea Plants: The Principle of Independent Assortment 57
Crosses with Two Traits 57
Methods, Results, and Conclusions 57
The Principle of Independent Assortment 58
CONCEPTS AND CONTROVERSIES Evaluating Results—The Chi-Square Test
Mendelian Inheritance and Meiosis: The Idea that Genes
Are on Chromosomes 62
Many Genes Have More Than Two Alleles 64
Variations on a Theme by Mendel 65
Codominant Alleles Are Both Expressed in the Phenotype 65
Incomplete Dominance Has a Distinctive Phenotype 65
The Concepts of Dominance and Recessiveness 66
Mendelian Inheritance in Humans 66
Pedigree Analysis in Human Genetics 67
CONCEPTS AND CONTROVERSIES Solving Genetics Problems 69
Summary 71
Questions and Problems 71
Science and Society 73
Internet Activities 74
For Further Reading 74

Chapter 4

PEDIGREE ANALYSIS IN HUMAN GENETICS 75

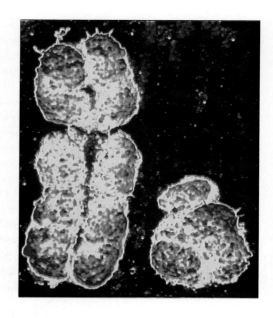

Humans as a Subject for Genetics 76
Pedigree Analysis 77
The Catalog of Mendelian Genetic Disorders 78
CONCEPTS AND CONTROVERSIES   Was Noah an Albino? 79
Autosomal Recessive Traits 79
  Cystic Fibrosis 80
  Sickle Cell Anemia 84
Autosomal Dominant Traits 85
  Pattern of Inheritance 85
  Marfan Syndrome 87
Sex-Linked Inheritance 88
  X-Linked Dominant Inheritance 89
  X-Linked Recessive Inheritance 90
SIDEBAR   Hemophilia, HIV, and AIDS 92
CONCEPTS AND CONTROVERSIES   Hemophilia and History 94
  Muscular Dystrophy 94
  Y-Linked Inheritance 95
Mitochondrial Inheritance 95
Variations in Gene Expression 96
  Temperature and Gene Expression 96
  Age and Gene Expression 97
GUEST ESSAY   Exploring Membranes by Anne Walter 98
  Penetrance and Expressivity 99
  Pleiotropy 100
Linkage and Genetic Maps 100
Linkage Analysis and Lod Scores 102
Summary 103
Questions and Problems 104
Science and Society 107
Internet Activities 107
For Further Reading 108

Chapter 5

POLYGENES AND MULTIFACTORIAL INHERITANCE 109

Some Traits Are Controlled by Two or More Genes 110
Polygenes and Variations in Phenotype 111
  The Additive Model for Polygenic Inheritance 114
  Averaging Out the Phenotype: Regression to the Mean 115
Polygenes and the Environment: Multifactorial Traits 116
  Threshold Effects and the Expression of Multifactorial Traits 116
  Estimating the Interaction between Genotype and Environment 117
Heritability Measures Phenotypic Variation 117
CONCEPTS AND CONTROVERSIES   Baseball Genes and Baseball Environment 118
  Using Fingerprints to Estimate Heritability 119
  Twin Studies and Multifactorial Traits 120

The Biology of Twins 120
Concordance and Twins 121
Using Twins to Study Obesity 122
CONCEPTS AND CONTROVERSIES Twins, Quintuplets, and Armadillos 123
Genetic Clues to Obesity 125
SIDEBAR Leptin and Female Athletes 126
A Survey of Some Multifactorial Traits 126
Cardiovascular Disease Has Genetic and Environmental
Components 126
Skin Color is a Polygenic Trait 128
Intelligence and IQ: Are They Related? 130
The Controversy about IQ and Race 132
Summary 133
Questions and Problems 133
Science and Society 134
Internet Activities 135
For Further Reading 135

 Chapter **6**

CYTOGENETICS 136

Analyzing Chromosomes and Karyotypes 137
Getting Cells for Chromosome Studies 140
Amniocentesis Collects Cells from the Fluid Surrounding the Fetus 140
Chorionic Villus Sampling Retrieves Fetal Tissue from the Placenta 141
CONCEPTS AND CONTROVERSIES Using Fetal Cells from the Mother's Blood 142
Variations in Chromosome Number 142
Polyploidy Changes the Number of Chromosome Sets 143
Triploidy 144
Tetraploidy 144
Aneuploidy Changes the Number of Individual Chromosomes 144
Monosomy is Rare 146
Trisomy is Relatively Common 146
Trisomy 13: Platau Syndrome (47,+13) 146
Trisomy 18: Edwards Syndrome (47,+18) 147
Trisomy 21: Down Syndrome (47,+21) 147
Risks for Autosomal Trisomy 148
Maternal Age is a Risk Factor 148
Why is Age a Risk Factor? 149
Aneuploidy of the Sex Chromosomes 149
Turner Syndrome (45,X) 149
Klinefelter Syndrome (47,XXY) 151
XYY Syndrome (47,XYY) 151
XXX Syndrome (47,XXX) 152
Aneuploidy of the Sex Chromosomes: Some Conclusions 152
Structural Alterations within Chromosomes 153
Deletions Involve Loss of Chromosomal Material 154
Cri du chat Syndrome 154
Prader-Willi Syndrome 154
Translocations Involve Exchange of Chromosome Parts 155
CONCEPTS AND CONTROVERSIES The Oldest Known Chromosome Aberration 156
Consequences of Aneuploidy 158
Other Forms of Chromosome Abnormalities 159

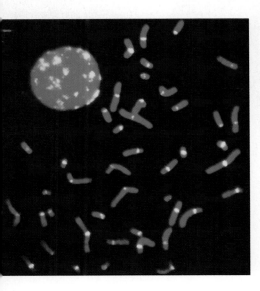

Uniparental Disomy 159
Fragile Sites 161
    Fragile-X Syndrome is Associated with Mental
    Retardation 161
SIDEBAR   Fragile Sites and Cancer 162
Summary 162
Questions and Problems 163
Science and Society 164
Internet Activities 165
For Further Reading 165

Chapter 7

REPRODUCTION AND DEVELOPMENT 166

Human Reproduction 167
    Anatomy of the Male Reproductive System 167
    Anatomy of the Female Reproductive System 170
Human Development from Fertilization to Birth 172
    Human Development Is Divided into Three Stages 174
        Organ Formation Occurs in the First Trimester 175
        The Second Trimester Is a Period of Organ Maturation 176
        Rapid Growth Takes Place in the Third Trimester 177
    Birth Occurs in Stages 177
Reproduction and Technology 177
    Contraception Uncouples Sexual Intercourse from Pregnancy 177
    Technology Expands Reproductive Choices 178
Teratogens Pose a Risk to the Developing Fetus 179
    Little Is Known about Teratogens 179
    Fetal Alcohol Syndrome 180
Sex Determination in Humans 181
    Chromosomes Can Help Determine Sex 181
    The Sex Ratio in Humans 182
Sex Differentiation Follows Sex Determination 183
    Chromosomal Sex and Phenotypic Sex 183
    Events in Embryogenesis Begin Sexual Differentiation 183
CONCEPTS AND CONTROVERSIES   Sex Testing in International Athletics—
Is It Necessary? 184
Genetic Control of Sexual Differentiation 186
    Testicular Feminization and Phenotypic Sex 187
Gene Expression and Sexual Phenotype 188
CONCEPTS AND CONTROVERSIES   Joan of Arc—Was It Really
John of Arc? 189
Dosage Compensation and the X Chromosome 189
    Expression of Genes on the X Chromosome 189
    Barr Bodies and X Inactivation 189
    Females Are Mosaics for X-Linked Genes 190
Sex-Influenced and Sex-Limited Traits 192
Summary 192
Questions and Problems 193
Science and Society 194
Internet Activities 194
For Further Reading 195

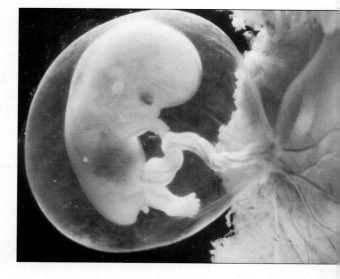

Chapter 8

DNA STRUCTURE AND CHROMOSOME ORGANIZATION   196

DNA as a Carrier of Genetic Information 197
  Transfer of Genetic Traits in Bacteria 198
  Reproduction in Bacterial Viruses Involves DNA 199
      CONCEPTS AND CONTROVERSIES   DNA as a Commercial Product 201
      Watson, Crick, and the Structure of DNA 202
          Reviewing Some Basic Chemistry 202
          Nucleotides: The Building Blocks of Nucleic Acids 203
          DNA Is a Double Helix 204
  SIDEBAR   DNA Organization and Disease 206
          Structure of RNA 207
  DNA Is Coiled with Proteins to Form Chromosomes 208
          The Mitochondrial Chromosome Is a Circular DNA Molecule 208
          Nuclear Chromosomes Have a Complex Structure 209
  DNA Replication Depends on Base Pairing 211
  Summary 212
  Questions and Problems 212
  Science and Society 214
  Internet Activities 214
  For Further Reading 215

Chapter 9

GENE EXPRESSION: HOW PROTEINS ARE MADE   216

Genes and Proteins: Unresolved Questions 217
  Genes and Metabolism 218
  The Relationship between Genes and Enzymes 218
How Is Genetic Information Stored in DNA? 219
The Flow of Genetic Information Is a Multistep Process 220
  Transcription Produces Genetic Messages 220
  Genes Can Have a Complex Internal Organization 221
  Messenger RNA Is Processed and Spliced 222
  Translation Requires the Interaction of Several Components 222
CONCEPTS AND CONTROVERSIES   Antibiotics and Protein Synthesis 227
The Genetic Code: The Key to Life 228
          The Polypeptide Product of Translation 229
              Levels of Structure in Proteins 230
              Proteins Have Many Functions 232
          SIDEBAR   Selective Breeding Gone Bad 232
          Summary 233
          Questions and Problems 233
          Science and Society 235
          Internet Activities 235
          For Further Reading 236

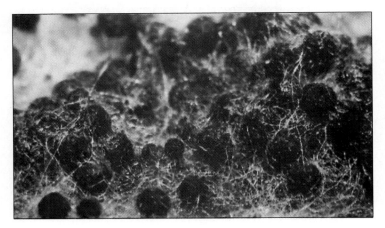

Chapter **10**

FROM PROTEINS TO PHENOTYPES: METABOLIC DISORDERS 237

The Role of Proteins 238
Metabolic Pathways and Genetic Disorders 239
CONCEPTS AND CONTROVERSIES   Garrod and Metabolic Disease 240
    Phenylketonuria: A Defect in Amino Acid Metabolism 241
        Dietary Control of the PKU Phenotype 242
        PKU Females and Reproduction 242
    Other Metabolic Disorders in the Phenylalanine Pathway 242
CONCEPTS AND CONTROVERSIES   Dietary Management and Metabolic Disorders 243
    Defects in Carbohydrate Metabolism 244
    Metabolic Disorders without Serious Phenotypic Consequences 246
    Lesch-Nyhan Syndrome Is a Disorder of Nucleic Acid Metabolism 246
Mutations in Receptor Proteins: Familial Hypercholesterolemia 248
SIDEBAR   Population Genetics of Sickle Cell Genes 250
Defects in Transport Proteins: The Globin Genes 250
    Hemoglobin Variants 253
    Sickle Cell Anemia 253
    Other Hemoglobin Variants 254
    Thalassemias 255
    Treatment of Hemoglobin Disorders by Gene Switching 257
Structural Proteins: Inherited Disorders of Connective Tissue 258
    Collagen Fibers: Structure and Function 258
    Osteogenesis Imperfecta and Collagen Genes 259
Transcription Factors and Genetic Disorders 260
    Xeroderma Pigmentosum 260
    Grieg Syndrome 260
Summary 261
Questions and Problems 262
Science and Society 264
Internet Activities 264
For Further Reading 265

 Chapter **11**

MUTATION: THE SOURCE OF GENETIC VARIATION 266

The Nature of Mutation 267
Detecting Mutation 267
Measuring Mutation Rates 269
    Gene-Specific Mutation Rates 269
    Indirect Measurement of Mutation Rates 271
Factors That Influence the Mutation Rate 271
    Radiation as a Mutagen 271
    Action of Chemical Mutagens 272
    Finding Mutagenic Chemicals: The Ames Test 273
CONCEPTS AND CONTROVERSIES   Irradiated Food 274
Mutation at the Molecular Level: DNA as a Target 274
    Nucleotide Substitutions 275
    Deletions and Insertions 276
    Trinucleotide Repeats and Allelic Expansion 277
    Allelic Expansion and Anticipation 279

DNA Repair Mechanisms 279
   Assessing Damage to DNA 279
   Repairing Damage to DNA 280
Mutation, Genotypes, and Phenotypes 280
   Mutation Can Cause a Range of Phenotypes 281
   Genomic Imprinting: Reversible Alterations to the Genome 282
Summary 283
Questions and Problems 284
Science and Society 285
Internet Activities 286
For Further Reading 286

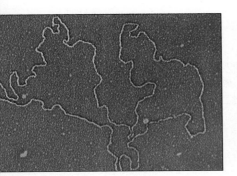

Chapter 12

RECOMBINANT DNA TECHNOLOGY 287

What Are Clones? 288
   Plants Can Be Cloned from Single Cells 289
   Animals Can Be Cloned by Two Methods 290
Cloning Genes Is a Multistep Process 291
   Restriction Enzymes Cut DNA at Specific Sites 291
   Vectors Serve as Carriers of DNA 293
   Steps in the Process of Cloning DNA 294
   Cloned Libraries 297
   Finding a Specific Clone in a Library 298
CONCEPTS AND CONTROVERSIES Asilomar: Scientists Get Involved 299
Analyzing Cloned Sequences 299
   Southern Blotting 299
   DNA Sequencing 300
The Polymerase Chain Reaction 302
GUEST ESSAY The Human Genome Project: Reading Our Own Genetic Blueprint by
  Francis Sellers Collins 304
Summary 305
Questions and Problems 305
Science and Society 306
Internet Activities 307
For Further Reading 307

Chapter 13

APPLICATIONS OF RECOMBINANT DNA TECHNOLOGY 308

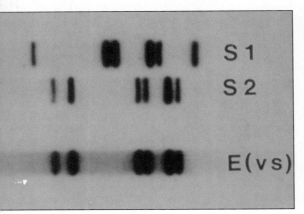

Recombinant DNA Techniques Have Revolutionized Genetic Mapping 309
   RFLPs Are Heritable Genetic Markers 310
   Mapping Genes Using RFLPs and Positional Cloning 311
   Mapping at the Chromosomal Level 312
DNA Fingerprinting 313
   Analyzing DNA Fingerprints 314
   Other Applications of DNA Fingerprinting 315
Prenatal and Presymptomatic Testing for Genetic Disorders 315
CONCEPTS AND CONTROVERSIES Death of a Czar 316
The Human Genome Project Is an International Effort 318

    Steps in the Project 319
        The Human Genome Project: A Progress Report 320
        Implications of the Human Genome Project 320
    Gene Transfer Technology Has Many Applications 321
        Proteins Can Be Manufactured by Recombinant DNA Technology 321
        Genetic Disorders Can Be Corrected by Gene Therapy 322
        New Plants and Animals Can Be Created by Gene Transfer 324
    Ethical Questions about Recombinant DNA 325
    Summary 326
    Questions and Problems 326
    Science and Society 328
    Internet Activities 329
    For Further Reading 329

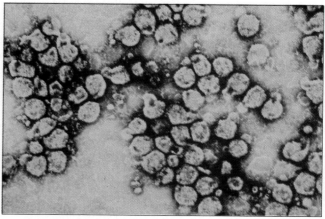

 Chapter **14**

GENES AND CANCER 330

Tumors and Cancer: What Are They? 332
Genes That Predispose to Cancer 332
Tumor Suppressor Genes and the Cell Cycle 333
    Retinoblastoma 334
    The Search for Breast Cancer Genes 335
    Colon Cancer Requires Multiple Mutations 336
    Genetic Instability and Cancer 338
Oncogenes and Cancer 338
    Rous Sarcoma Virus and Oncogenes 339
    Oncogenes and Mutation 341
Chromosomes and Cancer 342
    Chromosome Instability Syndromes 343
    Chromosome Aberrations and Leukemia 343
Cancer and the Environment 344
    Epidemiology and Links to Environmental Factors 345
    Occupational Hazards and Cancer Risk 345
    Environmental Factors and Cancer 346
CONCEPTS AND CONTROVERSIES Epidemiology, Asbestos, and Cancer 347
GUEST ESSAY A Journey through Science by Bruce Ames 348
    Genetic Models for Susceptibility 349
Summary 349
Questions and Problems 350
Science and Society 352
Internet Activities 352
For Further Reading 352

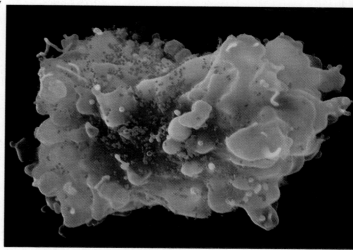

 Chapter **15**

GENETICS OF THE IMMUNE SYSTEM 354

The Immune System Defends the Body against Infection 355
The Inflammatory Response is a General Reaction 356
    Nonspecific Responses Are Activated by the Inflammatory Reaction 356

The Complement System Kills Microorganisms Directly 357
The Immune Response Is a Specific Defense against Infection 358
  An Overview of the Immune Response 358
  Antibody-Mediated Immunity Uses Molecular Weapons 359
  Antibodies Are Molecular Weapons against Antigens 361
  Rearrangement in Antibody Genes 362
  T Cells Mediate the Cellular Immune Response 364
  The Immune System Has a Memory Function 364
Blood Types Are Determined by Cell Surface Antigens 366
  ABO Blood Typing Allows Safe Blood Transfusions 366
  Rh Blood Types Can Cause Immune Reactions between Mother and Fetus 366
Organ Transplants Must Be Immunologically Matched 368
  Successful Transplants Depend on HLA Matching 368
  SIDEBAR Genetically Engineered Blood 369
  Animal-Human Transplants 369
  The HLA System and Disease Associations 369
Disorders of the Immune System 370
  Overreaction in the Immune System Causes Allergies 370
  Autoimmune Reactions Cause the Immune System to Attack the Body 372
  Genetic Disorders Can Impair the Immune System 372
CONCEPTS AND CONTROVERSIES Why Bee Stings Can Be Fatal 373
  AIDS Attacks the Immune System 374
GUEST ESSAY Medicine—A Scientific Safari by M. Michael Glovsky 375
Summary 376
Questions and Problems 376
Science and Society 377
Internet Activities 378
For Further Reading 378

Chapter 16

GENETICS OF BEHAVIOR 379

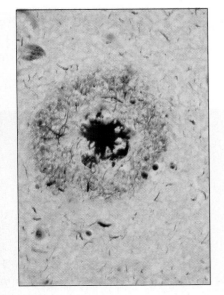

Models, Methods, and Phenotypes 381
  Genetic Models of Inheritance and Behavior 381
CONCEPTS AND CONTROVERSIES Is Going to Medical School a Genetic Trait? 382
  Methods of Studying Behavior Genetics 382
  Phenotypes: What Is Behavior? 383
Animal Models: The Search for Behavior Genes 383
  Open-Field Behavior 383
  Learning in *Drosophila* 384
Single-Gene Effects on Human Behavior 385
  Charcot-Marie-Tooth Disease 386
  Friedreich Ataxia 387
  Menkes Kinky-Hair Disease 387
  Huntington Disease 388
Aggressive Behavior and Brain Metabolism 389
SIDEBAR A Genetic Link to a Personality Trait 389
The Genetics of Mood Disorders and Schizophrenia 390
  Mood Disorders: Unipolar and Bipolar Illnesses 390
  Schizophrenia 393
CONCEPTS AND CONTROVERSIES The Link between Madness and Genius 394
Genetics and Social Behavior 395
  Tourette Syndrome 395
  Alzheimer Disease 396
  Alcoholism 397

Sexual Orientation 398
GUEST ESSAY   Neurogenetics: From Mutants to Molecules by Barry S. Ganetzky 400
Summing Up: The Current Status of Human Behavior Genetics 401
Summary 402
Questions and Problems 402
Science and Society 403
Internet Activities 404
For Further Reading 404

Chapter 17

GENES IN POPULATIONS   406

The Population as a Genetic Reservoir 408
Measuring Allele Frequencies 410
    Codominant Alleles 410
    Recessive Allele Frequencies Cannot Be Measured Directly 411
The Hardy-Weinberg Law 411
CONCEPTS AND CONTROVERSIES   The Thrifty Genotype 412
    Assumptions for the Hardy-Weinberg Law 412
    Calculating Allele Frequencies and Genotype Frequencies 412
    Genetic Equilibrium 414
Using the Hardy-Weinberg Law in Human Genetics 414
    Autosomal Codominant Alleles 414
    Autosomal Dominant and Recessive Alleles 414
    X-Linked Traits 415
    Multiple Alleles 415
    Estimating Heterozygote Frequency 416
Anthropology and Population Structure 419
Summary 421
Questions and Problems 421
Science and Society 422
Internet Activities 423
For Further Reading 423

Chapter 18

HUMAN DIVERSITY AND EVOLUTION   424

Genetic Diversity in Human Populations 425
    New Alleles Are Generated by Mutation 425
    Genetic Drift 427
    Natural Selection Acts on Variation in Populations 428
    Selection and the Genetic History of a Population 430
Natural Selection and the Frequency of Human Genetic Disorders 430
Human Activity as a Force in Changing Allele Frequencies 431
SIDEBAR   Stone Age Fabrics 441
    Migration 432
    Mate Selection 433
    Culture 435
Allele Differences between Populations 437
    Tracking Gene Flow in Populations 437
    Gene Flow between Populations 438
Primate Evolution and Human Origins 440

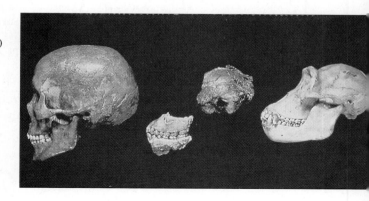

Human-like Hominids Appeared about Four Million Years Ago 440
The Genus *Homo* Appeared about Two Million Years Ago 442
Homo erectus Originated in Africa 443
The Appearance and Spread of *Homo sapiens* 443
CONCEPTS AND CONTROVERSIES   Tool Time: Did *Homo erectus* Use Killer Frisbees 444
Two Theories Differ on How and Where *Homo sapiens* Originated 444
The Transition to Agriculture Is a Cultural Adaptation 445
Human Migration to the Americas Is a Recent Event 446
Summary 448
Questions and Problems 448
Science and Society 449
Internet Activities 449
For Further Reading 450

Chapter 19

GENETIC SCREENING AND GENETIC COUNSELING   451

Genetic Screening 452
Newborn and Carrier Screening 453
Tay-Sachs Disease 453
Sickle Cell Trait 453
Cystic Fibrosis 454
Occupational Screening 455
Reproductive Screening 457
Cost-Benefit Analysis in Genetic Screening 457
Prenatal Testing 458
Ultrasonography 460
Fetoscopy 460
Testing Embryonic Blastomeres 461
Risks and Problems Associated with Prenatal Testing 462
Genetic Counseling 462
Who Are Genetic Counselors? 462
CONCEPTS AND CONTROVERSIES   The Business of Making Babies 463
Reasons to Seek Genetic Counseling 464
How Does Genetic Counseling Work? 464
Future Directions 466
The Impact of Genetic Testing and Genetic Screening 466
Personal Consequences 466
Social Consequences 467
Legal Implications 468
Summary 469
Questions and Problems 469
Science and Society 470
Internet Activities 471
For Further Reading 471

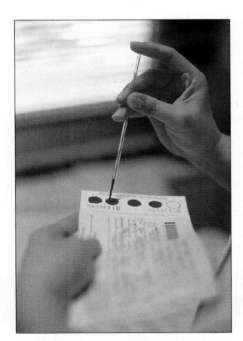

APPENDIX A   Probability 473
APPENDIX B   Answers to Questions and Problems 477

GLOSSARY 499
INDEX 509

PREFACE TO THE FOURTH EDITION

Since the third edition of *Human Heredity* was published three years ago, the dynamic field of human genetics has continued moving forward rapidly. Much of this momentum comes from the Human Genome Project. Major strides have been made in mapping and sequencing the human genome, understanding the nature of genetic disorders, and using recombinant DNA technology for gene therapy. These exciting developments reinforce the need for an accessible text that can provide the degree of scientific literacy necessary to comprehend and interpret these advances.

This book is intended to teach the basic concepts of human genetics, leading the reader to an understanding of the genetic uniqueness of each person and the impact of advances in human genetics on health care, biotechnology, public policy, and law. As with previous editions, the text is primarily intended for use in one-term courses for undergraduates with little or no background in biology, chemistry, and mathematics. Although some chemistry and mathematics are used in the text, they are presented in a descriptive fashion and at an elementary level.

The text serves those who will become users of genetic technology, including prenatal testing for inherited disorders and presymptomatic testing for breast cancer or Huntington disease. It also serves students who will become health care providers by showing how an understanding of basic mechanisms in human genetics is transformed into the technologies for detecting, treating, and preventing genetic disorders. Hopefully, this text will also enable those who formulate public policy and laws to make informed decisions rooted in an understanding of the potential and the limitations of genetics.

The goals of this fourth edition of the text are as follows:

- Present the principles of human genetics and their applications in a clear, concise manner that conveys a working knowledge of genetic concepts.
- Provide an understanding of the origin and amount of genetic diversity present in the human population and how the forces of selection and evolution have shaped our genotypes and phenotypes.
- Examine the social, cultural, and ethical implications of human genetic technology and how these are applied to individuals and society.
- Through examples, descriptions, and essays, help students understand how scientists think and approach research problems. Leading scientists such as Francis Collins, Craig Ventner, and Barry Ganetzky have been solicited to write essays, describing their background and their area of research.

To achieve these goals, emphasis has been placed on clear writing, up-to-date coverage, and flexible organization. A conscious effort has been made to present the material in a straightforward fashion with a minimum of scientific jargon. Previous editions have been used by a wide range of instructors. Their comments and suggestions have once again been most helpful in presenting concepts, providing new and interesting examples, clarifying language, and improving the reading level.

Although the text has been revised, and the order of chapters has changed, the text can still be divided into three sections: Chapters 1 through 7 cover cell division, transmission of traits, and reproduction. Chapters 8 through 13 emphasize molecular aspects of genetics, including gene action, mutation, the production of phenotype, and recombinant DNA. Chapters 14 through 19 cover specialized topics such as cancer, the immune system, population genetics, and evolution; they also consider the social aspects of genetics, including behavior, genetic screening, and counseling.

Recognizing that instructors have many ideas about course organization and the sequence of topics, the text has been written to accommodate different presentation formats. After the section on transmission genetics, the chapters can be used in whatever order suits the needs of the course. Within each chapter, the outline lets the instructor and the student easily identify central ideas.

✱ FEATURES OF THE NEW EDITION

Since each week seems to bring important new discoveries in human genetics, this edition has undergone significant restructuring and rewriting. It includes new organization, new chapters, new supplements, a new, full-color art program, and links to electronic databases and the World Wide Web. Because the book is intended for the non-specialist, much of the text has been rewritten to place the principles of human genetics in a wider biological context.

New Organization

The chapter on multifactorial traits (Chapter 5) has been moved forward to follow that on Mendelian inheritance (Chapter 4) in order to cover all aspects of transmission genetics in one section. The chapters on mutation and mutagens have been combined into a single chapter (Chapter 11) that now precedes the material on recombinant DNA. This new order allows a more logical flow of the discussion in the central chapters, beginning with DNA (Chapter 8), gene action and phenotype (Chapters 9 and 10), and mutation (Chapter 11), followed by recombinant DNA (Chapter 12) and applications of recombinant DNA (Chapter 13). Lastly, the chapter on genetics, law, and bioethics has been partly combined with Chapter 19 (genetic screening and counseling), with the rest of the material placed in other chapters.

New Chapters

A new chapter on reproduction and development (Chapter 7) has been added in order to put the topics of sex determination and sex differentiation into a wider biological context. This chapter begins with a discussion of the human reproductive systems and then briefly describes human development from fertilization to birth, contraception, and teratogens. With this as background, the chapter concludes with sections on sex determination and sex differentiation.

In response to developments in the field, the topic of recombinant DNA technology has been expanded to two chapters. The new chapter (Chapter 13) covers the applications of recombinant DNA technology. Topics include genetic mapping, DNA fingerprinting, prenatal and presymptomatic diagnosis of genetic diseases, and gene transfer technology. The chapter ends with a discussion of the ethical questions that have been generated with the use of recombinant DNA technology in many fields.

New Art Program

The art for the book has been completely revamped, and a new, four-color art program has been developed for this edition. The art program is concept-driven: the illustrations are designed to clearly summarize a concept under discussion, free of unnecessary text, labels, or detail. This is accomplished by supporting the illustrations with detailed explanations in the text, allowing the art to be an unencumbered summary of a process or concept.

To emphasize the parallel importance and interaction of text and art, the description of a concept and its accompanying illustration appear on the same page or the same two-page spread. Students will not have to turn pages to find figures related to the points being discussed. In addition, colored icons highlight the figure references

in the text, allowing the students to return quickly to the appropriate place in the text after studying the figure.

Expanded Questions and Problems

One of the most significant features of this edition is the revision of the questions and problems at the end of each chapter. There are now more than 365 end-of-chapter questions and problems, an increase of over 65%. Many of these have been contributed by adopters of the text or experts in a specialized field of human genetics. The questions and problems use both an objective and a problem format, and are arranged by level of difficulty. Because some quantitative skills are needed in human genetics, almost all chapters include some problems that require the student to organize the concepts in the chapter, and to use these concepts in reasoning to a conclusion.

Sidebars

Throughout the book, sidebars are used to highlight applications of concepts, present controversial ideas, and communicate the latest results in human genetics, without interrupting the flow of the text.

Science and Society Questions and Mini-Cases

To make problems in human genetics relevant to situations that students may encounter outside the classroom, a new section, "Science and Society," has been added at the end of each chapter. This section contains questions that apply situations and cases in human genetics to larger issues of health care, ethics, public policy, and personal decision-making. The answers to these questions are often open-ended and can be used as the basis for classroom discussions or student presentations.

Guest Essays

The fourth edition features a series of essays to emphasize that human genetics, like all of science, is a human endeavor. These essays, written by distinguished scientists, describe how these people became interested in science, what they study, and how their research relates to the larger context of human society. These essays are not just *about* scientists; they are written *by* scientists, giving the non-science major insights into the lives, thoughts, and motives of biologists.

Genetic Disorders and Electronic Databases

The field of genetics has been quick to embrace the concept of computer databases to organize and disperse information, rapidly communicate new findings, and even publish research articles. Informed citizens need to be aware of the existence as well as the relevance of these databases.

To foster this awareness, genetic disorders mentioned in this edition are followed by the number assigned to them in the comprehensive catalog assembled by Victor McKusick and his colleagues at Johns Hopkins University. This catalog is available in book form as *Mendelian Inheritance in Man: Catalog of Human Genes and Genetic Disorders*. It is also available at several World Wide Web sites as *Online Mendelian Inheritance in Man (OMIM)*. The online version (with daily updates) contains text, pictures and videos, and references and links to other databases, including the Genome Data Base (GDB). The GDB coordinates, catalogs, and disseminates the information gathered by the Human Genome Project.

Students wishing to learn more about a genetic disorder can use OMIM to obtain a detailed listing that includes the latest information and references available about

the mode of inheritance, phenotype, biochemical basis of the defect, mapping information, molecular nature of mutations, and alleles. OMIM and its links can also be used as the basis for student projects and presentations.

Internet Activities

The World Wide Web (WWW) is a resource that can be used to expand the discussion of genetic concepts as well as specific disorders into other areas, including support groups, ethics, and the transition between basic research and clinical activities. At the end of each chapter, there are one or more Internet activities. These activities use WWW resources to enhance the topics covered in the chapter, and are designed to generate interaction and thought rather than passive observation. Sites for these activities can be reached through the book's home page. Because WWW addresses often change, and because new sites are constantly being generated, the addresses for these activities are monitored and updated as needed.

PEDAGOGICAL FEATURES

The basic organization within chapters, which has been successfully used as a teaching resource, has been retained for this edition. Many of the elements have been revised and updated to reflect current topics to engage student interest and, as mentioned earlier, several new features have been added.

Chapter Outlines

At the beginning of each chapter, an outline provides an overview of the main concepts, secondary ideas, and examples. Most of the headings have been rewritten as descriptive, summary statements that preview the material and often summarize the point of the section. Chapter outlines give the student a convenient way of reviewing the material in the chapter.

Opening Vignettes

Each chapter begins with a short prologue directly related to the main ideas of the chapter, often drawn from real life. Topics include accounts of genetic disorders found in ancient manuscripts, genetic discoveries, and attempts to use genetics for political ends—such as the early attempts to breed human giants. These prologues are designed to engage student interest and to demonstrate the relationship between science and the applications to everyday life.

Concepts and Controversies

Within each chapter, students will find boxes that present topics elaborating on ideas discussed in the chapter. Other boxes offer interesting but tangential examples that should be of interest to the student, or that examine the controversies that often arise when genetic knowledge is transferred into technology and services.

Guest Essays

Scattered throughout the book are seven essays, written by prominent scientists. The scientists summarize how they became interested in science and explain how their work relates to larger issues in society. These essays are intended to introduce students to scientists who work in human genetics and related fields.

Margin Glossary

A glossary in the page margins gives students immediate access to definitions of terms as they are introduced in the text. This format also allows definitions to be easily identified when students are studying the material or preparing for examinations. The same definitions have been gathered into an alphabetical glossary at the back of the text. Because understanding the language of genetics is important in learning concepts, more than 350 terms are included.

 ## END-OF-CHAPTER FEATURES

New end-of-chapter features have been added to this edition. They are designed to help students review the concepts presented and to find additional information.

Summary

Each chapter ends with a summary that restates the major ideas covered in the chapter. Beginning each chapter with an outline and ending with a numbered list of the concepts and their applications helps focus the students' attention on the conceptual framework and minimizes the chance that they will attempt to learn by rote memorization of facts.

Questions and Problems

Questions and problems at the end of each chapter are designed to test students' knowledge of the facts and their ability to reason from the facts to conclusions. This section has been greatly expanded by contributions from adopters of previous editions, by professionals in genetic research and health care services, and by students themselves, who suggested many revisions and new problems.

Science and Society Questions and Mini-Cases

As described earlier, open-ended questions at the end of each chapter ask the students to apply what they have learned to everyday situations. These questions are wide-ranging, from consideration of ethical uses of genetic technology to personal opinions about issues of public policy.

Internet Activities

To demonstrate the resources available on the World Wide Web, and to gain further insights, activities at the end of each chapter utilize one or more Web sites to engage the students in an activity that is related to the concepts discussed in the chapter.

For Further Reading

A list of readings is presented at the end of each chapter. These readings include review and general articles that are accessible to the non-scientist, and key scientific papers for discoveries covered in the chapter. The references have been updated just before publication to provide the most up-to-date coverage of the literature.

 ## ANCILLARY MATERIALS

The expanded ancillary materials that accompany this edition are designed to assist instructors in human genetics in preparing lectures and examinations, and to help keep instructors and students informed about new discoveries in the field.

Instructor's Manual

An expanded, updated, and revised instructor's manual is available to assist the instructor in preparing lectures and examinations. This edition, prepared by Patricia DeLeon of the University of Delaware, contains an outline of each chapter, a list of learning objectives, and questions and problems that can be used for problem sets or examinations. For some chapters, the manual contains additional material not covered in the text or a more detailed consideration of a topic.

Study Guide

A student study guide has been prepared by Nancy Shontz of Grand Valley State University. It contains learning objectives, key word lists, and four types of questions: multiple-choice, fill-in the blank, questions to be edited, and short essay questions/problems.

Transparencies

The most important figures and tables have been reproduced in a set of 150 full-color transparencies that are available to adopters of the text.

Readings Book

An annual book of readings, *Current Perspectives in Genetics,* is prepared by Shelly Cummings of the University of Chicago. The book, which contains over 40 readings selected from general-interest and science magazines, is published concurrently with the text. The readings have been selected to report on the latest discoveries and to convey some of the excitement generated by these discoveries. The book begins with a brief discussion and timeline for the history of genetic research and discoveries. Each article begins with a short synopsis, followed by questions that test the student's knowledge and understanding of the material. Answers to these questions are provided in an appendix. Also provided are URL addresses for Web sites with related information.

Electronic Newsletter

Previous editions of the text were accompanied by a newsletter, published twice yearly, that contained 10 to 12 short articles about new and important discoveries in human genetics. Each article contained references to the relevant papers and was keyed to the chapter in the text where the concept was discussed.

To keep pace with the discoveries in human genetics, the newsletter has been converted to an electronic format, available on the book's home page. As before, each article covers a significant new discovery in human genetics and includes references to the relevant papers. Each article now features an Internet link to one or more sites that have additional information or related articles of interest. The newsletter has been and will continue to be updated monthly, so new research findings can be converted quickly into classroom material. Log onto the book's home page at http://www.wadsworth.com/biology and follow the links to the newsletter.

Contacting the Author

I welcome questions and comments from faculty and students about the book or about human genetics. Please contact me at:

cummings @ uic.edu

❀ ACKNOWLEDGMENTS

By the time a book reaches the fourth edition, it is no longer just the product of the author, but has been shaped and refined by many others, including reviewers, editors, instructors, and students. Over the course of four editions, three reviewers have provided me with valuable guidance and counsel. Their collective wisdom and sharp eyes have improved the presentation of concepts and nuance of language. I owe a debt of gratitude to these colleagues, who gave so generously of their time and input: George Hudock of Indiana University, H. Eldon Sutton of the University of Texas, and Werner Heim of Colorado College.

To all the reviewers who were involved in the preparation of this edition, I extend thanks and gratitude for their efforts and many suggestions. Their efforts greatly enhance the focus and presentation of the material.

Patricia DeLeon
University of Delaware

Kim R. Finer
Kent State University

Werner G. Heim
Colorado College

George A. Hudock
Indiana University

Charles C. Lanbert
California State University, Fullerton

Michelle Murphy
University of Notre Dame

Harold James Price
Texas A & M University

H. Eldon Sutton
University of Texas at Austin

Patricia M. Walsh
University of Delaware

Roberta Williams
University of Nevada

The task of revising the existing end-of-chapter questions and writing new questions at various levels of difficulty was undertaken by Michelle Murphy of Notre Dame University, with contributions by her students. Questions in some chapters were prepared by Shelly Cummings of the University of Chicago. Good end-of-chapter questions are a lot like art—everybody knows what they like, but very few can define what it takes to be good art or a good question. These fearless individuals stepped in where many others feared to tread; the result is an expanded and pedagogically improved feature that is an important part of the learning process. Thanks to you all for your creative and relevant contributions. The "Science and Society" questions were researched and written by Shelly Cummings, whose hard work, optimism, and cheerful attitude produced a new and valuable feature of this edition that enhances the learning process. Many of the "Internet Activities" were contributed by Kim Finer of Kent State University, who is one of the pioneers in using electronic resources in the classroom. Her expertise and efforts have helped set the standard for future editions and texts in this field.

This edition was prepared during a time of transition at West Publishing. Over the years, I have worked with more than a half-dozen publishing houses involved in the production of college textbooks. I was always impressed with, and will always remember, the care and dedication with which the people at West crafted books. A spirit of cooperation, civility, and mutual respect was always evident at all levels; those attributes are increasingly rare in a time when both public and private discourse is becoming coarser and sometimes mean-spirited.

More than anything, it was the insight, encouragement, and persistence of my editor, Jerry Westby, that helped bring this book into existence. His creative contributions, ability to look at things from the student's point of view, and his commitment to undergraduate education have helped shape each edition. Over the twelve years we worked together, his advice, guidance, and friendship have always been the most valuable benefits of this project. Matt Thurber, my production editor for this and the previous edition, worked through and around the inevitable distractions to convert this edition into a full-color book, while managing the galleys, layouts,

proofs, and pages. His high standards in all aspects of manuscript and art preparation, photo selection, and his attention to detail have greatly enhanced the book. Friendship and a shared enthusiasm for jazz and the cuisine at Al's Beef is a lasting sidelight to working with Matt.

Thanks also to Halee Dinsey, my developmental editor. Her analysis of the reviews and summary of the strengths and weaknesses of the book, along with her insights and recommendations, laid the foundation for the reorganization of the text and the development of the new chapters found in this edition. My copy editor, Chris Thillen, kept me safe from the shoals of dangling modifiers and comma splices. Her detailed and welcome analysis of my writing will improve future editions of this and my other texts. Diane Beasley, a talented and award-winning designer, brought the elements of this edition to life by creating an outstanding design for the book, the cover, and the page layout. Ann Hillstrom developed an original and effective marketing promotion for this edition, highlighting the book's goals, aims, and extensive revisions.

Finally, special thanks go to my colleague, Suzanne McCutcheon, for so generously giving her time to supervise the research in my lab during the preparation of this edition.

Michael R. Cummings

GENETICS AS A HUMAN ENDEAVOR

Chapter Outline

THE DOMESTICATION OF PLANTS AND
   ANIMALS
ANCIENT CONCEPTS ABOUT GENETICS
IDEAS ABOUT HEREDITY CHANGED IN
   THE 18TH AND 19TH CENTURY
Ancient Theories Remained Influential
New Theories Revolutionized Biology
Darwin and Wallace Developed the Theory of
   Natural Selection
Mendel Changed Ideas about Inheritance
NATURAL SELECTION AND EUGENICS
The Eugenics Movement in the United States
CONCEPTS AND CONTROVERSIES   *Genetics,*
   Eugenics, and Nazi Germany
Eugenics and the Nazi Movement
THE EMERGENCE OF HUMAN GENETICS
   AS A DISTINCT BRANCH OF GENETICS
GUEST ESSAY   *Genomic Research*
THE FUTURE OF HUMAN GENETICS
CONCEPTS AND CONTROVERSIES   *Genetic*
   Disorders in Society, History, and Art

Chapter 1

OPENING IMAGE
The development of art was an important
stage in human evolution.

THE DOMESTICATION OF PLANTS AND ANIMALS

Interest in heredity and the transmission of traits from generation to generation can be traced back more than 10,000 years to preliterate cultures. Evidence from animal remains and pictorial representations (■ Figure 1.1) indicates that dogs, sheep, goats, oxen, camels, and other animals were domesticated some 10,000 to 12,000 years ago. How domestication took place is still unknown, but it may have proceeded from the capture of young members of a herd and their maintenance and reproduction under human control. Once animals were domesticated, heritable traits were manipulated by selective breeding to produce strains with characteristics tailored to human needs. Distinctive breeds of a species can be developed rapidly under selective breeding. As Charles Darwin pointed out, a wide array of mink breeds with different coat colors was produced in only 25 generations.

Cultivated plants were developed at about the same time as domesticated animals. The existence of two distinct sexes of date palms was

FIGURE 1.1

Carving from the Old Kingdom (2700–2200 B.C.) tomb of the Egyptian Nefer el Ka-Hay. This panel shows agricultural activities, including the harvesting of papyrus and herding of cattle, indicating that the domestication of plants and animals is an ancient practice.

known by the Assyrians and Babylonians as early as 5000 B.C. Artificial fertilization of date palms (Figure 1.2) was common in the reign of Hammurabi (2000 B.C.). Records on clay tablets indicate that date pollen was a commercial product at that time. Several hundred varieties of dates—developed by selective breeding—were available, each differing in a characteristic such as size, color, time of maturation, and taste. Many of these ancient strains are still grown in the Middle East and other parts of the world.

Selective breeding and the development of domesticated plants and animals eventually became part of the economy of many cultures. Ancient poets recount that part of the wealth and reputation of the Trojan empire was derived from skills in horse breeding.

ANCIENT CONCEPTS ABOUT GENETICS

In Greek civilization, philosophy concerned itself with explaining the origin and organization of the universe and of living systems, including humans. The search for laws governing reproduction and heredity produced theories that had a profound influence on European science that lasted well into the 19th century. We will briefly consider three of these ideas: pangenesis, male and female contributions to offspring, and inheritance of acquired characteristics.

To explain how characteristics are transmitted from parent to offspring, the Greek philosophers proposed that semen is formed as small particles in every part of the body. These particles, known as pangenes, travel through the blood to the testicles, from which they are transferred to the female during intercourse. The transmission of abnormally formed particles explained the appearance of deformities in some newborns. Some of the ancient Greek philosophers believed that females also formed semen in a similar fashion and passed traits to their children. The theory that hereditary particles were formed in organs, moved through the blood, and were transmitted to the offspring is known as **pangenesis.** This theory remained influential until the middle of the 19th century.

Pangenesis
A discarded theory of heredity that postulated the existence of pangenes, small particles from all parts of the body that concentrated in the gametes, passing traits from generation to generation and blending the traits of the parents in the offspring.

● FIGURE 1.2
Artifical pollination of date palms is depicted in a relief carving done in the reign of the Assyrian king Assurnasirpal II (883–859 B.C). Many varieties of date palms are still grown today in the Middle East.

Greek philosophers also considered the question of whether each parent makes an equal contribution to the characteristics of the offspring. On this point there was much debate and little agreement. The philosopher Aeschylus felt that the male parent determined all the characteristics of the offspring. In 458 B.C. he wrote:

> The mother of what is called her child is no parent of it, but nurse only of the young life that is sown in her. The parent is the male, and she but a stranger, a friend, who, if fate spares his plant, preserves it till it puts forth.

Most of the Greek philosophers agreed that characteristics acquired through accident or experience were transmitted to the offspring. This view is reflected in the writings of Aristotle:

> . . . the children of parents who bore scars are also scarred in just the same way and in just the same place. In Chalcedon, for example, a man who had been branded on the arm had a child who showed the same branded letter, though it was not so distinctly marked and had become blurred.

In part it was necessary to introduce the idea of the inheritance of acquired characteristics to explain why children often have traits that are different from those of their parents.

✺ IDEAS ABOUT HEREDITY CHANGED IN THE 18TH AND 19TH CENTURY

Attention was again focused on the mechanisms of heredity and development in the 17th and 18th centuries. At this time, two competing theories emerged: epigenesis and preformationism. According to the theory of **epigenesis,** the organs and struc-

Epigenesis
The idea that development proceeds by the appearance and growth of new structures.

Preformationism
An idea that an organism develops by the growth of preformed structures already present in the egg.

Homunculus
The preformed, miniature individual thought to be present in the sperm or egg.

⬤ FIGURE 1.3

An engraving showing a preformed human infant or homunculus contained within a sperm. Preformationism, the idea that sperm or eggs contain an intact, miniature human, was first proposed in the late 1600s.

Natural selection
The process by which the organisms possessing heritable variations that make them better adapted to the environment leave more offspring than those organisms not possessing such variations.

Evolution
The appearance of new species of plants and animals.

tures of the adult are not present initially, but arise during the course of development. Opposed to this was the idea of **preformationism,** which held that the sperm or the egg contained a completely formed miniature adult, known as a **homunculus** (⬤ Figure 1.3). Among the preformationists, ovists held that the egg contained the preformed individual and that the sperm served to stimulate growth. Spermists, on the other hand, believed that the sperm contained the homunculus.

Ancient Theories Remained Influential

By the middle of the 19th century, the theories formulated by the ancient Greeks to explain heredity and development remained influential. Pangenesis was still regarded as a valid way of explaining the transmission of traits from parent to offspring. The issue of what contributions to the offspring were made by each parent was still unresolved, and the inheritance of acquired characteristics had been incorporated into a theory of evolution formulated by Jean Baptiste-Lamarck in the early 1800s (⬤ Figure 1.4). Although Greek philosophers speculated that living organisms might have arisen from ancestral forms, serious inquiry into the formation of plant and animal species from preexisting species began only in the 18th century. These ideas gained little support, so that in the mid-19th century, the idea that species did not change after their appearance (the fixity of species) still predominated.

New Theories Revolutionized Biology

In the mid-19th century, a series of new theories revolutionized biology. These new ideas included the cell theory proposed by Schleiden and Schwann. According to this theory, all organisms are composed of cells, which are derived from preexisting cells. The concept of natural selection—and Mendel's work on heredity along with the cell theory—overturned ancient ideas about how traits were inherited, and how new species of plants and animals arose, and set the stage for the remarkable advances that followed in this century.

Darwin and Wallace Developed the Theory of Natural Selection

Against this background, the discovery of the principles of natural selection and genetics rank as two of the greatest achievements in the history of science. After observing the natural history of a great number of different organisms, Alfred Russel Wallace and Charles Darwin formulated the principle of **natural selection.** They observed that all organisms produce more progeny than can reasonably survive. Some of the individuals among the progeny often contain small, heritable variations that enhance their ability for survival and reproduction. Through the process of natural selection, those variations gradually spread through a population. Darwin called this process "descent with modification." According to Wallace and Darwin, the spread of favorable variations occurs in response to alterations in environmental conditions. Over long periods, accumulated changes bring about the formation of new species: the process of **evolution** (Figure 1.4). Those species that do not respond to changes in the environment become extinct. As species become extinct, they are replaced by new species that are adapted to survive in the new conditions.

Understanding the mechanisms that generate these variations is basic to an understanding of evolution. Variations that promote differential survival and reproduction are valuable only if they are passed on from generation to generation. Darwin knew nothing of the process of inheritance but recognized the need for such a mechanism for natural selection to be successful.

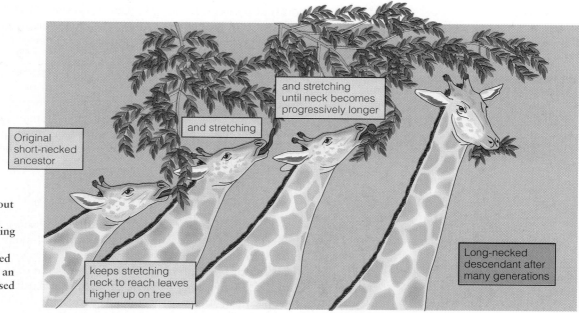

FIGURE 1.4

Contrasting ideas about the mechanism of evolution. (a) According to Lamarck's theory, characteristics acquired during the lifetime of an individual can be passed on to subsequent generations. In this example, short-necked giraffes stretch their necks to reach higher into the trees for food, and during their lifetime, their necks become longer. This trait is passed on to offspring, who were born with longer necks. (b) According to the Wallace-Darwin theory of natural selection, some giraffes have slightly longer necks as a naturally occurring variation. If this is advantageous for feeding, giraffes with this trait will have an advantage in feeding and more of these giraffes will survive to pass the trait to their offspring. Over time and many generations, natural selection will lead to an increase in the length of giraffe necks.

In figure (a): Original short-necked ancestor; keeps stretching neck to reach leaves higher up on tree; and stretching; and stretching until neck becomes progressively longer; Long-necked descendant after many generations. (a)

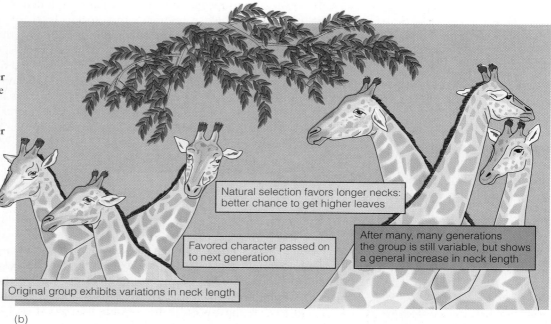

In figure (b): Original group exhibits variations in neck length; Favored character passed on to next generation; Natural selection favors longer necks: better chance to get higher leaves; After many, many generations the group is still variable, but shows a general increase in neck length. (b)

Mendel Changed Ideas about Inheritance

Following the publication of Darwin's book *The Origin of Species*, the work of an Augustinian monk named Gregor Mendel dramatically changed ideas about inheritance that had gone unchallenged for thousands of years. Working with pea plants, Mendel showed that traits are passed from parent to offspring through the inheritance of factors we now call **genes**. He reasoned that each parent contributes one factor to the traits shown in the offspring, and that pairs of traits separate from each other during the formation of egg and sperm.

Mendel's work showed that the male and female parent make equal contributions to the traits of the offspring, and that there is no inheritance of acquired character-

Genes
The fundamental units of heredity.

Genetics
The scientific study of heredity.

Biometrics
The application of statistical methods to problems in biological sciences.

Eugenics
The attempt to improve the human species by selective breeding.

Hereditarianism
The idea that human traits are determined solely by the genotype, ignoring the contribution of the environment.

● FIGURE 1.5
Sir Francis Galton, cousin of Charles Darwin and the founder of the eugenics movement.

istics. In the short time between 1859, when Darwin published *The Origin of Species,* and 1866, when Mendel published his work on the inheritance of traits in pea plants, ideas that had held sway for centuries were replaced with new theories based on specific and fundamental biological mechanisms.

The term **genetics** was coined by William Bateson to describe the study of inheritance and the expression of inherited traits. Genetics as an organized discipline began in the 20th century and has progressed to the point where we have transferred human genes into animals and are replacing defective human genes with normal genes. Although genetics has progressed rapidly in this century, progress in human genetics has been uneven, and on occasion, human genetics has been badly used for social and political purposes.

✿ NATURAL SELECTION AND EUGENICS

The Origin of Species contains few references to human evolution. However, the concept of natural selection had a great impact on the study of human society, and it became popular to explain culture and social progress in terms of natural selection. Progress was the result of selection of the fit and elimination of the unfit. Sir Francis Galton (● Figure 1.5), a cousin of Darwin, thought that natural selection could be used as a tool to consciously improve the human species. He developed statistical and mathematical tools to study human traits, established the value of twin studies in genetics, and founded **biometrics,** a field that statistically analyzes the variation observed in traits such as height and weight. He also founded **eugenics,** a method of improving the intellectual, economic, and social level of humans by allowing differential reproduction of superior people to prevail over those designated as inferior. Galton studied the inheritance of many traits in families, such as musical ability and leadership, and concluded that such traits were handed down without environmental influence. As he phrased it, nature was more important than nurture (the idea that all human traits are genetically determined is known as **hereditarianism**).

Galton's ideas were summarized in the book *Natural Inheritance,* published in 1889. He proposed that individuals having desirable traits be encouraged to have large families (positive eugenics), while those having traits regarded as undesirable should be discouraged from reproducing (negative eugenics). In this way the evolution of the human species could be controlled and directed by an artificial form of natural selection.

The Eugenics Movement in the United States

In the United States, eugenics and genetics were first united in the American Breeder's Association, founded in 1903 by biology professors and stock breeders to encourage Mendelian research. One of the committees set up by the association was the Eugenics Committee, which was to "investigate and report on heredity in the human race" and to "emphasize the value of superior blood and the menace of inferior blood."

Charles Davenport, chairman of the Eugenics Committee, was instrumental in setting up a Eugenics Record Office at Cold Springs Harbor, New York, which later served as the center of the eugenics movement in America. The office trained eugenic field workers, who in turn went to prisons, asylums, and reformatories to construct pedigrees of the inmates. This information was sent to the Record Office, where it became part of a repository on human heredity. Unfortunately, Davenport and many others in the eugenics movement thought that most human traits were controlled by single genes, just as Mendel had reported for traits such as seed color and height in pea plants. As a result, human traits such as insanity, alcoholism, morality, tuberculosis, religious preference, love of the sea, and quickness of temper were all considered to be inherited as genetic traits (● Figure 1.6). The emphasis in all these studies was on the gene; little thought was given to the effects of environment.

Having accepted that most social problems were rooted in genetics, eugenicists in the United States worked to promote selective breeding in the human population (● Figure 1.7), to regulate immigration and to control reproduction of those designated as genetically defective. From about 1905 through 1933, eugenics became a powerful and influential force in the development of laws formulating social policy. This influence reached a peak in the passage of federal laws restricting immigration from southern and eastern Europe and the implementation of forced sterilization as a eugenic policy.

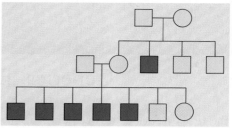

● FIGURE 1.6

A family history or pedigree, collected by eugenicists at the beginning of this century, showing that nomadism, or love of wandering, is an inherited trait. In this pedigree, males are represented by squares, females by circles, and affected individuals by shaded symbols.

Eugenics and Immigration Laws   In the early decades of this century, the rationale for restricting immigration was based on the argument that heredity alone was responsible for all aspects of the human personality and human behavior. Since immigrants with prolific reproductive patterns and high frequency of deleterious mutations were likely to lower the quality of American life, immigration of these groups should be controlled. The high levels of unemployment, poverty, and crime among immigrants from southern and eastern Europe was taken as evidence of genetic inferiority. In addition, surveys of those confined to institutions for the insane and feebleminded were reported in a manner designed to show that a disproportionate number were from eastern and southern Europe. Expert testimony by leading authorities on eugenics indicated that many recent immigrants also carried recessive deleterious traits that would become evident in their homozygous recessive children and contaminate the American gene pool.

Based on what were presented as established scientific principles of biology and genetics, Congress enacted the Immigration Act of 1924, which was signed by President Calvin Coolidge. The law, in effect, closed the door to America for millions of people in southern and eastern Europe, marking the end of the idea that America was a land of opportunity open to all. Forty-one years later, in 1965, the Cellar Act—sponsored by Rep. Emanuel Cellar of New York—reformed the immigration laws, with immigrants admitted by the order in which they applied, rather than by their country of origin.

● FIGURE 1.7

In the early part of the century, eugenics exhibits were a common feature at fairs and similar events. Such exhibits served to educate the public about genetics and the benefits of eugenics as public policy. These exhibits often included contests to find the eugenically perfect family.

CONCEPTS AND CONTROVERSIES

Genetics, Eugenics, and Nazi Germany

In the first decades of this century, eugenics advocates in Germany were concerned with preservation of racial "purity," as were their colleagues in other countries, including the United States and England. By 1927, many states in the United States had enacted laws that prohibited marriage by "social misfits," and made sterilization compulsory for the "genetically unfit" and for certain crimes. In Germany, the laws of the Weimar government prohibited sterilization, and there were no laws restricting marriage on eugenic grounds. As a result, several leading eugenicists became associated with the National Socialist Party (Nazis), which advocated forced sterilization and other eugenic measures to preserve the purity of the Aryan "race."

Adolf Hitler and the Nazi party came to power in January 1933. By July of that year a sterilization law was in effect, and before the end of that year, it had been amended to broaden its powers. Under the law, those regarded as having lives not worth living, including the feebleminded, epileptics, the deformed, those having hereditary forms of blindness or deafness, and alcoholics, were to be sterilized.

By the end of 1933, the policy was extended to include mercy killing (Gnadentod) of newborns who were incurably ill with hereditary disorders or birth defects. This program was gradually expanded to include children up to 3 or 4 years of age, then adolescents, and finally, all institutionalized children, including juvenile delinquents and Jewish children. More than two dozen institutions in Germany, Austria, and Poland were assigned to carry out this program. Children were usually killed by poison, or by starvation.

In 1939, the program was extended to include mentally retarded and mentally defective adults, and adults with certain genetic disorders. This program began by killing adults in psychiatric hospitals. As increasing numbers were killed, gas chambers were installed at several institutions to dispose of the impaired and the defective. This practice spread from mental hospitals to include defective individuals in concentration camps, and then to whole groups of people in concentration camps, most of whom were Jews, Gypsies, Communists, homosexuals, and political opponents of the government.

Eugenics and Reproductive Rights The first law in the United States regulating marriage for the purposes of preventing reproduction among those regarded as defective was passed in Connecticut in 1896. By 1905, five other states had similar laws. Typically, marriage by epileptics, criminals, alcoholics, the insane, and the feebleminded was made a violation of state law. Many of these laws were promoted and supported by local groups such as physicians, church organizations, and charities. By the time the eugenics movement was fading away in the mid-1930s, 41 (out of 48) states had laws preventing marriage by several groups defined as socially or genetically defective.

The eugenics movement in the United States became closely identified with laws that required sterilization for those labeled as socially defective. A committee of the American Breeder's Association concluded that 10% of the American population was socially inadequate, and proposed that these individuals should be segregated from the rest of the American gene pool either by being institutionalized or sterilized.

The first sterilization law was passed in 1907 in Indiana. In the next 10 years, similar laws were passed in 15 other states. Most of these laws were punitive, providing for sterilization of those labeled as genetic defectives as well as those convicted of certain crimes. These early laws were criticized for not allowing due process and protection of constitutional rights. Through the 1920s and 1930s, revisions in sterilization laws removed most of these objections. But in spite of these reforms, there was widespread feeling that in matters of genetic defects, the rights of the state far outweighed the rights of the individual.

The *Buck vs. Bell* decision by the U.S. Supreme Court in 1927 established the legal principle that it is within the power of the state to use forced sterilization for eugenic reasons. In rendering the decision of the Court, Justice Oliver Wendell Holmes emphasized the right of the state to employ sterilization:

We have seen more than once that the public welfare may call upon the best citizens for their lives. It would be strange if it could not call upon those who already sap the strength of the state for these lesser sacrifices, often not felt to be such by those concerned, in order to prevent our being swamped with incompetence. It is better for all the world, if instead of waiting to execute degenerate offspring for crime, or to let them starve for their imbecility, society can prevent those who are manifestly unfit from continuing their kind. The principle that sustains compulsory vaccination is broad enough to cover cutting the fallopian tubes.

What such reasoning fails to take into account is that sterilization is an ineffective eugenic measure. In most cases, sterilization will have almost no effect on the frequency of a genetic disorder. Sterilization laws are still on the books in about 20 states, and although they are sporadically enforced, they remain as testimony to the effectiveness of the eugenics movement.

Eugenics and the Nazi Movement

In Germany, eugenics (known as Rassenhygiene) fused with genetics and the political philosophy of the Nazi movement (see "Concepts and Controversies" on page 000). This relationship evolved into a government policy that began with sterilization and, later, the systematic killing of those individuals defined as social defectives. This included the retarded, the physically deformed, and the mentally ill. Later this rationale was used in an attempt to eradicate entire ethnic groups, such as the Gypsies and Jews. The association of eugenics with the policies of the government of Nazi Germany led to the rapid decline of the eugenics movement in the United States by the mid-1930s.

✿ THE EMERGENCE OF HUMAN GENETICS AS A DISTINCT BRANCH OF GENETICS

During and immediately after World War II, research in human genetics focused on the identification of Mendelian traits and the use of mathematical formulas to study genes in different human populations. During this period, human genetics emerged as a separate branch of genetics. Studies on the effects of atomic radiation on residents of Nagasaki and Hiroshima and their offspring by a Japanese-American team of scientists under the leadership of James Neel of the University of Michigan provided a new direction for human genetics. Another group, led by Linus Pauling at Cal Tech, discovered that a genetic disorder known as sickle cell anemia was caused by a defective hemoglobin molecule (▬ Figure 1.8), giving birth to the field of human molecular genetics. Human cytogenetics began in 1956 when J. H. Tijo and A. Levan determined that humans carried 46 chromosomes, and in 1959 the chromosomal basis of Down syndrome was identified.

The revolution in molecular genetics that began with the discovery of the structure of DNA in 1952, and the elucidation of the genetic code, had an immediate impact on hu-

▬ **FIGURE 1.8**

Hemoglobin is an oxygen-transporting protein found in red blood cells.

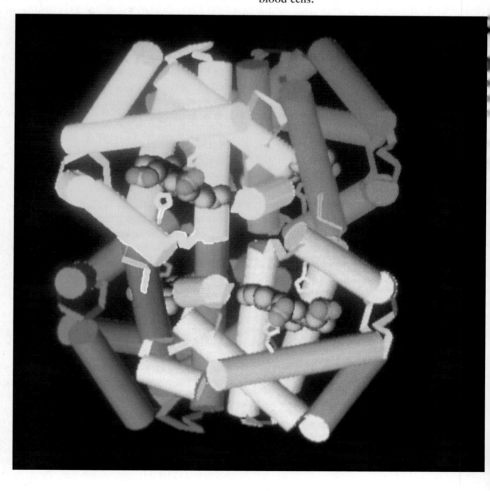

Genomic Research

J. CRAIG VENTER

My high school days were devoted more to competitive swimming and the building of hydroplanes than to my studies. As a result, I barely graduated. After high school, I moved to Newport Beach, California, to concentrate on surfing. Because I was not in school, I was drafted in 1965, but I took the option to enlist in the Navy, where I was to serve on the swim team, until Lyndon Johnson further escalated the war in Vietnam.

Out of an interest in medicine, I became a medical corpsman. One and a half years of training later, I ended up in DaNang, Vietnam, at the Navy hospital. The schedule was twelve hours a day, seven days a week. In addition, there was a nearby Vietnamese orphanage without any medical care, and I volunteered to spend one day a week there. I was learning at an incredible rate, making a difference, and I loved it. I turned 21 in Vietnam, and I left the Navy with a clear, new direction. I wanted to go into medicine.

I completed my undergraduate work in three years and went on to do the same in graduate school, receiving a Ph.D. in physiology and pharmacology in 1975. My route to medical practice was altered by my introduction to fundamental science. I was fascinated by how cells worked at the molecular level and by how little was actually known. I was very fortunate to be able to study under Nathan O. Kaplan, the discoverer of co-enzyme A and the lactate dehydrogenase isoenzymes. I learned from Kaplan not to be afraid to take on any new technique, an approach that has helped me throughout my career.

In 1984, my lab moved to the National Institutes of Health (NIH). Using a manual DNA sequencing technique, we sequenced the gene for one of the first human receptors from the brain.

The Human Genome Project was just being discussed. I found the prospect of identifying the entire human genome with its 50,000 to 100,000 genes exciting. Having the human genes characterized would alter medicine, change fundamental, basic science, and rewrite molecular evolution. I was hooked.

Because of our team's sequencing experience and capacity, in 1991 we were asked by the Secretary of Health and Human Services and the Centers for Disease Control to sequence the 186,000 bp genome of the small pox virus (variola) as a prelude to its final destruction. We have since embarked on a major program to sequence the genomes of a number of microbes. As of 1995, we have sequenced the first two genomes of free living organisms, *Haemophilus influenzae* (1,831,000 bp, *Science*, July 18, 1995) and *Mycoplasma genitalism* (581,000 bp, *Science*, October 1995).

Because of the conservation of genes throughout evolution, many human genes have counterparts in other organisms, including animals and plants. Thus, it is possible to assign probable function to newly discovered genes by their sequence similarity to genes that have been studied in other organisms. This occurred in December 1993 at our institute when in collaboration with Bert Vogelstein and his coworkers, at Johns Hopkins University we identified the function of three new human genes in our database through their sequence similarity to mismatch repair genes in bacteria. The human genes are associated with non-polyposis colon cancer. This ability to rapidly compare genes sequences from different organisms comes from the emerging science of bioinformatics, which will serve as a powerful tool for all of the biological sciences, including evolutionary biology.

J. CRAIG VENTER *is the founder, director, and president of The Institute for Genomic Research, a not-for-profit research center located in Rockville, Maryland. He earned a B.S. and Ph.D. from the University of California, San Diego. The Institute applies high-throughput sequencing methods and bioinformatic to identify and characterize genes and entire genomes in a variety of organisms, including plant, animal, and human, with the overall goal of describing evolution at the whole genome level.*

man genetics (Figure 1.9). In the years following these discoveries, the molecular basis of a number of human genetic disorders was explained. This allowed the use of dietary restrictions to treat genetic disorders such as phenylketonuria and galactosemia.

With the development of recombinant DNA techniques in the 1970s, human genetics has made rapid strides. In the span of about 20 years, we have learned how to predict the sex of unborn children, to diagnose many genetic disorders prenatally, and to manufacture gene products to prevent the deleterious effects of some genetic diseases. The Human Genome Project, started in 1991, is an international effort to

map all the genetic information carried by humans at its most elemental level: the 3 billion nucleotide subunits of DNA. As of this writing, the project is ahead of its 15 year timetable, and has produced detailed genetic maps of all human chromosomes.

Genetic technology has made it possible to produce human embryos by fusion of sperm and eggs in a laboratory dish and transfer the developing embryo to the womb of a surrogate mother (Figure 1.10). Embryos can also be frozen for transfer to a womb at a later time. Genetic defects are being corrected by inserting normal genes to replace mutant genes, a technique called gene therapy. We can even insert human genes into animals, creating new types of organisms.

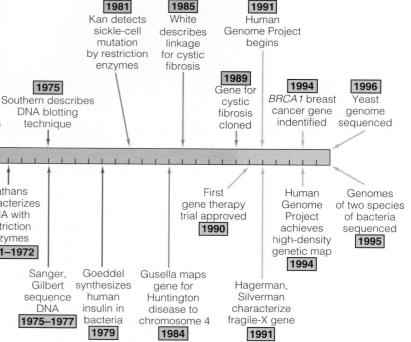

 FIGURE 1.9

The structure of DNA, discovered by James Watson and Francis Crick in 1952, marked the beginning of molecular genetics.

THE FUTURE OF HUMAN GENETICS

Although genetic knowledge has been accumulating for thousands of years (see "Concepts and Controversies" on page 12), almost all of what we know has been discovered in this century (Figure 1.11). The amount of scientific

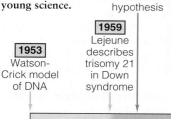

 FIGURE 1.10

Human embryo, shortly after fertilization in the laboratory. Embryos at this stage of development can be analyzed for genetic disorders before implantation into the uterus of the egg donor, or that of another, surrogate mother.

 FIGURE 1.11

A time line showing the major advances in genetics that have had an impact on human genetics. Most of the advances have occurred in the last 50 years, making human genetics a relatively young science.

1961
Lyon proposes X-inactivation hypothesis

1959
Lejeune describes trisomy 21 in Down syndrome

1953
Watson-Crick model of DNA

1966–1968
Linn, Arber, Smith discover restriction enzymes

1975
Southern describes DNA blotting technique

1981
Kan detects sickle-cell mutation by restriction enzymes

1985
White describes linkage for cystic fibrosis

1991
Human Genome Project begins

1989
Gene for cystic fibrosis cloned

1994
BRCA1 breast cancer gene indentified

1996
Yeast genome sequenced

Tijo, Levan find chromosome number in humans is 46
1956

Khorana, Nirenberg, Ochoa decipher the genetic code
1966

Nathans characterizes DNA with restriction enzymes
1971–1972

First gene therapy trial approved
1990

Human Genome Project achieves high-density genetic map
1994

Genomes of two species of bacteria sequenced
1995

Sanger, Gilbert sequence DNA
1975–1977

Goeddel synthesizes human insulin in bacteria
1979

Gusella maps gene for Huntington disease to chromosome 4
1984

Hagerman, Silverman characterize fragile-X gene
1991

CONCEPTS AND CONTROVERSIES

Genetic Disorders in Society, History, and Art

It is difficult to pinpoint when the inheritance of specific traits in humans was first recognized. Descriptions of heritable disorders often appear in myths and legends in many different cultures. Other ancient cultures assigned social roles in a hereditary fashion—from prophets and priests to kings and queens. The belief that certain traits were heritable helped shape the development of many cultures and social customs.

In some ancient societies, the birth of a deformed child was regarded as a sign of impending war or famine. Clay tablets from Babylonian cities record more than 60 types of birth defects, along with the dire consequences thought to accompany such births. Later societies, ranging from the Romans to 18th-century Europe, regarded malformed individuals (such as dwarfs) as curiosities rather than figures of impending doom, and they were highly prized by royalty as courtiers and entertainers.

Whether motivated by fear, curiosity, or an urge to record the many variations of the human form, both famous and anonymous individuals with genetic disorders have been

portrayed in paintings, sculptures, and other forms of the visual arts. These portrayals are often detailed, highly accurate, and are easily recognizable today. In fact, across time, culture, and artistic medium, affected individuals shown in these portraits often resemble each other more closely than they do their siblings, peers, or family members. In some cases, the representations allow the disorder to be clearly diagnosed at a distance of several thousand years.

To the left is a painting of a child with the short stature, short extremities, obesity, and facial features characteristic of a genetic disorder known as Prader-Willi syndrome. Throughout the book you will find fine-art representations of individuals afflicted with genetic disorders. These portraits represent the long-standing link between science and the arts in many cultures. They are not intended as a gallery of freaks or monsters, but as a reminder that being human encompasses a wide range of conditions. A more thorough discussion of genetic disorders in art is in *Genetics and Malformations in Art*, by J. Kunze and I. Nippert, published by Grosse Verläg, Berlin, 1986.

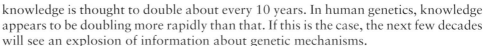

knowledge is thought to double about every 10 years. In human genetics, knowledge appears to be doubling more rapidly than that. If this is the case, the next few decades will see an explosion of information about genetic mechanisms.

More importantly, we are beginning to apply genetic knowledge in ways that will affect us all, and this trend will probably accelerate in the coming years. One of the most visible applications is the Human Genome Project. This work will generate new knowledge about complex genetic disorders such as heart disease and mental disorders and will provide insight into cellular processes that may help unravel the causes of cancer.

Developments in biotechnology have produced fundamental changes in the diagnosis of genetic disorders and infectious diseases. They have also led to the develop-

ment of genetically engineered plants and animals. In the pharmaceutical industry, genetically engineered bacteria are being used to produce human gene products for therapeutic purposes. Human insulin was the first such product, and it is one of over two dozen now available.

The application of much of this knowledge raises new ethical questions that we must face and answer in the near future. As a student of human genetics, you have elected to become involved in the search for answers to these important questions.

FOR FURTHER READING

Adams, M. B. (1990). *The wellborn science: Eugenics in Germany, France, Brazil, and Russia.* New York: Oxford University Press.

Ahmed, I. (Ed.). (1992). *Biotechnology: A Hope or Threat?* London: St. Martin's Press.

Anderson, W. F., & Dircumakos, E. G. (1981, July). Genetic engineering in mammalian cells. *Sci. Am., 245* 106–121.

Bishop, J. E., & Waldholz, M. (1990). *Genome.* New York: Simon and Schuster.

Brackman, A. C. (1980). *A Delicate Arrangement: The Strange Case of Charles Darwin and Alfred Russel Wallace.* New York: Times Books.

Brooks, J. L. (1984). *Just Before the Origin: Alfred Russel Wallace's Theory of Evolution.* New York: Columbia University Press.

Bud, R. (1993). *The Use of Life: A History of Biotechnology.* New York: Cambridge University Press.

Carter, G. S. (1957). *A Hundred Years of Evolution.* London: Sidgwick & Jackson.

Corcos, A. (1984). Reproductive hereditary beliefs of the Hindus, based on their sacred books. *J. Hered., 75,* 152–154.

Davis, B. D., ed. (1991). *The Genetic Revolution: Scientific Prospects and Public Perceptions.* Baltimore: Johns Hopkins Press.

Dunn, L. C. (1962). Cross currents in the history of human genetics. *Am. J. Hum. Genet., 14,* 1–13.

Dunn, L. C. (1965). *A short history of genetics.* New York: McGraw-Hill.

Hopwood, D. A. (1981, September). The genetic programming of industrial microorganisms. *Sci. Am., 245,* 91–102.

Kevles, D. J. (1985). *In the Name of Eugenics: Genetics and the Use of Human Heredity.* New York: Knopf.

Kevles, D. J., Hood, L. (Eds.). (1992). *The code of codes: Scientific and social issues in the Human Genome Project.* Cambridge, MA: Harvard University Press.

Kuhl, S. (1994). *The Nazi connection: Eugenics, American racism, and the German national socialism.* New York: Oxford University Press.

Larson, E. J. (1995). *Sex, race and science: Eugenics in the deep South.* Baltimore: Johns Hopkins University Press.

Lifton, R. J. (1986). *The Nazi doctors: Medical killing and the psychology of genocide.* New York: Knopf.

McKusick, V. J. (1975). The growth and development of human genetics as a clinical discipline. *Am. J. Hum. Genet., 27,* 261–273.

Muller-Hill, B. (1988). *Murderous science: Elimination by scientific selection of Jews, Gypsies, and others, Germany, 1933–1945.* Oxford: Oxford University Press.

Proctor, R. N. (1988). *Racial hygiene: Medicine under the Nazis.* Cambridge, MA: Harvard University Press.

Rafter, N. H. (1988). *White trash.* Boston: Northeastern University Press.

Reilly, P. R. (1991). *The surgical solution: A history of involuntary sterilization in the United States.* Baltimore: Johns Hopkins University Press.

Ryder, M. I. (1987, January). The evolution of fleece. *Sci. Am., 256,* 112–119.

Stern, C., & Sherwood, E. (1966). *The origin of genetics: A Mendel sourcebook.* San Francisco: Freeman.

Stubbe, H. (1972). *History of genetics: From prehistoric times to the rediscovery of Mendel's laws.* Cambridge, MA: MIT Press.

Tijo, H. J., & Levan, A. (1956). The chromosome number of man. *Hereditas, 42,* 1–6.

Torrey, J. G. (1985). The development of plant biotechnology. *Am. Sci., 73,* 354–363.

Weiss, S. F. (1988). *Race hygiene and national efficiency: The eugenics of William Schallmeyer.* Berkeley: University of California Press.

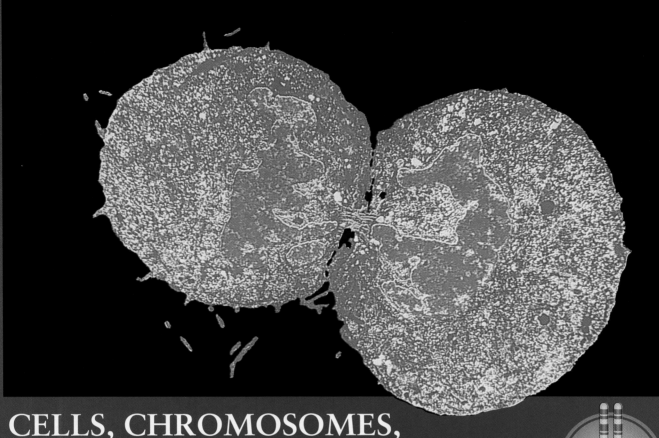

CELLS, CHROMOSOMES, AND CELL DIVISION

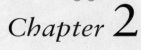

Chapter 2

Chapter Outline

THERE ARE TWO MAIN TYPES OF
   CELLS: PROKARYOTIC AND
   EUKARYOTIC
CELL STRUCTURES AND FUNCTIONS
There Is a Wide Range of Cell Sizes
The Plasma Membrane and the Cytoplasm
Organelles Are Specialized Structures in the
   Cytoplasm
SIDEBAR   *A Fatal Membrane Flaw*
IDENTIFICATION AND
   CLASSIFICATION OF
   CHROMOSOMES

THE CELL CYCLE DESCRIBES THE LIFE
   HISTORY OF A CELL
Interphase Has Three Stages
SIDEBAR   *Cell Division and Spinal Cord
   Injuries*
CONCEPTS AND CONTROVERSIES   *HeLa
   Cells: The Ultimate Growth Industry*
Cell Division by Mitosis Occurs in Four
   Stages
Cytokinesis Begins during Telophase
SIGNIFICANCE OF MITOSIS
THE HUMAN CHROMOSOME SET

CELL DIVISION BY MEIOSIS: THE BASIS
   OF SEX
CONCEPTS AND CONTROVERSIES   *Making
   a Karyotype*
Meiosis I Reduces the Chromosome Number
GUEST ESSAY   *Nothing in Biology Makes
   Sense without Evolution*
Meiosis II Begins with Haploid Cells
Meiosis Produces New Combinations of
   Genes in Two Ways
Formation of Gametes: Spermatogenesis and
   Oogenesis

OPENING IMAGE
A cell in the final stages of mitosis.

E merging *from the womb, a newborn human represents the culmination
of a series of genetically programmed events that began some 38 weeks
earlier. At birth an infant contains trillions of cells derived from the fertilized egg by cell division, under control of genetic information contributed*

by each parent. Its body contains several hundred different cell types, each with a distinctive organization, often associated with highly specialized functions.

In spite of their apparent variation in size and shape, all cells carry the same set of genetic information, and share a basic architecture. Each is surrounded by a plasm membrane and each possesses a membrane-enclosed nucleus for all or part of its life cycle. In addition, cells possess internal structures known as organelles. Because the shape, structure, and internal components of each cell are determined by genetic information, a large part of human genetics involves the study of cells. Many genetic diseases are expressed at the cellular level; for example, a mutant gene in sickle cell anemia causes an alteration in the shape of red blood cells, and most of the resulting physical symptoms are a direct result of this altered shape.

As cells grow and divide, the genetic information they carry must be faithfully copied and distributed to their progeny. This is accomplished by structures within the nucleus known as chromosomes. The process of chromosome distribution and cell division is known as mitosis. The sperm and egg that fuse to form the fertilized egg or zygote are the products of a special form of cell division known as meiosis. Mistakes in either of these processes can have serious genetic consequences.

Because cells are the building blocks of the body and because the reproduction and transmission of genetic traits are mediated by cells, we will begin with an outline of their basic structural features. We will also consider cell division, with emphasis on the replication and distribution of chromosomes. Chromosome preparations are important tools in genetics, and the methods used in the analysis of chromosome number and structure will be presented. Human reproduction is accomplished via specialized cells known as gametes, and knowledge of how genetic traits are distributed during gamete formation is essential to an understanding of heredity.

THERE ARE TWO MAIN TYPES OF CELLS: PROKARYOTIC AND EUKARYOTIC

At the cellular level, organisms can be classified as eukaryotes or prokaryotes.

Prokaryotic cells include the bacteria and blue-green algae. These cells are enclosed by a plasma membrane, but do not contain a membrane-bounded nucleus. Instead, the genetic information carried by the cell (in the form of a naked DNA molecule) is in direct contact with the cytoplasm. In addition, prokaryotic cells do not contain any of the membranous organelles found in eukaryotic cells.

Eukaryotic cells are found in the protists (a group of single-celled organisms) in the fungi, plants, and in animals, including humans. These cells contain a membrane-bound **nucleus,** and the cytoplasm is divided into a number of compartments by internal membrane systems

CELL STRUCTURES AND FUNCTIONS

In the following discussion, we will consider several aspects of eukaryotic cell structure (Figure 2.1).

Prokaryote
Organism without a nucleus.

Eukaryote
Organism with a nuclear membrane surrounding the genetic material and with other membrane-bound organelles in the cytoplasm.

Nucleus
The membrane-bounded organelle, present in eukaryotic cells, that contains the chromosomes.

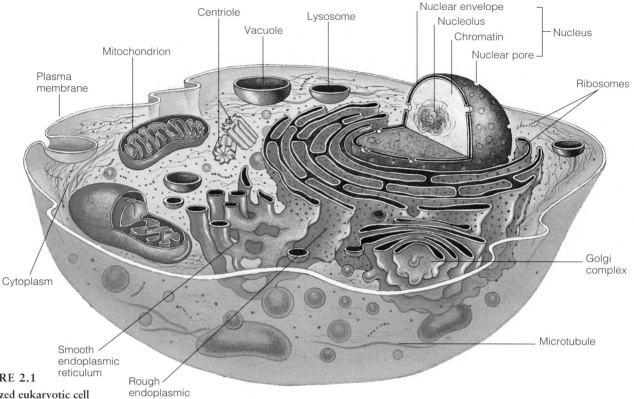

FIGURE 2.1

A generalized eukaryotic cell showing the organization and distribution of organelles as they would appear in the transmission electron microscope. The type, number, and distribution of organelles found in cells is related to cell function.

There Is a Wide Range of Cell Sizes

Most of the cells in the human body are too small to be seen without the aid of a microscope. Cell size is usually measured in micrometers (μm). There are 1 million micrometers in a meter, 25,000 per inch, and 1000 in a millimeter. Objects larger than 80 μm in diameter are visible to the unaided eye. Within the human body, cell size varies from small blood cells at around 5 μm to certain nerve cells with processes that may extend up to 3 ft (■ Figure 2.2). In the body, most of the cells average between 10 and 30 μm in diameter.

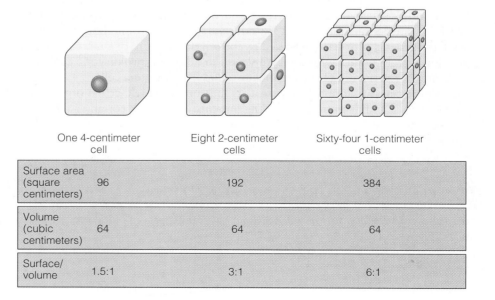

FIGURE 2.2

The range of cell sizes. The largest cell produced in the life cycle of animals (including humans) is usually the egg. The human egg is about 100 micrometers in diameter. In humans, red blood cells are among the smallest cells, with a diameter about 7–8 micrometers.

	One 4-centimeter cell	Eight 2-centimeter cells	Sixty-four 1-centimeter cells
Surface area (square centimeters)	96	192	384
Volume (cubic centimeters)	64	64	64
Surface/ volume	1.5:1	3:1	6:1

The Plasma Membrane and the Cytoplasm

Bordering all cells is a double-layered plasma membrane that is a dynamic and active component of cell function (Table 2.1). This structure controls the exchange of materials with the environment outside the cell (Figure 2.3). Gases, water, and some

TABLE 2.1	
Overview of Plasma Membrane Transport	
PROCESS	DESCRIPTION
Simple diffusion	Flow of ions and molecules from high concentrations to low. Water-soluble ions and molecules probably pass through pores; water-insoluble molecules pass directly through the lipid layer.
Facilitated diffusion	Flow of ions and molecules from high concentrations to low concentrations with the aid of protein carrier molecules in the membrane.
Active transport	Transport of molecules from regions of low concentration to regions of high concentration with the aid of transport proteins in the cell membrane and ATP.
Endocytosis	Active incorporation of liquid and solid materials outside the cell by the plasma membrane. Materials are engulfed by the cell and become surrounded by a membrane.
Exocytosis	Release of materials packaged in secretory vesicles.
Osmosis	Diffusion of water molecules from regions of high water (low solute) concentration to regions of low water (high solute) concentration.

 FIGURE 2.3

The plasma membrane. Proteins are embedded in a double layer of lipids. Short carbohydrate chains are attached to some proteins on the outer surface of the membrane.

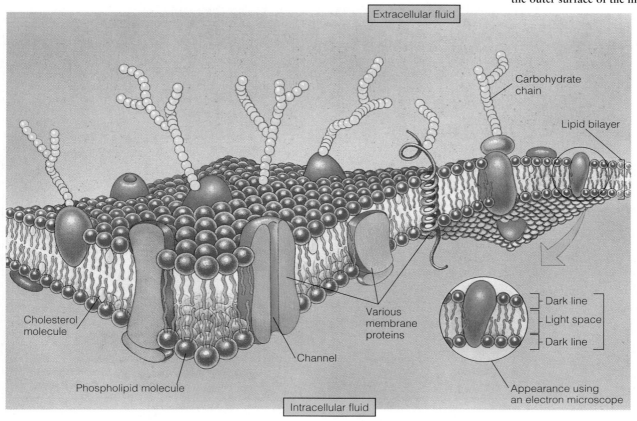

Extracellular fluid

Carbohydrate chain

Lipid bilayer

Cholesterol molecule

Various membrane proteins

Channel

Phospholipid molecule

Dark line
Light space
Dark line

Appearance using an electron microscope

Intracellular fluid

small molecules pass through the membrane easily, while large molecules are moved across by processes that require energy. Molecules in and on the plasma membrane confer a form of molecular identity on all cells. The form and number of these molecules are genetically controlled and are responsible for many important properties of cells, including blood type and compatibility in organ transplants.

The plasma membrane encloses the cytoplasm, a complex mixture of **molecules** and supramolecular structures. Within the cytoplasm, a three-dimensional network of protein microfilaments and microtubules known as the **cytoskeleton** helps establish and maintain cell shape, and serves to anchor cellular structures. It also functions in cell movement and cell division. The cytoplasm also contains a number of specialized structures known collectively as **organelles.**

Organelles Are Specialized Structures in the Cytoplasm

The organization of the cytoplasm in a eukaryotic cell is related to its function, and can differ from cell type to cell type. Cytoplasmic organelles are formed from membranes and divide the cell into a number of functional compartments. Table 2.2 summarizes the major organelles and their functions.

Molecule
A structure composed of two or more atoms held together by chemical bonds.

Cytoskeleton
A system of protein microfilaments and microtubules that allows a cell to have a characteristic shape.

Organelle
A cytoplasmic structure having a specialized function.

TABLE 2.2
Overview of Cell Organelles

ORGANELLE	STRUCTURE	FUNCTION
Nucleus	Round or oval body; surrounded by nuclear envelope.	Contains the genetic information necessary for control of cell structure and function. DNA contains heredity information.
Nucleolus	Round or oval body in the nucleus consisting of DNA and RNA.	Produces ribosomal RNA.
Endoplasmic reticulum	Network of membranous tubules in the cytoplasm of the cell. Smooth endoplasmic reticulum contains no ribosomes. Rough endoplasmic reticulum is studded with ribosomes.	Smooth endoplasmic reticulum (SER) is involved in the production of phospholipids and has many different functions in different cells; rough endoplasmic reticulum (RER) is the site of the synthesis of lysosomal enzymes and proteins for extracellular use.
Ribosomes	Small particles found in the cytoplasm; made of RNA and protein.	Aid in the production of proteins on the RER and ribosome complexes (polysomes).
Golgi apparatus	Series of flattened sacs usually located near the nucleus.	Sorts, chemically modifies, and packages proteins produced on the RER.
Secretory vesicles	Membrane-bound vesicles containing proteins produced by the RER and repackaged by the Golgi apparatus; contain protein hormones or enzymes.	Store protein hormones or enzymes in the cytoplasm awaiting a signal for release.
Lysosome	Membrane-bound structure containing digestive enzymes.	Combines with food vacules and digests materials engulfed by cells.
Mitochondria	Round, oval, or elongated structures with a double membrane. The inner membrane is thrown into folds.	Complete the breakdown of glucose, producing NADH and ATP.
Cytoskeleton	Network of microtubules and microfilaments in the cytoplasm.	Gives the cell internal support, helps transport molecules and some organelles inside the cell, and binds to enzymes of metabolic pathways.

FIGURE 2.4

(a) Three-dimensional representation of the endoplasmic reticulum (ER), showing the relationship between the smooth and rough ER. (b) An electron micrograph of ribosome-studded rough ER.

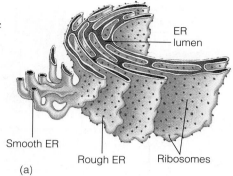

ER lumen

Smooth ER

Rough ER

Ribosomes

(a)

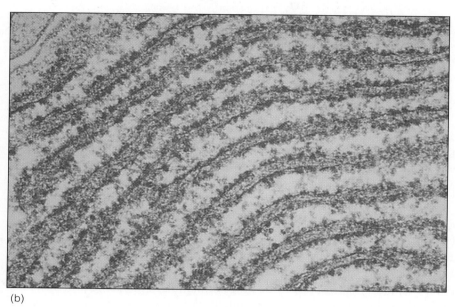

(b)

SIDEBAR

A Fatal Membrane Flaw

Cystic fibrosis is a genetic disorder that leads to an early death. Affected individuals have thick, sticky secretions of the pancreas and lungs. Diagnosis is often made by finding elevated levels of chloride ions in sweat. According to folklore, midwives would lick the forehead of newborns. If the sweat was salty, they predicted that the infant would die a premature death. Despite intensive therapy and drug treatments, the average survival of persons with this disorder is only about 25 years. Cystic fibrosis is caused by a functional defect in a membrane protein that controls the movement of chloride ions across the plasma membrane. In normal cells, this protein functions as a pore or channel controlling the flow of chloride; but in cystic fibrosis, the channel is unable to open. This causes chloride ions to accumulate inside the cell. To balance the chloride ions, the cells absorb excess sodium. In secretory glands, this leads to decreases in fluid production, resulting in blockage of flow from the pancreas and the accumulation of thick mucus in the lungs. The symptoms and premature death associated with this disorder point out the important role of membranes in controlling cell function.

Endoplasmic Reticulum   The **endoplasmic reticulum (ER)** is a network of membranous channels within the cytoplasm. The ER is a dynamic structure predominant in cells that make large amounts of protein (Figure 2.4). The ER is the cellular site of protein synthesis. The inside of the ER, called the lumen, is a separate compartment within the cell, where proteins are modified and prepared for transport to other locations within the cell, and for secretion out of the cell. In addition to being the site of protein synthesis, the ER is the source of most of the new membranes produced in the cell for maintenance and growth.

The outer surface of the ER is often studded with **ribosomes,** another cytoplasmic component (Figure 2.4). Ribosomes are the most numerous cellular structures and can be found free in the cytoplasm, attached to the outer surface of the ER, or the nuclear membrane. Under an electron microscope, ribosomes appear as spherical structures but are actually composed of two subunits that function to assemble the proteins necessary for cellular growth and metabolism. The process of protein synthesis is covered in detail in Chapter 9.

Golgi Apparatus   Animal cells contain clusters of flattened membrane sacs, called the **Golgi apparatus** (Figure 2.5). The Golgi chemically modify and distribute proteins synthesized by the ER, and serve as a source of membranes for other organelles, including lysosomes. **Lysosomes** are membrane-enclosed vesicles that store a collection of digestive enzymes. The enzymes stored here originate in the ER and are trans-

Endoplasmic reticulum (ER)
A system of cytoplasmic membranes arranged into sheets and channels that functions in the synthesis and transport of gene products.

Ribosomes
Cytoplasmic particles composed of two subunits that are the site of protein synthesis.

Golgi apparatus
Membranous organelles composed of a series of flattened sacs. They sort, modify, and package proteins synthesized in the ER.

Lysosomes
Membrane-enclosed organelles containing digestive enzymes.

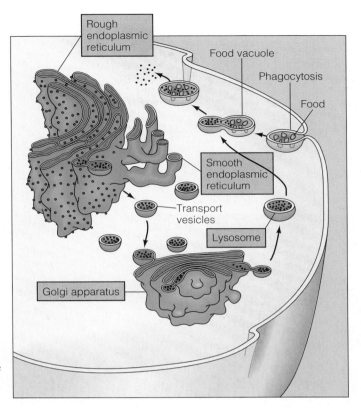

FIGURE 2.5

The relationship between the Golgi complex and lysosomes. Digestive enzymes are synthesized in the ER, and move to the Golgi in transport vesicles. In the Golgi, the enzymes are modified and packaged. Lysosomes pinch off the end of the Golgi membrane. In the cytoplasm, lysosomes fuse with and digest the contents of vesicles that are internalized from the plasma membrane.

Mitochondria (singular: mitochondrion)
Membrane-bound organelles present in the cytoplasm of all eukaryotic cells. They are the sites of energy production within cells.

Nucleolus (plural: nucleoli)
A nuclear region that functions in the synthesis of ribosomes.

Chromatin
The component material of chromosomes, visible as clumps or threads in nuclei examined under a microscope.

Chromosomes
The threadlike structures in the nucleus that carry genetic information.

ported to the Golgi, where they are packaged into vesicles. The vesicles bud off the Golgi to form the lysosomes (▬ Figure 2.5).

Lysosomes   Lysosomes degrade a wide range of materials, including proteins, fats, carbohydrates, and invading viruses that might enter the cell. The importance of lysosomes in cellular maintenance is underscored by several genetic disorders that disrupt or halt lysosome function. These disorders include **Tay-Sachs** (MIM/OMIM 272800) disease and **Pompe's** (MIM/OMIM 232300) disease. These disorders act at the level of organelles within the cell, but their outcomes can include severe mental retardation, blindness, and death by the age of 3 or 4 years. These disorders serve to reinforce the point made earlier that the functioning of the organism can be explained by events that occur within its cells.

Mitochondria   Mitochondria are centers of energy transformation (▬ Figure 2.6). They are somewhat variable in shape but are always enclosed by two double-layered membranes. Mitochondria carry genetic information in the form of circular molecules of DNA. A typical liver cell might contain about 1000 mitochondria. Mutations in mitochondrial DNA can cause a number of genetic disorders, and some of these will be discussed in Chapter 4.

Nucleus   The largest and most prominent cellular organelle is the nucleus (▬ Figure 2.7). This structure's double membrane is known as the nuclear envelope. The envelope is studded with pores that allow direct communication between the nucleus and cytoplasm (Figure 2.7). Within the nucleus, one or more dense regions known as **nucleoli** (singular: nucleolus) function in the synthesis of ribosomes. Under an electron microscope, thin strands and clumps of **chromatin** are seen throughout the nucleus (Figure 2.7). As the cells prepare to divide, the chromatin condenses and coils to form the **chromosomes**.

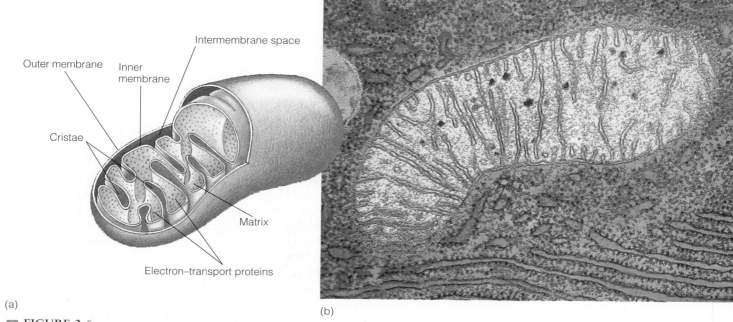

Outer membrane
Inner membrane
Intermembrane space
Cristae
Matrix
Electron–transport proteins

(a)

(b)

● **FIGURE 2.6**

The mitochondrion is a cell organelle involved in energy transformation. (a) The infolded inner membrane forms two compartments where chemical reactions transfer energy from one form to another. (b) A transmission electron micrograph of a mitochondrion.

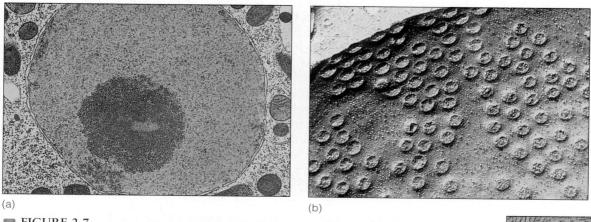

(a)

(b)

● **FIGURE 2.7**

(a) The nucleus is bounded by a double-layered plasma membrane. The nucleolus is a prominent structure in the nucleus. (b) The plasma membrane is studded with pores to allow the exchange of materials between the nucleus and the cytoplasm. (c) During interphase the chromosomes are uncoiled and dispersed throughout the nucleus as clumps of chromatin, clustered near the nuclear membrane.

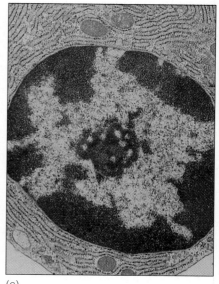

(c)

The nucleus is of central importance to genetics, because it acts to regulate the activity of the cytoplasm. The nucleus can function as a control center because it contains the genetic information that ultimately determines the structure and shape of the cell as well as the range of functions carried out by the cell. This information, in the form of genes, resides in the chromosomes carried in the nucleus. Because chromosomes carry genetic information, they occupy a central position in human genetics. The correct number of chromosomes in humans (46) was not determined until 1956. In the 1970s, developments in chromosome staining and refined methods of preparing chromosomes for examination led to advances in prenatal diagnosis, genetic screening, and locating or mapping genes to specific chromosome regions.

✺ IDENTIFICATION AND CLASSIFICATION OF CHROMOSOMES

Chromosomes, though present, are not usually visible in the nuclei of nondividing cells. As a cell prepares to divide, the thin strands of chromatin distributed throughout the nucleus begin to condense into the coiled structures recognizable as chromosomes. As they become visible, certain structural features allow the chromosomes to be distinguished from one another. The number of chromosomes present in the nucleus is characteristic for a given species: the fruit fly *Drosophila melanogaster* has 8, corn plants have 20, and humans contain 46 chromosomes. The chromosome number for several species of plants and animals is given in Table 2.3. The chromosomes of humans and most other eukaryotic organisms occur in pairs. One member of each chromosome pair is derived from the female parent and the other from the male parent. Members of a chromosome pair are known as **homologues.**

Cells that contain pairs of homologous chromosomes are known as **diploid** cells, and the number of chromosomes carried in such cells is known as the diploid, or $2n$, number of chromosomes. In humans, the diploid number of chromosomes is 46. Certain cells, such as eggs and sperm (gametes), contain only one copy of each chromosome and are referred to as **haploid** cells. The chromosome number in these cells is known as the haploid, or n, number of chromosomes. In humans, the haploid number of chromosomes is 23. At fertilization the fusion of haploid gametes and their nuclei produces a cell, known as a **zygote,** carrying the diploid number of chromosomes.

Each chromosome contains a specialized region known as the **centromere.** The position of the centromere divides the chromosome into two arms, and its location is characteristic for a given chromosome (➡ Figure 2.8). Chromosomes with centromeres at or near the middle have arms of equal length and are known as **metacentric** chromosomes (➡ Figure 2.9). If the centromere is not centrally located and the arms are unequal in length, the chromosome is known as **submetacentric;** if the centromere is located very close to one end, the chromosome is known as an **acrocentric** chromosome. In telocentric chromosomes, the centromere is at one end. Although **telocentric** chromosomes are common in mice and some other rodents, human chromosomes are telocentric. In a later section we will use centromere location, and chromosome size and banding patterns, produced by certain stains, to distinguish chromosomes in the human diploid chromosome set.

Homologues
Members of a chromosome pair.

Diploid
The condition in which each chromosome is represented twice, as a member of a homologous pair.

Haploid
The condition in which each chromosome is represented once, in an unpaired condition.

Zygote
The diploid cell resulting from the union of a male haploid gamete and a female haploid gamete.

Centromere
A region of a chromosome to which fibers attach during cell division. Location of a centromere gives a chromosome its characteristic shape.

Metacentric
A chromosome with a centrally placed centromere.

Submetacentric
A chromosome with a centromere placed closer to one end than the other.

Acrocentric
A chromosome with the centromere placed very close to, but not at, one end.

Telocentric
A chromosome with the centromere located at one end.

TABLE 2.3		
Chromosome Number in Selected Organisms		
ORGANISM	**DIPLOID NUMBER ($2n$)**	**HAPLOID NUMBER (n)**
Human (*Homo sapiens*)	46	23
Chimpanzee (*Pan troglodytes*)	48	24
Gorilla (*Gorilla gorilla*)	48	24
Dog (*Canis familiaris*)	78	39
Chicken (*Gallus domesticus*)	78	39
Frog (*Rana pipiens*)	26	13
Housefly (*Musca domestica*)	12	6
Onion (*Allium cepa*)	16	8
Corn (*Zea mays*)	20	10
Tobacco (*Nicotiana tobacum*)	48	24
House mouse (*Mus musculus*)	40	20
Fruit fly (*Drosophila melanogaster*)	8	4
Nematode (*Caenorhabditis elegans*)	12	6

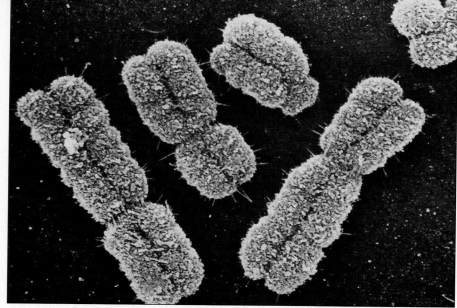

FIGURE 2.8

Human chromosomes as seen at metaphase of mitosis in the scanning electron microscope. The replicated chromosomes appear as double structures, consisting of sister chromatids, joined by a single centromere.

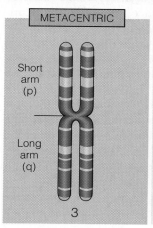

METACENTRIC

Short arm (p)

Long arm (q)

3

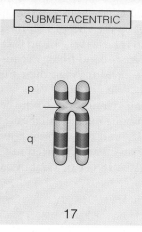

SUBMETACENTRIC

p

q

17

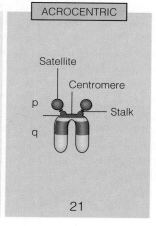

ACROCENTRIC

Satellite

Centromere

p

Stalk

q

21

FIGURE 2.10 (below)

The cell cycle has two stages: interphase and mitosis. Interphase has three components: G1, S, and G2. Times shown for the stages are representative for cells grown in the laboratory.

FIGURE 2.9 (above)

Human metaphase chromosomes are identified by size, centromere location, and banding pattern. The relative size, centromere locations, and banding patterns for three representative human chromosomes is shown. Chromosome 3 is one of the largest human chromosomes, and because the centromere is centrally located, is a metacentric chromosome. Chromosome 17 is a submetacentric chromosome because the centromere divides the chromosome into two arms of unequal size. Chromosome 21 has a centromere placed very close to one end, and is called an acrocentric chromosome. In humans, the short arm of each chromosome is called the p arm, and the long arm is called the q arm.

THE CELL CYCLE

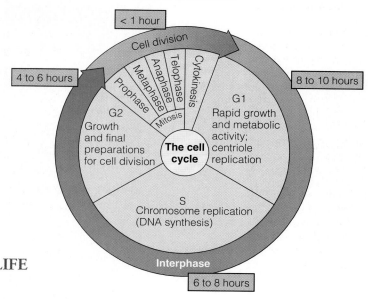

THE CELL CYCLE

< 1 hour

Cell division

4 to 6 hours

Cytokinesis

Telophase

Anaphase

Metaphase

Prophase

Mitosis

8 to 10 hours

G1
Rapid growth and metabolic activity; centriole replication

G2
Growth and final preparations for cell division

The cell cycle

S
Chromosome replication (DNA synthesis)

Interphase

6 to 8 hours

THE CELL CYCLE DESCRIBES THE LIFE HISTORY OF A CELL

Many cells in the body alternate between states of division and nondivision. The interval between divisions can vary from minutes in embryonic cells to months or even years in some cells of adults. The sequence of events from one division to another is called the **cell cycle** (Figure 2.10). The period of division itself consists

Cell cycle
The sequence of events that takes place between successive mitotic divisions.

Mitosis
Form of cell division that produces two cells, each with the same complement of chromosomes as the parent cell.

Cytokinesis
The process of cytoplasmic division that accompanies cell division.

Interphase
The period of time in the cell cycle between mitotic divisions.

of two phases, **mitosis** and **cytokinesis.** Mitosis is the division of the chromosomes, and cytokinesis is the division or partitioning of the cytoplasm. The period between cell (mitotic) divisions is known as **interphase,** the first major part of the cell cycle.

Interphase Has Three Stages

A good place to begin a discussion of the cell cycle is with a cell that has just been formed by division. After a cell divides, the resulting daughter cells are about one half the size of the parental cell. Before they can divide again, they must undergo a period of growth and synthesis. These events take place during the three stages of interphase: G1, S, and G2.

The G1 stage, known as gap 1, begins immediately after division and is a period when many cytoplasmic components, including organelles, membranes, and ribosomes, are replaced. The synthetic activity in G1 almost doubles the cell size and replaces components lost in the previous division. G1 is followed by the S (synthesis) phase, during which a duplicate copy of each chromosome is made. A second period of cellular growth, known as the G2 phase (gap 2), takes place before the cell is ready to begin a new round of division. By the end of G2, the cell is ready to divide. The time spent in the three stages of interphase (G1, S, and G2) varies from 18 to 24 hours in animal cells grown under laboratory conditions. Because the events of mitosis usually take less than one hour, cells spend most of their time in interphase. Table 2.4 summarizes the phases of the cell cycle.

The life history of cells and their relationship to the cell cycle varies for different cell types. Some cells, like those in bone marrow that give rise to red blood cells, pass through the cell cycle continuously and divide on a regular basis. At the other extreme, some cell types become permanently arrested in G1 and never divide. In between are cell types that are arrested in G1 or G2 but can divide under certain circumstances.

	TABLE 2.4
	Phases of the Cell Cycle

PHASE	CHARACTERISTICS
Interphase	
G1 (gap 1)	Stage begins immediately after mitosis. RNA, protein, and other molecules are synthesized.
S (synthesis)	DNA is replicated. Chromosomes become double stranded.
G2 (gap 2)	Mitochondria divide; precursors of spindle fibers are synthesized.
Mitosis	
Prophase	Chromosomes condense. Nuclear envelope disappears. Centrioles divide and migrate to opposite poles of the dividing cell. Spindle fibers form and attach to chromosomes.
Metaphase	Chromosomes line up on equatorial plate of the dividing cell.
Anaphase	Chromosomes begin to separate.
Telophase	Chromosomes migrate or are pulled to opposite poles. New nuclear envelope forms. Chromosomes uncoil.
Cytokinesis	Cleavage furrow forms and deepens. Cytoplasm divides.

HeLa Cells: The Ultimate Growth Industry

Many advances in human genetics and other fields, such as cancer research, have been made with cells grown outside the body, using *in vitro* culture (*in vitro* is a Latin phrase meaning "in glass"). Efforts to grow human cells *in vitro* began in the late 1940s and early 1950s. These early attempts usually met with failure; the cells died after a few days or weeks. One day in February 1951, a researcher at Johns Hopkins University received a sample of cervical cancer tissue from a patient named Henrietta Lacks. Following convention, the cell culture was named HeLa, by combining the first two letters of the first and last name of the donor. These cervical cancer cells easily adapted to growth *in vitro*, and became one of the first cell lines successfully grown outside the body.

Researchers were eager to have human cells available on demand to study the effects of drugs, toxic chemicals, radiation, and viruses on human tissue. Success in establishing the HeLa cell line spurred improvements in methods of growing cells, and cell lines from other cancers and normal tissues were soon commonplace. By the early 1960s, a central repository of cell lines was established in Washington, D.C., and cultured human cells became an important tool in many areas of biological research.

The first clouds in this picture began to gather in 1966 when Stanley Gartler, a geneticist at the University of Washington, analyzed 18 different human cell lines and found that they all had been contaminated and taken over by HeLa cells. Over the next two years, investigation revealed that 24 of the 34 cell lines in the repository were actually HeLa cells. Researchers who had spent years studying what they thought were heart or kidney cells had been working with cervical cancer cells. This meant that thousands of experiments performed in laboratories around the world were now worthless.

As painful as this lesson was, scientists started over. They prepared new cell lines and established strict rules to prevent these cell lines from being contaminated. Unfortunately, this was not the end of the problem. In 1974, Walter Nelson-Rees showed that five cell lines used in cancer research were actually HeLa cells. In 1976, another paper showed that 11 additional lines, widely used in research, were also contaminated with HeLa cells. In 1981, Nelson-Rees listed 22 more cell lines that were actually HeLa cells. In all, it was clear that about one third of all cell lines used in cancer research were contaminated with HeLa cells.

How did this happen? HeLa cells are fast-growing cells adaptable to a wide range of growth conditions. They can survive for a long time as contaminants on pipette tips and glassware, and not enough care was taken to prevent the spread of these cells to other cell lines. In other cases, poor record keeping and mislabeling of cultures were responsible. It is clear that Henrietta Lack's gift to science is a two-edged sword: a valuable cell line that must be used very carefully.

When cells escape from the controls that are part of the cell cycle, they become cancerous (see Concepts & Controversies on this page).

Cell Division by Mitosis Occurs in Four Stages

When the cell reaches the end of the G2 stage, it is ready to undergo mitosis, the second major part of the cell cycle. During this period, two important steps are completed: a complete set of chromosomes is distributed to each daughter cell, and cytokinesis distributes the cytoplasm more or less equally to the two daughter cells. The division of the cytoplasm is accomplished by splitting the cell into two parts, with each receiving multiple copies of organelles and a sufficient supply of plasma membrane to enclose the new cells. While cytokinesis can be somewhat imprecise and still be operational, the division and distribution of the chromosomes must be accurate and unerring for the cell to function. The chromosomes and the genetic information they contain are precisely replicated during the S stage of interphase, and during mitosis a complete set of diploid chromosomes is distributed to each of the daughter cells. The net result of this replication and distribution is two diploid daughter cells, each of which contains 46 chromosomes derived from a single parental cell with 46 chromosomes. Although the distribution of chromosomes in cell division should be precise, errors in this process do occur. These mistakes often have serious genetic consequences and will be discussed in detail in Chapter 6.

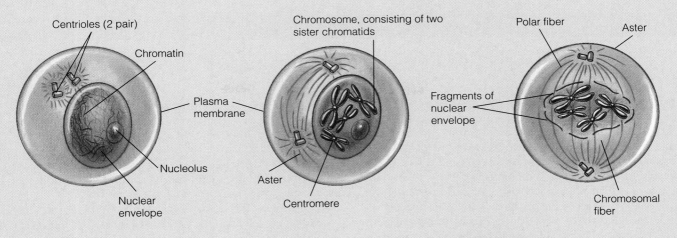

(a) Interphase

(b) Prophase

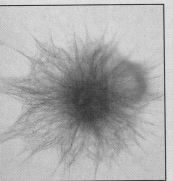

Interphase.

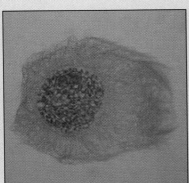

Early prophase.

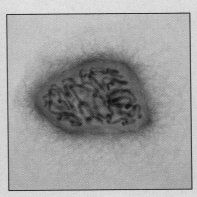

Midprophase.

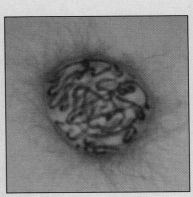

Late prophase.

▬ FIGURE 2.11

Stages of mitosis. During interphase (a) replication of chromosomes takes place. (b) In prophase, the chromosomes coil and become visible as thread-like structures. In late prophase, they form a double structure, consisting of sister chromatids joined by a single centromere. At the end of prophase, the nuclear membrane breaks down. In metaphase (c), chromosomes become aligned at the equator of the cell. In anaphase (d), the centromeres divide, converting the sister chromatids into chromosomes, which move toward opposite sides of the cell. At telophase (e) the chromosomes uncoil, the nuclear membrane reforms, and the cytoplasm divides.

Mitosis takes place in somatic cells and in the germ cells of the ovary and testis. Progeny of the germ cells undergo meiosis, a form of cell division that will be described below. Although mitosis is a continuous process, for the sake of discussion it has been divided into four phases: prophase, metaphase, anaphase, and telophase (▬ Figure 2.11). Throughout the cell cycle, the chromosomes alternately condense and decondense. In an extended configuration, the chromosomal material is dispersed throughout the nucleus and is recognizable as clumps of chromatin. In the G2 stage prior to entry into mitosis, the replicated chromosomes begin to condense, thicken, and shorten.

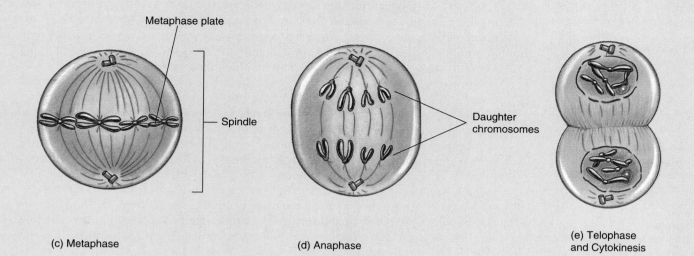

(c) Metaphase

(d) Anaphase

(e) Telophase and Cytokinesis

Metaphase plate

Spindle

Daughter chromosomes

Early metaphase.

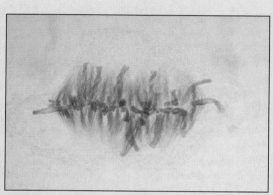

Metaphase.

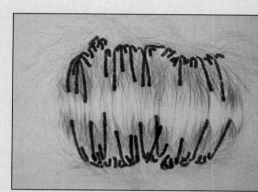

Mid-anaphase.

Late anaphase.

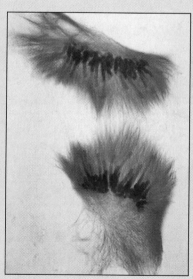

Telophase.

Interphase.

Prophase
A stage in mitosis during which the chromosomes become visible and split longitudinally except at the centromere.

Chromatid
One of the strands of a duplicated chromosome, joined by a single centromere to its sister chromatid.

Sister chromatids
Two chromatids joined by a common centromere. Each chromatid carries identical genetic information.

Metaphase
A stage in mitosis during which the chromosomes move and become arranged near the middle of the cell.

Metaphase plate
The cluster of chromosomes aligned at the equator of the cell during mitosis.

Prophase   During mitosis the chromosomes coil tightly and are recognizable as distinct structures. As they coil, the chromosomes become thick enough to be recognized under a microscope. When first seen, the chromosomes appear as long, thin, intertwined threads; this marks the beginning of **prophase.** In the cytoplasm a collection of specialized tubules known as spindle fibers begins to form.

As prophase continues, the chromosomes continue to coil and become shorter and thicker; in human cells, 46 such structures can be seen. The condensation of chromosomes at the beginning of prophase serves an important function. In a shortened and contracted form, the chromosomes untangle from each other and move freely during mitosis. Near the end of prophase, each chromosome can be seen to consist of two longitudinal strands known as **chromatids.** The chromatids are separate structures, held together at the centromere. Two chromatids joined by a common centromere are known as **sister chromatids** (Figure 2.12). Near the end of prophase, the nucleolus disappears, and the nuclear membrane breaks down. In the cytoplasm the spindle fibers become fully organized and stretch from centriole to centriole, forming an axis along which mitosis will occur.   Figure 2.13 illustrates the events at this stage of mitosis.

Metaphase   **Metaphase** begins when the nuclear membrane has completely disappeared. The two chromatids are still attached at a single centromere, giving chromosomes an X-shaped appearance. The chromosomes become aligned along a plane in the midline, or equator, of the cell, in an arrangement called the **metaphase plate.** At the completion of metaphase, each chromosome is present on the metaphase plate and has spindle fibers attached to its centromere (Figure 2.13). At this stage there are 46 centromeres, each attached to two sister chromatids.

One chromosome (unreplicated)

One chromosome (replicated)

a chromatid

its sister chromatid

centromere

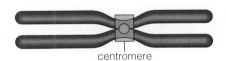

FIGURE 2.12

Chromosomes replicate during the S phase. While attached to the centromere, the replicated chromosomes are called sister chromatids.

FIGURE 2.13

Microtubules form the mitotic spindle during prophase. Some of the fibers connect to the centromeres and help move the chromosomes to opposite sides of the cell during anaphase.

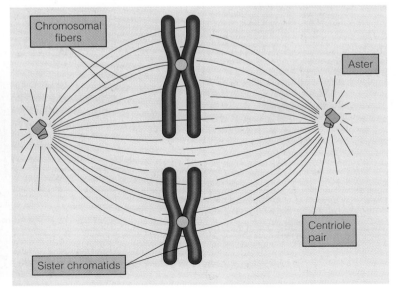

Chromosomal fibers

Aster

Centriole pair

Sister chromatids

Anaphase At the beginning of **anaphase,** centromeres joining sister chromatids divide, converting each sister chromatid into a chromosome (Figure 2.11). The two chromosomes derived from sister chromatids will be genetically and structurally identical. Spindle fibers attached to the centromeres begin to shorten, and the chromosomes derived from sister chromatids migrate toward opposite centrioles. Movement of chromosomes depends on the correct attachment of spindle fibers to the centromere. As the spindle fibers shorten, the centromere moves first, and the chromosome arms trail behind, making the chromosomes appear V-shaped or J-shaped. By the end of anaphase a complete set of chromosomes is present at each pole of the cell. Although anaphase is the briefest stage of mitosis, it is essential to ensuring that each daughter cell receives an intact and identical set of 46 chromosomes. An abnormality of centromere function during prenatal development is responsible for **Roberts syndrome** (MIM/OMIM 268300, ⬤ Figure 2.14)

Telophase The final stage of mitosis is **telophase,** characterized by cytokinesis and the formation of nuclei. As the chromosomes reach opposite poles of the cell, the spindle fibers break down into subunits, which are stored in the cytoplasm, or become incorporated into the cytoskeleton. Membrane buds from the ER form a new nuclear membrane. Inside the new nucleus, the chromsomes begin to uncoil, become dispersed as chromatin, and nucleoli appear. The uncoiling of chromosomes represents a functionally specialized state. The cycle of chromosome uncoiling extends from telophase through G1, and the cycle of condensation runs from G2 to anaphase. It is likely that genetic information in an uncoiled chromosome is more accessible, and able to direct the synthesis of gene products during interphase.

Cytokinesis Begins during Telophase

Cytokinesis, the division of the cytoplasm, begins with the formation of the **cell furrow,** a constriction of the cell membrane that forms at the equator of the cell (⬤ Figure 2.15). The constriction gradually tightens and divides the cell in two. The major features of mitosis are summarized in Table 2.5.

⬤ **FIGURE 2.15**

Cytokinesis. (a) A scanning electron micrograph of cleavage as seen from the outside of the cell. (b) A transmission electron micrograph of cytokinesis in a cross-section of a dividing cell.

⬤ **FIGURE 2.14**

Roberts syndrome is a genetic disorder caused by malfunction of centromeres during mitosis. In this painting by Goya (1746–1828), the child on the mother's lap has a lack of limb development that is characteristic of this syndrome.

Anaphase
A stage in mitosis during which the centromeres split and the daughter chromosomes begin to separate.

Telophase
The last stage of mitosis, during which division of the cytoplasm occurs, the chromosomes of the daughter cells disperse, and the nucleus reforms.

Cell furrow
A constriction of the cell membrane that forms at the point of cytoplasmic cleavage during cell division.

(a)

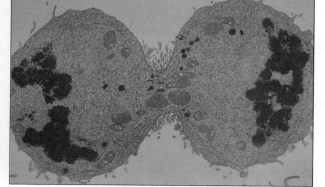

(b)

TABLE 2.5	
Summary of Mitosis	
STAGE	CHARACTERISTICS
Interphase	Replication of chromosomes takes place.
Prophase	Chromosomes become visible as threadlike structures; later, as they continue to condense, they are seen to be double, with sister chromatids joined at a single centromere.
Metaphase	Chromosomes become aligned at equator of cell.
Anaphase	Centromeres divide, and chromosomes move toward opposite poles.
Telophase	Chromosomes uncoil, nuclear membrane forms, and cytoplasm divides.

SIGNIFICANCE OF MITOSIS

Mitosis is an essential process in all multicellular organisms. In humans—throughout adult life—some cells retain their capacity to divide, while others do not divide after adulthood is reached. Cells in the bone marrow move through the cell cycle and divide continually to produce about 2 million red blood cells each second. Cells in the epidermis remain mitotically active and divide to replace dead epidermal cells that are continually sloughed off the surface of the body. The healing of wounds also involves mitosis in the damaged tissues. By contrast, most cells in the nervous system remain permanently in G1 and cannot undergo division. Thus, when nerves are damaged or destroyed, they cannot be replaced. For this reason many injuries to the spinal cord result in permanent paralysis. Occasionally, cells escape regulation and grow continuously, forming tumors, including cancer.

The mechanism that determines whether cells are cycling or noncycling operates in the G1 phase of the cell cycle. The general features of this regulation are known, and will be discussed in Chapter 14, "The Genetics of Cancer."

Studies of many organisms have established that each species has a characteristic life span, or longevity. In humans this is estimated to be about 110 to 120 years. Studies of cells grown in the laboratory indicate that cells are programmed to undergo a finite number of mitotic divisions. Once this number, known as the Hayflick limit, is reached, the cells die. Cells cultured from human embryos have a limit of about 50 doublings, a capacity that includes all divisions necessary to produce a human adult and cell replacement during a lifetime. Cells from adults and elderly individuals can divide only about 10 to 30 times in tissue culture before dying.

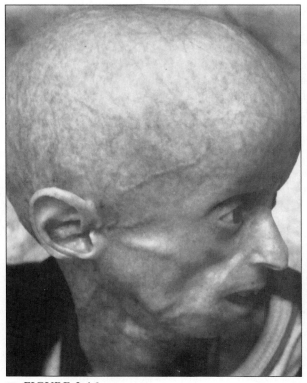

● FIGURE 2.16

A 13-year-old girl with progeria.

It appears that cells of many higher organisms, including humans, contain an internal mechanism that determines the maximum number of divisions, which in turn determines the ultimate life span of the individual. The process appears to be under genetic control because several mutations that affect the aging process are known. One of these is a rare heritable condition known as **progeria** (MIM/OMIM 176670), in which affected individuals age rapidly. Seven- or 8-year-old children with this disease physically and mentally resemble individuals of 70 or 80 years of age (◗ Figure 2.16). Affected individuals usually die of old age by the age of 14. **Werner syndrome** (MIM/OMIM 277700)is another genetic condition associated with premature aging. In this case, the disease process begins between the ages of 15 and 20 years, and affected individuals die of age-related problems by 45 to 50 years of age.

 ## THE HUMAN CHROMOSOME SET

Human chromosomes are most often studied by microscopic examination and photography of cells in mitotic metaphase. For convenience, the chromosomes are cut out from a photographic print and, by convention, are arranged in pairs according to size and centromere location. This construction is known as a **karyotype.** Examination of human karyotypes reveals that one pair of chromosomes is not always homologous. Members of this pair are involved in the process of sex determination and are known as **sex chromosomes.** There are two types of sex chromosomes, X and Y. Females have two homologous X chromosomes, and males have a nonhomologous pair consisting of one X and one Y chromosome. Both males and females have two copies of the remaining 22 pairs of chromosomes, known as **autosomes.**

By convention, the chromosomes in the human karyotype are numbered and arranged into seven groups, A through G. Each group is defined by chromosome size and centromere location. Staining procedures, which produce patterns of bands that are unique for each chromosome, allow individual chromosomes to be clearly identified (◗ Figure 2.17). The standardized G-banding pattern for the human chromo-

Progeria
A genetic trait in humans associated with premature aging and early death.

Werner syndrome
A genetic trait in humans that causes aging to accelerate in adolescence, leading to death by about age 50.

Karyotype
The chromosome complement of a cell line or a person, photographed at metaphase and arranged in a standard sequence.

Sex chromosomes
Chromosomes involved in sex determination. In humans, the X and Y chromosomes are the sex chromosomes.

Autosomes
Chromosomes other than the sex chromosomes. In humans, chromosomes 1–22 are autosomes.

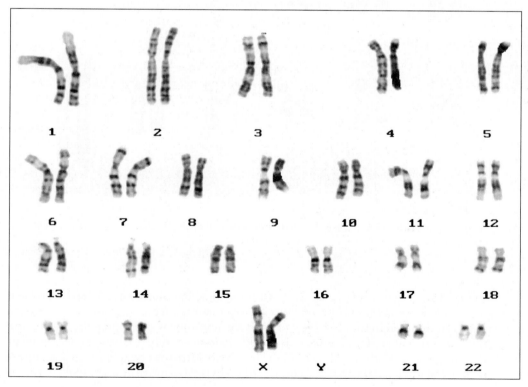

◗ **FIGURE 2.17**

A human karyotype showing replicated chromosomes from a cell in metaphase of mitosis. This female has 46 chromosomes, including two X chromosomes.

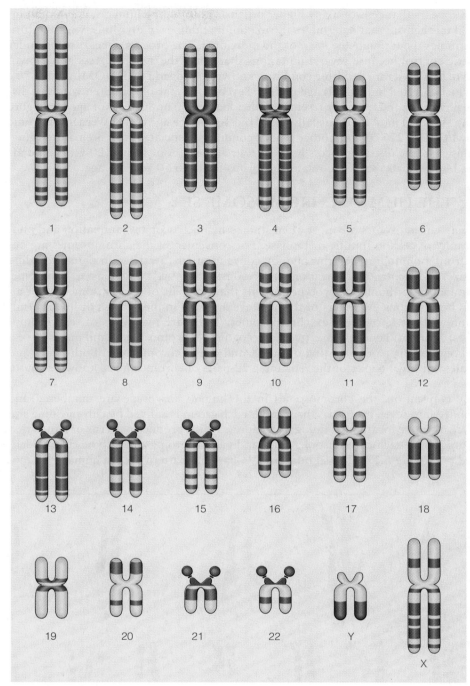

⬛ **FIGURE 2.18**

⬛ **FIGURE 2.18**

A karyogram of the human chromosome set, showing the distinctive banding pattern of each chromosome.

some set is shown in ⬛ Figure 2.18. Chromosome banding patterns have also been used as the basis for identifying specific regions on each chromosome (⬛ Figure 2.19). In this system the short arm of each chromosome is designated the p arm, and the long arm the q arm. Each arm is subdivided into numbered regions beginning at the centromere. Within each region, the bands are identified by number. Thus any region in the human karyotype can be identified by a descriptive address such as 1q2.4.

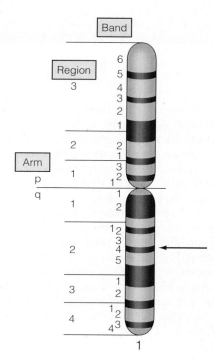

 FIGURE 2.19

The system of naming chromosome bands. Each autosome is numbered from 1–22. The sex chromosomes are X and Y. Within a chromosome, the short arm is the p arm, and the long arm is the q arm. Each arm is divided into numbered regions. Within each region, the bands are designated by number. The area marked by the arrow is designated as 1q2.4 (chromosome 1, long arm, region 2, band 4).

The address consists of the chromosome number (1), the arm (q), the region (2), and the band (4) (Figure 2.19).

The development of banding techniques and related methods has provided the clinician and researcher with a powerful tool for chromosome studies (see "Concepts and Controversies," page 34). Chromosome studies are usually performed at metaphase, since the chromosomes are maximally condensed at this stage. Preparations can be made from lymphocytes, a type of white blood cell that can be induced to divide in the laboratory, or from fibroblasts, a cell type that can be recovered by skin biopsy. Chromosome analysis has many important applications in human genetics, some of which will be discussed in later chapters. These include prenatal diagnosis, gene mapping, and cancer research.

CELL DIVISION BY MEIOSIS: THE BASIS OF SEX

The genetic information we inherit is contained in two cells, the sperm and the egg. These cells are produced by a form of cell division known as **meiosis.** Recall that in mitosis, each daughter cell receives 46 chromosomes. In meiosis, however, members of a chromosome pair are separated from each other to produce haploid cells, or **gametes,** each with 23 chromosomes. Union of the two gametes in fertilization restores the chromosome number to 46 and provides a full complement of genetic information to the zygote.

The distribution of chromosomes in meiosis is an exact process; each gamete must contain not just 23 chromosomes, but one member of each chromosome pair rather than a random selection of 23 of the 46 chromosomes. How the precise reduction in the chromosome number is accomplished is of central importance in human genetics.

Cells in the testis and ovary that give rise to gametes are diploid and divide by mitosis. Some of the progeny of these germ cells, but no other cells in the body, undergo meiosis. In meiosis, diploid ($2n$) cells undergo one round of chromosome replication followed by two divisions to produce four cells, each with the haploid (n) number of chromosomes. The two division events are referred to as meiosis I and II, respectively.

Meiosis
The process of cell division during which one cycle of chromosome replication is followed by two successive cell divisions to produce four haploid cells.

Gamete
A haploid reproductive cell, such as the sperm or egg.

Making a Karyotype

Chromosome analysis can be performed using cells from a number of sources, including white blood cells (lymphocytes), skin cells (fibroblasts), amniotic fluid cells (amniocytes), and chorionic villus cells (placental cells). One of the most common methods begins with collection of a blood sample from a vein in the arm. A few drops of the collected blood are added to a flask containing a nutrient growth medium. Since the lymphocytes in the blood sample do not normally divide, a mitosis-inducing chemical such as phytohemagglutinin is added to the flask, and the cells are grown for two or three days at body temperature (37°C) in an incubator. At the end of this time, a drug such as colcemid is added to stop dividing cells at metaphase. Over a period of about 2 hours of colcemid treatment, cells entering mitosis are arrested in metaphase.

The blood cells are then concentrated by centrifugation, and a salt solution is added to break open the red blood cells (which are nondividing) and to swell the lymphocytes. This treatment prevents the chromosomes in dividing cells from sticking together, and makes the lymphocytes easier to break open. After fixation in a mixture of methanol and acetic acid, the cells are dropped onto a microscope slide. The impact causes the fragile lymphocytes to break open, spreading the metaphase chromosomes. After being stained to reveal banding patterns, the preparation is examined with a microscope, and the spread of metaphase chromosomes is photographed. A print of this photograph is used to construct a karyotype. The chromosome images are cut from the photograph and arranged according to size, centromere location, and banding pattern. The presence of chro-

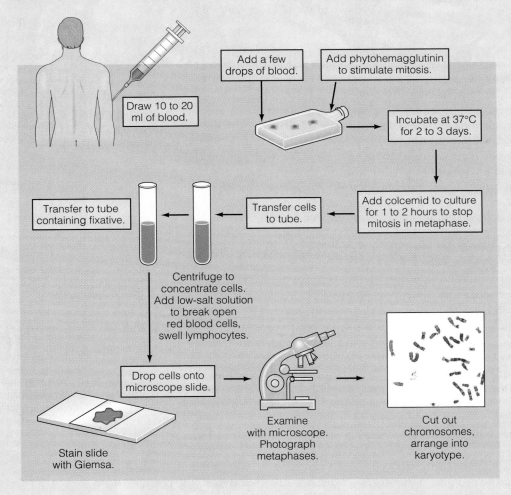

mosomal abnormalities can be detected by a trained cytogeneticist.

The process of cutting chromosome images from photographs by hand and arranging them into karyotypes is tedious and time-consuming. Computer-assisted karyotype preparation is now available in most cytogenetic laboratories. In this system, a television camera and a computer are linked to a microscope. As metaphase chromosomes are located using the microscope, the image is recorded by the camera, digitized, and transmitted to the computer, where it is processed into a karyotype and printed. In the photographs below, a metaphase array of chromosomes has been printed by such a system. At the right is the computer-derived karyotype. Note that the image has been processed to straighten the chromosomes as they are arranged into a karyotype.

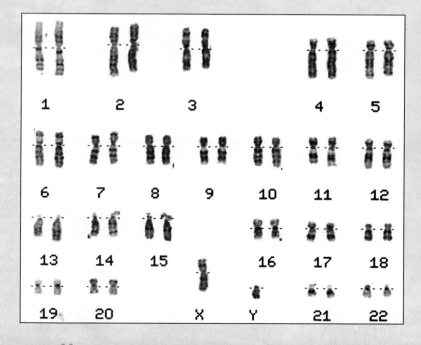

Meiosis I Reduces the Chromosome Number

Before cells enter meiosis, the chromosomes are replicated during interphase (◖ Figure 2.20a). As in mitosis, each replicated chromosome has a single centromere. In the first part of prophase I, the chromosomes coil and condense and be-

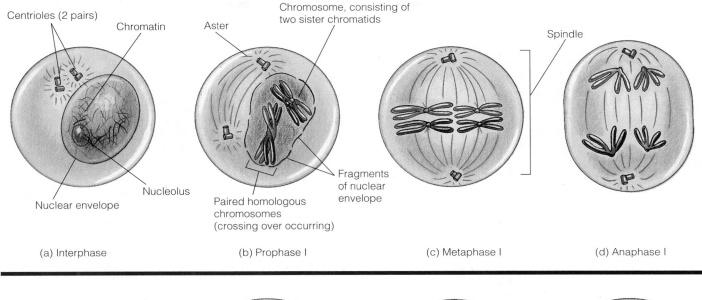

(a) Interphase (b) Prophase I (c) Metaphase I (d) Anaphase I

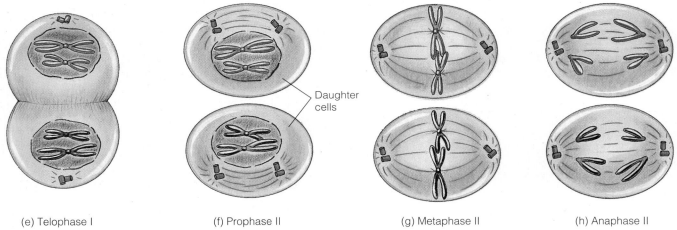

(e) Telophase I (f) Prophase II (g) Metaphase II (h) Anaphase II

(i) Telophase II (j) Haploid daughter cells

◖ **FIGURE 2.20**

The stages of meiosis. Chromosomes become visible as thread-like structures early in prophase I (b). Once visible, homologous chromosomes pair, and split longitudinally except at centromeres. While paired, homologous chromosomes undergo crossing over. In metaphase I (c), the chromosomes become arranged at the cell's equator. In anaphase I (d), members of all chromosome pairs separate from each other and migrate to opposite sides of the cell. The result is the formation of two new cells (e, f). In prophase II (f), the nuclear membrane breaks down, and the chromosomes align at the metaphase plate (g). In anaphase II, the centromeres split, converting the sister chromatids into chromosomes, and the newly formed chromosomes move apart. After telophase (i), the result is four haploid daughter cells (j), each containing one copy of each chromosome.

Nothing in Biology Makes Sense
without Evolution

MICHAEL ROSE

The best course I took in high school, maybe the best course I've ever taken, was comparative vertebrate anatomy. I loved taking apart the bodies, learning the names of each part, carefully removing material to see little holes and tiny nerves. But before the gore came the scientific theory: fossils, Lamarck, Darwin, Mendel. The theory animated the corpses, made them meaningful, gave them some sense. At the time, I was a big science fiction fan, a genre in which every story had to have a portentous meaning. Evolution is the deep meaning behind life, and without it biology becomes a lot of details.

When I started my doctoral studies, I was given the task of showing experimentally that evolution could make sense of biological aging. At first I was dismayed. Aging, throughout human history, has been a mystery. The people who talk or write most about it are charlatans, quacks, and hustlers. I feared that my career would be aborted by the combination of my failure to accomplish the task and my spattering with the mud of quackery about aging. So far, my fears have proven erroneous.

Consider two genetic diseases, progeria and Huntington disease. It is now thought that each of these is caused by a specific mutation at a single copy of a normal human gene, one gene for each disease. Progeria strikes children between 5 and 10 years of age and is an extremely rare disorder. Huntington disease, on the other hand, strikes almost entirely after the age of 30 and affects thousands of individuals around the world.

Progeria strikes children, prevents their reproduction, and also completely precludes transmission of progeria into the next generation. With 100% success, natural selection screens out new mutations for progeria. With Huntington disease, the patients may already have children before they show any symptoms. Natural selection fails to screen the Huntington mutation out of the population because the gene has effects primarily at later ages, not earlier ages. The key is that *the force of natural selection falls with adult age.*

Genes that have effects on the health or development of young animals are sharply scrutinized by natural selection. This fundamental idea was first proposed by evolutionary bi-ologists in the 1930s and 1940s. My role has been to test this idea. When this kind of reproductive pattern is imposed on laboratory populations of the fruit fly *Drosophila,* they evolve an increased life span over dozens of generations. This happens because we are artificially strengthening natural selection at later ages. Fruit flies that can't survive to reproduce in their middle age, in this experiment, are selected against. Thus natural selection alters the genetic basis of aging and increases the life span.

The flies that live longer are interesting beasts. They have a lot of physiological differences that can be related to their ability to live longer. They reproduce less when young, even when they have opportunity to do so. They resist stresses better, including starvation and desiccation. They move around more when they are older, whether walking or flying. They can reproduce more at later ages. Longer lived flies appear, for now, to be superior organisms—"superflies!"

When I present these superflies to audiences, people want to know if I will ever be able to do the same things for them. Literally, the answer is no. But there is the possibility of learning more about the genetics of postponed aging in fruit flies in the hope that we can apply our findings to humans. If this is ever done, it will transform the human life cycle, as aging becomes something that can be controlled–instead of merely endured.

MICHAEL ROBERTSON ROSE *is a professor of evolutionary biology at the University of California, Irvine. He received B.S. and M.S. degrees from Queen's University, Ontario, Canada, and a Ph.D. from University of Sussex in England. He is a member of the editorial board of the* Journal of Evolutionary Biology *and the* Journal of Theoretical Biology. *In 1992 he won the President's Prize from the American Society of Naturalists.*

---

come visible under a microscope (Figure 2.20b). As the chromosomes coil, the nucleoli and nuclear membrane disappear, and the spindle becomes organized. Each chromosome physically associates with its homologue, and the two chromosomes line up side by side, in a process known as **synapsis.** Chromosome pairing usually begins at one or more points along the chromosome and proceeds until the chromosomes are aligned.

Synapsis
The pairing of homologous chromosomes during prophase I of meiosis.

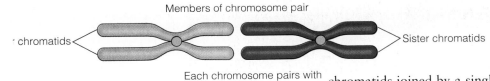
Members of chromosome pair

chromatids

Sister chromatids

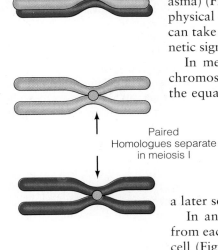
Each chromosome pairs with its homologue

● FIGURE 2.21

Summary of chromosome movements in meiosis. Homologous chromosomes appear and pair in prophase I. At metaphase I, members of a homologous pair align at the equator of the cell and separate from each other in anaphase I. In meiosis II, the centromeres split, and sister chromatids are converted into individual chromosomes. The resulting haploid cells each have one set of chromosomes.

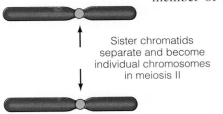
Paired Homologues separate in meiosis I

Sister chromatids separate and become individual chromosomes in meiosis II

Chiasmata
The crossing of nonsister chromatid strands seen in the first meiotic prophase. Chiasmata represent the structural evidence for crossing over.

Crossing over
The process of exchanging parts between homologous chromosomes during meiosis; produces new combinations of genetic information.

Next, the sister chromatids of each chromosome become visible (Figure 2.20b). At this stage, each chromosome consists of two sister chromatids joined by a single centromere. Also during this stage, evidence for a physical exchange of chromosomal material between homologous chromosomes may become visible at cross-shaped or X-shaped regions known as **chiasmata** (singular: chiasma) (Figure 2.20b). These structures are the points at which the physical exchange of chromosome material between chromatids can take place. This event, known as **crossing over,** is of great genetic significance and will be discussed later.

In metaphase I (Figure 2.20c), the synapsed members of a chromosome pair move to the center of the cell and line up on the equatorial plate. An important feature of meiosis should be noted here. The orientation of each chromosome pair at metaphase is random. Remember that one chromosome in each pair is paternal, and the other is maternal; there is no fixed pattern of arrangement of these chromosomes. The genetic consequences of this random arrangement at metaphase I will be discussed in a later section.

In anaphase I, members of each chromosome pair separate from each other and move toward opposite poles of the dividing cell (Figure 2.20d). In this way, each daughter cell receives one member of each chromosome pair. The chromosomes begin to unwind slightly in telophase I, and cytokinesis occurs, producing two haploid cells (Figure 2.20e). Two major events take place during meiosis I: *reduction*, the random separation of maternal and paternal chromatids, and *crossing over*, the physical exchange of segments between homologous chromosomes.

Meiosis II Begins with Haploid Cells

In prophase II, the chromosomes coil and become visible, a spindle forms, and the nuclear membrane (if present) disappears. The chromosomes cannot synapse because there are no homologues with which to pair (Figure 2.20f). As the chromosomes become more condensed, they begin moving toward the equator of the cell. At metaphase II (Figure 2.20g), the 23 chromosomes, each consisting of a centromere and two sister chromatids, line up on the metaphase plate with spindle fibers attached to the centromeres. At the beginning of anaphase II (Figure 2.20h) the centromere of each chromosome divides for the first time, and the 46 chromatids are converted to independent chromosomes and move to opposite poles of the cell.

In telophase II the chromosomes uncoil and become diffuse, the nuclear membrane reforms, and division of the cytoplasm takes place (Figure 2.20i). The process of meiosis is now complete. One diploid cell containing 46 chromosomes has undergone one round of chromosome replication and two rounds of division to produce four haploid cells, each containing one copy of each chromosome for a total of 23 chromosomes (Figure 2.20j).

The movement of chromosomes is summarized in ● Figure 2.21, and the events of meiosis are presented in Table 2.6 on p. 40. ● Figure 2.22 compares the events of mitosis and meiosis.

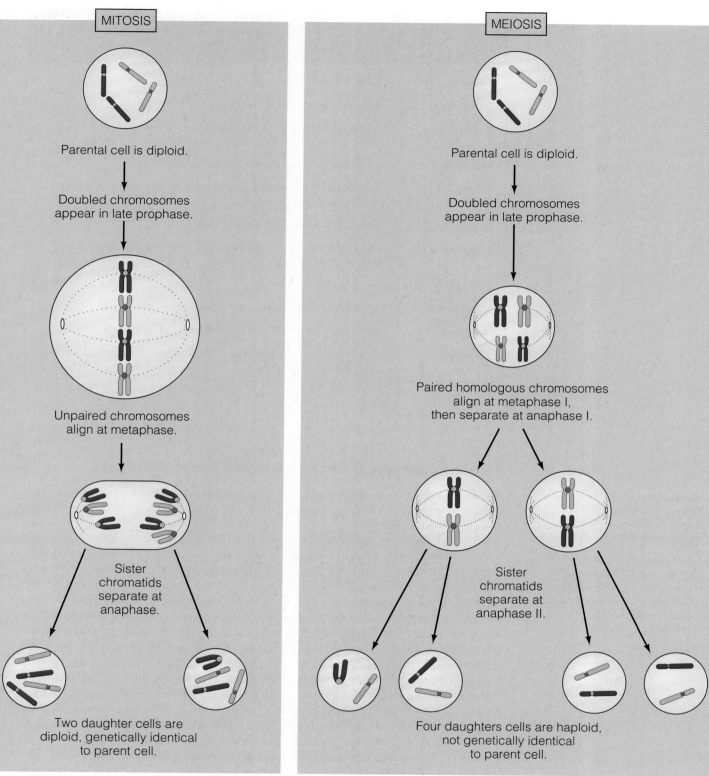

MITOSIS

Parental cell is diploid.

Doubled chromosomes appear in late prophase.

Unpaired chromosomes align at metaphase.

Sister chromatids separate at anaphase.

Two daughter cells are diploid, genetically identical to parent cell.

MEIOSIS

Parental cell is diploid.

Doubled chromosomes appear in late prophase.

Paired homologous chromosomes align at metaphase I, then separate at anaphase I.

Sister chromatids separate at anaphase II.

Four daughters cells are haploid, not genetically identical to parent cell.

FIGURE 2.22

A comparison of the events in mitosis and meiosis. In mitosis (left) a diploid parental cell undergoes chromosomal replication, and then enters prophase. The chromosomes appear doubled during late prophase, and unpaired chromosomes align at the middle (equator) of the cell during metaphase. In anaphase, the centromeres split converting the sister chromatids into chromosomes. The result is two daughter cells, each of which is genetically identical to the parental cell. In meiosis I (right), the parental diploid cell undergoes chromosome replication and then enters prophase. Homologous chromosomes pair, and each chromosome appears doubled, except at the centromeres. Paired homologues align at the equator of the cell during metaphase, and members of a chromosome pair separate during anaphase. In meiosis II, the unpaired chromosomes in each cell align at the equator of the cell, and during anaphase II, the centromeres split, and one copy of each chromosome is distributed to daughter cells. The result is four haploid daughter cells, which are not genetically equivalent to the parental cell.

TABLE 2.6

Summary of Meiosis

STAGE	CHARACTERISTICS
Interphase I	Chromosome replication takes place.
Prophase I	Chromosomes become visible, homologous chromosomes pair, and sister chromatids become visible; recombination takes place.
Metaphase I	Paired chromosomes align at equator of cell.
Anaphase I	Homologous chromosomes separate; members of each chromosome pair move to opposite poles.
Telophase I	Cytoplasm divides, producing two cells.
Interphase II	Following a brief pause, chromosomes uncoil slightly; this is not a real interphase as such.
Prophase II	Chromosomes re-coil.
Metaphase II	Unpaired chromosomes become aligned at equator of cell.
Anaphase II	Centromeres split; daughter chromosomes pull apart.
Telophase II	Chromosomes uncoil, nuclear membrane reforms, cytoplasm divides, and meiosis is complete.

Meiosis Produces New Combinations of Genes in Two Ways

Assortment
The random distribution of members of homologous chromosome pairs during meiosis.

Recombination
The process of exchanging chromosome parts between homologous chromosomes during meiosis; produces new combinations of genetic material.

Meiosis produces new combinations of genes in two ways: by **assortment** of chromosomes in meoisis I and by **recombination,** the physical exchange of homologous chromosome parts that also occurrs in meoisis I. As discussed earlier, each chromosome pair consists of one maternally derived (M) and one paternally derived (P) chromosome. When synapsed chromosome pairs line up on the cell's equator in metaphase I, there is no fixed pattern of arrangement of the maternal or paternal chromosomes (● Figure 2.23). The alignment of any chromosome pair can be maternal:paternal or paternal:maternal. As a result, each daughter cell is more likely to receive an assortment of maternal and paternal chromosomes than a complete set of maternal or paternal chromosomes. The number of maternal and paternal chromosome combinations produced by meiosis is equal to 2^n, where 2 represents the chromosomes in each pair, and n represents the number of chromosomes in the haploid set. Since humans have 23 chromosomes in the haploid set, then 2^{23} or 8,388,608 different combinations of maternal and paternal chromosomes are possible in haploid cells. If each parent has this many combinations possible, they could produce more than 7×10^{13} offspring with different combinations of parental chromosomes.

This astronomic number does not take into account the variability generated by the physical exchange of chromosome parts, or crossing over, that takes place during meiosis. Crossing over or recombination is a second mechanism through which new combinations of genes are produced by meiosis. During prophase I homologous chromosomes pair with each other and the sister chromatids of each chromosome become visible. During this stage, the arms of two nonsister chromatids can overlap, forming chiasma (● Figure 2.24). These sites of overlap are associated with the physical exchange of chromosome segments and the genes they contain. If, for example, a pair of homologous chromosomes carries different forms of a gene (e.g., *A*

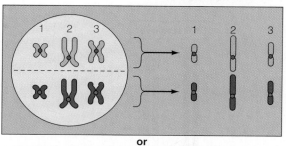

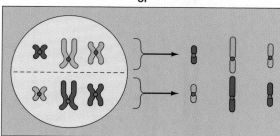

or

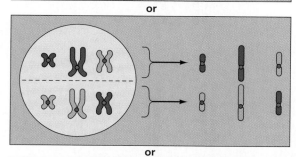

or

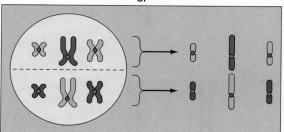

or

— FIGURE 2.23

The orientation of members of a chromosome pair at meiosis is random. Here three chromosomes (1, 2, and 3) have four possible alignments (maternal members of each chromosome pair are light blue, patental members are dark blue). There are eight possible combinations of maternal and paternal chromosomes in the resulting haploid cells.

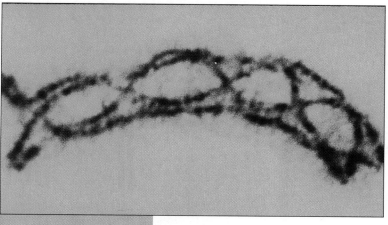

— FIGURE 2.24

Crossing over is the physical exchange of chromosome parts between homologous chromosomes. The X-shaped regions are the site of crossing over.

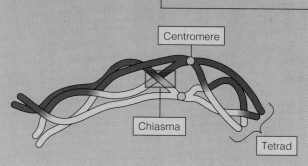

Centromere

Chiasma

Tetrad

and *a* or *B* and *b*), crossing over reshuffles this genetic information, creating new chromosomal combinations (● Figure 2.25).

● **FIGURE 2.25**

Crossing over increases genetic variation by combining genes from both parents on the same chromatid. At left is shown the combination of maternal and paternal genes when no crossing over occurs. At right, new combinations (*Ab, aB*) are produced by crossing over, increasing genetic variability in the haploid cells that will form gametes.

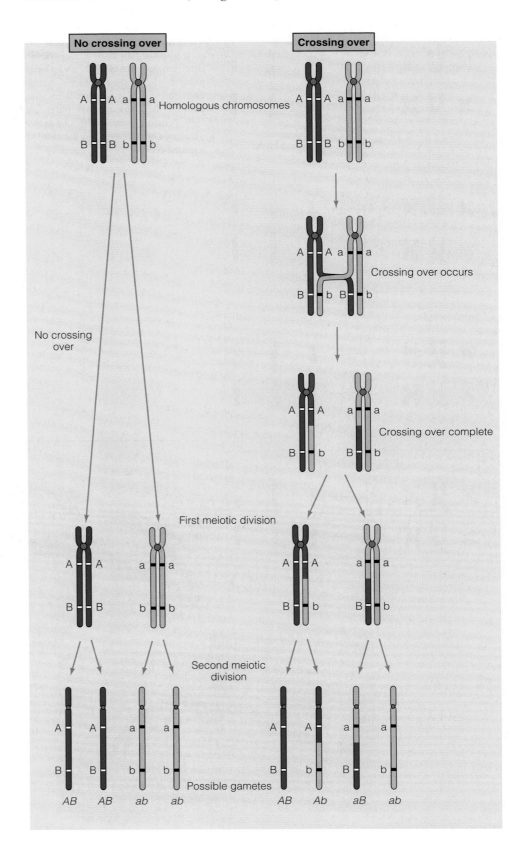

Without crossing over, the combination of genes on a particular chromosome would remain coupled together indefinitely. Crossing over allows new and perhaps advantageous combinations of genes to be produced. When the variability generated by crossing over is added to that produced by random chromosome combinations, the number of different genetic combinations that a couple can produce in their offspring has been estimated to be 80^{23}. Obviously the offspring of a couple will represent only a very small fraction of all these possible gamete combinations. For this reason, it is almost impossible for any two children (aside from identical twins) to be genetically identical.

Formation of Gametes: Spermatogenesis and Oogenesis

Gametogenesis is the formation of mature ova and spermatozoa. In males the production of sperm occurs in the testis and is known as **spermatogenesis**. Germ cells, or **spermatogonia**, line the tubules in the testis and are mitotically active from puberty until death and produce daughter cells called **primary spermatocytes** (━ Figure 2.26). The spermatocytes undergo meiosis, and the four haploid cells that result are known as **spermatids**. Each spermatid undergoes a period of development into mature **sperm**. During this period the nucleus, containing 23 chromosomes (sperm carry 22 autosomes and an X or a Y chromosome) becomes condensed and forms the head

Spermatogenesis
The process of sperm production, including meiosis and the cellular events of sperm formation.

Spermatogonia
Mitotically active cells in the gonads of males that give rise to primary spermatocytes.

Primary spermatocytes
Cells in the testis that undergo meiosis.

Spermatids
The four haploid cells produced by meiotic division of a primary spermatocyte.

Sperm
Male haploid gametes produced by morphological transformation of spermatids.

━ **FIGURE 2.26**

The process of spermatogenesis. Germ cells (spermatocytes) divide by mitosis, and some cells produced in this way enter meiosis as primary spermatocytes beginning at puberty. After meiosis I, the secondary spermatocytes contain 23 double-stranded chromosomes. After meiosis II, the haploid spermatids contain 23 single-stranded chromosomes. Spermatids undergo a series of developmental changes (spermiogenesis) and become converted into mature spermatozoa.

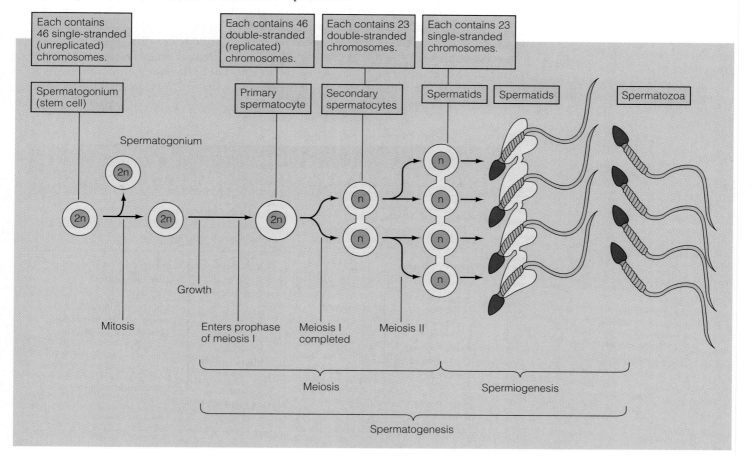

of the sperm. In the cytoplasm a neck and whiplike tail develop, and most of the remaining cytoplasm is lost. In human males, meiosis and sperm production begin at puberty and continue throughout life. The entire process of spermatogenesis takes about 48 days: 16 for meiosis I, 16 for meiosis II, and 16 for the conversion of the spermatid into the mature sperm. The tubules within the testis contain large numbers of spermatocytes, and large numbers of sperm are always in production. A single ejaculate may contain 200 to 300 million sperm, and over a lifetime a male will produce billions of sperm.

In females the production of gametes is known as oogenesis and takes place in the ovary. Germ cells, or **oogonia,** divide by mitosis and form **primary oocytes** that undergo meiosis (Figure 2.27). However, the cytoplasmic cleavage in meiosis I does not produce cells of equal size. One cell, destined to become the oocyte, receives about 95% of the cytoplasm and is known as the **secondary oocyte.** In the second meiotic division, the same disproportionate cleavage results in one cell retaining most of the cytoplasm. The large cell, known as an **ootid,** will become the functional gamete, and the nonfunctional, smaller cells are known as **polar bodies.** Thus in females, only one of the four cells produced by meiosis becomes a gamete. All oocytes contain 22 autosomes and an X chromosome.

The timing of meiosis and gamete formation in the human female is different than in the male (Table 2.7). The mitotic divisions of oogonia begin early in embryonic development and are completed at 7 to 8 weeks of gestation. Since no more divisions take place, the female is born with all the primary oocytes she will ever possess. The primary oocytes enter late meiotic prophase I well before birth and remain in meiosis I until the female undergoes puberty. Under hormonal influence, usually one oocyte per menstrual cycle completes the first meiotic division and is released from the ovary (ovulated). If the egg is fertilized as it passes down the fallopian tube, it will quickly complete meiosis II, resulting in a diploid zygote. Unfertilized eggs are sloughed off during menstruation, along with uterine tissue. The production of secondary oocytes continues until menopause. Since ovulation occurs once in each menstrual cycle, the female releases about 450 secondary oocytes during the reproductive period of her life. In females meiosis stretches over a range of years, from the initiation of prophase I, while she is still an embryo, to the completion of meiosis II following fertilization. Depending on the time of ovulation, meiosis can take from 12 to 50 years in human females.

Oogonia
Mitotically active cells that produce primary oocytes.

Primary oocytes
Cells in the ovary that undergo meiosis.

Secondary oocyte
The cell produced by the first meiotic division.

Ootid
The haploid cell produced by meiosis that will become the functional gamete.

Polar body
A cell produced in the first or second division in female meiosis that contains little cytoplasm and will not function as a gamete.

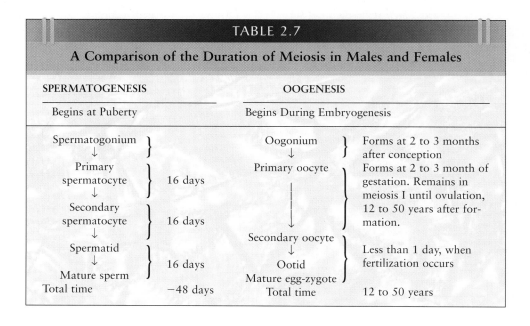

TABLE 2.7			
A Comparison of the Duration of Meiosis in Males and Females			
SPERMATOGENESIS		**OOGENESIS**	
Begins at Puberty		Begins During Embryogenesis	
Spermatogonium ↓	}	Oogonium ↓	} Forms at 2 to 3 months after conception
Primary spermatocyte ↓	} 16 days	Primary oocyte ↓	Forms at 2 to 3 month of gestation. Remains in meiosis I until ovulation, 12 to 50 years after formation.
Secondary spermatocyte ↓	} 16 days	↓	
Spermatid ↓	} 16 days	Secondary oocyte ↓ Ootid	} Less than 1 day, when fertilization occurs
Mature sperm		Mature egg-zygote	
Total time	~48 days	Total time	12 to 50 years

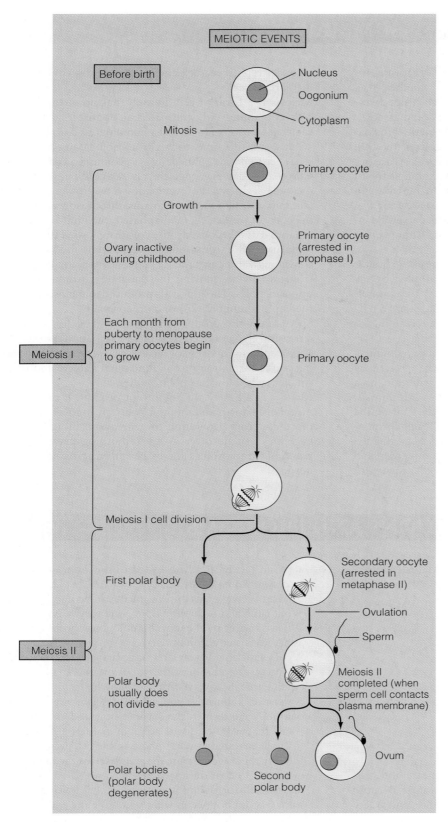

MEIOTIC EVENTS

Before birth

Nucleus
Oogonium
Cytoplasm

Mitosis

Primary oocyte

Growth

Ovary inactive
during childhood

Primary oocyte
(arrested in
prophase I)

Each month from
puberty to menopause
primary oocytes begin
to grow

Meiosis I

Primary oocyte

Meiosis I cell division

First polar body

Secondary oocyte
(arrested in
metaphase II)

Ovulation

Sperm

Meiosis II

Polar body
usually does
not divide

Meiosis II
completed (when
sperm cell contacts
plasma membrane)

Polar bodies
(polar body
degenerates)

Second
polar body

Ovum

▬ FIGURE 2.27

The process of oogenesis. Germ cells (oogonia) divide by mitosis, and some cells enter meiosis as primary oocytes during embryonic development. The primary oocytes arrest in prophase I. At puberty, one oocyte per menstrual cycle continues meiosis, and the product of the first meiotic division—the secondary oocyte—is released from the ovary. Production of the secondary oocyte is accompanied by unequal cytoplasmic cleavage, producing the secondary oocyte and a polar body. The secondary oocyte is arrested in meiosis II until fertilization. Penetration of the sperm stimulates completion of the second meiotic division, producing the ovum and the second polar body.

1. The cell is the basic unit in the bodies of all organisms, including humans. Since genes control the number, size, shape, and function of cells, the study of cell structure often reveals much about the normal expression of genes.

2. Within the cell the nucleus contains the genetic information that controls the structure and function of the cell. This genetic information is carried in nuclear structures known as chromosomes. The number, size, and shape of chromosomes are species-specific traits. In humans, 46 chromosomes, the *2n,* or diploid, number, are found in most cells, while specialized cells known as gametes contain half of that number, the haploid, or *n,* number of chromosomes.

3. In humans, chromosomes exist in pairs known as homologues. One member of each pair is contributed by the mother and one by the father. Females carry two homologous X chromosomes, while males have an X and a partially nonhomologous Y chromosome. The remaining 22 pairs of chromosomes are known as autosomes.

4. For cells to survive and function, they must contain a complete set of genetic information. This is ensured by replication of each chromosome and distribution of a complete chromosome set in the process of mitosis. Mitosis represents one part of the cell cycle. During the other part, interphase, a duplicate copy of each chromosome is made. The process of mitosis has been divided into four stages: prophase, metaphase, anaphase, and telophase. Mitosis results in two diploid cells, each with an exact replica of the genetic information contained in the parental cell.

5. Meiosis is a form of cell division that produces haploid cells containing only the paternal or maternal copy of each chromosome. In meiosis, homologous chromosomes synapse. At this time, each chromosome consists of two sister chromatids joined by a common centromere. Chromatids can engage in the physical exchange of chromosome segments, an event known as crossing over. In metaphase I, paired, homologous chromosomes align at the equator of the cell; in anaphase I, the homologues are separated and become dyads. Before meiosis II there is no replication of chromosomes, and the unpaired chromosomes align at the metaphase plate. In anaphase II the centromeres divide, moving the daughter chromosomes to opposite poles. The four cells produced in meiosis contain the haploid number (23) of chromosomes.

6. Spermatids, the products of meiosis in males, undergo structural changes to convert them to functional sperm. In female meiosis, division of the cytoplasm is unequal, leading to the formation of one functional gamete and three smaller cells known as polar bodies.

7. Meiosis is a genetically important process. It provides a mechanism for maintaining a constant number of chromosomes from generation to generation. In addition, it generates genetic diversity by reshuffling maternal and paternal chromosomes and by permitting crossing over to occur.

QUESTIONS AND PROBLEMS

1. Assign a function(s) to the following cellular structures:
   a. plasma membrane
   b. mitochondrion
   c. nucleus
   d. ribosome

2. Define the following terms:
   a. chromosome
   b. chromatin
   c. chromatid

3. Human haploid gametes (sperm and eggs) contain:
   a. 46 chromosomes, 46 chromatids
   b. 46 chromosomes, 23 chromatids
   c. 23 chromosomes, 46 chromatids
   d. 23 chromosomes, 23 chromatids

4. Originally, karyotypic analysis relied on size and centromere placement to identify chromosomes. Because many chromosomes are similar in size and centromere placement, the identification of individual chromosomes was difficult, and chromosomes were placed into eight groups, identified by letters A-G. Today, each human chromosome can be readily identified.

   a. What technical advances led to this improvement in chromosome identification?
   b. List two ways this improvement can be implemented.

5. What clinical information does a karyotype give you?

6. What is meant by the term homologous chromosomes?

7. What are sister chromatids?

8. A colleague emails you a message that she has identified an interesting chromosome variation at 21q13. In discussing this discovery with a friend who is not a cytogeneticist, explain how you would describe the location, defining each term in the chromosome address 21q13.

9. A cell that will not divide again in its lifetime will most likely be arrested at what phase of the cell cycle?

10. Identify the stages of mitosis, and describe the important events that occur during each stage.

11. Why is cell furrowing important in cell division? If cytokinesis did not occur, what would be the end result?

12. Which of the following statements is not true when comparing mitosis and meiosis?
   a. twice the number of cells are produced in meiosis versus mitosis

b. meiosis is involved in the production of gametes, unlike mitosis

c. crossing over occurs in meiosis I, not in meiosis II or mitosis

d. meiosis and mitosis both produce cells that are genetically identical

e. in both mitosis and meiosis, the parental cell is diploid

13. In what stage are the following diploid cells ($2n = 4$).
   a. anaphase of meiosis I
   b. interphase of mitosis
   c. metaphase of mitosis
   d. metaphase of meiosis I
   e. metaphase of meiosis II

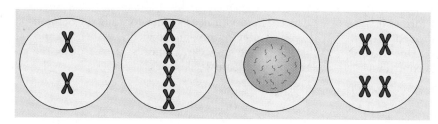

14. A cell from a human female has just undergone mitosis. For unknown reasons, the centromere of chromosome 7 failed to divide. Describe the chromosomal contents of the daughter cells.

15. During which phases of the mitotic cycle would the terms *chromosome* and *chromatid* refer to identical structures?

16. Describe the critical events of mitosis that are responsible for ensuring that each daughter cell receives a full set of chromosomes from the parent cell.

17. What is meant by the term *cycle* in the cell cycle? What is happening at the S phase and the M phase?

18. Does the cell cycle refer to meiosis as well as meiosis?

19. It is possible that an alternative mechanism for generating germ cells could have evolved. Consider meiosis in a germ cell precursor with such a way of producing germ cells. If the S phase were skipped, which meiotic division (meiosis I or meiosis II) would no longer be required?

20. A cell has a diploid number of 6 ($2n = 6$).
   a. Draw the cell in metaphase of meiosis I.
   b. Draw the cell in metaphase of mitosis.
   c. How many chromosomes are present in a daughter cell after meiosis I?
   d. How many chromatids are present in a daughter cell after meiosis II?
   e. How many chromosomes are present in a daughter cell after mitosis?
   f. During meiosis I, how many tetrads are visible in this cell?

21. A cell ($2n = 4$) has undergone cell division. Two daughter cells have the following chromosome content. Has this cell undergone mitosis or meiosis I or meiosis II?

a.

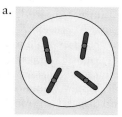

b.

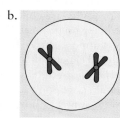

c.

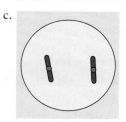

22. We are following the progress of human chromosome 1 during meiosis. At the end of synapsis, how many chromosomes, chromatids and centromeres are present to ensure that chromosome 1 faithfully traverses meiosis?

23. What is the physical structure that is associated with crossing over?

24. Compare meiotic anaphase I with meiotic anaphase II. Which meiotic anaphase is similar to mitotic anaphase?

25. Discuss and compare the products of meiosis in human females and males. How many functional gametes are produced from the daughter cells in each sex?

26. Explain how meiosis leads to genetic variation in diploid organisms?

27. A human female is conceived on April 1, 1949 and is born on January 1, 1950. Onset of puberty occurs on January 1, 1962. She conceives a child on July 1, 1994. How long did it take for the ovum that was fertilized on July 1, 1994 to complete meiosis?

SCIENCE AND SOCIETY

1. All cancers are characterized by uncontrollable cell growth, and when untreated, are fatal. Early diagnosis and treatment are vital to prevent death of affected individuals. Cancers that occur in childhood are usually more malignant that those that develop later in life. Although all cancers involve mutant genes (most often in somatic cells) those that develop in childhood are more likely to have a hereditary predisposition transmitted by the germ cells. What homeostatic mechanisms have gone awry when cancer develops? Why are childhood cancers more likely to have a hereditary predisposition than adult-onset forms? Why do you suppose there is a higher degree of malignancy in childhood cancers than in adult forms? It is estimated that nearly 1 in 3 adults will be affected with some form of cancer at some point in their life. Does this seem like a high or low number? What factors contribute to this incidence of cancer?

2. Electromagnetic fields from power lines or electrical appliances have been implicated as a cause of some childhood cancers, especially leukemia and brain tumors. This link is derived from studies of populations and the incidence of cancers (an epidemiological study). Other epidemiological studies contradict this finding. For example, the state of Connecticut has the oldest cancer registry in the United States, and data from this registry indicates that leukemia rates have remained constant for the last half-century despite an increase in power consumption. In addition, there is no direct scientific evidence for a link between electromagnetic fields and cancer. What scientific evidence would you need before forming an opinion on the ability of electromagnetic fields to cause cancers? What would be an accurate means of measuring the effects of magnetic fields on genes?

INTERNET ACTIVITIES

The following activities use the resources of the World Wide Web to enhance the topics covered in this chapter. To investigate the topics described below, log on to the book's home page at:

http://www.wadsworth.com/biology

1. For a look at the diversity of various cell types at the microscopic level, access the nanoworld site from the book's homepage. Not only does this site have great photos, but it also illustrates the power of the World Wide Web to allow instantaneous sharing of information across the globe. Look at a variety of images of cells, cell organelles and cell division to gain an appreciation of this imagery.

2. Use the link on the book's homepage to find the Cells Alive! homepage. Available quick-time movies show a number of cell functions, including bacterial reproduction and phagocytosis. Scroll down to the Inside-Vintage section and click on *How Big is a* .... Compare the size of a virus, bacterium, red blood cell, lymphocyte and human sperm by using the line scale provided.

FOR FURTHER READING

Bretscher, M. (1985). Molecules of the cell membrane. *Sci. Am.* 253, 100-109.

Cross, P. C. (1993). Cell and tissue ultrastructure: A functional perspective. Upper Saddle River, NJ: Prentice-Hall.

Kessel, R., & Shih, C. (1974). *Scanning electron microscopy in biology: A student's atlas of biological organization.* New York: Springer-Verlag.

Therman, E., & Susman, M. (1993). *Human chromosomes: Structure, behavior, effects (3rd ed.).* New York: Springer-Verlag.

Travis, J. (1996). What's in the vault? *Science News* 150, 56-57.

Wagner, R.P, Maguire, M.P., & Stallings, R.L. (1993). *Chromosomes: A synthesis.* New York: Wiley-Liss.

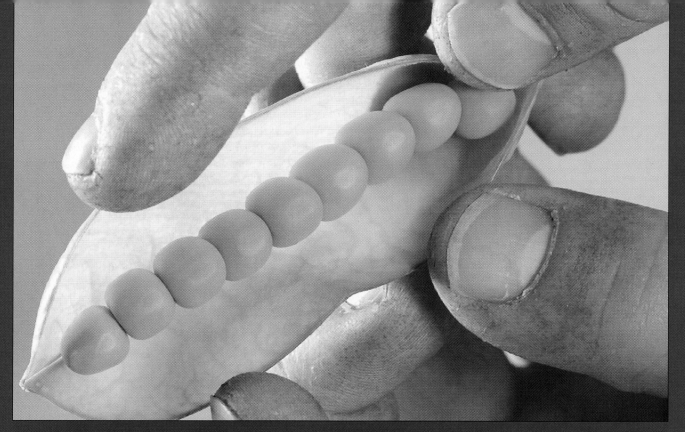

TRANSMISSION OF GENES FROM GENERATION TO GENERATION

Chapter **3**

Chapter Outline

HEREDITY: HOW DOES IT WORK?
SIDEBAR   *Mendel and Test Anxiety*
MENDEL'S EXPERIMENTAL APPROACH
  RESOLVED MANY UNANSWERED
  QUESTIONS
CROSSING PEA PLANTS: THE
  PRINCIPLE OF SEGREGATION
Results and Conclusions from Mendel's
  First Series of Crosses
SIDEBAR   *Why Wrinkled Peas are Wrinkled*
CONCEPTS AND CONTROVERSIES
  Ockham's Razor
Inheritance of a Single Trait: The Principle
  of Segregation

MORE CROSSES WITH PEA PLANTS:
  THE PRINCIPLE OF INDEPENDENT
  ASSORTMENT
Crosses with Two Traits
Methods, Results, and Conclusions
The Principle of Independent Assortment
CONCEPTS AND CONTROVERSIES
  Evaluating Results—The Chi-Square Test
MENDELIAN INHERITANCE AND
  MEIOSIS: THE IDEA THAT GENES
  ARE ON CHROMOSOMES
MANY GENES HAVE MORE THAN TWO
  ALLELES

VARIATIONS ON A THEME BY MENDEL
Codominant Alleles Are Both Expressed in
  the Phenotype
Incomplete Dominance Has a Distinctive
  Phenotype
The Concepts of Dominance and
  Recessiveness
MENDELIAN INHERITANCE IN
  HUMANS
Pedigree Analysis in Human Genetics
CONCEPTS AND CONTROVERSIES   *Solving
  Genetics Problems*
Pedigree Analysis in Humans

OPENING IMAGE
*Pea plants were carefully selected by
Mendel for his heredity experiments.*

*C*harles Darwin was not the only member of his family to make significant contributions to our understanding of genetics and evolution in
the latter part of the 19th century. Darwin's cousin, Francis Galton, was
concerned that Darwin's account of evolution did not explain how small
variations in appearance were generated, and set out to experimentally test
Darwin's idea about how traits were inherited.

Darwin subscribed to the generally accepted idea of the time that parental traits are blended in the offspring. According to the blending idea, if a plant with red flowers is crossed to a plant with white flowers, the offspring should have pink flowers (a blend of red and white). But Darwin realized that if traits were blended generation after generation, variation would be reduced, not increased. To get around this problem, Darwin decided to support a second idea about how traits were inherited. This idea was really the ancient theory of pangenesis presented in a slightly different form. According to this concept, instructions to form structures of the body are contained in particles called "gemmules." These particles, formed in various parts of the body, move through the blood to the reproductive organs, and are transmitted from there to the offspring. Gemmules from each parent make a contribution to the traits expressed in the offspring.

Galton decided to put the idea of gemmules to a test. He used rabbits with different coat colors, and transfused blood between them. He thought that a transfusion should mix the gemmules from the two rabbits, changing the coat color in the offspring. Blood from black-coated rabbits was transfused into rabbits with white coats, and these white rabbits were bred to each other. If the gemmules from the black rabbits mixed with the gemmules in the white rabbits, then crossing the transfused white rabbits with each other should produce at least some offspring with gray coats (a blend of black and white).

The results of Galton's experiments did not support the idea of pangenesis. No mixing of fur color occurred when transfused rabbits were interbred. He presented his results to the Royal Society, the highest scientific body in England on March 30, 1871, and said: "The conclusion from this large series of experiments is not to be avoided, that the doctrine of Pangenesis, pure and simple, as I have interpreted it, is incorrect." The report showed that traits were not transmitted by pangenesis, but it left the question of how traits were inherited unanswered.

Galton went on to make other significant contributions to the study of inheritance. He set up the mathematical basis for studying traits controlled by several genes, and pointed out the importance of twin studies in human genetics.

Unfortunately, it appears that neither Galton nor Darwin read the work of Gregor Mendel on the inheritance of traits in the garden pea published in 1866. This work, titled "Experiments in Plant Hybrids," is one of the most important scientific papers ever published. Here Mendel departs from the usual reporting of observations and takes the additional step of fitting his experimental results into a conceptual framework that can be used to explain the mechanism of heredity in any organism, not just the garden pea. In this chapter, we will reconstruct the experiments of Mendel and show how he moved from recording his results to drawing conclusions about the principles of heredity.

HEREDITY: HOW DOES IT WORK?

Johann Gregor Mendel was born in 1822 in Hynice, Moravia, a region that is now part of the Czech Republic. He showed great promise as a student, but poverty prevented him from beginning university studies. At the age of 21, he entered the Augustinian monastery at Brno as a way of continuing his interests in natural history. After completing his monastic studies, Mendel enrolled at the University of Vienna in the fall of 1851. In his first year he took courses in physics, mathematics, chemistry, and the natural sciences.

In his botany courses, Mendel encountered the new concept that all organisms are composed of cells and that cells are the fundamental unit of all living things. The cell theory raised several new questions and many controversial issues. One was the ques-

tion of whether both parents contributed equally to the traits of the offspring. Because the germ cells in most female plants and animals are so much larger than those of the male, this was a logical and much debated question. Related to this was the question of whether the traits present in the offspring were produced by blending the traits of the parents. If so, in what ratios? Did the female contribute 40%, 50%, 60%, or more of the traits? In 1854 Mendel returned to Brno to teach physics and began a series of experiments that were to resolve these questions.

MENDEL'S EXPERIMENTAL APPROACH RESOLVED MANY UNANSWERED QUESTIONS

Mendel's success in uncovering the mechanisms of inheritance was not blind luck, but was the result of carefully planned experiments. Having determined what he wanted to investigate, Mendel set about choosing an organism for these experiments. Near the beginning of his landmark paper on inheritance, Mendel wrote:

> The value and validity of any experiment are determined by the suitability of the means as well as by the way they are applied. In the present case as well, it can not be unimportant which plant species were chosen for the experiments and how these were carried out.
>
> Selection of the plant group for experiments of this kind must be made with the greatest possible care if one does not want to jeopardize all possibility of success from the very outset.

He then listed the properties that an experimental organism should have. First, it should have a number of differing traits that can be studied; second, the plant should be self-fertilizing and have a flower structure that minimizes accidental contamination with foreign pollen; and third, the offspring of self-fertilized plants should be fully fertile so that further crosses can be made.

He paid particular attention to a plant group known as the legumes because their flower structure allows self-pollination or cross-pollination (with a minimum chance of accidental pollination) by other plants. Among the legumes, he noted that 34 varieties of pea plants with different traits were available to him from seed dealers; the plant had a relatively short growth period, could be grown in the ground or in pots in the greenhouse, and could be self-fertilized or artificially fertilized by hand when necessary (￼ Figure 3.1).

Mendel then tested all 34 varieties of pea plants for 2 years to ensure that the traits they carried were true-breeding; that is, that self-fertilization gave rise to the same traits in all offspring, generation after generation. From these, 22 varieties were planted annually for the next 8 years

￼ **FIGURE 3.1**

The study of how traits in pea plants are passed from generation to generation provided the material for Mendel's work on heredity.

Monohybrid cross
A cross between individuals that
differ with respect to a single gene
pair.

to provide plants for his experiments (■ Figure 3.2). For his work, he
selected seven characters that affected the seeds, pods, flowers, and
stems of the plant (Table 3.1). Each character he studied was represented by two distinct forms or traits: plant height by tall and short, seed
shape by wrinkled and smooth, and so forth.

To avoid errors caused by small sample sizes, he planned experiments
on a large scale. Over the next 8 years, Mendel used some 28,000 pea
plants in his experiments. In all his experiments, he kept track of each
character separately for several generations. He began by studying one
pair of traits at a time and repeated his experiments for each of the traits
to confirm his results. Using his training in physics and mathematics,
Mendel analyzed his data according to the principles of probability and
statistics. His methodical and thorough approach to his work, and his
lack of preconceived notions, were the secrets of his success.

CROSSING PEA PLANTS: THE PRINCIPLE OF SEGREGATION

To show how Mendel developed his ideas about inheritance, we will first describe
some of his experiments and outline the results he obtained. Then, we will follow the
reasoning Mendel used in reaching his conclusions, and outline some of the further
experiments that confirmed his ideas.

In the first set of experiments, Mendel followed the inheritance of seed shape.
Since this cross involved only one character (seed shape), he called it a **monohybrid
cross.** He took plants with smooth seeds and crossed them to a variety with wrinkled seeds. In making this cross, flowers from one variety were fertilized by hand
using pollen from the other variety. In this first experiment, Mendel performed 60
fertilizations on 15 plants. The seeds that formed as a result of these fertilizations
were all smooth. This result was true whether the pollen was contributed by a plant
with smooth peas or by a plant with wrinkled peas. The next year, Mendel planted
the smooth seeds from this cross. When the plants matured, the flowers were self-
fertilized, and a total of 7324 seeds were collected. Of these, 5474 were smooth and
1850 were wrinkled.

P_1 : Smooth × wrinkled

F_1 : All Smooth

F_2 : 5474 Smooth and 1850 wrinkled

TABLE 3.1		
Traits Selected for Study by Mendel		
STRUCTURE STUDIED	**DOMINANT**	**RECESSIVE**
SEEDS		
Shape	Smooth	Wrinkled
Color	Yellow	Green
Seed Coat Color	Gray	White
PODS		
Shape	Full	Constricted
Color	Green	Yellow
FLOWERS		
Placement	Axial (along stems)	Terminal (top of stems)
STEMS		
Length	Long	Short

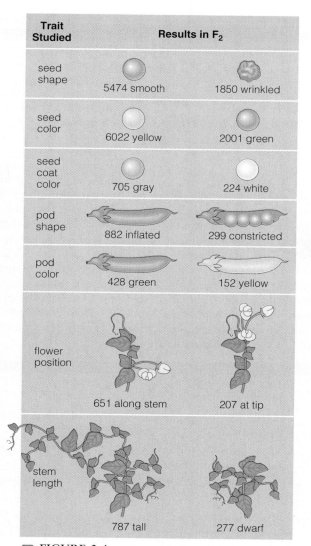

Trait Studied	Results in F₂	
seed shape	5474 smooth	1850 wrinkled
seed color	6022 yellow	2001 green
seed coat color	705 gray	224 white
pod shape	882 inflated	299 constricted
pod color	428 green	152 yellow
flower position	651 along stem	207 at tip
stem length	787 tall	277 dwarf

P₁ Smooth × wrinkled

F₁ Smooth

self-fertilize F₁ plants

F₂ 5474 Smooth | 1850 wrinkled

Total peas in F₂: 7324

¾ Smooth
¼ wrinkled

 FIGURE 3.3

One of Mendel's crosses. Pure-breeding varieties of peas (smooth and wrinkled) were used as the P₁ generation. The offspring in the F₁ had all smooth seeds. Self-fertilization of F₁ plants gave rise to both smooth and wrinkled progeny in the F₂ generation. About ¾ of the offspring were smooth, and about ¼ were wrinkled.

FIGURE 3.4

Results of Mendel's monohybrid crosses in peas. The numbers represent the F₂ plants showing a given trait. On average, ¾ of the offspring showed one trait, and ¼ showed the other (a 3 : 1 ratio).

SIDEBAR

Why Wrinkled Peas Are Wrinkled

Wrinkled peas was one variety used by Mendel in his experiments. At the time, nothing was known about how peas became wrinkled or smooth. All Mendel needed to know was that a factor controls seed shape, and that it has two alleles—a dominant one for smooth shape and a recessive one for wrinkled shape.

Recently, scientists have discovered how peas become wrinkled, providing a connection between a gene and its phenotype. While the pea is developing, starch is synthesized and stored as a food source. Starch is a large, branched molecule made up of sugar molecules, and the ability to form branches is controlled by a gene. Normally, starch molecules are highly branched structures; this allows more sugar to be stored in each molecule. In peas with the wrinkled genotype, the branching gene is inactive. The developing pea thus converts sugar into starch very slowly, and excess sugar accumulates. The excess sugar causes the pea to take up large amounts of water, and the seed swells. In a final stage of development, water is lost from the seed. In homozygous *wrinkled* peas, more water is lost than in the smooth seeds, causing the outer shell of the pea to become wrinkled.

Mendel's contribution was to show that a specific factor controlled a trait, and that a given gene could have different forms. We now know that genes exert their effect on phenotype through the production of a gene product.

He conducted similar experiments on the inheritance of the other six characters. In his experiments, Mendel designated the parental generation as the P₁ generation and the offspring as the F₁ (first filial) generation. The second generation, produced by self-fertilizing the F₁ plants, was called the F₂ (or second filial) generation. The experiments with seed shape are summarized in Figure 3.3.

Results and Conclusions from Mendel's First Series of Crosses

The results from experiments with all seven characters were similar to those seen in the cross with smooth and wrinkled seeds, and are summarized in Figure 3.4. In all crosses, the following results were obtained:

CONCEPTS AND CONTROVERSIES

Ockham's Razor

When Mendel proposed the simplest explanation for the number of factors contained in the F_1 plants in his monohybrid crosses, he was using a principle of scientific reasoning known as the principle of parsimony, or Ockham's razor.

William of Ockham (also spelled Occam) was a Franciscan monk and scholastic philosopher who lived from about 1300 to 1349. He had a strong interest in the study of thought processes and in logical methods. He is the author of the maxim known as Ockham's razor: "Pluralites non est pondera sine necessitate," which translates from the Latin as "entities must not be multiplied without necessity." In the study of philosophy and theology of the Middle Ages, this was taken to mean that when constructing an argument, do not go beyond the simplest argument unless it is necessary. While Ockham was not the first to use this approach, he used this tool of logic so well and so often to dissect the arguments of his opponents that it became known as Ockham's razor.

The principle was adapted to the construction of scientific hypotheses in the 15th century. Galileo used the principle of parsimony to argue that since his model of the solar system was the simplest, it was probably correct. In modern terms, the phrase is taken to mean that in proposing a mechanism or hypothesis, use the least number of steps possible. The simplest mechanism is not necessarily correct, but it is usually the easiest to prove or disprove by doing experiments, and the most likely to produce scientific progress.

For a given trait, Mendel concluded that both parents contribute an equal number of factors to the offspring. In this case, the simplest assumption is that each parent contributes one such factor, and that the F_1 offspring contained two such factors. Further experiments proved this conclusion correct.

- The F_1 offspring showed only one of the two parental traits, and always the same trait.
- In all crosses, it did not matter which variety served as the male parent (that is, which plant donated the pollen). The results were always the same.
- The trait not shown in the F_1 offspring reappeared in about 25% of the F_2 offspring.

The results of these crosses were the basis for Mendel's first discoveries. His experiments showed that traits remained unchanged as they passed from parent to offspring: traits did not blend together in any of the offspring. Although they might be unexpressed, they remained unchanged from generation to generation. This convinced him that inheritance did not work by blending the traits of the parents in the offspring; rather, traits were inherited as if they were separate units that did not blend together.

In his experiments, Mendel made reciprocal crosses, so that the variety used as a male plant in one set of experiments was used as the female plant in the next set of crosses. In all cases, it did not matter whether the male or female plant had smooth or wrinkled seeds; the result were the same. From these experiments he concluded that each parent makes an equal contribution to the genetic makeup of the offspring.

Based on the results of his crosses with each of the seven characters, Mendel came to several conclusions:

- Factors that determine traits can be hidden or unexpressed. All the F_1 seeds resembled the smooth parent, but when these seeds were grown and self-fertilized, they produced some plants with wrinkled seeds. This means that the F_1 seeds contained a hereditary factor for wrinkled that was present but not expressed. The trait that is not expressed in the F_1 but is present in the F_2 he called the **recessive** trait. The trait expressed in the F_1 is called the **dominant** trait. Mendel called this phenomenon dominance.
- Comparison of the P_1 smooth plants and the F_1 smooth plants showed that despite identical appearances, their genetic makeup must be different. When P_1

Recessive
The trait unexpressed in the F_1 but reexpressed in some members of the F_2 generation.

Dominant
The trait expressed in the F_1 (or heterozygous) condition.

plants are self-fertilized, they give rise to plants that produce only smooth seeds. But when F_1 plants are self-fertilized, they give rise to plants with both smooth and wrinkled seeds. Mendel realized that it was important to make a distinction between the appearance of an organism and its genetic constitution. The term **phenotype** is now used to refer to the observed properties or outward appearance of a trait, and the term **genotype** refers to the genetic makeup of an organism with regard to the trait. In our example, it is apparent that the P_1 and F_1 plants with smooth seeds have identical phenotypes, but must have different genotypes.

• The results of these self-fertilization experiments indicate that the F_1 plants must have contained factors for smooth and wrinkled traits, since both types of seeds are present in the F_2 generation. The question is, how many factors for seed shape are carried in the F_1 plants? From the results of his crosses, since Mendel had reasoned that the male and female parent contributed equally to the traits of the offspring, the simplest interpretation is that each F_1 plant contained two hereditary factors, one for smooth that was expressed, and one for wrinkled that remained unexpressed (see "Concepts and Controversies," page 54). By extension of this reasoning, each P_1 and F_2 plant must also contain two factors that determine seed shape. Traditionally, uppercase letters are used to represent the factor with a dominant pattern of inheritance, and lowercase letters are used to represent the factor with a recessive pattern of inheritance (S = smooth, and s = wrinkled). Using this shorthand, we can reconstruct the genotypes and phenotypes of the P_1 and F_1 as shown in ● Figure 3.5.

Phenotype
The observable properties of an organism.

Genotype
The specific genetic constitution of an organism.

● **FIGURE 3.5**

The phenotypes and genotypes of the parents and offspring in Mendel's cross involving seed shape.

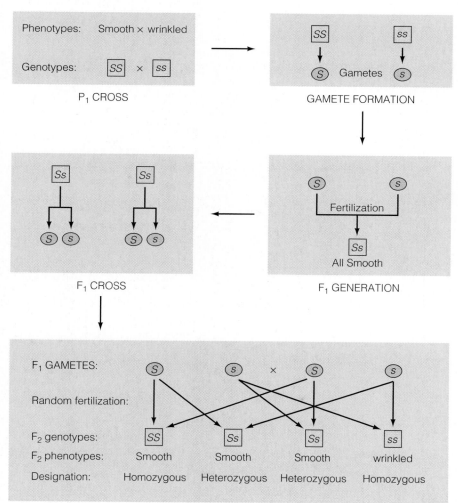

Inheritance of a Single Trait: The Principle of Segregation

If factors that determine traits exist in pairs, then some mechanism must exist to prevent these factors from being doubled in each succeeding generation. If each parent has two factors for a given trait, why doesn't the offspring have four? Mendel reasoned that members of a pair of factors must separate or segregate from each other during gamete formation. In doing so, each gamete receives only one of the factors for a given trait. The separation of paired factors during gamete formation is called the **principle of segregation,** or Mendel's First Law.

As shown in ⬤ Figure 3.6, members of a gene pair separate (or segregate) from each other so that only one or the other is included in each gamete. In the F_1 generation, the parents each make two kinds of gametes in equal proportions. At fertilization, the random combination of these gametes produces the genotypic combinations shown in the Punnett square (a method for analyzing genetic crosses devised by R. C. Punnett). The F_2 genotypic ratio of 1 SS : 2 Ss : 1 ss is expressed as a phenotypic ratio that is ¾ dominant and ¼ recessive. This is usually abbreviated as a 3 : 1 ratio.

Mendel's experiments with the six other sets of traits can also be explained in this way. His reasoning makes a prediction about the genotypes of the F_2 generation. One-fourth of the F_2 plants should carry only smooth factors (SS) and give rise to only smooth plants when self-fertilized. One half of the F_2 plants should carry factors for both smooth and wrinkled (Ss) and give rise to smooth and wrinkled progeny in a ¾ to ¼ ratio when self-fertilized (⬤ Figure 3.7). Finally, one-fourth of the

Segregation
The separation of members of a gene pair from each other during gamete formation.

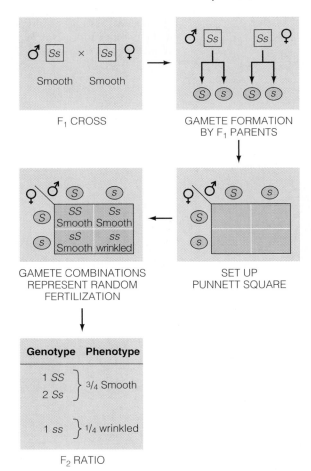

⬤ **FIGURE 3.6**
How a Punnett square can be used to generate the F_2 ratio in a cross from the F_1 generation.

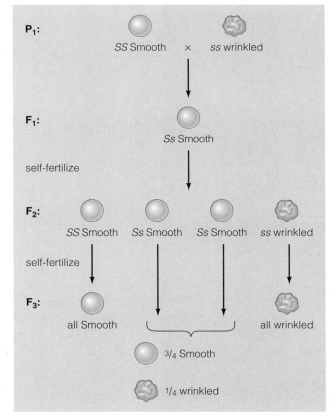

⬤ **FIGURE 3.7**
Self-crossing the F_2 plants demonstrates that there are two different genotypes among the plants with smooth peas in the F_2 generation.

F₂ plants should be homozygous for wrinkled (*ss*) and give rise to all wrinkled progeny if self-fertilized. In fact, Mendel fertilized a number of plants from the F₂ generation and five succeeding generations to confirm these predictions.

Mendel carried out his experiments before the discovery of mitosis and meiosis, and before the discovery of chromosomes. As we will discuss in a later section, his deductions about the way traits are inherited are in fact descriptions of the way chromosomes behave in meiosis. Seen in this light, his discoveries are all the more remarkable.

Today we call Mendel's factors **genes** and refer to the alternate forms of a gene as **alleles**. In the example we have been discussing, the gene for seed shape has two alleles, smooth and wrinkled. Individuals carrying identical alleles of a given gene (*SS* or *ss*) are said to be **homozygous** for the gene in question. Similarly, when two different alleles are present in a gene pair (*Ss*), the individual is said to have a **heterozygous** genotype. The *SS* homozygotes and the *Ss* heterozygotes will show dominant phenotypes (because *S* is dominant to *s*), and *ss* homozygotes will show recessive phenotypes.

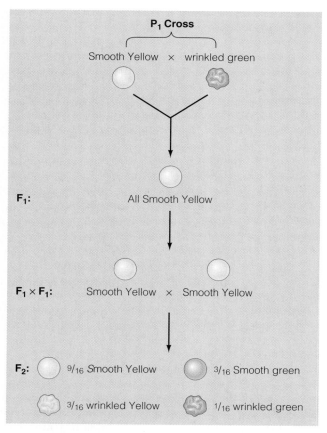

● **FIGURE 3.8**

The phenotypic distribution in a dihybrid cross. Plants in the F₂ generation show the parental phenotypes and two new phenotypic combinations.

✺ MORE CROSSES WITH PEA PLANTS: THE PRINCIPLE OF INDEPENDENT ASSORTMENT

Mendel realized the need to extend his studies on the inheritance from monohybrid crosses to more complex situations. He wrote:

> In the experiments discussed above, plants were used which differed in only one essential trait. The next task consisted in investigating whether the law of development thus found would also apply to a pair of differing traits.

For this work, he selected seed shape and seed color as traits to be studied, because as he put it: "Experiments with seed traits lead most easily and assuredly to success." A cross that involves two sets of characters is called a **dihybrid cross**.

Crosses with Two Traits

As in the first set of crosses, we will analyze the actual experiments of Mendel, outline the results, and summarize the conclusions he drew from them. From previous crosses it is known that in seeds, smooth is dominant to wrinkled and yellow is dominant to green. In our reconstruction of these experiments, we will represent smooth by an uppercase *S*, wrinkled by a lowercase *s*, yellow by an uppercase *Y* and green by a lowercase *y*.

Methods, Results, and Conclusions

Mendel selected true-breeding plants with smooth, yellow seeds and crossed them to true-breeding plants with wrinkled, green seeds (● Figure 3.8). The seeds of the F₁ plants were all smooth and yellow, confirming that smooth and yellow are dominant traits. He then self-fertilized the F₁ and produced an F₂ generation. These F₂ plants produced seeds of four types, often found together in a single pod. From 15 plants, he counted a total of 556 seeds with the following phenotypic distributions:

Gene
The fundamental unit of heredity.

Allele
One of the possible alternative forms of a gene, usually distinguished from other alleles by its phenotypic effects.

Homozygous
Having identical alleles for one or more genes.

Heterozygous
Carrying two different alleles for one or more genes.

Dihybrid cross
A cross between individuals who differ with respect to two gene pairs.

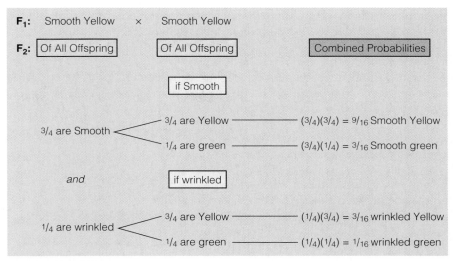

FIGURE 3.9

Analysis of a dihybrid cross for the separate inheritance of each trait.

315 Smooth and Yellow

108 Smooth and green

101 wrinkled and Yellow

32 wrinkled and green

The F$_2$ phenotypes include not only the parental phenotypes, but two new combinations (smooth green and wrinkled yellow).

To determine how the two genes in a dihybrid cross were inherited, Mendel first analyzed the results of the F$_2$ for each trait separately, as if the other trait were not present (Figure 3.9). If we consider only seed shape (smooth or wrinkled) and ignore color, we expect to obtain ¾ smooth and ¼ wrinkled offspring in the F$_2$. Analyzing the actual results, we find that the total number of smooth offspring is 315 + 108 = 423. The total number of wrinkled seeds is 101 + 32 = 133. The proportion of smooth to wrinkled seeds (423 : 133) is close to a ratio of 3 : 1. Similarly, if we consider only seed color (yellow or green), there are 416 yellow seeds (315 + 101) and 140 green seeds (108 + 32) in the F$_2$ generation. These results are also close to a 3 : 1 distribution.

Once he established a pattern of 3 : 1 inheritance for each trait separately (consistent with the principle of segregation), Mendel then considered the inheritance of both traits simultaneously.

The Principle of Independent Assortment

Before we discuss what is meant by independent assortment, let's see how the phenotypes and genotypes of the F$_1$ and F$_2$ were generated. The F$_1$ plants with smooth yellow seeds were heterozygous for both seed shape and seed color. This means that the genotype of the F$_1$ plant must have been *SsYy*, with the *S* and *Y* alleles dominant to *s* and *y*. Mendel postulated that members of a gene pair separate or segregate from each other during gamete formation. In this case, with two genes present, the segregation of the *S* and *s* alleles must have occurred independently from the segregation of the *Y* and *y* alleles (Figure 3.10).

Because each gene pair segregated independently, the gametes formed by the F$_1$ plants contained all combinations of these alleles in equal proportions: *SY*, *Sy*, *sY*, and *sy*. If fertilizations involving the four types of male and female gametes occurred at random (as expected), 16 possible combinations would result (Figure 3.10).

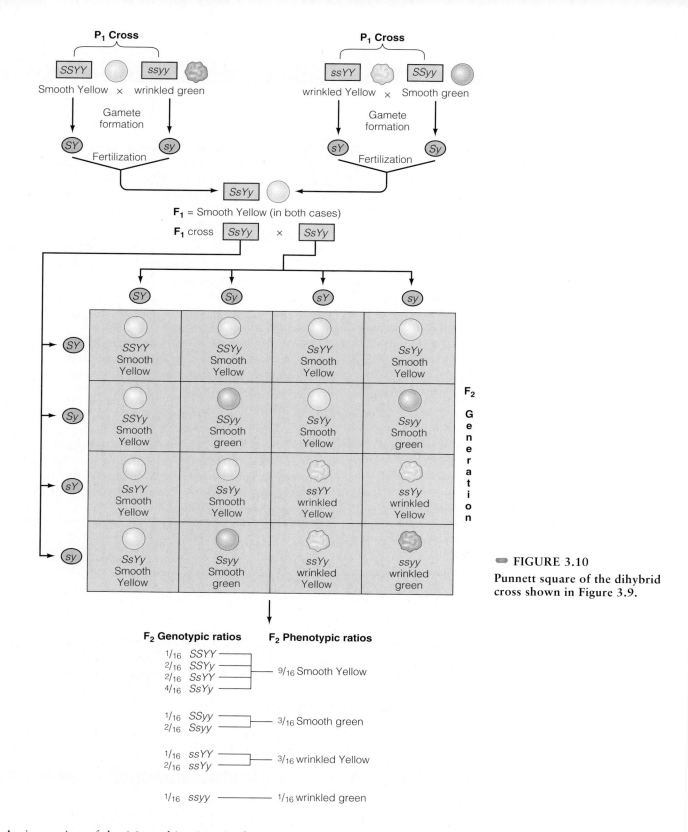

FIGURE 3.10
Punnett square of the dihybrid cross shown in Figure 3.9.

An inspection of the 16 combinations in the Punnett square shows that:

- 9 have at least one copy of each dominant allele, *S* and *Y*.
- 3 have at least one copy of the dominant allele *S* and are homozygous *yy*.
- 3 have at least one copy of the dominant allele *Y* and are homozygous *ss*.
- 1 combination is homozygous for *ss* and *yy*.

CONCEPTS AND CONTROVERSIES

Evaluating Results—The Chi-Square Test

One of Mendel's innovations was the application of mathematics and combinatorial theory to biological research. This allowed him to predict the genotypic and phenotypic ratios in his crosses and to follow the inheritance of several traits simultaneously. If the cross involved two alleles of a gene (e.g., A and a), the expected outcome was an F_2 phenotypic ratio of $3A:1a$ and a genotypic ratio of $1AA:2aA:1aa$. What Mendel was unable to analyze mathematically was how well the actual outcome of the cross fulfilled his predictions. He apparently realized this problem and compensated for it by conducting his experiments on a large scale, counting substantial numbers of individuals in each experiment in an attempt to reduce the chance of error.

Shortly after the turn of the century an English scientist named Karl Pearson developed a statistical test to determine whether the observed distribution of individuals in phenotypic categories is as predicted or occurs by chance. This simple test, regarded as one of the fundamental advances in statistics, is a valuable tool in genetic research. The method is known as the chi-square (χ^2) test (pronounced "kye square"). In use, this test requires several steps:

1. Record the observed numbers of organisms in each phenotypic class.
2. Calculate the expected values for each phenotypic class based on the predicted ratios.
3. If O is the observed number of organisms in a phenotypic class, or category, and E is the expected number, calculate the difference d in each category by subtraction $(O - E) = d$ (Table 3.2).
4. For each phenotypic category, square the difference d, and divide by the number expected (E) in that phenotypic class.
5. Add all the numbers in step 4 to get the χ^2 value.

If there are no differences between the observed and the expected ratios, the value for χ^2 will be zero. The value of χ^2 will increase with the size of the difference between the observed and the expected classes. The formula can be expressed in the general form

$$\chi^2 = \Sigma \frac{d^2}{E}$$

Using this formula, we can do what Mendel could not: analyze his data for the dihybrid cross involving wrinkled and smooth seeds and yellow and green cotyledons that produced a 9:3:3:1 ratio. In the F_2, Mendel counted a total of 556 peas; the number in each phenotypic class is the observed number (Table 3.2). Using the total of 556 peas, we can calculate that the expected number in each class for a 9:3:3:1 ratio would be 313:104:104:35 ($\frac{9}{16}$ of 556 is 313, $\frac{3}{16}$ of 556 is 104, etc). Substituting these numbers into the formula, we obtain

$$\chi^2 = \frac{2^2}{313} + \frac{4^2}{104} + \frac{3^2}{104} + \frac{3^2}{35}$$
$$= 0.371$$

The χ^2 value is very low, confirming that there is very little difference between the number of peas observed and the number expected in each class. In other words, the results are close enough to the expectation that we need not reject them.

The question remains, however, how much deviation is permitted from the expected numbers before we will decide that the observations do not fit our expectation that a 9:3:3:1 ratio will be fulfilled. To decide this we must have a way of interpreting the χ^2 value. We need to convert this value into a probability and to ask, what is the probability that the calculated χ^2 value is acceptable? In making this calculation we must first establish something called degrees of freedom, df, which is one less than the number of phenotypic classes, n. In the dihybrid cross we expect four phenotypic classes, so the degrees of freedom are as follows:

$$df = n-1$$
$$df = 4-1$$
$$df = 3$$

Next we can calculate the probability of obtaining the given set of results by consulting a probability chart (Table 3.3). First, find the line corresponding to a df value of 3. Look across on this line for the number corresponding to the χ^2 value. The calculated value is 0.37, which is between the columns headed 0.95 and 0.90. This means that we can expect a deviation of this magnitude at least 90% of the time when we do this experiment. In other words, we can be con-

---

In other words, the 16 combinations of fertilization events (genotypes) fall into four phenotypic classes:

$\frac{9}{16}$ smooth and yellow

$\frac{3}{16}$ smooth and green

$\frac{3}{16}$ wrinkled and yellow

$\frac{1}{16}$ wrinkled and green

TABLE 3.2

Chi-Square Analysis of Mendel's Data

SEED SHAPE	COTYLEDON COLOR	OBSERVED NUMBERS	EXPECTED NUMBERS (BASED ON A 9:3:3:1 RATIO)	DIFFERENCE (d) (O−E)
Smooth	Yellow	315	313	+2
Smooth	Green	108	104	+4
Wrinkled	Yellow	101	104	−3
Wrinkled	Green	32	35	−3

TABLE 3.3

Probability Values for Chi-Square Analysis

PROBABILITIES

df	0.95	0.90	0.70	0.50	0.30	0.20	0.10	0.05	0.01
1	.004	.016	.15	.46	1.07	1.64	2.71	3.84	6.64
2	.10	.21	.71	1.39	2.41	3.22	4.61	5.99	9.21
3	.35	.58	1.42	2.37	3.67	4.64	6.25	7.82	11.35
4	.71	1.06	2.20	3.36	4.88	5.99	7.78	9.49	13.28
5	1.15	1.61	3.00	4.35	6.06	7.29	9.24	11.07	15.09
6	1.64	2.20	3.83	5.35	7.23	8.56	10.65	12.59	16.81
7	2.17	2.83	4.67	6.35	8.38	9.80	12.02	14.07	18.48
8	2.73	3.49	5.53	7.34	9.52	11.03	13.36	15.51	20.09
9	3.33	4.17	6.39	8.34	10.66	12.24	14.68	16.92	21.67
10	3.94	4.87	7.27	9.34	11.78	13.44	15.99	18.31	23.21

◄─────────────── Acceptable ───────────────► | Unacceptable

Note. From *Statistical Tables for Biological, Agricultural and Medical Research* (6th ed.), Table IV, by R. Fisher and F. Yates, 1963, Edinburgh; Longman Essex.

fident that our expectations of a 9:3:3:1 ratio are correct. In general, a *P* value of less than .05 means that the observations do not fit the expected distribution into phenotypic classes, and that the expectation needs to be reexamined. The acceptable range of values is indicated by a line in Table 3.3. The use of $p = 0.05$ as the border for acceptability has been arbitrarily set.

In the case of Mendel's data, there is very little difference between the observed and expected results (Table 3.2).

Several writers have commented that Mendel's results fit the expectations too closely and that perhaps he adjusted his results to fit a preconceived standard.

In human genetics, the χ^2 method is very valuable and has wide applications. It is used in deciding modes of inheritance (autosomal or sex linked), deciding whether the pattern of inheritance shown by two genes indicates that they are on the same chromosome, and deciding whether marriage patterns have produced genetically divergent groups in a population.

These phenotypic combinations correspond to the number of phenotypic classes seen in the F_2 generation and to the proportions of progeny seen in each class (Figure 3.10). For example, 315 of 556 seeds were smooth and yellow, corresponding to about $9/16$ of the total number of offspring; 108 of 556 seeds were smooth and green, corresponding to about $3/16$ of the offspring; and so forth. This distribution of offspring in the F_2 corresponds to a phenotypic ratio of 9:3:3:1 (see "Concepts and Controversies," page 60). The results of this cross can be explained by assuming (as

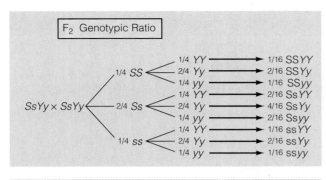

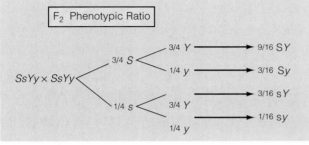

➥ FIGURE 3.11

The phenotypic and genotypic ratios of a dihybrid cross can be derived using a forked-line method instead of a Punnett square.

Independent assortment
The random distribution of genes into gametes during meiosis.

Genetics
The scientific study of heredity.

Chromosome theory of inheritance
The theory that genes are carried on chromosomes and that the behavior of chromosomes during meiosis is the physical explanation for Mendel's observations on the segregation and independent assortment of genes.

Mendel did) that during gamete formation, alleles in one gene pair segregate into gametes independently of the alleles belonging to other gene pairs, resulting in the production of gametes containing all combinations of alleles. This second fundamental principle of genetics outlined by Mendel is called the **principle of independent assortment**, or Mendel's Second Law.

Instead of using a Punnett square to determine the distribution and frequencies of phenotypes and genotypes in the F_2, we can also use a branch diagram, or forked-line method, which is based on probability. In the dihybrid F_2, the probability that a plant will be smooth is ¾, and the chance that it will be wrinkled is ¼. Since each trait is inherited independently, each smooth plant has a ¾ chance of being yellow and a ¼ chance of being green. The same is true for each wrinkled plant. ➥ Figure 3.11 shows how these probabilities combine to give the phenotypic ratios.

After 10 years of experimentation involving thousands of pea plants, Mendel presented his results in 1865 at the February and March meetings of his local Natural Science Society. The text of these lectures was published in the following year in the Proceedings of the Society. Although his work was cited in several bibliographies, and copies of the journal were widely read, the significance of Mendel's findings was unappreciated. Even Charles Darwin, continuing his search for a mechanism to explain heredity and its role in natural selection, failed to realize the significance of Mendel's work. Darwin's own copy of the Proceedings has many notes scribbled in the margin of the paper next to Mendel's, but not one pencil mark anywhere in Mendel's paper.

Finally, in 1900 three scientists, each working independently on the mechanism of heredity, confirmed Mendel's findings and brought his paper to widespread attention. These events stimulated a great interest in the study of what is now called **genetics**. Unfortunately, Mendel died in 1884—unaware that he had founded an entire scientific discipline.

✾ MENDELIAN INHERITANCE AND MEIOSIS: THE IDEA THAT GENES ARE ON CHROMOSOMES

It is generally accepted that the year 1900 marks the beginning of genetics as a scientific discipline. When Mendel performed his experiments, the behavior of chromosomes in mitosis and meiosis had not been described. By 1900, however, cytology was a well-established field, and the principles of mitosis and meiosis were well known. As scientists confirmed that the fundamentals of Mendelian inheritance operated in many organisms, it soon became apparent that genes and chromosomes had much in common (Table 3.4). Both chromosomes and genes occur in pairs, and in each pair one member is maternally derived and one is paternally derived. In meiosis, members of a chromosome pair separate from each other. In addition, the arrangement of a given chromosome pair at metaphase I in meiosis is independent of the way all other chromosome pairs are arranged. The result is that gametes receive different combinations of maternal and paternal chromosomes. Likewise, members of a gene pair assort themselves into gametes independently of all other gene pairs, producing gametes with all combinations of genes. Finally, fertilization restores the diploid number of chromosomes and two copies of each gene to the zygote.

In 1903 Walter Sutton and Theodore Boveri each noted these similarities and independently proposed that chromosomes are the cellular components that physically contain the genes. This **chromosome theory of inheritance** has been confirmed by

TABLE 3.4

Genes, Chromosomes, and Meiosis

GENES	CHROMOSOMES
Occur in pairs (alleles)	Occur in pairs (homologues)
Members of a gene pair separate from each other during meiosis	Members of a pair of homologues separate from each other during meiosis
Members of one gene pair independently assort from other gene pairs during meiosis	Members of one chromosome pair independently assort from other chromosome pairs during meiosis

Locus
The position occupied by a gene on a chromosome.

many experiments in the following decades and is one of the foundations of modern genetics. Each gene occupies a place, or **locus** (plural: loci), on a chromosome and each chromosome carries many genes. In humans it is estimated that 50,000 to 100,000 genes are carried on the 23 different chromosomes. Although each gene may have different forms (alleles), any normal individual carries only two such alleles, since he or she has only two copies of each chromosome. Obviously, different individuals can have different combinations of alleles. ⬤ Figure 3.12 shows the distribution of chromosomes and genes at meiosis.

⬤ **FIGURE 3.12**

Mendel's observations about segregation and independent assortment are explained by the behavior of chromosomes during meiosis. The arrangement of chromosomes at metaphase I is at random. As a result, all combinations of the alleles of the two genes are produced in the gametes.

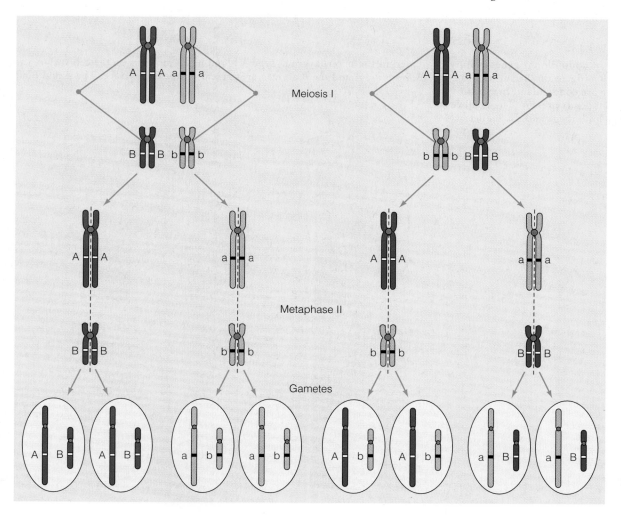

⚛ MANY GENES HAVE MORE THAN TWO ALLELES

So far, our discussion has been confined to genes with two alleles. Since alleles represent different forms of a gene, there is no reason why a gene has to have only two alleles. In fact, many genes have more than two alleles. Any individual can carry only two alleles of a gene, but in a population, many different alleles of a gene can be present. In humans, the gene that determines ABO blood groups is an example of a gene with **multiple alleles**. The ABO blood types are determined by molecules (proteins with polysaccharides attached) on the surface of human red blood cell membranes. These molecules provide the cell with an identity tag recognized by the body's immune system.

Multiple alleles
Genes with more than two alleles have multiple alleles.

ABO blood types are controlled by a single gene, I, with three alleles, I^A, I^B, and I^O. The A and B alleles control the formation of slightly different forms of a molecule (called an antigen) present on the surface of blood cells and other cells in the body. Individuals homozygous for the A allele (AA) carry the A antigen on cells, and have blood type A. Those who are homozygous for the B allele (BB) carry the B antigen and are type B. The third allele, (O), does not make any antigen, and individuals homozygous for the third allele for this gene, I^O, carry neither the A nor the B antigen on their cells. The O allele is recessive to the A and B alleles. Because there are three alleles, there are six possible genotypes (⚬ Figure 3.13).

Blood type can be determined by a simple test, and it is important to match blood types in transfusions. The ABO blood groups are also used as evidence in paternity cases. Blood typing can provide evidence that rules out a man as the father of a given child.

⚬ **FIGURE 3.13**

Each allele of codominant genes is fully expressed in the heterozygote. Type A blood has *A* antigens on the cell surface, and type B has *B* antigens on the surface. In type AB, both the *A* and the *B* antigen are present on the cell surface. The *A* and *B* alleles of the *I* gene are codominant. In type O blood, no antigen is present. The O allele is recessive to both the *A* and the *B* allele.

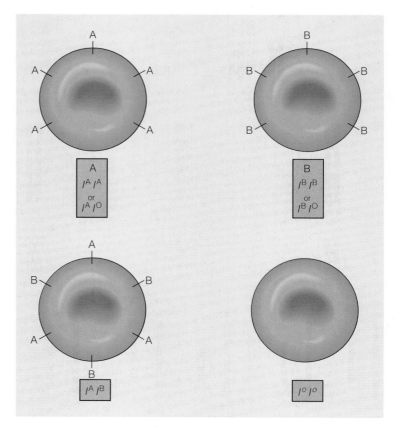

VARIATIONS ON A THEME BY MENDEL

After Mendel's work became widely known, geneticists in the early years of this century turned up cases in which the phenotypes of the F_1 offspring did not resemble one or the other of the parents. In some cases, the offspring had a phenotype intermediate to that of the parents, or a phenotype in which the traits of both parents were expressed. These findings led to a debate as to whether these cases could be explained by Mendelian principles of inheritance, or whether there might be another, separate mechanism of inheritance that did not follow the laws of segregation and independent assortment.

Eventually, experiments with several different organisms showed that these cases were not exceptions to Mendelian inheritance and could be explained by the way in which genes act to produce phenotypes. In this section, we will discuss some of these phenotypic variations, and show that while the phenotypes may not follow the predicted Mendelian ratios for complete phenotypic dominance, the outcome of crosses involving these traits can be predicted according to the Mendelian distribution of genotypes.

Codominant Alleles Are Both Expressed in the Phenotype

In **codominance**, heterozygotes fully express *both* alleles. In the ABO blood type, *AB* heterozygotes have both the *A* and *B* antigens on their cell membranes and are blood type AB. In AB heterozygotes, neither allele is dominant over the other, and since each allele is fully expressed, they are said to be codominant (Figure 3.13). As a result, the three alleles of the ABO system have six genotypic combinations contributing to four phenotypes (Table 3.5).

Incomplete Dominance Has a Distinctive Phenotype

In the case of **incomplete dominance**, the heterozygote has a phenotype intermediate to those of the homozygous parents. An example of this type of inheritance is flower color in snapdragons (➤ Figure 3.14). If a true-breeding variety bearing red flowers is crossed to a variety that produces white flowers, the F_1 offspring will all have pink flowers. The phenotype of the F_1 is different from that of either parent, and is intermediate to the phenotypes of the parents.

➤ **FIGURE 3.14**
Incomplete dominance in snapdragon flower color. Red-flowered snapdragons crossed with white-flowered snapdragons produce offspring with pink flowers in the F_1. In heterozygotes, the allele for red flowers is incompletely dominant over the allele for white.

TABLE 3.5

ABO Blood Types

GENOTYPES	PHENOTYPES
$I^A I^A$, $I^A I^O$	Type A
$I^B I^B$, $I^B I^O$	Type B
$I^A I^B$	Type AB
$I^O I^O$	Type O

Codominance
Full phenotypic expression of both members of a gene pair in the heterozygous condition.

Incomplete dominance
Expression of a phenotype that is intermediate between those of the parents.

When the F_1 plants are self-fertilized, they produce plants with red, pink, and white flowers in a 1 : 2 : 1 ratio (Figure 3.14). This would not be expected if true blending occurred, since crossing plants with pink flowers should produce offspring with pink flowers.

The results of this cross can be explained using Mendelian principles. Each genotype in this cross has a distinct phenotype, and the phenotypic ratio of 1 red : 2 pink : 1 white is the same as the genotypic ratio of 1 *RR* : 2 *Rr* : 1 *rr*. It takes two doses of the *R* allele to produce red flowers. One dose will result in pink flowers, and as a result, the *R* allele is incompletely dominant over the *r* allele. Because the *r* allele produces no color, the absence of *R* alleles produces white flowers.

The Concepts of Dominance and Recessiveness

Earlier in this chapter, genes were said to have dominant or recessive patterns of inheritance. Dominant alleles were represented by uppercase letters (such as *A*) and recessive alleles were represented by lowercase letters (such as *a*). If a trait is present when inherited from only one parent, the allele is said to be dominant. If the phenotype is shown only when identical alleles have been inherited from each parent, the trait is recessive. Dominant traits are expressed in the heterozygous condition, and recessive traits are not. Referring to alleles as dominant or recessive is a shorthand way of talking about genes; remember that the terms *dominant* and *recessive* actually refer to phenotypes and not to the gene itself. As we will see in later chapters the terms *dominant* and *recessive* are somewhat relative. Heterozygotes for recessive traits can often be identified because they produce half as much of a gene product as those with the homozygous dominant genotype. This does not change the recessive nature of the phenotype, since usually only homozygous recessive individuals are phenotypically affected by the mutant condition.

In general, recessive traits tend to have more serious phenotypic effects than those controlled by dominant genes. One reason is that recessive alleles can remain in the population in the heterozygous condition at a high frequency, affecting only a small number of homozygotes. If, on the other hand, a dominant mutation prevented survival or reproduction, it would quickly be eliminated from the population. As a result, many dominant genetic diseases are more variable and diffuse in their phenotypic effects. If dominant traits have lethal effects, it is usually after reproductive age has been reached. In other words, deleterious dominant traits survive because of low penetrance, variable expressivity, and delayed onset.

 MENDELIAN INHERITANCE IN HUMANS

After 1900, the principles of segregation and independent assortment discovered by Mendel were studied in a wide range of organisms. Although some believed that inheritance of traits in humans might be an exception to these principles, the first Mendelian trait (a hand deformity called brachydactyly, MIM/OMIM 112500) was identified in 1905. Since then, over 4500 such traits have been described.

To illustrate how segregation and independent assortment apply to the inheritance of human traits, we will follow the inheritance of a recessive trait called albinism (*a*, MIM/OMIM 203100). Individuals who are homozygous (*aa*) for this recessive trait have no pigment in skin, hair and eyes; and have very pale, white skin, white hair, and colorless eyes—actually, the eyes may appear pink because of the blood vessels in the iris (● Figure 3.15). The dominant allele (*A*) controls normal pigmentation.

In the example we will consider, both parents have normal pigmentation, but are heterozygous for the recessive allele causing albinism (● Figure 3.16). In each parent, the dominant and recessive alleles separate or segregate from each other at the time of gamete formation. Since each parent can produce two different types of gametes (one containing the dominant allele *A* and another type carrying the recessive allele *a*), there are four possible combinations of these gametes at fertilization. If

● **FIGURE 3.15**
Albino individuals lack pigment in the skin, hair, and eyes.

enough offspring are produced, these four possible types of fertilization events will show a predicted phenotypic ratio of 3 pigmented : 1 albino offspring, and a genotypic ratio of 1 *AA* : 2*Aa* : 1*aa* (Figure 3.16). In other words, segregation of alleles during gamete formation produces the same outcome in both pea plants and humans. This does not mean that in every such family with four children there will be one albino child and three normally pigmented children. It does mean that in a mating between heterozygotes, each child has a 25% chance of being albino and a 75% chance of having normal pigmentation.

The simultaneous inheritance of two traits in humans follows the Mendelian principle of independent assortment (Figure 3.17). To illustrate, let's examine a family in which each parent is heterozygous for albinism (*Aa*) and heterozygous for another recessive trait, hereditary deafness (*Dd*, MIM/OMIM 220290). The normal allele (*D*) is dominant and expressed in the homozygous dominant (*DD*) or heterozygous condition (*Dd*). During gamete formation, the alleles for skin color and the alleles for hearing will assort into gametes independently. As a result, each parent will produce equal proportions of four different types of gametes. If each parent produces four types of gametes, there are 16 possible combinations of these gametes at fertilization (four types of gametes in all possible combinations), resulting in four different phenotypic classes (Figure 3.17). An examination of the possible genotypes shows that there is a 1 in 16 chance that a child would be both deaf *and* an albino.

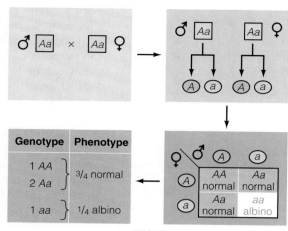

 FIGURE 3.16

The segregation of albinism, a recessive trait in humans. As in pea plants, alleles of a gene pair separate from each other during gamete formation.

Pedigree Analysis in Human Genetics

In pea plants and other organisms such as *Drosophila*, genetic analysis can be performed by experimental crosses. In the case of humans, geneticists must base their work on matings that have already taken place, and cannot design crosses to directly

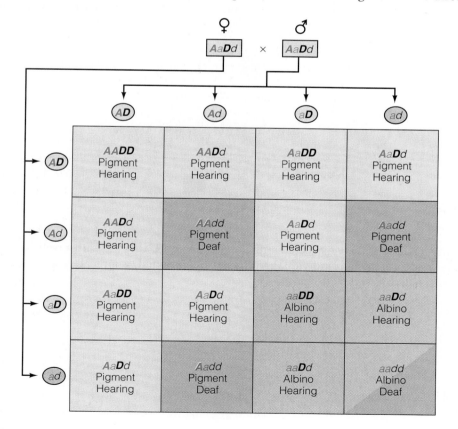

 FIGURE 3.17

Independent assortment for two traits in humans follows the same pattern of inheritance as do traits in pea plants.

Pedigree analysis
Use of family history to determine how a trait is inherited, and to determine risk factors for family members.

test a hypothesis. A basic method of genetic analysis in humans is to follow a trait for several generations in a family to determine how it is inherited. This method is called **pedigree analysis.** A pedigree is the orderly presentation of family information in the form of an easily readable chart. From such a family tree, the inheritance of a trait can be followed through several generations. Using Mendelian principles, the information in the pedigree can be analyzed to determine whether the trait has a dominant or recessive pattern of inheritance, and whether the gene in question is located on an autosome or a sex chromosome.

Pedigrees use a set of standardized symbols, many of which are borrowed from genealogy. In constructing a **pedigree chart,** males are represented by squares (□) and females by circles (○). An individual who exhibits a trait in question is represented by a filled symbol (■ or ●). Heterozygotes, when known, are indicated by half-filled symbols (◧ or ◑). The relationships between individuals in a pedigree are indicated by a series of lines. A horizontal line between two symbols represents a mating (□—○). Matings between brother and sister or between close relatives are known as *consanguineous* matings and are symbolized by a double horizontal line. The offspring, listed from left to right in birth order, are connected to each other by a horizontal line (○ ○ □) and to the parents by a vertical line:

Pedigree chart
A diagram listing the members and ancestral relationships in a family; used in the study of human heredity.

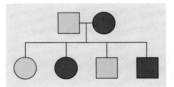

If twins are present as offspring, they are identified either as identical (monozygotic) twins (⚯), arising from a single egg, or nonidentical (dizygotic) twins (⚯), arising from the fertilization of two eggs.

To identify individuals in a pedigree, a numbering system is employed. Each generation is indicated by a roman numeral, and within a generation, each individual is numbered by birth order using arabic numbers:

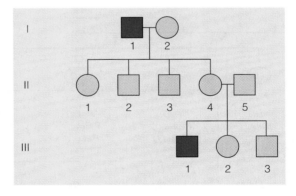

Often pedigrees are constructed after a family member afflicted with a genetic trait has been identified. This individual, known as the **proband,** is indicated on the pedigree by an arrow and the letter P:

Proband
First affected family member seeking medical attention.

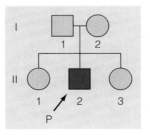

CONCEPTS AND CONTROVERSIES

Solving Genetics Problems

In solving genetics problems, several steps must be followed to ensure success. The process of analyzing and solving these problems depends on several steps: (1) analyze each problem carefully to determine what information is provided, and what information is asked for; (2) translate the terms and words of the problems into symbols, and (3) solve the problem using logic.

The most basic problems involving Mendelian inheritance usually provide some information about the parental generation (P_1), and ask you to employ your knowledge of Mendelian principles to come to conclusions about the genotypes or phenotypes of the F_1 or F_2 generation. The solution uses several steps:

1. Carefully read the problem and establish the genotype of each parent, assigning letter symbols if necessary.
2. Based on their genotypes, determine what types of gametes can be formed by each parent.
3. Unite the gametes from the parents in all combinations. Use a Punnett square if necessary. This will automatically give you all possible genotypes and their ratios for the F_1 generation.
4. If necessary, use all combinations of F_1 individuals as parents for the F_2, and repeat steps 2 and 3 to derive the genotypes and phenotypes of the F generation.

As an example, consider the following problem. The recessive allele *wrinkled* (s) causes peas to appear wrinkled when homozygous. The dominant allele *smooth* (S) causes peas to appear smooth when homozygous or heterozygous. In the following cross, what phenotypic ratio would you expect in the offspring? One parent is a plant that bears wrinkled seeds. The other is a plant that bears smooth seeds and is the offspring of a cross between true-breeding smooth and wrinkled parents.

The solution to this problem depends on an understanding of the principle of segregation and the relationship between dominance and recessiveness. To derive the genotypes of the parental plants, the following are relevant:

1. Since one parental plant bears wrinkled seeds, this plant is homozygous for the recessive allele (ss). The other parental plant bears smooth seeds, and carries at least one dominant allele (S). Since this

parent is the offspring from a cross between true-breeding smooth and true-breeding wrinkled plants, it must have received a wrinkled allele, and therefore must be heterozygous (Ss).
2. The cross is therefore $Ss \times ss$. The gametes each parent can make and their combinations in fertilizations are shown below:

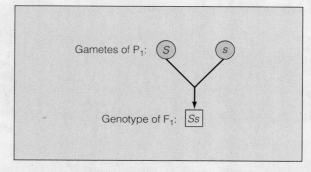

3. In this cross, half of the F_1 offspring will be heterozygous smooth individuals (Ss), and half will be homozygous wrinkled (ss).

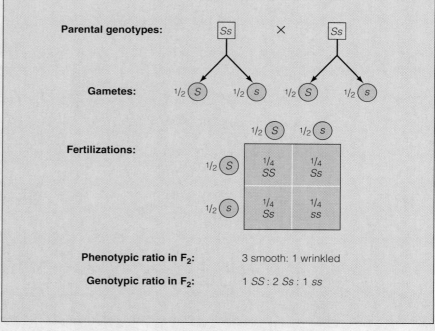

The phenotypic ratio will be 1 smooth : 1 wrinkled.

Because pedigree analysis is essentially a reconstruction of a family history, details about earlier generations may be uncertain. If the sex of someone is unknown or unimportant, this is indicated by a diamond shape: (◇). In some cases, spouses in a pedigree are omitted if they are not essential to the inheritance of the trait. If there is doubt that a family member possessed the trait in question, this is indicated by a question mark above the symbol. Many of the symbols and terminology used in the construction of pedigrees are presented in ⬤ Figure 3.18. A completed pedigree is a form of symbolic communication used by clinicians and human genetics researchers (⬤ Figure 3.19). It contains information that can establish the pattern of inheritance for a trait, identify those at risk of developing or transmitting the trait, and serves as a resource for establishing biological relationships within a family. Establishing genotypes of parents and predicting the chances of having affected children is part of **genetic counseling**, a topic that will be discussed in Chapter 19.

Genetic counseling
Analysis of genetic risk within families, and presentation of available options to avoid or reduce risks.

⬤ **FIGURE 3.18**
Symbols used in pedigree analysis.

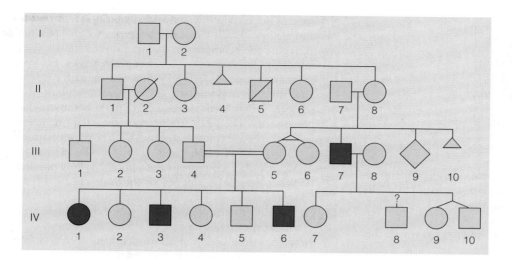

■ FIGURE 3.19

A pedigree chart showing the inheritance of a trait in several generations of a family. This pedigree, and all those in this book, use the standardized set of symbols adopted in 1995 by the American Society of Human Genetics.

SUMMARY

1. In the centuries before Gregor Mendel experimented with the inheritance of traits in the garden pea, several competing theories attempted to explain how traits were passed from generation to generation. In his decade-long series of experiments, Mendel established the foundation for the science of genetics.

2. Mendel studied crosses in the garden pea that involved one pair of alleles, and demonstrated that the phenotypes associated with these traits are controlled by pairs of factors, now known as genes. These factors separate or segregate from each other during gamete formation, and exhibit dominant/recessive relationships.

3. In later experiments, Mendel discovered that members of one gene pair separate or segregate independently of other gene pairs. This principle of independent assortment leads to the formation of all possible combinations of gametes with equal probability in a cross between two individuals.

4. The principles of segregation and independent assortment proposed by Mendel apply to all sexually reproducing organisms, including humans.

5. Instead of direct experimental crosses, traits in humans are traced by the construction of pedigrees that follow a trait through several generations.

6. Because genes for human genetic disorders exhibit segregation and independent assortment, the inheritance of certain human traits is predictable, making it possible to provide genetic counseling to those at risk of having children affected with genetic disorders.

QUESTIONS AND PROBLEMS

1. Explain the difference between the following terms:
   a. gene versus allele
   b. genotype versus phenotype
   c. dominant versus recessive
   d. complete dominance versus incomplete dominance versus codominance

2. An organism has the following genotype: $AABb$. What type of gametes can be produced, and in what proportions?

3. Suppose that this organism is mated to one with the genotype $Aabb$. What are the predicted phenotypic ratios and genotypic ratios of the offspring?

4. A woman is heterozygous for two genes. How many different types of gametes can she produce, and in what proportions?

5. Brown eyes (B) are fully dominant to blue eyes (b).
   a. A 3:1 phenotypic ratio of F_1 progeny indicates that the parents are of what genotype?
   b. A 1:1 phenotypic ratio of F_1 progeny indicates that the parents of what genotype.

6. An unspecified character controlled by a single gene is examined in pea plants. Only two phenotypic states exist for this trait. One phenotypic state is completely dominant to the other. A heterozygous plant is self-crossed. What proportion of the progeny plants exhibiting the dominant phenotype are homozygous?

7. The following diagram shows a hypothetical diploid cell. The recessive allele for albinism is represented by a, and d represents the recessive allele for deafness. The normal alleles for these conditions are represented by A and D respectively.

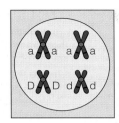

a. According to the principle of segregation, what is segregating in this cell?

b. According to Mendel's principle of independent assortment, what is independently assorting in this cell?

c. How many chromatids are in this cell?

d. How many tetrads are in this cell?

e. Write the genotype of the individual from whom this cell was taken.

f. What is the phenotype of this individual?

g. What stage of cell division is represent by this cell? (prophase, metaphase anaphase or telophase of meiosis I, meiosis II or mitosis).

h. After meiosis II is complete, how many chromatids and chromosomes will be present in one of the four progeny cells?

8. Use the Punnett square and then the forked-line method to determine the possible genotypes and phenotypes of the F_1 offspring from the following cross to show that the two methods achieve the same results.
P_1: AaBb × AaBb

9. Two traits are simultaneously examined in a cross of two pure-breeding pea-plant varieties. Pod shape can be either swollen or pinched. Seed color can be either green or yellow. A swollen, green plant is crossed with a pinched, yellow plant, and a resulting F_1 plant is self-crossed. A total of 640 F_2 progeny are phenotypically categorized as follows:
swollen, yellow 360
swollen, green 120
pinched, yellow 120
pinched, green 40

a. What is the phenotypic ratio observed for pod shape? seed color?

b. What is the phenotypic ratio observed for both traits considered together?

c. What is the dominance relationship for pod shape? seed color?

d. Deduce the genotypes of the P_1 and F_1 generations.

10. Sickle cell anemia (SCA) is a human genetic disorder caused by a recessive allele. A couple plan to marry and want to know the probability that they will have an affected child. With your knowledge of Mendelian inheritance, what can you tell them if (a) both are normal, but each has one affected parent and the other parent has no family history of SCA; and (b) the man is affected by the disorder, but the woman has no family history of SCA.

11. Consider the following cross in pea plants, where smooth seed shape is dominant to wrinkled and yellow seed color is dominant to green. A plant with smooth, yellow seeds is crossed to a plant with wrinkled, green seeds. The peas produced by the offspring are all smooth and yellow. What are the genotypes of the parents? What are the genotypes of the offspring?

12. Consider another cross involving the genes for seed color and shape. As before, yellow is dominant to green, and smooth is dominant to wrinkled. A plant with smooth, yellow seeds is crossed to a plant with wrinkled, green seeds. The peas produced by the offspring are as follows: 1/4 are smooth, yellow, 1/4 are smooth, green, 1/4 are wrinkled, yellow, and 1/4 are wrinkled, green.

a. What is the genotype of the smooth, yellow parent?

b. What are the genotypes of the four classes of offspring?

13. Stem length in pea plants is controlled by a single gene. Consider the cross of a true-breeding long-stemmed variety to a true-breeding short-stemmed variety where long stems are completely dominant.

a. 120 F_1 plants are examined. How many plants are expected to be long stemmed? short stemmed?

b. Assign genotypes to both P_1 varieties and to all phenotypes listed in (a).

c. A long-stemmed F_1 plant is self-crossed. Of 300 F_2 plants, how many should be long stemmed? short stemmed?

d. For the F_2 plants mentioned in (c), what is the expected genotypic ratio?

14. A pea plant that is AaBb is self-crossed. A 9:3:3:1 phenotypic ratio is obtained, as expected in a simple dihybrid cross. What is the underlying genotypic ratio? (Assign genotypes to each element of the ratio.)

15. Another character of pea plants amenable to genetic analysis is flower color. Imagine that a true-breeding purple-flowered variety is crossed to a pure line having white flowers. The progeny are exclusively pink flowered. Diagram this cross, including genotypes for all P_1 and F_1 phenotypes. What is the mode of inheritance? Let F = purple and f = white.

16. In peas, straight stems *(S)* are dominant to gnarled (s), and round seeds *(R)* are dominant to wrinkled *(r)*. The following cross (a test cross) is performed: *SsRr × ssrr*. Determine the expected progeny phenotypes and what fraction of the progeny should exhibit each phenotype.

17. A strange pea-plant variant is found that has orange flowers. A self-cross of this plant yields the following phenotypes:
red flowers 30
orange flowers 62
yellow flowers 33
What mode of inheritance can you infer for flower color in this pea plant variant?

18. Determine the possible genotypes of the parents shown below by analyzing the phenotypes of their children. In this case, we will assume that brown eyes (B) is dominant to blue (b) and that right handedness (R) is dominant to lefthandness (r).

a. Parents: brown eyes, right handed × brown eyes, right handed
Offspring: 3/4 brown eyes, right handed
1/4 blue eyes, left handed

b. Parents: brown eyes, right handed × blue eyes, right handed

   Offspring: 6/16 blue eyes, right handed
   2/16 blue eyes, left handed
   6/16 brown eyes, right handed
   2/16 brown eyes, left handed

c. Parents: brown eyes, right handed × blue eyes, left handed

   Offspring: 1/4 brown eyes, right handed
   1/4 brown eyes, left handed
   1/4 blue eyes, right handed
   1/4 blue eyes, left handed

19. In the following cross:

   P_1: AABBCCDDEE × aabbccddee
   F_1: AaBbCcDdEe (self cross to get F_2)

   What is the chance of getting an AaBBccDdee individual in the F_2 generation?

20. In the following trihybrid cross, determine the chance that an individual could be phenotypically A,b,C in the F_1 generation.

   P_1: AaBbCc × AabbCC

21. Suppose Mendel had ignored the advice contained in Ockham's razor. Based on a crude estimate of pollen and ovule size, he postulates that one hereditary factor is contributed by the pollen and three hereditary factors are contributed by the ovule. The anthers from a pure variety of pea possessing round seeds are applied to the stigma of a true-breeding variety having wrinkled seeds. Round seeds are completely dominant to wrinkled seeds, and independent assortment is operating in this cross.

   a. 200 F_1 plants are examined. How many plants are expected to bear round seeds? wrinkled?

   b. An F_1 plant bearing round seeds is self-crossed. Of 400 F_2 plants, how many are expected to bear round seeds? wrinkled?

22. In pea plants, long stems are dominant to short stems, purple flowers are dominant to white, and round seeds are dominant to wrinkled. Each trait is determined by a single, different gene. A plant that is heterozygous at all three loci is self-crossed, and 2048 progeny are examined. How many of these plants would you expect to be long stemmed with purple flowers, producing wrinkled seeds?

23. A pea plant exhibits the dominant phenotype for two traits: its seed color is yellow and its pods are swollen. A self-cross produces 178 progeny with the following phenotypes:

   yellow, swollen 132
   yellow, pinched 46

   From this information, can you infer the relevant genotype of the plant that was self-crossed?

24. A plant geneticist is examining the mode of inheritance of flower color in two closely related species of exotic plants. Analysis of one species has resulted in the identification of two pure-breeding lines: one produces a distinct red flower and the other produces either a very pale yellow color or no color at all, he cannot be sure. A cross of these varieties produces all pink-flowered progeny. The second species exhibits similar pure-breeding varieties; that is, one variety produces red flowers, and the other produces an ambiguous yellow or albino flower. A cross of these two varieties, however, produces orange-flowered progeny exclusively. Analyze the mode of inheritance of flower color in these two plant species.

25. Think about this one carefully. Albinism and hair color are governed by different genes. A recessively inherited form of albinism causes affected individuals to lack pigment in their skin, hair and eyes. Hair color itself is governed by a gene where red hair is inherited as a recessive trait, and brown hair is inherited as a dominant trait. An albino whose parents both have red hair has two children with someone who is normally pigmented and has brown hair. The brown-haired partner has one parent with red hair. The first child is normally pigmented and has brown hair. The second child is albino. What is the hair color (phenotype) of the albino parent? What is the genotype of the albino parent for hair color? What is the genotype of the brown-haired parent with respect to hair color? skin pigmentation? What is the genotype of the first child for hair color and skin pigmentation? What are the possible genotypes of the second child for hair color? What is the phenotype of the second child for hair color? Can you explain this?

26. Discuss the pertinent features of meiosis that provide a physical correlate to Mendel's abstract genetic laws of random segregation and independent assortment.

27. If you are told that being right- or left-handed is heritable and that a right-handed couple is expecting a child, can you conclude that the child will be right-handed?

SCIENCE AND SOCIETY

1. A pedigree illustrates information about a family to show the pattern of inheritance for a trait or disease. In many cases, this pattern has features that suggest a dominant or recessive mode of inheritance. Most pedigrees contain a relatively small number of individuals, and the number of offspring in each generation is too small for the observed phenotypic ratio to be a reliable indicator of the mode of inheritance. Conclusions about the inheritance of a trait are often made by pooling the information from several pedigrees. Do you think that genetic information about you or your family should be made public? Should such information be part of your medical records, or be available to employers or insurance companies? How much do you know about the genetic history of your family? What

are the advantages and disadvantages of knowing your family's genetic history?

2. Construct a pedigree given the following information. The proband, Mary, is a 35 year-old woman who is 16 weeks pregnant, and was referred for genetic counseling because of advanced maternal age. Mary has one daughter, Sarah, who is 5 years old. Mary has three older sisters and four younger brothers. The two oldest sisters are married and each have one son. All her brothers are married, but none has any children. Mary's parents are both alive, and she has two maternal uncles and three paternal aunts. Mary's husband John has two brothers, one older and one younger, neither of whom is married. John's mother is alive, but his father is deceased.

INTERNET ACTIVITIES

The following activities use the resources of the World Wide Web to enhance the topics covered in this chapter. To investigate the topics described below, log on to the book's home page at:

http://www.wadsworth.com/biology

1. Perform fly crosses demonstrating Mendelian principles by linking to the Virtual Fly Lab. By selecting traits and performing crosses you can demonstrate the concepts of dominant and recessive phenotypes, segregation and independent assortment.

a. For an experimental cross, select *Designing a Cross*. Scroll through the characteristics and choose a mutant strain. Next, click on the *Mate Flies* button and then record your results.

b. Click on *Other Places to Go* and select *Design and Mate Flies*. Pick two mutations for two of the nine genes. Click on the *Mate Flies* button and then record your results.

2. By connecting to the MendelWeb site, you can read Mendel's original paper, both in English and German. In addition to the original manuscript, the site contains critical interpretations of the work.

FOR FURTHER READING

Corcos, A. F., and Monaghan, F. 1985. Role of de Vries in the recovery of Mendel's work. I. Was de Vries really an independent discoverer of Mendel? *J. Hered.* **76:** 187–190.

Dahl, H. 1993. Things Mendel never dreamed of. Med. J. Aust. 158: 247–252.

Dunn, L. C. 1965. *A Short History of Genetics.* New York: McGraw-Hill.

Edwards, A. W. 1986. Are Mendel's results really too close? *Biol. Rev. Cambridge Philos. Soc.* **61:** 295–312.

Finney, D. J. 1980. *Statistics for Biologists.* New York: Chapman & Hall.

Gasking, E. B. 1959. Why was Mendel's work ignored? *J. Hist. Ideas* **20:** 62–84.

George, W. 1975. *Gregor Mendel and Heredity.* London: Priory Press.

Hartl, D. and Orel, V. 1992. What did Gregor Mendel think he discovered? Genetics **131:** 245–253.

Heim, W. G. 1991. What is a recessive allele? *Amer Biol Teacher* 53: 94–97.

Mather, K. 1965. *Statistical Analysis in Biology.* London: Methuen.

Monaghan, F. V., and Corcos, A. F. 1985. Mendel, the empiricist. J. Hered. **76:** 49–54.

Orel, V. 1973. The scientific milieu in Brno during the era of Mendel's research. *J. Hered.* **64:** 314–318.

Orel, V. 1984. *Mendel.* New York: Oxford University Press.

Piegorsch, W.W. 1990. Fisher's contributions to genetics and heredity, with special emphasis on the Gregor Mendel controversy. Biometrics **46:** 915–924.

Pilgrim, I. 1986. A solution to the too-good-to-be-true paradox and Gregor Mendel. *J. Hered.* **77:** 218–220.

Sandler, I., and Sandler, L. 1985. A conceptual ambiguity that contributed to the neglect of Mendel's paper. *Publ. Stn. Zool. Napoli* **7:** 3–70.

Stern, C., and Sherwood, E. 1966. *The Origins of Genetics: A Mendel Sourcebook.* San Francisco: Freeman.

Voipio, P. 1990. When and how did Mendel become convinced of the idea of general, successive evolution? Hereditas **113:** 179–181.

Voller, B. R., ed. 1968. *The Chromosome Theory of Inheritance. Classic Papers in Development and Heredity.* New York: Appleton-Century-Crofts.

Weiling, F. 1991. Historical study: Johann Gregor Mendel 1822–1884. Am. J. Med. Genet. **40:** 1–25.

PEDIGREE ANALYSIS IN HUMAN GENETICS

Chapter 4

Chapter Outline

HUMANS AS A SUBJECT FOR GENETICS
PEDIGREE ANALYSIS
THE CATALOG OF MENDELIAN
  GENETIC DISORDERS
CONCEPTS AND CONTROVERSIES *Was*
  Noah an Albino?
AUTOSOMAL RECESSIVE TRAITS
Cystic Fibrosis
Sickle Cell Anemia
AUTOSOMAL DOMINANT TRAITS

Pattern of Inheritance
Marfan Syndrome
SEX-LINKED INHERITANCE
X-Linked Dominant Inheritance
X-Linked Recessive Inheritance
SIDEBAR *Homophilia, HIV, and AIDS*
CONCEPTS AND CONTROVERSIES
  Hemophilia and History
Muscular Dystrophy
Y-Linked Inheritance

MITOCHONDRIAL INHERITANCE
VARIATIONS IN GENE EXPRESSION
Temperature and Gene Expression
Age and Gene Expression
GUEST ESSAY *Exploring Membranes*
Penetrance and Expressivity
Pleiotropy
LINKAGE AND GENETIC MAPS
LINKAGE ANALYSIS AND LOD SCORES

OPENING IMAGE
*Constructing the human genetic map is a
complex process.*

W as Abraham Lincoln, the 16th president of the United States, affected
with a genetic disorder? Several writers have speculated that Lincoln had
a genetic disease known as Marfan syndrome. The evidence offered to support
this idea is based on Lincoln's physical appearance and the report of Marfan
syndrome in a distant relative.

    Photographs, written descriptions, and medical reports are available to
provide ample information about Lincoln's physical appearance. He was 6 ft
4 in. tall and thin, weighing between 160 and 180 lbs. for most of his adult
life. He had long arms and legs, with large, narrow hands and feet.

Contemporary descriptions of his appearance indicate that he was stoop-shouldered, loose jointed, and walked with a shuffling gait. In addition, he wore eyeglasses to correct a visual problem.

Lincoln's appearance and ocular problems are suggestive of Marfan syndrome, a genetic condition that affects the connective tissue of the body, resulting in a tall, thin individual often affected with a shifted lens in the eye, blood vessel defects, and loose joints.

In 1960 a man diagnosed as having Marfan syndrome was found to have ancestors in common with Lincoln (the common ancestor was Lincoln's great-great-grandfather). Added to the evidence based on physical appearance, the family history suggests that Lincoln had Marfan syndrome.

Others strongly disagree with this speculation, arguing that the length of Lincoln's extremities and the proportions of his body were well within the normal limits for tall, thin individuals. In addition, although Lincoln had visual problems, an examination of his eyeglasses indicates that he was farsighted, while those with the classical form of Marfan syndrome are nearsighted. Lastly, Lincoln showed no outward signs of problems with major blood vessels such as the aorta.

Did Lincoln really have Marfan syndrome, and should we care? Interest in this issue probably grows from our interest in the lives of historic figures and our fascination with the intimate details of the lives of the famous and the infamous. At the present time there is no solid evidence to suggest that Lincoln had Marfan syndrome, although molecular testing on bone and hair fragments (discussed below) have been proposed. For now we are left only with speculation and inferential reasoning.

The more important question for this chapter is how we can tell when someone is affected with a genetic disorder? Lincoln's family history shows only one documented case of Marfan syndrome in nine generations. Is this enough to decide that he was also affected with this genetic condition?

In this chapter we will show that the principles of inheritance discovered by Mendel in peas also apply to humans. Even though the methods employed in human genetics differ significantly from those used in other organisms, the rules for the inheritance of traits in humans are the same as those for pea plants.

HUMANS AS A SUBJECT FOR GENETICS

Pea plants were selected by Mendel for two primary reasons. First, they can be crossed in any combination; second, each cross is likely to produce large numbers of offspring, an important factor in understanding how a trait is inherited. If you were picking an organism for genetic studies, humans would not be a good choice. With pea plants, it's easy to carry out crosses between plants with purple flowers and plants with white flowers and to repeat this cross as often as necessary. For obvious reasons, experimental matings in humans are not possible. You can't ask all albino humans to mate with homozygous normally pigmented individuals and have their progeny interbreed to produce an F_2. For the most part, human geneticists base their work on matings that have already taken place, whether or not such matings would be the most genetically informative.

Compared with the progeny that can be counted in a single cross with peas, humans produce very few offspring, and these usually represent only a small fraction of the possible genetic combinations. If two heterozygous pea plants are crossed ($Aa \times Aa$), about three-fourths of the offspring will express the dominant phenotype, while the recessive phenotype will be expressed in the remaining one fourth of the

progeny (Figure 4.1). Mendel was able to count hundreds and sometimes thousands of offspring from such a cross, recording progeny in all expected phenotypic classes, clearly establishing a ratio of 3:1 for recessive traits. As a parallel, consider two humans, each of whom is phenotypically normal. Suppose this couple have two children, one of whom is a son affected with a genetic disorder. The ratio of phenotypes in this case is 1:1. This makes it difficult to decide whether the trait is carried on an autosome or a sex chromosome, whether it is a dominant or recessive trait, and whether it is controlled by a single gene or by two or more genes.

These examples should serve to demonstrate that the basic method of genetic analysis in humans is observational rather than experimental and requires the reconstruction of events that have already taken place rather than the design and execution of experiments to directly test a hypothesis. One of the first steps in studying a human trait is to construct a pedigree. The information in the pedigree is then used to determine how a trait is inherited.

PEDIGREE ANALYSIS

As outlined in the previous chapter, a pedigree chart is an orderly presentation of family information, using standardized symbols. Once a pedigree has been constructed, the principles of Mendelian inheritance are used to determine whether the trait is inherited in a dominant or recessive fashion, and whether the gene in question is located on an autosome or a sex chromosome.

The actual collection of pedigree information is not always straightforward. Knowledge about distant relatives is often incomplete, and recollections about medical conditions can be blurred by the passage of time. Older family members are sometimes reluctant to discuss relatives who had abnormalities or who were placed in institutions. As a result, collecting accurate pedigree information for a large family over several generations can be a challenge for the geneticist. The collection and storage of pedigree information can now be done using computer programs such as Cryllic (Figure 4.2).

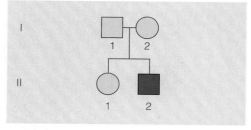
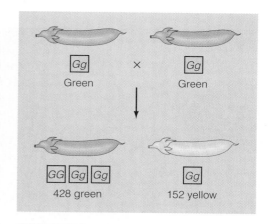

◆ **FIGURE 4.1**

Inheritance in pea plants and humans. (a) In pea plants, a cross between two heterozygotes provides enough offspring in each phenotypic class to allow the mode of inheritance of the trait to be determined. **(b)** Humans have relatively few offspring, often making it difficult to interpret how a trait is inherited.

◆ **FIGURE 4.2**

Programs such as Cryllic can be used to store and interpret information gathered for pedigree analysis.

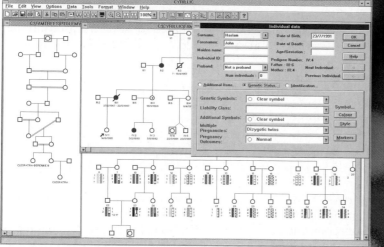

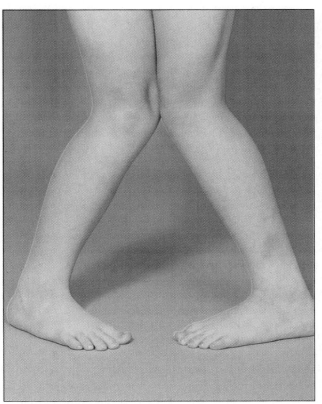

FIGURE 4.3

Ehlers-Danlos syndrome. This disorder can be inherited as an autosomal dominant, autosomal recessive, or X-linked recessive trait. People with the common autosomal dominant form have loose joints and highly elastic skin, which can be stretched by several inches but returns to its normal position when released.

These programs give on-screen displays of pedigrees and genetic information, and can be used to analyze patterns of inheritance.

Once a pedigree has been constructed, the information in the pedigree is analyzed to determine how the trait is inherited. The modes of inheritance we will consider in this chapter include

- Autosomal recessive
- Autosomal dominant
- X-linked dominant
- X-linked recessive
- Y-linked
- Mitochondrial

As outlined above, pedigrees can be difficult to construct. For several reasons, they can also be difficult to analyze. In analyzing a pedigree, a geneticist first forms a hypothesis about how the trait is inherited (for example, is it autosomal dominant?). The pedigree is then examined for evidence that will support or reject this mode of inheritance. Even if the information in the pedigree supports the hypothesis, the analysis of the pedigree is complete only when *all* possible modes of inheritance have been considered. If only one mode of inheritance is supported by the information in the pedigree, it is accepted as the mode of inheritance for the trait being examined.

It may turn out that the pedigree does not provide enough information to rule out all other possible modes of inheritance. For example, analysis of a pedigree may indicate that a trait can be inherited in an autosomal dominant or an X-linked dominant fashion. If this is the case, the pedigree is examined to determine whether one mode of transmission is more likely than another. The most likely mode of inheritance is then used as the basis for further work.

As a further complication, a genetic disorder can have more than one mode of inheritance. Ehlers-Danlos syndrome (Figure 4.3) (MIM/OMIM 130000, and other numbers), characterized by loose joints, and easily stretched skin can be inherited as an autosomal dominant, autosomal recessive or an X-linked recessive trait. In other cases, a trait can have single mode of inheritance, but be caused by mutation in any of several genes. Porphyria (MIM/OMIM 176200, and other numbers), a disorder associated with abnormal metabolism which causes abnormal behavior, is inherited as an autosomal dominant trait. It can be caused by the mutations of genes on chromosomes 1, 9, 11, and 14.

It is important to establish how a trait is inherited for several reasons. If the mode of inheritance can be established, it can be used to predict genetic risk in several situations, including:

- Pregnancy outcome
- Adult onset disorders
- Recurrence risks in future offspring

THE CATALOG OF MENDELIAN GENETIC DISORDERS

In this chapter we will deal with the six possible modes of inheritance listed above, and use Mendelian principles to analyze pedigrees for these traits. We will limit our discussion to traits controlled by a single gene. Near the end of the chapter, we will consider factors that can influence gene expression. In the next chapter, we will discuss traits that are controlled by two or more genes.

Was Noah an Albino?

The biblical character Noah, along with the ark and its animals, are among the most recognizable figures in the Book of Genesis. His birth is recorded in a single sentence, and although the story of how the ark was built and survived a great flood is told later, there is no mention of Noah's physical appearance. But other sources contain references to Noah that are consistent with the idea that Noah was one of the first albinos mentioned in recorded history.

The birth of Noah is recorded in several sources, including the Book of Enoch the Prophet, written about 200 B.C. This book, quoted several times in the New Testament, was regarded as lost until 1773, when an Ethiopian version of the text was discovered. In describing the birth of Noah, the text relates that his "flesh was white as snow, and red as a rose; the hair of whose head was white like wool, and long, and whose eyes were beautiful."

A reconstructed fragment of one of the Dead Sea Scrolls describes Noah as an abnormal child born to normal parents. This fragment of the scroll also provides some insight into the pedigree of Noah's family, as does the Book of Jubilees. According to these sources, Noah's father (Lamech) and his mother (Betenos) were first cousins. Lamech was the son of Methuselah, and Lamech's wife was a daughter of Methuselah's sister. This is important because marriage between close relatives is sometimes involved in pedigrees of autosomal recessive traits such as albinism.

If this interpretation of ancient texts is correct, Noah's albinism is the result of a consanguineous marriage, and not only is he one of the earliest albinos on record, but his grandfather Methuselah and Methuselah's sister are the first recorded heterozygous carriers of a recessive genetic trait.

To date, over 5000 genetic traits have been identified in humans. The chromosomal location for a few thousand of these genes has been determined, and the molecular basis of traits associated with deleterious phenotypes is known in a smaller number of cases. Victor McKusick, a geneticist at Johns Hopkins University, and his colleagues have compiled a catalog of human genetic traits. The catalog is published in book form as *Mendelian Inheritance in Man: Catalogs of Human Genes and Genetic Disorders*. The catalog is also available at several World Wide Web sites as *Online Mendelian Inheritance in Man*. The online version contains text, pictures, references and links to other databases (Figure 4.4). Each trait is assigned a catalog number (called the MIM or OMIM number). In this chapter and throughout the book, the MIM/OMIM number for each trait discussed is listed. You can use the MIM/OMIM number to obtain more information about these traits. Access to OMIM is available through the book's Home Page.

AUTOSOMAL RECESSIVE TRAITS

Although human families are relatively small, analysis of the affected and unaffected members over several generations usually provides enough information to determine whether a trait has a recessive pattern of inheritance, and is carried on an autosome (as opposed to a sex chromosome). Recessive traits carried on autosomes have several characteristics that can be established by pedigree analysis. Some of these are listed below:

 FIGURE 4.4

OMIM is an online database containing information about human genetic disorders.

TABLE 4.1

Some Autosomal Recessive Traits

TRAIT NUMBER	PHENOTYPE	MIM/OMIM NUMBER
Albinism	Absence of pigment in skin, eyes, hair	203100
Ataxia telangiectasia	Progressive degeneration of nervous system	208900
Bloom syndrome	Dwarfism, skin rash, increased cancer rate	210900
Cystic fibrosis	Mucous production that blocks ducts of certain glands, lung passages; often fatal by early adulthood	219700
Fanconi anemia	Slow growth, heart defects, high rate of leukemia	227650
Galactosemia	Accumulation of galactose in liver; mental retardation	230400
Phenylketonuria	Excess accumulation of phenylalanine in blood, mental retardation	261600
Sickle cell anemia	Abnormal hemoglobin, blood vessel blockage, early death	141900
Thalassemia	Improper hemoglobin production; symptoms range from mild to fatal	141900 / 141800
Xeroderma pigmentosum	Lack of DNA repair enzymes, sensitivity to UV light, skin cancer, early death	278700
Tay-Sachs disease	Improper metabolism of gangliosides in nerve cells, early death	272800

- For recessive traits that are rare or relatively rare, most affected individuals are the children of unaffected parents.
- All the children of two affected (homozygous) individuals are affected.
- The risk of an affected child from a mating of two heterozygotes is 25%.
- Because the trait is autosomal, it is expressed in both males and females, who are affected in roughly equal numbers. The trait can also be transmitted by either male or female parents.
- In pedigrees involving rare traits, the unaffected (heterozygous) parents of an affected (homozygous) individual may be related to each other.

Table 4.1 lists a number of autosomal recessive genetic disorders. A pedigree illustrating a pattern of inheritance typical of autosomal recessive genes is shown in ● Figure 4.5.

Some autosomal recessive traits represent minor variations in phenotype, such as hair color and eye color; others result in phenotypes that can be life threatening or even fatal. Examples of these more severe phenotypes include cystic fibrosis and sickle cell anemia.

Cystic Fibrosis

Cystic fibrosis
A fatal recessive genetic disorder associated with abnormal secretions of the exocrine glands.

Cystic fibrosis (CF, MIM/OMIM 219700) is a disabling and fatal genetic disorder inherited as an autosomal recessive trait. The mutant gene affects the exocrine glands, which produce mucus, digestive enzymes, and sweat. Because the sweat glands are

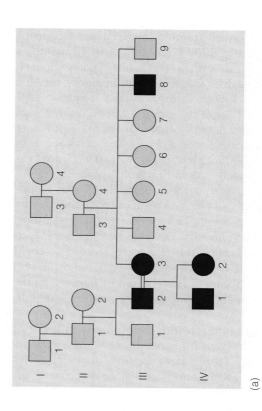

(a)

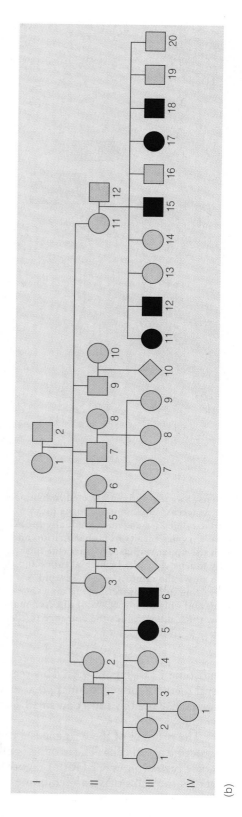

(b)

FIGURE 4.5

Pedigrees for autosomal recessive traits.
(a) This pedigree has many of the
characteristics for autosomal recessive
inheritance: most affected individuals have
normal parents, about one fourth of the
children in large affected families show the
trait, both sexes are affected in roughly
equal numbers, and affected parents
produce only affected children. (b) A
pedigree for an autosomal recessive trait.

defective, they release excessive amounts of salt, and the disease is often diagnosed
by analyzing the amount of salt present in sweat. According to folklore, midwives
would lick the forehead of newborns. If the sweat tasted too salty, they predicted that
the child would die prematurely of lung congestion.

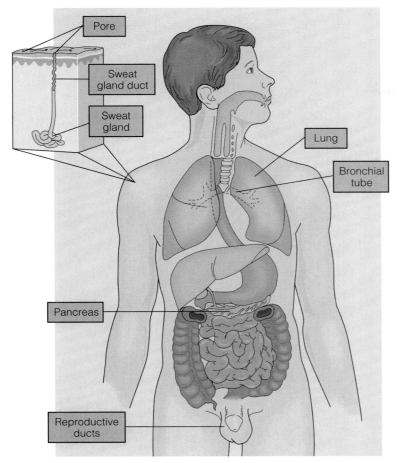

➡ FIGURE 4.6

Organ systems affected by cystic fibrosis. Sweat glands in affected individuals secrete excessive amounts of salt. In the pancreas, thick mucus blocks the transport of digestive enzymes. The trapped digestive enzymes gradually break down the pancreas. The lack of digestive enzymes results in poor nutrition and slow growth. Cystic fibrosis affects both the upper respiratory tract (the nose and sinuses) and the lungs. Thick, sticky mucus clogs the bronchial tubes and the lungs, making breathing difficult. It also slows the removal of viruses and bacteria from the respiratory system, resulting in lung infections. In males, mucus blocks the ducts that carry sperm, and only about 2–3% of affected males are fertile. In women with cystic fibrosis, thick mucus plugs the entrance to the uterus, lowering fertility.

This disease has far-reaching effects because exocrine glands perform a number of vital functions. CF causes the production of thick mucus, which clogs the ducts that carry digestive enzymes from the pancreas to the small intestine, reducing the effectiveness of digestion. As a result, affected children often suffer from malnutrition in spite of an increased appetite and food intake. Eventually, cysts form in the pancreas, and the gland degenerates into a fibrous structure, giving rise to the name of the disease. A similar pattern of events affects all the exocrine glands of the body. Because CF causes the production of thick mucus that blocks the airways in the lungs, most patients with cystic fibrosis develop obstructive lung diseases and infections that lead to premature death (➡ Figure 4.6).

Many affected individuals are infertile because their reproductive ducts are blocked. As a result, almost all cases of CF are children of phenotypically normal, heterozygous parents. Cystic fibrosis is relatively common in some populations, but rare in others (➡ Figure 4.7). Among the U.S. white population, CF has a frequency of 1 in 2000 births, and 1 in 22 members of this group are heterozygous carriers. The disease is less common among the U.S. black population and has a frequency of 1 in 17,000 to one in 19,000. Among U.S. citizens with origins in Asia, CF is a rare disease, with a frequency of about 1 in 90,000. Heterozygote carriers are extremely rare in this population.

The underlying defect in CF was identified in 1989 by a team of researchers led by Lap-chee Tsui and Francis Collins. Recombinant DNA techniques were used to localize the gene to region q31 of chromosome 7 (➡ Figure 4.8). This region of the chromosome was explored using several methods of genetic mapping, and the CF gene was identified by comparing the molecular organization of a small segment of chromosome 7 in normal and CF individuals.

The product of the CF gene is a protein that inserts into the plasma membrane of exocrine gland cells. The protein is called the *cystic fibrosis transmembrane conductance regulator,* or CFTR (➡ Figure 4.9). CFTR regulates the flow of chloride ions across the cell's plasma membrane. The CFTR protein is absent or defective in affected individuals. Because fluids move across plasma membranes in response to the movement of ions, a defective CFTR protein causes less fluid to be added to the secretions of exocrine glands. The thickened secretions produce the characteristic symptoms of CF. It is hoped that further studies of the structure of the CF gene and the function of CFTR will lead to the development of new methods of treatment for this deadly disease.

FIGURE 4.7

About 1 in 25 Americans of European descent, 1 in 46 Hispanics, 1 in 60–65 African Americans, and 1 in 150 Asian Americans is a carrier for cystic fibrosis. A crowd such as this may contain a carrier.

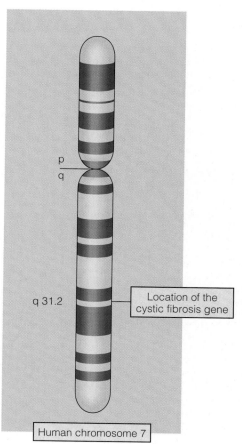

p
q

q 31.2 — Location of the cystic fibrosis gene

Human chromosome 7

FIGURE 4.8

Human chromosome 7. The gene for cystic fibrosis (CF) maps to region 7q31.2-31.3, about two-thirds of the way down the long arm of the chromosome.

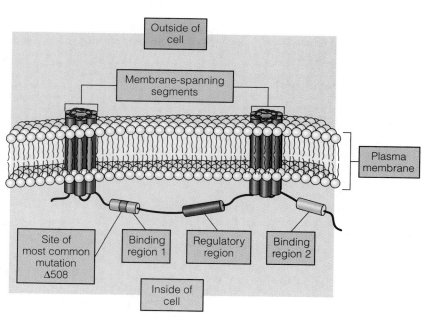

Outside of cell

Membrane-spanning segments

Plasma membrane

Site of most common mutation Δ508

Binding region 1

Regulatory region

Binding region 2

Inside of cell

FIGURE 4.9

The cystic fibrosis gene product. The CFTR protein is located in the plasma membrane of the cell, and regulates the movement of chloride ions across the cell membrane. The regulatory region controls the activity of the CFTR molecule in response to signals from inside the cell. In most cases (about 70%), the protein is defective in the shaded region.

Sickle Cell Anemia

Sickle cell anemia
A recessive genetic disorder associated with an abnormal type of hemoglobin, a blood transport protein.

Americans whose ancestors lived in parts of West Africa, the lowlands around the Mediterranean Sea, or in parts of the Indian subcontinent have a high frequency of **sickle cell anemia** (MIM/OMIM 141900). Individuals with this recessive genetic disorder produce an abnormal type of hemoglobin, a protein found in red blood cells. Normally, this protein functions in the transport of oxygen from the lungs to the tissues of the body, and each red cell contains millions of hemoglobin molecules.

In sickle cell anemia, the abnormal hemoglobin molecules pack together to form rods (➡ Figure 4.10). This causes the red blood cells to become crescent- or sickle-shaped (➡ Figure 4.11). The deformed red blood cells are fragile, and break open as they circulate through the body. New blood cells are not produced fast enough to replace those that are lost, and the oxygen-carrying capacity of the blood is reduced, causing anemia. Individuals with sickle cell anemia tire easily and often develop heart failure because of the increased load on the circulatory system. The deformed blood cells also clog small blood vessels and capillaries, further reducing oxygen transport, sometimes initiating a sickling crisis. As oxygen levels in the circulatory system fall, more and more red blood cells become sickled, bringing on intense pain as blood vessels become blocked. In some affected areas, ulcers and sores appear on the body surface. Blockage of the blood vessels in the brain leads to strokes and can result in partial paralysis.

Because of the number of systems in the body affected and the severity of the effects, untreated sickle cell anemia can be lethal. Some affected individuals die in childhood or adolescence, but aggressive medical treatment allows survival into adulthood. As in cystic fibrosis, most affected individuals are children of phenotypically normal, heterozygous parents.

The high frequency of sickle cell anemia in certain populations is related to the frequency of malaria, an infectious disease. Sickle cell heterozygotes are more resistant

➡ **FIGURE 4.10**

Hemoglobin molecules aggregate in sickle cell anemia. The mutant hemoglobin molecules in red blood cells stack together to form rod-like structures. The formation of these aggregates in the cytoplasm causes the red blood cells to deform and become elongated or sickle-shaped.

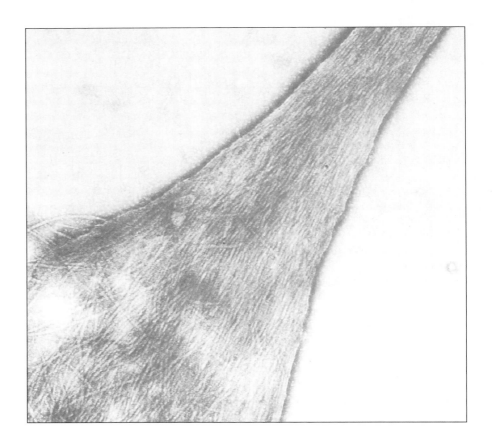

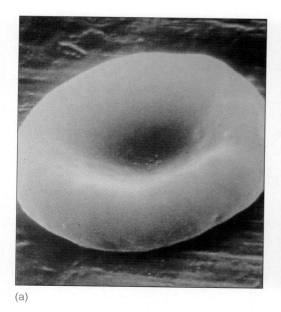

(a)

(b)

 FIGURE 4.11
Red blood cells. (a) Normal red blood cells are flat, disk-shaped cells, indented in the middle on both sides. (b) In sickle cell anemia, the cells become elongated and fragile.

to malarial infection than homozygous normal individuals. As a result, this mutation is widespread in certain populations. Among the U.S. black population, sickle cell anemia occurs with a frequency of 1 in every 500 births, and approximately 1 in every 12 individuals is a heterozygote. The high frequency of this mutation in the black population is a genetic vestige of African origins. The same is true for U.S. residents whose ancestral origins are in lowland regions of Italy, Sicily, Cyprus, Greece, and the Middle East. This mutation in a hemoglobin molecule has a double effect: it causes sickle cell anemia but also confers resistance to malaria. The molecular basis of this disease is well known and will be discussed in later chapters.

AUTOSOMAL DOMINANT TRAITS

In autosomal dominant disorders, heterozygotes and those with a homozygous dominant genotype show expression of the abnormal phenotype. Unaffected individuals carry two recessive alleles. Careful analysis of pedigrees is necessary to determine whether a trait is caused by a dominant allele.

Pattern of Inheritance

Dominant traits that are fully expressed have a distinctive pattern of inheritance:

- Every affected individual should have at least one affected parent. Exceptions can occur in cases where the gene has a high mutation rate. Mutation is the sudden appearance of a heritable allele that was not transmitted by the biological parents.
- Because most affected individuals are heterozygotes who mate with unaffected (homozygous recessive) individuals, there is a 50% chance of transmitting the trait to each child.
- Because the trait is autosomal, the number of affected males and females are roughly equal.
- Two affected individuals may have unaffected children, again because most affected individuals are heterozygotes. In contrast, two individuals affected with an autosomal recessive trait have only affected children.
- In homozygous dominant individuals, the phenotype is often more severe than the heterozygous phenotype.

Table 4.2 lists a number of human genetic disorders caused by autosomal dominant genes. The pedigree in ⬤ Figure 4.12 is typical of the pattern found in autosomal dominant conditions.

⬤ **FIGURE 4.12**

Pedigrees for autosomal dominant traits. (a) This pedigree shows many of the characteristics of autosomal dominant inheritance: affected individuals have at least one affected parent, about one half of the children with one affected parent are affected, both sexes are affected with roughly equal frequency, and affected parents can have unaffected children. (b) Pedigree of Huntington disease, an autosomal dominant disorder, in a large family from Venezuela.

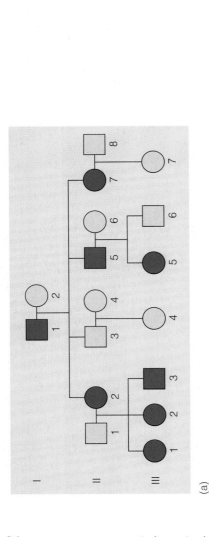

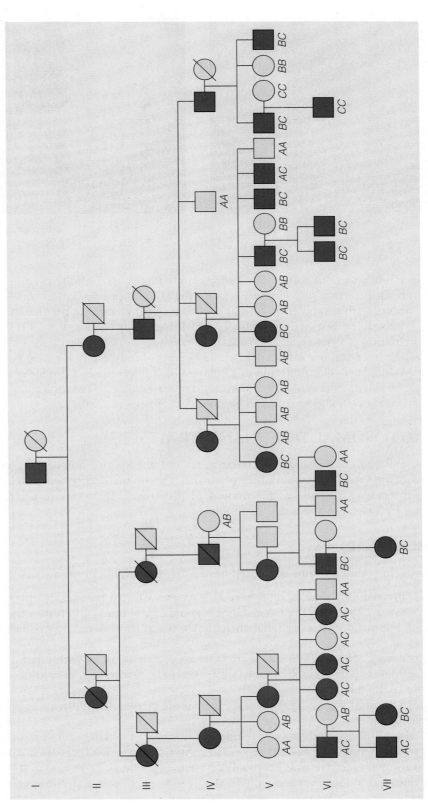

TABLE 4.2

Some Autosomal Dominant Traits

TRAIT	PHENOTYPE	MIM/OMIM NUMBER
Achondroplasia	Dwarfism associated with defects in growth regions of long bones	100800
Brachydactyly	Malformed hands with shortened fingers	112500
Camptodactyly	Stiff, permanently bent little fingers	114200
Crouzon syndrome	Defective development of midface region, protruding eyes, hook nose	123500
Ehlers-Danlos syndrome	Connective tissue disorder, elastic skin, loose joints	130000
Familial hyper-cholesterolemia	Elevated levels of cholesterol; predisposes to plaque formation, cardiac disease; may be most prevalent genetic disease	144010
Adult polycystic kidney disease	Formation of cysts in kidneys; leads to hypertension, kidney failure	173900
Huntington disease	Progressive degeneration of nervous system, dementia, early death	143100
Hypercalcemia	Elevated levels of calcium in blood serum	143880
Marfan syndrome	Connective tissue defect; death by aortic rupture	154700
Nail-patella syndrome	Absence of nails, kneecaps	161200
Porphyria	Inability to metabolize porphyrins, episodes of mental derangement	176200

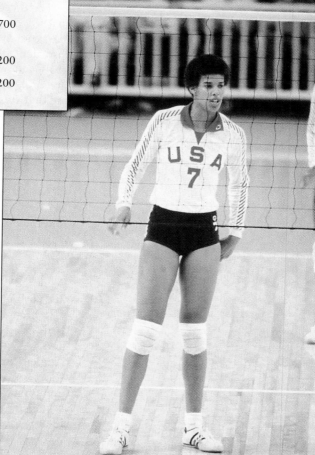

Marfan syndrome
An autosomal dominant genetic disorder that affects the skeletal system, the cardiovascular system, and the eyes.

Marfan Syndrome

Marfan syndrome (MIM/OMIM 154700) is an autosomal dominant disorder which affects the skeletal system, the eyes, and the cardiovascular system. It was first described in 1896 by A. B. Marfan, a French physician. Affected individuals tend to be tall and thin with long arms and legs and long, thin fingers. Because of their height and long limbs, those with Marfan syndrome often excel in sports like basketball and volleyball, although nearsightedness and defects in the lens of the eye are also common (➥ Figure 4.13).

The most dangerous effects of Marfan syndrome are on the cardiovascular system, especially the aorta. The aorta is the main blood-carrying vessel in the body. As it leaves the heart, the aorta arches back and downward, feeding blood to all the major organ systems. Marfan syndrome weakens the connective tissue around

➥ **FIGURE 4.13**
Flo Hyman was a star on the U.S. women's volleyball team in the 1984 Olympics. Two years later, she died in a volleyball game from a ruptured aorta caused by Marfan syndrome.

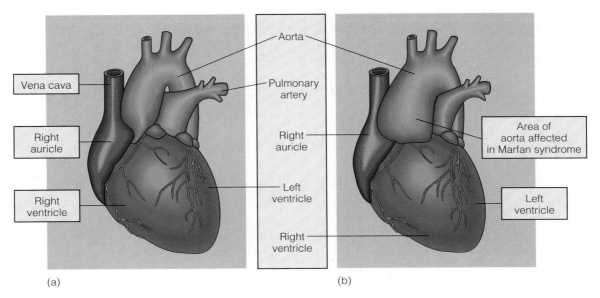

FIGURE 4.14

The heart and its major blood vessels. Oxygen-rich blood is pumped from the lungs to the left side of the heart. From there, blood is pumped through the aorta to all parts of the body.

the base of the aorta, causing it to enlarge and eventually to split open (Figure 4.14). It is the first few inches of the aorta that are most likely to enlarge and split, and in cases where the enlargement can be detected, it can be repaired by surgery.

The defective gene that causes Marfan syndrome was mapped to chromosome 15 in 1989. In 1991, the Marfan protein was identified as fibrillin, a component of the elastic connective tissue in the aorta, the eye, and the sheath covering long bones. The disorder affects males and females with equal frequency and is found in all ethnic groups at a frequency of about 1 in 10,000 individuals. About 25% of affected individuals appear in families with no previous history of Marfan syndrome, indicating that this gene undergoes mutation at a high rate. As discussed in the chapter introduction, it has been suggested that Abraham Lincoln had Marfan syndrome.

Bone fragments and hair from Lincoln's body are preserved at the National Medical Library in Washington, D.C.. Recently, a group of research scientists asked permission to analyze these samples using recombinant DNA techniques to decide whether Lincoln did, in fact, have Marfan syndrome. A committee appointed to review the request has agreed that this material can be tested, but it has recommended that testing be delayed until more is known about the fibrillin gene and the nature and the population distribution of mutant alleles.

SEX-LINKED INHERITANCE

As noted in Chapter 2, females have two X chromosomes, and males have an X and a Y chromosome. These two chromosomes are very different in size and appearance. The X chromosome is a medium-sized, metacentric chromosome with a well-defined banding pattern. The Y chromosome is a much smaller, acrocentric chromosome, about 25% as large as the X, and has a variable banding pattern (Figure 4.15). At meiosis, the X and Y chromosomes pair only along a small region at the tip of the short arms. The absence of pairing along most of the chromosome suggests that the great majority of genes present on the X chromosome are not represented on the Y.

This lack of genetic equivalence between the X and Y chromosomes is responsible for a pattern of transmission known as sex-linked inheritance. For genes on the X chromosome, the pattern is **X-linked,** and genes on the Y exhibit Y-linkage. Females carry two copies of all X-linked genes, and can be heterozygous or ho-

X-linkage
The pattern of inheritance that results from genes located on the X chromosome.

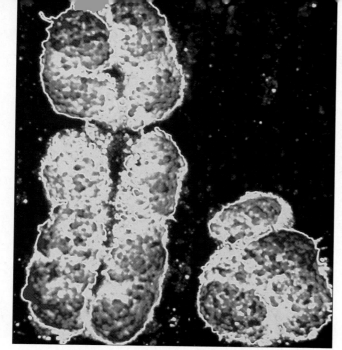

The human X and Y chromosome. This false-color scanning electron micrograph shows the differences between these chromosomes.

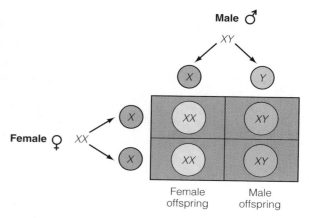

■ FIGURE 4.16

Distribution of sex chromosomes by parents. All children receive an X chromosome from their mothers. Fathers pass their X chromosome to all daughters, and a Y chromosome to all their sons. The sex chromosome content of the sperm determines the sex of the child.

mozygous for any of them. Males, on the other hand, have only one copy of the X chromosome. Since the Y chromosome does not carry copies of most X-linked genes, a male cannot be heterozygous for genes on the X chromosome.

This situation explains why males are affected by X-linked recessive genetic disorders more often than females. The term **hemizygous** is used for genes present in a single dose on the X chromosome in males. Since males cannot be heterozygous for these genes, recessive traits on the X chromosome are expressed in males (traits controlled by genes on the X chromosome are defined as dominant or recessive by their pattern of expression in females). The distinctive pattern of sex-linked inheritance derives from the fact that males transmit their X chromosome to all daughters and their Y chromosome to all sons. Females randomly pass on one or the other X chromosome to all daughters and to all sons (■ Figure 4.16). If a trait is X-linked, a male will pass it to all his daughters, who may be heterozygous or homozygous for the condition. If their mother is heterozygous for an X-linked recessive trait, sons have a 50% chance of receiving the recessive allele. In the following sections, we will consider examples of sex-linked inheritance and explore the characteristic pedigrees in detail.

Hemizygous
A gene present on the X chromosome that is expressed in males in both the recessive and dominant condition.

X-Linked Dominant Inheritance

Only a small number of dominant traits map to the X chromosome. One of these is a phosphate deficiency known as **hypophosphatemia** (MIM/OMIM 307800), which causes a type of rickets, or bowleggedness. Dominant X-linked traits have a distinctive pattern of transmission with three characteristics:

Hypophosphatemia
An X-linked dominant disorder. Those affected have low phosphate levels in blood, and skeletal deformaties.

- Affected males produce all affected daughters and no affected sons.
- A heterozygous affected female will transmit the trait to half her children, with males and females equally affected.
- On average, twice as many females will be affected as males.

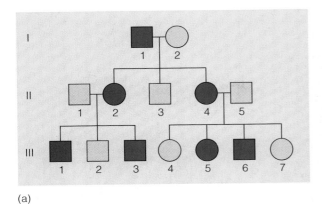

(a)

● FIGURE 4.17

FIGURE 4.17

Pedigrees for X-linked dominant traits. (a) This pedigree shows the characteristics of X-linked dominant traits: affected males produce all affected daughters and no affected sons, affected females transmit the trait to roughly half their children, with males and females equally affected, and twice as many females are affected with the trait as males. (b) A pedigree for hypophosphatemia, an X-linked dominant trait.

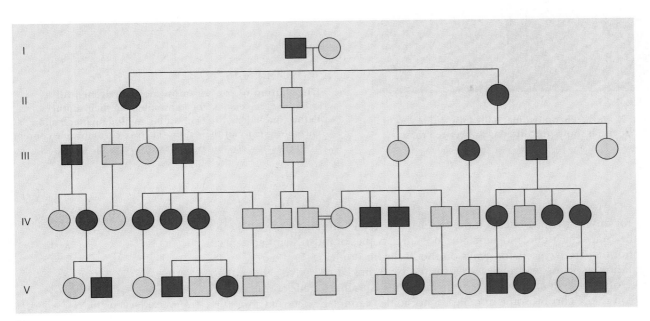

(b)

As expected, a homozygous female will transmit the trait to all her offspring. A pedigree for the inheritance of hyperphosphatemia is shown in ● Figure 4.17. To determine whether a trait is X-linked dominant or autosomal dominant, the children of affected males should be carefully analyzed. In X-linked dominant traits, affected males transmit the trait only to daughters. In autosomal dominant conditions, affected males pass the trait to both daughters and sons, with about half the daughters and about half the sons being affected.

X-Linked Recessive Inheritance

Color blindness

Defective color vision caused by reduction or absence of visual pigments. There are three forms: red, green, and blue blindness.

The X-linked recessive trait for **color blindness** is actually a collection of several abnormalities of color vision. The most common forms of color blindness, known as red-green blindness, affect about 8% of the male population in the United States. Red blindness (MIM/OMIM 303900) is characterized by the inability to see red as a distinct color (● Figure 4.18). Green blindness (MIM/OMIM 303800) is the inability to see green and other colors in the middle of the visual spectrum (● Figure 4.19). Both red blindness and green blindness are inherited as X-linked recessive traits. A rare form of blue color blindness (MIM/OMIM 190900) is inherited as an autosomal dominant condition that maps to chromosome 7.

These three genes for color blindness encode different forms of opsins, which are proteins found in the cone cells of the retina (● Figure 4.20). Normally, opsins bind

(a)

(b)

FIGURE 4.18

People who are color-blind see colors differently. (a) Those with normal vision see a red cable car. (b) Someone with red-green color blindness would see the cable car as gray.

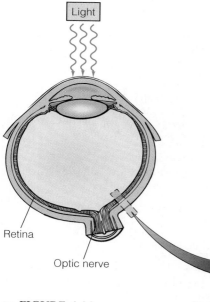

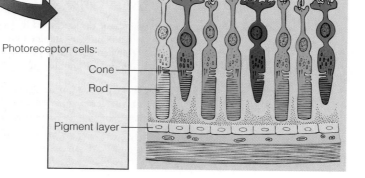

FIGURE 4.19

People with normal color vision see the number 29 in the chart, but those who are color-blind cannot see any number.

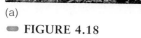

FIGURE 4.20

In the retina, there are two types of light receptor cells: rods are sensitive to differences in light intensity, and cones are sensitive to differences in color. There are three types of cones: red-sensitive, green-sensitive, and blue-sensitive.

to visual pigments in the red-, green-, or blue-cone cells, making the visual pigment/opsin complex sensitive to light of a given wavelength. If the red-opsin gene product is defective or absent, function of the red cones is impaired, and red color blindness results. Similarly, defects in the green or blue opsins produce green and blue blindness.

Pedigrees of color blindness can be used to demonstrate the patterns of transmission for sex-linked recessive traits (● Figure 4.21). These patterns can be summarized as follows:

- Both hemizygous males and homozygous females are affected.
- Phenotypic expression is much more common in males than in females, and in the case of rare alleles, males are almost exclusively affected.
- Affected males get the mutant allele from their mothers, and transmit it to all their daughters, but not to any sons.
- Daughters of affected males will usually be heterozygous and therefore unaffected. Sons of heterozygous females have a 50% chance of receiving the recessive gene.

Table 4.3 lists some sex-linked recessive conditions.

TABLE 4.3

Some X-linked Recessive Traits

TRAIT	PHENOTYPE	MIM/OMIM NUMBER
Adrenoleukodystrophy	Atrophy of adrenal glands, mental deterioration; death 1 to 5 years after onset	300100
Color blindness		
Green blindness	Insensitivity to green light; 60% to 75% of color blindness	303800
Red blindness	Insensitivity to red light; 25% to 40% of colorblindness	303900
Fabry disease	Metabolic defect caused by lack of enzyme alpha-galactosidase A; progressive cardiac renal problems, early death	301500
Glucose-6-phosphate dehydrogenase deficiency	Benign condition that can produce severe, even fatal anemia in presence of certain foods, drugs	305900
Hemophilia A	Inability to form blood clots; caused by lack of clotting factor VIII	306700
Hemophilia B	"Christmas disease"; clotting defect cause by lack of factor IX	306900
Ichthyosis	Skin disorder causing large, dark scales on extremities, trunk	308100
Lesch-Nyhan syndrome	Metabolic defect caused by lack of enzyme hypoxanthine-guanine phosphoribosyl transferase (HGPRT); causes mental retardation, self-mutilation, early death	308000
Muscular dystrophy	Duchenne-type, progressive; fatal condition accompanied by muscle wasting	310200

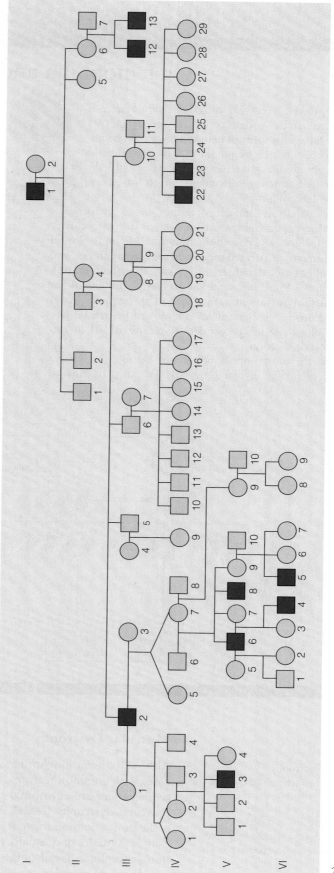

► FIGURE 4.21

Pedigrees for X-linked recessive traits. (a) This pedigree shows the characteristics of X-linked recessive traits: hemizygous males are affected, and transmit the trait to all daughters, who become heterozygous carriers, and phenotypic expression is much more common in males than in females. (b) A pedigree for an X-linked recessive trait associated with improper tooth development.

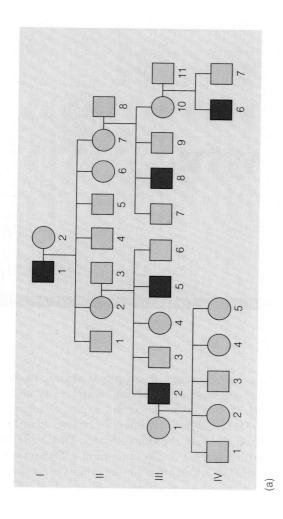

Hemophilia and History

The X-linked recessive disorder, *hemophilia,* is characterized by defects in the mechanism of blood clotting. This form of hemophilia, called hemophilia A, occurs with a frequency of 1 in 10,000 males. Because only homozygous recessive females can have hemophilia, the frequency in females is much lower, on the order of 1 in 100 million.

Pedigree analysis indicates that Queen Victoria of England (the granddaughter of King George III) was a carrier for this gene. Since she passed the mutant allele on to several of her children (one affected male, two carrier daughters, and one possible carrier daughter), it is likely that the mutation occurred in the X chromosome she received from one of her parents. Although this mutation spread through the royal houses of Europe, the present royal family of England is free of hemophilia, since it is descended from Edward VII, an unaffected son of Victoria.

Perhaps the most important case of hemophilia among Victoria's offspring involved the royal family of Russia.

Victoria's granddaughter Alix, a carrier, married Czar Nicholas II of Russia. She gave birth to four daughters and then a son, Alexis, who had hemophilia. Frustrated by the failure of the medical community to cure Alexis, the royal couple turned to a series of spiritualists, including the monk Rasputin. While under Rasputin's care, Alexis recovered from several episodes of bleeding, and Rasputin became a powerful adviser to the royal family. Some historians have argued that the czar's preoccupation with Alexis's health and the insidious influence of Rasputin contributed to the revolution that overthrew the throne. Other historians point out that Nicholas II was a weak czar and that revolution was inevitable; but it is interesting to speculate that much of Russian history in the 20th century turns on a mutation carried by an English queen at the beginning of the century.

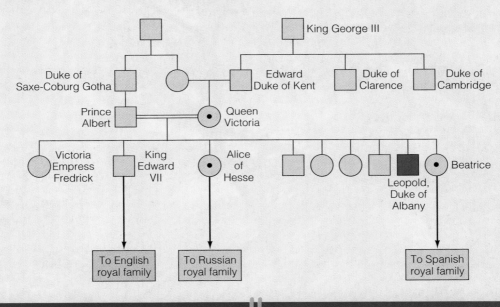

Muscular Dystrophy

Muscular dystrophy
A group of genetic diseases associated with progressive degeneration of muscles. Two of these, Duchenne and Becker muscular dystrophy, are inherited as X-linked, allelic, recessive traits.

Although often thought of as a single disorder, **muscular dystrophy** is a group of diseases with common features, including progressive weakness and wasting of muscle tissue. There are autosomal and X-linked forms of muscular dystrophy. Duchenne muscular dystrophy (DMD, MIM/OMIM 310200), an X-linked recessive disorder, is the most common form of muscular dystrophy. In the United States, DMD affects 1 in 3500 males and usually has an onset between 1 and 6 years of age. Progressive muscle weakness is one of the first signs of DMD, and affected individuals use a characteristic set of maneuvers in rising from the prone position (● Figure 4.22). The

disease progresses rapidly, and by 12 years of age, affected individuals are usually confined to a wheelchair because of muscle degeneration. Death usually occurs by the age of 20 years due to respiratory infection or cardiac failure.

DMD was mapped to band Xp21, a region in the middle of the short arm of the X chromosome, in 1986. The gene was identified by Louis Kunkle and his colleagues. It encodes a protein called *dystrophin*. Normal forms of dystrophin attach to the cytoplasmic side of the plasma membrane in muscle cells and stabilize the membrane during the mechanical strains of muscle contraction. In the absence of dystrophin, the plasma membranes gradually break down, causing the death of muscle tissue.

Most individuals with DMD have no detectable amounts of dystrophin in muscle tissue. A second form of X-linked muscular dystrophy, Becker muscular dystrophy (BMD, MIM/OMIM 310200), is distinguished from DMD by later age of onset, milder symptoms, and longer survival. Those with BMD synthesize an abnormal, usually shortened dystrophin that is only partially functional. This finding indicates that DMD and BMD represent different allelic forms of the same disease. The gene associated with these two forms of muscular dystrophy has been isolated and cloned using recombinant DNA techniques. The dystrophin gene is one of the largest yet identified, covering some 2 million base pairs of DNA. Future work on the structure and function of dystrophin will hopefully lead to the development of an effective treatment for muscular dystrophy.

FIGURE 4.22

A sign of Duchenne muscular dystrophy. Children with muscular dystrophy use a characteristic set of movements when rising from the prone position. Once the legs are pulled under the body, the child uses his arms to push the torso into an upright position.

Y-Linked Inheritance

Genes that occur only on the Y chromosome are said to be **Y-linked.** Since only males have Y chromosomes, Y-linked traits appear only in males and are passed directly from father to son. Furthermore, every Y-linked trait should be expressed, since males would be hemizygous for all genes on the Y chromosome. Although the distinctive pattern of inheritance should make such genes easy to identify, only about two dozen Y-linked traits have been discovered. These include a gene that encodes a protein confined to the cell nucleus that shares characteristics with proteins known to regulate gene expression. Another gene mapped to the Y chromosome, testis-determining factor (TDF, MIM/OMIM 480000), is involved in determining maleness in developing embryos. The TDF gene and early human development will be discussed in Chapter 7. Table 4.4 on p. 96 lists some of the genes mapped to the Y chromosome.

Y-linked
Genes located only on the Y chromosome.

MITOCHONDRIAL INHERITANCE

Mitochondria are cytoplasmic organelles that convert energy from food molecules into ATP, a molecule that powers many cellular functions. Billions of years ago, ancestors of mitochondria were probably free-living prokaryotes that formed a symbiotic relationship with primitive eukaryotes. As an evolutionary relic of their free-living ancestry, mitochondria carry DNA molecules that encode information necessary for mitochondrial gene products. Most mitochondria carry 5–10 copies of this information, and there can be from several hundred to over a thousand mitochondria in each cell (red blood cells are an exception; they have none).

TABLE 4.4

Some of the Genes Mapped to Y Chromosome

GENE	PRODUCT	MIM/OMIM NUMBER
ANT3 ADP/ATP translocase	Enzyme that moves ADP into, ATP out of mitochondria	403000
CSF2RA	Cell surface receptor for growth factor	425000
MIC2	Cell surface receptor	450000
TDF/SRY	Protein involved in early stage of testis differentiation	480000
H-Y antigen	Plasma membrane protein	426000
ZFY	DNA binding protein that may regulate gene expression	490000

Because mitochondria carry genetic information, mutations in these genes can cause human genetic disorders. Mitochondria are transmitted through the cytoplasm of the egg (sperm lose all cytoplasm during maturation). As a result, mutations in mitochondrial genes are maternally inherited. Both males and females can be affected by such disorders, but only females can transmit these mutant genes from generation to generation (Figure 4.23).

Several genetic disorders are known to be transmitted in this fashion, and all are caused by defects in energy conversion and ATP production. Tissues with the highest energy requirements are most affected, including the nervous system, skeletal muscle, heart muscle, liver and kidneys. Some of the disorders associated with mutations in mitochondria genes are listed in Table 4.5.

 ## VARIATIONS IN GENE EXPRESSION

Many genes have a regular and consistent pattern of expression, but others produce a wide range of phenotypes. In some cases, a mutant genotype may be present but remain unexpressed, resulting in a normal phenotype. Variation in phenotypic expression is caused by a number of factors, including interactions with other genes in the genotype, and by interactions between genes and the environment.

Temperature and Gene Expression

Siamese cats and Himalayan rabbits have light-colored bodies with dark fur on their paws, nose, ears, and tail (Figure 4.24). In these animals, a gene that controls pig-

 FIGURE 4.23

Mitochondrial inheritance. Both males and females can be affected by mitochondrial disorders, but only females can transmit the trait to offspring.

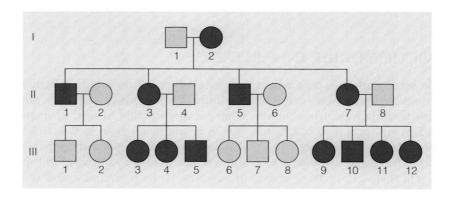

FIGURE 4.24
Animals such as Siamese cats have dark fur at the tips of the nose, paws, and ears. These colors are the result of expression of an allele for coat color that is active only at the slightly lower body temperatures found in the extremities.

ment production is expressed at the lower temperatures found in the extremities, but not at the slightly higher temperatures throughout the rest of the body. All cells of these animals carry the genes for pigment production, but the environment determines the phenotypic pattern of expression.

Age and Gene Expression

While a large number of genes act prenatally or early in development, the expression of other genes is delayed until later in life. One of the best-known examples is **Huntington disease** (HD, MIM/OMIM 143100), which is inherited as an autosomal dominant trait. The phenotype of this disorder is first expressed between the ages of 30 and 50 years. Affected individuals undergo a progressive degeneration of the nervous system, causing mental deterioration and uncontrolled, jerky movements of the head and limbs. The disease progresses slowly, and death occurs some 5 to 15 years after onset. This disorder is particularly insidious, since onset usually occurs after the affected person has started a family. Because most affected individuals are heterozygotes, each child of an affected parent has a 50% chance of developing the disease. The gene for HD has been identified and cloned using recombinant DNA techniques, making it possible to test family members and identify those who will develop the disorder.

Porphyria (MIM/OMIM 176200), an autosomal dominant disorder, is also expressed later in life. This disease is caused by the inability to correctly metabolize porphyrin, a chemical component of hemoglobin. As blood levels of porphyrin increase, some is excreted, producing wine-colored urine. The elevated levels also cause

Huntington disease
A dominant genetic disorder characterized by involuntary movements of the limbs, mental deterioration, and death within 15 years of onset. Symptoms appear between 30 and 50 years of age.

Porphyria
A genetic disorder inherited as a dominant trait that leads to intermittent attacks of pain and dementia, with symptoms first appearing in adulthood.

TABLE 4.5		
Some Mitochondrial Traits		
TRAIT	**PHENOTYPE**	**MIM/OMIM NUMBER**
Kearns-Sayre Syndrome	Short stature, retinal degeneration	530000
Leber optic atrophy (LHON)	Loss of vision in center of visual field, adult onset	535000
MELAS Syndrome	Episodes of vomiting, seizures, and stroke-like episodes	540000
MERRF Syndrome	Deficiencies in the enzyme complexes associated with energy transfer	545000
Oncocytoma	Benign tumors of the kidney	553000

Exploring Membranes

ANNE WALTER

While growing up it seemed to me that a biologist could be only a physician or a quintessential naturalist with sensible shoes, binoculars, and field notebook. Yet even though I loved biology, neither of these futures felt right. Fortunately, two wonderful teachers, Miss Hill and Miss Strosneider, taught biology in the Washington, D.C., public schools. With a paper chromatography experiment to extract plant pigments and a lab on enzymes that I remember to this day, these two remarkable teachers were the first to show me that the basis for much of biology was the precise and intricate interactions of specialized molecules. This was amazing! My interest must have showed, because I was encouraged to compete for an American Heart Association research opportunity that resulted in a summer at George Washington University working on lipid metabolism. Little did I expect lipids to be in my future.

My experiences in college helped me decide that I was interested in physiology and I started graduate studies with Maryanne Hughes, who wanted to understand how seagulls are able to drink seawater. These birds have several special adaptations including a gland that secretes an incredibly salty solution after they've had a salty drink. I had learned that because water permeability across cell membranes is high, cells equilibrate rapidly with their external medium. So why didn't the seagull salt glands rapidly lose water and shrink? I concluded that there must be something unusual about their membrane lipids and went on to study at Duke University in a department that specialized in membranes. My research problem was to define the permeability properties of the lipid bilayer in the absence of protein. My results confirmed that hydrophobic solutes like CO_2, ethanol, and aspirin all penetrate the membrane rapidly, whereas hydrophilic molecules such as glucose or amino acids penetrate very slowly. Part of my research was to test our methods thoroughly to ensure our values reflected the true permeabilities, allowing us to be very confident in our conclusion that the membrane behaves like a hydrocarbon that is very constrained . . . like an oil, but not like an oil. One potential application of this research may be a phospholipid "sponge" for cleaning up hydrocarbon pollutants. If lipid bilayers can be a sponge to soak up other molecules they can also release molecules. This idea is being used by the cosmetics and pharmaceutical industries to develop phospholipid dispersions as safe, slow-release systems.

My current research asks whether the behavior of transmembrane proteins is affected by their environment. With Neal Rote's research group at Wright State University, I have helped explore the possibility that the autoimmune disease called "antiphospholipid antibody syndrome" might be due to antibodies against phosphatidylserine that react when this lipid is exposed on the outside of the cell during platelet activation and possibly during placenta formation. I never would have guessed that expertise with membranes and lipids would be important in trying to figure out a disease process that has as one of its main symptoms blood clotting disorders and poor placental development.

Lipid bilayers are essential to all living cells. In fact, it has been suggested that the "primordial soup" contained lipids that spontaneously formed closed vesicles and bilayer surfaces that both protected and concentrated the protoenzymes as one of the first steps in the origin of living cells. Discovering the molecular basis for these properties is a puzzle that is turning out to be quite exciting to put together.

ANNE WALTER *is an associate professor in the Biology Department of St. Olaf College in Northfield, Minnesota. She received a B.A. in biology in 1973 from Grinnell College in Iowa and a Ph.D. in physiology and pharmacology in 1981 from Duke University, North Carolina.*

episodes of seizures, intense physical pain, dementia, and psychosis. These symptoms rarely appear before puberty and usually appear in middle age. King George III, the British monarch during the American revolution, may have suffered from porphyria (▬ Figure 4.25). He had a major attack in 1788 at the age of 50 years. He became delirious and suffered convulsions. His physical condition soon improved, but he remained irrational and confused. Early in 1789 his mental functions spontaneously improved, although his physicians took the credit. Later, after two more episodes, the

king was replaced on the throne by his son George IV. He died years later, blind and senile. The 1994 movie, "The Madness of King George," is a fictionalized account of how porphyria affected King George, his family, and the politics of Great Britain.

Penetrance and Expressivity

The terms *penetrance* and *expressivity* define two different aspects of variation in gene expression. **Penetrance** is the probability that a disease phenotype will appear when a disease-related genotype is present. If all individuals carrying the gene for a dominant disorder have the mutant phenotype, the gene is said to have 100% penetrance. If only 25% of those carrying the mutant gene show the mutant phenotype, the penetrance is 25%. Both genetic and environmental factors can affect penetrance. **Expressivity** refers to the range of phenotypic variation that is present. For example, an inherited disorder such as cystic fibrosis can have severe or mild symptoms.

The autosomal dominant trait, **camptodactyly** (MIM/OMIM 114200), is caused by the improper attachment of muscles to bones in the little finger. The result is an immobile, bent little finger. In some people, both little fingers are bent; in others, only one finger is affected; and in a small percentage of cases, neither finger is affected, even though a mutant allele is present (➥ Figure 4.26). Since the trait is dominant, all heterozygotes and homozygotes should be affected on both hands. The pedigree shows that one individual (III-4) is not affected even though he passed the trait to his offspring.

Penetrance can be assessed only by examining a population of individuals. The pedigree in Figure 4.27 shows that nine people must carry the dominant allele for camptodactyly, but phenotypic expression is seen only in eight, giving 8/9, or 88%, penetrance. This is only an estimate because II-1, II-2, and III-1 produced no offspring and could also carry the dominant gene with no penetrance. Many more samples from other pedigrees would be necessary to establish a reliable figure for penetrance of this gene.

Expressivity defines the *degree* of expression for a given trait. In the pedigree for camptodactyly, some individuals are affected on the left hand, others on the right hand; in one case both hands are affected; in another, neither hand is affected. This variable gene expression results from interactions with other genes and with nongenetic factors in the environment.

➥ FIGURE 4.25

King George III of Great Britain (1738–1820) was probably afflicted with porphyria, a genetic disorder that appears in adulthood and affects behavior.

Penetrance
The probability that a disease phenotype will appear when a disease-related genotype is present.

Expressivity
The range of phenotypes resulting from a given genotype.

Camptodactyly
A dominant human genetic trait that is expressed as immobile, bent little fingers.

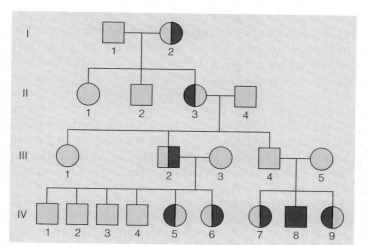

➥ FIGURE 4.26

Penetrance and expressivity. This pedigree shows the transmission of camptodactyly in a family. Those with two affected hands are shown as a fully shaded symbol. Those affected only in the left hand are indicated by shading the left half of the symbol, and those affected only in the right hand have the right half of the symbol shaded. Symbols without shading indicate unaffected family members.

Pleiotropy

Many genetic disorders have multiple phenotypic effects that are seemingly unrelated. In Marfan syndrome mutation of a single gene produces a weakened aorta, nearsightedness, and malformations of the sternum, or breastbone. Genes that produce several effects that seem unrelated are called *pleiotropic* genes, and the phenomenon is known as **pleiotropy.**

Sickle cell anemia produces a wide range of defects and is another example of a pleiotropic gene. The phenotype in sickle cell anemia includes changes in the shape of red blood cells, intense pain, skin ulcers, weakness, and early death. The range of symptoms exhibited in pleiotropy usually arises from a single gene defect but is ultimately the result of developmental and environmental interactions. Pleiotropic effects are the rule rather than the exception in human genetics.

The variations in gene expression that we have discussed are all the result of the relationship between a gene and the mechanisms that produce the gene's phenotype. The inheritance of these genes follows the predictable pattern worked out by Mendel for traits in the pea plant, but expression can be complicated by factors that include temperature and age.

LINKAGE AND GENETIC MAPS

There are 50,000 to 100,000 genes distributed on the 24 human chromosomes (22 autosomes and the X and the Y chromosome). Each chromosome carries many genes, all arranged in a linear order along the chromosome. Genes present on the same chromosome are said to show **linkage,** because they tend to be inherited together. Although linked genes *tend* to be inherited together, they *do* separate from each other in some offspring because of crossing over between homologous chromosomes (Figure 4.27). Early in this century, Alfred Sturtevant, working with the fruit fly, *Drosophila*, realized that the further apart two genes are on a chromosome, the greater the chance that they will be separated by crossing over. He concluded that the amount of crossing over between genes can be used to determine the order and distance between genes on a chromosome, producing a genetic map.

In a **genetic map,** genes are arranged in a linear order, and the distance between any two genes is measured by how frequently crossing over takes place between them (Figure 4.28). In other words, genetic distance is measured by the frequency of recombination between loci on the same chromosome. The units are expressed as percentage of recombination, with 1 map unit equal to a frequency of 1% recombination. (This unit is also known as a *centimorgan,* or *cM*). Remember, it is possible to construct genetic maps only because linked genes separate from each other by crossing over during meiosis. How often this event happens depends on the distance between the genes. The farther apart two genes are on a chromosome, the more likely it is that a crossover event will separate them. Conversely, the closer together two genes are on a chromosome, the less frequently they will be separated by a crossover event.

 Figure 4.29 shows a pedigree in which linkage is indicated between the gene for the ABO blood group (the *I* locus, (MIM/OMIM 110300) and a condition called nail-patella syndrome (MIM/OMIM 161200). Nail-patella syndrome is an autosomal dominant condition associated with deformities in the nails and kneecaps. In this pedigree, the B allele (I^B) and the allele for nail-patella syndrome occur together in I-2. In generations II and III, these two alleles tend to be inherited together. Individuals with type B blood tend to have nail-patella syndrome. In generation II, the B allele and the nail patella allele show linkage in II-1, II-2, II-5, II-6 and II-14. In generation III, the two alleles are linked in III-1 and III-2. But type B blood and nail-patella syndrome are not *always* inherited together. Examination of the pedigree shows that 2 of the 16 individuals have inherited one of the two alleles, but not both (individuals II-8 and III-3). This separation of the two alleles is the result of recombination be-

Pleiotropy
The appearance of several apparently unrelated phenotypic effects caused by a single gene.

Linkage
A condition in which two or more genes do not show independent assortment. Rather, they tend to be inherited together. Such genes are located on the same chromosome. By measuring the degree of recombination between such genes, the distance between them can be determined.

Genetic map
The arrangement and distance between genes on a chromosome deduced from studies of genetic recombination.

ABO groups
Three alleles of a gene on human chromosome 9 that specify the presence and/or identity of certain molecules on the surface of red blood cells.

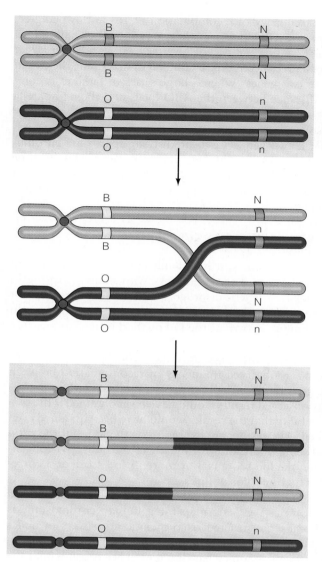

■ FIGURE 4.27 (left)

Crossing over between homologous chromosomes during meiosis involves the exchange of chromosome parts. In this case, crossing over between the genes for blood type (alleles B, O, of gene I) and nail-patella syndrome (N) produce new allele combinations. The frequency of crossing over is proportional to the distance between the genes, allowing a genetic map for this region of the chromosome to be constructed.

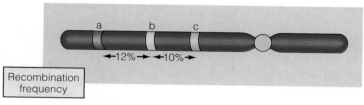

Recombination frequency

■ FIGURE 4.28 (above)

Linked genes are carried on the same chromosome. Recombination frequencies can be used to construct genetic maps, giving the order and distance between genes.

■ FIGURE 4.29

Linkage between nail-patella syndrome and the ABO blood type locus. Shaded symbols in this pedigree represent those with nail-patella syndrome, an autosomal dominant trait. Genotypes for the ABO locus are shown below each symbol. Nail-patella syndrome and the B allele are present in I-2, they tend to be inherited together in this family, and they are identified as linked genes. Individuals marked with an asterisk (II-8 and III-3) inherited the nail-patella allele or the B allele alone. This separation of the two alleles occurred by recombination.

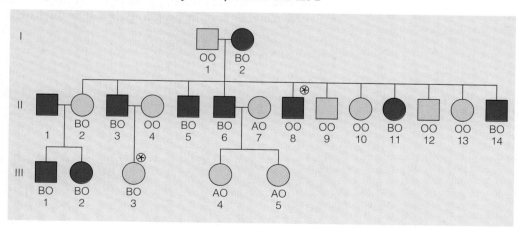

tween the two genes. From the frequency of recombination (2/16) in this pedigree, the distance between the gene for the ABO locus and the gene controlling nail-patella syndrome can be calculated as 12.5 map units. For accuracy, either a much larger pedigree or many more small pedigrees need to be examined to determine the extent of recombination between these two genes. When a large series of families is combined in an analysis, the map distance between the ABO locus and the nail-patella locus is about 10 units.

Mapping by observing crossovers is more accurate when the two genes being studied are relatively close together. If two genes are located so far apart on a chromosome that they undergo crossing over 50% of the time, the results would be the same as independent assortment. As a result, mapping can directly measure distances of less than 50 map units. Longer distances can be mapped by adding together the distances between intermediate loci.

 ## LINKAGE ANALYSIS AND LOD SCORES

In many, if not most, human linkage studies, it is difficult to establish linkage and measure genetic distance between genes. Large pedigrees with many offspring in three or more generations in which two genetic disorders are present are rare. In most cases, pedigrees cover three generations—the grandparents, parents, and children. In these situations, a statistical technique known as the **lod method** is used to measure the distance between genes.

This measurement is done with computer programs (like LINKMAP) designed to carry out linkage analysis. First, an observed frequency of recombination between two genes is derived from pedigree studies. Then the program calculates two probabilities: the probability that the observed results would have been obtained if the two genes were linked and the probability that the results would have been obtained even if the two genes were *not* linked. The results are expressed as the $\log_{10}$ of the *ratio* of the two probabilities, or lod score (*lod* stands for the log of the odds). By convention, linkage is established when the lod score is 3 or more. A lod score of 3 corresponds to odds of at least 1000 to 1 in favor of linkage.

Using both pedigree analysis and lod scores, genetic maps have been constructed for all of the human chromosomes. A genetic map for a human chromosome is shown in ● Figure 4.30. The map constructed from meiotic crossovers in males gives the same order as a map constructed using crossovers in females, but the distance between genes in the two maps is somewhat different. The reason is that the frequency of crossovers is different in males and females, and genetic maps, of course, are based on the frequency of crossovers. The reasons for the difference in recombination frequency between males and females are not yet understood.

Newer methods of mapping use recombinant DNA techniques to map human chromosomes. These methods, along with linkage mapping, are part of the Human Genome Project, an international effort to map all the genes in the human genome. These methods and the project itself will be discussed in Chapter 13.

Lod method
A probability technique used to determine whether genes are linked.

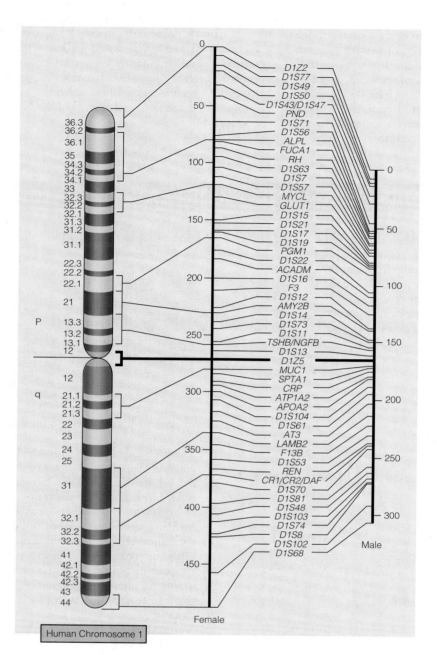

FIGURE 4.30

Genetic map of human chromosome 1. At the left is a drawing of the chromosome. The two vertical lines at the right represent genetic maps derived from studies of recombination in males and females. Between the genetic maps are the order and location of 58 loci, some of which are genes (red) and others (blue) that are genetic markers detected using recombinant DNA techniques. The map in females is about 500 cM long, and in males it is just over 300 cM. This is a result of differences in the frequency of crossing over in males and females. This map provides a framework for locating genes on the chromosome as part of the Human Genome Project.

SUMMARY

1. The inheritance of single gene traits in humans is often referred to as Mendelian inheritance because of the pattern of segregation within families. These traits produce phenotypic ratios similar to those observed by Mendel in the pea plant. While the results of studies in peas and humans may be similar, the methods are somewhat different. Instead of direct experimental crosses, human traits are traced by the construction of pedigrees that follow a trait through several generations of a family.

2. Information in the pedigree is used to determine the mode of inheritance. These modes include autosomal dominant, autosomal recessive, X-linked dominant, X-linked recessive, and Y-linked.

3. The results of pedigree analysis depend on the distribution of alleles via gametes from parent to child. Since the number of offspring is usually small, large deviations from expected ratios of segregation are often encountered. This effect can be controlled by examining pedigrees from a large number of families and pooling the information from many sources to confirm the mode of inheritance for a given trait.

4. Guidelines for pedigree analysis can be used to determine if a trait is inherited in an autosomal recessive fashion. Other guidelines can be used to establish whether a trait has an autosomal dominant, X-linked recessive, X-linked dominant, or mitochondrial pattern of inheritance.
5. Several factors can alter an expected pattern of inheritance, including the age of onset, penetrance, expressivity, pleiotropy, and environmental interactions.
6. Genes on the same chromosome tend to be inherited together, and are called linked genes. Within limits, the amount of recombination between two genes can be used to measure the distance between genes, creating genetic maps of chromosomes. Maps of all the human chromosomes are being prepared as part of the Human Genome Project.

QUESTIONS AND PROBLEMS

1. What is the main reason that pedigree charts are used?
2. Pedigree analysis permits all of the following except:
   a. an orderly presentation of family information
   b. the determination of whether a trait is genetic
   c. whether a trait is dominant or recessive
   d. which gene is involved in a heritable disorder
   e. whether a trait is X-linked or autosomal
3. Define the following pedigree symbols:

4. Identify the mode of inheritance suggested by the following pedigree:

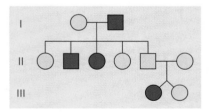

5. What mode of inheritance is suggested by the following pedigree?

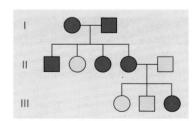

6. Does the indicated individual (III-5) show the trait in question?

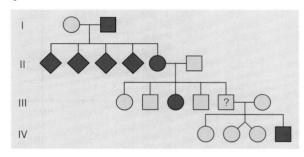

7. a. Construct a pedigree based on the following information:
   1. The proband (affected individual that led to the construction of the pedigree) exhibits the trait.
   2. neither her husband nor her only sibling, an older brother) exhibit the trait.
   3. the proband has five children by her current husband: the oldest is a boy, followed by a girl, then another boy, and then identical twin girls. Only the second oldest fails to exhibit the trait.
   4. the parents of the proband both show the trait.
   b. Determine the mode of inheritance of the trait (go step by step to examine each possible mode of inheritance).
   c. Can you deduce the genotype of the proband's husband for this trait?
8. What is the mode of inheritance of this autosomal trait and why?

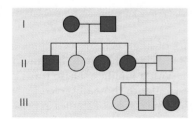

9. In the following pedigree, assume that the father of the proband is homozygous for the trait in question. Explain a mode of inheritance consistent with this pedigree. In particular, explain the phenotype of the proband.

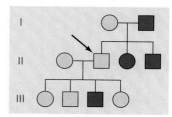

10. Using the following pedigree:

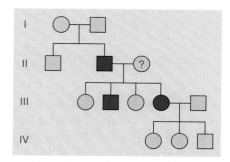

   a. Deduce a compatible mode of inheritance.
   b. Identify the genotype of the individual in question.
11. From the pedigrees illustrated below, choose the one consistent with the following human diseases/conditions: a) ocular-cutaneous albinism, b) Marfan syndrome, c) camptodactly.

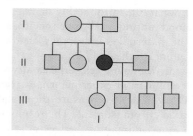

I.

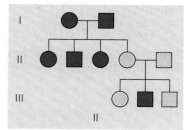

II.

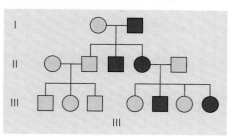

III.

12. List and describe two diesease inherited in the following fashion:
   a. autosomal dominant
   b. autosomal recessive
13. The X and Y chromosomes are structurally and genetically distinct. However, they do pair during meiosis at a small region near the tips of their short arms, indicating that the chromosomes are homologous in this region. If a gene lies in this region, will its mode of transmission be sex-linked or autosomal? Why?
14. A young boy is colorblind. His one brother and five sisters are not. The boy has three maternal uncles and four maternal aunts. None of his uncles' children or grandchildren are colorblind. One of the maternal aunts married a colorblind man, and half of her children, both male and female, are colorblind. The other aunts married men with normal color vision. All their daughters have normal vision, but half their sons are colorblind.
   a. Which of the boy's four grandparents transmitted the gene for colorblindness?
   b. Are any of the boy's aunts or uncles colorblind?
   c. Are either of the boy's parents colorblind?
15. The following is a pedigree for a common genetic trait. Analyze the pedigree to determine whether the trait is inherited as an:
   a. autosomal dominant
   b. autosomal recessive
   c. X-linked dominant
   d. X-linked recessive
   e. Y linked

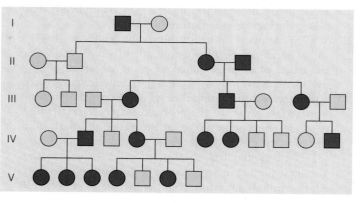

16. As a genetic counselor investigating a genetic disorder in a family, you are able to collect a four generation pedigree that details the inheritance of the disorder in question. Analyze the information in the pedigree to determine whether the trait is inherited as an:
    a. autosomal dominant
    b. autosomal recessive
    c. X-linked dominant
    d. X-linked recessive
    e. Y-linked

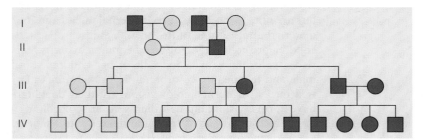

17. Define penetrance and expressivity.
18. Suppose that space explorers discover an alien species that has the same genetic principles that apply to humans. Although all 19 aliens analyzed to date carry a gene for a third eye, only 15 display this phenotype. What is the penetrance of the third eye gene in this population?
19. A genetic disorder characterized by falling asleep in genetics lectures is known to be 20% penetrant. All 90 students in a genetics class are homozygous for this gene. How many of the 90 students will theoretically fall asleep during the next lecture?
20. Why are humans difficult subjects for genetic analysis?
21. A proband suffering from an unidentified disease seeks the advice of a genetic counselor prior to starting a family. Based on the following data, the counselor constructs a pedigree encompassing three generations: (1) The maternal grandfather of the proband suffers from the disease. (2) The mother of the proband is unaffected and is the youngest of five children, the three oldest being male. (3) The proband has an affected older sister, but the youngest siblings are unaffected twins (boy and girl). (4) All individuals suffering from the disease have been revealed. Duplicate the counselor's feat.
22. The father of 12 children begins to show symptoms of neurofibromatosis.
    a. What is the probability that Sam, the man's second oldest son (II-2), will suffer from the disease if he lives a normal life span? (Sam's mother and her ancestors do not have the disease.)
    b. Can you infer anything about the presence of the disease in Sam's paternal grandparents?
23. The only daughter of an only son has blood serum possessing antibodies directed against type A and type B blood. Her mother possesses type A antigens. Her paternal grandfather possesses antibodies to type B blood, and he can neither give nor receive blood from his wife due to ABO incompatibility. However, their son can donate blood to either of them. Construct a pedigree containing this information, and include ABO genotypes.
24. A hypothetical human trait is controlled by a single gene. Four alleles of this gene have been identified: a, b, c, and d. Alleles a, b, and c are all codominant; allele d is recessive to all other alleles.
    a. How many phenotypes are possible?
    b. How many genotypes are possible?
25. A 54-year-old man begins showing signs of Huntington disease. His daughter is 29 years old and has three children. What is the probability that her youngest child will develop Huntington disease if neither the father's family nor the maternal grandmother has the disease? (Assume a long life for the child.)
26. How can dominant lethal alleles survive in a population?
27. A recombination experiment is carried out in the fruit fly, Drosophila, to measure the distance between two genes on chromosome 2. The results indicate that there is 58% recombination between the two loci. Are these genes linked?
28. The frequency of recombination between gene A and gene B is 8%; between gene B and gene C the frequency is 12%, and between gene A and gene C the frequency is 4%. From this information, deduce the gene order.

1. Muscular dystrophies are a group of hereditary disorders characterized by muscle weakness and wasting and are distinguished from one another by clinical and genetic patterns. Duchenne muscular dystrophy (DMD) is the most common and most serious form of muscular dystrophy. It is an X-linked recessive condition, and affects primarily males carrying the mutant gene on their X chromosome. At birth, clinical symptoms are typically mild, and therefore often overlooked. Diagnosis is usually made by the age of three years, when more severe manifestations appear. The gene for DMD has been isolated and prenatal testing is available.

   a. Why are males primarily affected with this condition? If a woman carries the gene for DMD, what are the chances that her sons will inherit the mutant gene? Prenatal diagnosis for DMD allows couples to know before birth whether their child carries the gene for DMD. Should parents end a pregnancy if they know the child carries the gene for DMD? Why or Why not? Is this a form of eugenics?

   b. Before the development of recombinant DNA techniques, women with a history of DMD in their family relied upon ultrasound and karyotype analysis for sex determination. If the woman was a known carrier and her fetus was a male, the dif-

ficult decision of terminating the pregnancy had to be made. In this situation the woman had to take the risk of terminating a genotypically normal male. What was her chance of terminating a genotypically normal male? Do you think new DNA technology has enabled couples to make a more informed decision about their reproductive options or increased the difficulty in making reproductive decisions? Explain your reasoning.

2. In the 18th century a young boy suffered from a skin condition known as ichthyosis hystrix gravior. The phenotype of this disorder includes thickening of skin and the formation of loose spines that are periodically sloughed off. This "porcupine man" married and had six sons, all of whom had this same condition. He also had several daughters, all of whom were unaffected. In all succeeding generations, this condition was passed on from father to son. What can you theorize about the location of the gene that causes ichthyosis hystrix gravior.

3. Huntington disease is a rare, fatal disease, usually developing in the fourth or fifth decade of life. It is caused by a single dominant autosomal allele. A phenotypically normal man in his twenties, who has a two year old son of his own, learns that his father has developed Huntington disease. What is the probability that he himself will develop the disease? What is the chance that his young son might eventually develop the disease?

The following activities use the resources of the World Wide Web to enhance the topics covered in this chapter. To investigate the topics described below, log on to the book's home page at:

http://www.wadsworth.com/biology

1. Online Mendelian Inheritance in Man (OMIM) is an online catalog of human genetic disorders that is updated daily. For any given genetic disorder, information on clinical features, mode of inheritance, molecular genetics, diagnosis, therapies, and more is presented.

   a. Access OMIM through the homepage, and select a genetic disorder mentioned in the chapter and read the material to supplement the information provided in the chapter.

   b. OMIM also contains information about human traits not associated with disease, such as eye color,

handedness, uncontrolled sneezing (the achoo syndrome), alteration of taste senations, earlobe creases, cleft chins, earwax, baldness, and many more. Access OMIM and read the material about one or more of these traits.

2. Information about genetic disorders, support groups and organizations is available on the World Wide Web. If you, a member of your family or someone you know has a genetic disorder, information about the disorder, treatments, and parent groups can be accessed. If you are interested in a genetic disorder, the book's homepage has a link to a listing of genetic support groups. Write to one of these groups to obtain more information about a specific genetic disorder.

Cawthon, R. M., Weiss, R., Xu, G., Viskochil, D., Culver, M., Stevens, J., Robertson, M., Dunn, D., Gesteland, R., O'Connell, P., and White, R. 1990. A major segment of the neurofibromatosis type 1 gene: cDNA sequence, genomic structure, and point mutations. *Cell* 62: 193–201.

Collins, F. S., Ponder, B. A., Seizinger, B. R., and Epstein, C. J. 1989. The von Recklinghausen neurofibromatosis region on chromosome 17: Genetic and physical maps come into focus. *Am. J. Hum. Genet. 44:* 1–5.

Eaton, W., and Hofrichter, J. 1995. The biophysics of sickle cell hydrozyurea therapy. *Science 268:* 1142–1143.

Embury, S. H. 1986. The clinical pathology of sickle cell disease. *Ann. Rev. Med.* 37:361–376.

Francomano, C. A., Le, P. L., and Pyeritz, R. E. 1988. Molecular genetic studies in achondroplasia. *Basic Life Sci.* 48: 53–58.

Huntington's Disease Collaborative Research Group. 1993. A novel gene containing a trinucleotide repeat that is expanded and unstable on Huntington's disease chromosomes. *Cell 72:* 971–983.

Kinnear, P. E., Jay, B., and Witkop, C. J., Jr. 1985. Albinism. Surv. *Ophthalmol. 30:* 75–101.

Lucky, P. A., and Nordlund, J. J. 1985. The biology of the pigmentary system and its disorders. *Dermatol. Clin. 3:* 197–216.

Macalpine, I., and Hunter, R. 1969. Porphyria and King George III. *Sci. Am.* 221 (July):38–46.

Peltonen, L. and Kainulainen, K. 1992. Elucidation of the gene defect in Marfan syndrome. Success by two complementary research strategies. *FEBS Letters 307:* 116–121.

Prockop, D. J. 1985. Mutations in collagen genes: Consequences for rare and common diseases. *J. Clin. Invest. 75:* 783–787.

Ramirez, F., Sangiorgi, F. O., and Tsipouras, P. 1986. Human collagens: Biochemical, molecular and genetic features in normal and diseased states. *Horiz. Biochem. Biophys. 8:* 341–375.

Rommens, J. M., Iannuzzi, M. C., Bat-Sheva, K., Drumm, M. L., Melmer, G., Dean, M., Rozmahel, R., Cole, J. L., Kennedy, D., Hidaka, N., Zsiga, M., Buchwald, M., Riordan, J. R., Tsui, L. C., and Collins, F. S. 1989. Identification of the cystic fibrosis gene: Chromosome walking and jumping. *Science 245:* 1059–1065.

Rouleau, G. A., Wertelecki, W., Haines, J. L., Hobbs, W., Trofatter, J. A., Seizinger, B., Martuza, R., Superneau, D., Conneally, P. M., and Gusella, J. 1987. Genetic linkage of bilateral acoustic neurofibromatosis to a DNA marker on chromosome 22. *Nature 329:* 246–248.

Smithies, O. 1993. Animal models of human genetic diseases. *Trends Genet. 9:* 112–116.

Stanbury, J. B., Wyngaarden, J. B., and Fredrickson, D. S. 1983. *The Metabolic Basis of Inherited Disease.* 5th ed. New York: McGraw-Hill.

Stern, C. 1973. *Principles of Human Genetics.* 3d ed. San Francisco: Freeman.

Stokes, R. W. 1986. Neurofibromatosis: A review of the literature. *J. Am. Osteopath. Assoc. 86:* 49–52.

Tsipouras, P., and Ramirez, F. 1987. Genetic disorders of collagen. *J. Med. Genet. 24:* 2–8.

Wallace, M. R., Marchuk, D. A., Anderson, L. B., Letcher, R., Odeh, H. M., Saulino, A. M., Fountain, J. W., Brereton, A., Nicholson, J., Mitchell, A. L., Brownstein, B. H., and Collins, F. S. 1990. Type 1 neurofibromatosis gene: identification of a large transcript disrupted in three NF1 patients. *Science 249:* 181–186.

Welsh, M. and Smith, A. 1995. Cystic fibrosis. *Sci. Amer. 273:* 52–59.

Worton, R. 1995. Muscular dystrophies: diseases of the dystrophin-glycoportein complex. *Science 270:* 755–756.

Yoshida, A. 1982. Biochemical genetics of the human blood group ABO system. *Am. J. Hum. Genet. 34:* 1–14.

POLYGENES AND MULTIFACTORIAL INHERITANCE

Chapter 5

Chapter Outline

SOME TRAITS ARE CONTROLLED BY
   TWO OR MORE GENES
POLYGENES AND VARIATION IN
   PHENOTYPE
The Additive Model for Polygenic
   Inheritance
Averaging Out the Phenotype: Regression to
   the Mean
POLYGENES AND THE ENVIRONMENT:
   MULTIFACTORIAL TRAITS
Threshold Effects and the Expression of
   Multifactorial Traits

Estimating the Interaction between Genotype
   and Environment
HERITABILITY MEASURES
   PHENOTYPIC VARIATION
CONCEPTS AND CONTROVERSIES   *Baseball
   Genes and Baseball Environment*
Using Fingerprints to Estimate Heritability
Twin Studies and Multifactorial Traits
The Biology of Twins
Concordance and Twins
Using Twins to Study Obesity

CONCEPTS AND CONTROVERSIES   *Twins,
   Quintuplets, and Armadillos*
Genetic Clues to Obesity
SIDEBAR   *Leptin and Female Athletes*
A SURVEY OF SOME MULTIFACTORIAL
   TRAITS
Cardiovascular Disease Has Genetic and
   Environmental Components
Skin Color Is a Polygenic Trait
Intelligence and IQ: Are They Related?
The Controversy about IQ and Race

OPENING IMAGE
*Analysis of polygenic traits in twins is an
important method in genetic analysis.*

I n 1713, a new king was crowned in Prussia, and began one of the largest military buildups of the 18th century. In the space of 20 years King Frederick William I, ruler of fewer than 2 million citizens, enlarged his army from around 38,000 men to just under 100,000 troops. Compare this situation to that in the neighboring kingdom of Austria, which had a population of 20 million, and an army of just under 100,000

men, and you will understand why Frederick William was regarded as a military monomaniac. The crowning glory of his military machine was the king's personal guard, known as the Potsdam Grenadier Guards. This unit was composed of the tallest men obtainable. Frederick William was obsessed with having giants in this guard, and his recruiters used bribery, kidnapping, and smuggling to fill the ranks of this unit. It is said that members of the guard could lock arms while marching on either side of the king's carriage. Many members were close to 7 feet tall. Although in professional basketball a height of 7 feet is not much of a novelty, in 18th-century Prussia anyone taller than about 5 feet 4 inches was above average height.

Frederick William was also rather miserly, and because this recruiting was costing him millions, he decided it would be more economical to simply breed giants to serve in his elite unit. To accomplish this, he ordered that every tall man in the kingdom was to marry a tall, robust woman, with the expectation that the offspring would all be giants. Unfortunately this idea was a frustrating failure. Not only was it slow, but most of the children were shorter than their parents. While continuing this breeding program, Frederick William reverted to kidnapping and bounties, and he also let it be known that the best way for foreign governments to gain his favor was to send giants to be members of his guard. This human breeding experiment continued until shortly after Frederick William's death in 1740, when his son, Frederick the Great, disbanded the Potsdam Guards.

SOME TRAITS ARE CONTROLLED BY TWO OR MORE GENES

What exactly went wrong with Frederick William's experiment in human genetics? Selecting the tallest men and women as parents should result in tall children. We have the advantage of knowing that when Mendel intercrossed true-breeding tall pea plants, the offspring were all tall. Even when heterozygous tall pea plants are crossed, three-fourths of the offspring are tall.

The problem is that height in pea plants is controlled by a single gene pair, while in humans, height is determined by several gene pairs and is a **polygenic trait**. The tall and short phenotypes in pea plants are two distinct phenotypes, and are examples of **discontinuous variation**. In measuring height in humans, it is difficult to set up only two phenotypes. Instead, height in humans is an example of **continuous variation**. Unlike Mendel's pea plants, people are not either 18 in. or 84 in. tall; they fall into a series of overlapping phenotypic classes. Traits with a gradation of phenotypes are often controlled by two or more separate gene pairs.

Understanding the distinction between discontinuous and continuous traits was an important advance in genetics, and is based on acceptance of the idea that genes interact with each other and with the environment. All genes can interact with the environment, and they differ only in the degree of this interaction. **Multifactorial traits** are those that involve two or more genes and strong interaction with the environment.

In this chapter, we will examine traits controlled by genes at two or more loci and consider how nongenetic factors such as the environment affect gene expression. The degree of genetic effects on a trait can be estimated by measuring *heritability*. We will consider this concept and the use of twins as a means of measuring the heritability of a trait. In the last part of the chapter we will examine a number of human polygenic traits, some of which have been the subject of political and social controversy.

Polygenic trait
A phenotype that is dependent upon the action of a number of genes.

Discontinuous variation
Phenotypes that fall into two or more distinct, nonoverlapping classes.

Continuous variation
A distribution of phenotypic characters that is distributed from one extreme to another in an overlapping, or continuous, fashion.

Multifactorial traits
Traits that result from the interaction of one or more environmental factors and two or more genes.

POLYGENES AND VARIATION IN PHENOTYPE

Mendel was not the only scientist in the late 19th century experimenting with the inheritance of traits. In one series of experiments, Josef Kölreuter crossed tall and dwarf tobacco plants. The F_1 plants were all intermediate in height to the parents. When self-crossed, the F_1 produced an F_2 that contained plants of many different heights. Some of the F_2 were as tall or short as the parents, but most of the F_2 were intermediate in height when compared with the parents (Figure 5.1). Mendel's results with pea plants, however, produced evidence of discontinuous variation (Figure 5.1).

Shortly after the turn of the century, traits in a variety of organisms were found to show continuous variation in phenotype. In each of these cases, the offspring had a phenotype that seemed to be a blend of the parental traits. Analyzing these results, geneticists debated whether the phenomenon of continuous variation could be reconciled with the inheritance of Mendelian factors, or whether this apparent blending of traits signaled the existence of another mechanism of inheritance. This argument is of importance to human genetics because many human traits and many genetic disorders show continuous variation.

In the years immediately after the rediscovery of Mendel's work only a few traits were known in humans, and these were controlled by single genes. At the time, interest in human genetics was largely centered on discovering whether "social" traits such as alcoholism, feeblemindedness, and criminal behavior were inherited. Some

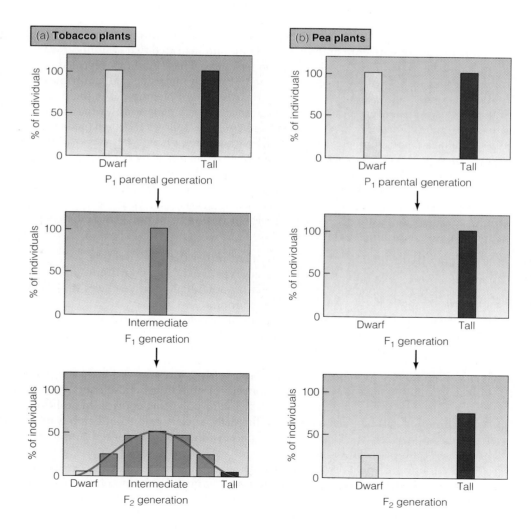

 FIGURE 5.1

A comparison of traits with continuous and discontinuous phenotypes. (a) Histograms showing the percentage of plants with different heights in crosses between tall and dwarf strains of tobacco plants carried to the F_2 generation. The F_1 generation is intermediate to the parents in height, and the F_2 shows a range of phenotypes from dwarf to tall. Most plants have a height intermediate to those of the P_1 generation. (b) Histograms showing the percentage of plants with different heights in crosses between tall and dwarf strains of the pea plant. The F_1 generation has the tall phenotype, and the F_2 has two distinct phenotypic classes; 75% of the offspring are tall, and 25% are dwarf. The differences between tobacco plants and pea plants are explained by the fact that height in tobacco plants is controlled by two or more gene pairs, while in peas, height is controlled by a single gene.

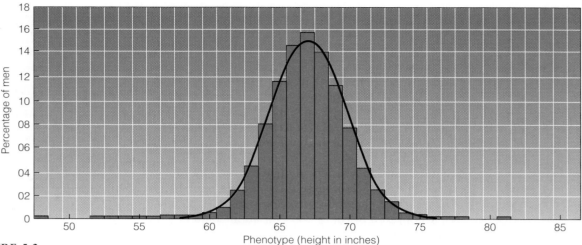

FIGURE 5.2

A bell-shaped or "normal" curve shows the distribution of phenotypes for traits controlled by two or more genes. A normal curve is characterized by few individuals at the extremes of the phenotype, with most individuals clustered around the average value. In this case, the phenotype is height measured in a population of human males.

geneticists simply assumed that these traits were controlled by single genes, and constructed pedigrees accordingly. Other geneticists pointed out that these traits were not inherited in the phenotypic ratios observed in experimental organisms, and discounted the importance of Mendelian inheritance in humans. In fact, the biomathematician Karl Pearson is reported to have said that "there is no truth in Mendelism at all."

Between 1910 and 1930, the controversy over continuous variation was resolved. Experimental work with corn and tobacco plants demonstrated that continuous variation could be explained by Mendelian inheritance. These findings revealed that traits determined by a number of alleles, each of which makes a small contribution to the phenotype, will exhibit a continuous distribution of phenotypes in the F_2 generation. This is true even though the inheritance of each gene follows the rules of Mendelian inheritance. This distribution of phenotypes follows a bell-shaped curve, and contains a small number of individuals with exteme phenotypes (very short or very tall, for example). Most individuals, however, have phenotypes between the extremes; their distribution follows what statisticians call a "normal curve" (Figure 5.2). This pattern of inheritance—known as polygenic or quantitative inheritance—is additive, because each allele adds an incremental amount to the phenotype.

The continuous variation of phenotypes that results from polygenic inheritance has several distinguishing characteristics:

- Traits are usually quantified by measurement rather than by counting.
- Two or more genes contribute to the phenotype. Each gene contributes in an additive way to the phenotype. The effect of individual additive alleles may be small, with some alleles making no contribution.
- Phenotypic expression of polygenic and multifactorial traits varies within a wide range. This variation is produced by gene interaction and by environmental factors and is best analyzed in populations rather than in individuals (Figure 5.3).

Polygenic inheritance is an important concept in human genetics. Traits such as height, weight, skin color, and intelligence are under polygenic control. In addition, congenital malformations such as neural tube defects, cleft palate, and club foot as well as genetic disorders such as diabetes, hypertension, and behavioral disorders are polygenic, or multifactorial, traits.

The distribution of phenotypes and F_2 ratios in traits involving two, three, and four genes is shown in Figure 5.4. If the trait is controlled by two loci, there are five phenotypic classes in the F_2, each class having 4, 3, 2, 1, or 0 dominant alleles.

FIGURE 5.3

Skin color is a polygenic trait, and is controlled by three or four genes, producing a wide range of phenotypes. Environmental factors (exposure to the sun and weather) also contribute to the phenotypic variation.

The F_2 ratio of 1:4:6:4:1 results from the number of genotypic combinations that produce each phenotype. At each extreme are the homozygous dominant (*AABB*) and homozygous recessive (*aabb*) genotypes, having 4 and 0 dominant alleles respectively. The largest class (6/16) has 6 genotypic combinations of 2 dominant alleles. As the number of genes controlling the trait increases, and the amount of phenotypic variation increases because of environmental factors, the phenotypes blend together, generating a continuous distribution.

As the number of loci controlling a trait increases, the number of phenotypic classes increases. As the number of classes increases, there is less phenotypic difference between each class. This means that there is a greater chance for environmental factors to override the small difference between classes. For example, exposure to sunlight can alter skin color and obscure phenotypic differences.

FIGURE 5.4

The number of phenotypic classes in the F_2 generation increases as the number of genes controlling the trait increases. This relationship allows geneticists to estimate the number of genes involved in the expression of a polygenic trait. As the number of phenotypic classes increases, the distribution of phenotypes becomes a normal curve.

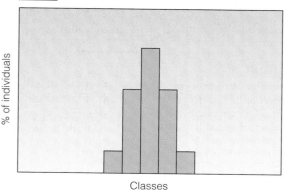

2 loci

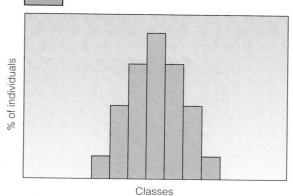

3 loci

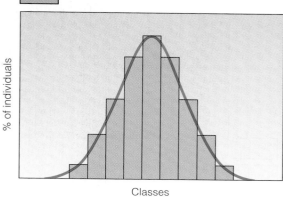

4 loci

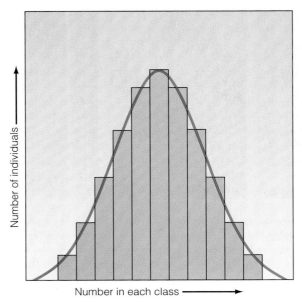

FIGURE 5.5

The results of phenotypic measurements in polygenic inheritance expressed as a frequency diagram, resulting from an interaction of polygenes with environmental factors.

The results of phenotypic measurements in polygenic inheritance are usually expressed as a frequency diagram. ▬ Figure 5.5 shows a frequency distribution for a polygenic trait.

The Additive Model for Polygenic Inheritance

To explain how polygenes contribute to a trait, and how genotypes contribute to variation in phenotypic expression, let's consider a model for polygenic inheritance. To simplify the analysis, the model will be examined assuming the following conditions:

- The trait is controlled by several loci. We will assume three loci, each with two alleles (A,a, B,b, C,c).
- The dominant alleles each make an equal contribution to the phenotype, and the recessive alleles make no contribution.
- The effect of each active (dominant) allele on the phenotype is small, and additive.
- The genes controlling the trait are not linked; they assort independently.

This model will be applied to the inheritance of height. In this model, we will assume that each dominant allele adds 3 inches to a base height of 5 ft. The recessive alleles a, b, and c add nothing to the base height. An individual with the genotype *aabbcc* is 5 ft tall, and someone with the genotype *AABBCC* is 6 ft 6 in. tall. If the environment acts equally on all genotypes, the average height (5 ft 9 in.) would be represented by those carrying three of the six possible dominant alleles.

▬ Figure 5.6a shows the genotypic frequencies and their phenotypes. With three alleles, there are seven phenotypic classes, having 6, 5, 4, 3, 2, 1, and 0 dominant al-

FIGURE 5.6

(a) The distribution of height in a three-gene model, where each dominant allele adds three inches above a base (homozygous recessive *aabbcc*) level of 5 ft. In this model, the phenotypic extremes are represented by 5 ft and 6 ft 6 in. (b) In reality, the interaction of genotypes with the environment produces a continuous distribution of phenotypes (height).

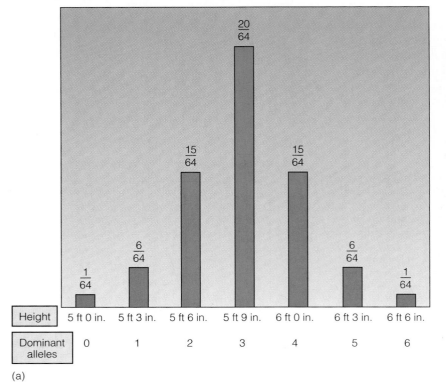

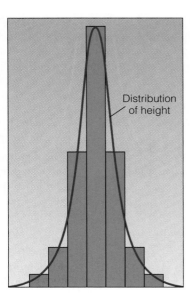

(a)

(b)

leles. In real-life situations, the action of environmental factors blurs the distinction between the phenotypic classes, producing the continuous variation in height that is actually observed (Figure 5.6b). The most frequent phenotype (with three dominant alleles) produces the average height of 5 ft 9 in. At either end of the phenotypic range, the frequencies decline, and only 1/64 of the individuals will be as short as 5 ft, or as tall as 6 ft 6 in.

In this example, and in polygenic traits in general, the genotype represents the genetic potential for height. Full expression of the genotype depends on the environment. Poor nutrition during childhood can result in someone not reaching their potential height. On the other hand, optimal nutrition from birth to adulthood cannot make someone taller than what is dictated by the genotype.

Averaging Out the Phenotype: Regression to the Mean

A distinguishing characteristic of polygenic traits is that most of the offspring of individuals with a phenotype from one of the extremes (tall x tall, for example) will have a less extreme phenotype. This phenomenon is known as **regression to the mean.**

As an example, let's look at King Frederick William's attempt to breed giants for his elite guard unit. We will assume that this breeding program used individuals at least 5 ft 9 in. tall. For simplicity, we'll also assume that the dominant alleles *A*, *B*, and *C* each add 3 in. above a base height of 5 ft 9 in., and the recessive alleles *a*, *b*, and *c* add nothing above the base height. An individual with the genotype *aabbcc* would be 5 ft 9 in. tall, and an individual with the genotype *AABBCC* would be 7 ft 3 in. tall.

Suppose that a 6 ft 9 in. member of the guard carrying the genotype *AaBbCC* mates with a 6 ft 3 in. woman with the genotype *AaBbcc*. The possible outcomes are diagrammed in ➡ Figure 5.7. In this case, there are four paternal and four maternal gamete combinations, and 16 possible types of fertilizations, with five phenotypic classes.

Regression to the mean
In a polygenic system, the tendency of offspring of parents with extreme differences in phenotype to exhibit a phenotype that is the average of the two parental phenotypes.

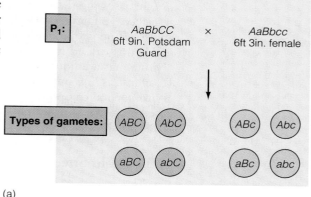

(a)

➡ **FIGURE 5.7**

A model for inheritance of height in the Potsdam Guards. In this example, the guards and their mates represent a subset of individuals in a population where height can range from 5 ft 9 in. (*aabbcc*) to 7 ft 3 in. (*AABBCC*). (a) Gametes produced by a 6 ft 9 in. male and a 6 ft 3 in. female. (b) Punnett square showing the 16 genotypic and 5 phenotypic combinations that result from fertilization of all combinations of gametes. The genotypes resulting in children who are as tall or taller than their father are noted. Most of the children will have a height intermediate to their parents, showing regression to a mean height.

♂ Gametes / ♀ Gametes

♀ Gametes	ABC	AbC	aBC	abC
ABc	AABBCc 7 ft	AABbCc 6 ft 9 in.	AaBBCc 6 ft 9 in.	AaBbCc 6 ft 9 in.
Abc	AABbCc 6 ft 9 in.	AAbbCc 6 ft 6 in.	AaBbCc 6 ft 6 in.	AabbCc 6 ft 3 in.
aBc	AaBBCc 6 ft 9 in.	AaBbCc 6 ft 6 in.	aaBBCc 6 ft 6 in.	aaBbCc 6 ft 3 in.
abc	AaBbCc 6 ft 6 in.	AabbCc 6 ft 3 in.	aaBbCc 6 ft 3 in.	aabbCc 6ft

(b)

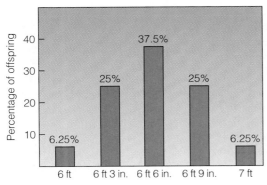

FIGURE 5.8

Frequency distribution of phenotypes from the possible offspring in Figure 5.7. Height of the offspring shows regression to the mean.

The phenotypic classes and ratio of possible offspring are diagrammed in Figure 5.8. As the king discovered (after waiting about 18 years for them to grow up), most of the children tended toward the average height (6 ft 6 in.) between the two parents. In fact, 11 of the 16 genotypic combinations will result in children shorter than their father. In succeeding generations, further regression to the mean will occur. To make matters worse, many of the Potsdam Grenadier Guards were tall because of endocrine malfunctions, and did not have the genotypes to produce tall offspring under any circumstances.

Regression to the mean is brought about not only by dominance and additive effects but also by gene interaction and environmental effects. If these other factors were included in our crosses, and if the genotypes included individuals of average height (say, 5 ft 4 in.), the regression toward the mean would be even more pronounced.

POLYGENES AND THE ENVIRONMENT: MULTIFACTORIAL TRAITS

We have looked at the interaction between genes and the environment in previous chapters, but always in the context of single genes. In considering the interaction of polygenes and the environment, we will begin by reviewing some basic concepts. Recall that the genotype represents the genetic constitution of an individual; it is fixed at the moment of fertilization and, barring mutation, is unchanging. The phenotype is the sum of the observable characteristics; it is variable and undergoes continuous change throughout the life of the organism. The environment of a gene includes all other genes in the genotype, their effects and interactions, and all nongenetic factors, whether physical or social, that can interact with the genotype.

In assessing the interaction between the genotype and the environment, as in all science, you have to ask the right question (see "Concepts and Controversies," page 118). Suppose the question is posed as "How much of a given phenotype in an individual is caused by heredity, and how much by environment?" Because each individual has a unique genotype and has been exposed to a unique set of environment conditions, it is impossible to quantitatively evaluate the phenotype's genetic and environmental components. Thus, for a given individual, the question as posed cannot be answered. However, in a later section we will see that if the question is changed, it is possible to estimate the genotypic contribution to a phenotype.

Threshold Effects and the Expression of Multifactorial Traits

Although the degree of interaction between a genotype and the environment can be difficult to estimate, family studies indicate that such interactions do occur. Some multifactorial traits do not show a continuous distribution of phenotypes; individuals are either affected or not. Congenital birth defects such as club foot or cleft palate are examples of traits that are distributed in a discontinuous fashion but are, in fact, multifactorial.

A model has been developed to explain the phenotypic expression of such traits. In this model, genotype frequencies are distributed in a bell-shaped curve, but only a limited number of genotypes are liable to express the phenotype (Figure 5.9). This liability is caused by a number of genes, each contributing to the liability in an additive fashion. Those individuals with a liability above a threshold will develop the genetic disorder if exposed to certain environmental conditions (Figure 5.9). In other words, environmental conditions are most likely to have the greatest impact on genetically predisposed individuals.

The threshold model is useful in explaining the occurrence of certain disorders and congenital malformations. Evidence for such a threshold in any given disorder is indirect and comes mainly from family studies. The frequency of the trait among rela-

tives of affected individuals is compared with the frequency of the trait in the general population. In a family, first-degree relatives (parent-child) have one half of their genes in common, second-degree relatives (grandparent-grandchild) have one-fourth of their genes in common, and third-degree relatives (uncle-niece or uncle-nephew, aunt-niece or aunt-nephew) have one-eighth of their genes in common. As the degree of relatedness declines, so does the probability that individuals will share the same combination of alleles at multiple loci.

According to the threshold model, the risk for a disorder should also decrease as the degree of relatedness decreases. The distribution of family patterns for some congenital malformations is shown in Table 5.1, indicating a relationship of declining risk as the degree of relatedness declines.

The multifactorial threshold model provides only indirect evidence for the effect of genotype on traits and for the degree of interaction between the genotype and the environment. The model is helpful, however, in genetic counseling, where it is used to predict recurrence risks in families with certain congenital malformations and multifactorial disorders.

Estimating the Interaction between Genotype and Environment

To assess accurately the degree of interaction between the genotype and the environment, we must examine the total variation in phenotype that is exhibited by a population of individuals rather than looking at individual members of the population. This phenotypic variation is derived from two sources: (1) the presence of different genotypes in members of the population and (2) the presence of different environments in which all the genotypes have been expressed. Assessing the role of these factors in the production of phenotypic variability in a population is embodied in the concept known as **heritability**.

HERITABILITY MEASURES PHENOTYPIC VARIATION

Variation in phenotypic expression that results from different genotypes is known as **genetic variance**. Any variation in phenotype between individuals of the same genotype is known as **environmental variance**. The heritability of a trait, symbolized by H, is that proportion of the total phenotypic variance caused by genetic differences. Heritability is always a variable, and it is not possible to obtain an absolute heritability value for any given trait. The value obtained depends on several factors, in-

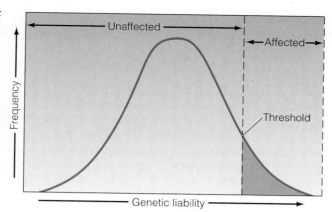

● **FIGURE 5.9**

A model to explain the discontinuous distribution of some multifactorial traits. In this model, liability for a genetic disorder is distributed among individuals in a normal curve. This liability is caused by a number of genes, each acting in an additive fashion. Only those individuals with a genetic liability above a certain threshold will be affected if exposed to certain environmental conditions.

Heritability
An expression of how much of the observed variation in a phenotype is due to differences in genotype.

Genetic variance
The phenotypic variance of a trait in a population that is attributed to genotypic differences.

Environmental variance
The phenotypic variance of a trait in a population that is attributed to differences in the environment.

TABLE 5.1

Familial Risks for Multifactorial Threshold Traits

MULTIFACTORIAL TRAIT	RISK RELATIVE TO GENERAL POPULATION			
	MZ Twins	First-Degree Relatives	Second-Degree Relatives	Third-Degree Relatives
Club foot	300x	25x	5x	2x
Cleft lip	400x	40x	7x	3x
Congenital hip dislocation (females only)	200x	25x	3x	2x
Congenital pyloric stenosis (males only)	80x	10x	5x	1.5

CONCEPTS AND CONTROVERSIES

Baseball Genes and Baseball Environment

Some traits are certainly familial; the degree to which they may be genetically determined is often a matter of question. In the last half of the 19th century, Sir Francis Galton began tracing traits through families to detemine whether there was a pattern of inheritance. As a modern example of the type of trait he studied, consider the case of the Boone family and baseball talent. Ray Boone played 13 years in the major leagues and is now a scout for the Boston Red Sox. His son, Bob Boone, played 18 years in the major leagues and is now the manager for the Kansas City Royals. Bob's son, Bret, now plays for the Cincinnati Reds. Bret's brother, Aaron, played college baseball at the University of Southern California.

It seems that baseball talent runs in the Boone family. In Galton's time, the presence of such talent in several generations of a family would have been taken as evidence for genetic control of this trait, because genetic factors were overestimated and environmental factors were underestimated. To estimate the degree of interaction between the genotype (genes for athletic ability) and environmental factors (growing up in a family of major league baseball players), geneticists today would examine the phenotypes and the amount of phenotypic variation (from high baseball ability to no baseball ability) present in a population, rather than just the individuals in one family. The results of such a study would be interpreted in terms of heritability, which provides a description of the genetic influences among a population living in a particular set of environmental conditions. It is important to remember that heritability does not imply a fixed genetic contribution to a trait in the way we can determine the genetic contribution to cystic fibrosis. Rather, it describes how much of the phenotypic variation in baseball ability is caused by genetic factors.

Boones by the Numbers

BRET BOONE

Born: 4-6-69. Home: Villa Park, Calif. Ht.: 5-10. Wt.: 170.
Bats/Throws: Right.
2B-SS, Southern California 1988-1990.

MAJOR LEAGUES	AVG	AB	R	H	2B	3B	HR	RBI	BB	SO	SB
Five years	.271	1323	173	359	75	6	43	192	87	252	11

BOB BOONE

Born: 11-19-47. Home: Villa Park, Calif. Ht.: 6-2. Wt.: 205.
Bats/Throws: Right.
3B-P, Stanford 1966-69; Drafted by Philadelphia Phillies, 6th round, June 1969 C, Philadelphia 1972-81, California 1982-88, Kansas City 1989-1990.

MAJOR LEAGUES	AVG	AB	R	H	2B	3B	HR	RBI	BB	SO	SB
18 years	.254	7245	679	1838	303	26	105	826	663	608	38

RAY BOONE

Born: 7-27-23. Home: El Cajon, Calif. Ht.: 6-0. Wt.: 172.
Batted/Threw: Right.
SS, Cleveland 1948-53; 3B, Detroit 1954-58; 1B, Milwaukee, 1960.

MAJOR LEAGUES	AVG	AB	R	H	2B	3B	HR	RBI	BB	SO	SB
13 years	.275	4587	645	1260	162	46	151	737	608	463	21

cluding the population being measured and the amount of environmental variability present at the time of measurement. Remember that heritability is a population phenomenon and applies to groups, not to individuals. In general, if the heritability is 100% ($H = 1.0$), the environment has no effect, and all phenotypic variation seen in the population is genetic. If the heritability is zero ($H = 0.0$), all phenotypic variation is due to the environment.

Heritability in humans is calculated from observations made among relatives. We know the fraction of genes that related individuals have in common: one half between parents and children, one fourth between grandparents and children, and so forth. These relationships are expressed as **correlation coefficients**. The half-set of genes received by a child from its parent corresponds to a correlation coefficient of 0.5. The genetic relatedness of identical twins is 100%, and is expressed as a correlation coefficient of 1.0. Unless a mother and father are related by descent, they should be genetically unrelated, and the correlation coefficient for this relationship is 0.0.

Correlation coefficient
A measure of the degree to which variables vary together.

Using Fingerprints to Estimate Heritability

It is difficult to find multifactorial traits to assess the degree of heritability because of interactions between genes and the environment. Fingerprint ridges are one multifactorial trait that is used to measure heritability.

Fingerprint patterns are laid down in the first 3 months of embryonic development (weeks 6–13). They are a polygenic trait, and can be influenced by the environment only during this short period of time. Everyone, including identical twins, has a unique set of fingerprints. Even though identical twins share the same set of genes and occupy the same uterus at the same time, they each live in slightly different environments. These subtle environmental factors are enough of an influence to create different fingerprint patterns.

Fingerprints are composed of ridges of skin cells called dermal ridges. As they develop, these ridges are laid down in distinctive patterns. Similar patterns are formed from the ridges on the palms, toes, and soles. Analysis of these patterns is known as **dermatoglyphics** (translated literally, the term means skin writing). The lines in the palms, known as flexion creases (the heart, life, and head lines of palmistry) are formed at the same time as the dermal ridges (Figure 5.10).

Fingerprint patterns are classified by shape as loops, whorls, and arches (Figure 5.11) and by ridge counts. Ridge counts are the most useful feature of fingerprints to the study of phenotypic variance and heritability. They are easily and objectively measured and once established are not subject to social and environmental factors (Figure 5.11).

Using correlation coefficients, one study of total ridge counts (TRC) sampled 825 British males and 825 British females (Table 5.2). The results provide no information about the number or nature of the genes involved, but the almost total agreement be-

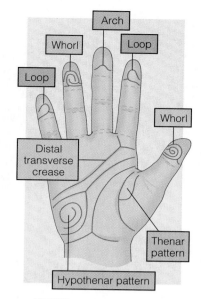

 FIGURE 5.10
The dermatoglyphic patterns on the fingers and palms are laid down early in fetal development.

Dermatoglyphics
The study of the skin ridges on the fingers, palms, toes, and soles.

 FIGURE 5.11
The three basic patterns of fingerprints. (a) arch (b) loop and (c) whorl. The triangular areas in (b) and (c) where ridge patterns diverge are called triradii. Ridge counts are made from prints of loops and whorls by superimposing a line from the triradius to the center of the print, and counting the number of ridges that cross the line.

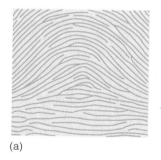
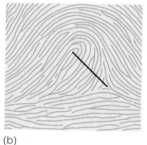
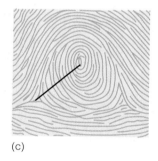

(a)   (b)   (c)

TABLE 5.2

Correlations between Relatives for the Total Ridge Count (TRC)

RELATIONSHIP	NUMBER OF PAIRS	OBSERVED CORRELATION COEFFICIENT	EXPECTED CORRELATION COEFFICIENT BETWEEN RELATIVES	HERITABILITY
Mother-child	405	0.48 ± 0.04	0.50	0.96
Father-child	405	0.49 ± 0.04	0.50	0.98
Husband-wife	200	0.05 ± 0.07	0.00	—
Sibling-sibling	642	0.50 ± 0.04	0.50	1.0
Monozygotic twins	80	0.95 ± 0.01	1.00	0.95
Dizygotic twins	92	0.49 ± 0.08	0.50	0.98

Note. From "Quantitative genetics of fingerprint patterns," by S. B. Holt, 1961, Br. Med. Bull., 17, pp. 247–250.

FIGURE 5.12

Identical twins (monozygotic twins) are of the same sex, and share a single genotype.

Monozygotic (MZ) twins
Twins derived from a single fertilization event involving one egg and one sperm; such twins are genetically identical.

Dizygotic (DZ) twins
Twins derived from two separate and nearly simultaneous fertilization events, each involving one egg and one sperm. Such twins share, on average, 50% of their genes.

tween the observed and expected values indicates that TRC is almost totally under genetic control, with environmental factors playing only a minor role.

Analysis of the results of ridge counts of parents and their children can be used to estimate the heritability of ridge counts. These estimates indicate a heritability of about 0.95. A heritability value of 0.95 means that most of the phenotypic variation in fingerprint ridges is genetically transmitted from parent to offspring. In fact, 95% of the phenotypic variation that is observed in ridge counts is due to differences in genotype. The small amount of nongenetic variation helps explain why identical twins have different fingerprint patterns.

Twin Studies and Multifactorial Traits

Use correlation coefficients to measure the degree of observed phenotypic variability provides an estimate of heritability. This method, however, has one main problem: The closer the genetic relationship, the more likely it is that the relatives share a common environment. In other words, parents and children may be similar because they have one half of their genes in common, but they may also be similar because they share a similar environment. How can the effects of genotype be separated from the effects of the environment?

To bypass this problem, human geneticists seek out situations in which genetic and environmental influences are clearly separated. One way to do this is to study twins (Figure 5.12). Identical twins share the same genotype. If identical twins are separated at birth and raised in different environments, the genotype is constant, and the environment is different. To reverse the situation, geneticists study traits in unrelated adopted children with those of natural children in the same family. This represents a situation with a constant environment and maximum genetic variability. The study of twins and adopted children is therefore an important tool in measuring heritability in humans.

The Biology of Twins

Sir Francis Galton (a cousin of Charles Darwin), the founder of eugenics, a movement to improve humans through selective breeding, pointed out in 1875 the value of studying twins to obtain information about the effects of environment on heredity. Before examining the results of such studies, we need to look briefly at the biology of twinning.

There are two types of twins, **monozygotic (MZ)** (identical) and **dizygotic (DZ)** (fraternal). Monozygotic twins originate from a single fertilization event: a single egg fertilized by a single sperm. During mitosis at an early stage of development, two separate embryos are formed. Additional splitting is also possible (see "Concepts and Controversies," page 123). This separation may take place at the time when the zygote undergoes its first mitotic division, or at any time up to the first 2 weeks of development (Figure 5.13). Conjoined twins (so-called Siamese twins) are thought to arise from an incomplete division of the embryo. Because they arise from a single fertilization event, MZ twins share the same genotype, are of the same sex, and carry the same genetic markers such as blood types. Dizygotic twins originate from two

separate fertilization events: two eggs, ovulated in the same menstrual cycle, are fertilized independently. DZ twins are no more related than other pairs of siblings, have half their genes in common, can be of different sex, and may have different genetic markers such as blood types.

For heritability studies, it is essential to identify a pair of twins as MZ or DZ. An accurate diagnosis of twins as MZ or DZ is made only by extensive tests. Comparison of many traits with absolute correlation between individuals can be used to identify twins as MZ. Divergence for one or more traits means that the twins are DZ. Among the characters used are blood groups, sex, eye color, hair color, fingerprints, palm and sole prints, DNA fingerprinting, and analysis of other DNA molecular markers.

Concordance
Agreement between traits exhibited by both twins.

Concordance and Twins

A simple method for evaluating phenotypic differences between twins is the use of traits that can be scored as present or absent rather than measured quantitatively. Twins are concordant if both have a trait and discordant if only one twin has the trait. As noted, MZ twins have 100% of their genes in common, while DZ twins, on average, have 50% in common. For any genetically determined trait the correlation in MZ twins should be higher than that in DZ twins. If the trait is completely heritable, the **concordance** should be 1.0 in MZ twins and close to 0.5 in DZ twins.

In evaluating the results of twin studies, it is the degree of difference between concordance in MZ twins versus DZ twins that is important. The greater the difference, the greater the resultant heritability. Table 5.3 lists concordance values in twins for a variety of traits. Examination of the table shows that the concordance value for cleft lip in MZ twins is higher than that for DZ twins (42% versus 5%). Although this difference suggests a genetic component to this trait, the value is so far below 100% that environmental factors (perhaps teratogens) are obviously important in the majority of cases. In all cases, concordance values must be interpreted cautiously.

Concordance values can be converted to heritability values through a number of statistical formulas. Heritability values derived in this manner are given in the last column of Tables 5.2 and 5.5. Remember that heritability is a relative value, valid only for the population measured and only under the environmental conditions in effect at the time of measurement. Heritability determinations made within one group cannot be compared with heritability measurements for the same trait in another group, since the two groups differ in genotypes and environmental variables in unknown ways.

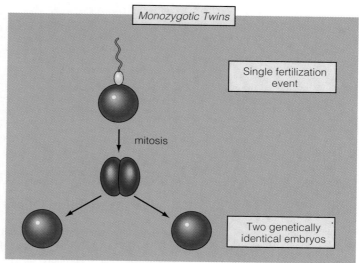

(a)

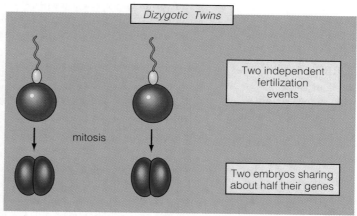

(b)

▬ FIGURE 5.13

(a) Monozygotic (MZ) twins result from the fertilization of a single egg by a single sperm. After one or more mitotic divisions, the embryo splits in two, and forms two genetically identical individuals. (b) Dizygotic (DZ) twins result from the indepenedent fertilization of two eggs by two sperm during the same ovulatory cycle. Although these two embryos share the same uterine environment at the same time, they share only about half their genes.

TABLE 5.3

Concordance Values in Monozygotic (MZ) and Dizygotic (DZ) Twins

TRAIT	CONCORDANCE VALUES (%)	
	MZ	DZ
Blood types	100	66
Eye color	99	28
Mental retardation	97	37
Hair color	89	22
Down syndrome	89	7
Handedness (left or right)	79	77
Epilepsy	72	15
Diabetes	65	18
Tuberculosis	56	22
Cleft lip	42	5

Using Twins to Study Obesity

Heritability estimates derived from studies of twins and adopted children are indirect ways of studying multifactorial traits. These studies are based on correlations rather than direct demonstration of cause and effect and are also subject to a number of uncertainties, as shown in the following sections.

Obesity is a trait that can be said to "run" in families. Obesity is also a national health problem. A federal study has estimated that up to 30% of the adult U.S. population between the ages of 20 and 75 years is overweight (Figure 5.14). These individuals are at risk for diseases such as high blood pressure, elevated levels of cholesterol in the blood, coronary artery disease, and adult-onset diabetes.

 FIGURE 5.14
About 30% of the U.S. population is overweight, making this a serious health problem.

CONCEPTS AND CONTROVERSIES

Twins, Quintuplets, and Armadillos

Because of the way in which they are formed, monozygotic twins (MZ) are genetically identical. The process of embryo splitting that gives rise to MZ twins can be considered a form of human asexual reproduction. In fact, another mammal, the nine-banded armadillo, produces litters of genetically identical, same-sex offspring that arise by embryo splitting. In armadillo reproduction a single fertilized egg splits in two, and daughter embryos can split again, resulting in litters of two to six genitically identical offspring.

In humans, multiple births occur rarely. About 1 in 7500 births are triplets, and 1 in 658,000 births are quadruplets. In many cases, both embryo splitting and multiple fertilizations are responsible for naturally occurring multiple births. Triplets may arise by fertilization of two eggs, with one of them undergoing embryo splitting. The use of hormones to enhance fertility has slightly increased the frequency of multiple births. These drugs work by inducing the production of multiple eggs in a single menstrual cycle. The resulting fertilizations have resulted in multiple births ranging from twins to septuplets.

Embryo splitting in naturally occurring births was documented in the Dionne quintuplets, born in May, 1934. This case was the first one in which all five members of a set of quintuplets survived. Blood tests and physical similarities indicate that these quintuplets arose from a single fertilization event followed by several embryo splits, according to the following diagram:

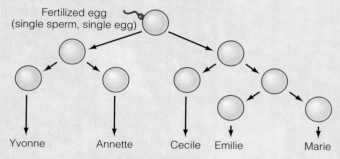

From this, it seems that MZ twins, armadillos, and the Dionne quintuplets have something in common: they all arise by embryo splitting.

Twins have been used to estimate the heritability of obesity. One large-scale study used 1974 pairs of MZ twins and 2097 pairs of DZ twins who were born between 1917 and 1927 and who served in the armed forces. Weights and heights measured at induction into the armed forces were compared with similar measurements taken 25 years later. Obesity was measured by body mass index (BMI; weight in kilograms divided by height in meters squared), and by reference to tables listing ideal weight-height relationships. Table 5.4 shows the concordance values from this study, for five

	TABLE 5.4			
	Concordance Values for Obesity in Twins			
% OVERWEIGHT	% CONCORDANT AT MILITARY INDUCTION		% CONCORDANT 25 YEARS LATER	
	MZ	DZ	MZ	DZ
15	61	31	68	49
20	57	27	60	40
25	46	24	54	26
30	51	19	47	16
40	44	0	36	6

Note. From A twin study of human obesity, by A. J. Stunkard, T. T. Foch, and Z. Hrubec, 1986, JAMA, 256, pp. 51–54.

levels of obesity. At military induction, concordance for MZ twins was much higher than that for DZ twins at all five levels of obesity. Twenty-five years later, the concordance levels for MZ twins were still much higher than those for DZ twins. The heritability values derived from these studies are shown in Table 5.5. The results show high values of heritability for obesity, suggesting that this condition has a strong genetic component.

But, let's consider some potential problems with this type of study that can affect the conclusions. First, the study included only men who had passed a preinduction physical that eliminated individuals with marked obesity, skewing the population studied to less obese individuals. This would tend to underestimate the contribution of heredity to obesity. Second, because the study did not include women or children, or men excluded from military service for other causes, it limited the researchers' ability to generalize the conclusions. Last, the study did not attempt to directly study the role of environmental factors such as diet in obesity. Even with these limitations, however, the heritability values are high enough to indicate that obesity is under strong genetic control.

Perhaps the most effective way of separating the effects of genes and environment and of controlling external factors is to study identical and fraternal twins reared under different environmental conditions. In a study of body mass index (BMI) in identical and fraternal twins reared together or apart, heritability values for BMI were calculated as 0.70 for men and 0.66 for women (Table 5.5). This indicates that 66–70% of the phenotypic variation (obesity) observed is due to differences in genotype, linking the condition to genetic factors.

Another method of assessing the role of genes and the environment in obesity is to study adopted unrelated children, who bring maximum genotypic differences into a family that is subjected to a relatively constant environment. Studies comparing obesity in adopted children with obesity in the biological and adopted parents confirm the role of genetic factors as important influences on obesity and assign a minor role to the family environment. One such study compared obesity in 3580 adoptees and their brothers and sisters, who were reared separately. The results indicate that obese adoptees tend to have obese siblings, even though they were raised in different environments. This reinforces the conclusion mentioned earlier that heredity plays an important role in obesity. The analysis also indicates that polygenic inheritance can account for body mass, ranging from thin to obese. These results are consistent with other studies showing that 75% of the phenotypic variation in obesity is explained by genetic factors.

TABLE 5.5	
Heritability Estimates for Obesity in Twins (from Several Studies)	
CONDITION	**HERITABILITY**
Obesity in children	0.77–0.88
Obesity in adults (weight at age 45)	0.64
Obesity in adults (body mass index at age 20)	0.80
Obesity in adults (weight at induction into armed forces)	0.77
Obesity in twins reared together or apart Men Women	 0.70 0.66

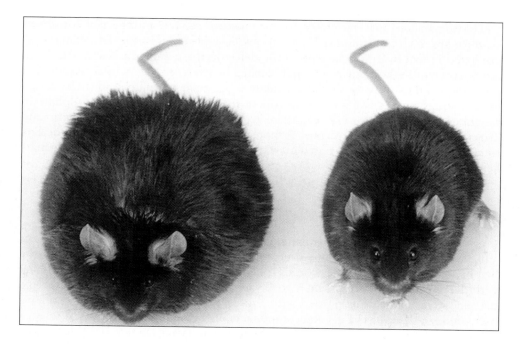

■ FIGURE 5.15
The *obese (ob)* mouse mutant, shown here on the left (a normal mouse is on the right), has provided many clues about how weight is controlled in humans.

Genetic Clues to Obesity

Further studies using twins have provided some clues as to how genes control body weight. Metabolic studies using identical twins have suggested that genetic factors determine how much food energy is converted into lean muscle, and how much is converted into fat.

Recent breakthroughs in understanding how genes regulate body weight have come from studies in mice. The mouse mutants *obese (ob)* and *diabetes (db)* are both obese (■ Figure 5.15). Using recombinant DNA techniques, these genes and their human equivalents have been isolated, mapped, and studied in detail. The *ob* gene encodes a weight-controlling hormone, **leptin** (from the Greek word for *thin*) produced by fat cells. In mice, the hormone is released from fat cells and travels through the blood to the brain, where cells of the hypothalamus carry leptin receptors encoded by the *db* gene. Binding of leptin activates the leptin receptor and initiates a response by the hypothalamus. This response might involve the production of an appetite-suppressing hormone, GLP-1 (glucagon-like protein-1). In normal individuals, the control system may regulate the relative amounts of food converted into fat or muscle mass, or alter the rate of energy consumption to maintain weight within a relatively narrow range (■ Figure 5.16). Control of weight in mice may involve other genes such as *tubby (tb)*, which also has an obese phenotype.

Leptin
A hormone produced by fat cells that signals the brain and ovary.

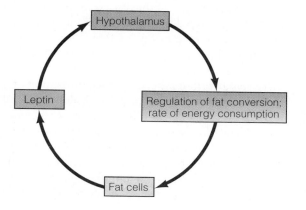

■ FIGURE 5.16
The hormone leptin is produced in fat cells, moves through the blood, and binds to receptors in the hypothalamus. Binding presumably activates a control mechanism (still unknown) that controls weight by regulating the conversion of food energy into fat and the rate of energy consumption. As fat levels become depleted, secretion of leptin slows and eventually stops.

Hypertension
Elevated blood pressure, consistently above 140/90 mm Hg.

Atherosclerosis
Arterial disease associated with deposition of plaques on inner surface of blood vessels.

The human gene for leptin maps to chromosome 7q31.1, and the gene for the receptor maps to chromosome 1p31. Most obese people do not have defects in the *ob* gene, and in fact overproduce leptin. The defect in these individuals seems to be in the receptor, or in the control systems activated by the receptor. An understanding of how leptin and its receptor work to regulate weight will hopefully lead to the design of new drugs to treat obesity. Since Americans spend over $30 billion dollars in weight control products every year, there is potentially a large market for leptin and drugs that affect the leptin receptor. A biotech company has paid $20 million dollars for a license to develop drugs based on leptin, and these products may be on the market in a few years.

A SURVEY OF SOME MULTIFACTORIAL TRAITS

Much of the phenotypic diversity in humans is the result of interaction between genes and environmental factors. Many traits involve a number of genes which, taken one by one, have only a small effect on the phenotype. Each of these genes can interact with the environment, producing a wide range of phenotypes, and often obscuring the genetic components associated with a disease. Varying degrees of progress have been made in defining the genetic components of the multifactorial traits discussed below. New methods of screening for polygenes that have been developed in the last few years and the identification of genes in the Human Genome Project may help explain how genetic and environmental factors contribute to complex traits.

Cardiovascular Disease Has Genetic and Environmental Components

Two significant factors lead to cardiovascular disease: **hypertension** (MIM/OMIM 145500, high blood pressure) and **atherosclerosis** (MIM/OMIM 143890, deposition of plaque on artery walls). Both traits have significant environmental contributions (Table 5.6) but also have well-established genetic components.

Hypertension occurs when the blood pressure (➡ Figure 5.17) is consistently above 140/90 mm Hg (140 is the pressure generated when the heart ventricles contract, and 90 is the pressure when the ventricles are relaxed). Many genes are involved in controlling blood pressure, including those that control sodium transport, and the gene for angiotensinogen (AGT). AGT (MIM/OMIM 106150) is a protein made in the liver and present in blood at a high concentration, which in its active form controls salt and water retention, which in turn affect blood pressure. Some variants of this protein have been linked to a predisposition to hypertension, which is a silent killer, since there are no obvious symptoms in early stages of the disease. Some 10–20% of the adult population of the United States suffers from hypertension, making it a serious health problem.

Atherosclerosis is the result of an imbalance between dietary intake, synthesis, utilization and breakdown of lipids, especially cholesterol, and leads to the blockage of blood vessels (➡ Figure 5.18). The most serious consequences come from blockage in the brain and heart, causing strokes and heart attacks. Cholesterol is needed for the synthesis of plasma membranes, steroid hormones (such as estrogen and testosterone), and

TABLE 5.6
Risk Factors for Cardiovascular Disease
Heredity (history of cardiovascular disease before age 55 in family members)
Being male
Hypertension
High blood cholesterol (high LDL and/or low HDL)
Smoking
Obesity
Lack of exercise
Stress

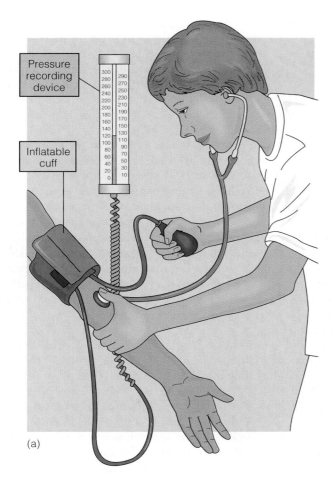

(a)

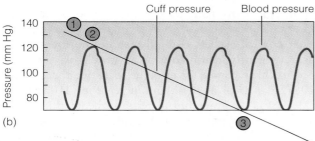

(b)

FIGURE 5.17

Blood pressure readings. (a) A blood presssure cuff is used to determine blood pressure. As shown in (b), blood pressure rises and falls as the left ventricle of the heart contracts and relaxes. To measure blood pressure, air is pumped into the cuff until it stops blood flow into the lower arm, and no sound can be heard (1). Air is gradually let out of the cuff, and when blood is heard flowing past the cuff, the pressure measured at this point is taken as the systolic pressure—the upper number in a blood pressure (2). As pressure in the cuff is gradually released, the artery becomes fully open, and no sound is heard. This is the diastolic pressure—the lower number in a blood pressure (3).

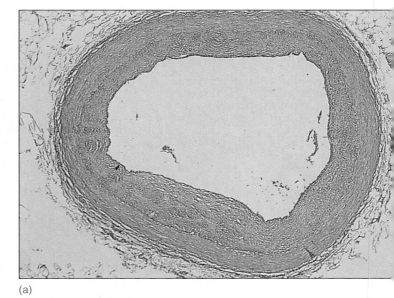

(a)

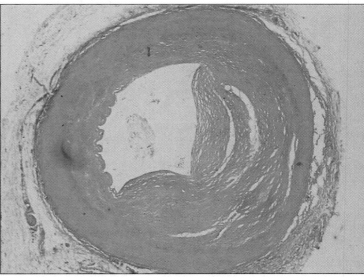

(b)

FIGURE 5.18

(a) A cross-section of a normal artery. (b) A cross-section of an artery partially blocked by athersclerotic plaque. As excess cholesterol accumulates in the body, it accumulates in plaques, leading to cardiovascular disease.

Lipoproteins
Particles with protein and phosopholipid coats that transport cholesterol and other lipids in the bloodstream.

Familial hypercholesteremia (FH)
Autosomal dominant disorder with defective or absent LDL receptors. Affected individuals are at increased risk for cardiovascular disease.

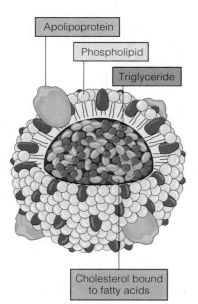

Apolipoprotein

Phospholipid

Triglyceride

Cholesterol bound to fatty acids

FIGURE 5.19
Lipoproteins carry cholesterol and other lipids through the blood enclosed in a protein and phosopholipid coating. There are several types of lipoproteins, with different proportions of lipids. LDLs are composed of about 45% cholesterol, and HDLs are made of about 20% cholesterol. High levels of LDLs and a low level of HDLs are risk factors for cardiovascular disease.

as a component of bile. The liver synthesizes cholesterol, and it is not a necessary part of the diet. But the accumulation of cholesterol in arterial plaque is an important factor in cardiovascular disease.

Large lipid molecules such as cholesterol are not soluble in blood plasma, and are wrapped in a coat of proteins and phosopholipids for transport. The coat and its contents are known as **lipoproteins** (Figure 5.19). Lipoproteins are classified by their size and density. Cholesterol is carried by both low-density (LDL) and high-density lipoproteins (HDL). LDLs are about 45% cholesterol and HDLs are about 20% cholesterol. LDLs transport cholesterol from the liver to tissues in the body for utilization and breakdown. HDLs transport cholesterol to the liver. The risk of atherosclerosis is related to the HDL/total cholesterol ratio. Higher HDL levels mean lower risk.

Cholesterol levels in the body are controlled by many genes, including those that encode apolipoproteins (part of the lipoprotein that attaches to cell receptors), cell receptors that bind to and internalize lipoproteins, and enzymes that degrade lipoproteins inside the cell. One of these chains is discussed below.

The autosomal dominant disease **familial hypercholesterolemia** (MIM/OMIM 143890) is caused by defective cell surface receptors that regulate the uptake of LDLs. Affected heterozygotes have elevated cholesterol levels in their blood serum, and usually develop coronary artery disease between ages 40–50. Two general types of defects are known: defective receptors and absent receptors. Several classes of defective receptors are known, including one that is unable to recognize and bind to LDLs, another with reduced ability to bind LDLs, and a third that recognizes and binds LDL, but is unable to move the LDL into the cell. Altogether, over 150 mutations of the gene on chromosome 19 encoding the LDL receptor have been identified. Each of these mutations results in elevated levels of LDL-derived cholesterol in the blood serum and the deposition of plaques on the inner surface of arteries, leading to premature heart disease.

The frequency of heterozygotes for familial hypercholesterolemia in European, Japanese, and U.S. populations is about 1 in 500, although in regions of Quebec the frequency is 1 in 122. The highest reported frequency is in a community of South Africa, where the frequency is 1 in 71. The average frequency of 1 in 500 makes this disorder one of the most common genetic disorders known, and is one of the major causes of cardiovascular disease.

Mutations in other genes that control aspects of lipid metabolism are also involved in cardiovascular disease. A recently identified gene, athrosclerosis susceptibility (ATHS), has been mapped to chromosome 19 near the locus for the LDL receptor. ATHS (MIM/OMIM 108725) is associated with an increase in LDL levels in the blood, a decrease in HDL levels, and a threefold increase in heart attack risk. Apolipoproteins are part of LDL and HDL lipoproteins, and have several functions, including interacting with cell surface receptors to bind lipoproteins to cell surfaces. Allelic variations of apolipoproteins play an important role in determining blood levels of cholesterol.

Skin Color is a Polygenic Trait

The theory of polygenic inheritance in humans was first tested by Charles and Gertrude Davenport, leading figures in the American eugenics movement. Between 1910 and 1914, they collected information on skin color in black-white marriages in Bermuda and in the Caribbean. To measure skin color, they used a top with a disk composed of colored sectors of various sizes (Figure 5.20). The colors used were black, white, red, and yellow. When the top was spun, the colored sectors blended together and produced a color that could be matched to a given skin color by changing the size of the black- and white-colored sectors. Based on the size of the black sector, individuals were assigned to one of five categories, 0 to 4.

The results of the Davenports' study illustrate several properties of polygenic traits. The offspring (F_1) of such marriages have skin color values intermediate be-

tween those of their parents. In the F₂ generation, a small number of children were as white as one grandparent, a small number were as black as the other grandparent, and most were distributed between these extremes (● Figure 5.21). Because individuals in the F₂ could be grouped into five classes, the Davenports hypothesized that skin color was controlled by two gene pairs. Each class represented a genotype that resulted from the segregation and assortment of two gene pairs. Suppose these genes are *A* and *B* respectively. Class 0 with the lightest skin represents the genotype *aabb*, Class 1 has the genotype *Aabb* or

● FIGURE 5.20

(a) The top used by the Davenports to measure skin color with overlaid disks. The color produced when the top is spun can be changed by changing the size of the sectors in the colored disks stacked together on the top. (b) The disks used to measure skin color. Disks of different amounts of black and white can be mounted on the top to produce a color that matches that of the person being studied. (c) Arrangement of sectors producing skin colors characteristic of white and black persons studied by the Davenports.

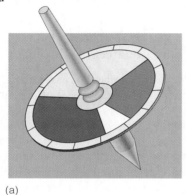

(a)

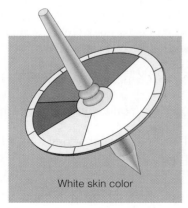

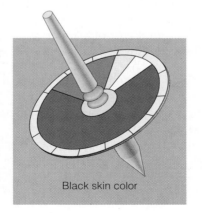

(c)

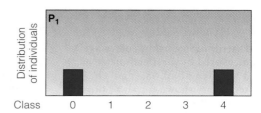

(a)

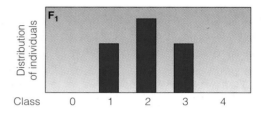

(b)

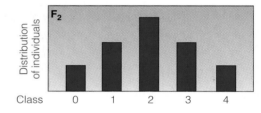

(c)

● FIGURE 5.21

Frequency diagrams of skin colors obtained by the Davenports. (a) Skin color distribution in the parents falls into two discontinuous classes. (b) Color values of seven children from the parents in (a) are intermediate to those of their parents. (c) Skin colors of 32 children of the parents in (b). Color values range from one phenotypic extreme to the other, with most clustered around a mean value. This normal distribution of phenotypes is characteristic of a polygenic trait.

White   Yellow   Red   Black

(b)

White skin color   Black skin color

Distribution of skin colors as measured by a reflectometer at a wavelength of 685 nm. The results are shown for an additive model of skin color, with environmental effects, for 1–4 gene pairs. Distributions observed in several populations indicate that 3 or 4 gene pairs control skin color.

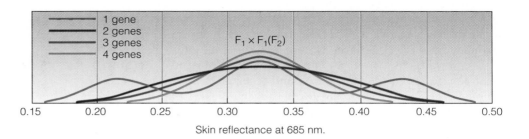

aaBb, and so forth, up to Class 5, which is homozygous dominant (*AABB*) and has the darkest skin.

Subsequent work using a more sophisticated instrument that measures the reflection of light from the skin surface (a reflectometer) has shown that skin color is actually controlled by more than two gene pairs, and the current estimate is that between three and six gene pairs are involved. The data are most consistent with a model involving three or four genes (● Figure 5.22).

Intelligence and IQ: Are They Related?

The idea that intelligence is a distinct entity that can be quantified began in the late 18th and early 19th centuries with the development of phrenology. Phrenologists believed that the brain has a series of compartments, each of which controls a single function, such as musical ability, courage, or intelligence. Since each area of the brain has an assigned function, the capacities of an individual can be determined by an examination of the shape and size of a particular region of the skull (● Figure 5.23). Later, many scientists related intelligence to overall brain size. Craniometry, the measurement of brain size (by weight or volume) then became the dominant means of assessing intelligence.

At the turn of the 20th century, Alfred Binet, a French psychologist, turned to psychological rather than physical methods for measuring intelligence. To identify children whose classroom performance indicated a need for special education, he developed a graded series of tasks related to basic mental processes such as comprehension, direction (sorting), and correction. Each child began by performing the simplest tasks and progressing in sequence until the tasks became too difficult. The age assigned for the last task performed became the child's mental age, and the intellectual age was calculated by subtracting the mental age from the chronological age. Binet's test became the basis of the Stanford-Binet intelligence tests in use today.

Another psychologist, Wilhelm Stern, divided mental age by chronological age, and the number became known as the **intelligence quotient,** or IQ. If a child of 7 years (chronological age) was able to successfully perform tasks for a 7-year-old but not tasks for an 8-year-old, a mental age of 7 would be assigned. To determine the IQ for this child, divide mental age by chronological age:

$$\frac{\text{mental age} = 7}{\text{chronological age} = 7} = 1.0 \times 100 = 100 = \text{IQ}$$

Multiply the quotient by 100 to eliminate the decimal point, and we obtain an IQ of 100 as the average for any given age.

The substitution of psychological for physical methods for measuring intelligence does not change the underlying assumption that intelligence is an entity with a biological basis that can be expressed as a single number. In fact, the use of IQ tests has

Intelligence quotient (IQ)
A score derived from standardized tests that is calculated by dividing the individual's mental age (determined by the test) by his or her chronologic age, and multiplying the quotient by 100.

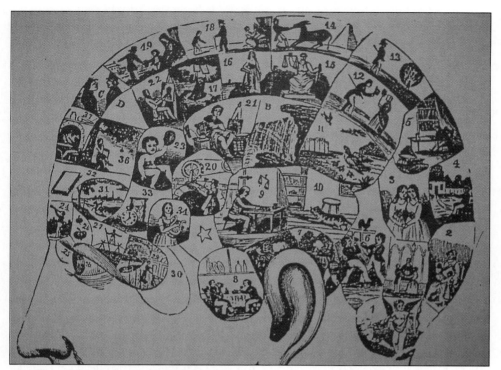

FIGURE 5.23

Phrenology model showing areas of the head overlying brain regions controlling different traits. Intelligence was estimated by measuring the area of the skull overlying the region of the brain thought to control this trait.

strengthened the assumption that IQ measures a fundamental, genetically determined physiological or biochemical property of the brain related to intelligence. The question is whether psychological methods such as IQ tests can measure intelligence any more accurately than the discredited physical methods of phrenology or craniometry.

To determine whether IQ tests or any other method accurately measure intelligence, we must first define intelligence in a way that it can be objectively measured, in the same way we can measure height, weight, or fingerprint ridge counts. Properties such as abstract reasoning, mathematical skills, verbal expression, ability to diagnose and to solve problems, and creativity are often cited as important components of intelligence. Unfortunately, there is no evidence that any of these properties are directly measured by an IQ test, and there is no objective way to quantitate such components of intelligence.

Dozens of distinct neural processes may be involved in mental functions, many of which may contribute to intelligence. In spite of the rapid advances in neurobiology, little or no information is available about the biological basis of any of these processes. Without knowledge of the mechanisms involved, it is difficult to quantitatively measure the outcome of these mechanisms.

The values obtained in IQ measurements, however, have significant heritable components. The evidence that IQ has genetic components comes from two areas: studies that estimate IQ heritability, and which show a range of heritability from 0.6 to 0.8, and comparison of IQs in groups of individuals raised together (unrelated individuals, parents and children, siblings, and MZ and DZ twins), and individuals raised separately (unrelated individuals, siblings, and MZ twins). The high correlation observed for MZ twins raised together indicates that genetics plays a significant

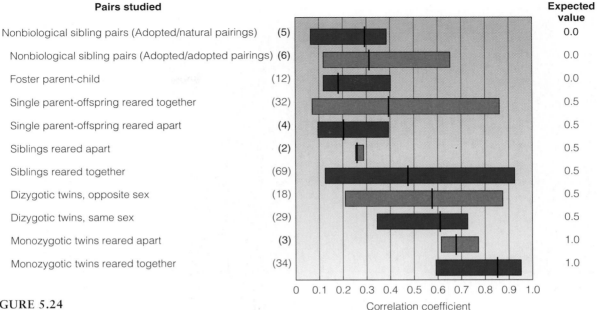

Pairs studied		Expected value
Nonbiological sibling pairs (Adopted/natural pairings)	(5)	0.0
Nonbiological sibling pairs (Adopted/adopted pairings)	(6)	0.0
Foster parent-child	(12)	0.0
Single parent-offspring reared together	(32)	0.5
Single parent-offspring reared apart	(4)	0.5
Siblings reared apart	(2)	0.5
Siblings reared together	(69)	0.5
Dizygotic twins, opposite sex	(18)	0.5
Dizygotic twins, same sex	(29)	0.5
Monozygotic twins reared apart	(3)	1.0
Monozygotic twins reared together	(34)	1.0

0 0.1 0.2 0.3 0.4 0.5 0.6 0.7 0.8 0.9 1.0
Correlation coefficient

FIGURE 5.24

A graphical representation of correlations in IQ measurements in different sets of individuals. The expected correlation coefficients are determined by the degree of genetic relatedness in each set of individuals. The vertical line represents the median correlation coefficient in each case.

role in determining IQ (Figure 5.24). But rearing MZ twins apart or raising siblings in different environments significantly reduces the correlation, and provides evidence that there is a substantial role for the environment in determining IQ.

The Controversy about IQ and Race

The assumption that intelligence is solely determined by biological factors coupled with the misuse or misunderstanding of the limits of heritability estimates have led to the conclusion that differences in IQ among different racial and ethnic groups are genetically determined. On standardized IQ tests, black persons score an average of 15 points lower than the average white person's score of 100. These differences are consistent across different tests, and the scores themselves do not seem to be a serious issue. The controversy is over what causes these differences. Are such differences genetic in origin, or do they reflect environmental differences, or are both factors at work? If both, to what degree does inheritance contribute to the differences? The debate about these questions has been renewed by the recent book *The Bell Curve* by Herrnstein and Murray.

Heritability studies have been used to support the argument that intelligence is mainly innate and inherited, citing heritability values of 0.8 for intelligence. In most cases, however, the reasoning used to support this argument misuses the concept of heritability. Recall that a measured heritability of 0.8 (for example) means that 80% of the phenotypic variation being measured is due to genetic differences within that population. Differences observed between two populations in heritability for a trait simply cannot be compared, because heritability measures only variation within a population at the time of measurement and cannot be used to estimate genetic variation between populations. In other words, we cannot use heritability differences among groups to conclude that there are genetic differences among those groups.

It is quite evident that both genetic and environmental factors make important contributions to intelligence. Clearly, the relative amount each contributes cannot be measured accurately at this time. Several points about this debate should be kept in mind. First, it is clear that IQ test scores cannot be equated with intelligence. Second, IQ scores are not fixed and can be changed significantly with training in problem solving and, in fact, change somewhat throughout the life of an individual. Variation

in IQ scores is quite wide, and measurements in one racial or ethnic group overlap those of other groups.

The problem in discussing the differences in IQ scores arises when the quantitative differences in scores are converted into qualitative judgments used to rank groups as superior or inferior. Genetics, like all sciences, progresses by the formulation of hypotheses that can be rigorously and objectively tested. The Human Genome Project may help define the number and action of genes involved in higher mental processes, and provide insight into the genetics of intelligence.

SUMMARY

1. In this chapter we have considered genes that affect traits in an additive or quantitative manner. The pattern of inheritance that controls metric characters (those that can be measured in a quantitative fashion) is called polygenic inheritance because two or more genes are usually involved.

2. The distribution of polygenic traits through the population follows a bell-shaped, or normal, curve. Parents whose phenotypes are near the extremes of this curve usually have children whose phenotypes are less extreme than the parents' and are closer to the mean of the population. This phenomenon, known as regression to the mean, is characteristic of systems in which the phenotype is produced by the additive action of many genes.

3. Variations in the expression of polygenic traits are often due to the action of environmental factors. Because of this, organisms that share a common genotype will show a range of phenotypic variation.

4. The impact of environment on genotype can cause genetically susceptible individuals to exhibit a trait in a discontinuous fashion even though there is an underlying continuous distribution of genotypes for the trait.

5. The degree of phenotypic variation produced by the genotype in a given population can be estimated by calculating the heritability of a trait. Heritability is estimated by observing the amount of variation among relatives having a known fraction of genes in common. MZ twins have 100% of their genes in common and when raised in separate environments provide an estimate of the degree of environmental influence on gene expression.

6. Heritability is a variable, validly calculated only for the population under study and the environmental condition in effect at the time of the study. It provides an estimate of the degree of genetic variance within a population, and heritability values cannot be compared among populations because of differences in genotypes and environmental factors.

7. In twin studies, the degree of concordance for a trait is compared in MZ and DZ twins reared together or apart. MZ twins result from the splitting of an embryo produced by a single fertilization event, while DZ twins are the products of multiple fertilization events. While twin studies can be useful in determining whether a trait is inherited, they cannot provide any information on the mode of inheritance or the number of genes involved.

8. Many human traits are controlled by polygenes, including skin color, intelligence, and aspects of behavior. The genetics of these traits has often been misused and misrepresented in the service of ideological, or political ends.

QUESTIONS AND PROBLEMS

1. Describe why continuous variation is common in humans and provide examples of such traits.

2. The text outlines some of the problems Frederick William I encountered in his attempt to breed tall Potsdam Guards.
   a. Why were the results he obtained so different from those obtained by Mendel with short and tall pea plants?
   b. Why were most of the children shorter than their tall parents?

3. A club foot is a common congenital birth defect in the Smith family. This defect is caused by a number of genes but appears to be phenotypically distributed in a noncontinuous fashion. Geneticists use the multifactorial threshold model to explain the occurrence of this defect. Explain this model. Explain predisposition to the defect in an individual that has a genotypic liability above the threshold versus an individual that has a liability below the threshold.

4. What role might the environment have played in causing Frederick William problems, especially in a time when nutrition varied greatly from town to town and from family to family?

5. Do you think his experiment would have worked better if he had ordered brother-sister marriages within tall families instead of just choosing the tallest individuals from throughout the country?

6. As it turned out, one of the tallest Potsdam Guards had an unquenchable attraction to short women. During his tenure as guard he had numerous clandestine affairs. In each case children resulted. Subsequently, some of the children, who had no way of knowing that they were related, married and had children of their own. Assume that height is determined by two pairs of genes. The genotype of the 7-ft-tall Potsdam Guard was $A'A'B'B'$, and the genotype of all his 5-ft clandestine lovers was AABB, where an A' or B' allele adds 6 in to the base height of 5 ft conferred by the AABB genotype.
   a. What were the genotypes and phenotypes of all the F1 children?
   b. Diagram the cross between the F1 offspring, and give all possible genotypes and phenotypes of the F2 progeny.

7. Describe why there is a fundamental difference between the expression of a trait that is determined by polygenes and the expression of a trait determined monogenetically.

8. Define genetic variance.

9. Define environmental variance.

10. How is heritability related to genetic and environmental variance?

11. Why are relatives used in the calculation of heritability?

12. Dizygotic twins:
   a. are as closely related as monozygotic twins
   b. are as closely related as non-twin siblings
   c. share 100% of their genetic material
   d. share 05 of their genetic material
   e. none of the above

13. Discuss the difficulties in attempting to determine whether intelligence is genetically based.

14. Why are monozygotic twins, reared apart, so useful in the calculation of heritability?

15. Monozygotic (MZ) twins have a concordance value of 44% for a specific trait, where dizygotic twins have a concordance value of less that 5% for the same trait. What could explain why the value for MZ twins is significantly less than 100%?

16. What is the importance of the comparison of traits between adopted and natural children in the determination of heritability?

17. If monozygotic twins show complete concordance for a trait whether they are reared together or apart, what does this suggest about the heritability of the trait?

18. If there is no genetic variation within a population for a given trait, what is the heritability for the trait in the population?

19. At the age of nine years, your genetics instructor was able to perform the mental tasks of an 11 year-old. According to Wilhelm Stern's method, calculate his or her IQ.

20. Suppose a team of researchers analyzes the heritability of SAT scores and assigns a heritability of 0.75 for this skill. This team also determines that a certain ethnic group has a heritability value that is 0.12 lower when compared to other ethnic groups. The group draws the conclusion that there must be a genetic explanation for the differences in scores. Why is this an invalid conclusion?

SCIENCE AND SOCIETY

1. Sickle cell anemia is an autosomal recessive condition caused by a single amino acid substitution in the beta globin gene, one of the protein components of hemoglobin. Individuals with this condition are subject to a wide range of problems, including anemia, pain swelling of the hands and feet, and are at risk for stroke and heart problems.

   Malaria is a disease caused by infection by a parasite known as Plasmodium falciparum, and the disease is transmitted to humans by mosquitoes. Victims of malaria are more susceptible to other diseases, and causes premature death. Heterozygotes and homozygotes for sickle cell anemia are more resistant to malarial infections than are those homozygous for the normal allele. The relationship between malaria and sickle cell anemia is an example of a genetic variation that interacts with an environmental factor to promote differential survival and reproduction. Thinking about sickle cell anemia, do you think that fitness (the ability to survive and reproduce) is greater for an individual who is homozygous for sickle cell anemia, a heterozygote or a homozygous normal individual? In areas where malaria is common, which genotype would have a greater fitness? What would happen to the frequency of the sickle cell allele if the mosquito population were controlled or eliminated? Why?

2. The late nineteenth and early twentieth century witnessed the development eugenics, a program of selective breeding to improve the human species (review this topic in Chapter 1). Eugenics includes positive eugenics (encouraging and rewarding the breeding of those with "desirable" traits) and negative eugenics (discouraging breeding of those with "undesirable" traits). Just before World War II, eugenics fell into disfavor, but recent advances in genetic technologies have stirred interest in this topic. Is eugenics a practical approach to the elimination of disease genes? What about polygenic traits? Are they amenable to manipulation by selective breeding? Are there examples from other organisms that support your answer?

INTERNET ACTIVITIES

The following activities use the resources of the World Wide Web to enhance the topics covered in this chapter. To investigate the topics described below, log on to the book's home page at:

http://www.wadsworth.com/biology

1. Traits that show continuous phenotypic variation (examples of polygenic inheritance) in domesticated plants and animals are of great interest because of their economic value. The loci that control such traits are called quantitative trait loci (QTLs). Mapping QTLs with molecular markers allows plant and animal breeders to select organisms for breeding and reduces the time for improving plant and animal stocks. Access the site on QTLs and read about them. If a polygenic trait is altered by selective breeding, is this any different than modifying the organism by the use of recombinant DNA techniques in order to produce the same phenotype?

2. Multifactorial traits are those having a strong interaction with environmental factors. Two such traits are handedness (MIM/OMIM 139900) and longevity (MIM/OMIM 152430). Access these listings in the OMIM database, and read one or more of the references on the multifactorial nature of these traits. Have twin studies played a role in identifying the genetic components of these traits? If a trait is controlled by more than one gene, and each gene contributes only a small amount to the phenotype, how can such genes be identified and mapped?

FOR FURTHER READING

Aldhous, P. 1992. The promise and pitfalls of molecular genetics. *Science* 257: 164–165.

Balmor, M. G. 1970. *The Biology of Twinning in Man.* Oxford, England: Clarendon.

Baringa, M. 1996. Researchers nail down leptin receptor. *Science* 271: 913.

Benirschke, K. 1972. Origin and clinical significance of twinning. *Clin. Obstet. Gynecol.* 15: 220–235.

Bouchard, C., Tremblay, A., Despres, J.-P., Nadeau, A., Lupien, P. J., Theriault, G., Dussault, J., Moorjani, S., Pinault, S., and Fournier, G. 1990. The response to long-term overfeeding in identical twins. *New Engl. J. Med.* 322: 1477–1481.

Bouchard, C., Aderusse, L. 1993. Genetics of obesity. *Ann. Rev. Nutrition* 13: 337–354.

Bouchard, T. 1994. Genes, environment and personality. *Science* 264: 1700–1701.

Feldman, M. W., and Lewontin, R. 1975. The heritability hangup. *Science* 190: 1163–1166.

Harrison, G. A., and Owens, J. J. T. 1964. Studies on the inheritance of human skin color. *Ann. Hum. Genet.* 28: 27–37.

Horgan, J. 1995. Get smart, take a test. *Sci. Amer.* 273: 12–14.

Mackintosh, N. J. 1986. The biology of intelligence? *Br. J. Psychol.* 77: 1–18.

Moll, P., Burns, T. and Laver, R. 1991. The genetic and environmental sources of body mass index variability: The Muscatine ponderosity family study. *Am. J. Hum. Genet.* 49: 1243–1255.

Sorenson, T. I., Price, R. A., Stunkard, A. J., and Schulsinger, F. 1989. Genetics of obesity in adult adoptees and their biological siblings. *Br. Med. J.* 298: 87–90.

Stern, C. 1970. Model estimates for the number of gene pairs involved in pigmentation variability in Negro-Americans. *Hum Hered.* 20: 165–168.

Stunkard, A. J., Foch, T., and Hrubec, Z. 1986. A twin study of human obesity. *JAMA* 256: 51–54.

Stunkard, A. J., Harrus, J. R., Pedersen, N. L., and McClearn, G. E. 1990. The body-mass index of twins who have been reared apart. *New Engl. J. Med.* 322: 1483–1487.

CYTOGENETICS

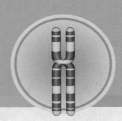

Chapter 6

Chapter Outline

ANALYZING CHROMOSOMES AND KARYOTYPES
Getting Cells for Chromosome Studies
Amniocentesis Collects Cells from the Fluid Surrounding the Fetus
Chorionic Villus Sampling Retrieves Fetal Tissue from the Placenta
CONCEPTS AND CONTROVERSIES   *Using Fetal Cells from the Mother's Blood*
VARIATIONS IN CHROMOSOME NUMBER
Polyploidy Changes the Number of Chromosome Sets
Aneuploidy Changes the Number of Individual Chromosomes

Monosomy Is Rare
Trisomy Is Relatively Common
RISKS FOR AUTOSOMAL TRISOMY
Maternal Age Is a Risk Factor
Why Is Age a Risk Factor?
ANEUPLOIDY OF THE SEX CHROMOSOMES
Turner Syndrome (45,X)
Klinefelter Syndrome (47,XXY)
XYY Syndrome (47,XXY)
XXX Syndrome (47,XXX)
Aneuploidy of the Sex Chromosomes: Some Conclusions

STRUCTURAL ALTERATIONS WITHIN CHROMOSOMES
Deletions Involve Loss of Chromosomal Material
Translocations Involve Exchange of Chromosome Parts
CONCEPTS AND CONTROVERSIES   *The Oldest Known Chromosome Aberration*
CONSEQUENCES OF ANEUPLOIDY
OTHER FORMS OF CHROMOSOME ABNORMALITIES
Uniparental Disomy
Fragile Sites
SIDEBAR   *Fragile Sites and Cancer*

OPENING IMAGE

A young girl with Down syndrome, a condition caused by an extra copy of chromosome 21.

I n 1953 a French physician named Jérôme Lejeune began working on a condition first described in 1866 by an English physician named John Langdon Down. Individuals with this condition have a distinctive physical appearance and are mentally retarded. Lejeune suspected that there was a genetic link to this phenotype.

He began by studying the fingerprints and palm prints of children with the condition, known as Down syndrome, and comparing them with the prints of unaffected children. The prints from Down syndrome children showed a high frequency of abnormalities. Because fingerprints and palm prints are laid down very early in development, they serve as a record of events that take place early in embryogenesis. From his studies on the disturbances in the print patterns of affected children, Lejeune became convinced that such significant changes in print patterns were probably not caused by the action of only one or two genes. Instead he reasoned that many genes must be involved; perhaps even an entire chromosome might play a role in Down syndrome.

It was a logical step to examine the chromosomes of Down syndrome children, but Lejeune lacked access to the proper equipment and techniques required. In 1957, in cooperation with a colleague, he began culturing cells from Down syndrome children. Lejeune examined the chromosomes in these cells using a microscope that had been discarded by the bacteriology laboratory in the hospital where he worked. He repaired the instrument by inserting a foil wrapper from a candy bar into the gears so that the image could be focused. His chromosome counts indicated that the cells of Down syndrome individuals contained 47 chromosomes, while those of unaffected individuals contained 46 chromosomes. He and his colleagues published a short paper in 1959 in which they reported that Down syndrome is caused by the presence of an extra chromosome. This chromosome was later identified as chromosome 21.

This remarkable discovery was the first human chromosome abnormality to be identified and marked an important turning point in human genetics. The discovery made clear that genetic disorders can be associated with changes in chromosome number, not just mutations of single genes inherited in Mendelian fashion.

ANALYZING CHROMOSOMES AND KARYOTYPES

Developments in cytogenetic techniques over the last 25 years have made it possible to selectively stain and identify each chromosome in the karyotype, to selectively stain specific regions of chromosomes (Figure 6.1), and to identify the location of genes directly on chromosomes. These advances have revolutionized the study of human chromosomes, and cytogenetic methods are routinely used in parallel with molecular techniques in the study of human genes.

Chromosome banding methods use stains and dyes to produce a pattern of bands that is different for each chromosome (although homologous chromosomes have the same pattern). One of the most common staining methods is G-banding, in which chromosomes are first treated with an enzyme (trypsin) to partially digest some chromosomal proteins, and then exposed to Giemsa stain (a mixture of dyes). The resulting pattern of bands is visible under the microscope, and is used to identify individual chromosomes in cytogenetic analysis. Usually, metaphase chromosomes are stained, because this is the stage of maximum chromosome condensation. Normally, cytogeneticists use metaphase chromosomes with about 550 bands. More detailed banding patterns can be obtained by staining chromosomes at early metaphase or late prophase. In these earlier stages, the chromosomes are longer and less con-

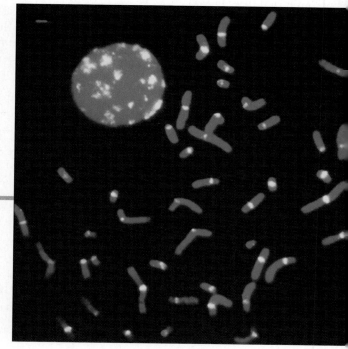

 FIGURE 6.1

Metaphase chromosomes stained to highlight centromeres (yellow). The chromosomes themselves were stained red. At upper left is an intact nucleus, with centromeres of chromosomes inside stained yellow.

densed, and about 2000 bands can be identified in the normal human karyotype. Some other banding methods are reviewed in ⬤ Figure 6.2.

Bands produced by Giemsa staining are consistent chromosomal landmarks that form the basis of a standardized code (presented in Chapter 2) used to identify any region of a chromosome by giving the chromosome number, the arm (p or q), the region number, and the band number within that region. For example, 21q23 refers to band 3 in region 2 of the long arm of chromosome 21 (review this code in Chapter 2).

In analyzing karyotypes, a similar standardized system of terminology is used. In this system, a karyotype is described by (1) the number of chromosomes, (2) the sex chromosome status, (3) the presence or absence of an individual chromosome, and (4) the nature and extent of any structural abnormality. The symbols for structural alterations include **t** for a translocation, **dup** for duplication, and **del** for deletion. These structural aberrations will be discussed later in the chapter. If a male has a deletion in the short arm of chromosome 5, but otherwise is chromosomally normal, this would be represented as 46,XY,del(5p). Table 6.1 lists some chromosomal aberrations using this system of terminology.

Cytogenetic analysis is a painstaking procedure done by cytogeneticists who study karyotypes stained to reveal black and white banding patterns. In hopes of making it easier to spot abnormalities, scientists have introduced a technique called chromosome painting. This method uses fluorescent markers, which attach to chromosome-specific DNA sequences. This labeling can use more than one DNA sequence and more than one fluorescent marker to produce a unique pattern for each of the 24 human chromosomes (22 autosomes and the X and Y chromosomes). Using this method, it is easier to find chromosomal abnormalities (⬤ Figure 6.3). Eventually, chromosome analysis may be done by automated scanning of painted chromosomes.

Translocation
A chromosomal aberration in which a chromosome segment is transferred to another, non-homologous chromosome.

Duplication
A chromosomal aberration in which a segment of a chromosome is repeated and therefore is present in more than one copy within the chromosome.

Deletion
A chromosomal aberration in whch a segment of a chromosome is missing.

⬤ **FIGURE 6.2**

Four common staining procedures used in chromosome analysis. Most karyotypes are prepared using G-banding. Q-banding and R-banding produce a pattern of bands that is the reverse of those in G-banded chromosomes.

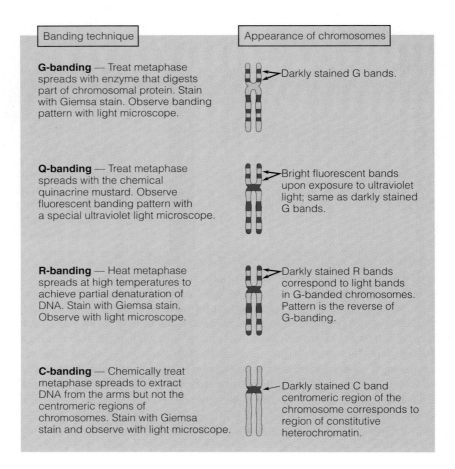

Banding technique	Appearance of chromosomes

G-banding — Treat metaphase spreads with enzyme that digests part of chromosomal protein. Stain with Giemsa stain. Observe banding pattern with light microscope.
Darkly stained G bands.

Q-banding — Treat metaphase spreads with the chemical quinacrine mustard. Observe fluorescent banding pattern with a special ultraviolet light microscope.
Bright fluorescent bands upon exposure to ultraviolet light; same as darkly stained G bands.

R-banding — Heat metaphase spreads at high temperatures to achieve partial denaturation of DNA. Stain with Giemsa stain. Observe with light microscope.
Darkly stained R bands correspond to light bands in G-banded chromosomes. Pattern is the reverse of G-banding.

C-banding — Chemically treat metaphase spreads to extract DNA from the arms but not the centromeric regions of chromosomes. Stain with Giemsa stain and observe with light microscope.
Darkly stained C band centromeric region of the chromosome corresponds to region of constitutive heterochromatin.

TABLE 6.1

Chromosome Aberrations

CHROMOSOME ABNORMALITY	SYNDROME	PHENOTYPE
46,del(4p)	Wolf-Hirschhorn syndrome	Mental retardation; midline facial defects consisting of broad nose, wide-set eyes, small lower jaw, and cleft palate; heart, lung, and skeletal abnormalities common; severely reduced survival
46,del(11)(p13)	WAGR syndrome	Tumors of the kidney (Wilms tumor) and of the gonad (gonadoblastoma); aniridia (absence of the iris); ambiguous genitalia; mental retardation
46,t(9;22)(q34q11)	CML (chronic myelogenous leukemia)	Enlargement of liver and spleen; anemia; excessive, unrestrained growth of white cells (granulocytes) in the bone marrow
46,t(8;14)	Burkitt's lymphoma	Malignancy of B lymphocytes that mature into the antibody-producing plasma cells; solid tumors, typically in the bones of the jaw and organs of the abdomen

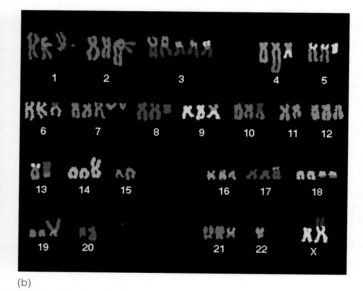

(a)

(b)

(c)

FIGURE 6.3

Chromosome painting with five different-colored markers in a normal cell (a) produces a pattern that highlights the translocations and deletions found in cancer cells (b and c).

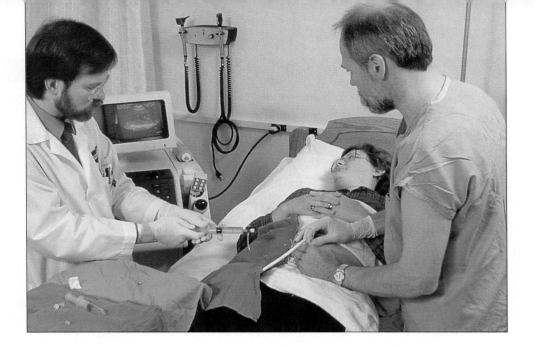

● **FIGURE 6.4**

A patient undergoing amniocentesis.

Amniocentesis

A method of sampling the fluid surrounding the developing fetus by inserting a hollow needle and withdrawing suspended fetal cells and fluid; used in diagnosing fetal genetic and developmental disorders; usually performed in the 16th week of pregnancy.

Chorionic villus sampling

A method of sampling fetal chorionic cells by inserting a catheter through the vagina or abdominal wall into the uterus. Used in diagnosing biochemical and cytogenetic defects in the embryo. Usually performed in the 8th or 9th week of pregnancy.

Getting Cells for Chromosome Studies

Almost any cell with a nucleus (red blood cells have no nuclei) can be used for chromosome analysis. In adults, white blood cells (lymphocytes), skin cells (fibroblasts), and cells from biopsies or surgically removed tumor cells are routinely used to make chromosome preparations.

The development of methods for prenatal diagnosis of chromosome abnormalities was a major advance in human genetics. Using **amniocentesis** and **chorionic villus sampling,** it is possible to diagnose chromosome abnormalities before birth. Another method that detects and analyzes fetal cells in the maternal circulation is now undergoing clinical testing, and may eventually be the method of choice for prenatal diagnosis (see "Concepts and Controversies," p. 142).

Amniocentesis Collects Cells from the Fluid Surrounding the Fetus

Until the 1960s, amniocentesis was used to diagnose and to follow the progress of high-risk and potentially fatal disorders such as fetal hemolytic anemia. In the mid-1960s, amniocentesis was successfully used for cytogenetic analysis. During amniocentesis, the fetus and the placenta are located by ultrasound, and a needle is inserted through the abdominal and uterine walls (avoiding the placenta and fetus) into the amniotic sac (● Figure 6.4). Approximately 10 to 30 ml of fluid is withdrawn using a syringe.

The amniotic fluid is mostly composed of fetal urine that contains cells shed from the skin, respiratory tract, and urinary tract of the fetus. The cells can be separated from the fluid by centrifugation (● Figure 6.5). The fluid can be tested for biochemical abnormalities that indicate the presence of a genetic defect. More than 100 biochemical disorders can be diagnosed by amniocentesis. The amniotic cells can be assayed for biochemical defects or grown in culture for karyotypic analysis following the procedures outlined in Chapter 2 for metaphase preparations. Once a karyotype has been prepared, it is possible to diagnose the sex of the fetus and the presence of chromosomal abnormalities.

Amniocentesis is not usually performed until the 16th week of pregnancy. Before this time, there is very little amniotic fluid, and contamination of the sample with maternal cells is often a problem. Several studies in the United States, Britain, and Canada have shown that amniocentesis involves a small but measurable risk to both the fetus and mother. There is a risk of maternal infection and a slight increase (less

than 1%) in the probability of a spontaneous abortion. To offset these risks, amniocentesis is normally used only under certain conditions:

- **Advanced maternal age.** Since the risk for aneuploid offspring increases dramatically after the age of 35 years, this procedure is recommended when the prospective mother is 35 years or older. This risk factor accounts for the majority of all cases in which amniocentesis is used.
- **Previous child with chromosomal aberration.** If a previous child had a chromosome abnormality, the recurrence risk is about 1% to 2%, and amniocentesis is recommended.
- **Presence of a balanced chromosomal rearrangement.** If either parent carries a chromosomal translocation or other rearrangement that can cause an unbalanced karyotype in the child, amniocentesis should be considered.
- **X-linked disorder.** If the mother is a carrier of an X-linked biochemical disorder that cannot be diagnosed prenatally and she is willing to abort if the fetus is male, then amniocentesis is recommended.

Chorionic Villus Sampling Retrieves Fetal Tissue from the Placenta

Chorionic villus sampling (CVS) is used for prenatal diagnosis in the first trimester of pregnancy. This technique has several advantages over amniocentesis. CVS can be performed at 8 to 10 weeks of gestation, compared with the 15 to 16 weeks for amniocentesis. Cytogenetic results from CVS can be available within a few hours or a few days, and biochemical tests can be performed directly on the sampled fetal tis-

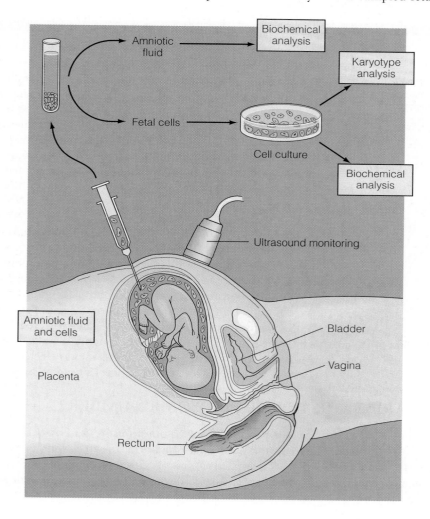

FIGURE 6.5

In amniocentesis, a syringe needle is inserted through the abdominal wall and uterine wall to collect a small sample of the amniotic fluid. The fluid contains fetal cells that can be collected and used for prenatal chromosomal or biochemical analysis.

Using Fetal Cells from the Mother's Blood

More than a century has passed since placental cells from the fetus were first discovered in the circulatory systems of pregnant women. In 1969, cytogeneticists observed cells carrying a Y chromosome in the blood of women who later gave birth to male infants. Since then, research has been directed at finding ways to recover and use fetal cells from the maternal circulation for prenatal diagnosis. The goal is to be able to carry out chromosome analysis on fetal cells in a 20-ml sample of maternal blood without using the invasive procedures of amniocentesis and chorionic villus sampling (CVS). Use of fetal blood for prenatal diagnosis would lower the risk of injury to the mother and fetus. Several types of fetal cells enter the maternal circulation, including placental cells (trophoblasts) and white blood cells (lymphocytes). These cells probably enter the bloodstream in detectable amounts between the 6th and 12th week of pregnancy. But since less than 1 in every 100,000 cells in the mother's blood are from the fetus, collecting enough fetal cells from a blood sample is one of the challenges facing those working to develop this technique.

Several methods are being tried to isolate fetal cells from maternal blood, and no single technique has emerged as the best. Even though these methods are still under development, several studies have found it possible to diagnose chromosome abnormalities in fetal cells collected from maternal blood. These encouraging results have led the National Institute of Child Health and Human Development to begin a clinical trial designed to test the accuracy of chromosomal analysis on fetal blood cells. In this trial, 3000 women who are having amniocentesis or chorionic villus biopsy for a high-risk pregnancy will be asked to donate a blood sample for chromosome analysis. The results from the fetal blood cells will be compared to those from amniocentesis and CVS. The trial will be completed and evaluated in 1997. If successful, fetal blood sampling may gradually replace more invasive procedures for prenatal chromosome analysis.

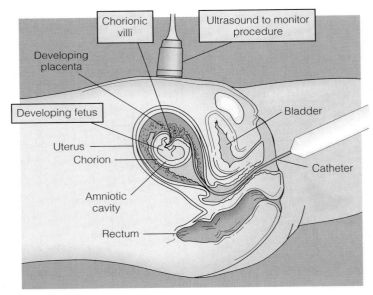

● FIGURE 6.6

The chorionic villus sampling technique. A catheter is inserted into the uterus through the vagina to remove a sample of fetal tissue from the chorion. Cells in the tissue can be used for chromosomal or biochemical analysis.

sue rather than after tissue culture, as required following amniocentesis. For CVS, a small flexible catheter is inserted through the vagina or abdomen into the uterus, and is guided by ultrasound images. A small sample from the chorionic villi, a fetal tissue that forms part of the placenta is obtained by suction (● Figure 6.6). This tissue is mitotically active and can be used immediately in the preparation of a karyotype. As with amniocentesis, enough material is usually obtained with CVS to allow biochemical testing or the preparation of DNA samples for molecular analysis. The use of DNA analysis for prenatal diagnosis will be discussed in Chapter 13.

CVS is a more specialized technique than amniocentesis and at present is used less often. Although early studies indicated that the procedure posed a higher risk to mother and fetus than amniocentesis, improvements in the instruments and technique have lowered the risk somewhat. CVS offers early diagnosis of genetic diseases, and if termination of pregnancy is elected, maternal risks are lower at 9 to 12 weeks than at 16 weeks.

 ## VARIATIONS IN CHROMOSOME NUMBER

At the birth of a child, anxious parents have two questions: is it a boy or a girl, and is the baby normal? The term *normal* in this context means free from all birth defects. The causes of such defects are, of course, both environmental and genetic. Among the genetic causes, we have considered disorders such as sickle cell anemia or Marfan syndrome, caused by the mutation of single genes. Other genetic causes of

defects are changes in chromosome number or structural alterations in chromosomes. Such changes may involve entire chromosome sets, individual chromosomes, or alterations within individual chromosomes. Recall that the set of 46 chromosomes present in each somatic cell is referred to as the diploid, or $2n$, number of chromosomes. Similarly, the set of 23 chromosomes (constituting the n number) is the haploid set. Together these normal conditions are referred to as the euploid condition.

Variation in the number of haploid sets of chromosomes is known as **polyploidy.** A cell with three sets of chromosomes is triploid, one with four sets is tetraploid, and so forth. A change in chromosome number that involves less than an entire diploid set of chromosomes is known as **aneuploidy.** The number of chromosomes present in aneuploidy is not a simple multiple of the haploid set. In humans the most common forms of aneuploidy involve the gain or loss of a single chromosome. The loss of a chromosome is known as **monosomy** ($2n - 1$), and the addition of a chromosome to the diploid set is known as **trisomy** ($2n + 1$). Since the discovery of trisomy 21 in 1959 as the first example of aneuploidy in humans, cytogenetic studies have revealed that alterations in chromosome number are fairly common in humans and are a major cause of reproductive failure. It is now estimated that as many as 1 in every 2 conceptions may be aneuploid, and that 70% of early embryonic deaths and spontaneous abortions are caused by aneuploidy. About 1 in every 170 live births is at least partially aneuploid, and from 5% to 7% of all deaths in early childhood are related to aneuploidy.

Humans have a rate of aneuploidy that is up to 10 times higher than that of other mammals, including other primates. This difference may represent a considerable reproductive disadvantage for our species. Understanding the causes of aneuploidy in humans remains one of the great challenges in human genetics.

Polyploidy
A chromosome number that is a multiple of the normal diploid chromosome set.

Aneuploidy
A chromosome number that is not an exact multiple of the haploid set.

Monosomy
A condition in which one member of a chromosome pair is missing; having one less than the diploid number ($2n - 1$).

Trisomy
A condition in which one chromosome is present in three copies while all others are diploid; having one more than the diploid number ($2n + 1$).

Polyploidy Changes the Number of Chromosome Sets

Abnormalities in the number of haploid chromosome sets can arise in several ways: (1) errors in meiosis during gamete formation, (2) events at fertilization, or (3) errors in mitosis following fertilization. Polyploidy sometimes occurs through a process called endoreduplication. In endoreduplication, cleavage of the cytoplasm (cytokinesis) fails to occur in the last stage of cell division. This can occur in either mitosis or meiosis. Recall that mitotic divisions precede meiosis in the ovary and testis. If, during one of these mitotic cycles, the chromosomes replicate and sister chromatids divide but there is no cytoplasmic division, the result is a tetraploid cell containing four copies of each chromosome. If this cell undergoes meiosis in a normal fashion, the result will be gametes that contain the diploid instead of the haploid number of chromosomes. Fusion between this genetically unbalanced gamete and a normal haploid gamete will produce a triploid zygote (Figure 6.7).

A diploid gamete can also arise through meiotic errors. An error in meiosis I can result in the failure of homologous chromosomes to separate, producing diploid gametes after meiosis II. Alternatively, in meiosis II, if all chromosomes move to the same pole after cen-

 FIGURE 6.7

The karyotype of a triploid individual contains three copies of each chromosome.

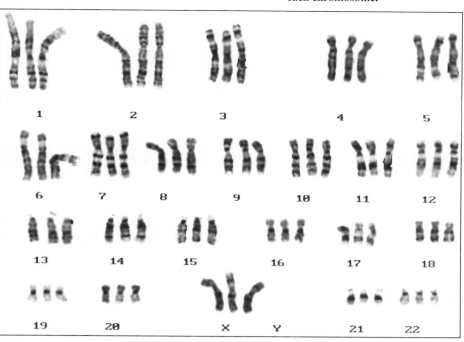

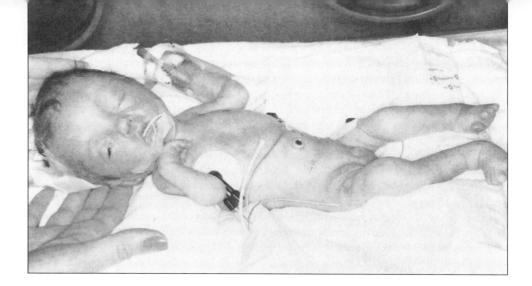

FIGURE 6.8
A triploid infant, showing the characteristic enlarged head.

Dispermy
Fertilization of haploid egg by two haploid sperm, forming a triploid zygote.

Triploidy
A chromosome number that is three times the haploid number, having three copies of all autosomes and three sex chromosomes.

Tetraploidy
A chromosome number that is four times the haploid number, having four copies of all autosomes and four sex chromosomes.

Nondisjunction
The failure of homologous chromosomes to properly separate during meiosis or mitosis.

tromere separation, diploid gametes will also result. Another event that can result in polyploidy is **dispermy**, the simultaneous fertilization of a haploid egg by two haploid sperm. The result is a zygote containing three haploid chromosome sets, or triploidy.

Triploidy   The most common form of polyploidy in humans is **triploidy**, which is found in 15% to 18% of spontaneous abortions. Three types of triploid chromosome sets have been observed: 69,XXY; 69,XXX; and 69,XYY. Approximately 75% of all cases of triploidy have two sets of paternal chromosomes. Accidents in male gamete formation do not occur this often, and most triploid zygotes probably arise as the result of dispermy. Although biochemical changes that accompany fertilization normally prevent such fertilizations, this system is not fail-safe.

Almost 1% of all conceptions are triploid, but over 99% of these die before birth, and only 1 in 10,000 live births is triploid. Survival for triploids is limited, and most die within a month. Triploid newborns have multiple abnormalities including an enlarged head, fusion of fingers and toes (syndactyly), and malformations of the mouth, eyes, and genitals (► Figure 6.8). The high rate of embryonic death and failure to survive as a newborn indicates that triploidy is incompatible with life and should be regarded as a lethal condition.

Tetraploidy   Tetraploidy is observed in about 5% of all spontaneous abortions and is reported only rarely in live births. The sex chromosome constitution of all tetraploid embryos is either XXXX or XXYY. **Tetraploidy** can arise in the first mitotic division after fertilization if there is no cytoplasmic division (cytokinesis) after chromosome division. The result will be a tetraploid cell. Subsequent rounds of mitosis will result in a tetraploid embryo. If tetraploidy arises sometime after the first mitotic division, two different cell lines will coexist in the embryo, one a normal diploid line and the other a tetraploid cell line. Such mosaic individuals survive somewhat longer than complete polyploids, but the condition is still life-threatening.

In summary, polyploidy in humans can arise by at least two different mechanisms, but is inevitably lethal. Polyploidy does not involve mutation of any genes, but only changes in the number of gene copies. How this quantitative change in gene number is related to lethality in development is unknown.

Aneuploidy Changes the Number of Individual Chromosomes

As defined earlier, aneuploidy is the addition or deletion of individual chromosomes from the normal diploid set of 46. Aneuploidy can be caused in several ways, the most important of which is **nondisjunction**, a process in which chromosomes fail to

separate properly at anaphase. Although this failure can occur in either meiosis or mitosis, nondisjunction in meiosis is the leading cause of aneuploidy in humans. There are two cell divisions in meiosis, and nondisjunction can occur in either the first or second division, with different genetic consequences (━ Figure 6.9).

If nondisjunction takes place in meiosis I, all the gametes will be abnormal. These gametes will carry both members of a chromosome pair, or neither member of the pair. Nondisjunction in meiosis II results in two normal gametes and two abnormal gametes (Figure 6.9). Gametes missing a copy of a given chromosome will produce a monosomic zygote; those containing an extra copy of a chromosome will give rise to a trisomic zygote.

As a group, aneuploid individuals have distinct and characteristic phenotypic features. Those with a given form of aneuploidy, such as Down syndrome, tend to resemble each other more closely than their own brothers and sisters. The phenotypic effects of aneuploidy range from minor physical symptoms to devastating and lethal deficiencies in major organ systems. Among survivors, phenotypic effects often include behavioral deficits and mental retardation. In the following section, we will look at some of the important features of autosomal aneuploid phenotypes. Then we will consider the phenotypic effects of sex chromosome aneuploidy.

━ **FIGURE 6.9**

Nondisjunction in the first meiotic division (left) results in four abnormal gametes. Two gametes carry both members of a chromosome pair, and two are missing one chromosome. Nondisjunction in the second meiotic division (right) produces two normal gametes and two abnormal gametes. One gamete carries both members of a chromosome pair, and one is missing a chromosome.

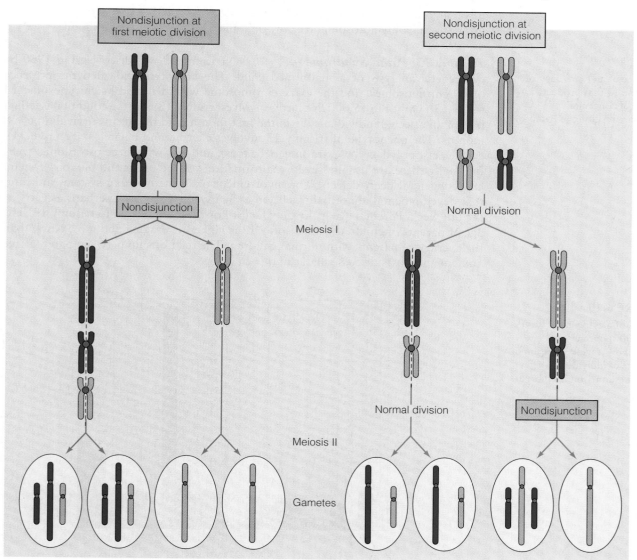

Monosomy is Rare

Meiotic nondisjunction during gamete formation should result in equal numbers of monosomic and trisomic embryos. However, autosomal monosomies are only rarely observed among spontaneous abortions and live births. The likely explanation is that the majority of autosomal monosomic embryos are lost very early, even before pregnancy is recognized.

Trisomy is Relatively Common

Most autosomal trisomies are lethal conditions; but unlike monosomy, the presence of an extra chromosome allows varying degrees of development to occur. Autosomal trisomy is found in about 50% of all cases of chromosome abnormalities in fetal death. The findings also indicate that the autosomes are differentially involved in trisomy (Figure 6.10). Trisomies for chromosomes 1, 3, 12, and 19 are rarely observed in spontaneous abortions, while trisomy for chromosome 16 accounts for almost one third of all cases. As a group, the acrocentric chromosomes (13–15, 21, and 22) are represented in 40% of all spontaneous abortions. Reasons for this differential involvement include differences in the rate of nondisjunction, in the rate of fetal death before recognition of pregnancy, or a combination of factors. Only a few autosomal trisomies result in live birth (trisomy 8, 13, and 18). Trisomy 21(Down syndrome) is the only autosomal trisomy that allows survival into adulthood.

Trisomy 13
The presence of an extra copy of chromosome 13 that produces a distinct set of congenital abnormalities resulting in Patau syndrome.

Trisomy 13: Patau Syndrome (47,+ 13)   **Trisomy 13** was discovered in 1960 by cytogenetic analysis of a malformed child. The karyotype indicated the presence of 47 chromosomes, and the extra chromosome was identified as chromosome 13 (47,+ 13). Only 1 in 15,000 live births involves trisomy 13, and the condition is lethal; half of all affected individuals die in the first month, and the mean survival time is 6 months. The phenotype of trisomy 13 involves cleft lip and palate (Figure 6.11), eye defects, polydactyly (extra fingers or toes), and feet with large protruding heels. Internally there are usually severe malformations of the brain and nervous system, and congenital heart defects. The involvement of so many organ systems indicates that developmental abnormalities begin early in embryogenesis, perhaps as early as the 6th week. Parental age is the only factor known to be related to trisomy 13. The age of parents of children with trisomy 13 is higher (averaging about 32 years) than the average of parents with normal children. The relationship between parental age and aneuploidy is discussed later in this chapter.

 FIGURE 6.10

The results of a cytogenetic survey of over 4000 spontaneous abortions show a wide variation in the presence of individual chromosomes in trisomic embryos.

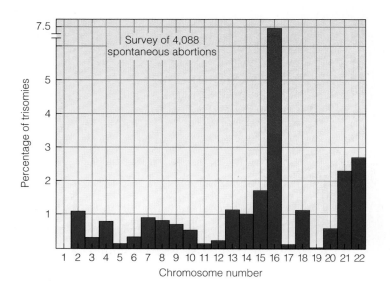

Survey of 4,088 spontaneous abortions

Trisomy 18: Edwards Syndrome (47,+ 18) In 1960 John Edwards and his colleagues reported the first case of **trisomy 18** (47,+ 18). Infants with this condition are small at birth, grow very slowly, and are mentally retarded. For reasons still unknown, 80% of all trisomy 18 births are female. Clenched fists, with the second and fifth finger overlapping the third and fourth fingers, and malformed feet are also characteristic (➡ Figure 6.12). Heart malformations are almost always present, and death is usually caused by heart failure or pneumonia. Trisomy 18 occurs with a frequency of 1 in 11,000 live births, and the average survival time is 2 to 4 months. As in trisomy 13, advanced maternal age is a factor predisposing to trisomy 18.

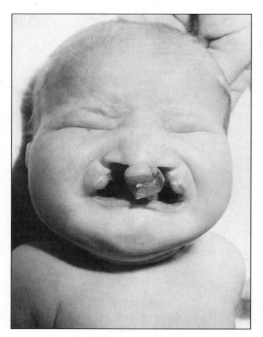

Trisomy 21: Down Syndrome (47,+ 21) The phenotypic features of **trisomy 21**(MIM/OMIM 190685) were first described by John Langdon Down in 1866. He called the condition mongolism because of the distinctive fold of skin, known as an epicanthic fold, in

Trisomy 18
The presence of an extra copy of chromosome 18 that results in a clinically distinct set of invariably lethal abnormalities known as Edwards syndrome.

Trisomy 21
Aneuploidy involving the presence of an extra copy of chromosome 21, resulting in Down syndrome.

➡ **FIGURE 6.11**
An infant with trisomy 13, showing a cleft lip and palate (the roof of the mouth).

➡ **FIGURE 6.12**
An infant with trisomy 18 and a karyotype.

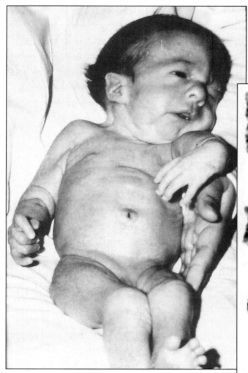

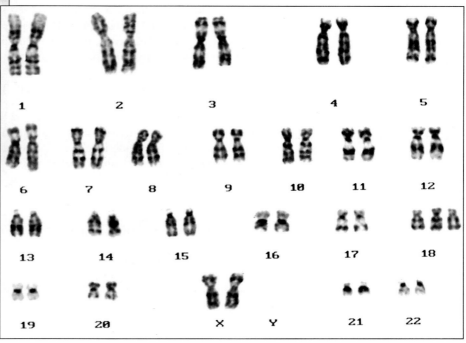

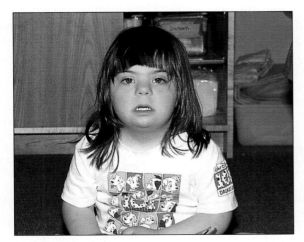

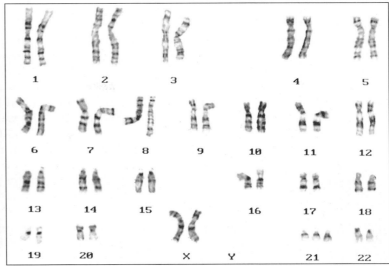

FIGURE 6.13

A child with trisomy 21 and a karyotype. This child has three copies of chromosome 21.

the corner of the eye (Figure 6.13). To remove the racist implications inherent in the term, Lionel Penrose and others changed the designation to Down syndrome. As described in the chapter opening, the presence of an extra copy of chromosome 21 as the underlying cause of Down syndrome was discovered by Jérôme Lejeune and his colleagues in 1959 and represents the first chromosome abnormality discovered in humans. Trisomy 21 has also been observed in other primate species including the chimpanzee.

Down syndrome is one of the most common chromosome defects in humans and occurs in about 0.5% of all conceptions and in 1 in 900 live births (Figure 6.13). It is a leading cause of childhood mental retardation and heart defects in the United States. Affected individuals have a wide skull that is flatter than normal at the back. The eyelids have an epicanthic fold, and the iris contains spots, known as Brushfield spots. The tongue may be furrowed and protruding, causing the mouth to remain partially open. Physical growth, behavior, and mental development are retarded, and approximately 40% of all affected individuals have congenital heart defects. In addition, children with Down syndrome are prone to respiratory infections and contract leukemia at a rate far above the normal population. In the past decade improvements in medical care have increased survival rates dramatically, so that many affected individuals survive into adulthood, although few reach the age of 50 years. In spite of these handicaps, many individuals with Down syndrome lead rich, productive lives and can serve as an inspiration to us all.

RISKS FOR AUTOSOMAL TRISOMY

The causes of autosomal trisomies such as Down syndrome are unknown; but a variety of genetic and environmental factors have been proposed, including radiation, viral infection, hormone levels, and genetic predisposition. To date the only factor clearly related to autosomal aneuploidy is advanced maternal age. In fact, a relationship between maternal age and Down syndrome was well established 25 years before the chromosomal basis for the condition was discovered.

Maternal Age is a Risk Factor

The risk of having children with trisomy 21 is low for young mothers, but increases rapidly after the age of 35 years. At the age of 20 the incidence of Down syndrome offspring is 0.05%, by age 35 the risk of having a child with Down syndrome has climbed to 0.9%, and at 45 years 3% of all births are trisomy 21 (Figure 6.14). The effect of maternal age on other aneuploidies has been documented, and the re-

lationship between advanced maternal age and autosomal trisomy is very striking (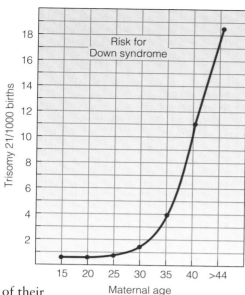 Figure 6.15). Paternal age has also been proposed as a factor in trisomy, but the evidence is weak, and no clear-cut link has been demonstrated.

The evidence that advanced maternal age is a risk factor for aneuploid offspring comes from studies on the parental origin of nondisjunction events documented by chromosome banding of the affected child and both parents, and by studies using recombinant DNA technology. Occasionally, chromosomes have some minor variations in banding patterns. By examining banded chromosomes from the trisomic child and the parents, the parental origin of the nondisjunction can often be determined. For trisomy 21, the nondisjunction event is maternal about 94% of the time and paternal about 6% of the time. In other autosomal trisomies studied, the paternal contribution is about 7%. In all trisomies, the great majority of maternal nondisjunction events occur at meiosis I.

FIGURE 6.14

The relationship between maternal age and the frequency of trisomy 21 (Down syndrome). The risk increases rapidly after 34 years of age.

Why is Age a Risk Factor?

Nondisjunction during gamete formation increases as women reach the end of their reproductive period, but the mechanisms controlling this increase remain obscure. One idea about the relationship between maternal age and nondisjunction focuses on the duration of meiosis in females. Recall from Chapter 2 that primary oocytes are formed early in development, and enter the first meiotic prophase well before birth. Meiosis I is not completed until ovulation, so that eggs produced at age 40 have been in meiosis I for over 40 years. During this time metabolic errors or environmental agents may damage the cell so that aneuploidy results when meiosis resumes. However, it is not yet known whether the age of the ovum is directly related to the increased frequency of nondisjunction.

A second idea proposed to account for the relationship between an increase in aneuploid children with advanced maternal age is related to the interaction between the implanting embryo and the uterine environment. According to this idea, the embryo-uterus interaction normally results in the spontaneous abortion of chromosomally abnormal embryos, a process called maternal selection. As women age, this process may become less effective, allowing more chromosomally abnormal embryos to implant and develop. This second theory to explain the relationship between advanced maternal age and aneuploid offspring is called relaxed maternal selection.

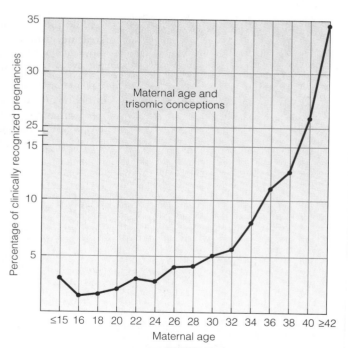

FIGURE 6.15

Maternal age is the major risk factor for autosomal trisomies of all types. By age 42, about 1 in 3 identified pregnancies is trisomic.

ANEUPLOIDY OF THE SEX CHROMOSOMES

The incidence of sex chromosome aneuploidy is higher than for autosomes. The overall incidence of sex chromosome anomalies in live births is 1 in 400 for males and 1 in 650 for females. Unlike the situation with autosomes, where monosomy is always fatal, monosomy for the X chromosome is a viable condition. Monosomy for the Y chromosome (45,Y), however, is always lethal.

Turner Syndrome (45,X)

Monosomy for the X chromosome (45,X) was reported as a chromosomal disorder in 1959, but the cytogenetic findings were only the finishing touch to a larger piece of genetic detective work. In 1954, Paul Polani, working on the causes of congenital

heart defects, examined three women who suffered from a defect of the aorta usually found only in males. Polani noted that all three women also had phenotypic features originally described by Henry Turner in 1938: short stature, extra folds of skin on the neck, and rudimentary sexual development. Examining cells scraped from the inside of their cheeks, Polani discovered that, like males, these females lacked a sex chromatin, or Barr body. Because of this, he suspected that females with **Turner syndrome** might be affected by X-linked traits as frequently as males.

Assembling a large group of females lacking ovarian development, including those with Turner syndrome, Polani tested them for colorblindness, a sex-linked trait. Four of the 25 females tested were color blind, a result that was much higher than expected in a population of females and similar to that expected in males. In a paper published in 1956, he suggested that Turner syndrome females might have only one X chromosome and in effect be hemizygous for traits on the X chromosome.

After a careful cytogenetic study, Polani and Charles Ford published a paper in 1959 confirming that Turner females are indeed 45,X. The unraveling of the chromosomal basis of Turner syndrome illustrates a basic property of scientific research: work in one area—in this case, congenital heart disease—often leads to significant findings in another field.

Turner syndrome females are short and wide chested, with underdeveloped breasts and rudimentary ovaries (● Figure 6.16). At birth a puffiness of the hands and feet is prominent, but this disappears in infancy. As reported by Polani, such individuals also have a narrowing, or coarctation, of the aorta. There is no mental retardation associated with this syndrome, although evidence suggests that Turner syndrome is associated with reduced skills in interpreting spatial relationships. This chromosome disorder occurs with a frequency of 1 in 10,000 female births, and while affected newborns suffer no life-threatening problems, 95% to 99% of all 45,X embryos die before birth. It is estimated that 1% of all conceptions are 45,X. Another notable feature of this syndrome is that in 75% of all cases, the nondisjunction event apparently originates in the father.

The phenotypic impact of the single X chromosome in Turner syndrome is strikingly illustrated in a case of identical twins, one of them 46,XX and the other 45,X. This situation apparently arose by mitotic nondisjunction after fertilization and twinning. These twins (● Figure 6.17) were judged to be identical on the basis of blood types and chromosome banding studies. They show significant differences in height, sexual development, hearing, dental maturity, and performance on tests that measure numerical skills and space perception. While some environmental factors may contribute to these differences, the major role of the second X chromosome in normal female development is apparent. These

Turner syndrome
A monosomy of the X chromosome (45,X) that results in female sterility.

● **FIGURE 6.16**

A girl with Turner syndrome and the associated karyotype, containing a single X chromosome. Turner syndrome is characterized by short stature, a broad chest, and lack of sexual development. Stature and sexual development can be treated using hormones.

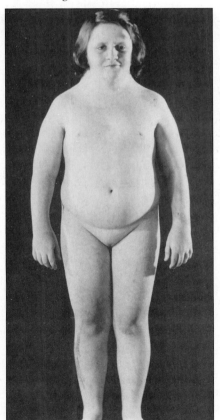

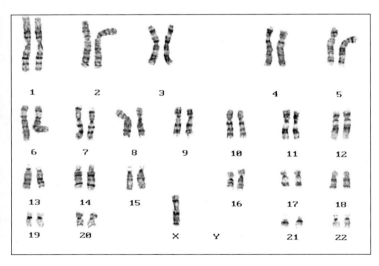

and similar results from other studies on individuals with Turner syndrome indicate that a second X chromosome is necessary for normal development of the ovary, normal growth patterns, and development of the nervous system. Complete absence of an X chromosome, with or without the presence of a Y chromosome, is always lethal, emphasizing that the X chromosome is an essential component of the karyotype.

Klinefelter syndrome
Aneuploidy of the sex chromosomes involving an XXY chromosome constitution.

Klinefelter Syndrome (47,XXY)

The phenotype of Klinefelter syndrome was first described in 1942, and the XXY chromosome constitution was reported in 1959 by Patricia Jacobs and John Strong. The frequency of **Klinefelter syndrome** is approximately 1 in 1000 male births. The phenotypic features of this syndrome do not develop until puberty. Affected individuals are male but show poor sexual development and have very low fertility. Some degree of breast development occurs in about 50% of the cases (Figure 6.18). A degree of subnormal intelligence appears in some affected individuals.

A significant fraction of Klinefelter males are mosaics, with XY and XXY cell lines present in the body. About 60% of the cases are the result of maternal nondisjunction, and advanced maternal age is known to increase the risk of affected offspring. Other forms of Klinefelter include XXYY, XXXY, and XXXXY. The presence of additional X chromosomes in these karyotypes increases the severity of the phenotypic symptoms and brings on clear-cut mental retardation.

XYY Syndrome (47,XYY)

In 1965 the results of a cytogenetic survey by Patricia Jacobs of 197 males institutionalized for violent and dangerous antisocial behavior aroused a great deal of interest in the scientific community and the popular press. The findings indicated that nine of these males (about 4.5% of the institution-

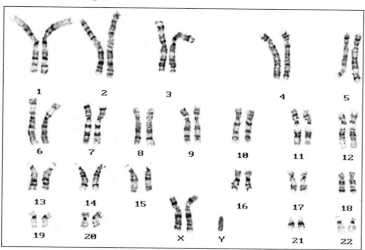

 FIGURE 6.17

Monozygotic twins, one of which has Turner syndrome. The twin with Turner syndrome (left) is 45, X; the normal twin (right) is 46, XX.

 FIGURE 6.18

A young man with Klinefelter syndrome and its characteristic karyotype. In some cases, Klinefelter syndrome is associated with breast development.

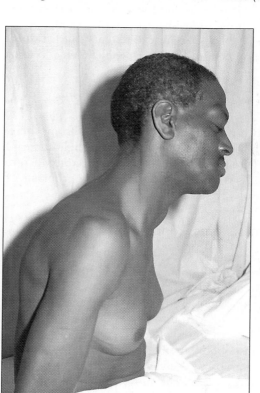

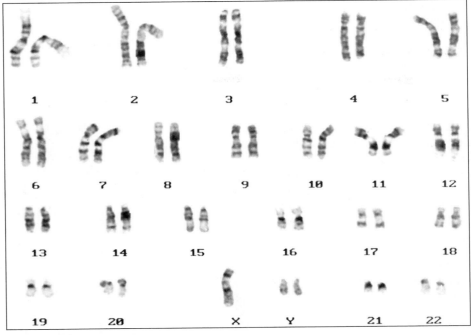

FIGURE 6.19

The karyotype of an XYY male. Affected individuals are usually taller than normal, and some—but not all—suffer from personality disorders.

XYY karyotype
Aneuploidy of the sex chromosomes involving XYY chromosome constitution.

alized males in the survey) had an XYY karyotype (● Figure 6.19). These XYY individuals were all above average in height, all suffered personality disorders, and seven of the nine were of subnormal intelligence. Subsequent studies indicated that the frequency of XYY males in the general population is 1 in 1000 male births (about 0.1% of the males in the general population), and that the frequency of XYY individuals in penal and mental institutions is significantly higher than in the population at large.

Early investigators associated the tendency to violent criminal behavior with the presence of an extra Y chromosome. In effect, this would mean that some forms of violent behavior were brought about by genetic predisposition. In fact, the XYY karyotype has been used on several occasions as a legal defense (unsuccessfully, so far) in criminal trials. The question is this: is there really a causal relationship between the XYY condition and criminal behavior? There is no strong evidence to support such a link; in fact, the vast majority of XYY males lead socially normal lives. In the United States, long-term studies of the relationship between antisocial behavior and the 47,XYY karyotype have been discontinued because of the fear that identifying someone with potential behavior problems might lead parents to treat those children differently, resulting in the development of behavior problems as a kind of self-fulfilling prophecy.

XXX Syndrome (47,XXX)

Approximately 1 in 1000 females are born with three copies of the X chromosome. In most cases these females are clinically normal, although there is a slight increase in sterility and mental retardation compared with the population at large. In rare cases 48,XXXX and 49,XXXXX karyotypes have been reported, and problems of sexual development and mental retardation are severe.

Aneuploidy of the Sex Chromosomes: Some Conclusions

Several conclusions can be drawn from the study of sex chromosome disorders. First, at least one copy of an X chromosome is essential for survival. Embryos without any X chromosomes (44,-XX and 45,OY) are inviable and are not observed in studies of spontaneous abortions. They must be eliminated even before pregnancy is recognized, emphasizing the role of the X chromosome in normal development. The second general conclusion is that addition of extra copies of either sex chromosome interferes with normal development and causes both physical and mental problems. As the number of sex chromosomes in the karyotype increases, the derangements become more severe, indicating that a balance of sex-chromosome gene dosage and gene products is essential to normal development in both males and females.

STRUCTURAL ALTERATIONS WITHIN CHROMOSOMES

Changes in chromosome structure can involve one, two, or more chromosomes, and result from the breakage and reunion of chromosome parts. In some cases the pieces in chromosome breaks are rejoined to restore the original structure; in others an array of abnormal chromosomes results. Breaks can occur spontaneously through errors in replication or recombination. They can also be produced by environmental agents such as ultraviolet light, radiation, viruses, and chemicals. Structural alterations include deletions, the loss of a chromosome segment; duplications, which are extra copies of a chromosome segment; translocations, which move a segment from one chromosome to another; and **inversions,** or reversal in the order of a chromosome segment (⬤ Figure 6.20). Rather than considering how such aberrations are produced, we will concentrate on the phenotypic effects of these structural alter-

Inversion
A chromosomal aberration in which a chromosome segment has been rotated 180° from its usual orientation.

⬤ **FIGURE 6.20**

Some of the common structural abnormalities seen in chromosomes. (a) In a deletion, part of the chromosome is lost. This can occur at the tip of the chromosome as shown, or an internal segment can be lost. (b) In an inversion, the order of part of the chromosome is reversed. This does not change the amount of genetic information carried by the chromosome, only its arrangement. (c) A duplication has a chromosome segment repeated (in this example, gene D and its surrounding region are duplicated). (d) In a translocation, chromosome parts are exchanged.

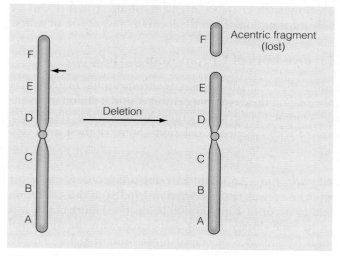

(a)

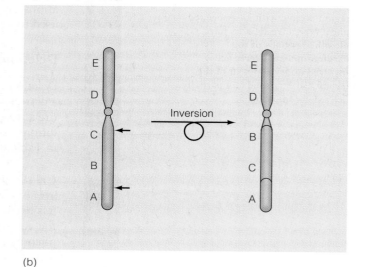

(b)

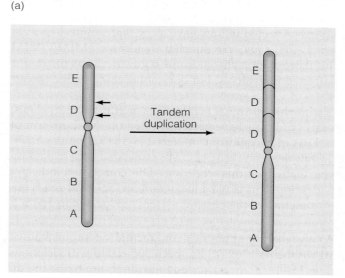

(c)

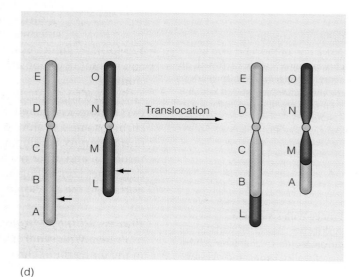

(d)

TABLE 6.2		
Chromosome Deletions		
DELETION	SYNDROME	PHENOTYPE
5p-	Cri du chat syndrome	Infants have catlike cry, some facial anomalies, severe mental retardation
11q-	Wilms tumor	Kidney tumors, genital and urinary tract abnormalities
13q-	Retinoblastoma	Cancer of eye, increased risk of other cancers
15q-	Prader-Willi syndrome	Infants: weak, slow growth; children and adults: obesity, compulsive eating

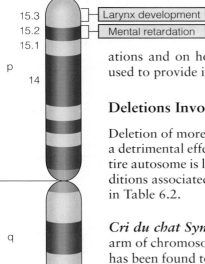

▬ **FIGURE 6.21**

A deletion of part of chromosome 5 is associated with cri du chat syndrome. (a) By comparing the region deleted with its associated phenotype, investigators have identified regions of the chromosome that carry genes involved in development of the larynx. (b) A normal and partially deleted chromosome 5.

ations and on how such changes in chromosome structure can be used to provide information about the location and action of genes.

Deletions Involve Loss of Chromosomal Material

Deletion of more than a small amount of chromosomal material has a detrimental effect on the developing embryo, and deletion of an entire autosome is lethal. Consequently there are only a few viable conditions associated with large-scale deletions. Some of these are listed in Table 6.2.

Cri du chat Syndrome   An infant carrying a deletion of the short arm of chromosome 5 was first reported in 1963, and this condition has been found to occur in 1 in 100,000 births (▬ Figure 6.21). It is the reduction in gene dosage that is associated with the abnormal phenotype, not the presence of one or more mutant genes. The affected infant is mentally retarded, with defects in facial development, gastrointestinal malformations, and abnormal development of the glottis and larynx. Affected infants have a cry that sounds like a cat meowing, hence the name **cri du chat syndrome** (MIM/OMIM 123450)(▬ Figure 6.22). This deletion of a chromosome segment affects the motor and mental development of affected individuals, but does not seem to be life threatening.

By correlating phenotypes with chromosomal breakpoints in affected individuals, two regions associated with this syndrome have been identified on the short arm of chromosome 5 (Figure 6.21). Loss of chromosome material in 5p15.3 results in abnormal larynx development, while deletions in 5p15.2 are associated with mental retardation and other phenotypic features of this syndrome. This correlation indicates that genes controlling larynx development may be located in 5p15.3, and genes important in the development or function of the nervous system are located in 5p15.2.

Prader-Willi Syndrome   A constellation of physical and mental symptoms known as **Prader-Willi syndrome** (MIM/OMIM 176270) has been correlated with deletions in the long arm of chromosome 15. As infants, affected individuals are weak and do

Cri du chat syndrome
A deletion of the short arm of chromosome 5 associated with an array of congenital malformations, the most characteristic of which is an infant cry that resembles a mewing cat.

Prader-Willi syndrome
A disorder associated with chromosome 15 characterized by uncontrolled eating and obesity.

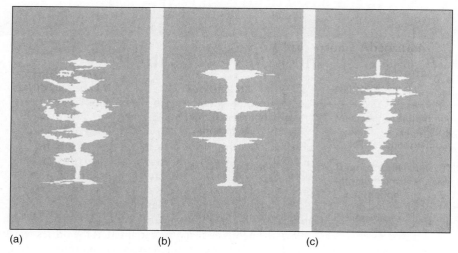

■ **FIGURE 6.22**

Sound recordings of (a) a normal infant, (b) an infant with cri du chat syndrome, and (c) a cat. The cry of the affected infant is much closer in sound pattern to that of the cat than a normal infant, giving rise to the name of the syndrome, cry of the cat.

(a)   (b)   (c)

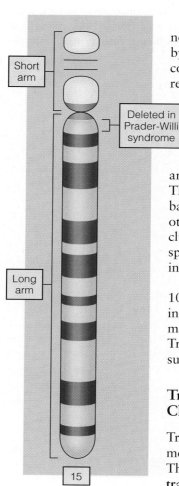

Short arm

Deleted in Prader-Willi syndrome

Long arm

15

■ **FIGURE 6.23**

Diagram of chromosome 15, showing the region deleted in Prader-Willi syndrome.

not feed well because of a poor sucking reflex. However, by the age of 5 or 6 years, these children develop an uncontrollable compulsion to eat that results in obesity and related health problems such as diabetes. Left untreated, victims will literally eat themselves to death. Other symptoms include poor sexual development in males, behavioral problems, and mental retardation. Careful examination of karyotypes from Prader-Willi patients shows deletions in the long arm of chromosome 15 between bands q11 and q13. The size of the deletion is variable but always includes band 15q11.2 (■ Figure 6.23). In about 5% of cases other chromosomal aberrations are found at this site, including duplications and translocations, giving rise to speculation that this region is predisposed to structural instability.

Prader-Willi syndrome is estimated to affect from 1 in 10,000 to 1 in 25,000 people, with males predominating. The cause of the eating disorder is unknown but may be related to disturbances in endocrine function. Treatment includes behavior modification with constant supervision of access to food.

Translocations Involve Exchange of Chromosome Parts

Transfer of a chromosome segment to another nonhomologous chromosome is known as a translocation. There are two major types of translocations: **reciprocal translocations** and **Robertsonian translocations**. If two nonhomologous chromosomes exchange segments, the event is a reciprocal translocation. In such exchanges there is no gain or loss of genetic information, only the rearrangement of gene sequences. In some cases no phenotypic effects are seen, and the translocation is passed through a family for generations (see "Concepts & Controversies," page 156). However, during meiosis, cells containing translocations can produce genetically

Reciprocal translocation
A chromosomal aberration resulting in a positional change of a chromosome segment. This changes the arrangement of genes, but not the number of genes.

Robertsonian translocation
Breakage in the short arms of acrocentric chromosomes followed by fusion of the long parts into a single chromosome.

The Oldest Known Chromosome Aberration

In conducting a chromosome analysis to confirm a diagnosis of Down syndrome, Paul Genest and his colleagues verified the presence of trisomy 21, but also noticed that the child had an abnormal-looking Y chromosome. This unusual-looking Y chromosome carried structures that looked like the short arms of an acrocentric chromosome. They used staining techniques that specifically stain only the short arms of acrocentric chromosomes, and found that the structures on the end of the abnormal-looking Y chromosome also stained. This chromosome, known as a satellited Y, probably arose as the result of a translocation between an acrocentric chromosome and a Y chromosome. The satellited Y was carried by the boy's father, brother, paternal uncle, and nephew, all of whom were phenotypically normal. Other relatives of the boy were screened, and the chromosome was found in many family members as shown in the following pedigree.

The family groups carrying this variant of the Y chromosome were related by a single common ancestor, Pierre R. (III–3). Pierre was born in France in 1635 and emigrated to Quebec in 1665. Because of the structure of the pedigree, and because only males carry a Y chromosome, he is the only person who could have passed the satellited Y chromosome to all male descendants in the family line. Filled symbols in the pedigree carry the satellited Y; the others were not tested. It is impossible to tell whether the translocation arose in Pierre R., or was only transmitted through him. Nonetheless—having arisen at least 350 years ago—this is the oldest translocation chromosome known in the human species.

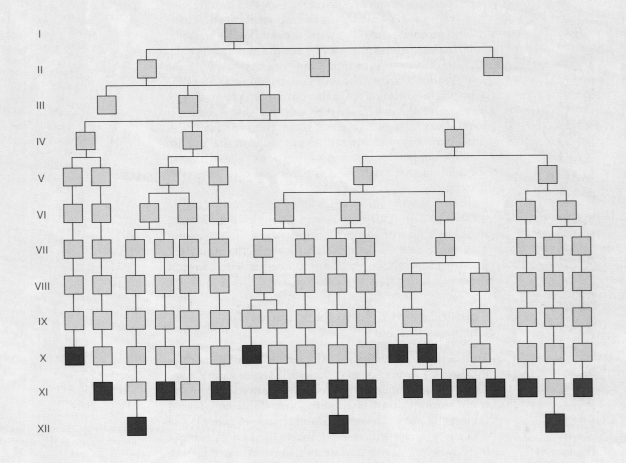

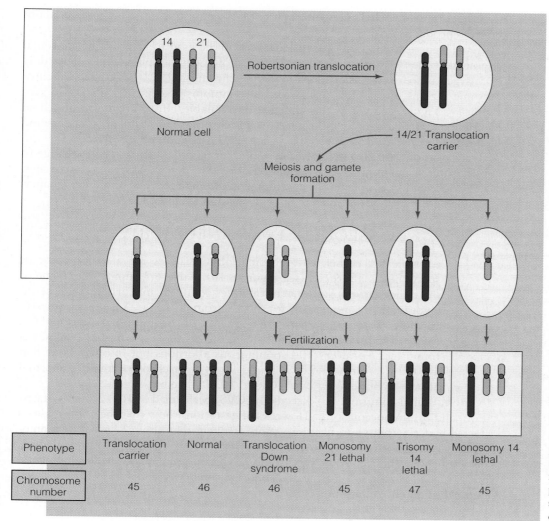

Phenotype	Translocation carrier	Normal	Translocation Down syndrome	Monosomy 21 lethal	Trisomy 14 lethal	Monosomy 14 lethal
Chromosome number	45	46	46	45	47	45

FIGURE 6.24

Segregation of chromosomes at meiosis in a 14–21 translocation carrier. Six types of gametes are produced. When these gametes fuse with those of a normal individual, six types of zygotes are produced. Of these, two (translocation carrier and normal) have a normal phenotype, one is Down syndrome, and three are lethal combinations.

unbalanced gametes containing duplicated or deleted chromosome segments. If these gametes participate in fertilization, the result is embryonic death or abnormal offspring.

About 5% of all cases of Down syndrome involve a Robertsonian translocation, most often between chromosomes 21 and 14. In this type of translocation, the centromeres of the two chromosomes fuse, and chromosome material is lost from the short arms (● Figure 6.24). The carrier of such a translocation is phenotypically normal, even though the short arms of both chromosomes may be lost. This carrier is actually aneuploid and has only 45 chromosomes. But, because the carrier has two copies of the long arm of chromosome 14 and two copies of the long arm of chromosome 21 (a normal 14, a normal 21, and a translocated 14/21), there is no phenotypic effect. At meiosis the carrier will produce six types of gametes in equal proportions (Figure 6.24). Three of these will result in zygotes that are inviable. Of the remaining three, one will produce a Down syndrome child. Theoretically this means that the chance of producing future children with Down syndrome is one third, or 33%. In practice, however, the observed risk is somewhat lower. It is important to remember that this risk does not increase with maternal age. In addition, there is also a 1 in 3 chance of producing a phenotypically normal translocation carrier, who is at risk of producing children with Down syndrome. For this reason it is important to karyotype a Down syndrome child and his or her parents to determine whether a

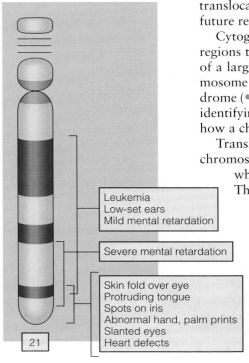

Leukemia
Low-set ears
Mild mental retardation

Severe mental retardation

Skin fold over eye
Protruding tongue
Spots on iris
Abnormal hand, palm prints
Slanted eyes
Heart defects

21

FIGURE 6.25

Chromosome 21, showing regions associated with various phenotypic features of Down syndrome. These assignments have been made by comparing various deletions in the chromosome with the phenotypes they produce.

translocation is involved. This information is essential in counseling parents about future reproductive risks.

Cytogenetic examination of translocations can be used to identify chromosomal regions that are most critical to the expression of aneuploid phenotypes. The study of a large number of translocations involving chromosome 21 has correlated chromosome regions on the long arm with the symptoms associated with Down syndrome (Figure 6.25). With this information available, efforts are now centered on identifying and characterizing the genes in this chromosome segment to understand how a change in gene dosage produces such serious phenotypic effects.

Translocations are also involved in specific forms of leukemia. The exchange of chromosome segments alters the regulation of a class of genes known as oncogenes, whose action is essential to development and maintenance of the malignancy. This topic will be considered in some detail in Chapter 11.

CONSEQUENCES OF ANEUPLOIDY

As indicated earlier, chromosomal abnormalities are a major cause of spontaneous abortions (see Figure 6.10). Table 6.3 summarizes some of the major chromosomal abnormalities found in miscarriages. These include triploidy, monosomy for the X chromosome (45,X), and trisomy 16. It is interesting to compare the frequency of chromosomal abnormalities found in spontaneous abortions with those seen in live births. Triploidy is found in 17 of every 100 spontaneous abortions but in only about 1 in 10,000 live births; 45,X is found in 18% of chromosomally abnormal abortuses but in only 1 in 7,000 to 10,000 live births.

Chromosomal abnormalities detected by CVS (performed at 10–12 weeks of gestation) and by amniocentesis (at 16 weeks of gestation) show that the abnormalities detected by CVS are two to five times more frequent than those detected by amniocentesis, which in turn are about two times higher than those found in newborns. This gradient in the frequency of chromosomal abnormalities over developmental time is evidence that karyotypically abnormal embryos and fetuses are selected against throughout gestation.

TABLE 6.3

Chromosome Abnormalities in Spontaneous Abortions

ABNORMALITY	FREQUENCY (%)
Trisomy 16	15
Trisomies 13, 18, 21	9
XXX, XXY, XYY	1
Other	27
45,X	18
Triploidy	17
Tetraploidy	6
Other	7

Note. Adapted from T. Hassold, 1986, Trends in Genetics, 2, pp. 105–110. Adapted with permission of the publisher.

TABLE 6.4	
Chromosome Abnormalities in Newborns	
ABNORMALITY	APPROXIMATE FREQUENCY
45,X	1/7500
XXX	1/1200
XXY	1/1000
XYY	1/1100
Trisomy 13	1/15,000
Trisomy 18	1/11,000
Trisomy 21	1/900
Structural abnormalities	1/400

Birth defects are another consequence of chromosome abnormalities. The frequency of chromosome aberrations detected in cytogenetic surveys of newborns are shown in Table 6.4. Among trisomies, trisomy 16, which is common in spontaneous abortions, is not found among infants, indicating that this condition is completely selected against. Although trisomy 21 occurs with a frequency of about 1 in 900 births, cytogenetic surveys of spontaneous abortions indicate that about two-thirds of such conceptions are lost by miscarriage. Similarly, over 99% of all 45,X conceptions are lost before birth. Overall, while selection against chromosomally abnormal embryos and fetuses is efficient, the high rate of nondisjunction means there is a significant reproductive risk for chromosomal abnormalities. Over 0.5% of all newborns are affected with an abnormal karyotype.

The relationship between the development of cancer in somatic cells of the body and accompanying chromosomal changes is a third consequence of chromosomal abnormalities. An increasing number of malignancies, especially leukemia, are known to be associated with specific chromosomal translocations. In many solid tumors, a wide range of chromosomal abnormalities is present. New evidence suggests that these abnormalities, which include aneuploidy, translocations, and duplications, may arise during a period of genomic instability that precedes or accompanies the transition of a normal cell into a malignant one. The mechanisms by which such chromosomal changes can cause or accompany the development of cancer will be discussed in Chapter 11.

OTHER FORMS OF CHROMOSOME ABNORMALITIES

In some forms of chromosome abnormalities, the karyotype and individual chromosomes appear to be normal. In uniparental disomy, both members of a chromosome pair are derived from one parent, resulting in an abnormal phenotype. Fragile sites appear only when cells are grown in the laboratory and certain chemicals are added to the growth medium.

Uniparental Disomy

Normally, meiosis ensures that one member of each chromosome pair is derived from the mother, and the other member is from the father. On rare occasions, however, a child gets both copies of a chromosome from one parent, a condition known as **uniparental disomy**. This condition can arise in several ways, all of which involve two

Uniparental disomy
A condition in which both copies of a chromosome are inherited from a single parent.

chromosomal errors in cell division (● Figure 6.26). These errors can occur in meiosis, or in mitotic divisions following fertilization.

The frequency of uniparental disomy is unknown, but this condition has been identified in some unusual situations including females who are affected with rare X-linked disorders such as hemophilia; father-to-son transmission of rare, X-linked disorders where the mother is homozygous normal; and cases where children are affected with rare autosomal recessive disorders, but only one parent is heterozygous. Prader-Willi syndrome and **Angelman syndrome** (MIM/OMIM 105830) can be caused by deletions in region 15q11.12 *or* by uniparental disomy. If both copies of chromosome 15 are derived from the mother, Prader-Willi syndrome results; if both copies of chromosome 15 are derived from the father, Angelman syndrome results. The origin of these disorders by uniparental disomy is discussed in detail in Chapter 11.

● **FIGURE 6.26**
Uniparental disomy can be produce by several mechanisms, involving nondisjunction in meiosis or nondisjunction in the zygote or early embryo. (a) Normally, gametes contain one copy of each chromosome, and fertilization produces a zygote carrying two copies of a chromosome, one derived from each parent. (b) Nondisjunction in both parents, with one gamete carrying both copies of a chromosome, and the other gamete missing a copy of that chromosome. Fertilization produces a diploid zygote, but both copies of one chromosome are inherited from a single parent. (c) Nondisjunction in one parent, resulting in the loss of a chromosome. This gamete fuses with a normal gamete to produce a zygote monosomic for a chromosome. An error in the first mitotic division results in the duplication of the monosomic chromosome, producing uniparental disomy. (d) Nondisjunction in one parent, producing a gamete carrying both copies of a chromosome. Fusion with a normal gamete produces a trisomic zygote, which loses one copy of the chromosome in a nondisjunction event, resulting in uniparental disomy. (e) Normal gametes can fuse to produce a normal zygote, which loses a chromosome at the first mitotic division. A second nondisjunction event restores the lost copy, but both copies are derived from one parent.

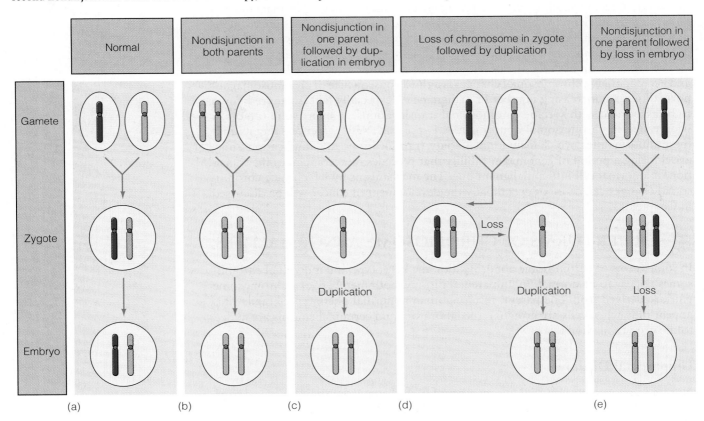

Fragile Sites

Fragile sites are structural features of chromosomes that become visible under certain conditions of cell culture. They appear as a gap or a break at a characteristic place on a chromosome, and are inherited in a codominant fashion. The fragile sites often produce chromosome fragments, deleted chromosomes, and other alterations in subsequent mitotic divisions. Seventeen heritable fragile sites have been identified in the human genome (Figure 6.27). The molecular nature of fragile sites is unknown but is of great interest, since the sites represent regions that are susceptible to breakage. Almost all studies of fragile sites have been carried out on cells in tissue culture, and it is currently not known whether such sites are expressed in meiotic cells. Most fragile sites do not appear to be associated with any clinical syndrome.

Fragile-X Syndrome is Associated with Mental Retardation   A fragile site near the tip of the long arm of the X chromosome is associated with an X-linked form of mental retardation known as Martin-Bell syndrome, or **fragile-X** (fra-X)

Fragile X
An X chromosome that carries a nonstaining gap, or break, at band q27. Associated with mental retardation in males.

 FIGURE 6.27

The location of the major fragile sites in the human karyotype. These sites appear as gaps or breaks in the chromosome only under certain conditions of cell culture. The site on the X chromosome is associated with mental retardation, and the site on chromosome 3 is associated with an increased risk for cancer. The nature and risk factors for the other sites are not yet known.

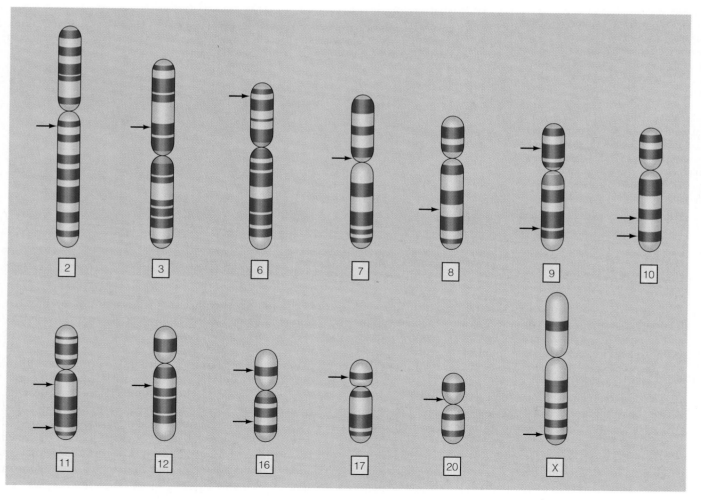

Over 175,000 cases of lung cancer are diagnosed each year in the U.S., and over 150,000 deaths are related to this form of cancer. The short arm of chromosome 3 is thought to carry one or more genes that when mutated, is involved in the development of lung cancer. A gene, called FHIT, located at the fragile site 3p14.2, has recently been shown to be abnormal in many cases of lung cancer. FHIT encodes an enzyme involved in nucleotide metabolism that is highly conserved in both prokaryotes and eukaryotes.

In lung cancer cells obtained from tumors and in laboratory-grown cell lines, 76% of the samples showed a loss of one or both FHIT alleles, and up to 80% of the samples were defective in the expression of the FHIT gene, mostly caused by deletions or rearrangements of the FHIT gene.

Expression of the fragile site at 3p14.2 is much higher in the circulating blood cells of lung cancer patients, indicating that this site has been damaged. Fragile sites are susceptible to breakage and chromosome damage by physical, chemical, or biological agents. Tobacco smoke contains compounds that interfere with the replication of DNA, and might lead to abnormalities in genes at fragile sites, such as FHIT. These abnormalities, along with other mutant gene, appear to be associated with the development of lung tumors.

(MIM/OMIM 309500) syndrome (Figure 6.28). Males with this syndrome have long, narrow faces with protruding chins and large ears. They also have enlarged testes and varying degrees of mental retardation. Fragile-X syndrome is the most common form of inherited mental retardation, and about 3% to 5% of the males institutionalized for mental retardation have a fragile X chromosome. Female carriers show no clear-cut physical symptoms, but as a group have a higher rate of mental retardation than normal individuals. The fragile-X syndrome is caused by an alteration in a gene (FMR-1) that will be discussed in Chapter 11.

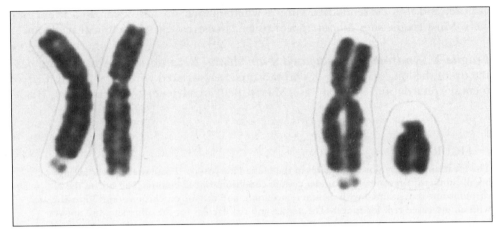

FIGURE 6.28

The fragile-X syndrome shown in a carrier female (left) and a male (right). This syndrome causes the lower tip of the X chromosome to appear as a fragile piece hanging by a thread. The nature of the mutation that causes this syndrome is discussed in Chapter 11.

SUMMARY

1. The study of variations in chromosome structure and number began in 1959 with the discovery that Down syndrome is caused by the presence of an extra copy of chromosome 21. Since then the number of genetic diseases known to be related to chromosome aberrations has steadily increased.

2. The development of chromosome banding and techniques for the resolution of small changes in chromosome structure have contributed greatly to the information that is now available.

3. There are two major types of chromosome changes: a change in chromosome number and a change in chromosome arrangement. Polyploidy, aneuploidy, and changes in chromosome number are major causes of reproductive failure in humans. Polyploidy is rarely seen in live births, but the rate of aneuploidy in humans is reported to be more than ten-fold higher than in other primates and mammals. The reasons for this difference are unknown, but this represents an area of intense scientific interest.

4. The loss of a single chromosome creates a monosomic condition, and the gain of a single chromosome is called a trisomic condition. Autosomal monosomy is eliminated early in development. Autosomal trisomy is selected against less stringently, and cases of partial development and live births of trisomic individuals are observed. Most cases of autosomal trisomy greatly shorten life ex-

pectancy, and only trisomy 21 individuals survive into adulthood.

5. Aneuploidy of sex chromosomes shows even more latitude, with monosomy X being a viable condition. Studies of sex chromosome aneuploidies indicate that at least one copy of the X chromosome is required for development. Increasing the number of copies of the X or Y chromosome above the normal range causes progressively greater disturbances in phenotype and behavior, indicating the need for a balance in gene products for normal development.

6. Changes in the arrangement of chromosomes include deletions, duplications, inversions, and translocations.

Deletions of chromosome segments are associated with several genetic disorders, including cri-du-chat and Prader-Willi syndromes. Translocations often produce no overt phenotypic effects but can result in genetically imbalanced and aneuploid gametes. We discussed a translocation resulting in Down syndrome that in effect makes Down syndrome a heritable genetic disease, potentially present in 1 in 3 offspring.

7. Fragile sites appear as gaps, or breaks, in chromosome-specific locations. One of these fragile sites, on the X chromosome, is associated with a common form of mental retardation that affects a significant number of males.

QUESTIONS AND PROBLEMS

1. As a physician, you deliver a baby with protruding heels, clenched fists with the second and fifth fingers overlapping the third and fourth fingers. (a) What genetic disorder do you suspect the baby has? (b) How do you confirm your suspicion?

2. Hypothetical human conditions have been found to have a genetic basis. The genetic defect responsible for condition 1 is similar in type to the one that causes Marfan syndrome. The defect responsible for condition 2 resembles the one responsible for Edwards syndrome. One of the two conditions results in more severe defects, and death occurs in infancy. The other condition produces a mild phenotypic abnormality and is not lethal. Which condition is most likely lethal and why?

3. Discuss the following sets of terms:
   trisomy and triploidy
   aneuploidy and euploidy
   euploidy and polyploidy

4. What chromosomal abnormality can result from dispermy?

5. Tetraploidy may result from :
   a. endoreduplication in meiosis II
   b. nondisjunction in meiosis I
   c. endoreduplication in mitosis in the embryo
   d. nondisjunction in mitosis in the embryo
   e. none of the above

6. A cytology student believes he has identified an individual suffering from monoploidy. The instructor views the cells under the microscope and correctly dismisses the claim.
   Why was the claim dismissed?
   What type of cells were being viewed?

7. Albinism is caused by an autosomal recessive allele of a single gene. An albino child is born to phenotypically normal parents. However, the paternal grandfather is albino. Exhaustive analysis suggests that neither the mother nor her ancestors carry the allele for albinism. Suggest a mechanism to explain this situation.

8. A geneticist discovers that a girl with Down syndrome has a Robertsonian translocation involving chromo-

somes 14 and 21. If she has an older brother who is phenotypically normal, what are the chances that he is a translocation carrier?

9. What is the relative rate of aneuploidy in humans compared with other mammals? Speculate as to what evolutionary role this rate might have.

10. An individual is found to have some tetraploid liver cells but diploid kidney cells. Be specific in explaining how this condition might arise.

11. A spermatogonial cell undergoes mitosis prior to entering the meiotic cell cycle enroute to the production of sperm. However, during mitosis the cytoplasm fails to divide, and only one "daughter" cell is produced. A resultant sperm eventually fertilizes a normal ovum. What is the chromosomal complement of the embryo?

12. A teratogen is present at conception. As a result, during the first mitotic division the centromeres fail to divide. The teratogen then loses its potency and has no further effect on the embryo. What will be the chromosomal complement of this embryo?

13. Describe the process of nondisjunction and when it takes place during cell division.

14. A woman gives birth to monozygotic twins. One boy has a normal genotype (46,XY), but the other boy has trisomy 13 (47,+13). What events, and in what sequence led to this situation?

15. Assume a meiotic nondisjunction event is responsible for an individual who is trisomic for chromosome 8. If two of the three copies of chromosome 8 are absolutely identical, when during meiosis did the nondisjunction event take place?

16. What is the genetic basis and phenotype for each of the following disorders (use proper genetic notation)?
    Edwards syndrome
    Turner syndrome
    Patau syndrome
    Kleinfelter syndrome
    Down syndrome

17. The majority of nondisjunction events leading to Down syndrome are maternal in origin. Based on the duration of meiosis in females, speculate on the possible reasons for females contributing aneuploid gametes more frequently than males.

18. Name and describe the theory, which deals with embryo-uterus interaction, that explains the relationship between advanced maternal age and the increased frequency of aneuploid offspring.

19. If all the nondisjunction events leading to Turner syndrome were paternal in origin, what trisomic condition might be expected to occur at least as frequently?

20. Identify the type of chromosome aberration described in each case:
    loss of a chromosome segment
    extra copies of a chromosome segment
    reversal in the order of a chromosome segment
    movement of a chromosome segment to another, non-homologous chromosome

21. What are the two prenatal diagnosis techniques used to detect genetic defects in a baby before birth? Which technique can be performed earlier, and why is this an advantage?

22. What are some conditions that warrant prenatal diagnosis?

SCIENCE AND SOCIETY

1. The chance of having a child affected with Down syndrome increases as a woman ages. Researchers attribute more than 95% of Down syndrome babies to maternal nondisjunction (failure of chromosomes to separate during meiosis) of chromosome number 21. Therefore, the cause of Down syndrome has been attributed to the age of the oocyte in women. A recent international study has shown that older women have a higher incidence of Down syndrome because they are more likely to carry a Down syndrome fetus to term than younger women. These investigators also found that the nondisjunction event involving chromosome 21 most often occurs during the first meiotic division, and that the frequency of nondisjunction was almost identical in older and younger women.

   If there is no difference in frequency of nondisjunction between older and younger women, why do you think older women have a higher incidence of Down syndrome babies?

   Does the uterine environment contribute to the continuation of a pregnancy? If it does, what is the process involved?

   If a younger woman had an older woman's ova implanted in her uterus, would the younger woman's chance of having a Down syndrome child change? Explain your reasoning.

   Can you think of ways to test whether the results of the international study are valid? Would comparing the ages of women who spontaneously miscarry a Down syndrome fetus help in testing this hypothesis? Why or why not?

   Should a woman's genetic, family, and medical history be taken into account in understanding the reasoning why older women have a higher percentage of Down syndrome babies than younger women? Why or why not?

2. A healthy 40-year old woman underwent prenatal diagnosis via chorionic villus sampling (CVS) because of advanced maternal age. The pregnancy was uncomplicated and family history was negative for genetic conditions or birth defects. The CVS results obtained at 15 weeks revealed cells with a 45,X constitution, and cells with 47,XXX. A single 46, XX cell was present in one culture. What is this phenomenon of two cell populations in a single sampling called?

   Could a child born with a single X chromosome survive? If so, what phenotypic features would you expect to see? How do the phenotypic features of sex chromosome aneuploidies change with increasing number of X chromosomes?

   What is the term for a 45,X individual? What is the term for an 47,XXX individual?

INTERNET ACTIVITIES

The following activities use the resources of the World Wide Web to enhance the topics covered in this chapter. To investigate the topics described below, log on to the book's home page at:

http://www.wadsworth.com/biology

1. The University of Utah maintains an Internet pathology laboratory with over 1800 images. In the cytogenetics index, you can find 28 images representing a broad range of genetic disorders. Use these images to supplement those found in your text.

   a. Look at some of the nondisjunction event-caused disorders like trisomy 21. It has been suggested that the nondisjunction of chromosome 21 occurs more frequently in females. How could this be substantiated?

   b. Many of the conditions shown have been represented in art in many cultures over thousands of years. What does this tell you about these conditions?

2. Fragile X syndrome is the leading genetic cause of mental retardation. The Fragile X Research Foundation maintains a Web site which contains information about the disease, and also posts information about current research projects. Use the information at this site to supplement what you know about the screening and treatment of fragile X syndrome.

   a. Describe the features of the fragile X children shown at this site. What differences can you see between the boys and the girls? Is it worth using physical appearance to identify children with this syndrome?

   b. What do you think might explain why most affected boys are mentally retarded, but only 1/3 to 1/2 of the girls are similarly impaired? Men who inherit the mutant gene (FMR1) that causes fragile X syndrome but have a normal phenotype are called transmitter males. Try to explain why mothers of transmitter males are normal, and have a low risk of having fragile X children, but daughters of transmitter males have a higher risk of having affected children (we will discuss this topic in Chapter 11).

FOR FURTHER READING

Borgaonkar, D. S. 1989. *Chromosome Variation in Man: A Catalogue of Chromosomal Variants and Anomalies.* 5th ed. New York: Liss.

Boue, A., Boue, J., and Gropp, A. 1985. Cytogenetics of pregnancy wastage. *Adv. Hum. Genet.* **14:** 1–57.

Cassidy, S.B. 1995. Uniparental disomy and genomic imprinting as causes of human genetic disease. Environ. Mol. Mutagen. 25: (Suppl. 26) 941–947.

Chu, C.E. and Connor, J.M. 1995. Molecular biology of Turner's syndrome. Arch. Dis. Child. 72: 285–286.

Dellarco, V., Voytek, P., and Hollaender, A. 1985. *Aneuploidy: Etiology and Mechanisms.* New York: Plenum.

Faix, R., Barr, M., Jr., and Waterson, J. 1984. Triploidy: Case report of a live-born male and an ethical dilemma. Pediatrics **74:** 296–299.

Friedmann, T. 1971. Prenatal diagnosis of genetic disease. Sci. Am. *225* (November): 34–42.

Green, J. E., Dorfmann, A., Jones, S., Bender, S., Patton, L., and Schulman, J. D. 1988. Chorionic villus sampling: Experience with an initial 940 cases. *Obstet. Gynecol.* **71:** 208–212.

Grouchy, J. de. 1984. *Clinical Atlas of Human Chromosomes.* New York: Wiley.

Jacobs, P.A. and Hassold, T. J. 1995. The origin of numerical chromosome abnormalities. Adv. Genet. 33: 101–133.

Linden, M.G., Bender, B.G, and Robinson, A. 1996. Intrauterine diagnosis of sex chromosome aneuploidy. Obstet. Gynecol. 87: 468–475.

Lurie, I.W. 1993. Autosomal imbalance syndromes: genetic interactions and the origin of congenital malformations in aneuploidy syndromes. Am. J. Med. Genet. 47: 410–416.

Neely, E.K. and Rosenfeld, R.G. 1994. Use and abuse of human growth hormone. Ann. Rev. Med. 45: 407–420.

Oostra, B.A. and Willems, P. J. 1995. A fragile gene. Bioessays 17: 941–947.

Philip, J., Bryndorf, T. and Christensen, B. 1994. Prenatal aneuploidy detection in interphase cells by fluorescence *in situ* hybridization (FISH). Prenatal Diagn. 14: 1203–1215.

Weiss, E., Loevy, H., Saunders, A., Pruzansky, S., and Rosenthal, I. 1982. Monozygotic twins discordant for Ullrich-Turner syndrome. Am J. Med Genet. **13:** 389–399.

Zinn, A.R., Page, D.C. and Fisher, E.M. 1993. Turner syndrome: the case of the missing chromosome. Trends Genet. 9: 90–93.

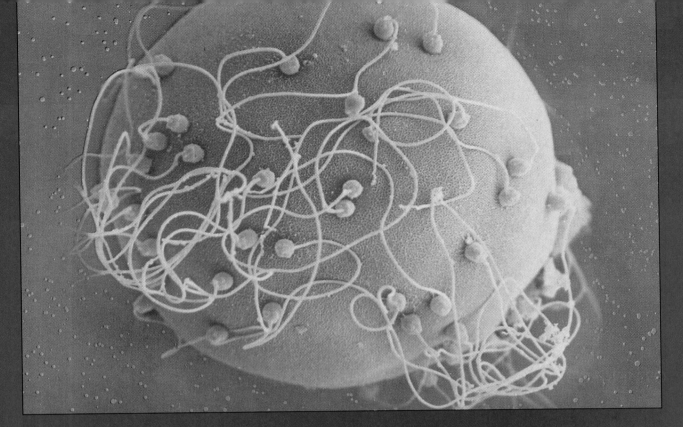

REPRODUCTION AND DEVELOPMENT

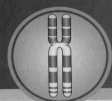

Chapter 7

Chapter Outline

HUMAN REPRODUCTION
Anatomy of the Male Reproductive System
Anatomy of the Female Reproductive System
HUMAN DEVELOPMENT FROM
    FERTILIZATION TO BIRTH
Human Development Is Divided into Three
    Stages
Birth Occurs in Stages
REPRODUCTION AND TECHNOLOGY
Contraception Uncouples Sexual Intercourse
    from Pregnancy
Technology Expands Reproductive Choices
TERATOGENS POSE A RISK TO THE
    DEVELOPING FETUS

Little is Known about Teratogens
Fetal Alcohol Syndrome
SEX DETERMINATION IN HUMANS
Chromosomes Can Help Determine Sex
The Sex Ratio in Humans
SEX DIFFERENTIATION FOLLOWS SEX
    DETERMINATION
Chromosomal Sex and Phenotypic Sex
Events in Embryogenesis Begin Sex
    Differentiation
CONCEPTS AND CONTROVERSIES *Sex
    Testing in International Athletics—Is It
    Necessary?*

GENETIC CONTROL OF SEXUAL
    DIFFERENTIATION
Testicular Feminization and Phenotypic Sex
Gene Expression and Sexual Phenotype
CONCEPTS AND CONTROVERSIES Joan of
    Arc—Was It Really John of Arc?
DOSAGE COMPENSATION AND THE X
    CHROMOSOME
Expression of Genes on the X Chromosome
Barr Bodies and X Inactivation
Females Are Mosaics for X-linked Genes
SEX-INFLUENCED AND SEX-LIMITED
    TRAITS

OPENING IMAGE
Sperm surrounding a mammalian oocyte.

L*ouise Brown was born in April, 1978 in England. Of the millions of
children born that year, Louise represents a landmark in human
reproduction and human genetics. She was the first human born after in vitro
fertilization (IVF), a procedure in which gametes are fertilized outside the
body, and the developing embryo is implanted into the uterus for develop-*

ment. Since then, hundreds of children have been born after IVF, and there are more than a dozen centers in the United States that offer IVF services.

The development of IVF by Robert Edwards and Patrick Steptoe was a long, slow process conducted over a number of years. After three years of experiments to determine the best conditions for a sperm to fertilize an egg in a petri dish, Edwards began a collaboration with Steptoe, an obstetrician who was an expert in the use of a laparascope to remove an egg from a woman's ovary. Nine years later, their work had progressed to the point where they were able to remove eggs, fertilize them, and implant the developing embryos into the uterus, but there were no resulting pregnancies. In the fall of 1977, Steptoe recovered an egg from Louise's mother, Lesly, by making a small incision (about one-half inch long) in her abdomen. He inserted the tube-like laparascope to examine the ovary, and another small incision was made through which a second instrument was used to remove an egg. A few minutes after removal, the egg was mixed with semen from Louise's father in a sterile dish, and fertilization took place. The developing embryo was implanted into the uterus via a tube inserted in the vagina, and Louise was born on April 25 of the following year.

This remarkable achievement led to the development of a profusion of reproductive alternatives for infertile couples, some of which will be discussed in this chapter. The combination of IVF with recombinant DNA techniques has created a powerful new technology for sex selection, the diagnosis of genetic disorders, and gene transfer. The use of these techniques will be covered in Chapter 13.

In this chapter, attention will focus on the biology of human development, and the genetics of sex determination and differentiation. The chapter begins with a discussion of gamete formation in males and females, and the major features of embryonic and fetal development, followed by a section on reproductive technology. The central portion of the chapter covers genetic aspects of sex determination and sex differentiation. The chapter concludes with an examination of how patterns of expression of genes on the X chromosome are different in males and females.

HUMAN REPRODUCTION

Human reproduction depends on the integrated action of the endocrine system and the reproductive organs. Males and females each possess a pair of **gonads,** with associated accessory glands and ducts. The **testes** of males produce spermatozoa and sex hormones. The **ovaries** of females produce eggs or ova and female sex hormones. Within the gonads, cells produced by meiosis mature into gametes.

Anatomy of the Male Reproductive System

The testes form in the abdominal cavity during male embryonic development and descend into the scrotum, a pouch of skin located outside the body cavity. The interior of the testis is divided into a series of lobes, each of which contains tightly coiled lengths of seminiferous tubules, where sperm are produced (● Figure 7.1). Altogether, about 250 meters (850 feet) of tubules are packed into each testis. Cells called spermatocytes in the tubules divide by meiosis to produce haploid spermatids (review this process in Chapter 2), which in turn differentiate into mature sperm (● Figure 7.2). Sperm production begins at puberty and continues throughout life; each day, several hundred million sperm are in various stages of maturation. Once formed, sperm move from the seminiferous tubules to the epididymis, where they mature and are stored.

Gonads
The male and female reproductive organs that produce gametes.

Testes
The male gonads; they produce sperm and male hormones.

Ovaries
The female gonads; they produce ova and female hormones.

In addition to the testes, the male reproductive system also includes (1) a duct system that transports sperm out of the body; (2) three sets of glands that secrete fluids to maintain sperm viability and motility; and (3) the penis (Figure 7.3).

 FIGURE 7.1
(a) Section through the testis showing the location and arrangement of the seminiferous tubules and the epididymis. (b) Light micrograph of a section through a seminiferous tubule. The undifferentiated spermatogonia are at the periphery, the mature spermatozoa in the lumen, with various stages of development between. (c) A scanning electron micrograph of a section through a seiminiferous tubule. (d) The location and relationship among the cells of the seminiferous tubule.

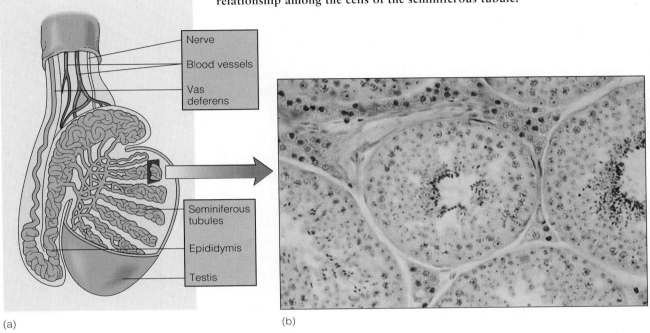

(a)

(b)

(c)

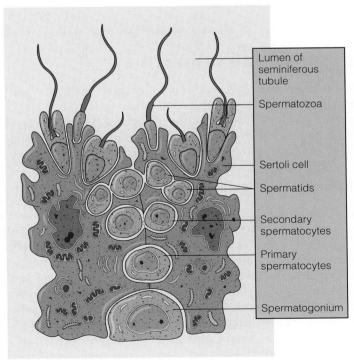

(d)

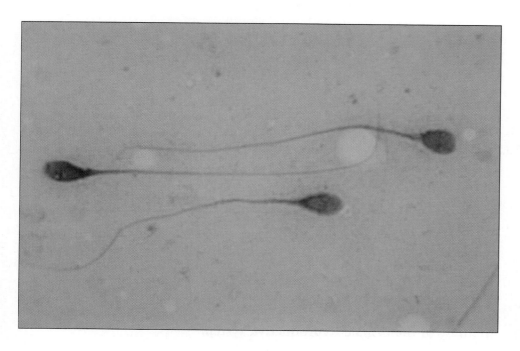

■ FIGURE 7.2
A light micrograph of mature
human sperm.

Sperm move from the epididymis into the vas deferens. The walls of the vas deferens are lined with muscles, which contract rhythmically to move sperm forward. The vas deferens from each testis join to form a short ejaculatory duct that connects to the urethra. The urethra (which also functions in urine transport) passes through the penis and opens to the outside. Sperm are propelled by muscular contractions accompanying orgasm from the vas deferens through the urethra and expelled from the body.

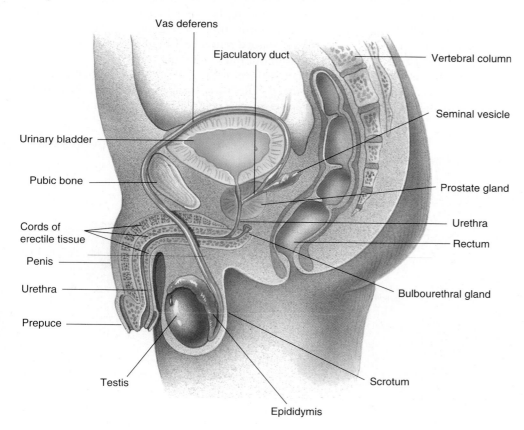

■ FIGURE 7.3
The anatomy of the male
reproductive system.

TABLE 7.1	
The Male Reproductive System	
COMPONENT	FUNCTION
Testes	Produce sperm and male sex steroids
Epididymis	Stores sperm
Vas deferens	Conducts sperm to urethra
Sex accessory glands	Produce seminal fluid that nourishes sperm
Urethra	Conducts sperm to outside
Penis	Organ of copulation
Scrotum	Provides proper temperature for testes

As sperm are transported through the duct system, secretions are added from the seminal vesicles, the prostate gland, and the bulbourethral glands. Together, the sperm and these various glandular secretions make up **semen,** a mixture that is about 95% secretions and about 5% spermatazoa. The components and functions of the male reproductive system are summarized in Table 7.1.

Anatomy of the Female Reproductive System

The female gonads are a pair of oval-shaped ovaries about 3 cm long, located in the abdominal cavity (Figure 7.4). The ovary contains many follicles, each consisting of a developing egg surrounded by a outer layer of cells (Figure 7.5). The developing egg is a primary oocyte, and begins meiosis in the third month of female prenatal development. At birth, the female carries a lifetime supply of developing oocytes, each of which is in the prophase of the first meiotic division. The first developing egg, called a secondary oocyte, is released from a follicle at puberty by **ovulation.** Over a woman's reproductive lifetime, about 400–500 gametes will be produced.

The ovulated cell, called a secondary oocyte, is swept by ciliary action into the oviduct, also called the fallopian tube or uterine tube (Figure 7.6). The oviduct is connected to the uterus, a hollow, pear-shaped muscular organ about 7.5 cm (3 in.) long and 5 cm (2 in.) wide. The uterus has a thick, muscular outer layer and an inner layer, the endometrium. The inner surface of the endometrium is shed at menstruation if fertilization has not occurred. The lower neck of the uterus, the cervix, opens into the vagina. The vagina receives the penis during intercourse and also

Semen
A mixture of sperm and various glandular secretions.

Ovulation
The release of an egg (ova) from the ovary.

 FIGURE 7.4

The ovary contains follicles in various stages of development.

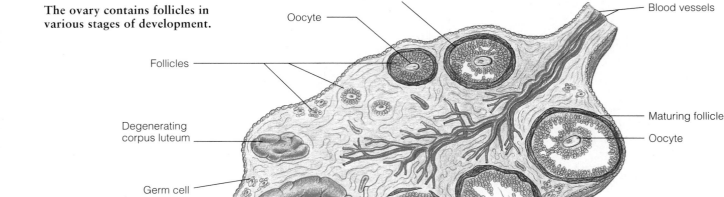

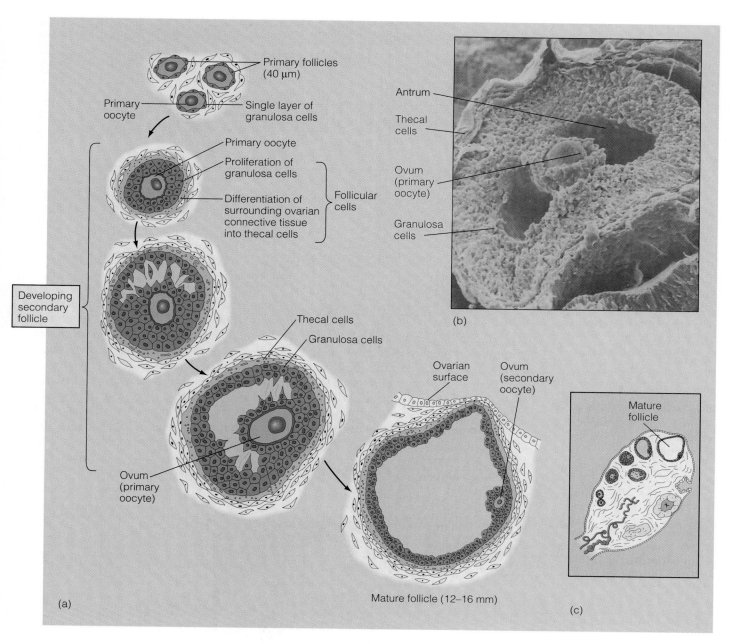

Primary follicles
(40 µm)

Primary oocyte

Single layer of
granulosa cells

Primary oocyte

Proliferation of
granulosa cells

Differentiation of
surrounding ovarian
connective tissue
into thecal cells

Follicular
cells

Developing
secondary
follicle

Thecal cells

Granulosa cells

Ovum
(primary
oocyte)

Ovarian
surface

Ovum
(secondary
oocyte)

Mature follicle (12–16 mm)

(a)

Antrum

Thecal
cells

Ovum
(primary
oocyte)

Granulosa
cells

(b)

Mature
follicle

(c)

FIGURE 7.5

(a) Development of follicles from primary
stages through the mature follicle. (b) A
scanning electron micrograph of a
developing oocyte. (c) Drawing of an
ovary (actual size) showing a mature
follicle.

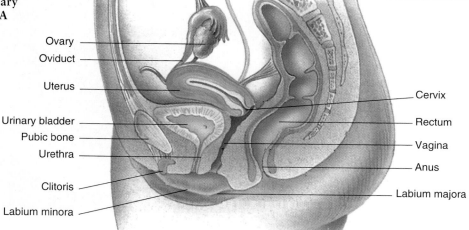

Ovary
Oviduct
Uterus
Urinary bladder
Pubic bone
Urethra
Clitoris
Labium minora

Vertebral column
Cervix
Rectum
Vagina
Anus
Labium majora

FIGURE 7.6

The anatomy of the female
reproductive system.

TABLE 7.2	
The Female Reproductive System	
COMPONENT	FUNCTION
Ovaries	Produce ova and female sex steroids
Uterine tubes	Transport sperm to ova; transport fertilized ova to uterus
Uterus	Nourishes and protects embryo and fetus
Vagina	Site of sperm deposition, birth canal

serves as the birth canal. The vagina opens to the outside of the body behind the urethra. The components and functions of the female reproductive system are summarized in Table 7.2.

HUMAN DEVELOPMENT FROM FERTILIZATION TO BIRTH

Fertilization, the fusion of male and female gametes, usually occurs in the upper third of the oviduct (⬤ Figure 7.7). Sperm deposited into the vagina travel through the cervix, up the uterus and into the oviduct. About 30 minutes after ejaculation, sperm are present in the oviduct (⬤ Figure 7.8). Sperm travel this distance by swimming via whip-like contractions of their tails, aided by muscular contractions of the uterus.

Only one sperm will fertilize the egg, but many other sperm assist in this process (⬤ Figure 7.9), perhaps by triggering chemical changes in the egg. A single sperm binds to receptors on the surface of the secondary oocyte, and fuses with its outer membrane. This attachment triggers a series of chemical changes in the membrane and prevents any other sperm from entering the oocyte. Movement of the sperm into the oocyte cytoplasm initiates the second meiotic division of the oocyte. Fusion of the haploid sperm nucleus with the resulting haploid oocyte nucleus forms a diploid **zygote.**

Fertilization
The fusion of two gametes to produce a zygote.

Zygote
The fertilized egg that develops into a new individual.

Blastocyst
The developmental stage at which the embryo implants into the uterine wall.

⬤ **FIGURE 7.7**
Scanning electron micrograph of an oocyte surrounded by sperm. Only one sperm will enter the egg.

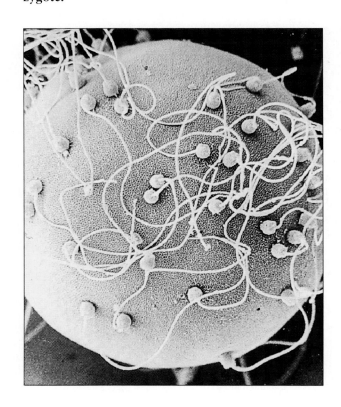

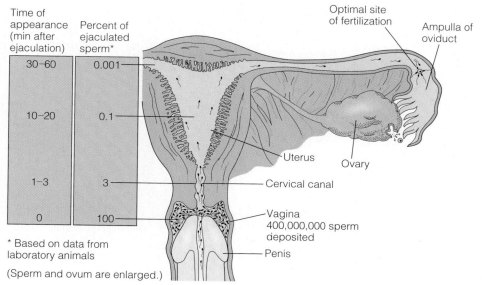

Time of appearance (min after ejaculation)	Percent of ejaculated sperm*	
30–60	0.001	
10–20	0.1	
1–3	3	
0	100	

* Based on data from laboratory animals

(Sperm and ovum are enlarged.)

Optimal site of fertilization

Ampulla of oviduct

Uterus

Ovary

Cervical canal

Vagina 400,000,000 sperm deposited

Penis

● **FIGURE 7.8**

The time and relative amounts of sperm transported from the vagina into the oviduct.

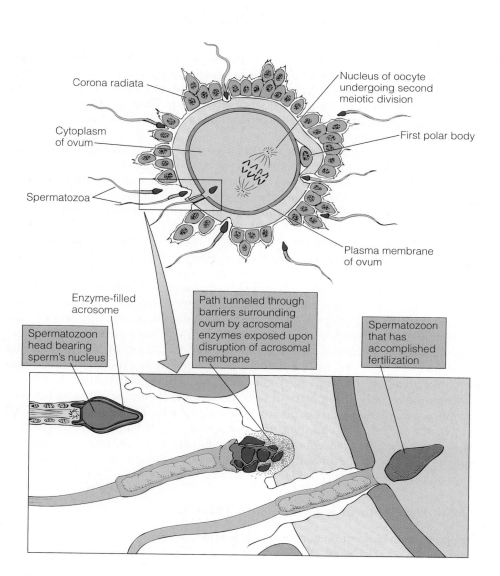

Corona radiata

Nucleus of oocyte undergoing second meiotic division

Cytoplasm of ovum

First polar body

Spermatozoa

Plasma membrane of ovum

Enzyme-filled acrosome

Path tunneled through barriers surrounding ovum by acrosomal enzymes exposed upon disruption of acrosomal membrane

Spermatozoon that has accomplished fertilization

Spermatozoon head bearing sperm's nucleus

● **FIGURE 7.9**

The process of fertilization. The tip of the sperm head, known as the acrosome, contains enzymes that dissolve the outer barriers surrounding the oocyte. Only the head of the sperm enters the egg.

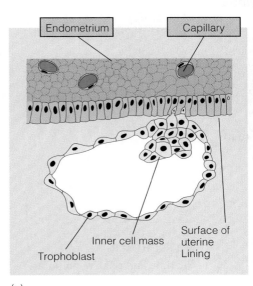

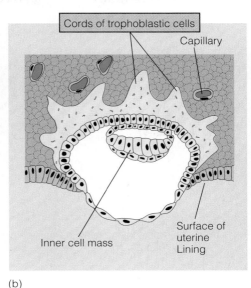

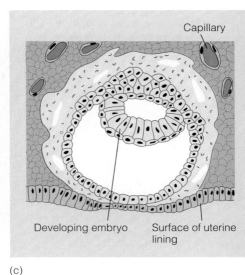

(a) (b) (c)

FIGURE 7.10

The process of implantation. (a) A blastocyst attaches to the endometrial lining of the uterus. (b) As the blastocyst implants, cords of chorionic cells form. (c) When implanatation is complete, the blastocyst is buried in the endometrium.

Inner cell mass
A cluster of cells in the blastocyst that gives rise to the body of the embryo.

Trophoblast
The outer layer of cells in the blastocyst that gives rise to the membranes surrounding the embryo.

Chorion
A two-layered structure formed from the trophoblast.

The zygote travels down the oviduct to the uterus over the next 3–4 days. While in the oviduct, the zygote undergoes a series of cell divisions to form a solid ball of cells called a morula. Once the zygote begins to divide, it becomes an embryo. The embryo descends into the uterus and floats unattached in the uterine interior for several days, drawing nutrients from the uterine fluids and continuing to divide to form a **blastocyst** (Figure 7.10).

The blastocyst is made up of the inner cell mass, an internal cavity, and an outer layer of cells (the trophoblast). During the week or so that the zygote is dividing, the endometrium of the uterus continues to enlarge and differentiate. During implantation, the trophoblast cells adhere to the endometrium and secrete enzymes that allow fingers of trophoblast cells to penetrate the endometrium, locking the embryo into place (Figure 7.10).

At twelve days after fertilization, the embryo is embedded in the endometrium, and the trophoblast has formed a two-layered structure, the **chorion.** One of the first events that follows implantation is the secretion of a peptide hormone, human chorionic gonadotropin (hCG), by the chorion. This hormone prevents breakdown of the uterine lining, which grows and begins secreting hormones to maintain the pregnancy. Excess hCG is eliminated in the urine, and home pregnancy tests work by detecting hCG levels, as early as two weeks after the first missed menstrual period.

As the chorion grows and expands, it forms a series of finger-like projections that extend into cavities filled with maternal blood. Embryonic capillaries extend into these projections, or villi. The embryonic circulation and the maternal pools of blood are separated by only a thin layer of cells, allowing exchange of nutrients between the embryonic and maternal circulation. These villi are the source of tissue gathered for prenatal diagnosis by chorionic villus sampling (CVS). Further development of this structure forms the placenta. The membranes connecting the embryo to the placenta develop to form the umbilical cord, containing two umbilical arteries and a single umbilical vein (Figure 7.11).

Human Development Is Divided into Three Stages

The period from conception to birth is divided into three trimesters, each about three months (12 weeks) in length. During this period of about 38 weeks, the single-celled

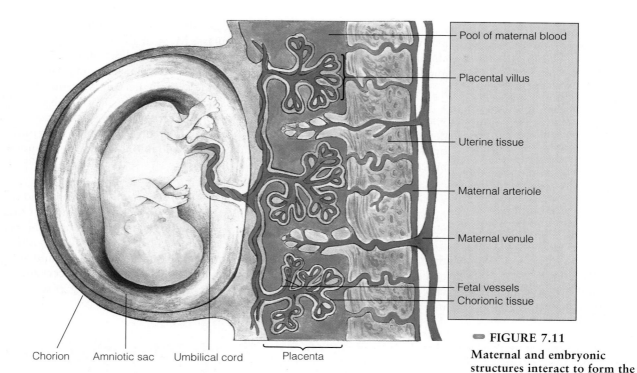

Pool of maternal blood

Placental villus

Uterine tissue

Maternal arteriole

Maternal venule

Fetal vessels

Chorionic tissue

Chorion   Amniotic sac   Umbilical cord   Placenta

FIGURE 7.11

Maternal and embryonic structures interact to form the placenta.

zygote undergoes about 40–44 rounds of mitosis, producing an infant containing trillions of cells organized into highly specialized tissues and organs.

Organ Formation Occurs in the First Trimester   The first 12 weeks of development are a period of radical changes in the size, shape, and complexity of the embryo (Figure 7.12). In the week after implantation, the basic tissue layers are formed, and by the end of the third week, formation of organ systems begins. At the end of the first month the embryo is about 5 mm in length, and much of the body is composed of paired segments.

FIGURE 7.12

A human embryo near the end of the first trimester of development.

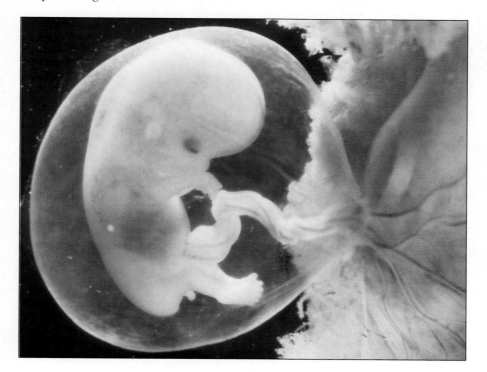

In the second month, the embryo grows dramatically to a length of about 3 cm, and undergoes a 500-fold increase in mass. Most of the major organ systems, including the four chambers of the heart, are formed. The limb buds develop into arms and legs, complete with fingers and toes. The head is very large in relation to the rest of the body, because of the rapid development of the nervous system.

By about seven weeks, the embryo is now called a fetus. Although chromosomal sex (XX females and XY males) is determined at the time of fertilization, at the beginning of the third month, the fetus is sexually neutral. In the third month, developmental pathways activate different gene sets and initiate sexual development. This process is discussed in detail later in this chapter.

The Second Trimester Is a Period of Organ Maturation In the second trimester, major changes include an increase in size and the further development of organ systems (Figure 7.13). Bony parts of the skeleton begin to form, and the heartbeat can be heard with a stethoscope. Fetal movements begin in the third month, and by the fourth month, the mother can feel movements of the fetus's arms and legs. At the end of the second trimester, the fetus weighs about 700 g (~27 ounces) and is 30–40 cm (about 13 inches) long. It has a well-formed face, toes and fingers with nails, and its eyes can open.

 FIGURE 7.13
Growth of the embryo and fetus during the first 16 weeks of development. The drawings represent actual sizes.

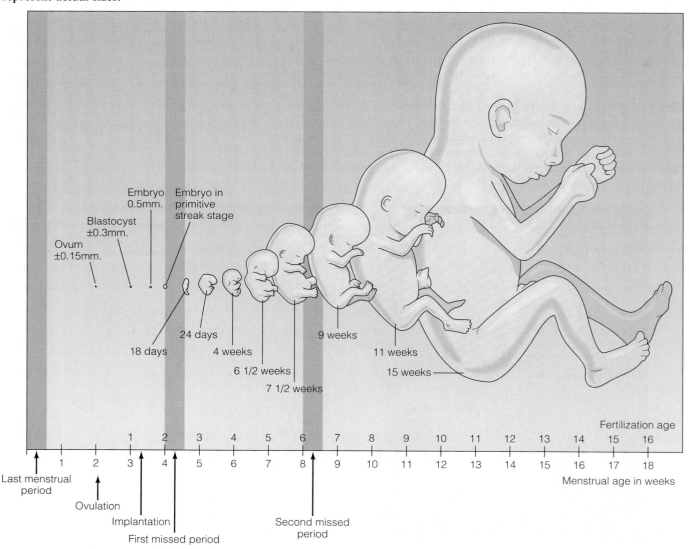

Ovum
±0.15mm.

Blastocyst
±0.3mm.

Embryo
0.5mm.

Embryo in primitive streak stage

18 days

24 days

4 weeks

6 1/2 weeks

7 1/2 weeks

9 weeks

11 weeks

15 weeks

Fertilization age

1 2 3 4 5 6 7 8 9 10 11 12 13 14 15 16

1 2 3 4 5 6 7 8 9 10 11 12 13 14 15 16 17 18

Last menstrual period

Ovulation

Implantation

First missed period

Second missed period

Menstrual age in weeks

Rapid Growth Takes Place in the Third Trimester In the third trimester the fetus grows rapidly, and the circulatory system and the respiratory systems mature in preparation for air breathing. During this period of rapid growth, maternal nutrition is important, since a large fraction of the protein the mother eats will be used for growth and development of the fetal brain and nervous system. Similarly, much of the calcium in the mother's diet will be used for development of the fetal skeletal system.

The fetus doubles in size during the last two months, and chances for survival outside the uterus increase rapidly during this time. In the last month, antibodies from the maternal circulation pass into the fetal circulation, conferring temporary immunity on the fetus. In the first months after birth, the baby's immune system will mature and begin to make its own antibodies, and the maternal antibodies disappear. At the end of the third trimester, the fetus is about 50 cm (19 in.) in length, and weighs from 2.5 to 4.8 kg (5.5 to 10.5 lbs).

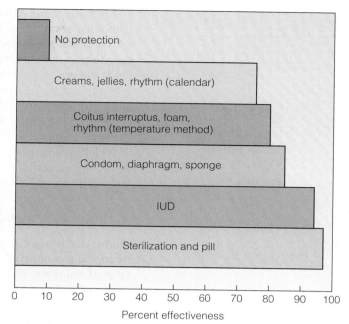

FIGURE 7.14

Effectiveness of various methods of birth control. The percent effectiveness is a measure of how many women in a group of 100 will not become pregnant in a year when using a given method of birth control.

Birth Occurs in Stages

Birth is a hormonally induced process. The cervix softens in the last trimester, and the fetus shifts downward, usually with its head pressed against the cervix. During birth, the cervical opening dilates to allow passage of the fetus, and uterine contractions expel the fetus. The head usually emerges first; if any other body part enters the birth canal first, the result is a breech birth.

A short time after delivery, a second round of uterine contractions begins delivery of the placenta. These contractions separate the placenta from the lining of the uterus, and the placenta is expelled through the vagina.

REPRODUCTION AND TECHNOLOGY

Advances in genetics, physiology, and molecular biology have led to the development of techniques that enhance or reduce the chances of conception. Reproductive technologies can correct defective functions and manipulate the physiology of reproduction.

Contraception Uncouples Sexual Intercourse from Pregnancy

The uncoupling of sexual intercourse from fertilization and pregnancy employs methods that block one of three stages in reproduction: release and transport of gametes, fertilization, and implantation. None of these methods is completely successful in preventing pregnancy or sexually transmitted diseases (STDs) except complete abstinence from sexual intercourse (Figure 7.14).

Aside from abstinence, methods that physically prevent the release and transport of gametes (such as vasectomy and tubal ligation) are the most effective. In **tubal ligation** the oviduct is cut, and the ends are tied off to prevent ovulated eggs from reaching the uterus. In **vasectomy,** the vas deferens is withdrawn through a small incision in the scrotum and cut. The cut ends are sealed to prevent transport of sperm.

Birth control pills are an effective method of birth control. The most common birth control pills contain a combination of hormones that prevent the release of an oocyte from the ovary. Time-release capsules (sold as Norplant) implanted under the skin release hormones slowly and offer long-term suppression of ovulation.

Tubal ligation
A contraceptive procedure in women in which the oviducts are cut, preventing ova from reaching the uterus.

Vasectomy
A contraceptive procedure in men in which the vas deferens is cut and sealed to prevent the transport of sperm.

Methods to prevent fertilization include the use of physical and chemical barriers. Condoms are latex or gut sheaths worn over the penis during intercourse. Only latex condoms prevent sexually transmitted diseases, including AIDS. Diaphragms are caps that fit over the cervix and are inserted before intercourse. Chemical barriers include the use of spermicidal jelly or foam that kill sperm on contact. They are placed into the vagina just before intercourse. Contraceptive sponges, filled with spermicides, combine physical and chemical barriers. Condoms treated with a chemical spermicide are more successful at preventing pregnancy than either condoms or chemical barriers alone.

RU-486, a drug developed in Europe, is being tested in the United States for use as a contraceptive. This drug, chemically related to reproductive hormones, interferes with events following fertilization and may inhibit implantation.

Technology Expands Reproductive Choices

About one in six couples are infertile, that is, unable to have children after a year of trying to conceive. Physical and physiological conditions prevent the production of gametes, fertilization, or implantation. Technologies to reduce or overcome these problems have been developed in the last two decades. Blocked oviducts, often the result of untreated STDs, are the leading cause of infertility in females. In males, low sperm count, low motility, and blocked ducts are causes of infertility. Hormone therapy can often be used to increase egg production, and surgical procedures can sometimes be used to open closed ducts in the reproductive tracts. Overall, about 40% of infertility is related to problems in the male reproductive tract, 40% is associated with the female tract, and in 20% of the cases, the infertility is of unknown origin.

One of the first methods of reproductive technology developed was artificial insemination. In the simplest application of this method, the male partner is infertile, and the female receives sperm collected from a donor (⬤ Figure 7.15). Sperm can be collected from donors and stored in liquid nitrogen at sperm banks, which offer artificial insemination.

Methods to recover and fertilize gametes outside the body, known as *in vitro* **fertilization (IVF),** are widely used. Several variations of this technology are available (Figure 7.15). IVF can be used when ovulation is normal, but the oviducts are blocked. IVF is mainly offered at reproductive clinics in major medical centers, at a cost of about $10,000 per procedure.

Reproductive technology has altered accepted patterns of reproduction. In the United States, variations of surrogate motherhood are a reproductive option. In one version, a woman is artifically inseminated by sperm and carries the child to term. After the child is born, she surrenders the child to the father and his mate. In this case, the surrogate is both the genetic and gestational mother of the child. In another version, a couple provides both the egg and the sperm, and the surrogate is implanted with the developing embryo, and serves as the gestational mother, but is genetically unrelated to the child she bears.

Following the discovery that it is the age of ova—not the reproductive system—that is responsible for infertility as women age, women are now becoming mothers in their late fifties and early sixties. After hormonal treatment, they receive zygotes for implantation, produced by fertilization of donated eggs from younger women. Fertilized eggs can now be collected and frozen for later use. This allows younger women to collect eggs while risks for chromosome abnormalities in the offspring are low, and to use them over a period of years, including menopause, to become mothers.

These and other unconventional means of generating a pregnancy have developed more rapidly than the social conventions and laws governing their use. In the process, controversy about the moral, ethical, and legal grounds for the use of these techniques has been generated, but not yet resolved.

In vitro fertilization (IVF)
A procedure in which gametes are fertilized in a dish in the laboratory, and the resulting zygote is implanted in the uterus for development.

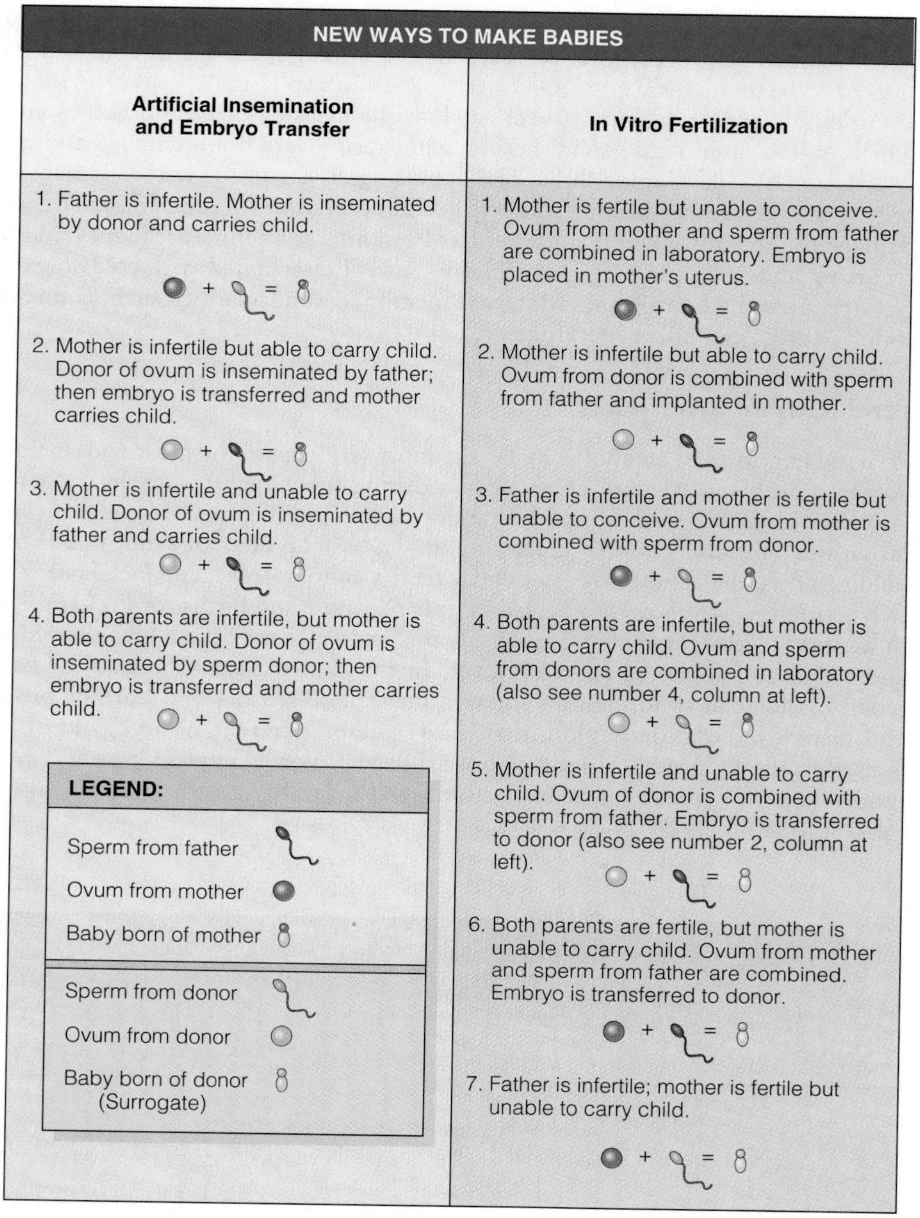

NEW WAYS TO MAKE BABIES	
Artificial Insemination and Embryo Transfer	**In Vitro Fertilization**
1. Father is infertile. Mother is inseminated by donor and carries child.	1. Mother is fertile but unable to conceive. Ovum from mother and sperm from father are combined in laboratory. Embryo is placed in mother's uterus.
2. Mother is infertile but able to carry child. Donor of ovum is inseminated by father; then embryo is transferred and mother carries child.	2. Mother is infertile but able to carry child. Ovum from donor is combined with sperm from father and implanted in mother.
3. Mother is infertile and unable to carry child. Donor of ovum is inseminated by father and carries child.	3. Father is infertile and mother is fertile but unable to conceive. Ovum from mother is combined with sperm from donor.
4. Both parents are infertile, but mother is able to carry child. Donor of ovum is inseminated by sperm donor; then embryo is transferred and mother carries child.	4. Both parents are infertile, but mother is able to carry child. Ovum and sperm from donors are combined in laboratory (also see number 4, column at left).
LEGEND: Sperm from father Ovum from mother Baby born of mother Sperm from donor Ovum from donor Baby born of donor (Surrogate)	5. Mother is infertile and unable to carry child. Ovum of donor is combined with sperm from father. Embryo is transferred to donor (also see number 2, column at left).
	6. Both parents are fertile, but mother is unable to carry child. Ovum from mother and sperm from father are combined. Embryo is transferred to donor.
	7. Father is infertile; mother is fertile but unable to carry child.

FIGURE 7.15

Some of the ways gametes can be combined to produce babies.

✳ TERATOGENS POSE A RISK TO THE DEVELOPING FETUS

Teratogens are agents that produce abnormalities during embryonic or fetal development. They produce nongenetic birth defects, and not heritable changes. In 1960 only four or five agents were known to be teratogens. The discovery that a tranquilizer, thalidomide, caused limb defects in unborn children helped focus attention on this field. Today, 30 to 40 teratogenic agents are known, with another 10 to 12 compounds strongly suspected.

Little Is Known about Teratogens

At present, little is known about how most teratogens produce fetal damage. Table 7.3 lists some known and suspected teratogens that cause defects in developing embryos and fetuses. Pregnant women should avoid all unnecessary x-rays, and no dose

Teratogen
Any physical or chemical agent that brings about an increase in congenital malformations.

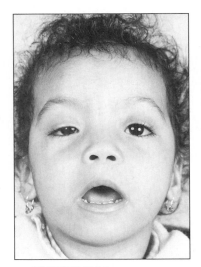

FIGURE 7.16

A child with fetal alcohol syndrome, with misshapen eyes, flat nose, and face characteristic of this condition.

Fetal alcohol syndrome
A constellation of birth defects caused by maternal drinking during pregnancy.

should be delivered to the abdomen of any woman of childbearing age unless she is known not to be pregnant. At present, the use of diagnostic ultrasound is not considered to be teratogenic.

Among infectious agents, viruses, such as the measles virus, and herpes virus II, which is associated with genital herpes, can cause severe brain damage and mental retardation in a developing fetus. The damaging effects of the herpes II virus occur only when the mother becomes infected with herpes *during* pregnancy. There is no damage to the fetus when the mother has been infected before pregnancy and has a recurring attack during pregnancy. Herpes virus I (associated with cold sores) does not appear to be teratogenic. Maternal metabolic abnormalities such as phenylketonuria (PKU) can also be teratogenic.

Fetal Alcohol Syndrome

Prenatal exposure to alcohol is by far the most serious and the most widespread teratogenic problem. Alcohol consumption during pregnancy results in spontaneous abortion, growth retardation, facial abnormalities (Figure 7.16), and mental retardation. This collection of defects is known as **fetal alcohol syndrome (FAS).** In milder forms, the condition is known as fetal alcohol effects. The incidence of these two conditions is about 1.9 affected infants per thousand births for FAS and 3.5 per thousand for fetal alcohol effects. While this incidence may seem low, the economic and social consequences are significant. In the United States the cost for surgical repair of all facial abnormalities and treatment of all sensory and learning problems and mental retardation is more than $320 million per year, a large part of which is used in the treatment of fetal alchol syndrome. For example, about 11% of the total budget for treatment of institutionalized mentally retarded individuals is for those affected by FAS.

TABLE 7.3		
Human Teratogens		
KNOWN		**POSSIBLE**
Radiation		Cigarette smoking
Fallout		High levels of vitamin A
X-rays		Lithium
		Zinc deficiency
Infectious Agents		
Cytomegalovirus		
Herpes virus II		
Rubella virus		
Toxoplasma gondii (spread in cat feces)		
Maternal Metabolic Problems		
Phenylketonuria (PKU)		
Diabetes		
Virilizing tumors		
Drugs and Chemicals		
Alcohol		
Aminopterins		
Chlorobiphenyls		
Coumarin anticoagulants		
Diethlystilbestrol		
Tetracyclines		
Thalidomide		

The teratogenic effects of alcohol can occur at any time during pregnancy, but weeks 8–12 are particularly sensitive periods. Even in the third trimester, alcohol can seriously impair fetal growth. Consumption of one ounce of absolute alcohol (the amount contained in two mixed drinks) per day in the third trimester of pregnancy reduces the birth weight of the fetus by about 160 gm. The equivalent of two mixed drinks in one day at any time in the last 3 months of pregnancy will reduce fetus birth weight by 5%. Each day of consumption of a similar amount will reduce the birth weight by another 5%. Low birth weight is associated with high rates of neonatal death; newborns below 50% of normal birth weight have a 45% mortality rate.

Alcohol produces its effects by constricting the blood vessels of the placenta and umbilical cord, reducing the supply of oxygen to the fetus. Measurements on placentas recovered from normal births show that umbilical blood vessels constrict in the presence of alcohol concentrations as low as 0.05%, the amount contained in 1 to 1.5 drinks. Oxygen deprivation may play a role in the behavioral defects and mental retardation associated with FAS. Low levels of blood alcohol can cause serious problems in fetal development, and pregnant women should avoid all alcohol during pregnancy.

While the actions of alcohol as a teratogen are now well known, work is needed to resolve the degree of risk involved with chemicals and substances that are suspected teratogens and to identify new teratogens among the thousands of chemicals in present use. More importantly, it is necessary to investigate the genetic basis of susceptibility to teratogenic agents, especially drugs and chemicals.

SEX DETERMINATION IN HUMANS

In humans, as in many other species, there are obvious phenotypic differences between the sexes, a condition known as **sexual dimorphism.** In some organisms the differences are limited to the gonads; in others, including humans, secondary sex characteristics such as body size, muscle mass, patterns of fat distribution, and amounts and distribution of body hair emphasize the differences between the sexes.

Chromosomes Can Help Determine Sex

What determines maleness and femaleness is a complex interaction between genes and the environment. In some organisms, environmental factors play a major role (Figure 7.17). For example, in some reptiles such as turtles or crocodiles, sex is determined by the temperature at which the eggs develop. Eggs incubated at higher temperatures produce females; those at lower temperatures produce males. In other reptiles, the opposite is true; higher incubation temperatures produce males, and lower temperatures result in females. In humans, on the other hand, sex determination is primarily associated with the sex chromosomes. As dis-

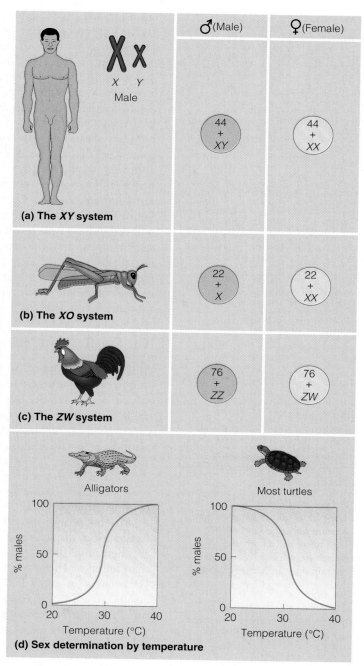

 FIGURE 7.17

(a–c) Animals have several mechanisms of sex determination involving chromosomes. (d) In some reptiles, the temperature at which the egg is incubated determines the sex of the offspring.

Sexual dimorphism
The presence of morphological traits that characterize males and females.

cussed in Chapter 2, females have two X chromosomes (XX) and males have an X and a Y chromosome.

Although the XX-XY mechanism of sex determination seems straightforward, it does not provide all the answers to the question of what determines maleness and femaleness. Is a male a male because he has a Y chromosome, or because he does not have two X chromosomes? This question was answered about 25 years ago by the discovery that some humans carry an abnormal number of sex chromosomes. Rarely, individuals with only 45 chromosomes (45,X) are born, and these individuals are female. At about the same time, males carrying two X chromosomes and a Y chromosome were discovered (47,XXY). From the study of these and other individuals with abnormal numbers of sex chromosomes, it is clear that some females may have only one X chromosome and that some males can have more than one X chromosome. Furthermore, anyone with a Y chromosome is almost always male, no matter how many X chromosomes he may have. From studies on the chromosomal status of normal individuals and those carrying abnormal numbers or structural variants of the sex chromosomes, the conclusion is that under normal circumstances, the male phenotype is associated with the presence of a Y chromosome, and the absence of a Y chromosome results in the female phenotype. However, two X chromosomes are required for female development to take place in a normal fashion, and a single X chromosome is required for normal male development.

The Sex Ratio in Humans

All gametes produced by females contain an X chromosome, while males produce roughly equal numbers of gametes carrying an X chromosome and gametes carrying a Y chromosome. Because the male makes two kinds of gametes, he is referred to as the **heterogametic** sex. The female is **homogametic** since she makes only one type of gamete. An egg fertilized by an X-bearing sperm results in an XX zygote that will develop as a female. Fertilization by a Y-bearing sperm will produce an XY, or male, zygote (⬤ Figure 7.18). It is the male gamete that determines the sex of the offspring.

Because sex of the offspring is determined by the presence or absence of a Y chromosome, and because males produce approximately equal numbers of X- and Y-bearing gametes, males and females should be produced in equal proportions (Figure 7.18). This proportion, known as the **sex ratio,** changes throughout the life cycle. At fertilization, the sex ratio (known as the primary sex ratio), should be 1:1. While direct determinations are impossible, estimates indicate that more males are conceived than females. The sex ratio at birth, known as the secondary sex ratio, is about 1.05 (105 males for every 100 females). The tertiary sex ratio is the ratio as measured in adults. At 20 to 25 years of age, the ratio is close to 1.00; thereafter, females outnumber males in ever-increasing proportions. There are several reasons for the higher death rate among males, including both environmental and genetic factors. Accidents

Heterogametic
The production of gametes that contain different kinds of sex chromosomes. In humans, males produce gametes that contain X or Y chromosomes.

Homogametic
The production of gametes that contain only one kind of sex chromosome. In humans, all gametes produced by females contain only an X chromosome.

Sex ratio
The relative proportion of males and females belonging to a specific age group in a population.

⬤ **FIGURE 7.18**

The segregation of sex chromosomes into gametes and the random combination of X-bearing or Y-bearing sperm with an X-bearing egg produces, on average, a 1:1 ratio of males to females.

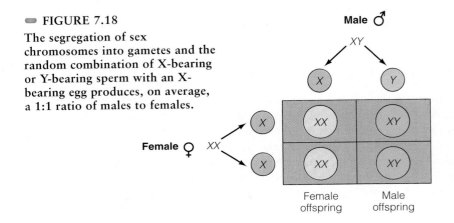

are the leading cause of death among males aged 15 to 35 years, and the expression of deleterious X-linked recessive genes also leads to a higher death rate among males.

SEX DIFFERENTIATION FOLLOWS SEX DETERMINATION

Sex is chromosomally determined at fertilization, but the expression of this chromosomal state as a phenotype occurs in stages over time. Factors influencing the course of these events are discussed below.

Chromosomal Sex and Phenotypic Sex

Sex determination by the XX-XY method provides a genetic framework for the developmental events that guide the zygote toward the acquisition of male or female phenotypes. The process of forming male or female reproductive structures depends on several factors, including gene action, interactions within the embryo, interaction with other embryos that may be present in the uterus, and interactions with the maternal environment. As a result of these interactions, the chromosomal sex (XX or XY) of an individual may be different from the phenotypic sex. These differences arise during embryonic and fetal development and can produce a phenotype opposite to the chromosomal sex, intermediate to the phenotypes of the two sexes, or a phenotype that has characteristics and genitalia of both sexes. The sex of an individual can be defined at several levels: chromosomal sex, gonadal sex, and phenotypic sex. In most cases, all these definitions are consistent, but in others they are not (see "Concepts and Controversies," page 184). To understand these variations and the interactions of genes with the environment, we will first consider the events in normal sexual development.

Events in Embryogenesis Begin Sexual Differentiation

The first step in sex differentiation occurs at fertilization with the formation of a diploid zygote having an XX or XY chromosome constitution. Although the chromosomal sex of the zygote is established at fertilization, the embryo that develops is sexually ambiguous for the first month or so. The external genitalia of early embryos are neither male nor female, but are indifferent. Internally, both male and female reproductive ducts and associated structures are present. The two internal duct systems are the Müllerian and Wolffian ducts (Figure 7.19). The Müllerian duct system will form the female reproductive ducts, and the Wolffian system gives rise to the male reproductive duct system.

At 7 weeks of development, diverging developmental pathways activate different sets of genes and establish the gonadal sex of the embryo. This process takes place over the next 4 to 6 weeks. While it is convenient to think of only two pathways, one leading to males and the other to females, there are many alternate pathways, producing intermediate outcomes in gonadal sex and in sexual phenotypes, some of which we will consider below.

 FIGURE 7.19

Two duct systems (Wolffian and Müllerian systems) are present in the early embryo. They enter different developmental pathways in the presence and absence of a Y chromosome.

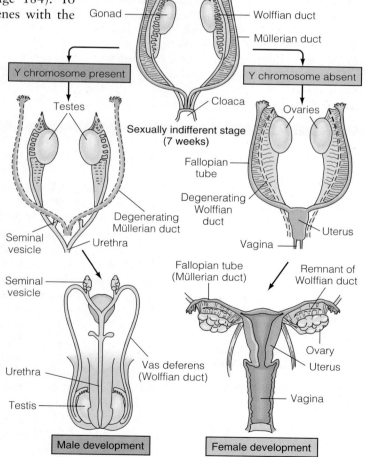

CONCEPTS AND CONTROVERSIES

Sex Testing in International Athletics—Is It Necessary?

Success in amateur athletics including the Olympics is often a prelude to financial rewards and acclaim as a professional athlete. Several methods are used to guard against cheating in competition. Competitors in many international events are required to submit urine samples (collected while someone watches) for drug testing. In other cases, this is done at random, in an attempt to eliminate the use of steroids or performance-enhancing drugs.

In the 1960s, concern about males attempting to compete as females led the International Olympic Committee (IOC) to institute sex testing for athletes, beginning with the 1968 Olympics. Sex testing may seem reasonable, given that men are usually larger, stronger, and faster than females, and males competing as females would have an unfair advantage. The IOC test involved analysis of epithelial cells recovered by scraping the inside of the mouth. In genetic females (XX), the inactivated X chromosome forms a Barr body, which can be stained and seen under a microscope. Genetic males (XY) do not have a Barr body. The procedure is noninvasive, and females are not required to submit to a physical examination of their genitals. If sexual identity were called into question as a result of the test, a karyotype was required, and if necessary, a gynecological examination followed.

In practice, the IOC test has been unsuccessful. The test for a Barr body is unreliable, and leads to both false positive and false negative results. It fails to take into account the sit-uation where a female can be XY, and have testicular feminization, and other conditions that result in a discrepancy between chromosomal and phenotypic sex.

In addition, the test does not take into account the psychological, social, and cultural factors that enter into one's identity as a male or a female. The test has not identified any men attempting to compete as females, but has barred several women from competition in every Olympic game since 1968.

An analysis of sex testing on more than 6000 women athletes has found that 1 in 500 had to withdraw from competition as a consequence of failing the sex test. In response to criticism, the IOC and the International Amateur Athletic Federation (IAAF) developed different responses. Since 1991, all IAAF athletes are required to have a physical examination, and have their sexual status certified. The IOC has instituted a new test, based on recombinant DNA technology, to detect the presence of the male-determining gene SRY, carried on the Y chromosome. A positive test makes the athlete ineligible to compete as a female. However, this new test remains controversial, and fails to recognize several chromosomal combinations that result in a female phenotype even though an SRY gene is present.

The basic question remains unanswered: Why are such sex tests needed in the first place? The IOF and the IAAF continue to debate the question and review their policies, but at this point are not willing to give up sex testing.

SRY
A gene called the sex-determining region of the Y, located near the end of the short arm of the Y chromosome, that plays a major role in causing the undifferentiated gonad to develop into a testis.

Testosterone
A steroid hormone produced by the testis; the male sex hormone.

Müllerian inhibiting hormone (MIH)
A hormone produced by the developing testis that causes the breakdown of the Müllerian ducts in the embryo.

In male development, the presence of a Y chromosome causes the indifferent gonad to begin development as a testis. The selection of this pathway is the result of the action of genes on the Y chromosome. Products from these activated genes stimulate the growth and differentiation of a small collection of cells within the indifferent gonad, causing the gonad to develop as a testis. A gene called the **sex-determining region of the Y (SRY)** (MIM/OMIM 480000), mapped to a region on the short arm of the Y chromosome, plays a major role in starting the cascade of gene action that causes the indifferent gonad to begin testis development. Other genes on the Y chromosome and on autosomes also play important roles at this time.

Once testis development is initiated, cells in the testis secrete two hormones, **testosterone** and the **Müllerian inhibiting hormone (MIH)**. Along with gene expression, these hormones control further sexual development. Testosterone stimulates the development of the male internal duct system (Wolffian ducts), including the epididymis, seminal vesicles, and vas deferens. MIH inhibits further development of female duct structure and causes degeneration of the Müllerian ducts (Figure 7.19).

In the case of female development, the absence of the Y chromosome and the presence of the second X chromosome causes the embryonic gonad to develop as an ovary. Cells along the outer edge of the gonad divide and push into the interior, form-

ing the ovary. In the absence of testosterone, the Wolffian duct system degenerates (Figure 7.19). In the absence of MIH, the Müllerian duct system develops to form the fallopian tubes, uterus, and parts of the vagina.

After gonadal sex has been established, the third phase of sexual differentiation, the appearance of sexual phenotype, begins (➡ Figure 7.20). In males, testosterone is metabolized and converted into another hormone, dihydroxytestosterone (DHT), which directs formation of the external genitalia. Under the influence of DHT and testosterone, the genital folds and genital tubercle develop into the penis, and the surrounding labioscrotal swelling form the scrotum.

In females, the genital tubercle develops into the clitoris, the genital folds form the labia minora, and the labioscrotal swellings form the labia majora (Figure 7.20).

➡ **FIGURE 7.20**

Steps in the development of phenotypic sex from the undifferentiated stage (a) to the male (b) or female (c) phenotype. The male pathway of development takes place in response to the presence of testosterone and dihydroxytestosterone (DHT). Female development takes place in the absence of these hormones.

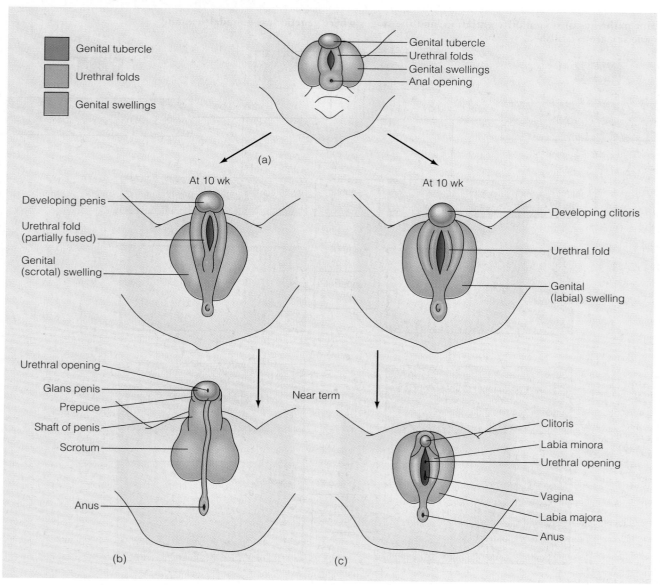

In terms of gene action, it is important to note that the development of gonadal sex and sexual phenotype in male and female humans results from different developmental pathways (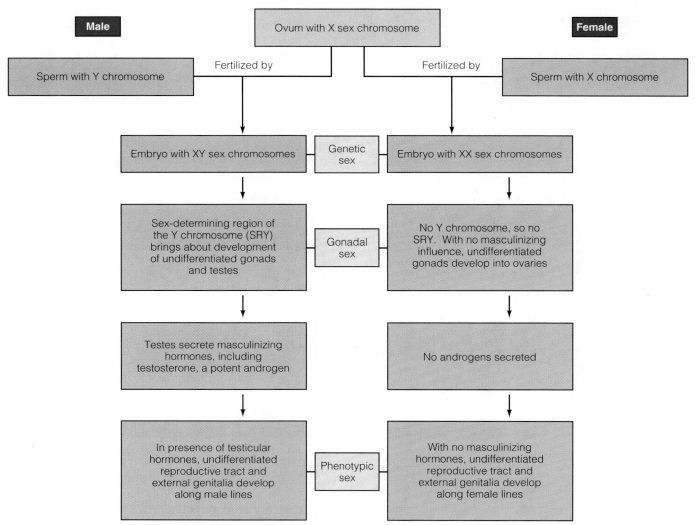 Figure 7.21). In males, this pathway involves induction by several genes on the Y chromosome, the presence of a single X chromosome, and possibly one or more autosomal genes. In females, this pathway involves the presence of two X chromosomes, the absence of Y chromosome genes, and presumably other autosomal genes. These distinctions indicate that there may be important differences in the way genes in these respective pathways are activated, and they may provide clues in the search for genes that regulate these pathways.

GENETIC CONTROL OF SEXUAL DIFFERENTIATION

Developmental pathways that begin with the indifferent gonad often result in a gonadal and/or sexual phenotype that is at variance with the chromosomal sex of XX

FIGURE 7.21

The major pathways of sexual differentiation, and the stages where genetic sex, gonadal sex, and phenotypic sex are established.

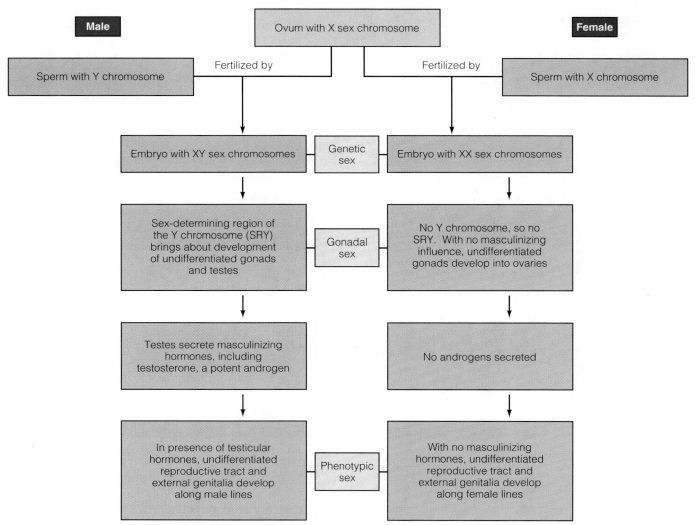

for females and XY for males. These differences in outcome can result from chromosomal events that exchange segments of the X and Y chromosomes, from mutations that affect the ability of cells to respond to the products of Y chromosome genes, or from the action of autosomal genes that control events on the X and/or Y chromosome. In addition, interactions between the embryo and maternal hormones in the uterus as well as the presence of other embryos in the uterus can affect the outcome of both the gonadal sex and the sexual phenotype.

Part of our understanding of sexual development is derived from the study of variations in this process, including single-gene mutations that produce altered sexual phenotypes. We will briefly consider three situations in which there is a lack of concordance among chromosomal sex, gonadal sex, and sexual phenotype.

True hermaphrodites are organisms that possess both ovaries and testes and the associated duct systems. In some species, such as the earthworm, this condition is normal. In humans, a true hermaphrodite is someone with ovarian and testicular tissue present in separate gonads or in a single combined gonad. Cytogenetic examination of several hermaphrodites has shown them to be sex chromosome mosaics, with some cells in the body being XX and others XY or XXY. In other cases, only XY cells were found.

Testicular Feminization and Phenotypic Sex

Testicular feminization (MIM/OMIM 313700) syndrome is an X-linked trait in which chromosomal males develop as females. In this case, chromosomal sex (XY) is opposite from phenotypic sex (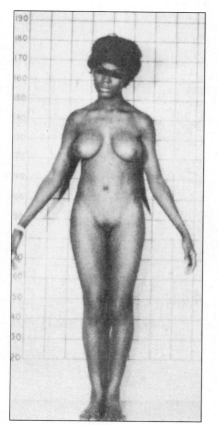 Figure 7.22). During sexual development, testis formation is induced normally, and testosterone and MIH production begins as expected. MIH brings about the degeneration of the Müllerian duct system so that no internal female reproductive tract is formed. However, a mutation in this X-chromosome gene blocks the ability of cells to respond to testosterone or DHT. As a result, development proceeds as if there is no testosterone or DHT present. The Wolffian duct system degenerates, and the indifferent genitalia develop as female structures. Individuals with this syndrome are females with well-developed breasts, very little pubic hair, and lack of menstruation (see "Concepts & Controversies," page 189).

Testicular feminization
An X-linked genetic trait that causes XY individuals to develop into phenotypic females.

⬛ **FIGURE 7.22**
An XY male with testicular feminization.

Gene Expression and Sexual Phenotype

Pseudohermaphroditism
An autosomal genetic condition that causes XY individuals to develop the phenotypic sex of females.

Pseudohermaphrodites usually have only one type of gonad and ambiguous genitalia. One form of **pseudohermaphroditism** (MIM/OMIM 264300) is known to be caused by an autosomal recessive gene. This condition, associated with an XY chromosome constitution, prevents the conversion of testosterone to DHT. In these cases, the Y chromosome initiates the development of testes, and the male duct system and internal organs are properly formed from the Wolffian ducts. MIH secretion prevents the development of female internal structures. However, the failure to produce DHT results in genitalia that are essentially female. The scrotum resembles the labia, a blind vaginal pouch is present, and the penis resembles a clitoris. Although chromosomally male, these individuals are raised as females.

At puberty, however, masculinization takes place. The testes descend into a developing scrotum, and the phallus develops into a functional penis. The voice deepens, beard growth occurs, and muscle mass increases as in normal males. Biopsy indicates that spermatogenesis is normal. These changes are mediated by the increased levels of testosterone that accompany puberty. This condition is rare, but in a group of small villages in the Dominican Republic, over 30 such cases are known. The high incidence of homozygous recessives can be attributed to common ancestry through intermarriage (● Figure 7.23). In 12 of the 13 families, a line of descent can be traced to a single ancestor (I-3). This mutation and the one that produces testicular feminization are evidence for the importance of gene interactions in normal development. Not only is the process of sexual development clearly under genetic control, but the ability to respond to the hormonal environment is critical to normal sexual differentiation.

● **FIGURE 7.23**

Pedigree of a pseudohermaphroditism in several generations of residents of a cluster of villages in the Dominican Republic. Although the condition was first diagnosed in generation V, members of earlier generations were probably affected.

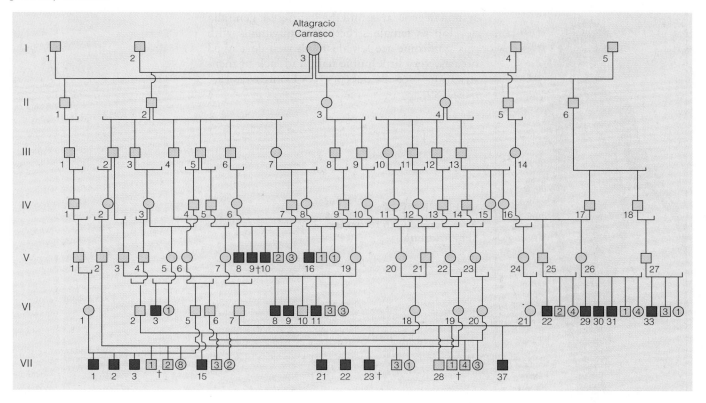

Joan of Arc—Was It Really John of Arc?

Joan of Arc, the national heroine of France, was born in a village in northeastern France in 1412, during the Hundred Years' War. At the age of 13 or 14 years, she began to have visions that directed her to help fight the English at Orléans. Following victory, she helped orchestrate the crowning of the new king, Charles VII. Joan was captured by the English during a siege of Paris, and in 1431, she was tried for heresy. Although her trial was technically a religious one conducted by the English-controlled Church, it was clearly a political trial. Shortly after being sentenced to life imprisonment, she was declared a relapsed heretic, and on May 30, 1431, she was burned at the stake in the marketplace at Rouen.

In 1455 Pope Callistus formed a commission to investigate the circumstances of her trial, and a Trial of Rehabilitation took place over a period of 7 months in 1456. The second trial took testimony from over 100 individuals who knew Joan personally. Extensive documentation from the original trial and the Trial of Rehabilitation exists. This material has served as the source for the more than 100 plays and countless books written about her life. Although the story of her life is well known, perhaps more remains to be discovered. From an examination of the original evidence, R. B. Greenblatt has proposed that Joan had phenotypic characteristics of testicular feminization. By all accounts, Joan was a healthy female with well-developed breasts. Those living with her in close quarters testified that she never menstruated, and physical examinations conducted during her imprisonment revealed a lack of pubic hair. While such circumstantial evidence is not enough for a diagnosis, it provides more than enough material for speculation. This speculation also provides a new impetus for those medicogenetic detectives who prowl through history, seeking information about the genetic makeup of the famous, infamous, the nortorious, and the obscure.

DOSAGE COMPENSATION AND THE X CHROMOSOME

Since females have two doses of all genes on the X chromosome and males have only one dose of most genes, it would seem that females should have twice as much of these gene products as males.

Expression of Genes on the X Chromosome

In Chapter 4, we discussed hemophilia A, an X-linked genetic disorder in which clotting factor VIII is deficient. Since normal females have two copies of this gene and normal males have only one, should the blood of females contain twice as much clotting factor VIII as that of males? Careful measurements indicate that females have the same amount of this clotting factor as males. In fact, the same is true for all X chromosome genes tested: the level of X-linked gene products is the same in males and females. Somehow, differences in gene dosage are regulated to produce equal amounts of gene products in both sexes. How that is accomplished in humans and how it came to be understood is an interesting story.

Barr Bodies and X Inactivation

An explanation of how **dosage compensation** works in humans is known as the **Lyon hypothesis,** after Mary Lyon, a British geneticist. She discovered that dosage compensation is accomplished by inactivating, or turning off, almost all the genes on one of the X chromosomes in females. She based this idea on both genetic and cytological evidence.

The genetic evidence came from studies on coat color in mice. In female mice heterozygous for X-linked coat-color genes, Lyon observed that coat color was not like

Dosage compensation
A mechanism that regulates the expression of sex-linked gene products.

Lyon hypothesis
The proposal that dosage compensation in mammalian females is accomplished by the partial and random inactivation of one of the two X chromosomes.

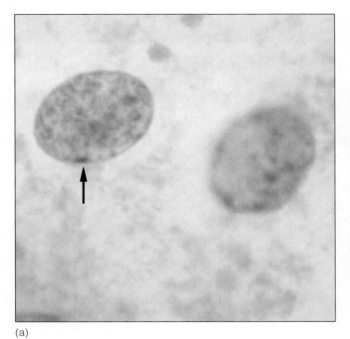

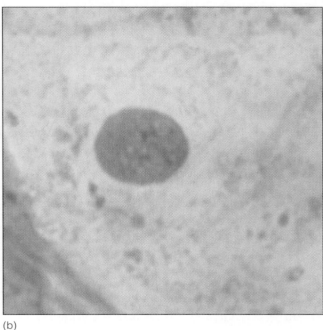

(a) (b)

● FIGURE 7.24

(a) Nucleus from a female cell showing a Barr body (arrow). (b) Nucleus from a male cell shows no Barr body.

that of either homozygote, nor was it intermediate to the homozygotes. Instead the coat was composed of patches of the two parental colors in a random arrangement. Males, hemizygous for either gene, never showed such patches and had coats of uniform color. This genetic evidence suggested to Lyon that in heterozygous females, both alleles were active but not in the same cells.

The relevant cytological observations were made by Murray Barr and his colleagues beginning in 1949. Barr, a physiologist, was studying nerve function and used nerve cells obtained from cats. He observed that the nuclei of nerve cells from female cats contained a small, dense mass of chromatin located near the inner surface of the nuclear membrane (● Figure 7.24). Nerve-cell nuclei from male cats did not contain this structure, referred to as the Barr body. Lyon suggested that the Barr body is actually an inactivated, condensed X chromosome and that either X chromosome can be inactivated. The Lyon hypothesis can be summarized as follows:

- In the somatic cells (not the germ cells) of female mammals, one X chromosome is active, and the second X chromosome is randomly inactivated and tightly coiled to form the Barr body.
- The inactive chromosome can be either paternally derived or maternally derived, and in each cell of the body, either the paternal or maternal X chromosome is randomly inactivated.
- Inactivation takes place early in development. After four to five rounds of mitosis following fertilization, each cell of the embryo randomly inactivates one X chromosome.
- This inactivation is permanent except in germ cells, and all descendants of a given cell will have the same X chromosome inactivated.
- The random inactivation of one X chromosome in females makes males and females equivalent for the activity of X-linked genes.

Mosaic
An individual composed of two or more cell types of different genetic or chromosomal constitution.

Females Are Mosaics for X-linked Genes

The Lyon hypothesis means that female mammals are actually **mosaics,** constructed of two different cell types: one with the maternal X chromosome active and one with

the paternal X chromosome active. This explains the pattern of coat color in the heterozygous mice that Lyon observed. In females heterozygous for X-linked coat-color genes, patches of one color are interspersed with patches of another color. According to the Lyon hypothesis, each patch represents a group of cells descended from a single cell in which the inactivation event occurred.

Another perhaps more familiar example of this mosaicism is the tortoiseshell cat (⬤ Figure 7.25). In cats, a gene for coat color on the X chromosome has two alleles, a dominant mutant allele *(O)* that produces an orange/yellow coat color and a recessive normal allele *(o)* that produces a black color. Heterozygous females *(O/o)* have a tortoiseshell coat, with patches of orange/yellow fur mixed with patches of black fur (white fur on the chest and abdomen in such cats is controlled by a different, autosomal gene). Tortoiseshell cats are therefore invariably female, as hemizygous males would be either all orange/yellow or all black.

In human females, mosaicism has also been demonstrated (⬤ Figure 7.26). A gene on the X chromosome encodes the information for an enzyme called G6PD (MIM/OMIM 305900), and has two alleles. Each allele produces a distinct and separable form of the enzyme. By pedigree analysis, heterozygous females were identified, and skin cells from these females were isolated and grown individually. Each culture, grown from a single cell, showed only one form or the other of the enzyme.

In humans, random inactivation of the X chromosome occurs very early in embryogenesis, usually at or before the 32-cell stage of development. Given the small number of cells present at the time of inactivation, it is possible that an imbalance in the ratio of inactivated paternal and maternal chromosomes might result by chance, causing females to express X-linked traits for which they are heterozygous. This imbalance has been demonstrated a number of times by observing monozygotic twins, one of whom exhibits an X-linked recessive trait while the other does not (⬤ Figure 7.27).

⬤ **FIGURE 7.25**
The different-colored patches of fur on this tortoiseshell cat are the result of X-chromosome inactivation.

⬤ **FIGURE 7.26**
Dosage compensation in humans. The X-linked gene encoding the enzyme G6PD has two alleles, one producing an active form of the enzyme; the other produces an inactive form. (a) Blood cells from an individual with two active alleles stained to show enzyme activity. (b) Blood cells from a heterozygous female. About half the cells are stained, reflecting the presence of an active allele. The unstained cells contain an inactive allele. Heterozygotes are mosaics composed of two cell types, one with G6PD enzyme activity and one with no activity.

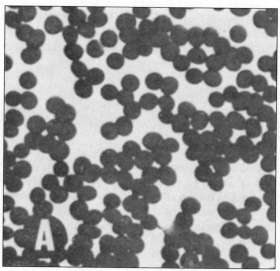

(a)

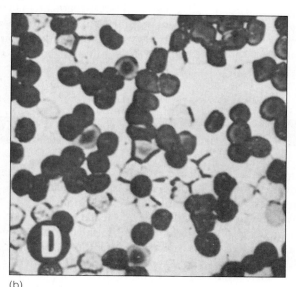

(b)

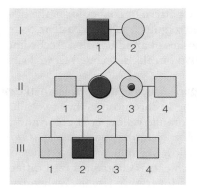

FIGURE 7.27

Pedigree showing monozygotic female twins (II-2 and II-3) discordant for color blindness. The twins inherited the allele for color blindness from their father. In the color-blind twin, almost all the active X chromosomes carry the mutant allele; in the twin with normal vision, almost all the active X chromosomes carry the allele for normal vision.

In this pedigree, two female identical twins are heterozygotes for red-green color-blindness through their color-blind father. One of the twins has normal color vision, and the other has red-green color blindness. The color-blind twin has three sons, two with normal vision and one who is color blind (see pedigree).

Analysis of X inactivation was carried out in these twins using molecular techniques, allowing the parental origin of active and inactive X chromosomes to be assigned. Testing of skin fibroblasts indicates that in the twin with color blindness, almost all the active X chromosomes are paternal X chromosomes carrying the allele for color blindness. In the twin with normal vision, the opposite situation is observed; almost all the active X chromosomes are maternal in origin.

The colorblindness in one twin and normal color vision in the other twin can be explained by X inactivation associated with twinning. One twin was formed from a small number of cells, most of which had the paternal X inactivated. The other twin originated from a small number of cells, most of which had the maternal X chromosome inactivated.

SEX-INFLUENCED AND SEX-LIMITED TRAITS

Sex-influenced genes
Loci that produce a phenotype that is conditioned by the sex of the individual.

Pattern baldness
A sex-influenced trait that acts like an autosomal dominant trait in males and an autosomal recessive trait in females.

Sex-limited genes
Loci that produce a phenotype that is produced in only one sex.

Precocius puberty
An autosomal dominant trait expressed in a sex-limited fashion. Heterozygous males are affected, but heterozygous females are not.

Sex-influenced genes are those that are expressed in both males and females but with frequencies much different than would be predicted by Mendelian ratios. These genes are usually autosomal and serve to illustrate the effect of sex on the level of gene expression. **Pattern baldness** (MIM/OMIM 109200) is an example of sex-influenced inheritance. This trait is expressed more often in males than in females. The gene acts as an autosomal dominant in males and as an autosomal recessive in females. In this case, the differential expression of pattern baldness in males and females is related to the different levels of testosterone present. In this case the hormonal environment and the genotype interact in determining expression of this gene.

Sex-limited genes are expressed only in one sex, whether they are inherited in an autosomal or sex-linked pattern. One such gene, an autosomal dominant that controls **precocious puberty** (MIM/OMIM 176410), is expressed in heterozygous males but not in heterozygous females. Affected males undergo puberty at 4 years of age or earlier. Heterozygous females are unaffected but pass this trait on to half their sons, making it hard to distinguish this trait from a sex-linked gene. Genes dealing with traits such as breast development in females and facial hair in males are other examples of sex-limited genes, as are virtually all other genes dealing with secondary sexual characteristics.

SUMMARY

1. The human reproductive system consists of gonads (testes in males, ovaries in females), ducts to transport gametes, and genital structures for copulation and fertilization.
2. Human development begins with fertilization and mitosis to form a blastocyst. The embryo implants in the uterine wall, and a placenta develops to nourish the embryo.

3. Human development is divided into three stages, or trimesters, of about 12 weeks each. The first trimester is a period of organ formation and growth to the fetal stage. Growth and maturation of the organ systems takes place in the second trimester. The third trimester is a period of rapid growth.

4. Although mechanisms of sex determination vary from species to species, the presence of a Y chromosome in humans is normally associated with male sexual development, and the absence of a Y chromosome is associated with female development.

5. Early in development, the Y chromosome signals the indifferent gonad to begin development as a testis. Further stages in male sexual differentiation, including the development of phenotypic sex, are controlled by hormones secreted by the testis.

6. In cases of sex-influenced and sex-limited inheritance, the sex of the individual affects whether a trait will be expressed and the degree to which the trait will be expressed. This holds true for both autosomal and sex-linked genes. Sex hormones and the developmental history of the individual are thought to modify expression of these genes, giving rise to altered phenotypic ratios.

QUESTIONS AND PROBLEMS

1. Describe, from fertilization, the major pathways of normal male sexual development, and include the stages where genetic sex, gonadal sex, and phenotypic sex are determined.

2. Give an example where genetic sex, gonadal sex and phenotypic sex do not coincide. Explain why they do not coincide.

3. Which pathway of sexual differentiation is regarded as the default pathway (male or female)? Why?

4. The absence of a Y chromosome in an early embryo causes:
   a. the embryonic testis to become an ovary
   b. The Wolffian duct system to develop
   c. The Mullerian duct system to degenerate
   d. the indifferent gonad to become an ovary

5. How can an individual who is XY be phenotypically female?

6. Discuss whether the following individuals are: 1) gonadally male or female, 2) phenotypically male or female (discuss Wolffian/Mullerian ducts and external genitalia), and 3) sterile or fertile:
   a. XY, homozygous for a recessive mutation in the testosterone gene, which renders the gene nonfunctional
   b. XX, heterozygous for a dominant mutation in the testosterone gene, which causes continuous production of testosterone
   c. XY, heterozygous for a recessive mutation in the MIH gene
   d. XY, homozygous for a recessive mutation in the TDF gene
   e. XY, homozygous for a recessive mutation in the MIH gene.

7. Individuals with an XXY genotype are sterile males. If one X is inactivated early in embryogenesis, the genotype of the individual effectively becomes XY. Why should not this individual develop as a normal male?

8. It has been shown that hormones interact with DNA to turn certain genes on and off. Use this fact to explain sex-limited and sex-influenced traits.

9. Assume that human-like creatures exist on Mars. As in the human population on Earth, there are two sexes and even sex-linked genes. The gene for eye color is an example of one such gene. It has two alleles. The purple allele is dominant to the yellow allele. A purple-eyed female alien mates with a purple-eyed male. All of the male offspring are purple-eyed, while half of the female offspring are purple-eyed and half are yellow-eyed. Which is the heterogametic sex?

10. Calico cats are almost invariably female. Why? (Explain genotype and phenotype of calico females and the theory of why calicos are females).

11. How many Barr bodies would the following individuals have:
    a. normal male
    b. normal female
    c. Kleinfelter male
    d. Turner female

12. Males have only one X chromosome and therefore only one copy of all genes on the X chromosome. Each gene is directly expressed, thus providing the basis of hemizygosity in males. Females have two X chromosomes, but one is always inactivated. Therefore females, like males, have only one functional copy of all the genes on the X chromosome. Again, each gene must be directly expressed. Why then are females not considered hemizygous, and why are they not afflicted with sex-linked recessive diseases as often as males?

13. What method of sex testing did the Olympics committee previously use? What method are they currently using? Do either of these methods conclusively test for "femaleness"? Explain.

SCIENCE AND SOCIETY

1. Researchers are currently learning how to transfer sperm-making cells from male mice into infertile male mice in the hopes of learning more about reproductive abnormalities. These donor spermatogonia cells have developed into mature spermatozoa in 70% of the cases and some recipients have gone on to father pups. This new advance opens the way for a host of experimental genetic manipulations. It also offers enormous potential for correcting human genetic disease. One human application that this procedure might be useful in is treating infertile males who wish to be fathers.

   Do you foresee any ethical or legal problems with the implementation of this technique? If so, elaborate on them. Could this procedure have the potential for misuse? If so, explain how.

   Should there be screening measures for donors? What kind of screening measures should be used for donors prior to their participation? What is your opinion on this issue?

2. What do you think are the legal and ethical issues surrounding the use of *in vitro* fertilization? How could these issues be resolved?

   Should the child, once he/she is old enough, be told how they were conceived? Why or why not?

   What should be done with the extra gametes that are removed from the woman's body but never implanted in her uterus?

   Should this technique be restricted to women of a certain age, race socio-economic class, or health background? Why or why not?

INTERNET ACTIVITIES

The following activities use the resources of the World Wide Web to enhance the topics covered in this chapter. To investigate the topics described below, log on to the book's home page at:

http://www.wadsworth.com/biology

1. An illustrated representation of the first four weeks of human development is found at the visible embryo web site. During gastrulation, the ectoderm, mesoderm and endoderm of the embryo are formed. Why is gastrulation so important for the embryo's future development?
2. Embryonic development of the nervous system, heart, eye, and ear is the focus of the Embryonic Development Web site maintained by the University of Pennsylvania.

   a. Examine the illustrations of the heart as it develops at 30, 40 and 50 days. Describe the changes and new structures formed at each of these stages.
   b. Consider the evolution of these organs for a moment. Can you formulate an evolutionary explanation for the development of a complex sensory organ such as the eye or the ear? What might be the starting point? Do you think the organ evolved in increments or by a revolutionary change? How do you explain these changes at the level of genes? Do you need new genes; if so where do they come from? Do you adapt genes to new functions: if so, what happens to their old functions?

Abel, E.L. 1995. An update on the incidence of FAS: FAS is not an equal opportunity birth defect. Neurotoxicol. Teratol. 17: 437–443.

Bratton, R.L. 1995. Fetal alcohol syndrome: how you can prevent it. Postgrad. Med. 98: 197–200.

Epstein, C.J. 1995. The new dysmorphology: applications of insights from basic developmental biology to the understanding of human birth defects. Proc. Nat. Acad. Sci. 92: 8566–8573.

Goodfellow, P. N., 1986. The case of the missing H-Y antigen. Trends in Genetics 2: 87.

Graves, J.A. 1995. The origin and function of the mammalian Y chromosome and Y-borne genes—an evolving understanding. Bioessays 17: 311–320.

Greenblatt, R. B. 1981. Case history: Jeanne d'Arc—Syndrome of feminizing testes. *Br. J. Sex Med. 8:* 54.

Hawkins, J.R. 1994. Sex determination. Hum. Mol. Genet. 3 Spec. Nos. 1463–1467.

Imperato-McGinley, J., Guerrero, L., Gautier, T., and Peterson, R. G. 1974. Steroid 5-alpha reductase deficiency in man: An inherited form of pseudo-hermaphroditism. *Science 186:* 1213–1215.

Kelley, R.L. and Kuroda, M.I. 1995. Equality for X chromosomes. Science 270: 1607–1610.

Lyon, M. F. 1962. Sex chromatin and gene action in the mammalian X-chromosome. *Am. J. Hum. Genet.* 14:135–148.

Lyon, M. R. 1989. X-chromosome inactivation as a system of gene dosage compensation to regulate gene expression. *Prog. Nucleic Acids Res. Mol. Biol. 36:* 119–130.

Nordqvist, K. 1995. Sex differentiation-gonadogenesis and novel genes. Int. J. Dev. Biol. 39: 727–736..

Ott, J. 1986. Y-linkage and pseudoautosomal linkage. *Am. J. Hum. Genet. 38:* 891–897.

Sulton, C., Lobaccaro, J., Belon, C., Terraza, A., and Lumbroso, S. 1992. Molecular biology of disorders of sex differentiation. Horm. Res. 38:105–113.

Whitfield, L., Lovell-Badge, R. and Goodfellow, P. 1993. Rapid sequence evolution of the mammalian sex-determining gene SRY. Nature 364:713–715.

Willard, H.F. 1996. X chromosome inactivation, XIST, and the pursuit of the X-inactivation center. Cell 86: 5–7.

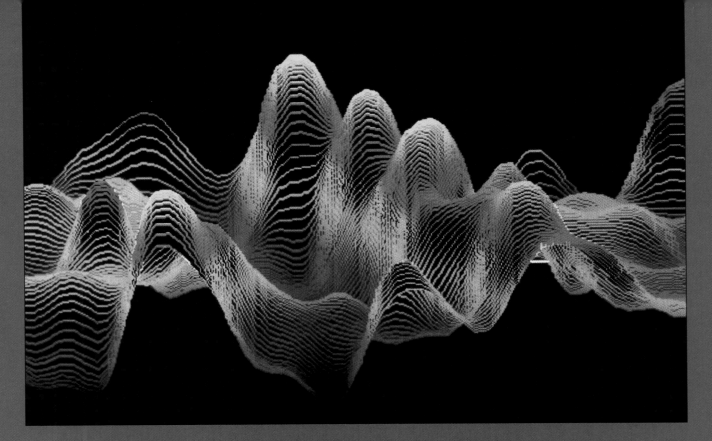

DNA STRUCTURE AND CHROMOSOME ORGANIZATION

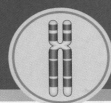

Chapter **8**

Chapter Outline

DNA AS A CARRIER OF GENETIC
INFORMATION
Transfer of Genetic Traits in Bacteria
Reproduction in Bacterial Viruses Involves
DNA
CONCEPTS AND CONTROVERSIES   *DNA as
a Commercial Product*
WATSON, CRICK, AND THE
STRUCTURE OF DNA

Reviewing Some Basic Chemistry
Nucleotides: The Building Blocks of Nucleic
Acids
DNA Is a Double Helix
SIDEBAR   *DNA Organization and Disease*
DNA IS COILED WITH PROTEINS TO
FORM CHROMOSOMES

The Mitochondrial Chromosome Is a
Circular DNA Molecule
Nuclear Chromosomes Have a Complex
Structure
DNA REPLICATION DEPENDS ON BASE
PAIRING

OPENING IMAGE
*A DNA molecule as seen in a computer-
enhanced image produced by a scanning-
tunneling micorgraph (STM).*

Early in the 1860s, Frederick Miescher set out to study the chemical
composition of human white blood cells with the hope of understanding
something of the nature of cellular mechanisms associated with life. But, such
cells were difficult to obtain in the quantities needed for chemical studies.
Miescher learned that cells present in the pus of infected wounds were derived
from the white blood cells. In the days before antibiotics, wound infections
were common. Miescher visited local hospitals to collect discarded bandages.
He scraped the pus from these bandages and developed a method of separating the pus cells from debris and bandage fragments by washing with a salt
solution.

In his early experiments Miescher recovered a chemical substance from the nuclei of the pus cells. To analyze this substance further, he decided to first purify the nuclei. As a first step, he broke open the pus cells by treating them with a protein-digesting substance called pepsin. To obtain pepsin, he prepared extracts of pig stomachs (a good source of pepsin, which functions in digestion). He then treated the pus cells with the extract of pig stomach for several hours. He noted that a gray sediment collected at the bottom of the flask. Under the microscope this sediment turned out to be pure nuclei. Miescher was therefore the first to isolate and to purify a cellular organelle.

By chemically extracting the purified nuclei, Miescher obtained a substance he called nuclein. Chemical analysis revealed that it contained hydrogen, carbon, nitrogen, oxygen, and phosphorus. Miescher showed that nuclein was found in other cell types, including kidney, liver, sperm, and yeast. He regarded it as an important component of most cells. Many years later his nuclein was shown to contain DNA.

At about the same time that Miescher was carrying out his experiments, Mendel outlined the rules for the inheritance of physical traits and developed the notion of what we now call genes. In the 1880s August Weismann and others emphasized the importance of the nucleus in heredity. At the turn of the century Walter Sutton and Theodore Boveri noted that the behavior of genes in inheritance paralleled that of nuclear components (the chromosomes) in meiosis. Later workers confirmed that, in fact, genes are part of chromosomes, and it was generally agreed that the genetic material was to be found in the nucleus. Through all this work, however, the most basic question remained unanswered: What is the nature of the genetic material?

The answer to this question will take us from the level of the gene as the physical unit of heredity to the level of nucleic acid molecules as the chemical components of cells most closely involved with the storage, expression, and transmission of genetic information. The path to this answer runs from the experiments of Miescher through 80 years to the experiments of Avery and his colleagues in the 1940s, and beyond. Although several lines of evidence provided clues pointing to nucleic acids, especially deoxyribonucleic acid (DNA), as the chemical answer to this problem, most theories were orginally based on proteins as the molecular carriers of genetic information. The general requirements for the genetic material, however, were clear and unambiguous. Any chemical structure proposed as the carrier of genetic information must explain the observed properties of genes: replication, information storage, expression of the stored information, and mutation. It was not until the middle of this century that this issue was resolved.

In this chapter we will examine the events that led to the confirmation of DNA as the molecule that carries genetic information, and we will consider the work of Watson and Crick on the organization and structure of DNA. We will also explore what is known about how DNA is incorporated into the structure of chromosomes.

DNA AS A CARRIER OF GENETIC INFORMATION

Research in the first few decades of this century established that genes existed and were carried on chromosomes. But what is a gene? As is often the case in science, the answer to this question came from a completely unexpected direction: the study of an infectious disease.

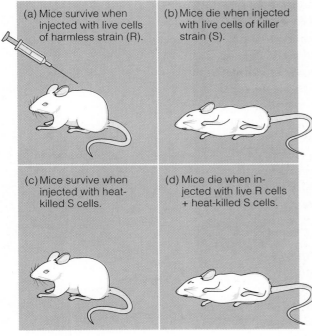

(a) Mice survive when injected with live cells of harmless strain (R).

(b) Mice die when injected with live cells of killer strain (S).

(c) Mice survive when injected with heat-killed S cells.

(d) Mice die when injected with live R cells + heat-killed S cells.

☞ FIGURE 8.1

Griffith discovered that the ability to cause pneumonia is a genetic trait that can be passed from one strain of bacteria to another. (a) Mice injected with strain R do not develop pneumonia. (b) Mice injected with strain S develop pneumonia and die. (c) When the S strain cells are killed by heat-treatment before injection, mice do not develop pneumonia. (d) When mice are injected with a mixture of heat-killed S cells and live R cells, they develop pneumonia and die. Griffith concluded that the live R cells acquired the ability to cause pneumonia from the dead S cells.

Transformation
The process of transferring genetic information between cells by means of DNA molecules.

Transforming factor
The molecular agent of transformation: DNA.

At the beginning of this century, pneumonia was a serious public health threat and the leading cause of death in the United States. Medical research was directed at understanding the nature of this infectious disease as a step toward developing an effective treatment, perhaps in the form of a vaccine. The unexpected outgrowth of this research was the discovery of the chemical nature of the gene.

Transfer of Genetic Traits in Bacteria

By the 1920s, it was known that pneumonia is caused by a bacterial infection, and that one form of pneumonia is caused by *Streptococcus pneumoniae*. Frederick Griffith studied the difference between two strains of this bacterium. In one strain (strain S), the cells were contained in a capsule. This strain was infective and caused pneumonia (that is, was a virulent strain). The other strain (strain R) did not form a capsule, and was not infective. The results of Griffith's experiment are straightforward and easily interpreted. Griffith showed that mice injected with living cells of strain R did not develop pneumonia, but mice injected with live cells from strain S developed pneumonia and soon died. Mice injected with heat-killed strain S cells survived and did not develop pneumonia (☞ Figure 8.1).

Mice injected with a mixture of heat-killed strain S cells and live cells from strain R developed pneumonia and died. From the bodies of the dead mice, Griffith recovered live strain S bacteria with capsules. When grown in the laboratory, the progeny of these transformed cells were always strain S. After further experiments, Griffith concluded that the living cells from strain R were transformed into strain S cells in the bodies of the mice. Griffith explained his results by proposing that hereditary information had passed from the dead strain S cells into the strain R cells, allowing them to make a capsule and become virulent. He called this process **transformation**, and the unknown material the **transforming factor**.

In 1944, after almost a decade of work, a team at the Rockefeller Institute in New York that included Oswald Avery, Colin MacLeod, and Maclyn McCarty discovered that the transforming factor is DNA. The story of this discovery is recounted in a readable memoir by Maclyn McCarty entitled *The transforming principle: Discovering that genes are made of DNA* (New York: Norton, 1985).

In a series of experiments that stretched over 10 years, Avery and his colleagues investigated a bacterial strain that causes pneumonia. Griffith had shown that the ability to cause pneumonia is associated with the presence of a thick capsule surrounding the bacterial cell. When an extract of heat-killed smooth bacteria (strain S) is mixed with living rough cells (strain R), a small fraction of the rough cells acquire the ability to form a capsule, grow as smooth colonies, and cause pneumonia. The bacteria that have acquired the ability to form a capsule transmit this trait to all their offspring, indicating that the trait is heritable.

Avery and his colleagues identified DNA as the active component present in the extract from the heat-killed cells. To confirm that DNA was the transforming substance, they treated the preparation with enzymes that destroy protein and RNA before transformation. This treatment removed any residual protein or RNA from the preparation but did not affect the transforming activity. As a final test the preparation was treated with deoxyribonuclease, an enzyme that digests DNA, whereupon transforming activity was abolished.

This work produced two important conclusions. In the bacterium Avery used:

- *DNA carries genetic information.* Only DNA is able to transfer heritable information from one strain to another strain.
- *DNA controls the synthesis of specific products.* Transfer of DNA also results in the transfer of the ability to synthesize a specific gene product (in the form of a capsule).

Although the evidence was strong, many in the scientific community were not persuaded. They remained convinced that proteins were the only molecule complex enough to be the carriers of genetic information. A few years later, conclusive evidence for the idea that DNA encodes genetic information came from the study of viruses.

Reproduction in Bacterial Viruses Involves DNA

In the late 1940s and early 1950s, scientists began working on a group of viruses that attack and kill bacterial cells (Figure 8.2). These viruses, known as **bacteriophages** (or phages for short), include one that infects and reproduces within *Escherichia coli*, the bacterium that inhabits the human intestinal tract. After gaining entry to the bacterial cell, a phage can reproduce rapidly; in 20–25 minutes about a hundred new phages burst from the ruptured bacterium, ready to invade other bacterial cells.

Bacteriophage
A virus that infects bacterial cells.

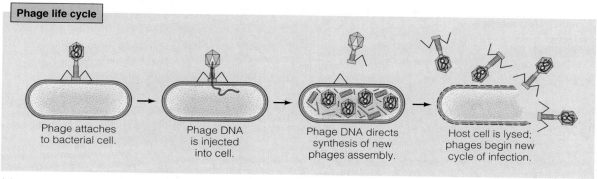

Phage life cycle

Phage attaches to bacterial cell.

Phage DNA is injected into cell.

Phage DNA directs synthesis of new phages assembly.

Host cell is lysed; phages begin new cycle of infection.

(a)

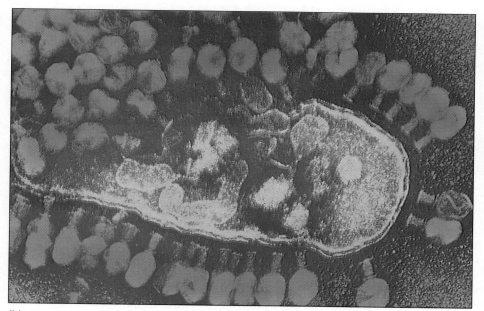

(b)

 FIGURE 8.2

(a) Bacteriophages are viruses that attack and kill bacteria. The virus attaches to the outside of the cell, and the viral DNA is injected. The phage DNA directs the synthesis and assembly of new phage particles that break open and destroy the bacterial cell, releasing new virus particles. (b) An electron micrograph of a bacteriophage attacking a bacterial cell.

Phages are composed only of DNA and protein, making them ideal candidates to help resolve which of these substances carries genetic information. Using what was then the new technique of labeling molecules with radioactive isotopes, in 1952 Alfred Hershey and Martha Chase labeled phage DNA with radioactive phosphorus (there is no phosphorus in proteins) and labeled phage protein with radioactive sulfur (there is no sulfur in DNA). Using radioactively labeled phage, they demonstrated that only radioactive phosphorus enters the bacterial cell and directs the production of new phages (● Figure 8.3). This work confirmed and extended the evidence from bacterial transformation that DNA, not protein, is the carrier of genetic information.

Studies on the genetic properties of DNA in viruses and bacteria did not immediately influence geneticists studying higher organisms. The reasons for this are complex and are partly scientific and partly sociological. At the experimental level, transformation cannot be performed on eukaryotic organisms, so it was not possible to directly replicate the results of Avery or Hershey with organisms such as *Drosophila* or mice. Because of this, acceptance of the idea that DNA is the genetic material in higher organisms was slow and was based mainly on indirect or circumstantial evidence.

● **FIGURE 8.3**

Phages contain only DNA and protein. Hershey and Chase used phages containing radioactively labeled protein (a) or radioactively labeled DNA (b). They found that only the radioactively labeled DNA entered the cell, and directed the synthesis of new phages. This strengthened the conclusion that DNA, not protein, encodes genetic information.

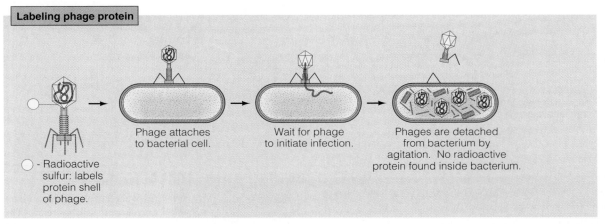

(a)

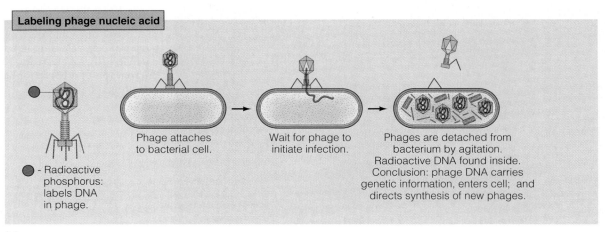

(b)

DNA as a Commercial Product

The ad for the perfume reads: "Where does love originate? Is it in the mind? Is it in the heart? Or in our genes?" A new perfume named DNA has been recently introduced, and is marketed in a helix-shaped bottle. There is no actual DNA in the fragrance, but the molecule is invoked to sell the idea that love emanates from the genes. Seem strange? Well, how about jewelry that actually contains DNA from your favorite celebrities? In this line of products, DNA in a single hair or cheek cell is amplified by a process called the polymerase chain reaction (PCR). The resulting solution, containing millions of copies of the DNA, is added to small channels drilled into acrylic earrings, pendants, or bracelets. The liquid can be colored to contrast with the acrylic and be more visible. Just as people wear tee shirts carrying pictures of Elvis or Einstein, they can now wear jewelry containing DNA from their favorite entertainer, poet, composer, scientist or athlete. For dead heroes, the DNA can come from a lock of hair; in fact, a single hair will do.

How about music composed from the base sequence of DNA? Composers have translated the four bases of DNA (adenine, guanine, cytosine, and thymine) into musical notes. Long sequences of bases, retrieved from computer databases, are converted into notes, transferred to sheet music, and played by instruments or synthesizers as the music of the genes. Those in the know say that the DNA near chromosome centromeres sounds much like the music of Bach or other Baroque composers, but that music from other parts of the genome has a contemporary sound.

From a scientific standpoint, this fascination with DNA may be a little difficult to understand, but DNA has clearly captured popular fancy, and is being used to sell an ever-increasing array of products. DNA has name recognition. Over the past 40 years, DNA has moved from scientific journals and textbooks to the popular press and even the comic strips. The relationship between genes and DNA is now well-known enough to be used in commercials and advertisements. In a few years, this fascination will probably fade and be replaced with another fad, but for now, if you want it to sell, relate it to DNA.

Since it was generally accepted that the chromosomes contain genetic information, indirect evidence was employed to strengthen the link between DNA and chromosomes. Refined methods of cytochemical staining indicated that not only is DNA largely confined to the nucleus, it is intimately associated with the chromosomes. Furthermore, DNA is present along the entire length of the chromosomes in a way that corresponds to the distribution of genetic loci. Last, within the cells of a given eukaryotic organism, the concentration of DNA is correlated with the number of chromosomes carried by the cell. In general, somatic diploid (2n) cells contain twice the number of chromosomes as haploid (n) gametes. Measurements of DNA concentration indicate that somatic cells have twice as much DNA as gametes. With the possible exception of a class of proteins known as histones, no such correlation between chromosome number and molecular concentration is apparent for other cellular components such as proteins, lipids, or carbohydrates. These and other forms of indirect evidence support the idea that DNA is the genetic material of eukaryotic organisms.

Today no one seriously doubts the validity of the circumstantial evidence that DNA is the repository of genetic information in higher organisms. In fact, as awareness of DNA and its role in genetics has grown, DNA is being used to sell products (see "Concepts and Controversies," above). Direct evidence for the role of DNA as the genetic material has come from the development of **recombinant DNA technology.** DNA segments from organisms such as humans can be spliced into bacterial DNA, and under the proper conditions this hybrid DNA molecule can direct the synthesis of a human gene product. The synthesis of human proteins in bacteria requires the presence of specific human DNA sequences, providing direct evidence for the role of DNA as the genetic material in higher organisms.

Recombinant DNA technology
Technique for joining DNA from two or more different organisms to produce hybrid, or recombined, DNA molecules.

WATSON, CRICK, AND THE STRUCTURE OF DNA

Recognition that DNA plays an important role in genetic processes coincided with efforts to understand the chemical structure of nucleic acids. In the years from the mid-1940s through 1953, several laboratories made significant strides in unraveling the structure of DNA, culminating in the Watson-Crick model for the DNA double helix in 1953. The scientific, intellectual, and personal intrigue that characterized the race to discover the structure of DNA has been documented in a number of books, beginning with *The Double Helix* by James Watson. These personal accounts and histories provide a rare glimpse into the ambitions, jealousies, and rivalries that entangled scientists involved in the dash to a Nobel Prize.

Reviewing Some Basic Chemistry

The structure of DNA in the Watson-Crick model, and in a later chapter the structure of proteins, is described and drawn using chemical terms and symbols. For this reason, a brief review of the terminology and definition of some terms is in order.

All matter is composed of atoms; the different types of atoms are known as elements (of which there are 103). In nature, atoms are rarely found as separate units. More often, they are combined into molecules, which we can define as units of two or more atoms chemically bonded together. Molecules can be represented as formulas that indicate how many of each type of atom are present. The type of atom is indicated by a symbol for the element it represents: H for hydrogen, N for nitrogen, C for carbon, O for oxygen, and so forth. For example, a water molecule, composed of two hydrogen atoms and one oxygen atom, has its chemical formula represented as H_2O:

two hydrogen atoms H_2O

one oxygen atom

Many molecules in cells are large and have more complex formulas. A molecule of glucose contains 24 atoms and is written as:

$$C_6H_{12}O_6$$

In molecules, the atomic components are held together by a stable interaction known as a **covalent bond.** In its simplest form, a covalent bond consists of a pair of electrons shared between two atoms. More complex covalent bonds can be formed by sharing two or more electrons. Figure 8.4 shows how such bonds are represented in structural formulas of molecules.

A second type of atomic interaction between molecules involves a weak attraction known as a **hydrogen bond.** In living systems, hydrogen bonds make a substantial contribution to the three-dimensional shape and, therefore, to the functional capacity of biological molecules. Hydrogen bonds are weak interactions between two atoms (one of which is hydrogen), carrying partial but opposite electrical charges. They are usually represented in structural formulas as dotted or dashed lines connecting two atoms (Figure 8.4).

When hydrogen forms a covalent bond with certain other atoms such as oxygen or nitrogen, it becomes partly positive. Because of this slight positive charge, the hydrogen is attracted to other atoms bearing a slight negative charge. This weak attraction is called a hydrogen bond. Hydrogen bonds usually form between atoms of different molecules or between atoms at different locations on a large molecule (such as DNA). Although individual hydrogen bonds are weak and easily broken, they function to hold molecules together by sheer force of numbers. As we will see in a following sec-

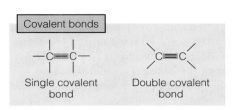

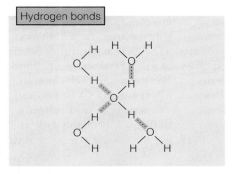

(a)

(b)

FIGURE 8.4

Representation of chemical bonds. (a) Covalent bonds are represented as solid lines connecting atoms. Depending on the degree of electron sharing, there can be one (left) or more (right) covalent bonds between atoms. Once formed, covalent bonds are stable, and are broken only in chemical reactions. (b) Hydrogen bonds are usually represented as dotted lines connecting two or more atoms. As shown, water molecules form hydrogen bonds with adjacent water molecules. These are weak interactions that are easily broken by heat and molecular tumbling, and can be reformed with other water molecules.

Covalent bond
A chemical bond that results from electron sharing between atoms. Covalent bonds are formed and broken during chemical reactions.

Hydrogen bond
A weak chemical bonding force between hydrogen and another atom.

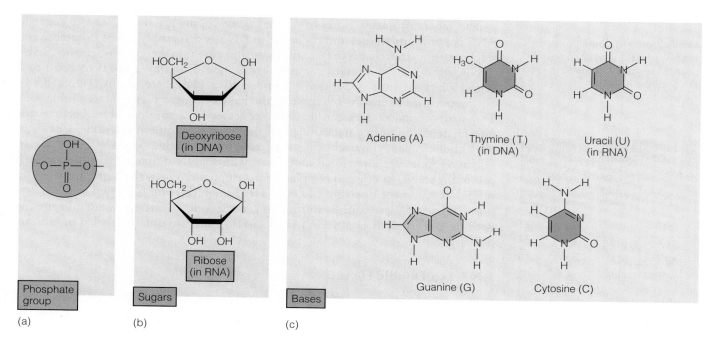

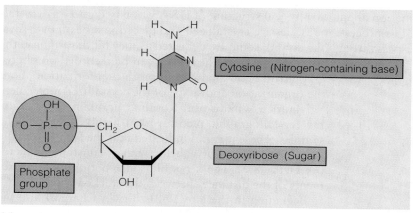

(d)

FIGURE 8.5

DNA is made up of subunits called nucleotides. Each nucleotide is composed of phosphorus (a), a sugar (b), and a base (c). A nucleotide (d).

tion, hydrogen bonds hold together the two strands in a DNA molecule and they are also responsible for the three-dimensional structure of proteins (Chapter 9).

Nucleotides: The Building Blocks of Nucleic Acids

There are two types of nucleic acids in biological organisms: **DNA** and **RNA**. Both are made up of subunits known as nucleotides. A **nucleotide** consists of a nitrogen-containing base (either a **purine** or a **pyrimidine**), a **pentose sugar** (either ribose or deoxyribose), and a phosphate group. The phosphate groups are strongly acidic and are the source of the designation nucleic acid. In the bases, both purines and pyrimidines have the same six-atom ring, but purines have an additional three-atom ring. The purine bases **adenine** (A) and **guanine** (G) are found in both RNA and DNA (Figure 8.5c). The pyrimidine bases include **thymine** (T), found in DNA; **uracil** (U), found in RNA; and **cytosine** (C), found in both RNA and DNA. RNA has four bases (A, G, U, C) and DNA has four bases (A, G, T, C).

Deoxyribonucleic acid (DNA)
A molecule consisting of antiparallel strands of polynucleotides that is the primary carrier of genetic information.

Ribonucleic acid (RNA)
A nucleic acid molecule that contains the pyrimidine uracil and the sugar ribose. The several forms of RNA function in gene expression.

Nucleotides
The basic building blocks of DNA and RNA. Each nucleotide consists of a base, a phosphate, and a sugar.

Nitrogen-containing base
A purine or pyrimidine that is a component of nucleotides.

Purine
A class of double-ringed organic bases found in nucleic acids.

Pyrimidines
A class of single-ringed organic bases found in nucleic acids.

Pentose sugar
A five-carbon sugar molecule found in nucleic acids.

Adenine and guanine
Purine nitrogenous bases found in nucleic acids.

Cytosine, thymine, and uracil
Pyrimidine nitrogenous bases found in nucleic acids.

TABLE 8.1

Nucleotides of RNA and DNA

RNA

Ribonucleotides
Adenylic acid
Cytidylic acid
Guanylic acid
Uridylic acid

DNA

Deoxyribonucleotides
Deoxyadenylic acid
Deoxycytidylic acid
Deoxyguanylic acid
Deoxythymidylic acid

The sugars in nucleic acids have five carbon atoms per molecule. The sugar in RNA is known as **ribose,** and the sugar in DNA is **deoxyribose.** The difference is a single oxygen atom that is present in ribose and absent in deoxyribose (Figure 8.5b).

Nucleotides are molecules composed of a base linked by a covalent bond to a sugar, which in turn is covalently bonded to a phosphate group (Figure 8.5d). Nucleotides are named by reference to the base and sugar they contain (Table 8.1). Two or more nucleotides can be linked together by a covalent bond between the phosphate group of one nucleotide and the sugar of another nucleotide. Chains of nucleotides called polynucleotides can be formed in this way (◀ Figure 8.6a). Polynucleotides are directional molecules, with slightly different structures at each end of the chain. At one end is a phosphate group; this end is the 5′ (pronounced "5 prime") end. At the opposite end is an OH group; this end is known as the 3′ ("3 prime") end of the chain. By convention, nucleotide chains are written beginning with the 5′ end, such as 5′-CGATATGCGAT-3′, and are usually labeled to indicate polarity.

DNA Is a Double Helix

In the early 1950s James Watson and Francis Crick began to work on a model for the structure of DNA. To build their model, they sifted through and organized the information that was already available about DNA. Their model is based on information about the chemistry of DNA and information on the physical structure of DNA. Information about the physical structure of DNA was based on x-ray crystallography. In this process, molecules are crystallized and placed in a beam of x-rays. As the x-rays pass through the crystal, some are deflected as they hit the atoms in the crystal. The pattern of x-rays emerging from the crystal can be recorded on photographic film and analyzed to produce information about the organization and shape of the crystallized molecule.

Maurice Wilkins and Rosalind Franklin obtained x-ray crystallographic pictures from highly purified DNA samples. These pictures indicated that the DNA molecule was in the shape of a helix with a constant diameter (◀ Figure 8.7). The x-ray films also permitted measurements of the distances between the stacked bases.

Beginning in the late 1940s, Erwin Chargaff and his colleagues extracted DNA from a variety of organisms and separated and analyzed the amounts of the four

◀ **FIGURE 8.6**

(a) Nucleotides can be joined together to form chains called polynucleotides. Polynucleotides are polar molecules, with a 5′ end (at the phosphate group) and a 3′ end (at the sugar group). (b) The components of a nucleotide.

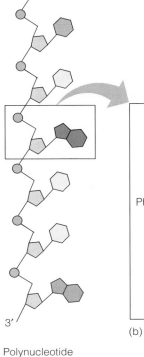

Polynucleotide chain

(a)

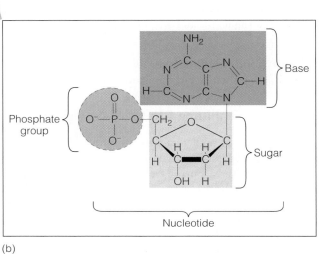

(b)

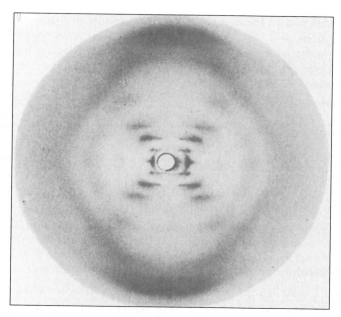

■ FIGURE 8.7

An x-ray diffraction photograph of a DNA crystal. The central x-shaped pattern is typical of helical structures, and the darker areas at the top and bottom indicate a regular arrangement of subunits in the molecule. Watson and Crick used this and other photographs to construct their model of DNA.

bases. The results indicated that DNA from all organisms tested had several common properties, which became known as Chargaff's rule:

- The total amount of purines (A + G) equals the total amount of pyrimidines (C + T).
- There is a 1:1 relationship between the amount of adenine and the amount of thymine and a 1:1 relationship between the amount of guanine and the amount of cytosine.

Using the information provided by the physical and chemical studies, Watson and Crick began building wire and metal models of potential DNA structures. They succeeded in producing a model that incorporated all the information described above (■ Figure 8.8). Their model has the following features:

- DNA is composed of two polynucleotide chains running in opposite directions.
- The two polynucleotide chains are coiled around a central axis to form a dou-

■ FIGURE 8.8

(a) The Watson-Crick model of DNA. Two polynucleotide strands are coiled around a central axis, forming a helix. (b) Hydrogen bonds between the bases hold the two strands together. In the molecule, A always pairs with T on the opposite strand, and C always pairs with G.

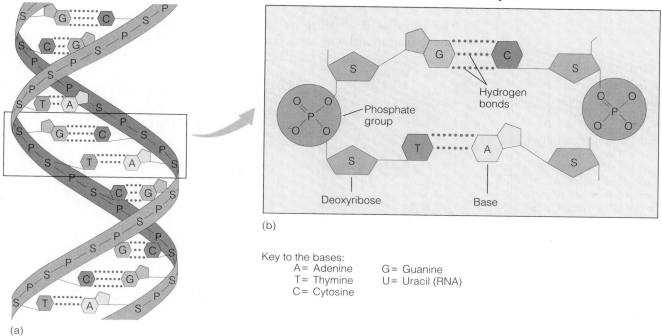

Key to the bases:
A = Adenine
T = Thymine
C = Cytosine
G = Guanine
U = Uracil (RNA)

ble helix. This part of the model fits the x-ray results of Rosalind Franklin and Maurice Wilkins.

- In each chain, the alternating sugar and phosphate groups are linked to form the backbone of the chain. The bases face inward, where they are paired by hydrogen bonds to bases in the opposite chain.
- In the model, base pairing is highly specific: A pairs only with T in the opposite chain, and C pairs only with G in the opposite chain. Each set of hydrogen-bonded bases is called a base pair. The pairing of A with T and C with G fits the results obtained by Chargaff.
- The base pairing of the model results in the two polynucleotide chains of DNA being complementary in base composition (⬤ Figure 8.9). If one strand has the sequence 5′-ACGTC-3′, the opposite strand must be 3′-TGCAG-5′, and the double-stranded structure would be written as:

$$5'\text{-ACGTC-}3'$$
$$3'\text{-TGCAG-}5'$$

Three important properties of this model should be considered:

- In this model, genetic information is stored in the sequence of bases in the DNA. The linear sequence of bases has a high coding capacity; a molecule n bases long has 4^n combinations. That means that a sequence of 10 nucleotides has 4^{10}, or 1,048,576, possible combinations of nucleotides. The complete set of genetic information carried by an organism (its genome) can be expressed as base pairs of DNA (Table 8.2). Genome sizes vary from a few thousand nucleotides (in viruses), encoding only a few genes, to billions of nucleotides, encoding perhaps 50,000 to 100,000 genes (as in humans). The human genome consists of about 3×10^9, or 3 billion, base pairs of DNA, distributed over 24 chromosomes (22 autosomes and two sex chromosomes).
- The model offers a molecular explanation for mutation. Because genetic information can be stored in the linear sequence of bases in DNA, any change in the order or number of bases in a gene can result in a mutation that produces an altered phenotype. This topic will be explored in more detail in Chapter 11.
- As Watson and Crick observed, the complementary strands in DNA can be used to explain the molecular basis of the replication of genetic information that takes place before each cell division. In such a model, each strand can be used as a template to reconstruct the base sequence in the opposite strand. This topic is discussed later in this chapter.

The Watson-Crick model was described in a brief paper in *Nature* in 1953. Although their model was based on the results of other workers, Watson and Crick

⬤ **FIGURE 8.9**
The two polynucleotide chains in DNA run in opposite directions. The top strand runs 5′ → 3′ and the bottom strand runs 3′ → 5′. The base sequences in each strand are complementary. An A in one strand pairs with a T in the other strand, and a C in one strand is paired with a G in the opposite strand.

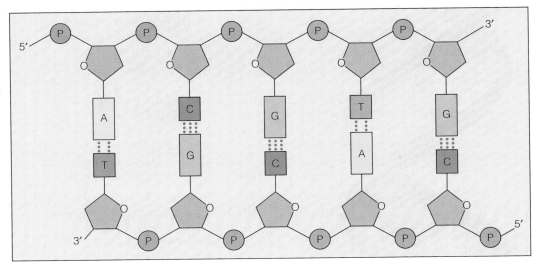

TABLE 8.2		
Genome Size in Various Organisms		
ORGANISM	SPECIES	GENOME SIZE IN NUCLEOTIDES
Bacterium	*E. coli*	4.2×10^6
Yeast	*S. cerevisiae*	1.3×10^7
Fruit fly	*D. melanogaster*	1.4×10^8
Tobacco plant	*N. tabacum*	4.8×10^9
Mouse	*M. musculus*	2.7×10^9
Human	*H. sapiens*	3.2×10^9

correctly incorporated the physical and chemical data into a model that also could be used to explain the properties expected of the genetic material (Figure 8.10). Present day applications, including genetic engineering, gene mapping, and gene therapy can be traced directly to this paper.

At the time there was no evidence to unequivocally support the Watson-Crick model, but in subsequent years it has been confirmed by experimental work in laboratories worldwide. The 1962 Nobel Prize for Medicine or Physiology was awarded to Watson, Crick, and Wilkins for their work on the structure of DNA. Although much of the x-ray data for the Watson-Crick model was provided by Rosalind Franklin, she did not receive a share of the prize. There has been some controversy over this, but she could not have shared in the prize, since it is awarded only to living individuals, and Franklin died of cancer in 1958. Her role in the discovery of the structure of DNA is presented in her biography, *Rosalind Franklin and the Discovery of DNA*.

Structure of RNA

RNA (ribonucleic acid) is found in both the nucleus and the cytoplasm. While DNA functions as a repository of genetic information, RNA functions to transfer genetic information from the nucleus to the cytoplasm (in a few viruses, RNA also functions to store genetic information). The nucleotides in RNA differ from those in DNA in two respects: the sugar in RNA nucleotides is ribose (deoxyribose in DNA), and the base uracil is used in place of the base thymine (Table 8.3).

TABLE 8.3		
Differences between DNA and RNA		
	DNA	RNA
Sugar	deoxyribose	ribose
Bases	adenine	adenine
	cytosine	cytosine
	guanine	guanine
	thymidine	uracil

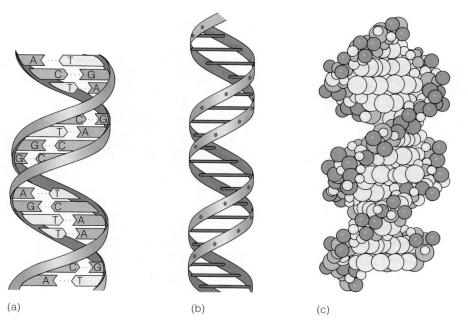

(a) (b) (c)

 FIGURE 8.10

Three different ways of representing DNA. (a) A model showing the complementary base pairing in the interior of the molecule. (b) A model showing the double helix wound around a central axis. (c) A space-filling model, showing the relative sizes of the atoms in the molecule.

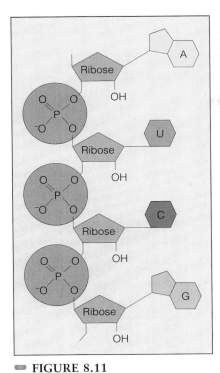

FIGURE 8.11

RNA is a single-stranded polynucleotide chain. RNA molecules contain a ribose sugar instead of a deoxyribose, and have uracil (U) in place of thymine (T).

Although two complementary strands of RNA can form a double helix similar to the one found in DNA, the RNA present in most cells is single stranded, and a complementary strand is not made (● Figure 8.11). But, RNA molecules can fold back upon themselves and form double-stranded regions. The functions of RNA will be considered in more detail in Chapter 9.

DNA IS COILED WITH PROTEINS TO FORM CHROMOSOMES

Although an understanding of DNA structure represents an important development in genetics, it provides no immediate information about how a chromosome is organized or about what regulates the cycle of condensation and decondensation of the chromosomes. This problem is significant, since the spatial arrangement of DNA may play an important role in regulating the expression of genetic information. In addition, the distribution of DNA into the 46 human chromosomes requires the packing of a little over 2 m (2 million μ) of DNA into a nucleus that measures about 5 μ in diameter. Within this cramped environment, the chromosomes unwind and become dispersed during interphase. In this condition they undergo replication, gene expression, homologous pairing during meiosis, and contraction and coiling to become visible again during prophase. An understanding of chromosome organization is necessary to understand these processes. In contrast to what is known about chromosomes in the nucleus, details of the structure and even the nucleotide sequence of the mitochondrial chromosome are well understood, and they will be considered first.

The Mitochondrial Chromosome is a Circular DNA Molecule

As discussed in Chapter 2, mitochondria are organelles involved in energy conversion. Mitochondria contain DNA that encodes genetic information, and this mitochondrial chromosome is transmitted maternally. In recent years, a number of genetic disorders resulting from mutations in mitochondrial DNA have been identified (see Chapter 4), and in this pattern of inheritance, all offspring of affected mothers are also affected.

The complete nucleotide sequence of the mitochondrial chromosome is known (● Figure 8.12). The chromosome consists of a circular DNA molecule containing

FIGURE 8.12

Mitochondrial genome. (a) Micrograph showing filaments of DNA in the mitochondrial matrix. (b) Mitochondrial DNA occurs in the form of circles 5 to 6 um in contour length.

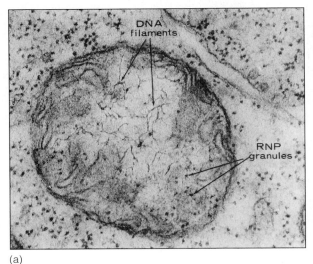

(a)

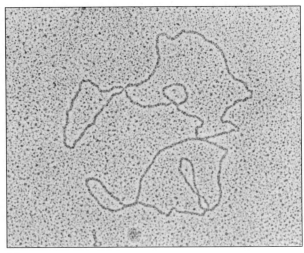

(b)

16,569 base pairs and encoding just over 40 genes. Alterations in the mitochondrial genome can lead to genetic disorders. Most mitochondria contain 5 to 10 copies of the mitochondrial chromosome, and because each cell has hundreds of mitochondria, thousands of mitochondrial genomes are present in each human cell. The DNA of the mitochondrial chromosome is not complexed with proteins and physically resembles the chromosomes of bacteria and other prokaryotes. This similarity reflects the evolutionary history of mitochondria and their transition from free-living prokaryotes to intracellular symbionts.

Nuclear Chromosomes Have a Complex Structure

A combination of biochemical and microscopic techniques developed in recent years has provided a great deal of information about the organization and structure of human chromosomes. In humans and other eukaryotes, each chromosome consists of a single DNA molecule complexed with proteins to form **chromatin.** There are two types of proteins in chromatin: **histones** and **nonhistone proteins.** The histones play a major role in chromosome structure, while the nonhistones are thought to be involved in gene regulation. Five types of histones are complexed with DNA to form small spherical bodies known as **nucleosomes** that are connected to each other by thin threads of DNA (Figure 8.13). Each nucleosome consists of DNA wound around a core composed of eight histone molecules.

The winding of DNA around the histones compresses the length of the DNA molecule by a factor of sixfold or sevenfold. But, in the mitotic chromosome the level of compaction is estimated to be 5000- to 10,000-fold. This suggests that there are several levels of organization between the nucleosome and the chromosome, each of

Chromatin
The complex of DNA and proteins that makes up a chromosome.

Histones
Small DNA-binding proteins that function in the coiling of DNA to produce the structure of chromosomes.

Nonhistone proteins
The array of proteins other than histones that are complexed with DNA in chromosomes.

Nucleosomes
A bead-like structure composed of histones wrapped by DNA.

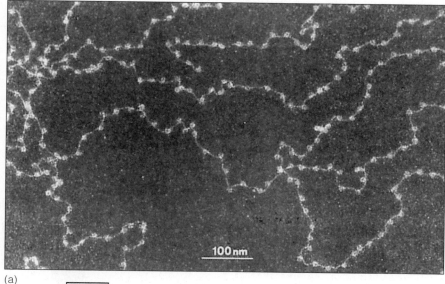

(a)

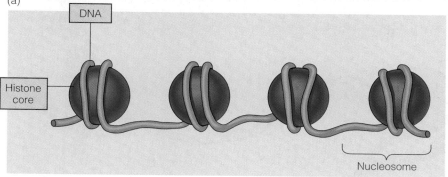

(b)

 FIGURE 8.13

Nucleosomes. (a) An electron micrograph showing the association of DNA with histones to form nucleosomes connected by threads of DNA in chromatin from chicken blood cells. (b) A diagram showing how DNA coils around the outside of a histone cluster in nucleosomes.

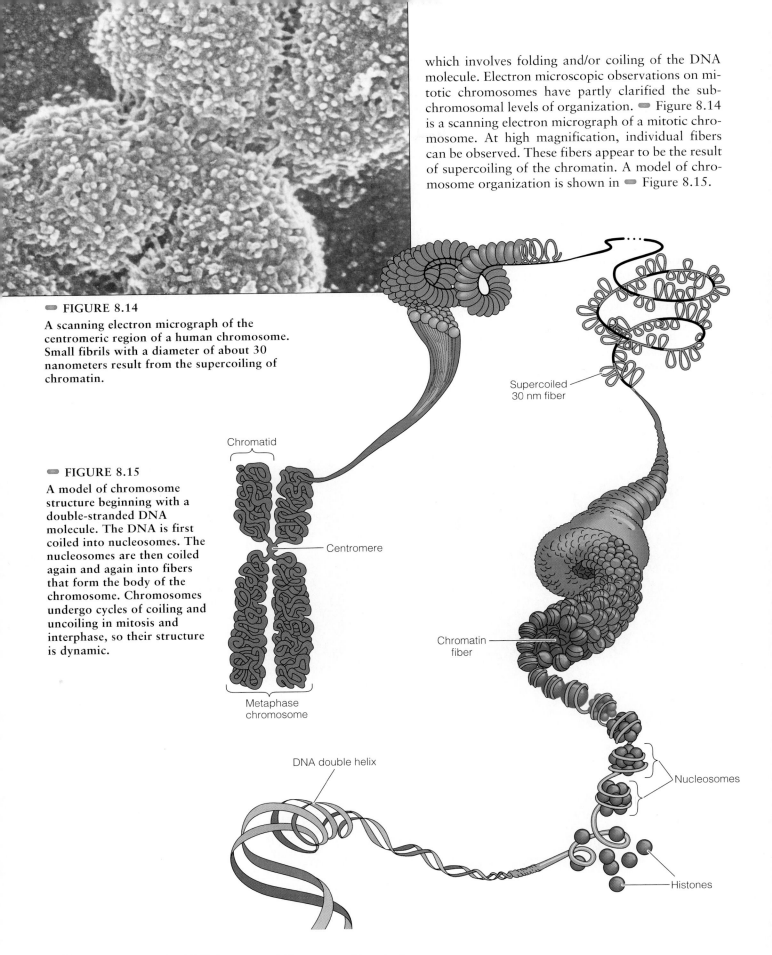

which involves folding and/or coiling of the DNA molecule. Electron microscopic observations on mitotic chromosomes have partly clarified the subchromosomal levels of organization. ● Figure 8.14 is a scanning electron micrograph of a mitotic chromosome. At high magnification, individual fibers can be observed. These fibers appear to be the result of supercoiling of the chromatin. A model of chromosome organization is shown in ● Figure 8.15.

● **FIGURE 8.14**

A scanning electron micrograph of the centromeric region of a human chromosome. Small fibrils with a diameter of about 30 nanometers result from the supercoiling of chromatin.

● **FIGURE 8.15**

A model of chromosome structure beginning with a double-stranded DNA molecule. The DNA is first coiled into nucleosomes. The nucleosomes are then coiled again and again into fibers that form the body of the chromosome. Chromosomes undergo cycles of coiling and uncoiling in mitosis and interphase, so their structure is dynamic.

Chromatid

Centromere

Metaphase chromosome

Supercoiled 30 nm fiber

Chromatin fiber

DNA double helix

Nucleosomes

Histones

DNA REPLICATION DEPENDS ON BASE PAIRING

Between cycles of division, all cells replicate their DNA so that each daughter cell receives a complete set of genetic information. In their paper on the structure of DNA, Watson and Crick note that "It has not escaped our notice that the specific pairing we have postulated immediately suggests a possible copying mechanism for the genetic material." In a subsequent paper, they proposed a mechanism for DNA replication that depends on the complementary base pairing in the polynucleotide chains of DNA. If the DNA helix is unwound, each strand can serve as a **template** or pattern for the synthesis of a new, complementary strand (Figure 8.16). This process is known as **semiconservative replication**, since one old strand is conserved in each new molecule.

The process of DNA replication in all cells, from bacteria to humans, is a complex process requiring the action of more than a dozen different enzymes. In humans, replication begins at sites called origins of replication that are present all along the length of the chromosome. At these sites, proteins unwind the double helix by breaking the hydrogen bonds between bases in adjacent strands. This process opens the molecule to the action of the enzyme **DNA polymerase**. DNA polymerase links the complementary nucleotides together to form newly synthesized strands.

Template
The single-stranded DNA that serves to specify the nucleotide sequence of a newly synthesized polynucleotide strand.

Semiconservative replication
A model of DNA replication that results in each daughter molecule containing one old strand and one newly synthesized strand. DNA replicates in this fashion.

DNA polymerase
An enzyme that catalyzes the synthesis of DNA using a template DNA strand and nucleotides.

 FIGURE 8.16

In DNA replication, the two polynucleotide strands uncoil, and each serves as a template for the synthesis of a new strand. As the strands uncoil, complementary base pairing occurs with the template strand. These are linked together by DNA polymerase, assisted by other enzymes that help uncoil the DNA and seal up gaps in the new strands. A completed DNA molecule contains one new strand and one old strand.

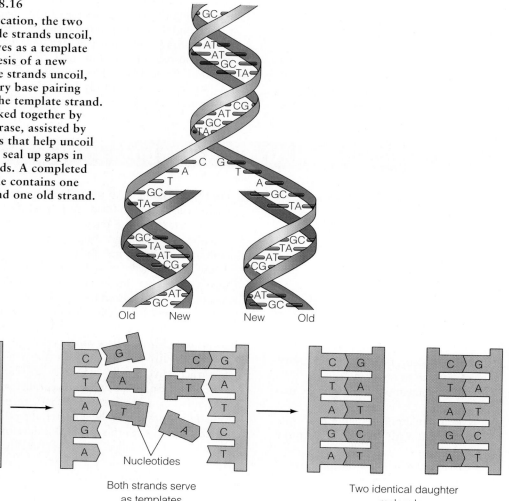

Old   New   New   Old

DNA to be replicated

Both strands serve as templates

Nucleotides

Two identical daughter molecules

Each chromosome contains one double-stranded DNA helix running from end to end. When replication is finished, the chromosome consists of two sister chromatids, joined at a common centromere. Each chromatid contains a DNA molecule consisting of one old strand and one new strand. When the centromeres divide at the beginning of anaphase, each chromatid becomes a separate chromosome containing an accurate copy of the genetic information present in the parental chromosome.

SUMMARY

1. At the turn of the century, scientists identified chromosomes as the cellular components that carried genes. This discovery focused efforts to identify the molecular nature of the gene on the chromosomes and the nucleus. Biochemical analysis of the nucleus began around 1870 when Frederick Miescher first separated nuclei from cytoplasm and described nuclein, a protein/nucleic acid complex now known as chromatin.

2. Originally, proteins were regarded as the only molecular component of the cell with the complexity to encode the genetic information. This changed in 1944 when Avery and his colleagues demonstrated that DNA was the genetic material in bacteria.

3. In 1953 Watson and Crick constructed a model of DNA structure that incorporated information from the chemical studies of Chargaff and the x-ray crystallographic work of Wilkins and Franklin. They proposed that DNA is composed of two polynucleotide chains oriented in opposite directions and held together by hydrogen bonding to complementary bases in the opposite strand. The two strands are wound around a central axis in a right-handed helix.

4. The mitochondrial chromosome, carrying genes that can cause maternally transmitted disorders, is a circular DNA molecule.

5. Within chromosomes, DNA is coiled around clusters of histones to form structures known as nucleosomes. Supercoiling of nucleosomes may form fibers that extend at right angles to the axis of the chromosome. The structure of chromosomes must be dynamic to allow the uncoiling and recoiling seen in successive phases of the cell cycle, but the details of this transition are still unknown.

6. In DNA replication, strands are copied to produce semi-conservatively replicated daughter strands.

QUESTIONS AND PROBLEMS

1. Until 1944, which cellular component was thought to carry genetic information?
   a. carbohydrate
   b. nucleic acid
   c. protein
   d. chromatin
   e. lipid

2. Summarize the arguments that were used against the role of nucleic acids as the genetic material.

3. The experiments of Avery and his co-workers led to the conclusion that:
   a. bacterial transformation occurs only in the laboratory.
   b. capsule proteins can attach to uncoated cells.
   c. DNA is the transforming agent and is the genetic material.
   d. transformation is an isolated phenomenon in *E coli*.
   e. DNA must be complexed with protein in bacterial chromosomes.

4. In the experiments of Avery, what was the purpose of treating the transforming extract with enzymes?

5. For this question, read the following experiment and interpret the results to form your conclusion.
   Experimental data: S bacteria were heat-killed and cell extracts were isolated. The extracts contained cellular components including lipids, proteins, DNA and RNA. These extracts were mixed with live R bacteria and then injected together into mice along with various enzymes (proteases, RNAses and DNAses) Proteases degrade proteins, RNAses degrade RNA and DNAses degrade DNA.

S extract + live R cells	kills mouse
S extract + live R cells + protease	kills mouse
S extract + live R cells + RNAse	kills mouse
S extract + live R cells + DNAse	mouse lives

   Based on these results, what is the transforming principle?

6. Recently, scientists discovered that a rare disorder called polkadotism is caused by a bacterial strain, *polkadotiae*. Mice injected with this strain (P), develop polkadots on their skin. Heat-killed P bacteria and live D bacteria, a non-virulent strain, do not produce polkadots when separately injected into mice. However, when a mixture of

heat-killed P cells and live D cells are injected together, the mice developed polkadots. What process explains this result? Describe what is happening in the mouse to cause this outcome.

7. List the pyrimidine bases, the purine bases, and the base pairing rules for DNA.

8. In analyzing the base composition of a DNA sample, a student loses the information on pyrimidine content. The purine content is A = 27% and G = 23%. Using Chargaff's rule, reconstruct the missing data, and list the base composition of the DNA sample.

9. The basic building blocks of nucleic acids are:
   a. nucleosides
   b. nucleotides
   c. ribose sugars
   d. amino acids
   e. purine bases

10. Adenine is a:
   a. nucleoside
   b. purine
   c. pyrimidine
   d. nucleotide
   e. base

11. Polynucleotide chains have a 5′ and a 3′ end. What groups are found at each of these ends?
   a. 5′ sugars, 3′ phosphates
   b. 3′ sugars, 5′ phosphates
   c. 3′ bases, 5′ sugars
   d. 5′ bases, 3′ sugars
   e. 5′ phosphates, 3′ bases

12. DNA contains many hydrogen bonds. Describe what a hydrogen bond is, and how this type of chemical bond holds DNA together.

13. Watson and Crick received the Nobel Prize for:
   a. proving their miracle diet works
   b. establishing that DNA replication is semiconservative
   c. solving the structure of DNA
   d. proving that DNA is the genetic material
   e. showing that the amount of A equals the amount of T

14. Summarize the elements of the Watson-Crick model of DNA.

15. The double helix of DNA involves:
   a. two strands coiled in a left-handed helix around a central core
   b. two polynucleotide strands coiled around each other
   c. a spiral of two strands
   d. two strands coiled in a right-handed helix around a central axis
   e. hydrogen bonding between nucleotides in the same chain

16. Using Figure 8.6 as a guide, draw a dinucleotide composed of C and A. Next to this, draw the complementary dinucleotide in an antiparallel fashion. Connect the dinucleotides with the appropriate hydrogen bonds.

17. DNA is said to be denatured when:
   a. the phosphates are removed from the backbone
   b. the sugar ring is broken
   c. it winds into a double helix
   d. the hydrogen bonds break
   e. none of the above

18. Nucleosomes are complexes of:
   a. nonhistone protein and DNA
   b. RNA and histone
   c. histones and DNA
   d. DNA, RNA, and protein
   e. histone H1 and DNA

19. Which of the following statements is *not* true about DNA replication.
   a. occurs during the M phase of the cell cycle
   b. makes a sister chromatid
   c. denatures DNA strands
   d. occurs semi-conservatively
   e. follows base pairing rules

20. Make the complementary strand to the following DNA template and label both strands as 5′ to 3′, or 3′ to 5′ (P = phosphate in the diagram). Draw an arrow showing the direction of synthesis of the new strand. How many hydrogen bonds are in this double strand of DNA?
   template   P - AGGCTCG - OH
   new strand:

21. A beginning genetics student is attempting to complete an assignment to draw a base pair from a DNA molecule, and asks your advice. The drawing is incomplete, and the student does not know how to finish. The assignment sheet shows that the drawing is to contain 3 hydrogen bonds, a purine and a pyrimidine. From your knowledge of the pairing rules and the number of hydrogen bonds in A/T and G/C base pairs, what base pair do you help the student draw?

22. How does DNA differ from RNA with respect to the following characteristics?
   a. Number of chains
   b. bases used
   c. sugar used
   d. function

23. Discuss the levels of chromosome organization, with reference to the following terms:
   a. nucleotide
   b. DNA double helix
   c. histones
   d. nucleosomes
   e. chromatin

1. The goal of the Human Genome Project (HGP) is to identify the nucleotide structure of each of the twenty four human chromosomes, and to deduce the exact location of each gene along the chromosome. As a result of the many new technologies and discoveries from the HGP, many commercial laboratories are seeking patents for their efforts. A dispute has arisen over the patenting of the nucleotide sequences recovered as part of this project. Some feel that these are discoveries that are patentable, while others feel that the sequence of nucleotides in a DNA molecule represent fundamental knowledge that should not be controlled or owned, but should be available to the all interested research workers.

The granting of a patent, by National Patent Offices, constitutes a contract between the inventor and the State. In return, the inventor reveals the invention to the public eighteen months after the invention was first filed. This publication is considered to be favored to the alternative of research secrecy, and ensures that others do not waste their intellect, time and money repeating an earlier invention. It also provides a new and publicly available knowledge base for further invention. There are defined technical requirements for a successful patent application. The patent officers assess applications against a number of basic detailed criteria.

1. Is the invention really new?
2. Was the invention obvious? This is judged by reference to an "individual skilled in the art." In other words, if an invention is made in molecular biology, was the invention the product of true inventiveness or would it have been obvious to any molecular biologist?
3. Does the invention have industrial use and is it of practical value?
4. Is the invention adequately described in the patent application?
5. Has the inventor conducted experiments to demonstrate the practical features of the invention, and is there adequate description to permit the "individual skilled in the art" to repeat those experiments?

In your opinion, do nucleotide sequences of DNA molecules meet these technical criteria for a successful patent?

If patents cannot be obtained for human genes what are the alternatives?

What are some of the consequences of successful patent applications of gene sequences?

The following activities use the resources of the World Wide Web to enhance the topics covered in this chapter. To investigate the topics described below, log on to the book's home page at:

http://www.wadsworth.com/biology

1. The Primer on Molecular Genetics produced by the Department of Energy presents basic information on DNA, genes, and chromosomes. Much of this information is applied to the mapping of the human genome. The introductory part of the Primer can provide you with a good review of DNA, RNA and proteins (proteins are discussed in Chapter 9).
   a. In what ways are DNA and RNA similar?
   b. In Figure 3 in the DNA section of the Primer, you will find that the Y chromosome is the smallest human chromosome with about 30 million base pairs of DNA. Does this surprise you? What implications does this suggest about sex determination?
   c. In light of the size and complexity of the human genome (which is present in all cells) does it surprise you to realize that blood cells reproduce at the rate of about 2 million per second?
2. Genetech, one of the world's largest biotechnology companies has a section on its homepage for teachers and students called Access Excellence. Scroll through this section and read the descriptions provided for the various sections. Click on the Activities Exchange icon and scroll to the AE Classics Collection. Click on this heading, which links to a number of interesting sites. Scroll to A Visit with Dr. Francis Crick, click, and read the interview with Dr. Crick.
   a. It's interesting to note that Dr. Crick studied math and physics until his curiosity motivated him to study the area that separates the living from the non-living. In your own situation, what genetic topics or diseases did you come to this course curious to learn more about (list at least four). Why is the discovery of the structure of DNA considered to be one of the most important advances in this century? Crick is now working to understand the biological basis of consciousness. Do you think that he or anyone else will be successful in understanding the structure of consciousness? Are there some similarities that may be present in the search for the structure of DNA versus the structure of consciousness?
   b. Are there any biases you can detect in the description of Acess Excellence? Describe some potentially positive and some potentially negative aspects of using educational information provided by a company in an emerging health technology field.

FOR FURTHER READING

Avery, O. T., Macleod, C. M., and McCarty, M. 1944. *J. Exp. Med. 70:* 137.

Felsenfeld, G. 1985. DNA, *Sci. Am. 253* (October): 58–67.

Judson, H. F. 1979. *The Eighth Day of Creation: The Makers of the Revolution in Biology.* New York: Simon & Schuster.

Kornberg, A. 1968. The synthesis of DNA. *Sci. Am. 219* (October): 64–79.

Kornberg, R., and Klug, A. 1981. Nucleosomes. *Sci. Am. 244* (February): 52–79.

McCarty, M. 1986. *The Transforming Principle: Discovery That Genes are Made of DNA.* New York: Norton.

Olby, R. 1974. *The Path to the Double Helix.* Seattle: University of Washington Press.

Sayre, A. 1975. *Rosalind Franklin and DNA.* New York: Norton.

Watson, J. D. 1968. *The Double Helix.* New York: Atheneum.

Watson, J. D., and Crick, F. H. C. 1953. Molecular structure of nucleic acids: A structure for deoxyribose nucleic acid. *Nature 171:* 737–738.

Watson, J. D., and Crick, F. H. C. 1953. Genetical implications of the structure of desoxyribonucleic acid. Nature 171: 964–967.

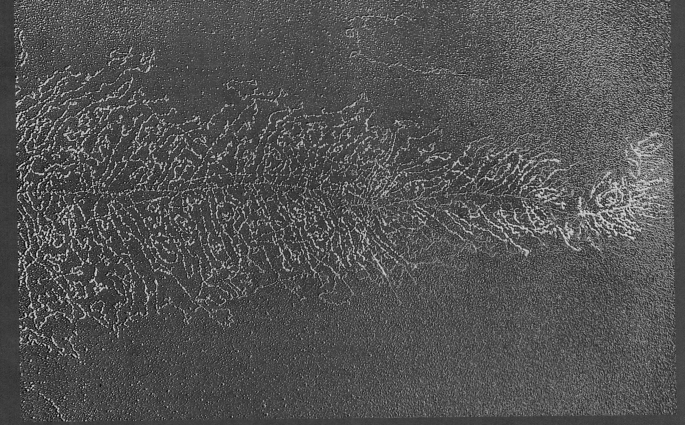

GENE EXPRESSION: HOW PROTEINS ARE MADE

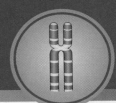

Chapter 9

Chapter Outline

GENES AND PROTEINS: UNRESOLVED
   QUESTIONS
Genes and Metabolism
The Relationship between Genes and
   Enzymes
HOW IS GENETIC INFORMATION
   STORED IN DNA?
THE FLOW OF GENETIC INFORMATION
   IS A MULTISTEP PROCESS

Transcription Produces Genetic Messages
Genes Can Have a Complex Internal
   Organization
Messenger RNA Is Processed and Spliced
Translation Requires the Interaction of
   Several Components
CONCEPTS AND CONTROVERSIES
   Antibiotics and Protein Synthesis
THE GENETIC CODE: THE KEY TO LIFE

THE POLYPEPTIDE PRODUCT OF
   TRANSLATION
Levels of Structure in Proteins
Proteins Have Many Functions
SIDEBAR   *Selective Breeding Gone Bad*
SUMMARY

OPENING IMAGE
*Transmission electron micrograph of
DNA and mRNA molecules forming a
feather-like, transcriptionally-active
structure.*

After a month of feeding on mulberry leaves, the caterpillar loses
   interest in food, and begins to move its head in a rotating motion.
*From two glands in the head, a liquid secretion emerges through an open-
ing called a spinneret. On contact with air, this secretion hardens into a
thin filament. Using a figure-eight movement, the caterpillar weaves this
long continuous filament into a cocoon slightly larger than a peanut. If
left undisturbed, the caterpillar will develop into an adult moth, called*

Bombyx mori. *This continuous filament is a protein called fibroin, and some 5000 years ago, Asians discovered how to use this filament to produce the fabric called silk.*

In making silk, a worker locates the end of the filament, and unwinds it from the cocoon. Each filament may be up to 3000 feet in length. Filaments from several cocoons are wound together to form a silk strand. The strands are reeled into skeins and bundled together to form books of 5–10 pounds, which in turn are packed into bales of about 140 pounds. In ancient times, these bales were shipped from China over a 4000-mile road to the shores of the Mediterranean Sea and shipped from there to Rome and other destinations in the West. The establishment of a weaving industry, its associated trade, and part of the culture of East Asia was founded on a single animal protein. This trade continues today, with the United States being the largest consumer of silk.

This example raises several questions relevant to genetics and gene expression. What are proteins? How and where are they made? How are proteins related to genes, and in particular to human genetics? As we will see in this chapter, proteins like silk fibroin, blood clotting factors, and digestive enzymes are gene products, encoded in the nucleotide sequence of DNA. Proteins are the intermediate between genes and phenotype. The phenotypes of a cell, tissue, and organism are the result of protein function. When these functions are absent or altered, the result is a mutant phenotype, which we describe as a genetic disorder. To discover how a genetic disorder produces an altered phenotype, an understanding of how genes control the synthesis of gene products is necessary.

The Watson-Crick model of DNA structure (discussed in Chapter 8) is the foundation for what is now called molecular biology, or molecular genetics. The model incorporates all the properties of the genetic material: replication, storage and expression of genetic information, and mutability. In this chapter we will examine the fundamental steps of DNA function in the storage and expression of genetic information. In this and the next chapter, we will be moving up from the level of DNA nucleotide sequence to cellular gene products to the production of phenotype. We have already considered how DNA replicates, and the property of mutability will be explored in Chapter 11.

✿ GENES AND PROTEINS: UNRESOLVED QUESTIONS

By the 1930s, genetics had surged forward on the strength of the chromosome theory of inheritance, and genetic maps were being prepared for several experimental organisms, including corn, *Drosophila*, and mice. Several important questions remained unanswered, often frustrating biologists who attempted to investigate these unresolved issues. What exactly are genes? How do they work? What produces the unique phenotype associated with a specific allele? In spite of the advances made using the newly developed techniques of genetics and cytology, these questions could not be answered with these methods. The answers came from other fields, including chemistry, physics, and the study of infectious disease.

Just as the merging of cytology and genetics produced the chromosome theory of inheritance, the fusion of these other disciplines with genetics gave rise to molecular genetics, an area that currently dominates research in genetics. In this chapter, we will examine some of the explanations provided for the questions posed above, beginning with some background information about what genes do.

Genes and Metabolism

Biochemical reactions in the cell are organized into chains of reactions known as *metabolic pathways*. The product of one reaction in a pathway serves as the substrate for the following reaction (⬤ Figure 9.1). *Enzymes* are protein molecules that serve as biological catalysts to carry out specific biochemical reactions. Loss of activity in a single enzyme can disrupt an entire biochemical pathway, causing an alteration in metabolism.

The relationship between metabolism and human genetic disease was first proposed by Archibald Garrod in 1902. He studied a condition called **alkaptonuria** (MIM/OMIM 203500). Affected individuals can be identified soon after birth because their urine turns black. Garrod found that alkaptonuria is associated with the excretion of large quantities of a compound he called alkapton (now called homogentisic acid). He reasoned that in unaffected individuals, homogentisic acid is metabolized to other products and does not build up in the urine. In alkaptonuria, however, the metabolic pathway is blocked, causing the buildup of homogentisic acid, which is excreted in the urine. He called this condition an "inborn error of metabolism." Garrod also discovered that alkaptonuria is inherited as a recessive Mendelian trait.

The Relationship between Genes and Enzymes

The connection between inborn errors of metabolism and enzymes was established by George Beadle and Edward Tatum in the late 1930s and early 1940s through their work on *Neurospora*, a common bread mold (⬤ Figure 9.2).

Using x-rays to cause genetic mutations, Beadle and Tatum generated mutant strains of *Neurospora* that were unable to carry out a specific biochemical reaction. The mutation was inherited in Mendelian fashion as a single gene, and was caused by the loss of activity in a single enzyme.

Beadle and Tatum reasoned that since each biochemical reaction in a metabolic pathway is regulated by a single enzyme, the production, activity, and specificity of that enzyme must be controlled by a single gene. Mutation in a gene whose product is involved in a metabolic pathway changes the ability of a cell to carry out a particular biochemical reaction, and disrupts the whole pathway. This idea was expressed as the **one gene–one enzyme hypothesis**, for which Beadle and Tatum received the Nobel Prize in 1958.

Alkaptonuria
An autosomal recessive condition that alters metabolism of homogentistic acid. Affected individuals do not produce the enzyme to metabolize this acid.

One gene–one enzyme hypothesis
The idea that individual genes encode the information for the synthesis and therefore the activity of a single enzyme. This provided the link between the gene and the phenotype.

⬤ **FIGURE 9.1**

A metabolic pathway, beginning with the amino acid phenylalanine. In humans, mutations cause blocks in this pathway, leading to genetic disorders including phenylketonuria (PKU), tyrosenemia, and alkaptonuria.

Phenylalanine → (Blocked in PKU) → Tyrosine → (Blocked in tyrosinemia) → *p*-hydroxy phenylpyruvic acid → Homogentisic acid → (Blocked in alkaptonuria) → Maleylacetoacetic acid

FIGURE 9.2

A culture of the mold *Neurospora crassa*, an organism used by George Beadle and Edward Tatum in their work on biochemical genetics.

What is it, then, that genes do? A gene encodes the information for the synthesis of a gene product in the form of a protein. The action of this protein, in turn, results in a particular phenotype. In some cases, the protein acts as an enzyme to catalyze a biochemical reaction. Blocking a biochemical reaction can disrupt a metabolic pathway, leading to an altered phenotype, as in alkaptonuria. In other cases, proteins function as transport molecules, hormones, structural components of cells, the contractile fibers of muscles, and in numerous other ways. Because some proteins are composed of more than one polypeptide chain, each of which is encoded by separate genes, the one gene–one enzyme hypothesis is now expressed as the **one gene–one polypeptide hypothesis**. A mutation in a gene encoding a specific polypeptide can alter the ability of the encoded protein to function, and in turn, produce an altered phenotype.

One gene–one polypeptide hypothesis
A refinement of the one gene–one enzyme hypothesis made necessary by the discovery that some proteins are composed of subunits encoded by different genes.

✿ HOW IS GENETIC INFORMATION STORED IN DNA?

An intriguing feature of the Watson-Crick model of DNA is that it offers an explanation for how genetic information is encoded in the structure of the molecule. Watson and Crick proposed that genetic information could be represented as the sequence of nucleotide bases in DNA. The amount of information stored in any cell is related to the number of base pairs in the DNA carried within the cell. This number ranges from a few thousand base pairs in some viruses, to over 3 billion base pairs in humans, and more than twice that amount in some amphibians and plants. A gene typically consists of hundreds or thousands of nucleotides. Each gene has a beginning and end, marked by specific nucleotide sequences, and a molecule of DNA can contain thousands of genes.

How do genes (in the form of DNA) control the production of proteins? Proteins are linear molecules composed of amino acid subunits. Twenty different types of amino acids can be used to assemble proteins. The diversity of proteins found in nature results from the number of possible combinations of these 20 different amino acids. Since each amino acid position in a protein can be occupied by any of 20 amino acids, the number of different combinations is 20^n, where n is the number of amino acids in the protein. In a protein composed of only 5 amino acids, 20^5, or 3,200,000 combinations are possible, each with a different amino acid sequence and a potentially different function. Most proteins are actually composed of several hundred amino acids, so literally billions and billions of combinations are possible.

Given that genes are linear sequences of nucleotides and proteins are linear sequences of amino acids, the question is: How is the linear sequence of nucleotides in a gene converted into the linear sequence of amino acids in a protein? In humans and other eukaryotes, the bulk of the cell's DNA is found in the nucleus, and almost all proteins are found in the cytoplasm. This means that the process of information transfer from gene to gene product must be indirect.

✿ THE FLOW OF GENETIC INFORMATION IS A MULTISTEP PROCESS

Transcription

Transfer of genetic information from the base sequence of DNA to the base sequence of RNA brought about by RNA synthesis.

Translation

The process of converting the information content in an mRNA molecule into the linear sequence of amino acids in a protein.

mRNA

A single-stranded complementary copy of the base sequence in a DNA molecule that constitutes a gene.

Codon

A triplet of bases in messenger RNA that encodes the information for the insertion of a specific amino acid in a protein.

RNA polymerase

An enzyme that catalyzes the formation of an RNA polynucleotide chain using a template DNA strand and ribonucleotides.

Promoter

A region of a DNA molecule to which RNA polymerase binds and initiates transcription.

The transfer of genetic information from DNA nucleotides into the amino acids of a protein has two main steps: **transcription** and **translation** (➾ Figure 9.3). In transcription, a single-stranded polynucleotide of RNA is synthesized at an unwound section of DNA, with one of the DNA strands serving as a template for the assembly of the RNA. The product is called an RNA transcript or mRNA molecule.

Both DNA and RNA carry genetic information in the sequence of their nucleotides. Recall that RNA differs from DNA in three ways:

• RNA is a single-stranded molecule.
• Nucleotides in RNA contain the sugar ribose rather than deoxyribose.
• RNA contains uracil in place of thymine.

To summarize, the genetic information encoded in DNA is transferred to RNA in transcription. RNA in turn carries this information to the cytoplasm and is directly involved with the synthesis of proteins.

In translation, **mRNA** moves to the cytoplasm and interacts with ribosomes to synthesize a protein containing a linear series of amino acids specified by the sequence of nucleotides in the RNA. In Figure 9.3, the brackets below the RNA indicate that genetic information is encoded in a sequence of three nucleotides, called **codons**. The four nucleotides of mRNA can be arranged to form 64 codons, each containing three letters (4^3 combinations), more than enough to specify the 20 amino acids used in proteins. Codons and the genetic code will be examined in a later section.

Transcription Produces Genetic Messages

In the nucleus, transcription begins when a section of a DNA double helix in chromosome unwinds, and one strand acts as a template for the formation of an mRNA molecule. The process of transcription occurs in three stages: initiation, elongation, and termination. In the first step, an enzyme called **RNA polymerase** binds to a specific nucleotide sequence in the DNA, which marks the beginning of a gene. This sequence is called a **promoter** region. After the polymerase is bound, the adjacent double-stranded DNA unwinds, exposing the template strand. Nucleotides that will make up the mRNA molecule form hydrogen bonds with the complementary nucleotides in the template DNA strand. In the elongation stage, RNA polymerase joins the RNA nucleotides into a polynucleotide chain (➾ Figure 9.4). The rules of base pairing in transcription are the same as in DNA replication, with one exception: an A on the DNA template specifies a U in the RNA transcript (there is no T in RNA).

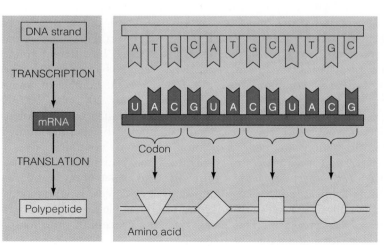

➾ FIGURE 9.3

The flow of genetic information. One strand of DNA is transcribed into a strand of mRNA. The mRNA moves to the cytoplasm, where it is converted into the amino acid sequence of a protein.

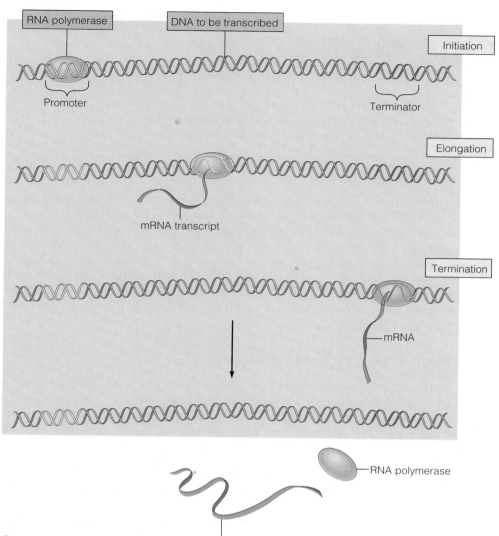

Initiation

RNA polymerase

DNA to be transcribed

Promoter

Terminator

Elongation

mRNA transcript

Termination

mRNA

RNA polymerase

Completed pre-mRNA

◖ **FIGURE 9.4**

Transcription begins when the enzyme RNA polymerase attaches to a promoter sequence that marks the beginning of a gene. One strand of DNA (the template strand) is transcribed into a complementary RNA molecule. Transcription ends when the RNA polymerase reaches a terminator sequence that marks the end of the gene.

In humans, 30–50 nucleotides per second are added to an mRNA molecule. In bacteria, up to 500 nucleotides per second are incorporated into mRNA.

The end of the gene is marked by a nucleotide sequence called a *terminator* region. When the RNA polymerase reaches this point, it detaches from the DNA template strand, the mRNA molecule is released, the DNA strands reform a double helix, and transcription is terminated (Figure 9.4). The length of the finished transcript depends on the size of the gene. In humans, most transcripts are about 5000 nucleotides, although lengths up to 200,000 nucleotides have been reported.

Genes Can Have a Complex Internal Organization

Many genes in humans contain nucleotide sequences that are transcribed, but not translated into the amino acid sequence of a polypeptide chain. These noncoding sequences, called **introns**, can vary in number from zero to 75 or more. Introns vary in size, ranging from about 100 nucleotides up to more than 100,000, and little is known about their function or significance.

The sequences in a gene that are transcribed and translated into the amino acid sequence of a protein are called **exons**. The internal organization of a typical gene is

Introns
DNA sequences present in some genes that are transcribed, but removed during processing, and therefore are not present in mRNA.

Exons
DNA sequences that are transcribed and joined to other exons during mRNA processing and are translated into the amino acid sequence of a protein.

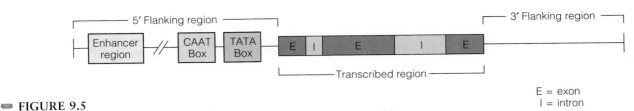

E = exon
I = intron

→ FIGURE 9.5

The organization of a typical eukaryotic gene. The part of the gene that is transcribed consists of all the introns and exons. Only the sequences in the exons will appear in the mature mRNA and be translated into the amino acid sequence of a protein.

5′ flanking region
A nucleotide region adjacent to the 5′ end of a gene that contains regulatory sequences.

shown in ← Figure 9.5. The combination of exons and introns determines the length of a gene, and often the exons make up only a fraction of the total length.

The regions on either side of a gene, known as the flanking regions, are important in regulating gene expression. The region adjacent to the site where transcription begins is called the **5′ flanking region**. In the first stage of transcription, RNA polymerase binds to the TATA sequence in this region, which is part of the promoter. It is thought that the TATA sequence helps to position the enzyme to ensure accurate transcription. Other sequences in this region serve as binding sites for proteins that assist in transcription.

Messenger RNA Is Processed and Spliced

In humans and other eukaryotes, transcription produces large RNA precursor molecules known as pre-mRNAs. These precursors are processed and modified in the nucleus to produce mature mRNA molecules that are transported to the cytoplasm, where they bind to ribosomes for translation (← Figure 9.6).

Cap
A modified base (guanine nucleotide) that is attached to the 5′ end of eukaryotic mRNA

Pre-mRNA molecules are processed by the addition of nucleotides to both the 5′ and 3′ ends. The sequence at the 5′ end, known as a **cap**, aids in the binding of the mRNA to ribosomes during translation. At the 3′ end a string of 30–100 A nucleotides, called the poly-A tail, is added. The role of the tail is unclear, since some mRNAs lack this modification.

After transcription, the pre-mRNA molecules are spliced and shortened by the removal of all introns. In splicing, the transcript is cut at the borders between introns and exons, and the exons are spliced together by enzymes to form the mature mRNA. The intron sequences are discarded. While a pre-mRNA transcript might be 5000 nucleotides long, the mature mRNA might be less than 1000 nucleotides in length. Proper splicing of pre-mRNA is essential for normal gene function. Several human genetic disorders are the result of abnormal pre-mRNA splicing. In β° thalassemia, one or more mutations at the border between introns and exons lowers the efficiency of splicing, and results in a deficiency in the amount of the gene product (beta globin) synthesized.

After processing and splicing, the mRNA moves from the nucleus to the cytoplasm, where the encoded information is translated into the linear series of amino acids in a protein.

Amino group
A chemical group (NH₂) found in amino acids and at one end of a polypeptide chain.

Carboxyl group
A chemical group (COOH) found in amino acids and at one end of a polypeptide chain.

R group
A term used to indicate the position of an unspecified group in a chemical structure.

Translation Requires the Interaction of Several Components

Proteins are polymers, assembled from amino acids. Twenty different amino acids are used in assembling proteins. The structure of each amino acid includes an **amino group** (NH_2), a **carboxyl group** ($COOH$), and an **R group** (← Figure 9.7). The R groups are side chains that are different for each amino acid. Some R groups are positively charged, some carry a negative charge, and others are electrically neutral. Table 9.1 lists the 20 amino acids typically found in proteins, with their abbreviations.

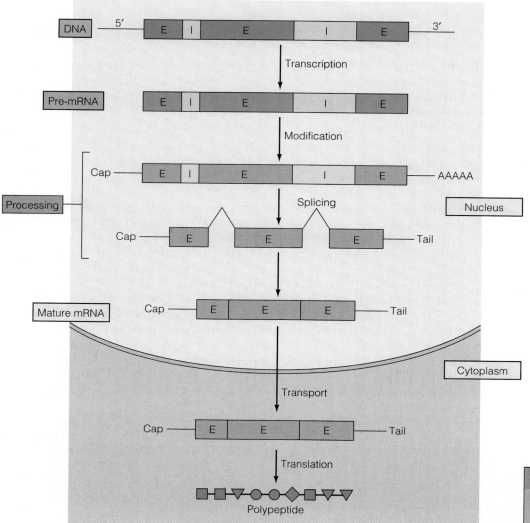

FIGURE 9.6

Steps in the processing and splicing of mRNA. The template strand of DNA is transcribed into a pre-mRNA molecule. The ends of this molecule are modified, and the introns are spliced out to produce a mature mRNA molecule. The mRNA is then moved to the cytoplasm for translation.

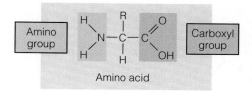

FIGURE 9.7

An amino acid, showing the amino group, the carboxyl group, and the chemical side chain known as an R group. The R groups are different in each of the 20 amino acids used in protein synthesis.

TABLE 9.1

Amino Acids Commonly Found in Proteins

AMINO ACID	ABBRE-VIATION
Alanine	ala
Arginine	arg
Asparagine	asn
Aspartic acid	asp
Cysteine	cys
Glutamic acid	glu
Glutamine	gln
Glycine	gly
Histidine	his
Isoleucine	ile
Leucine	leu
Lysine	lys
Methionine	met
Phenylalanine	phe
Proline	pro
Serine	ser
Threonine	thr
Tryptophan	trp
Tyrosine	tyr
Valine	val

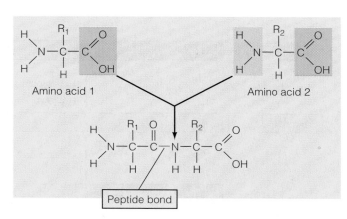

FIGURE 9.8

The formation of a peptide bond between two amino acids. An equivalent of a water molecule (H_2O) is split off during covalent bond formation. This reaction is catalyzed by an enzyme.

Peptide bond
A covalent chemical link between the carboxyl group of one amino acid and the amino group of another amino acid.

Polypeptide
A polymer made of amino acids joined together by peptide bonds.

N-terminus
The end of a polypeptide or protein that has a free amino group.

C-terminus
The end of a polypeptide or protein that has a free carboxyl group.

Transfer RNA (tRNA)
A small RNA molecule that contains a binding site for a specific type of amino acid and a three-base segment known as an anticodon that recognizes a specific base sequence in messenger RNA.

Ribosomal RNA (rRNA)
The RNA molecules that form part of the ribosome.

Anticodon loop
The region of a tRNA molecule that contains the three-base sequence (known as an anticodon) that pairs with a complementary sequence (known as codon) in an mRNA molecule.

Amino acids are linked together by the formation of a covalent **peptide bond** between the amino group of one amino acid and the carboxyl group of another amino acid (Figure 9.8). Two linked amino acid form a dipeptide, three form a tripeptide, and 10 or more make a **polypeptide**. Each polypeptide and protein is a directional molecule with a free amino group at one end, known as the **N-terminus,** and a free carboxyl group, called the **C-terminus** at the other.

Conversion of the information in the mRNA codons into the amino acids of a polypeptide chain is accomplished by the interaction of the mRNA with amino acids, and two other components of the cytoplasm: ribosomes and **transfer RNAs (tRNAs)** (Table 9.2).

Ribosomes are cellular organelles composed of two subunits, each containing RNA (rRNA) combined with proteins. Ribosomes, either free in the cytoplasm or bound to the membranes of the endoplasmic reticulum, are the site of protein synthesis.

Transfer RNA molecules help convert the mRNA codons into the amino acid sequence of a polypeptides. A tRNA molecule is a small (about 80 nucleotides) single-stranded molecule folded back upon itself to form several looped regions (Figure 9.9). Molecules of tRNA act as adaptors to match the codons in mRNA with the proper amino acids for incorporation into a polypeptide chain. As adaptors, tRNA molecules have two tasks: (1) bind to the appropriate amino acid and (2) recognize the proper codon in mRNA. The structure of tRNA molecules allows them to perform both tasks. A loop at one end of the molecule contains a triplet nucleotide sequence called an **anticodon**. The anticodon recognizes and pairs with a specific codon in an mRNA molecule. The other end of the tRNA contains a site that can bind to appropriate amino acid (Figure 9.9).

There are 20 different amino acids, and at least 20 different types of tRNA. Each tRNA carries an anticodon with a specific nucleotide sequence. If, for example, the

	TABLE 9.2			
	RNA Classes			
CLASS	**FUNCTION**	**NUMBER OF DIFFERENT TYPES**	**SIZE (NUCLEOTIDES)**	**% OF RNA IN CELL**
Ribosomal RNA (rRNA)	Structural, functional component of ribosomes	3	120 to 4,800	90
Messenger RNA (mRNA)	Carries genetic information from DNA to ribosomes	Many thousands	300 to 10,000	3 to 5
Transfer RNA (tRNA)	Adaptor recognizes nucleotide triplets and amino acids. Transports amino acids to ribosomes	50 to 60	75 to 90	5 to 7

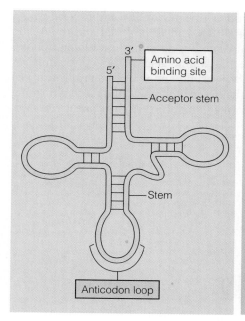

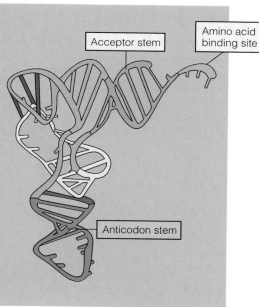

(a)   (b)

◉ FIGURE 9.9

(a) Transfer RNA acts as a molecular adaptor and can recognize mRNA codons (at the tRNA anticodon loop) and can bind the appropriate amino acid (at the amino acid binding site). (b) The three-dimensional structure of a tRNA molecule.

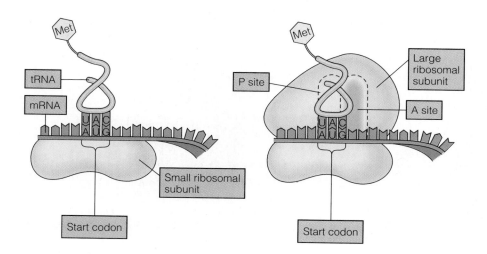

◉ FIGURE 9.10

Steps in the initiation of translation. In the cytoplasm, an mRNA molecule binds to a small ribosomal subunit. A tRNA carrying an amino acid (usually methionine) binds to the first codon (the start) codon in the mRNA. In a second step, a large ribosomal subunit binds to the small subunit, forming the initiation complex.

anticodon in a tRNA molecule is CCC, the amino acid glycine should bind at the other end of the molecule. But by themselves, tRNA molecules cannot recognize amino acids. This task is carried out by an enzyme that recognizes a specific amino acid and its proper tRNA. Because there are 20 amino acids, there is a family of 20 such enzymes to bind amino acids to the proper tRNAs. In turn, because of base-pairing rules, tRNAs with the anticodon CCC can only bind to the codon GGG on an mRNA molecule. In this way, the three nucleotides in each mRNA codon are matched with the proper amino acid to form the new polypeptide.

Translation takes place in a series of steps: initiation, elongation, and termination. In the first step, mRNA, the small ribosomal subunit, and a tRNA carrying the first amino acid join together to form an initiation complex (◉ Figure 9.10). Methionine is a unique amino acid in that it is usually inserted first in all polypeptide chains. Each mRNA molecule has codons marking the beginning of the message (**start codon** also called the **initiator codon**) and the end of the message (**stop codon**). The small ribosomal subunit binds at the start codon (AUG), and the anticodon (UAC) of a tRNA carrying methionine binds to the start codon. To complete initiation, a large ribosomal subunit binds to the small subunit.

Start codon or Initiator codon
A codon present in mRNA that signals the location for translation to begin. The codon AUG functions as an initiator codon.

Stop codons
Codons present in mRNA that signal the end of a growing polypeptide chain. UAA, UGA, and UAG function as stop codons.

Once initiation is complete, the polypeptide elongates by the addition of amino acids. Ribosomes have two binding sites for tRNA, called the P site and the A site. The tRNA carrying methionine binds to the P site during initiation. Elongation begins when a tRNA molecule, carrying the second amino acid, pairs with the mRNA codon in the A site (● Figure 9.11). When the second amino acid is in position, an enzyme associated with the ribosome joins the two amino acids together by forming a peptide bond. When this peptide bond is formed, the tRNA in the P site is released, and moves away from the ribosome.

● **FIGURE 9.11**

Steps in elongation during translation. (a) After initiation, the anticodon of a second tRNA binds to the second mRNA codon, which occupies the A site of the ribosome. (b) During peptide bond formation, the two amino acids are linked together by a covalent chemical bond. When the peptide bond is formed, the tRNA in the P site is released, leaving this site empty. (c–d) In translocation, the ribosome shifts down the mRNA by one codon, moving the tRNA carrying the growing polypeptide chain to the P site, and moving the next mRNA codon into the A site. A tRNA carrying an amino acid binds to the codon in the A site, and another peptide bond is formed. This process continues until a stop codon in the mRNA (UAA) is reached. When the stop codon occupies the A site, the translation complex comes apart, and the ribosome, mRNA, and completed polypeptide become separated.

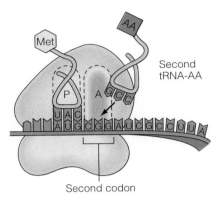

(a) As the first step in elongation, a tRNA-AA complex binds to the codon in the A site.

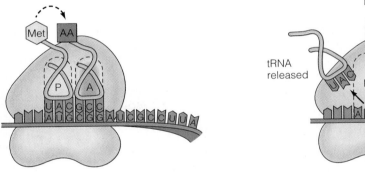
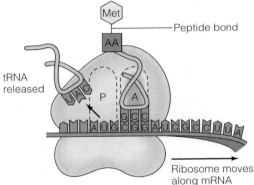

(b) An enzyme catalyzes the formation of a peptide bond between the two amino acids. The dipeptide that forms is attached to the second tRNA. This frees up the first tRNA, which vacates the P site.

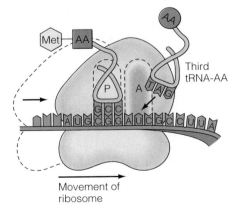
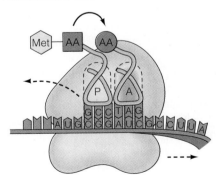

(c) The ribosome moves down the mRNA. The tRNA-dipeptide now occupies the P site and another tRNA-AA complex can occupy the A site.

(d) The dipeptide is linked by a peptide bond to the third amino acid. This frees the second tRNA. The ribosome moves down one more codon, exposing the A site and freeing it up for the addition of another tRNA-AA. This process repeats itself until the terminator codon (UUA) is reached.

CONCEPTS AND CONTROVERSIES

Antibiotics and Protein Synthesis

Antibiotics are chemicals produced by microorganisms as defense mechanisms. The most effective antibiotics work by interfering with essential biochemical or reproductive processes. Many antibiotics block or disrupt one or more stages in protein synthesis. Some of these are listed below.

Tetracyclines are a family of chemically similar antibiotics used to treat a range of bacterial infections. Tetracyclines interfere with the initiation of translation. The tetracycline molecule binds to the small ribosomal subunit and prevents the binding of the tRNA anticodon in the first step in initiation. Both eukaryotic and prokaryotic ribosomes are sensitive to the action of tetracycline. This antibiotic cannot pass through the plasma membrane of eukaryotic cells, but it can enter bacterial cells to inhibit protein synthesis and stop bacterial growth.

Streptomycin is an antibiotic used clinically to treat serious bacterial infections. It binds to the small ribosomal subunit but does not prevent initiation or elongation, although it alters the efficiency of protein synthesis. When streptomycin binds to a ribosome, it alters the interaction between codons in the mRNA and anticodons in the tRNA, so that incorrect amino acids are incorporated into the growing polypeptide chain. In addition, streptomycin causes the ribosome to fall off the mRNA at random, preventing the synthesis of complete proteins.

Puromcyin is an antibiotic that is not used clinically, but has played an important role in studying the mechanism of protein synthesis. Puromycin is about the size and shape of a tRNA-amino acid complex. As a result, it enters the ribosome and can be incorporated into a growing polypeptide chain. Once puromycin has been added to the polypeptide, further synthesis is terminated, and the shortened polypeptide with an attached puromycin falls off the ribosome.

Chloramphenicol was one of the first broad-spectrum antibiotics introduced. Eukaryotic cells are resistant to its actions, and it was widely used to treat bacterial infections. However, its use is now limited to external applications and serious infections because it has the potential to destroy cells in the bone marrow, the source of all blood cells. Chloramphenicol binds to the large ribosomal subunit of bacteria and inhibits the enzymatic reaction that forms the peptide bond. Another antibiotic, erythromycin, also binds to the large ribosomal subunit and inhibits the translocation step of protein synthesis.

Almost every step of protein synthesis can be inhibited by an antibiotic, and work on the design of new drugs to fight infections is based on the detailed knowledge of how the nucleotide sequence in mRNA is converted into the amino acid sequence of a protein.

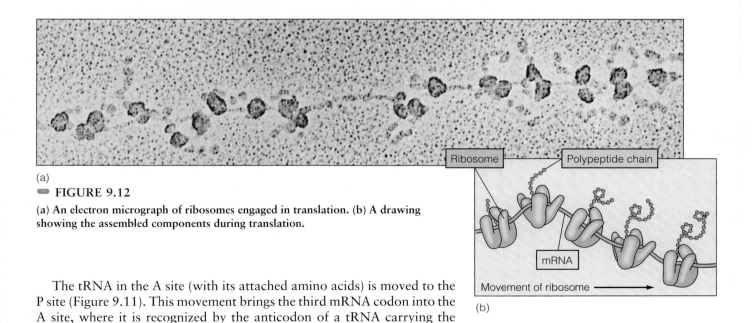

(a)

➡ FIGURE 9.12

(a) An electron micrograph of ribosomes engaged in translation. (b) A drawing showing the assembled components during translation.

The tRNA in the A site (with its attached amino acids) is moved to the P site (Figure 9.11). This movement brings the third mRNA codon into the A site, where it is recognized by the anticodon of a tRNA carrying the third amino acid. A peptide bond is formed between the second and third amino acid, and the process repeats itself, adding amino acids to the growing polypeptide chain (➡ Figure 9.12). Elongation continues until the ribosome reaches the stop codon.

Stop codons do not code for amino acids, and there are no tRNA anticodons for stop codons. At this point, polypeptide synthesis is terminated, and the polypeptide, mRNA, and tRNA are released from the ribosome. The role of antibiotics in dissecting the steps in protein synthesis is discussed in "Concepts and Controversies," page 227.

The process of protein synthesis occurs rapidly in prokaryotes, where the polypeptide grows at the rate of 15–20 amino acids per second, and more slowly in eukaryotes, where 2–10 amino acids are added per second.

THE GENETIC CODE: THE KEY TO LIFE

The information specifying the order of amino acids in a given polypeptide is encoded in the nucleotide sequence of a gene. Since DNA is composed of only four different nucleotides, at first glance it may seem difficult to envision how the information for literally billions of different combinations of 20 different amino acids can be carried in DNA. If each nucleotide encoded the information for one amino acid, only four different amino acids could be inserted into proteins (four nucleotides, taken one at a time, or 4^1). If a sequence of two nucleotides encoded an amino acid, only 16 combinations would be possible (four nucleotides, taken two at a time, or 4^2). On the other hand, a sequence of three nucleotides allows 64 combinations (four nucleotides, taken three at a time, or 4^3), 44 more than the 22 required.

The triplet nature of the genetic code was confirmed by Francis Crick, Sidney Brenner, and colleagues in a series of experiments using mutants of a gene in a phage called T4. They also proposed that some amino acids could be specified by more than one combination of three nucleotides, using most of the remaining 44 combinations. This work established that the genetic code consists of a linear series of nucleotides, read three at a time, and that each triplet specifies an amino acid.

The code itself was soon deciphered, and the coding nature of all 64 triplets was established (Table 9.3). By convention, the genetic code is written in mRNA codons.

TABLE 9.3

Codons on Messenger RNA and Their Corresponding Amino Acids

CODON	AMINO ACID	CODON	AMINO ACID	CODON	AMINO ACID	CODON	AMINO ACID
AAU AAC	} Asparagine	CAU CAC	} Histidine	GAU GAC	} Aspartic acid	UAU UAC	} Tyrosine
AAA AAG	} Lysine	CAA CAG	} Glutamine	GAA GAG	} Glutamic acid	UAA UAG	} Terminator*
ACU ACC ACA ACG	} Threonine	CCU CCC CCA CCG	} Proline	GCU GCC GCA GCG	} Alanine	UCU UCC UCA UCG	} Serine
AGU AGC	} Serine	CGU CGC	} Arginine	GGU GGC	} Glycine	UGU UGC	} Cystine
AGA AGG	} Arginine	CGA CGG		GGA GGG		UGA UGG	} Terminator* } Tryptophan
AUU AUC AUA	} Isoleucine	CUU CUC CUA	} Leucine	GUU GUC GUA	} Valine	UUU UUC	} Phenylalanine
AUG	} Methionine**	CUG		GUG		UUA UUG	} Leucine

*Terminator codons signal the end of the formation of a polypeptide chain.
**Codon has two functions: specifies the amino acid methionine and serves as the start codon, marking the beginning of a polypeptide chain.

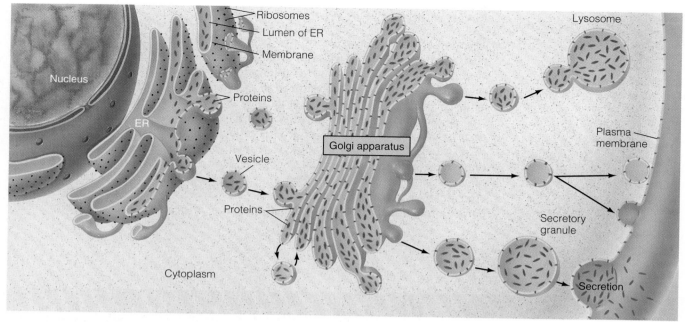

FIGURE 9.13

Processing, sorting, and transport of proteins synthesized in a eukaryotic cell. Proteins synthesized on ribosomes attached to ER are transferred into the lumen, where they are chemically modified. Many of these proteins are transferred to the Golgi apparatus in vesicles. In the Golgi the proteins are further modified, and sorted and packaged into vesicles for delivery to other parts of the cell and incorporated into organelles such as lysosomes, or transported to the surface for insertion into the plasma membrane. Proteins can also be packaged into vesicles for secretion.

Of these, 61 actually code for amino acids, while three (UAA, UAG, and UGA) serve as stop codons. The AUG codon serves two functions: it specifies the amino acid methionine and serves as the start codon, marking the beginning of a polypeptide chain.

An interesting feature of the genetic code is that the same codons are used for the same amino acids in all life forms, from viruses, bacteria, algae, fungi, and ciliates to multicellular plants and animals. The universal nature of the genetic code means that the nature of the genetic code was established very early during the evolution of life on this planet. The existence of a universal code is regarded as strong evidence that all living things are closely related and may have evolved from a common ancestor.

There are some rare exceptions to the universal nature of the genetic code, involving stop codons. In some species of the ciliates *Tetrahymena* and *Paramecium*, UAG and UAA encode glutamine. Other more substantial alterations in the genetic code have taken place in mitochondria, and point to a divergent evolutionary pathway for this organelle.

THE POLYPEPTIDE PRODUCT OF TRANSLATION

Once formed, the polypeptide chain can have several fates. In prokaryotes, the polypeptide folds into a three-dimensional shape determined by its amino acid sequence, and becomes functional. In eukaryotes, if the polypeptide is synthesized on ribosomes associated with endoplasmic reticulum (ER), it is released into the cisterna (the inside of the ER) where it can be chemically modified and transported to the Golgi complex for packaging and secretion from the cell (Figure 9.13). Alternately, if the polypeptide is synthesized on ribosomes free in the cytoplasm, it usually assumes a three-dimensional shape and becomes functional when released from the ribosome.

Primary structure
The amino acid sequence in a polypeptide chain.

Secondary structure
The pleated or helical structure in a protein molecule that is brought about by the formation of bonds between amino acids.

Tertiary structure
The three-dimensional structure of a protein molecule brought about by folding on itself.

Quaternary structure
The structure formed by the interaction of two or more polypeptide chains in a protein.

Levels of Structure in Proteins

The amino acid sequence determines the three-dimensional shape and functional capacity of proteins. Four levels of protein structure can be identified. The sequence of amino acids in a protein is known as its **primary structure** (⬤ Figure 9.14). The next two levels of structure are determined to a great extent by the R groups of each amino acid. The R groups interact with each other via hydrogen bonds to form a pleated or coiled **secondary structure**. Most proteins have regions containing each type of secondary structure. Folding the coiled helical or pleated regions back onto themselves forms the **tertiary structure**. Some functional proteins are composed of more than one polypeptide chain, and this level of interaction is known as **quaternary structure**. A newly synthesized polypeptide chain can be chemically modified and folded, and can interact with other polypeptide chains to achieve a functional state. When it becomes a functional, three-dimensional structure, it is called a protein.

TABLE 9.4

Biological Functions of Proteins

PROTEIN FUNCTION	EXAMPLES	OCCURRENCE OR ROLE
Catalysis	Lactate dehydrogenase	Oxidizes lactic acid
	Cytochrome c	Transfers electrons
	DNA polymerase	Replicates and repairs DNA
Structural	Viral-coat proteins	Sheath around nucleic acid of viruses
	Glycoproteins	Cell coats and walls
	α-keratin	Skin, hair, feathers, nails, and hoofs
	β-keratin	Silk of cocoons and spider webs
	Collagen	Fibrous connective tissue
	Elastin	Elastic connective tissue
Storage	Ovalbumin	Egg-white protein
	Casein	A milk protein
	Ferritin	Stores iron in the spleen
	Gliadin	Stores amino acids in wheat
	Zein	Stores amino acids in corn
Protection	Antibodies	Form complexes with foreign proteins
	Complement	Complexes with some antigen-antibody systems
	Fibrinogen	Involved in blood clotting
	Thrombin	Involved in blood clotting
Regulatory	Insulin	Regulates glucose metabolism
	Growth hormone	Stimulates growth of bone
Nerve impulse transmission	Rhodopsin	Involved in vision
	Acetylcholine receptor protein	Impulse transmission in nerve cells
Motion	Myosin	Thick filaments in muscle fiber
	Actin	Thin filaments in muscle fiber
	Dynein	Movement of cilia and flagella
Transport	Hemoglobin	Transports O_2 in blood
	Myoglobin	Transports O_2 in muscle cells
	Serum albumin	Transports fatty acids in blood
	Transferrin	Transports iron in blood
	Ceruloplasmin	Transports copper in blood

Proteins can have four levels of structure. (a) The primary structure is the amino acid sequence, which to a large extent determines the other levels of structure. (b) The secondary level of structure can be a pleated sheet or a random coil. (c) Folding of the secondary structures into a functional three-dimensional shape is the tertiary level of structure. (d) Some functional proteins are made up of more than one polypeptide chain. These interactions are the quaternary level of protein structure.

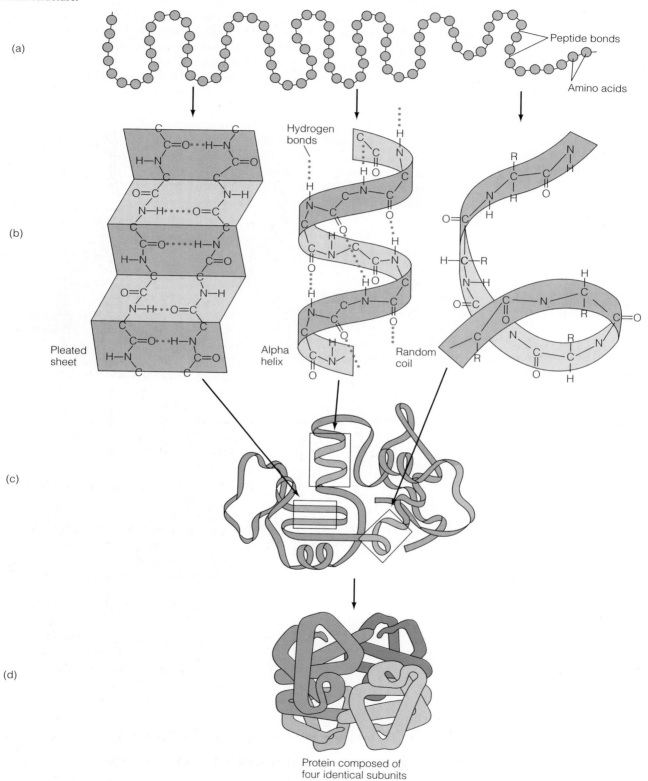

(a)

Peptide bonds

Amino acids

(b)

Hydrogen bonds

Pleated sheet

Alpha helix

Random coil

(c)

(d)

Protein composed of four identical subunits

Proteins Have Many Functions

Proteins are the most abundant class of molecules in the cell and participate in a wide range of functions (summarized in Table 9.4). Myosin and actin are contractile proteins found in muscle cells. Hemoglobin is a transport protein that shuttles oxygen to cells. The immune system depends on protein antibodies to identify and destroy invading organisms such as bacteria. Connective tissue and hair are rich in structural proteins such as keratin and collagen. Histones are structural proteins that complex with DNA to help form chromosomes. Many hormones, such as insulin, are proteins.

One of the most important classes of proteins is enzymes, molecules that act as catalysts in biochemical reactions (Figure 9.15). Enzymes accelerate the rate of a chemical reaction, but themselves remain unchanged by the reaction. The three-dimensional shape of the enzyme generates an **active site**. Molecules that bind to the active site and undergo a chemical change are known as substrates. Enzymes are usually named for their substrate, with the suffix "ase" added. The enzyme that catalyzes the breakdown of the sugar lactose is called lactase, and the enzyme that catalyzes the conversion of the amino acid phenylalanine to tyrosine is called phenylalanine hydroxylase. The relationship between enzymes and genetic disorders will be explored in Chapter 10.

The function of all proteins depends ultimately on the amino acid sequence of the polypeptide chain. The nucleotide sequence of DNA determines the amino acid sequence of proteins. If protein function is to be maintained from cell to cell and from generation to generation, the nucleotide sequence of a gene must remain unchanged. Alterations in the nucleotide sequence of DNA (a mutation) produce mutant gene products, with altered or impaired functions. The phenotypic consequences of changes in DNA will be discussed in Chapter 11.

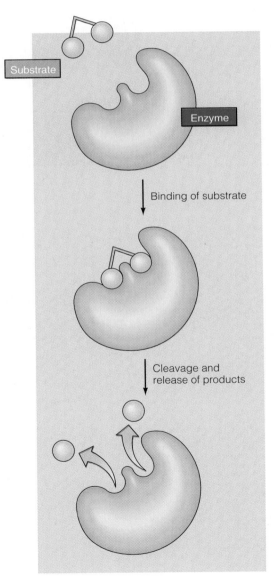

 FIGURE 9.15

Substrates bind to enzymes at active sites. The enzyme acts as a catalyst to carry out a chemical reaction, converting the substrate into a product.

SUMMARY

1. The idea that genetic disorders result from biochemical alterations was proposed by Garrod in the first decade of this century.

2. Evidence that gene action is mediated by proteins that control biochemical reactions was provided by Beadle and Tatum. In *Neurospora*, they demonstrated that mutations result in the loss of enzymatic activity, producing a mutant phenotype. Beadle proposed that genes function by controlling the synthesis of proteins and that protein function is responsible for the production of the phenotype.

3. Crick later summarized the molecular relationship between DNA and proteins: DNA makes RNA, which in turn makes protein.

4. The processes of transcription and translation require the interaction of many components, including ribosomes, mRNA, tRNA, amino acids, enzymes, and energy sources. Ribosomes serve as the workbenches upon which protein synthesis occurs; tRNA molecules are adaptors, recognizing amino acids as well as the nucleotide sequence in mRNA, the gene transcript.

5. In transcription, one of the DNA strands serves as a template for the synthesis of a complementary strand of RNA. The information transferred to RNA is encoded in triplet sequences of nucleotides. Of the 64 possible triplet codons, 61 code for amino acids, and 3 serve as stop codons.

6. Translation requires the interaction of charged tRNA molecules, ribosomes, mRNA, and energy sources. Within the ribosome, anticodons of charged tRNA molecules bind to complementary codons in the mRNA. The ribosome moves along the mRNA, producing a growing polypeptide chain. At termination this polypeptide is released from the ribosome and undergoes a conformational change to produce a functional protein.

7. Four levels of protein structure are recognized, three of which are a result of the primary sequence of amino acids in the backbone of the protein chain. Although proteins perform a wide range of tasks, enzyme activity is one of the primary tasks. Enzymes function by lowering the energy of activation required in biochemical reactions. The products of these biochemical reactions are inevitably involved in the production of phenotype.

QUESTIONS AND PROBLEMS

1. How do mutations in DNA alter proteins?
2. The 5′ promoter and the 3′ flanking regions of genes are important in:
   a. coding for amino acids
   b. regulation
   c. structural support for the gene
   d. intron removal
   e. anticodon recognition
3. Briefly describe the function of the following in protein synthesis:
   a. rRNA
   b. tRNA
   c. mRNA
4. What are the three modifications made to pre-mRNA molecules before they become mature mRNAs ready to be used in protein synthesis? What is the function of each modification?
5. The pre-mRNA transcript and protein made by several mutant genes were examined. The results are given below. Determine where in the gene the mutation lies in: the 5′ flanking region, exon, intron, cap and tail, or ribosome binding site.
   a. normal length transcript, normal length nonfunctional protein
   b. normal length transcript, no protein made
   c. normal length transcript, normal length mRNA, short nonfunctional protein
   d. normal length transcript, longer mRNA, longer nonfunctional protein
   e. transcript never made
   f. transcript made and rapidly degraded
6. If the genetic code is a triplet, how many different amino acids can be coded by a repeating RNA polymer composed of UA and UC (UAUCUAUCUAUC.....)
   a. one
   b. two
   c. three
   d. four
   e. five
7. Determine the percent of the gene below that will code for the protein product. Gene length is measured in kilobases kb) of DNA. Each kilobase is 1000 bases long.

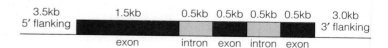

8. How many kilobases of the following DNA strand will actuallly code for amino acids in the protein product?

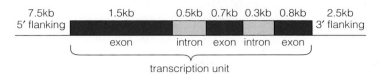

9. The following segment of DNA codes for a protein. The uppercase letters represent exons. The lowercase letters represent introns. The lower strand is the template strand. Draw the primary transcript and the mRNA resulting from this DNA:

GCTAAATGGCAaaattgccggatgacGCACATTGACTCGGaatcgaGGTCAGATGC

CGATTTACCGTtttaacggcctactgCGTGTAACTGAGCCttagctCCAGTCTACG

10. Given the following tRNA anticodon sequence, make the mRNA and the DNA template strand. Also, make the protein that is encoded by this message.

tRNA: UAC UCU CGA GGC
mRNA:
DNA:
protein:

How many hydrogen bonds would be present in the DNA segment?

11. Given the following mRNA, write the double stranded DNA segment that served as the template. In addition, indicate both the 5′ and the 3′ ends of both DNA strands. Also make the tRNA anticodons and the protein that is encoded by the mRNA message.

DNA:
mRNA: 5′- CCGCAUGUUCAGUGGGCGUAAACACUGA - 3′
protein:
tRNA:

12. The following is a portion of a protein:
met-trp-tyr-arg-gly-pro-thr-
Various mutant forms of this protein have been recovered. Using the normal and mutant sequences, determine the DNA and mRNA sequences that code for this portion of the protein and explain each of the mutations.
a. met-trp-
b. met-cys-ile-val-val-leu-gln-
c. met-trp-tyr-arg-ser-pro-thr-
d. met-trp-tyr-arg-gly-ala-val-ile-ser-pro-thr-

13. Write the mRNA and polypeptide encoded by the following DNA. The upper strand is the template strand:

TACGAACAGTGTCGGTTACCCATT

ATGCTTGTCACAGCCAATGGGTAA

14. A frameshift mutation causes:
a. a nucleotide substitution
b. a three base insertion
c. a three base deletion
d. a different amino acid sequence to be produced after the mutation
e. the same amino acid sequence to be produced after the mutation

15. Some mutations are suppressed by a second mutation. Explain how this might work, assuming that the second mutation occurs in the DNA that encodes a tRNA.

16. The following is the structure of glycine. Draw a tripeptide composed exclusively of glycine. Label the N-terminus and C-terminus. Draw a box around the peptide bonds.

$H_2N-\overset{\overset{\displaystyle H}{|}}{\underset{\underset{\displaystyle H}{|}}{C}}-C\overset{\displaystyle O}{\underset{\displaystyle OH}{\diagup}}$

17. Mutant ribosomes were isolated from different cells. Describe the most likely defect in each of the following ribosomes:
    a. unable to bind mRNA
    b. unable to join amino acids together
    c. unable to bind tRNA
18. Write the anticodon(s) for the following amino acids:
    a. met
    b. trp
    c. ser
    d. leu
19. Each of the following functions either in transcription or in translation. List each item in the proper category, transcription or translation: RNA polymerase, ribosomes, nucleotides, tRNA, pre-mRNA, DNA, A site, TATA box, anticodon, amino acids.

20. Enzyme X normally interacts with substrate A and water to produce compound B.
    a. What would happen to this reaction in the presence of another substance that resembles substrate A and was able to interact with enzyme X?
    b. What if a mutation in enzyme X changed the shape of the active site?
21. Can a mutation change a protein's tertiary structure without changing its primary structure? Can a mutation change a protein's primary structure without affecting its secondary structure?
22. Explain the role of proteins in the relationship between DNA and phenotype.

SCIENCE AND SOCIETY

1. Mad cow disease is thought to be caused by a prion. A prion is an infectious particle that consists only of protein, and is found in extracts prepared from the brains of diseased animals. The name is derived from the first letters of *proteinaceous* (pr) and *infectious* (i). Prions cause a neurological disorder in sheep and goats called scrapie, and Creutzfeldt-Jakob disease, a fatal neurological disorder in humans. They also are suspected as the causative agent in other diseases including multiple sclerosis, Parkinson disease, Lou Gehrig disease and Alzheimer dis-

ease. So far, it has not been possible to infect animals with any of these last mentioned diseases. Prions are able to retain their infectiveness when exposed to heat, chemicals, or radiation.

What makes prions resistant to agents that would normally destroy infectious agents such as viruses and bacteria?

How do you think a prion replicates since it contains no DNA or RNA?

INTERNET ACTIVITIES

The following activities use the resources of the World Wide Web to enhance the topics covered in this chapter. To investigate the topics described below, log on to the book's home page at:

http://www.wadsworth.com/biology

1. The Institute for Genomic Research (TIGR) has developed a human genome database for the use of researchers around the world. Access the TIGR cDNA Database (HCD) homepage, then read down to the highlighted word 'Overview.' Click on Overview and discover that over 345,000 DNA fragments and 30–45,000 human genes have been cataloged so far.

    This database is available to any one. Science has traditionally advanced through the open sharing of research results. Should this tradition continue, or do you think that information on the human genome should be restricted? Are there potential uses of genome information that are harmful?

2. The genome of *Haemophilus influenzae* was the first genome to be completely sequenced and mapped. Since then, the genomes of two other prokaryotic organisms have been sequenced. All three of these milestones were accomplished by the staff at TIGR. The TIGR homepage contains information about the DNA and protein sequence, as well as information about the cellular role of various gene products. View the map of *H. influenzae* and compare it with that of *Mycoplasma genitalium*, paying special attention to the relative sizes of the genomes, the number and sizes of the genes in each genome, and the cellular roles of their products.
    a) The genome of *M. genitalum* may be near the minimum size needed for a living organism. How many of the 482 genes from *M. genitalium* are found in *H. influenzae*? How about the reverse?
    b) Can you determine the cellular roles of the three largest genes in each genome?

Baralle, F. E. 1983. The functional significance of leader and trailer sequences in eucaryotic mRNAs. *Int. Rev. Cytol.* *85:* 71–106.

Beadle, G. W., and Tatum, E. L. 1941. Genetic control of biochemical reactions. *Neurospora. Proc. Natl. Acad. Sci. USA* *27:* 499–506.

Beato, M., Truss, M., and Chaves, S. 1996. Control of transcription by steroid hormones. Ann. N.Y. Acad. Sci. *784:* 93–123.

Bielka, H. (Ed.). 1983. *The Eukaryotic Ribosome.* New York: Springer-Verlag.

Chambon, P. 1981. Split genes. *Sci. Am. 244* (May): 60–71.

Crick, F. H. C. 1962. The genetic code. *Sci. Am. 207* (October): 66–77.

Danchin, A., and Slonimski, P. 1985. Split genes. *Endeavour 9:* 18–27.

Darnell, J. 1985. RNA. *Sci. Am. 253* (October): 68–87.

Doolittle, R. F. 1985. Proteins. *Sci. Am. 253* (October): 88–99.

Dreyfuss, G., Hentze, M. and Lammd, A.I. 1996. From transcript to protein. Cell *85:* 963–972.

Fesenfeld, G. 1996. Chromatin unfolds. Cell *86:* 3–9.

Garrod, A. 1902. The incidence of alkaptonuria: A study in chemical individuality. *Lancet 2:* 1666–1670.

Hamkalo, B. 1985. Visualizing transcription in chromosomes. Trends Genet. *1:* 255–260.

Holm, L. and Sander, C. 1996. Mapping the protein universe. Science *273:* 593–603.

Koshland, D. E. 1973. Protein shape and control. *Sci. Am. 229* (October): 52–64.

Krumm, A., Meulia, T., and Groudine, M. 1993. Common mechanisms for the control of eukaryotic transcriptional elongation. Bioessays *15:* 659–665.

Noller, H. F. 1985. Structure of ribosomal RNA. *Ann. Rev. Biochem. 53:* 119–162.

Pain, V.M. 1996. Initiation of protein synthesis in eukaryotic cells. Eur. J. Biochem. *236:* 747–771.

Sonnenberg, N. 1993. Remarks on the mechanism of ribosome binding to eukaryotic mRNAs. Gene Expr. *3:* 317–323.

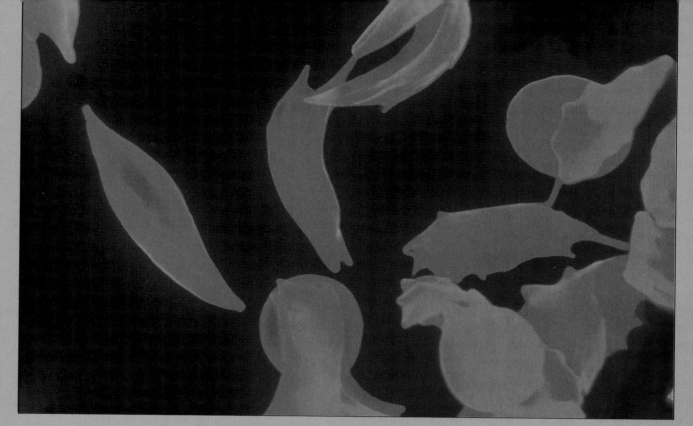

FROM PROTEINS TO PHENOTYPES: METABOLIC DISORDERS

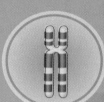

Chapter 10

Chapter Outline

THE ROLE OF PROTEINS

METABOLIC PATHWAYS AND GENETIC DISORDERS

CONCEPTS AND CONTROVERSIES
Garrod and Metabolic Disease

Phenylketonuria: A Defect in Amino Acid Metabolism

Other Metabolic Disorders in the Phenylalanine Pathway

CONCEPTS AND CONTROVERSIES
Dietary Management and Metabolic Disease

Defects in Carbohydrate Metabolism

Metabolic Disorders without Serious Phenotypic Consequences

Lesch-Nyhan Syndrome Is a Disorder of Nucleic Acid Metabolism

MUTATIONS IN RECEPTOR PROTEINS: FAMILIAL HYPERCHOLESTEROLEMIA

SIDEBAR *Population Genetics of Sickle Cell Genes*

DEFECTS IN TRANSPORT PROTEINS: THE GLOBIN GENES

Hemoglobin Variants

Sickle Cell Anemia

Other Hemoglobin Variants

Thalassemias

Treatment of Hemoglobin Disorders by Gene Switching

STRUCTURAL PROTEINS: INHERITED DISORDERS OF CONNECTIVE TISSUE

Collagen Fibers: Structure and Function

Osteogenesis Imperfecta and Collagen Genes

TRANSCRIPTION FACTORS AND GENETIC DISORDERS

Xeroderma Pigmentosum

Grieg Syndrome

OPENING IMAGE
De-oxygenated red blood cells.

A *young Norwegian mother had two children who were both mentally retarded. The first child, a girl, did not learn to walk until nearly 2 years of age, and spoke only a few words. The child also had a musty odor that could not be eliminated by bathing. Her younger brother was also slow to develop, and never learned to walk or talk. He had the same musty odor as his sister. To learn why both her children were retarded and had a musty odor, the mother went from doctor to doctor, but to no avail.*

Finally, in the spring of 1934, the persistent woman took the two children, then aged 4 and 7 years, to Dr. Asbjorn Fölling, a biochemist and a physician.

Because the urine from these children had a musty odor, the doctor first tested the urine for signs of infection, but there was none. He did find something in the urine that reacted with ferric chloride, producing a green color. Beginning with 20 liters of urine collected from the children, he began a series of biochemical extractions to isolate and identify the unknown substance. After 5 weeks, he was able to purify the compound; he then spent another 6 weeks identifying the substance as phenylpyruvic acid. To confirm that the compound in the urine was indeed phenylpyruvic acid, he synthesized and purified phenylpyruvic acid from organic chemicals, and demonstrated that both compounds had the same physical and chemical properties.

With his knowledge of chemistry, Dr. Fölling proposed that the phenylpyruvic acid was produced by a metabolic disorder that affected the breakdown of the amino acid phenylalanine. He further postulated that this biochemical abnormality might cause the phenotype of retardation. To confirm this, he examined the urine of several hundred patients in nursing homes and schools for the retarded and found phenylpyruvic acid in the urine of eight retarded individuals, but never in the urine of normal individuals. Less than 6 months after he began working on the problem, Dr. Fölling finished a manuscript for publication that described a condition now regarded as a prototype for metabolic genetic disorders. This condition, called phenylketonuria, helped establish the relationship between a gene product and a phenotype.

As we discussed in the last chapter, the discovery of biochemical mutations in fungi by George Beadle and Edward Tatum in 1941 was an important stage in understanding how gene expression results in a phenotype. We also considered how DNA encodes information for the chemical structure of proteins; in this chapter we will consider the relationship between proteins and the phenotype, using examples that emphasize the diverse role of proteins in living systems.

● **FIGURE 10.1**

Portrait of Count Boruwalski, artist unknown (1759). The body proportions of the Count are consistent with those seen in pituitary dwarfism I (primordial dwarfism), where the proportion of body parts to one another are normal, but the individual is a dwarf. This trait is inherited as an autosomal recessive, but some cases are sporadic. The disorder is caused by a deficiency of growth hormones, with all other endocrine functions being normal.

✿ THE ROLE OF PROTEINS

As outlined in Chapter 9, proteins are the most numerous and multifunctional class of macromolecules in the cell. They are essential to all cellular structures and biological processes carried out in every cell type. Proteins are components of membrane systems and the internal skeleton of cells. They form the glue that holds cells and tissues together, carry out biochemical reactions, destroy invading microorganisms, and act as hormones (● Figure 10.1), receptors, and transport molecules. Even the replication of DNA depends on the action of proteins. The importance of proteins to living systems is reflected in their name. The term *protein*, coined in the 19th century, is from the Greek word *proteios*, translated as "being of first importance."

The study of proteins played an interesting role in defining how biologists view living systems. In the late 19th century, most scientists thought that organisms were more than the sum of their parts and were infused with an immaterial force or spirit that made them alive. This idea was called by a variety of names, including vitalism and entelechy. In the 20th century the French philosopher Henri Bergson called this

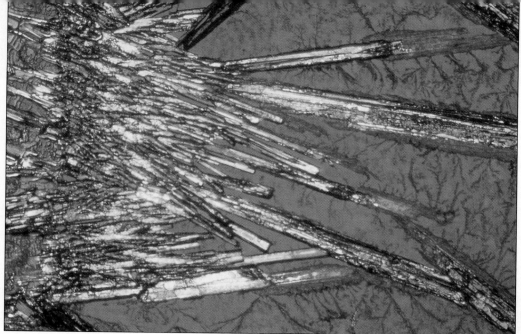

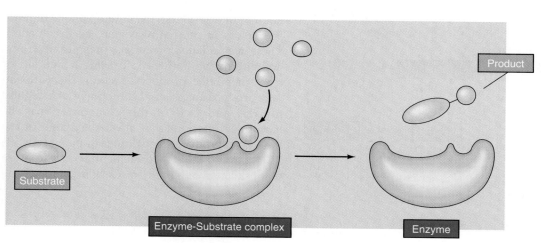

FIGURE 10.2

FIGURE 10.2

When purified, enzymes can be crystallized.

force an *elan vital*. Mechanists and reductionists, on the other hand, argued that the properties of living organisms could be explained by the action of lower levels of organization, including cells and molecules. As late as 1900, the chemist R. Willstätter (a vitalist) contended that although enzymes were bound to proteins, they could not themselves be proteins. Why? Because vitalists believed that an organic molecule could not have a property attributed to a living system.

This argument was resolved in 1926 when James Sumner crystallized the enzyme urease. Chemical analysis of this purified enzyme showed it to be a protein. By 1931, more than 30 different enzymes had been purified (━ Figure 10.2), and all were proteins capable of catalyzing a metabolic reaction, a property of living systems. After this, rapid progress was made in demonstrating that cellular metabolic events are associated with chains of biochemical reactions known as metabolic pathways.

METABOLIC PATHWAYS AND GENETIC DISORDERS

Since most proteins function as enzymes, we will first consider genetic disorders caused by defects in enzyme activity. Enzymes are biological catalysts that carry out biochemical reactions. They convert molecular **substrates** into **products** by a chemical reaction (━ Figure 10.3). Enzymatic reactions do not occur at random or in isolation; they are organized into a chain of reactions known as *biochemical pathways*

Substrate
The specific chemical compound that is acted upon by an enzyme.

Product
The specific chemical compound that is the result of enzyme action. In biochemical pathways, a compound can serve as the product of one reaction and the substrate for the next reaction.

━ FIGURE 10.3

Each step in a metabolic pathway is a separate chemical reaction catalyzed by an enzyme, in which a substrate is converted to a product.

Substrate

Enzyme-Substrate complex

Enzyme

Product

Garrod and Metabolic Disease

Sir Archibald Garrod was a distinguished physician, Oxford professor, and physician to the royal family. Garrod was widely trained; he was skilled in biology and biochemistry as well as clinical medicine. In studying alkaptonuria, he showed that the condition causes the excretion of abnormal amounts of a compound called homogentisic acid, which causes the urine to turn black upon exposure to air.

Garrod proposed that the presence of homogentisic acid in the urine of affected individuals was caused by a metabolic block, which prevented metabolism of the compound. He also speculated that the metabolic block was caused by an enzyme deficiency. Garrod observed that 60% of the affected individuals were the result of first-cousin marriages, and that the parents were unaffected. This led him to pro-

pose that alkaptonuria was inherited as a recessive Mendelian trait. Remember, Garrod did his work just a few years after Mendel's work was rediscoverd and widely publicized. Garrod studied other metabolic disorders, and published his findings in a book, *Inborn Errors of Metabolism,* that is widely regarded as a milestone in human genetics.

Why was Garrod's work, like that of Mendel, not immediately appreciated? From our perspective, it may seem strange, but Garrod worked in three areas that at the time were almost totally isolated from one another: genetics, medicine, and chemistry. Chemists had no interest in studying heredity, physicians regarded the conditions he studied as too rare to be important, and geneticists cared little about either metabolism or medicine.

Metabolism
The sum of all biochemical reactions by which cells convert and utilize energy.

Inborn error of metabolism
The concept advanced by Archibald Garrod that many genetic traits are the result of alterations in biochemical pathways.

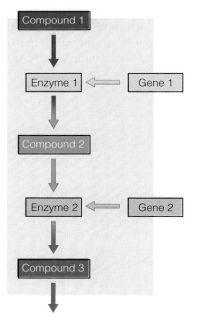

FIGURE 10.4

A sequence of reactions in a metabolic pathway. In this pathway, compound 1 is converted to compound 2, and 2 is converted to 3. Each step is controlled by an enzyme that catalyzes the reaction. Each enzyme is the product of a gene.

(Figure 10.4). The sum of all biochemical reactions in the cell is referred to as **metabolism,** and biochemical pathways are often referred to as metabolic pathways.

In a metabolic pathway, the product of one reaction serves as the substrate for the next reaction. Failure to carry out one of the reactions in a pathway shuts down all the following reactions beyond that point. It also results in the accumulation of substrates and products in the part of the pathway leading up to the block.

The relationship between human genetic disorders and metabolism was first proposed by Sir Archibald Garrod in 1901 (see "Concepts & Controversies," above). Garrod investigated a disease called alkaptonuria (MIM/OMIM 203500), in which large quantities of a compound called homogentisic acid are excreted in the urine. Garrod called this heritable condition an **inborn error of metabolism.** His work represented a pioneering study in applying Mendelian genetics to humans and in understanding the relationship between genes and biochemical reactions.

Mutations that cause the loss of activity in a single enzyme can have phenotypic effects in a number of ways. First, the buildup of one or more precursors in the pathway may be detrimental. These accumulated precursors may also overburden alternative pathways, causing a buildup of toxic metabolic products. Second, the pathway may produce an essential component of a cellular process, and lack of this component may be harmful. Mutations that affect the action of enzymes can produce a wide range of phenotypic effects, ranging from inconsequential ones to those that are lethal prenatally or early in infancy.

Phenylketonuria: A Defect in Amino Acid Metabolism

Most eukaryotes, including humans, can synthesize many of the 20 amino acids found in proteins. The amino acids that cannot be synthesized in the body are called **essential amino acids,** and must be part of the diet. In humans, there are nine essential amino acids: histidine, isoleucine, leucine, lysine, methionine, phenylalanine, threonine, tryptophan, and valine.

One of the essential amino acids, phenylalanine, serves as the starting point for a network of metabolic pathways, several of which are associated with human genetic disorders (⬤ Figure 10.5). Our focus will be on what happens when there is a block in the first step in the pathway: the conversion of phenylalanine to another amino acid, tyrosine. Failure to convert phenylalanine to tyrosine results in **phenylketonuria** (MIM/OMIM 261600); or PKU, the disorder described at the beginning of the chapter. PKU occurs about once in every 12,000 births, and is most often associated with a deficiency of the enzyme phenylalanine hydroxylase, which converts phenylalanine to tyrosine. Because of the defect in the enzyme, dietary phenylalanine accumulates in the body along with other metabolites, including phenylacetic acid, which is responsible for the musty odor of affected individuals.

The first sign of PKU is the accumulation of excess levels of phenylalanine in blood and other body fluids. If left untreated, affected individuals become mentally retarded, never learn to talk, and have enhanced reflexes that cause their arms and legs to move in a jerky fashion. Because the skin pigment melanin is also a product of the blocked metabolic pathway (Figure 10.5), most PKU victims usually have lighter hair and skin color than their siblings or other family members.

Essential amino acids
Amino acids that cannot be synthesized in the body and must be supplied in the diet.

Phenylketonuria (PKU)
An autosomal recessive disorder of amino acid metabolism that results in mental retardation if untreated.

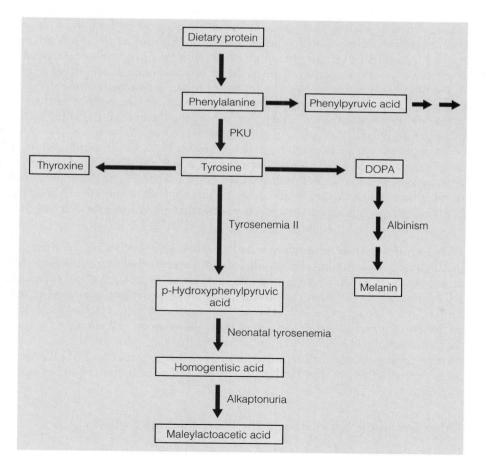

⬤ **FIGURE 10.5**
The metabolic pathway beginning with the essential amino acid, phenylalanine. Normally, phenylalanine is converted to tyrosine, and from there to many other compounds. A metabolic block, caused by a mutation in the gene encoding the enzyme phenylalanine hydroxylase, prevents the conversion of phenylalanine to tyrosine, and in homozygotes, produces the phenotype of phenylketonuria (PKU). The diagram also shows other metabolic diseases produced by mutations in genes encoding enzymes in this pathway.

How does the failure to convert phenylalanine to tyrosine produce mental retardation and the other neurological problems? These phenotypic effects are not caused by a lack of tyrosine, because tyrosine is available from the diet. The problem is caused by the accumulation of high levels of phenylalanine and metabolic by-products in secondary pathways (Figure 10.5) at a time when the nervous system is still developing.

In humans, the brain and nervous system continue to develop after birth, and require amino acids for protein synthesis. Special proteins in the plasma membrane of cells are responsible for moving amino acids and other metabolites into the cell. Phenylalanine and a group of other amino acids are transported by a single transport system. As phenylalanine accumulates in the fluid around cells of the nervous system, it blocks the uptake of several amino acids by the developing brain. These include tyrosine, leucine, isoleucine, valine, tryptophan, histidine, and methionine. It is not yet clear whether the damage is caused by the transport of too much phenylalanine or not enough of the other amino acids, but the result is brain damage, mental retardation, and other neurological symptoms.

Dietary Control of the PKU Phenotype   Most of those with PKU are born to heterozygous mothers, and are not affected before birth because the excess phenylalanine that accumulates in their bodies during fetal development is metabolized by maternal enzymes. PKU homozygotes suffer neurologic damage and become retarded only after birth when fed on a diet containing phenylalanine.

PKU can be treated by placing affected individuals on a diet with restricted phenylalanine intake (see "Concepts and Controversies" on page 243). This treatment is widely used and has been successful in reducing the effects of this disease. But managing PKU by controlling dietary intake is both difficult and expensive. A major problem is that phenylalanine is an amino acid present in many protein sources, and it is impossible to eliminate all protein from the diet. To overcome this problem, a synthetic mixture of amino acids (with very low levels of phenylalanine) is used as a protein substitute. The challenge is to maintain a level of phenylalanine in the blood that is high enough to permit normal development of the nervous system and yet low enough to prevent mental retardation. Treatment must be started in the first 1 or 2 months after birth. After that time the brain is damaged, and treatment has no effect.

All states now require screening of newborns for PKU, so the number of untreated cases is very low. Screening and treatment with a low phenylalanine diet allows PKU homozygotes to lead essentially normal lives. Some studies suggest that affected individuals can begin a normal diet by about 10 years of age without any effects on intellect or behavior, but some treatment centers recommend that the treatment be continued for life.

PKU Females and Reproduction   As PKU children treated with diet therapy have matured and reached reproductive age, an unforeseen problem has developed. If homozygous PKU females are on a regular diet during pregnancy, all of their children are born mentally retarded. Apparently the high levels of phenylalanine in the maternal circulation cross the placenta and damage the nervous system of the developing fetus in a way that is independent of the child's genotype. It is now recommended that PKU females stay on a PKU diet all through life, or return to the diet before becoming pregnant, and maintain the diet throughout pregnancy. PKU females have other reproductive options, including *in vitro* fertilization and the use of surrogate mothers.

Other Metabolic Disorders in the Phenylalanine Pathway

Several other genetic disorders are associated with blocks in the metabolic pathways leading from phenylalanine. For example, the pathway from tyrosine leads to the

Dietary Management and Metabolic Disorders

In several metabolic diseases, modifications of the diet are used to prevent full expression of the mutant phenotype. Diet can be manipulated to replace missing metabolites or to prevent the buildup of toxic intermediate compounds. This method is really a form of gene therapy. Dietary modification is used with varying degrees of success in several metabolic conditions including phenylketonuria (PKU), galactosemia, tyrosenemia, homocystinuria, and maple syrup urine disease.

The diet for each disorder usually is available in two versions, one for infants and one for children and adults that usually contains higher levels of proteins and other nutrients. For some amino acid disorders such as PKU, products prepared from enzymatically digested proteins or synthetic mixtures of amino acids are used as a protein source in the diet. These products often contain fats, usually in the form of corn oils, and carbohydrates from sugar, corn starch, or corn syrup. Vitamin and mineral supplements are also added. In one of the products available for PKU diets, casein (a protein extracted from milk) is enzymatically digested into individual amino acids. This mixture is poured over a column packed with activated charcoal, which removes phenylalanine, tyrosine, and tryptophan. These last two amino acids are added back to the remaining amino acids along with a source of fat, carbohydrates, vitamins, and minerals. Affected individuals use the powder at each meal as a source of amino acids. A typical menu for a school-age child is shown in the next column.

Up until the early 1980s, this protein-restricted diet was followed for 6–9 years. The rationale was that development of the nervous system is completed by this age, and that elevated levels of phenylalanine that accompany a normal diet would have no impact on intellectual development or behavior. This decision was also partly economic: the diet can cost more than $5,000 a year. Standard practice now is to continue the diet through adolescence, and some clinicians recommend the diet be continued for life. This decision is based on research indicating that withdrawal of the diet can be deleterious, and leads to a decline in intellectual ability and abnormal changes in electroencephalographic patterns.

Breakfast

⅔ cup dry rice cereal
½ banana
6 oz. formula

Lunch

½ can vegetable soup
3 crackers
1 cup fruit cocktail
4 oz formula

Dinner

2 cups low-protein noodles
½ cup meatless sphagetti sauce
1 cup of salad (lettuce)
French dressing
4 oz. formula

Snack

½ cup popcorn
1 tablespoon margarine

production of the thyroid hormones thyroxine and triiodothyronine, and a block in this pathway causes the recessive autosomal disorder called **genetic goitrous cretinism** (Figure 10.5). Newborn homozygotes are unaffected because maternal thyroid hormones cross the placenta and promote normal growth. But in the weeks following birth, physical development is slow, mental retardation occurs, and the thyroid gland greatly enlarges. This condition is caused by the failure to synthesize a metabolic end product (a hormone) and not by the accumulation of a metabolic intermediate as in PKU. If diagnosed early, this disorder can be treated by giving the affected infant regular doses of thyroid hormone.

In this same network of pathways, a lack of enzyme activity that leads to the buildup of homogentisic acid causes **alkaptonuria,** an autosomal recessive condition. This was the disorder first investigated by Garrod at the turn of the century. He postulated that it was under genetic control; this idea was confirmed in 1958 when the enzyme homogentisic acid oxidase was identified. Because of the metabolic block, excess homogentisic acid accumulates in the body and is excreted in the urine. The excess acid is converted to a dark pigment in cartilage areas that are exposed to light. As a result there is often discoloration of the ears, tip of the nose, palate, and whites of the eyes. Deposition in cartilage also produces a form of arthritis in later life.

Genetic goitrous cretinism
A hereditary disorder in which the failure to synthesize a needed hormone produces physical and mental abnormalities.

Alkaptonuria
A relatively benign autosomal recessive genetic disorder associated with the excretion of high levels of homogentisic acid.

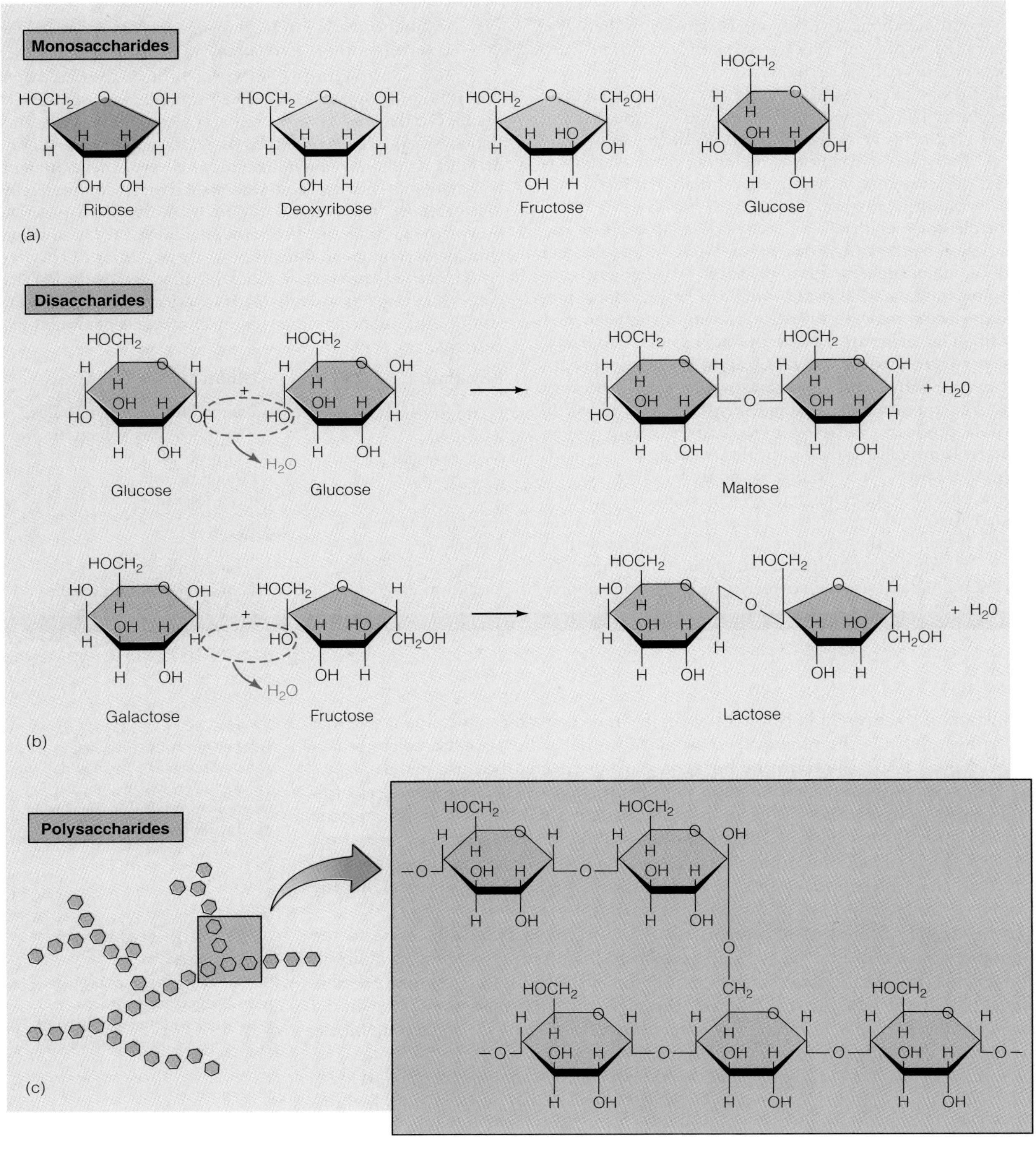

● FIGURE 10.6

(a) The formula and structures for four common monosaccharides. (b) Disaccharides. (c) Monosaccharides can combine in pairs to form disaccharides, or to form long chains of polysaccharides.

Defects in Carbohydrate Metabolism

Carbohydrates are organic molecules that include sugars, starches, glycogens, and celluloses. The simplest carbohydrates are sugars known as monosaccharides (Figure ● 10.6a). Sugars with six carbon atoms are hexoses and include glucose, galactose, and fructose. These sugars are important as metabolic energy sources. A combina-

Monosaccharides

Ribose   Deoxyribose   Fructose   Glucose

(a)

Disaccharides

Glucose   Glucose   Maltose $+ H_2O$

Galactose   Fructose   Lactose $+ H_2O$

(b)

Polysaccharides

(c)

tion of two monosaccharides produces a disaccharide (Figure 10.6b). Some common disaccharides include maltose (two glucose units, used in brewing beer), sucrose (a glucose and fructose unit, the sugar you buy at the store), and lactose (a glucose and a galactose unit, found in milk). Larger combinations of sugars form polysaccharides, including glycogen, starch, and cellulose (Figure 10.6c). In animals, including humans, the principal storage form of carbohydrate is glycogen, a molecule composed of long chains of glucose units.

Many different enzymes are required to catalyze the reactions that convert other sugars into glucose, those that store glucose as glycogen, and for the reactions that release glucose from glycogen. Metabolic blocks in any of these reactions can have serious phenotypic consequences. Some genetic disorders associated with the metabolism of glycogen are listed in Table 10.1.

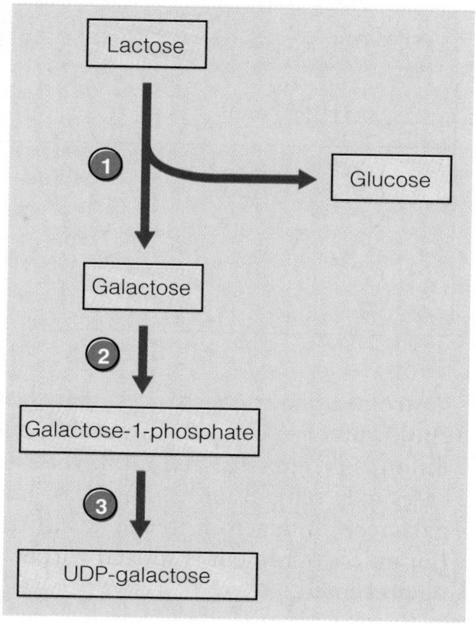

Galactosemia (MIM/OMIM 230400) is an autosomal recessive disorder caused by the inability to metabolize galactose, one of the components of lactose, the sugar found in human milk (Figure 10.7). Galactosemia occurs with a frequency of 1 in 57,000 births and is caused by lack of the enzyme galactose-1-phosphate uridyl transferase. In the absence of this enzyme, the metabolic intermediate galactose-1-phosphate accumulates to toxic levels in the body. Homozygous recessive individuals are unaffected at birth but develop symptoms a few days later. They begin with

 FIGURE 10.7

Metabolic pathway involving lactose and galactose. Lactose is the main sugar in milk, and is enzymatically digested to glucose and galactose in step 1. Step 2 is the conversion of galactose into galactose-1-phosphate. In galactosemia, a mutation in the gene controlling step 3 prevents the conversion of galactose-1-phosphate into UDP-galactose. As a result, the concentration of galactose-1-phosphate rises in the blood, causing mental retardation and blindness.

Galactosemia
A heritable trait associated with the inability to metabolize the sugar galactose. If it is left untreated, high levels of galactose-1-phosphate accumulate, causing cataracts and mental retardation.

TABLE 10.1

Some Inherited Diseases of Glycogen Metabolism

TYPE	DISEASE	METABOLIC DEFECT	INHERITANCE	PHENOTYPE	MIM/OMIM NUMBER
I	Glycogen storage disease—Von-Gierke disease	Glucose-6-phosphatase deficiency	Autosomal recessive	Severe enlargement of liver, often recognized in second or third decade of life; may cause death due to renal disease.	232200
II	Pompe disease	Lysosomal glucosidase deficiency	Autosomal recessive	Accumulation of membrane-bound glycogen deposits. First lysosomal disease known. Childhood form leads to early death.	232300
III	Forbes disease, Cori disease	Amylo 1, 6 glucosidase deficiency	Autosomal recessive	Accumulation of glycogen in muscle, liver. Mild enlargement of liver, some kidney problems.	232400
IV	Amylopectinosis, Andersen disease	Amylo 1, 4 transglucosidase deficiency	Autosomal recessive	Cirrhosis of liver, eventual liver failure, death.	232500

TABLE 10.2

Multiple Alleles of Galactosemia

GENOTYPE	ENZYME ACTIVITY	PHENOTYPE
G^+/G^+	100%	Normal
G^+/G^D	75%	Normal
G^D/G^D	50%	Normal
G^+/g	50%	Normal
G^D/g	25%	Borderline
g/g	0%	Galactosemia

gastrointestinal disturbances, dehydration, and loss of appetite; later symptoms include jaundice, cataract formation, and mental retardation. In severe cases the condition is progressive and fatal, with death occurring within a few months; but mild cases may remain undiagnosed for many years. A galactose-free diet and the use of galactose- and lactose-free milk substitutes and foods lead to a reversal of symptoms. But unless treatment is started within a few days of birth, mental retardation cannot be prevented.

Dietary treatment does not prevent long-term complications of this disorder, however. Affected individuals have difficulties in balance and impaired motor skills, including problems with handwriting. It is not clear whether this is due to damage to the nervous system that occurred during fetal development, or whether secondary metabolites build up to toxic levels. It is also not clear why galactose-1-phosphate is toxic.

Galactosemia is also an example of a multiple-allele system. In addition to the normal allele, *G,* and the recessive allele, *g,* a third allele, known as G^D (the Duarte allele, named after Duarte, California, the city in which it was discovered), has been found. Homozygous G^D/G^D individuals have only half the normal enzyme activity but show none of the symptoms of the disease. The existence of three alleles produces six possible genotypic combinations, with enzyme activities ranging from 100% to 0% (Table 10.2). This disease can be detected in newborns, and mandatory screening programs in some states test all newborns for galactosemia.

Metabolic Disorders without Serious Phenotypic Consequences

Two other disorders of carbohydrate metabolism, fructosuria and pentosuria, demonstrate that not all metabolic blocks have devastating effects. Although these genetic disorders are caused by the lack of a specific enzyme and the accumulation of metabolic intermediates, they do not produce clinically significant symptoms. The phenotypes in these diseases are characterized only by high levels of sugars in the blood and urine.

Fructosuria (MIM/OMIM 229800) is a rare autosomal recessive condition with a frequency of about 1 in 130,000. It is caused by a lack of the enzyme fructokinase. **Pentosuria** (MIM/OMIM 260800) is caused by the failure to convert the 5-carbon sugar xylulose to xylitol by the lack of the enzyme xylitol dehydrogenase. This autosomal recessive condition is found almost exclusively in Jews of East European (Ashkenazi) descent. The incidence is estimated to be 1 in 2500 among Jews in the United States and 1 in 5000 among Israeli Jews.

Lesch-Nyhan Syndrome Is a Disorder of Nucleic Acid Metabolism

In 1964, M. Lesch and W. L. Nyhan described an inherited disorder characterized by kidney failure, spastic movements, mental retardation, high levels of uric acid in the

Fructosuria
An autosomal recessive condition associated with the inability to metabolize the sugar fructose, which accumulates in the blood and urine.

Pentosuria
A relatively benign genetic disorder of sugar metabolism characterized by the accumulation of xylulose in the blood and urine.

blood and urine, and a strong tendency for self-mutilation. **Lesch-Nyhan syndrome** (MIM/OMIM 308000) is a rare X-linked recessive trait that affects 1 in 100,000 males. Hemizygous males are unaffected at birth, but delays in development appear at about 3 months. Later, writhing and uncontrollable spastic movements become apparent, but the most striking feature of this disease is the compulsive self-mutilation that usually appears between 2 and 4 years of age. Unless restrained, affected individuals bite off pieces of their fingers, lips, and cheeks. No affected females have been described, and most affected males die by the age of 20 years.

Lesch and Nyhan proposed that this condition was caused by an inborn error in purine metabolism (purines are bases found in DNA and RNA; review the structure of nucleic acids in Chapter 8). In 1967, J. E. Seegmiller and his colleagues demonstrated that the disease was caused by a lack of the enzyme hypoxanthine-guanine phosphoribosyltransferase (HGPRT) (● Figure 10.8). Normally, during cell turnover, nucleic acids are degraded into nucleotides, and the bases are stripped off. A large fraction of the purine bases are reused in nucleotide synthesis, and end up in newly synthesized DNA and RNA molecules. In the absence of HGPRT, the purine bases hypoxanthine and guanine are converted to uric acid, which build up in the blood to levels up to six times normal.

Lesch-Nyhan syndrome affects the function of the brain and nervous systems, but there are no detectable changes in the structure of cells in the nervous system. Normally, there is almost no production of new brain cells after the age of 1–2 years, and recent work has suggested that the progressive neurological degeneration seen in Lesch-Nyhan syndrome may result from the gradual accumulation of damage to

Lesch-Nyhan syndrome
An X-linked recessive condition associated with a defect in purine metabolism that causes an overproduction of uric acid.

● **FIGURE 10.8**

DNA and RNA are metabolically degraded into nucleotides. The bases are removed from the nucleotides by the action of enzymes. Most of the purines guanine and hypoxanthine (derived from adenine) are reused in making new nucleotides. Excess amounts are converted into uric acid, which is excreted in the urine. In Lesch-Nyhan syndrome, guanine and hypoxanthine cannot be reused and are converted to uric acid. The buildup of uric acid is toxic to the nervous system, and produces the symptoms of Lesch-Nyhan syndrome.

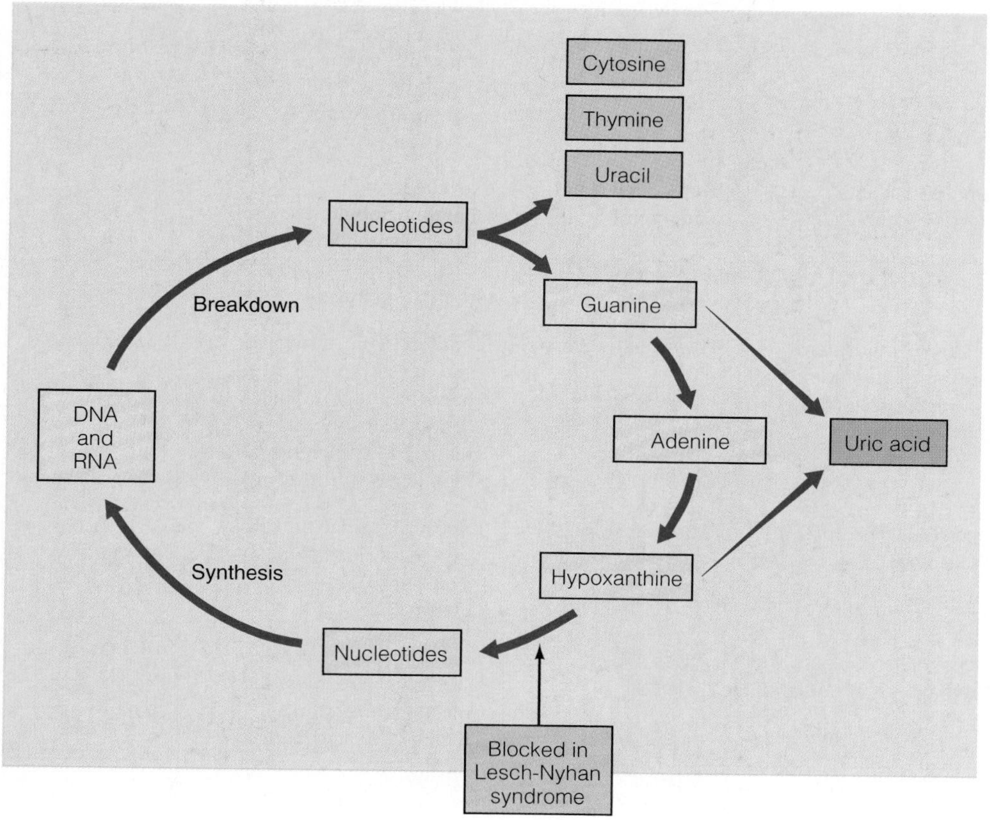

DNA in cells of the brain. How the lack of the HGPRT enzyme brings about DNA damage and the resulting phenotype is not known. Other disorders involved with metabolism of nucleic acids are listed in Table 10.3.

MUTATIONS IN RECEPTOR PROTEINS: FAMILIAL HYPERCHOLESTEROLEMIA

Although many, and perhaps most, proteins function as enzymes, proteins also act in other roles, including signal receptors and transducers. These functions usually take place in the plasma membrane of the cell, and mutations in receptor function can have drastic consequences. For example, in testicular feminization (discussed in Chapter 7), a defect in the ability to detect and bind the hormone testosterone leads to a change in sexual phenotype, causing a genotypic male to develop into a phenotypic female.

TABLE 10.3

Some Inherited Diseases of Nucleic Acid Metabolism

DISEASE	METABOLIC DEFECT	INHERITANCE	PHENOTYPE	MIM/OMIM NUMBER
Lesch-Nyhan syndrome	Hypoxanthine-guanine phosphoribosyl transferase	X-linked recessive	Mental retardation, motor impairment, self-mutilation, kidney failure, early death	308000
Hereditary xanthinuria	Xanthine oxidase	Autosomal recessive	Urinary purine is xanthine rather than uric acid; xanthine crystals in muscles; painful, debilitating disease	278300
Severe combined immunodeficiency	Adenosine deaminase	The deficiency syndrome is autosomal recessive	Reduced or absent immunoglobulins, defective immune response, reduced growth, recurrent infections, early death	102700
Defective T-cell immunity	Purine nucleoside phosphorylase	Autosomal dominant	Normal level of immunoglobulins, severe lack of lymphocytes, recurring infections of respiratory system	164050
Orotic aciduria	Oritidine-5′ phosphate decarboxylase and/or orotate phosphoribosyl transferase	Autosomal recessive	Lethargy; failure to grow and develop, moderate behavioral developmental delays, some mental retardation, excretion of high levels of orotic acid	258900
Xeroderma pigmentosum	Defective DNA repair after UV damage	Autosomal recessive	Exposure to sunlight causes skin lesions, pigment deposition, and malignancies	278700 and others
Ataxia telangiectasia	Defective DNA repair after gamma (x-ray) irradiation	Autosomal recessive	Skin lesions all over body, sensitivity to x-rays, some mental retardation, increased risk of cancer	208900

Another genetic disorder associated with a defect in a cellular receptor is **familial hypercholesterolemia** (MIM/OMIM 144010), an autosomal dominant condition with multiple alleles (see Chapter 5). Cholesterol and other fats are not very soluble in the bloodstream. In cells of the intestine, ingested cholesterol is coated with proteins and packaged into particles called low-density lipoproteins (LDL), which are soluble in the blood. Cells of the body take up LDLs from the circulatory system, using receptor molecules that project from the cell surface. The major site of uptake and metabolism of cholesterol is the liver. Once inside the cell, LDLs are broken down by enzymes, and the cholesterol is used for a variety of purposes, including the synthesis of new plasma membranes. Once uncoupled from the LDL, the receptor is returned to the plasma membrane to bind more LDL (Figure 10.9).

Familial hypercholesterolemia
A dominant autosomal genetic condition associated with a defect in cellular receptors that function in cholesterol metabolism. Affected individuals are susceptible to heart disease and early death.

 FIGURE 10.9

LDL receptors and cholesterol metabolism. LDL receptors are synthesized in the endoplasmic reticulum, modifed in the Golgi apparatus, and migrate to the outer surface of the plasma membrane. LDL complexed with cholesterol binds to the receptor on the cell surface and is internalized. Once in the cell, the LDL complex associates with a lysosome, which removes the cholesterol for metabolism, and the receptor returns to the cell surface. In familial hypercholesterolemia, LDL receptor defects prevent this cycle from occurring normally; cholesterol builds up in the bloodstream and is deposited on arterial walls, causing cardiovascular disease.

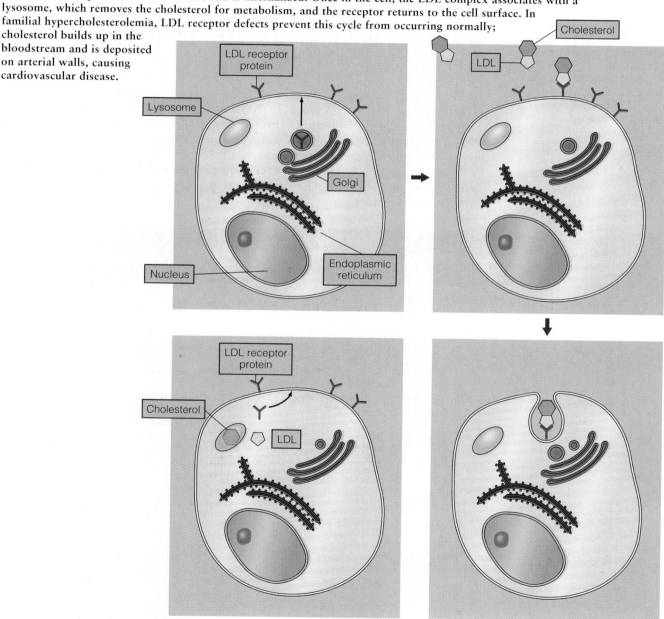

If cell surface receptors are absent or defective, LDL builds up in the blood and is deposited on the artery walls as atherosclerotic plaque, causing heart disease. The gene for familial hypercholesterolemia (FH), inherited as an autosomal dominant trait, controls the synthesis of the LDL receptor. There are two main types of mutant FH alleles—one class that makes no receptors, and one that makes defective receptors. Heterozygotes have half the usual number of functional receptors and twice the normal level of LDL. In FH, the connection between a gene product and the phenotype is relatively straightforward. When blood levels of cholesterol are too high, the cholesterol is deposited as plaque in the walls of blood vessels, causing atherosclerosis. As a result, heterozygotes for FH begin to have heart attacks in their early 30s. About 1 in 500 individuals is a heterozygote for an FH mutation. Homozygotes (about 1 in a million people) have two faulty genes for receptor synthesis and have no functional receptors. These individuals have LDL levels about six times normal, with heart attacks beginning as early as 2 years of age. Heart disease is unavoidable by the age of 20 years, with death in most cases by the age of 30 years. Other genetic disorders associated with receptors are listed in Table 10.4.

DEFECTS IN TRANSPORT PROTEINS: THE GLOBIN GENES

Hemoglobin, an iron-containing protein in red blood cells, is involved in the transport of oxygen from the lungs to the cells of the body. The hemoglobin molecule occupies a central position in human genetics. The study of hemoglobin led to an understanding of the molecular relationship between genes, proteins, and human disease. In addition, the study of hemoglobin in sickle cell anemia provided the first evidence that mutation results in a change in the amino acid sequence of proteins. The organization of the globin gene clusters has helped scientists understand how genes evolve and how gene expression is regulated. Heritable defects in globin structure or synthesis are well

TABLE 10.4

Some Heritable Traits Associated with Defective Receptors

DISEASE	DEFECTIVE/ABSENT RECEPTOR	INHERITANCE	PHENOTYPE	MIM/OMIM NUMBER
Familial hypercholesterolemia	Low-density lipoprotein (LDL)	Autosomal dominant	Elevated levels of cholesterol in blood, atherosclerosis, heart attacks; early death	144010
Pseudohypoparathyroidism	Parathormone (PTH)	X-linked dominant	Short stature, obesity, round face, mental retardation	300800
Diabetes insipidus	Vasopressin receptor defect	X-linked recessive	Failure to concentrate urine; high flow rate of dilute urine, severe thirst, dehydration; can produce mental retardation in infants unless diagnosed early	304800
Testicular feminization	Testosterone/ DHT receptor	X-linked recessive	Transformation of genotypic male into phenotypic female; malignancies often develop in intraabdominal testes	313700

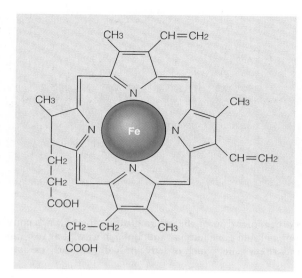

FIGURE 10.10

A heme group is a flat molecule that is inserted into the folds of a globin polypeptide. Each heme group carries an iron atom, which is important in binding oxygen in the lungs for transport to the cells and tissues of the body.

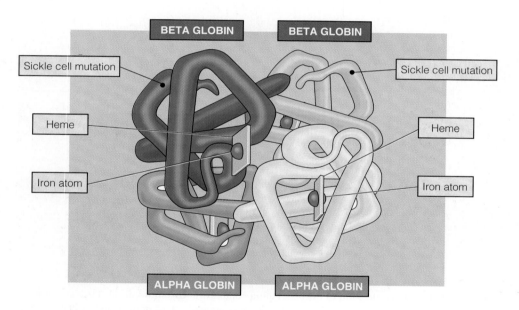

FIGURE 10.11

The functional hemoglobin molecule is composed of two alpha globin polypeptides and two beta polypeptides. Each globin molecule has an iron-containing heme group within its folds. The location of the mutation in beta globin that is responsible for sickle cell anemia is shown near the start of each beta chain.

understood at the molecular level and are truly "molecular diseases," as Linus Pauling called them. In this section we will consider the structure of the hemoglobin molecule, the organization of the globin genes, and some genetic disorders related to globin structure and synthesis.

Hemoglobin is a protein composed of four polypeptide chains; a heme group is bound to each globin molecule. Heme is an organic molecule that contains an iron-binding site (Figure 10.10). In the lungs, oxygen enters the red blood cell and binds to the iron atom in the heme group for transport to cells of the body. Although there are several different kinds of hemoglobin, the heme group is the same in all cases.

Adult hemoglobin (designated Hb A) has four subunits: two alpha chains and two beta chains (Figure 10.11). Each polypeptide chain is encoded by genes on different chromosomes. The alpha chains are in a gene cluster on chromosome 16, and the beta chains are in a gene cluster on chromosome 11. Each red blood cell contains about 280 million molecules of hemoglobin, and there are between 4.2 and 5.9 $\times$ 10^{12} red blood cells in each liter of blood. Each red blood cell is replaced every 10 to 20 days, so hemoglobin production is an important metabolic function.

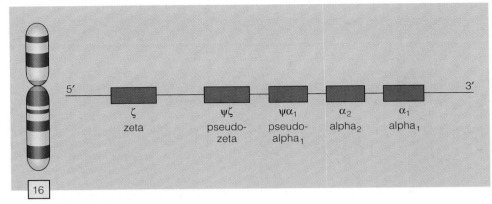

► FIGURE 10.12

The chromosomal location and organization of the alpha globin cluster. Each copy of chromosome 16 contains two copies of the alpha globin gene (alpha$_1$ and alpha$_2$), as well as two nonfunctional versions (called pseudogenes) and a zeta gene, which is active only during early embryonic development.

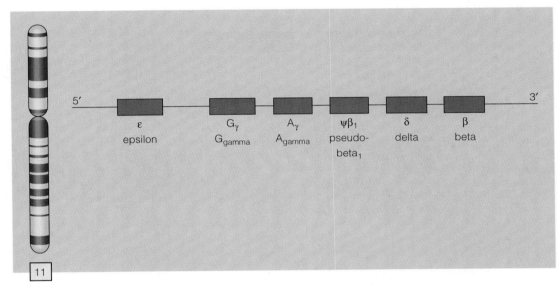

► FIGURE 10.13

The chromosomal location and organization of the beta globin complex on chromosome 11. Each copy of chromosome 11 has an epsilon gene, active during embryonic development, two gamma genes (gamma$_G$ and gamma$_A$) which are active in fetal development, and a delta gene and a beta gene, which are transcribed after birth.

Pseudogene

A nonfunctional gene that is closely related (by DNA sequence) to a functional gene present elsewhere in the genome.

In the alpha gene cluster on the short arm of chromosome 16 (► Figure 10.12), there are two copies of the alpha gene (designated alpha$_1$ and alpha$_2$) and three related genes: the zeta gene, pseudozeta and pseudoalpha-1. **Pseudogenes** are nonfunctional copies of genes with a nucleotide sequence that is similar to a functional gene, but they contain mutations that prevent their expression. The beta gene cluster is located on the short arm of chromosome 11 and contains several family members (► Figure 10.13). In order, these genes are the epsilon gene, ^{G}gamma and ^{A}gamma genes, a beta pseudogene, the delta gene, and the beta gene.

The alpha and beta globin genes have a similar internal organization, and the alpha and beta polypeptides are similar in size and amino acid composition. The alpha globin polypeptide is 141 amino acids long, and the beta globin molecule is 146 amino acids long. The amino acid sequences of the two polypeptides are very similar (► Figure 10.14). Because of these similarities, the alpha and beta genes fold into similar configurations, each cradling the heme group within internal folds of the polypeptide chain.

```
α-globin   V – L S P A D K T N V K A A W G K V G A H A G E Y G A  E A L E R M F L S F P  T T K T Y F P H F –  D L S H
β-globin   V H L T P E E K S A V T A L W G K V – – N V D E V G G  E A L G R L L V V Y P W T Q R F F E S F G  D L S T

α-globin   – – – G S A Q V K G H G K K V A – D A L T N A V A H V D D – M P N A L S A L  S D L H A H K L R V D P V N
β-globin   A V M G N P K V K A H G K K V L – G A F S D G L A H L D N – L K G T F A T L  S E L H C D K L H V D P E N

α-globin   L L S H C L L V T L A A H L P A E F T P A V H A S L D K F L A S V S T V L T S K Y R - 141
β-globin   L L G N V L V C V L A H H F G K E F T P P V Q A A Y Q K V V A G V A N A L A H K Y H - 146
```

FIGURE 10.14

The amino acid sequences of the alpha gene and the beta gene, using single-letter abbreviations for the amino acids. Shaded areas show regions where the amino acid sequences are identical. The two genes are descended from a common ancestor, and diverged from each other some 500 million years ago.

Heritable disorders of hemoglobin fall into two categories: the **hemoglobin variants,** which involve changes in the amino acid sequence of the globin polypeptides, and the **thalassemias,** which are characterized by imbalances in globin synthesis.

Hemoglobin Variants

Well over 300 variants of hemoglobin have been described, each originating as the result of genetic mutation. Over 90% of the variants are caused by the substitution of one amino acid for another in the globin chain, and over 60% of these are found in beta globin.

The simplest type of variant involves the substitution of one amino acid for another. The vast majority of these variants have been described in only one family or in small populations. But this category also includes Hb S and Hb C, which occur with high frequencies in certain populations and are associated with severe (Hb S) or mild (Hb C) phenotypic symptoms. Some of these variants are listed in Table 10.5. Note that many variants have no detectable phenotypic effect.

Sickle Cell Anemia

Sickle cell anemia (MIM/OMIM 141900) is inherited as an autosomal recessive trait and is caused by a mutation in the gene for the beta globin polypeptide. Hemoglobin

Hemoglobin variants
Alpha and beta globins with variant amino acid sequences.

Hemoglobinopathies
Disorders of hemoglobin synthesis and function.

TABLE 10.5

Beta Globin Chain Variants with Single Amino Acid Substitutions

HEMOGLOBIN	AMINO ACID POSITION	AMINO ACID	PHENOTYPE
A_1	6	glu	Normal
S	6	val	Sickle cell anemia
C	6	lys	Hemoglobin C disease
A_1	7	glu	Normal
Siriraj	7	lys	Normal
San Jose	7	gly	Normal
A_1	58	tyr	Normal
Hb Boston	58	his	Reduced O_2 affinity
A_1	145	cys	Normal
Bethesda	145	his	Increased O_2 affinity
Fort Gordon	145	asp	Increased O_2 affinity

FIGURE 10.15

(a) A computer-generated image of the stages in the polymerization of sickle cell beta globin to form rods. *Top*: a pair of intertwined fibers composed of stacked hemoglobin molecules. *Middle*: Seven pairs of fibers forming the structure that distorts the red blood cell. *Bottom*: A large fiber composed of many smaller fibers. (b) An electron micrograph of a ruptured sickled red blood cell, showing the internal fibers of polymerized hemoglobin.

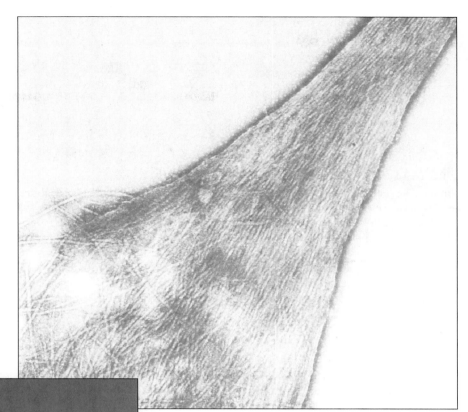

(b)

(a)

molecules containing mutant beta globin polypeptides become insoluble after oxygen is released. The insoluble molecules are sticky, and polymerize to form long tubular structures that form a rigid gel inside the cell (Figure 10.15). This distorts the membrane of the red blood cell, twisting the cell into a characteristic sickle shape. The deformed blood cells break easily and are removed from circulation, producing anemia; the sickled cells also clog blood vessels, producing tissue damage (micrographs of sickled cells are shown in Figure 4.11).

The differences between Hb A and Hb S were first demonstrated by Linus Pauling and his colleagues in 1949. They observed that these two forms of hemoglobin differed in their rate of migration in an electrical field. Since the R groups on many amino acids are electrically charged, they concluded that the amino acid structure of the two molecules must be different. This difference was confirmed by Vernon Ingram, who demonstrated that the difference between Hb A and Hb S was a single amino acid substitution at position 6 in the beta chain. This alteration in a single amino acid is the molecular basis of sickle cell anemia. All the symptoms of the disease and its inevitably fatal outcome, if untreated, derive from this alteration of one amino acid out of the 146 found in beta globin (Figure 10.16).

Other Hemoglobin Variants

It is interesting to examine the effects of another amino acid substitution at position 6 in the beta globin chain. Hb C is only slightly insoluble when it gives up its oxygen load, and forms intracellular crystals that make the erythrocyte membrane more rigid

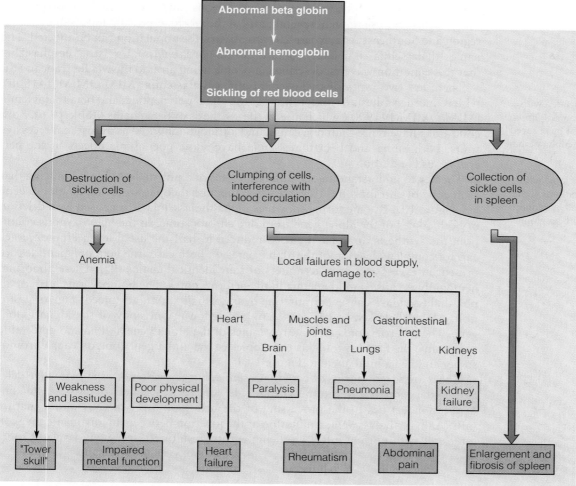

FIGURE 10.16

The cascade of phenotypic effects resulting from the mutation that causes sickle cell anemia. Affected homozygotes have effects at the molecular, cellular, and organ levels, all resulting from the substitution of a single amino acid in the beta globin polypeptide chain.

and leads to a reduced life span for the affected red blood cells. This produces a mild form of anemia, with accompanying enlargement of the spleen, but there is almost never a need for clinical treatment for this condition. The sequence of the first seven amino acids in Hb A, Hb S, and Hb C is shown below:

Hb A: val—his—leu—thr—pro—glu—glu—

Hb S: val—his—leu—thr—pro—val—glu—

Hb C: val—his—leu—thr—pro—lys—glu—

Recall from the discussion above that not all amino acid substitutions in the globin polypeptides are associated with a genetic disorder. Substitutions at position 7 (Table 10.5) in the beta globin chain have no detectable effects, although these variations are inherited in the same autosomal recessive fashion as sickle cell anemia.

Thalassemias

The thalassemias are a group of inherited hemoglobin disorders in which the synthesis of globin polypeptide chains is reduced or absent. This results in abnormal tetramers that do not have two alpha and two beta chains. These combinations do not

bind oxygen efficiently, and can have serious and even fatal consequences. Thalassemias are common in several parts of the world, especially the Mediterranean region and Southeast Asia, where 20% to 30% of the population can be affected. The name "thalassemia" is derived from the Greek word *thalassa*, for "sea," emphasizing that this condition was first described in people living around the Mediterranean Sea.

There are two types of thalassemia: **alpha thalassemia** (MIM/OMIM 141800), with reduced synthesis or no synthesis of the alpha polypeptide, and **beta thalassemia** (MIM/OMIM 141900), which affects the synthesis of beta chains (Table 10.6). Both conditions have more than one cause, and although inherited as autosomal recessive traits, both alpha and beta thalassemia have some phenotypic effects in the heterozygous condition.

The key to understanding the different forms of alpha thalassemia is knowing that each copy of chromosome 16 carries two functional copies of the alpha globin gene (● Figure 10.17). One form, known as alpha thalassemia-1, is caused by a deletion of both copies of the alpha gene from one chromosome. In the heterozygous condition, the synthesis of alpha chains is reduced to half the usual level. Homozygotes carry a complete deletion of the alpha genes. In both cases the beta polypeptides are present in excess and form tetramers of four identical chains (β_4). These abnormal hemoglobins cause a mild anemia in the heterozygotes. The homozygous form of alpha thalassemia-1 causes intrauterine death, usually at an advanced stage of gestation. Alpha thalassemia-2 is caused by a deletion in one copy of the alpha globin gene. The heterozygote carries three copies of the alpha gene and has no detectable symptoms; the homozygote has two copies of the alpha gene (one on each chromosome) and has a mild anemia (Figure 10.17).

There are several forms of beta thalassemia, but these do not usually involve deletion of the gene for the beta polypeptide. In some forms of beta thalassemia the underlying defect lies in the processing of the beta globin pre-mRNA into a mature mRNA. In β^0 thalassemia, a mutation at the junction between an intron and an exon interferes with normal mRNA splicing events, resulting in very low levels of func-

Alpha thalassemia
Genetic disorder associated with an imbalance in the ratio of alpha and beta globin caused by reduced or absent synthesis of alpha globin.

Beta thalassemia
Genetic disorder associated with an imbalance in the ratio of alpha and beta globin caused by reduced or absent synthesis of beta globin.

● **FIGURE 10.17**

Deletions and alpha thalassemia. (a) Normally, each copy of chromosome 16 carries two copies of the alpha globin gene (normal). One copy is deleted in the alpha-thal-2 allele, and in the alpha-thal-1 allele, both copies are deleted. **(b)** These three alleles can be combined to form six genotypic combinations, with 0–4 copies of the alpha globin gene. Genotypes with one copy have moderate anemia and other symptoms, and genotypes with no copies of the gene are lethal.

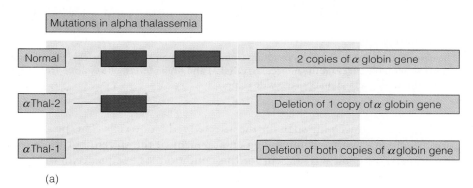

(a)

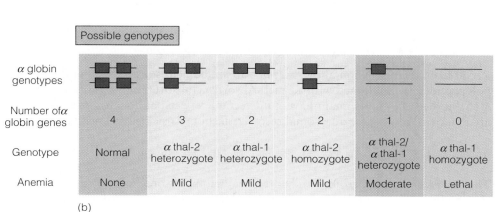

(b)

TABLE 10.6

Summary of Thalassemias

TYPE OF THALASSEMIA	NATURE OF DEFECT
α-Thalassemia-1	Deletion of two alpha globin genes/haploid genome
α-Thalassemia-2	Deletion of one alpha globin gene/haploid genome
β–Thalassemia	Deletion of beta and delta genes/haploid genome
Nondeletion α-Thalassemia	Absent, reduced, or inactive alpha globin mRNA
β^0-Thalassemia	Absent, reduced, or inactive beta globin mRNA. No beta globin produced.
β^+-Thalassemia	Absent, reduced, or inactive beta globin mRNA. Reduced beta globin production.

tional mRNA and, in turn, low levels of beta globin. Low levels of beta globin cause an excess of alpha globin polypeptides, which form hemoglobin molecules.

Treatment of Hemoglobin Disorders by Gene Switching

If untreated, sickle cell anemia is a fatal disease, and most affected individuals die by the age of 2 years. Even with an understanding of the molecular basis of the disease, treatments are only partially successful in relieving the symptoms. Years ago, treatments used chemicals such as sodium nitrite, sodium bicarbonate, and urea to prevent cells from sickling.

Recently, a discovery made with cancer drugs led to a new treatment. The drug hydroxyurea suppresses cell growth, and is used to treat cancer patients. Those treated with hydroxyurea have elevated levels of a form of hemoglobin usually seen only in developing fetuses. This hemoglobin is a combination of two alpha polypeptides and two gamma polypeptides. Gamma polypeptides are active in fetal development, and are switched off at birth, when the beta gene is activated (Figure 10.18). Treatment with hydroxyurea reactivates these genes, and makes fetal hemoglobin reappear in the red blood cells. When individuals with sickle cell anemia and beta thalassemia are treated with hydroxyurea, fetal hemoglobin is pro-

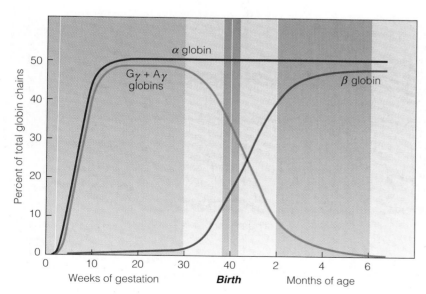

FIGURE 10.18

Patterns of globin gene expression during development. The alpha genes are switched on early in development, and continue throughout life. The gamma$_G$ and gamma$_A$ members of the beta family are active during fetal development, and switch off just before birth. The beta globin gene is switched on at birth, and is active throughout life. Sickle cell anemia and beta thalassemia are caused by mutations that affect beta globin. Research aimed at treating these conditions is directed at switching on the gamma genes, producing fetal hemoglobin to correct the conditions.

duced, and replaces the defective hemoglobin in red blood cells. Other drugs, including butyrate and sodium butyrate related to common chemicals used as a food additive also switch on the synthesis of fetal hemoglobin. In some patients, 25–30% of the hemoglobin in the blood was fetal hemoglobin. Because these chemicals are less toxic, they are being used in clinical trials to treat both sickle cell anemia and beta thalassemia by switching on genes that are normally turned off at birth.

STRUCTURAL PROTEINS: INHERITED DISORDERS OF CONNECTIVE TISSUE

Many inherited disorders of structural proteins are found in connective tissue. These include **osteogenesis imperfecta,** a group of inherited disorders that affect collagen, one of the main components of connective tissue; Marfan syndrome (described in Chapter 4), which affects fibrillin, a protein found in elastic connective tissue; and **Ehlers-Danlos** syndrome, a condition characterized by hyperflexible skin and joints (the molecular basis of this disorder is still unknown).

Collagen Fibers: Structure and Function

Collagen, the protein affected in osteogenesis imperfecta, is one of the most abundant proteins in the body and an important structural component of connective tissue. It is found in bone, cartilage, tendons, skin, and the arteries of the circulatory system. There are at least 12 types of collagen, and collagen genes are distributed on several different chromosomes. The basic structure common to all types of fibrillar collagen is a triple helix of three polypeptide chains (⬭ Figure 10.19). After synthe-

⬭ **FIGURE 10.19**

Three collagen molecules combine to form a helix of procollagen. The ends of the procollagen are trimmed by enzymatic action to produce collagen fibrils. Fibrils aggregate and crosslink together to form collagen fibers, which are found in connective tissues.

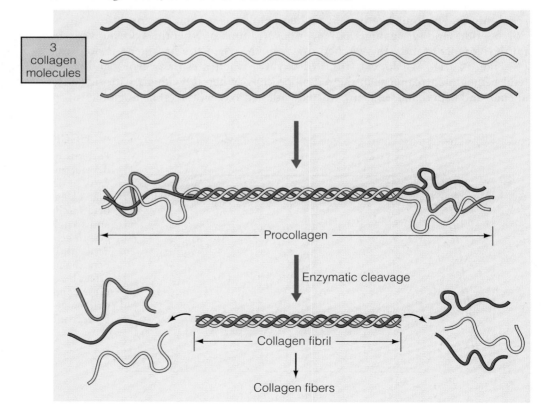

sis, the three polypeptide chains are assembled into a precursor molecule called *procollagen*, which is cleaved at each end to yield collagen fibrils. The fibrils crosslink to form long collagen fibers (Figure 10.20).

Osteogenesis Imperfecta and Collagen Genes

Osteogenesis imperfecta (OI) is a group of inherited connective disorders characterized by collagen defects (Table 10.7). Type I OI, associated with a defect in type I collagen, is the most common form of this disorder, and it is inherited as an autosomal dominant trait. Affected individuals have brittle bones that fracture easily and may develop deafness caused by abnormalities of the bones in the middle ear. In addition, the whites of the eyes often appear blue. Other forms of OI can be more serious; Type II OI causes severe bone malformations, multiple fractures, and early death (Figure 10.21).

In type I OI, one copy of the alpha 1 gene is inactive, resulting in a 50% decrease in the amount of type I collagen produced. This reduces the amount and thickness of collagen in tissues of the body, but the fibers that are produced are normal. In this disorder, I, the phenotype results from a reduction in the amount of a gene product, not the production of an abnormal product, or from the absence of a gene product.

The bones of affected individuals contain only half the normal amount of collagen, and because they are unable to withstand normal mechanical stresses, they frac-

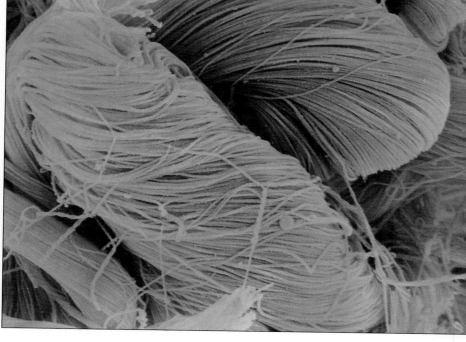

 FIGURE 10.20

Collagen fibers under the electron microscope. Normal connective tissue contains meshworks of collagen.

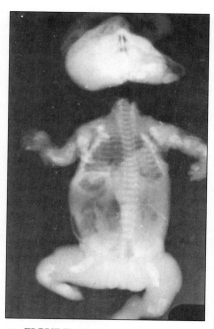

 FIGURE 10.21

Type II osteogeneis imperfecta (OI) is associated with severe bone deformaties and neonatal death. This form of OI is caused by a mutation in the type I collagen gene.

TABLE 10.7		
Types of osteogenesis imperfecta		
TYPE*	**PHENOTYPE**	**MIM/OMIM NUMBER**
I	Mild bone disease Blue sclerae (whites of eyes) Early onset deafness Tooth abnormalities	166200
II	Lethal soon after birth Many fractures and deformities	166210
III	Progressive deformity of bones Multiple fractures, short stature, deformity, deafness, and tooth abnormalities Scleral hue varies	259420
IV	Bone disease intermediate between OI I and III. Moderate deformity, short stature, tooth abnormalities, and hearing loss Normal sclerae	166200

Almost all types are inherited in an autosomal dominant fashion.

ture easily. The whites of the eyes appear blue because the sclera (a thin, fibrous tissue that covers the whites of the eye) is thinner than normal and somewhat transparent, allowing the veins underneath to show through.

TRANSCRIPTION FACTORS AND GENETIC DISORDERS

Transcription factors are proteins that bind to DNA and regulate gene expression. To date, more than 10 families of these proteins have been described. Each family has a distinct molecular configuration that permits binding to DNA. These are emerging as an important class of proteins that contribute to genetic disorders. The largest such family is the *zinc-finger* proteins, with tandemly repeated, folded loops of amino acids (extended like fingers), each stabilized by zinc ions (⬤ Figure 10.22). Over 200 zinc-finger genes have been identified, and all are thought to be involved in regulating transcription and controlling cellular growth and differentiation.

As more genetic disorders are characterized at the molecular level, mutant zinc-finger genes are emerging as important contributors to human genetic disorders. Two such disorders will be briefly described.

Xeroderma Pigmentosum

Xeroderma pigmentosum (XP) is a group of autosomal recessive disorders characterized by sensitivity to sunlight and the development of ultraviolet-light-induced skin cancers (⬤ Figure 10.23). Mutations in at least seven different genes (designated as XP-A through XP-G) can cause the symptoms of XP, and all are associated with the inability to repair damage to DNA caused by ultraviolet light. The gene for XP-A has been cloned, and from its nucleotide sequence it has been determined that the gene product is a zinc-finger protein. Its mechanism of action is not yet known, but the protein may bind to DNA to directly repair damage to DNA, or it may activate genes involved in DNA repair.

Grieg Syndrome

An autosomal dominant disorder known as **Greig syndrome** (MIM/OMIM 175700) affects limb and facial development, causing fusion of fingers and toes, as well as abnormalities of the face and skull. The gene, mapped to chromosome 7p13, encodes a zinc-finger protein known as GLI-3. The pattern of GLI-3 expression and the timing of its expression are consistent with the role of this protein as a regulator of limb and facial formation during prenatal development.

The role of zinc-finger proteins in programming gene transcription and the discovery that mutations in this group of genes can cause developmental defects indicate that investigation of DNA-binding proteins may be important in understanding mutations that exert their phenotypic effect during prenatal development or during infancy.

⬤ **FIGURE 10.22**

Zinc-finger proteins contain regions with cysteine (C) and histidine (H) amino acids that hold a zinc ion, causing the intervening amino acids to extend in a finger-like projection. Most zinc-finger proteins have 2–6 such fingers. These proteins bind to DNA and initiate transcription of genes.

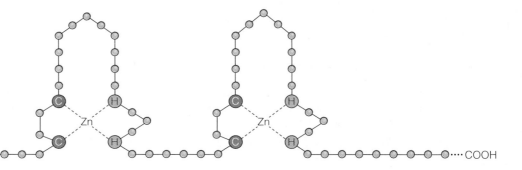

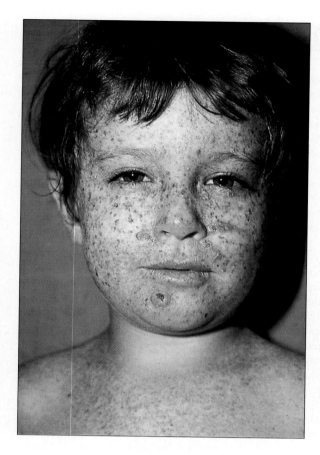

■ FIGURE 10.23
Child afflicted with xeroderma pigmentosum. One form, called xeroderma pigmentosum A, is caused by a mutation in a zinc-finger protein. Affected individuals are unable to repair damage to DNA caused by the ultraviolet light from the sun and other sources.

SUMMARY

1. In the early part of this century, Sir Archibald Garrod's studies on the human metabolic diseases cystinuria, albinism, and alkaptonuria provided the first hints that gene products control biochemical reactions. These diseases and many others are the result of mutations that cause metabolic blocks in biochemical pathways. In alkaptonuria, Garrod argued, the normal metabolic reaction is blocked by the lack of a needed enzyme. He speculated that the inability to carry out this reaction is the result of a recessive Mendelian gene.

2. In the late 1930s, George Beadle and his colleagues Boris Ephrussi and Edward Tatum studied genetic control of biochemical reactions in flies and fungi. Their work made it clear that single mutations led to the loss of activity in a single enzyme, an idea known as the one gene–one enzyme hypothesis. Subsequent work refined this into the one gene–one polypeptide hypothesis of today. Upon receiving the Nobel prize in 1958, Beadle said that he and Tatum had only "rediscovered what Garrod had seen so clearly."

3. Later investigations clearly identified enzyme defects in a large number of human metabolic diseases, and the role of mutations in nonenzymatic proteins became clear. In 1949, James Neel identified sickle cell anemia as a recessive disease, and Linus Pauling began to study the physical properties of hemoglobin, leading to Vernon Ingram's discovery that the molecular basis of sickle cell anemia is a single change in the amino acid sequence of a polypeptide chain. Logically this might involve changes in the nucleotide sequence of the genetic material, and this idea has been confirmed several times over.

4. Defects in receptor proteins, transport proteins, structural proteins, and other nonenzymatic proteins are able to cause phenotypic effects in the heterozygous state and show an incompletely dominant or dominant pattern of inheritance.

5. The examples of metabolic diseases outlined in this chapter serve to reinforce the notion of the biological uniqueness of the individual. The constellation of genes present within each person is the result of the random combination of parental genes as well as the sum of changes brought about by recombination and mutation. This genetic combination confers a distinctive phenotype upon each of us. Garrod referred to this metabolic uniqueness as chemical individuality. Understanding the molecular basis for this individuality remains one of the great challenges of human biochemical genetics.

1. Many individuals with metabolic diseases are normal at birth but show symptoms shortly thereafter. Why?
2. Describe the quaternary structure of the blood protein hemoglobin.
3. List the ways in which a metabolic block can have phenotypic effects.
4. A person was found to have very low levels of functional beta globin mRNA, and in turn, very low levels of the beta globin protein. Name the disease and explain what mutation may have occurred in the conversion of pre-mRNA into mRNA.
5. Familial hypercholesterolemia is caused by an autosomal dominant mutation in the gene that produces the LDL receptor. The LDL receptor is present in the plasma membrane of cells and binds cholesterol and helps remove it from the circulatory system for metabolism in the liver. What is the phenotype of the following individuals:

   HH
   Hh
   hh

6. Suppose the gene for the LDL receptor has been isolated by recombinant DNA techniques. Could you treat this disease by producing LDL receptor and injecting it into the bloodstream of affected individuals? Why or why not?
7. Some genes in humans are known to have a multiple phenotypic effects (these are called pleiotropic effects). Does this phenomenon contradict the one-gene-one-enzyme hypothesis? Explain. Cite examples of human genetic conditions where pleiotropic effects are part of the phenotype.
8. Suppose that in the formation of phenylalanine hydroxylase mRNA, the exons of the pre-mRNA fail to splice together properly, and the resulting enzyme is non-functional. This produces an accumulation of high levels of phenylalanine and other compounds which causes an neurological damage. What phenotype and disease would be produced in the affected individual?
9. The normal enzyme required for converting sugars into glucose is present in cells, but the conversion never takes place, and no glucose is produced. What could have occurred to cause this defect in a metabolic pathway?
10. If an extra nucleotide is present in the first exon of the beta globin gene, what effect would it have on the amino acid sequence of the globin polypeptides? Would the globin most likely be fully functional, partly functional or non-functional? Why?
11. The promoter region in the XP-A gene becomes mutated. How is transcription affected? How would an individual with this mutation be affected?
12. PKU is an autosomal recessive disorder that causes mental retardation. In PKU individuals, high levels of the essential amino acid phenylalanine are present due to a deficiency in the enzyme, phenylalanine hydroxylase. If phenylalanine was not an essential amino acid, would diet therapy (the elimination of phenylalanine from the diet) work?
13. Phenylketonuria and alkaptonuria are both autosomal recessive diseases. If a person with PKU marries a person with AKU, what will the phenotype of their children be?
14. If a chromosomal male has a defect in the cellular receptor that binds the hormone testosterone, what condition results? What is the genotype and phenotype of this individual?
15. Knowing that individuals who are homozygous for the G^D allele show no symptoms of galactosemia, is it surprising that galactosemia is a recessive disease? Why?
16. Transcriptional regulators are proteins that bind to promoters (the 5′-flanking regions of genes) to regulate their transcription. If a mutation makes nonfunctional the transcriptional regulator gene that normally turns on gene X, would the resulting phenotype be similar to a mutation in gene X itself? Why?
17. Mutations in the alpha thalassemia genes can result in a variety of abnormal phenotypes. If a heterozygous alpha thalassemia-1 man marries an heterozygous alpha thalassemia-2 woman, what are the phenotypes of their offspring? (Refer to Figure 10.16)
18. Use Figure 10.8 to answer this question. Severe immunodeficiency can be inherited as an autosomal or sex-linked recessive. A woman is a carrier for Lesch-Nyhan syndrome and the sex-linked form of severe combined immunodeficiency disease. She marries a normal man.
   a. List the phenotypes and phenotypic ratios of their children, assuming that the mutant alleles for both these diseases are on the same X chromosome.
   b. What will the phenotypes of the children be if the mutant alleles are not on the same X chromosome?

Questions 19–21 refer to the following hypothetical pathway in which substance A is converted to substance C by enzymes 1 and 2. Substance B is the intermediate produced in this pathway:

$$\text{enzyme} \quad \text{enzyme}$$
$$1 \qquad\quad 2$$
$$A \longrightarrow B \longrightarrow C$$

19. a. If an individual is homozygous for a null mutation in the gene that codes for enzyme 1, what will be the result?
   b. If an individual is homozygous for a null mutation in enzyme 2, what will be the result?
   c. What if an individual is heterozygous for a dominant mutation where enzyme 1 is overactive?
   d. What if an individual is heterozygous for a mutation that abolishes the activity of enzyme 2 (a null mutation)?

20. a. If the first individual in question 19 married the second individual, would their children be able to catabolize substance A into substance C?
   b. Suppose each of the aforementioned individuals were heterozygous for an autosomal dominant mutation. List the phenotypes of their children with respect to compounds A, B, and C. (Would the compound be in excess, not present, etc.?)
21. An individual is heterozygous for a recessive mutation in enzyme 1 and heterozygous for a recessive mutation in enzyme 2. This individual marries an individual of the same genotype. List the possible genotypes of their children. For every genotype, determine the activity of enzyme 1 and 2, assuming that the mutant alleles have 0% activity and the normal alleles have 50% activity. For every genotype, determine if compound C will be made. If compound C is not made, list the compound that will be in excess.
22. Explain why there are variant responses to drugs and why they act as heritable traits.

Questions 23 to 27 refer to a hypothetical metabolic disease in which protein E is not produced. Lack of protein E causes mental retardation in humans. Protein E's function is not known, but it is found in all cells of the body. Skin cells were taken from eight individuals who cannot produce protein E and were grown in culture. The defect in each of the individuals is due to a single recessive mutation. Each individual is homozygous for her or his mutation. The cells from one individual were grown with the cells from another individual in all possible combinations of two. After a few weeks of growth the mixed cultures were assayed for the presence of protein E. The results are given in the following table. A plus sign means that the two cell types produced protein E when grown together (but not separately), while a minus sign means that the two cell types still could not produce protein E:

	1	2	3	4	5	6	7	8
1	−	+	+	+	+	−	+	+
2		−	+	+	+	+	−	+
3			−	+	+	+	+	−
4				−	+	+	+	+
5					−	+	+	+
6						−	+	+
7							−	+
8								−

23. a. Which individuals seem to have the same defect in protein E production?
   b. If individual 2 married individual 3 would their children be able to make protein E?
   c. If individual 1 married individual 6 would their children be able to make protein E?

24. Assuming that these individuals represent all possible mutants in the synthesis of protein E, how many steps are there in the pathway to protein E production? Compounds A, B, C, and D are known to be intermediates in the pathway for production of protein E. To determine where the block in protein E production occurred in each individual, the various intermediates were given to each individual's cells in culture. After a few weeks of growth with the intermediate, the cells were assayed for the production of protein E. The results for each individual's cells are given in the following table. A plus means that protein E was produced after the cells were given the intermediate listed at the top of the column. A minus means that the cells still could not produce protein E even after being exposed to the intermediate at the top of the column:

	Compounds				
Cells	A	B	C	D	E
1	−	−	+	+	+
2	−	+	+	+	+
3	−	−	−	+	+
4	−	−	−	−	+
5	+	+	+	+	+
6	−	−	+	+	+
7	−	+	+	+	+
8	−	−	−	+	+

25. Draw the pathway leading to the production of protein E.
26. Denote the point in the pathway in which each individual is blocked.
27. a. If an individual who is homozygous for the mutation found in individual 2 and heterozygous for the mutation found in individual 4 marries an individual who is homozygous for the mutation found in individual 4 and heterozygous for the mutation found in individual 2, what will be the phenotype of their children?
   b. List the intermediate that would build up each of the types of children who could not produce protein E.

1. Proteins have been used for therapeutic purposes for over fifty years. Insulin, for example, is a protein that regulates the uptake of glucose from the bloodstream. Until 1981, it was extracted from animal carcasses and used to treat insulin-dependent diabetes. Now insulin, like many other proteins used in clinical treatment, can be manufactured using recombinant DNA techniques, and are readily available. The use of some of these proteins has raised social and ethical issues that have not been resolved. Growth hormone made by recombinant DNA techniques is used to treat growth defects that include some forms of dwarfism, and Turner syndrome. Treatment for these conditions is widely accepted, and non-controversial. However, growth hormone is also being used to treat children whose parents simply want their children to be slightly taller than normal. These parents feel that as adults, their children will have an increased chance of success if they are taller.

Do you think this is an appropriate use of this protein? Why or why not?

What if a parent wanted to have a child treated so that he or she would be much taller than average, and have a chance at a lucrative career as a professional basketball player or professional volleyball player?

What if a college coach approached you and said that your grammar school child has a great deal of athletic ability, and would qualify for a full athletic scholarship if they reached a certain height by the time they entered college? Would you seek treatment for your child? Why or why not?

Should there be a policy or law regulating the use of this and other therapeutic proteins? Who should draw up and enforce these regulations? To prevent abuse, some health professionals have called for access to some proteins to be regulated more strictly than access to prescription narcotics. Do you agree with this?

INTERNET ACTIVITIES

The following activities use the resources of the World Wide Web to enhance the topics covered in this chapter. To investigate the topics described below, log on to the book's home page at:

http://www.wadsworth.com/biology

1. PKU is one of a number of genetic disorders that is screened for at birth. By altering the diet of affected individuals at birth, the mental retardation associated with PKU can be avoided. The PKU homepage contains news and information about PKU including diets. An outline of British and European guidelines for treatment of PKU can also be found at this site. Learn about food choices for PKU individuals as well as lifestyle guidelines on this page.

   a. Scroll to the listing under PKU Pages: The Discovery of PKU by Dr. Asbjorn Fölling. Click on this entry and read the story of how and why PKU was identified. Please read the entire article; Dr. Fölling was a very interesting man, well ahead of his time in some of his thoughts and ideas. After his discovery, was a blanket conclusion about phenylpyruvic acid and mental retardation warranted? If gene therapy could be used to treat PKU, should it be used?

   b. On the same homepage, you will find an entry: British and European Guidelines for the Treatment of Phenylketonuria. Click on this site and compare the two sets of guidelines. What are the most important differences? How are they similar? How do these guidelines compare with what you have learned in this chapter about the treatment of PKU in the U.S.

2. Although we often are concerned only with the physical manifestations of genetic diseases, it is important to consider also the social and emotional impact of these disorders. The National Organization for Albinism and Hypopigmentation (NOAH) maintains a homepage which includes information bulletins. One of these addresses the social consequences of albinism. First, read NOAH's mission statement to get an overview of their goals. Then, return to the NOAH homepage, scroll to the highlighted Information Bulletins, click on this entry and read: What is Albinism, African-Americans and Social Aspects of Albinism.

   a. Having read the three articles, have your own thoughts about albinism changed? Do you know a classmate, member of your family or a member of your community with albinism? Have some of the things you read been consistent with what you've seen or felt?

   b. Would you classify albinism as a disability? Why or why not? Would you agree with the author of the article on social aspects that the media has often classified a person with albinism as a "villa, a deviant, cringing or sadistic?"

   c. Take a moment to communicate your thoughts about the homepage, albinism or any experiences you'd like to share through the highlighted NOAH Experiences Book or through the feedback link to NOAH.

Antonarakis, S., Kazazian, H., and Orkin, S. 1985. DNA polymorphisms and molecular pathology of the human globin gene clusters. *Hum. Genet. 69:* 1–14.

Beadle, G. W. 1945, Biochemical genetics. *Chem. Rev. 37:* 351.

Bearn, A. G., and Miller, E. D. 1979. Archibald Garrod and the development of the concept of inborn errors of metabolism. *Bull. Hist. Med. 53:* 317–324.

Benson, P. F., and Fenson, A. H. 1985. *Genetic Biochemical Disorders.* New York: Oxford University Press.

Childs, B. 1970. Sir Archibald Garrod's conception of chemical individuality: A modern appreciation. *N. Engl. J. Med. 282:* 4–5.

Eisensmith, R., Okano, Y., Dasovitch, M., Wang, T., Güttler, F., Lou, H., Guldberg, P., Lichter-Konecki, U., Konecki, D., et al, 1992. Multiple origins for phenylketonuna in Europe. Am. J. Hum. Genet. *51:* 1355–65.

Galjaard, H. 1980. *Genetic Metabolic Diseases: Early Diagnosis and Prenatal Analysis.* New York: Elsevier/North-Holland.

Garrod, A. E. 1902. The incidence of alkaptonuria: A study in chemical individuality. *Lancet 2:* 1616–1620.

Hobbs, H., Brown, M. and Goldstein, J. 1992. Molecular genetics of the LDL receptor gene in familial hypercholesterolemia. Human Mutat. *1:* 445–466.

Ingram, V. M. 1957. Gene mutations in human hemoglobin: The chemical differences between normal and sickle cell hemoglobin. *Nature 180:* 326–328.

King, R. A., and Olds, D. P. 1985. Hairbulb tyrosinase activity in oculocutaneous albinism: Suggestions for pathway control and block location. *Am. J. Med. Genet. 20:* 49–55.

Kivirkko, K. 1993. Collagens and their abnormalities in a wide spectrum of diseases. Ann. Med. *25:* 113–126.

McKusick, V. 1992. *Mendelian Inheritance in Man: catalogs of autosomal dominant, autosomal recessive and x-linked phenotypes.* 10th ed., Baltimore: Johns Hopkins Press.

Neel, J. V. 1949. The inheritance of sickle cell anemia. *Science 110:* 64–66.

Pauling, L., Itoh, H., Singer, S. J., and Wells, I. C. 1949. Sickle cell anemia: A molecular disease. *Science 110:* 543–548.

Scriver, C. R., Beaudet, A. L., Sly, W. S. and Valle, D. 1989. The Metabolic Basis of Inherited Disease. 6th ed. New York: McGraw-Hill.

Scriver, C. R., and Clow, C. L. 1980. Phenylketonuria and other phenylalanine hydroxylation mutants in man. *Ann. Rev. Genet. 14:* 179–202.

Sculley, D., Dawson, P., Emmerson, B. and Gordon, R. 1992. A review of the molecular basis of hypoxanthine-guanine phosphoribosyltransferase (HPRT) deficiency. Hum. Genet. *90:* 195–207.

Spritz, R. A., Strunk, K. M., Giebel, L. B., and King, R. A. 1990. Detection of mutations in the tyrosinase gene in a patient with Type LA oculocutaneous albinism. *New Engl. J. Med. 322:* 1724–1728.

Vella, F., 1980. Human hemoglobins and molecular disease. Biochem. Educ. *8:* 41–53.

Weatherall, D.J. 1993. Molecular medicine: towards the millenium. Trends Genet. *9:* 102.

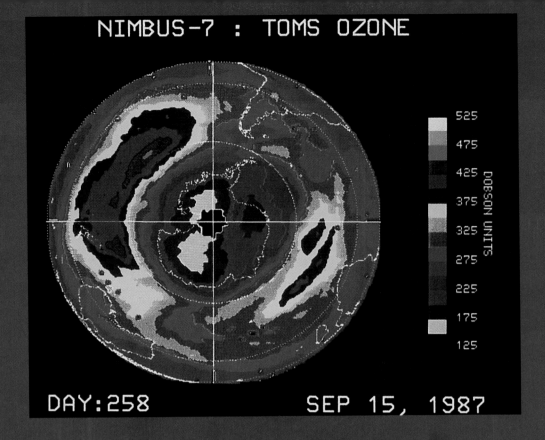

NIMBUS-7 : TOMS OZONE

DOBSON UNITS

525
475
425
375
325
275
225
175
125

DAY:258   SEP 15, 1987

MUTATION: THE SOURCE OF GENETIC VARIATION

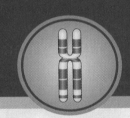

Chapter **11**

Chapter Outline

THE NATURE OF MUTATION
DETECTING MUTATION
MEASURING MUTATION RATES
Gene-Specific Mutation Rates
Indirect Measurement of Mutation Rates
FACTORS THAT INFLUENCE THE
   MUTATION RATE
Radiation as a Mutagen
Action of Chemical Mutagens

Finding Mutagenic Chemicals: The Ames
   Test
CONCEPTS AND CONTROVERSIES
   Irradiated Food
MUTATION AT THE MOLECULAR
   LEVEL: DNA AS A TARGET
Nucleotide Substitutions
Deletions and Insertions
Trinucleotide Repeats and Allelic Expansion

Allelic Expansion and Anticipation
DNA REPAIR MECHANISMS
Assessing Damage to DNA
Repairing Damage to DNA
MUTATION, GENOTYPES, AND
   PHENOTYPES
Mutation Can Cause a Range of Phenotypes
Genomic Imprinting: Reversible
   Alterations to the Genome

OPENING IMAGE
*The hole in the ozone layer over
Antarctica as seen from space.*

*C*hemist Linus Pauling once recalled that when he first heard a description
*of how red blood cells change shape in sickle cell anemia, it occurred to
him that sickle cell anemia was a molecular disease, involving an abnormality
of the hemoglobin molecule determined by a mutated gene.*

*Early in 1949, Linus Pauling and his student Harvey Itano began a series
of experiments to determine whether there was a difference between normal
hemoglobin and sickle cell hemoglobin. They obtained blood samples from
people with sickle cell anemia and from unaffected individuals and prepared
concentrated hemoglobin solutions from these samples. They placed the*

solution of concentrated hemoglobin in a tube fitted with an electrode at each end and passed an electrical current through the tube. Hemoglobin from individuals with sickle cell anemia migrated toward the cathode, indicating that it has a positive electrical charge. Samples of normal hemoglobin migrated in the opposite direction (toward the anode), indicating that it has a net negative electrical charge. In the same year, James Neel, working with sickle cell patients in the Detroit area, demonstrated that sickle cell anemia was an autosomal recessive trait, establishing the genetic link to this condition.

Pauling and his colleagues published a paper on their results, and incorporated Neel's findings into their discussion. They concluded that sickle cell anemia (and the heterozygous condition known as sickle cell trait) was caused by a mutant gene that was involved in the synthesis of hemoglobin. The idea that a genetic disorder could be caused by a defect in a single molecule was revolutionary. Pauling called sickle cell anemia a molecular disease. This idea established the foundation for human biochemical genetics, and played a key role in understanding the molecular nature of mutations.

Pauling's work on the hemoglobin protein influenced other researchers. After Watson and Crick worked out the structure of DNA, Crick was anxious to establish that mutant genes produced mutant proteins with amino acid sequences that differed from the normal protein. He persuaded Vernon Ingram to look for such differences. Because of Pauling's work, Ingram settled on hemoglobin as a subject for investigation. Beginning with concentrated hemoglobin preparations, Ingram first cut the protein into pieces using the enzyme trypsin, and separated the 30 resulting fragments. He noticed that normal hemoglobin and sickle cell hemoglobin differed only in one fragment, a peptide about 10 amino acids in length. Ingram then worked out the amino acid sequence in this fragment. In 1957, he reported that there was a difference of only a single amino acid (glutamine in normal hemoglobin and valine in sickle cell hemoglobin) between the two proteins. This finding confirmed the relationship between a mutant gene and a mutant gene product, but raised a more basic question: What is the nature of mutation?

 ## THE NATURE OF MUTATION

From a genetic point of view, mutation can be defined as any heritable change. These changes are the source of all genetic variation in humans and other organisms. The results of mutations can be classified in a number of ways. Mutations that produce dominant alleles are expressed in the heterozygous condition; mutations to recessive alleles are expressed only when homozygous. The effects of mutation can also be ranked in categories such as the severity of phenotype or age of onset. For our purposes, two general categories of mutations can be distinguished: chromosomal aberrations and changes in the nucleotide sequence of a gene. Chromosomal aberrations were discussed in Chapter 6. In this chapter we will discuss only those changes that occur within a single gene, specifically, alterations in the sequence or number of nucleotides in DNA. We will first consider how mutations are detected and then investigate at what rate these mutations take place. Finally, we will examine how mutation works at the molecular level.

 ## DETECTING MUTATION

How do we know that a mutation has taken place? In haploid organisms such as bacteria, experiments can be designed so that only new mutants will form colonies on nutrient agar plates. In humans, the appearance of a dominant mutation in a family

can be detected in a fairly straightforward manner. But mutation of a dominant allele to a recessive one can be detected only in the homozygous condition, posing a challenge for human geneticists. Because the human genome cannot be manipulated in genetic crosses to detect such heterozygotes, the methods of detecting whether a recessive mutation has occurred are indirect.

If an affected individual appears in an otherwise unaffected family, the first question is whether the trait is the result of genetic or nongenetic factors. For example, if a mother is exposed to the virus causing rubella (a form of measles) early in pregnancy, the fetus may develop a range of physical and neurologic symptoms that can resemble those seen in some metabolic genetic disorders. These symptoms are not the result of mutation, but the effect of the virus on the developing fetus. In general, the detection of mutations depends on pedigree analysis and the study of births in a family line.

If an allele is dominant, is fully penetrant, and appears in a family with no history of this condition over several generations, we can presume that a mutation has taken place. An example is presented in the pedigree in ⬭ Figure 11.1. In this case a severe blistering of the feet appeared in one out of six children, although the parents were unaffected. The trait was transmitted by the affected female to six of her eight children and was passed to the succeeding generation in the manner expected for an autosomal dominant condition. A reasonable explanation for this pedigree is that a mutation to a dominant allele occurred, and that II-5 was heterozygous for this dominant allele. On the other hand, a number of uncertainties can affect this conclusion. For example, if the father of this child was not the husband in the pedigree but an affected male, then it would only seem that a mutational event had taken place.

If mutation results in an allele that is recessive and sex linked, it often can be detected by examination of males in the family line. But it is difficult to determine whether a heterozygous female who transmits a trait to her son is the source of the mutation, or is only passing on a mutation that arose in an ancestor. The X-linked form of hemophilia that spread through the royal families of Western Europe and Russia probably originated with Queen Victoria (⬭ Figure 11.2; see "Concepts and Controversies: Hemophilia and History" in Chapter 4, page 94). An examination of the pedigree shows that none of Victoria's male ancestors had hemophilia. However, one of her sons was affected, and at least two of her daughters were carriers. Since Victoria transmitted the trait to a number of her children, it is reasonable to assume that she was a heterozygous carrier. Her father was not affected, and there is nothing in her mother's pedigree to indicate that she was a carrier. It is likely, therefore, that Victoria received a newly mutated allele from one of her parents. We can only speculate as to which parent.

⬭ **FIGURE 11.1**

A dominant trait, foot blistering, appeared (II-5) in a family with no previous history of this condition. The trait is transmitted through subsequent generations in an autosomal dominant fashion.

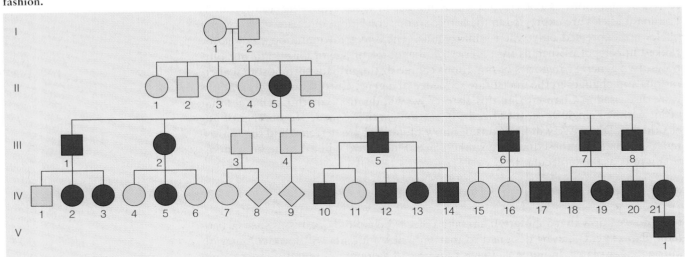

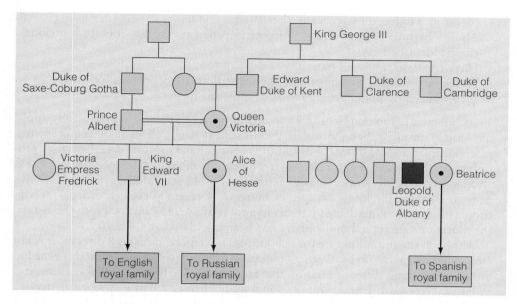

FIGURE 11.2
Pedigree of Queen Victoria of Britian, showing her immediate ancestors and children. Since she passed the mutant allele for hemophilia on to three of her children, she was probably a heterozygote rather than the source of the mutation.

If an autosomal recessive trait appears suddenly in a family, it is usually difficult or impossible to trace the trait through a pedigree to identify the person or even the generation in which the mutation first occurred, since only homozygotes are affected. Because of this, heterozygotes for autosomal recessive conditions can remain undetected for generations.

MEASURING MUTATION RATES

Analysis of human pedigrees indicates that mutation does take place in the human genome. The available evidence suggests that it is a rare event, but is it possible to measure the rate of mutation? Knowing the underlying rate of mutation would allow geneticists to monitor the rate over time to determine whether it is increasing, decreasing, or remaining the same. In organisms such as bacteria, fungi, *Drosophila*, and mice, experimental measurements have provided reliable information about the rate of mutation at a number of loci. For humans, the estimation of mutation rates is more difficult, and information is available for only a small number of genes.

Mutation rates are expressed as the number of mutated alleles per locus per generation. Suppose that for a certain gene, 4 out of 100,000 births show a mutation from a recessive to a dominant allele. Since each zygote producing these births carries two copies of the gene, we have sampled 200,000 copies of the gene. Because the mutations are dominant, the 4 births represent 4 mutated genes (we are assuming that the newborns are heterozygotes carrying only one mutant allele). In this case, then, the mutation rate is 4/200,000, or 2/100,000, and in scientific notation would be written as 2×10^{-5}/per allele/per generation.

If the locus were X-linked and if 100,000 male births were examined and 4 mutants were discovered, this would represent a sampling of 100,000 copies of the gene (since the males have only one copy of the X chromosome). Excluding contributions from female carriers, the mutation rate in this case would be 4/100,000, or 4×10^{-5}/per allele/per generation.

Mutation rate
The number of events producing mutated alleles per locus/per generation.

Gene-Specific Mutation Rates

Is there a way to measure directly the rate of mutation for a gene? For dominant alleles that fulfill certain conditions, the answer is yes. What are the conditions? To ensure accuracy in the measurement, the trait selected must:

- Never be produced by recessive alleles
- Always be fully expressed and completely penetrant so that mutant individuals can be identified
- Have clearly established paternity
- Never be produced by nongenetic agents such as drugs or infection
- Be produced by dominant mutation of only one locus

Although it is sometimes difficult to determine when these conditions fully apply, one dominant allele, achondroplasia, fulfills most if not all of these requirements. Achondroplasia (MIM/OMIM 100800) is a dominant form of dwarfism that produces short arms and legs and an enlarged skull. A definitive diagnosis by x-ray examination can be done shortly after birth. Since 1941 several surveys have used this gene to estimate the mutation rate in humans. A recent survey recorded 7 achondroplastic births to unaffected parents in a total of 242,257 births. From these data, the mutation rate for achondroplasia has been calculated at 1.4×10^{-5}.

Although the mutation rate for achondroplasia can be measured directly, it is not clear whether this is a typical rate of mutation for human genes. Maybe this gene has an inherently high rate of mutation that is atypical. For this and other reasons, it is important to measure mutation rates in a number of different genes before making any general statements. As it turns out, two other dominant mutations have widely different rates of mutations. Neurofibromatosis (MIM/OMIM 162200), an autosomal dominant condition, is characterized by pigmentation spots and tumors of the skin and nervous system (described in Chapter 4). About 1 in 3000 births are affected individuals. Many of these births (about 50%) occur in families with no previous history of neurofibromatosis, indicating that this locus has a high mutation rate. In fact, the mutation rate in this disease has been calculated to be as high as 1 in 10,000 (1×10^{-4}), one of the highest rates so far discovered in humans. For Huntington disease (MIM/OMIM 143100), the dominant condition that causes progressive degeneration of the nervous system (see Chapter 4), the mutation rate has been calculated as 1×10^{-6}, a rate some 100-fold lower than that for neurofibromatosis and 10-fold lower than that reported for achondroplasia.

Table 11.1 gives some estimates of mutation rates in human genes. These mutation rates average out to about 1×10^{-5}. Note that the genes listed in the table are all inherited as autosomal dominant or X-linked traits. It is almost impossible to measure directly the mutation rates in autosomal recessive alleles by inspection of phenotypes, but recombinant DNA methods are now being used to survey populations, and will provide estimates of the rate and type of mutations found in human genes.

TABLE 11.1

Mutation Rates for Selected Genes

TRAIT	MUTANTS/MILLION GAMETES	MUTATION RATE	MIM/OMIM NUMBER
Achondroplasia	10	1×10^{-5}	100800
Aniridia	2.6	2.6×10^{-6}	106200
Retinoblastoma	6	6×10^{-6}	180200
Osteogenesis imperfecta	10	1×10^{-5}	166200
Neurofibromatosis	50–100	$0.5–1 \times 10^{-4}$	162200
Polycystic kidney disease	60–120	$6–12 \times 10^{-4}$	173900
Marfan syndrome	4–6	$4–6 \times 10^{-6}$	154700
Von Hippel–Landau syndrome	<1	1.8×10^{-7}	193300
Duchenne muscular dystrophy	50–100	$0.5–1 \times 10^{-4}$	310200

Indirect Measurement of Mutation Rates

Several indirect methods for measuring mutation rates have been developed. They rely on statistical procedures derived from the principles of population genetics and will not be discussed in detail. The idea is that in many mutant traits, affected individuals leave few if any offspring, and over time the trait should be eliminated from the population. But since the allele frequencies for these traits remain constant, mutation must be replacing the mutant alleles lost by reproductive failure.

Average mutation rates in humans can also be estimated by comparison with the mutation rate in other mammals. The mouse, *Mus musculus,* has a genome about the same size as humans and presumably carries a similar number of genes. Observations on spontaneous mutations in laboratory mice and the experimental production of mutations indicate that the rate of mutation in the mouse is about 1.1×10^{-5}. The indirect and comparative methods support the observation that the average mutation rate in humans is about 1×10^{-5}.

Still, many geneticists feel that the genes in which the mutation rate can be measured might be those that have an inherently high rate of mutation. Other factors such as the size of a gene may also influence mutation rates. Larger genes may mutate more frequently than smaller genes because they contain more DNA. To reduce any potential bias, most human geneticists prefer to use a more conservative estimate of the mutation rate in humans; they generally use the number 1×10^{-6} as the average mutation rate.

FACTORS THAT INFLUENCE THE MUTATION RATE

Several factors influence the mutation rate and contribute to the observed variation in the mutation rate. Some of these factors include

- *Size of the gene.* Larger genes present larger targets for mutational events. Neurofibromatosis (NF-1) has a high mutation rate and is an extremely large gene. The NF-1 protein contains over 2000 amino acids, but including the non-coding regions, the gene extends over 300,000 base pairs of DNA. The gene for Duchenne and Becker muscular dystrophy is the largest gene identified to date in humans, and contains over 2 million base pairs. Both these genes have high rates of mutation.
- *Nucleotide sequence.* In some genes, short nucleotide repeats are present in the DNA. In the gene for fragile-X syndrome, a CGG repeat within the first coding region (exon) is present in 6 to 50 copies in unaffected individuals. Symptoms begin to appear in those with more than 52 copies and become more severe as the number of CGG repeats increases. The presence of these repeats may predispose a gene to mutation at a higher rate.
- *Spontaneous chemical changes.* Among the bases present in DNA, cytosine is especially susceptible to chemicals that can change the nucleotide sequence in DNA. These and other chemical changes will be discussed below. Genes rich in G-C base pairs are more likely to undergo spontaneous chemical changes than those rich in A-T pairs.

Radiation as a Mutagen

In physical terms, **radiation** is a process by which energy travels through space. There are two main forms of this energy: electromagnetic and corpuscular. Electromagnetic radiation is best described as waves of electrical or magnetic energy, while corpuscular radiation is composed of atomic and subatomic particles that move at high speeds and cause damage when they collide with other particles, including biological molecules.

Exposure to radiation is unavoidable. All forms of life are exposed continuously to radiation. Electromagnetic and corpuscular forms of radiation have been present

Radiation
The process by which electromagnetic energy travels through space or a medium such as air.

● FIGURE 11.3

In April 1986 the nuclear reactor at Chernobyl, Ukraine, exploded—spreading radioactive material across the Northern Hemisphere.

Free radical
An unstable and highly reactive molecule resulting from the interaction of ionizing radiation with water.

since the birth of the universe. These natural sources of radiation are referred to as background radiation. We are also exposed to manufactured sources of radiation from medical testing, nuclear testing, nuclear power, and consumer goods.

Radiation can cause damage at several levels in biological systems. Since the cell is about 80% water, radiation often generates **free radicals,** in the form of ionized hydrogen, or hydroxyl radicals (OH), derived from water. These react chemically to form other radicals or hydrogen peroxide (H_2O_2). Such molecules are highly reactive and can produce mutations in DNA. These mutations can be in somatic tissue, and induce cancer, or take place in germ cells, and be transmitted from generation to generation. As a result of the Chernobyl nuclear power plant accident (● Figure 11.3), the U.S. Nuclear Regulatory Commission has estimated that around 14,000 additional cancer deaths can be anticipated in Western Europe over the next 70 years.

As a mutagen, radiation increases the frequency of chromosome aberrations and other mutational events. At the molecular level, radiation induces DNA damage, including strand breaks and base deletions. At the chromosomal level, radiation may produce breaks that result in deletions, translocations, and chromosome fragments. Radiation can also induce aneuploidy through chromosome loss.

Action of Chemical Mutagens

Chemicals act as mutagens in several ways, and they are often classified by the type of damage they cause to DNA. Some chemicals cause mutations by altering the configuration of bases within a DNA molecule, changing them into other bases. For example, removing an amino group from cytosine (C) converts it to uracil (● Figure 11.4). What initially was a G-C pair is converted to a G-U pair. When present in DNA, uracil has the pairing properties of thymine (T). After two rounds of replication, the original G-C base pair is converted into an A-T pair (● Figure 11.5). Nitrous acid is a chemical that can convert cytosine into uracil. Although nitrous acid is not found in the environment outside certain manufacturing sites, nitrates and nitrites used in the preservation of meat, fish, and cheese are converted into nitrous acid during digestion. On their own, nitrates and nitrites are not considered mutagenic, but they can be activated or converted into mutagens by metabolic reactions or changing chemical conditions. Such compounds are known as **promutagens.** The mutagenic risk from nitrates and nitrites in food does not seem high, but has proven difficult to assess with any degree of accuracy.

Promutagen
A nonmutagenic compound that is a metabolic precursor to a mutagen.

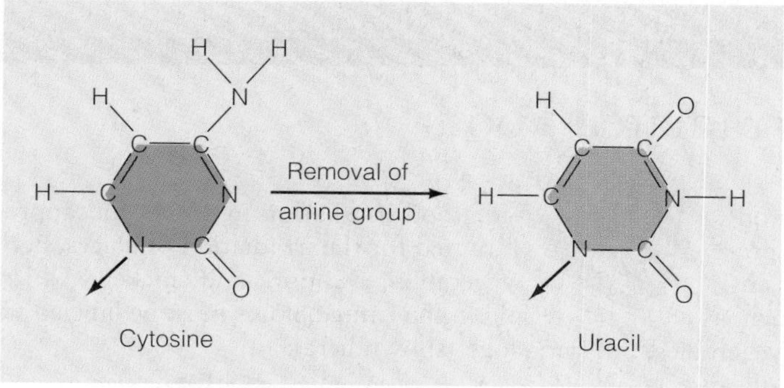

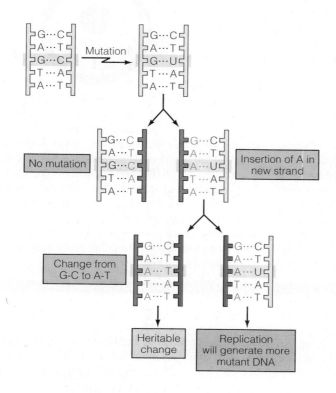

● FIGURE 11.4

The deamination of cytosine, which can occur by the action of chemical mutagens, converts the base to uracil. Replication will convert the original C-G base pair into an A-T base pair.

● FIGURE 11.5

Rounds of DNA replication following the conversion of cytosine to uracil in a DNA molecule. After two rounds of replication, the original G-C base pair is converted to an A-T base pair.

Mutagens that bind directly to DNA can result in frameshift mutations rather than base substitutions. Chemicals that insert themselves into DNA can distort the structure of the double helix, resulting in addition or deletion of bases during DNA replication. In addition to specific alterations in DNA structure, a wide range of chemicals can cause DNA strand breaks (single, double, or both) and crosslinking within or between strands.

Finding Mutagenic Chemicals: The Ames Test

One of the most widely used systems for finding mutagenic chemicals was devised by Bruce Ames and his colleagues. The **Ames test** can be used to rapidly screen chemicals for their mutagenic capacity. This procedure uses four tester strains of the bacterium *Salmonella typhimurium* that were genetically constructed for use in mutagenesis screening. One strain is used to detect base pair substitutions, and the other three detect frameshift mutations.

All four strains require the amino acid histidine for growth (they are called *his⁻*), and the assay detects the mutation of the *his⁻* gene to his⁺. In use, the cells are exposed to a mutagen and then plated on a medium lacking histidine. If the muta-

Ames test
A bioassay developed by Bruce Ames and his colleagues for identifying mutagenic compounds.

Irradiated Food

Over the past 40 years, research has demonstrated that radiation treatments can help preserve food and kill contaminating microorganisms. Irradiation prevents sprouting of root crops such as potatoes, extends the shelf life of many fruits and vegetables, destroys bacteria and fungi in meat and fish, and kills insects and other pests in spices.

For irradiation, food is placed on a conveyor and moved to a sealed, heavily shielded chamber where it is exposed to radiation from a radioactive source (x-rays or an electron beam). The dose is delivered using remote control by an operator who views the process on video camera. The food itself does not come in contact with the radioactive source, and the food is not made radioactive. Relatively low doses are used to inhibit sprouting of potatoes and to kill parasites in pork. Intermediate doses are used to retard spoilage in meat, poultry, and fish: and high doses can be used to sterilize foods, including meats. Worldwide, there are about 55 commercial facilities for food irradiation. The amount of food irradiated varies from country to country, ranging from a few tons of spices to hundreds of thousands of tons of grain.

Irradiated food has been used routinely by NASA to feed astronauts in space, and irradiated foods are sold in more than 20 countries, including the United States. The Food and Drug Administration (FDA) approved the first application for food irradiation in 1964, and approval has been granted for the irradiation of spices, herbs, fruits and vegetables, and pork and chicken. All irradiated food sold in the United States must be labeled with an identifying logo (shown here).

Public concern about radiation has prevented the widespread sale of irradiated food in this country. Advocates point out that irradiation can eliminate the use of many chemical preservatives, lower food costs by preventing spoilage, and reduce the incidence of food-borne illnesses transmitted by *Salmonella* and *E. coli*. Those opposed to food irradiation argue that irradiation produces chemical changes in food, and that the safety of these new chemicals has not been proven, although it should be noted that these same changes occur in foods preserved by other methods. Opponents also point out that treatment may select for radiation-resistant microorganisms.

---

gen has caused the *his* defect to be corrected, the bacteria can then grow on histidine-free medium. The number of colonies detected on the plate indicates the number of mutations that have occurred and is a measure of the degree of mutagenesis (⬤ Figure 11.6).

In some cases, metabolism can produce mutagenic chemicals from inactive precursors or promutagens. Detection of promutagens in the Ames test is achieved by first mixing the chemical with rat liver extracts. The enzymes present in the extract generate metabolic products to which the tester strains are exposed.

MUTATION AT THE MOLECULAR LEVEL: DNA AS A TARGET

At the molecular level, mutations can involve substitutions, insertions, or deletions of one or more nucleotides in a DNA molecule. Those mutations that involve an alteration in the sequence but not the number of nucleotides in a gene are called **nucleotide substitutions.** Generally, such substitutions involve one or a small number of nucleotides. A second type of mutation causes the *insertion* or *deletion* of one or more bases. Since codons are composed of three bases, changing the number of bases alters the sequence of all subsequent codons and results in large-scale changes in the amino acid sequence of the protein product of such mutated genes. We will begin by examining the simpler form of mutation, the substitution of one nucleotide for another, and will then consider mutations involving the addition or deletion of bases.

Nucleotide substitutions
Mutations that involve substitutions, insertions, or deletions of one or more nucleotides in a DNA molecule.

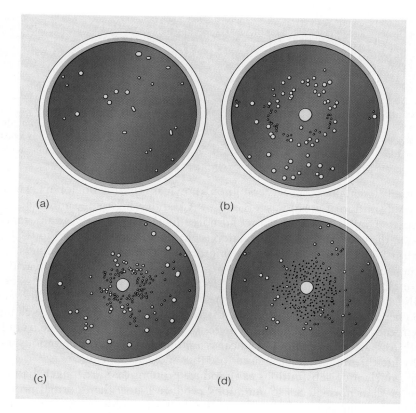

FIGURE 11.6

The Ames test. Dish A contains no mutagens. The colonies present represent spontaneous mutations in the tester strain of bacteria placed on the dish. The paper disks in dishes B, C, and D contain chemicals being tested for their ability to cause mutations. The number of bacterial colonies (greater than the number found in dish A) represent the relative mutational power of the chemicals being tested.

Nucleotide Substitutions

Several hundred variants of the alpha and beta globins with single amino-acid substitutions are known. These provide many well-studied examples of the effects of nucleotide substitutions on protein structure and function. Nucleotide substitutions in coding regions can have a number of outcomes, some of which are described in the following section. In this discussion, keep in mind that the term *codon* refers to the sequence of three nucleotides in mRNA that codes for an amino acid.

Missense mutations are single nucleotide changes that cause the substitution of one amino acid for another in a protein. This substitution may or may not affect the function of the gene product and may or may not have phenotypic consequences. In the gene coding for beta globin (Figure 11.7), a single nucleotide substitution in codon 6 from GAG (glu) to GUG (val) results in sickle cell anemia, a condition with

Missense mutation
A mutation that causes the substitution of one amino acid for another in a protein.

FIGURE 11.7

The DNA code word, mRNA codon, and the first 8 amino acids of normal adult hemoglobin (Hb A), hemoglobin C (Hb C), and sickle cell hemoglobin (Hb S). A single nucleotide substitution in codon 6 is responsible for the changes in the two variant forms of hemoglobin.

Normal Hb A		1	2	3	4	5	6	7	8
DNA		CAC	GTG	GAC	TGA	GGA	CTC	CTC	TTC
mRNA		GUG	CAC	CUG	ACU	CCU	GAG	GAG	AAG
Amino acid		val	his	leu	thr	pro	glu	glu	lys

Hb C		1	2	3	4	5	6	7	8
DNA		CAC	GTG	GAC	TGA	GGA	TTC	CTC	TTC
mRNA		GUG	CAC	CUG	ACU	CCU	AAG	GAG	AAG
Amino acid		val	his	leu	thr	pro	lys	glu	lys

Sickle Hb S		1	2	3	4	5	6	7	8
DNA		CAC	GTG	GAC	TGA	GGA	CAC	CTC	TTC
mRNA		GUG	CAC	CUG	ACU	CCU	GUG	GAG	AAG
Amino acid		val	his	leu	thr	pro	val	glu	lys

TABLE 11.2

Alpha Globins with Extended Chains Produced by Nucleotide Substitutions

HB	ABNORMAL CHAINS
Constant Springs–1	gln (142) + 30 amino acids
Icaria	lys (142) + 30 amino acids
Seal Rock	glu (142) + 30 amino acids
Koya Dora	ser (142) + 30 amino acids

a potentially lethal phenotype. A condition known as HbC (hemoglobin C) has a nucleotide subsitution at position six (GAG → AAG) that inserts the amino acid lysine and causes a mild set of clinical conditions. In a beta globin variant called Hb Makassar, the codon at the sixth position is changed from GAG (glu) to GCG (ala), a substitution that causes no clinical symptoms and is regarded as harmless.

In these examples, the resulting polypeptides differ only in the amino acid at position 6: Hb A has glutamic acid (glu), Hb S has valine (val), Hb C has lysine (lys), and Hb Makassar has alanine (ala). The sequence of the other 145 amino acids in the polypeptide is unchanged. In these three examples, single nucleotide changes in the sixth codon of the beta globin gene result in phenotypes that range from harmless (Hb Makassar), to the mild clinical symptoms of Hb C, to the serious and potentially life-threatening consequences of Hb S and sickle cell anemia.

Other nucleotide substitutions can produce proteins that are longer than normal or shorter than normal. **Sense mutations** produce longer-than-normal proteins by changing a termination codon into one that codes for amino acids. Several hemoglobin variants with longer-than-normal globin molecules are shown in Table 11.2. In each case, the extended polypeptide chain can be explained by a single nucleotide substitution in the normal termination codon.

Nonsense mutations change codons that specify amino acids into one of the three termination codons: UAA, UAG, or UGA (see Table 9.3). This leads to the formation of shortened polypeptide chains. In the beta globin variant McKees Rock, the last two amino acids are missing, and the protein is only 143 amino acids long. The change in codon 144 UAU (tyr) → UAA (termination) results in a beta chain that is shorter by two amino acids. This change has little or no effect on the function of the beta globin molecule as a carrier of oxygen. However, some nucleotide substitutions can produce more drastic changes in polypeptide length.

Deletions and Insertions

Deletions and insertions can range from mutations that involve single nucleotides to the deletion or duplication of an entire gene. As more genes are analyzed at the molecular level, deletions and insertions are emerging as a major cause of genetic disorders, accounting for 5% to 10% of all known mutations. **Frameshift mutations** are caused by the insertion or deletion of nucleotides within the coding sequence of a gene. Since codons consist of groups of three bases, adding or subtracting a base from a codon changes the coding sense of all subsequent codons. This results in a change in the amino acid sequence of the protein encoded by the mutated gene. Suppose that a codon series reads as the following sentence:

THE FAT CAT ATE HIS HAT

An insertion in the second codon destroys the sense of the remaining message:

insertion

THE FAA TCA TAT EHI SHA T

Sense mutation
A mutation that changes a termination codon into one that codes for an amino acid. Such mutations produce elongated proteins.

Nonsense mutation
A mutation that changes an amino-acid-specifying codon to one of the three termination codons.

Frameshift mutation
Mutational event in which one to three bases are added to or removed from DNA, causing a shift in the codon reading frame.

In a similar fashion, a deletion in the second codon can also generate an altered message:

THE FTC ATA TEH ISH AT

↓ deletion

In nucleotide substitutions, usually only one amino acid in the protein is altered. In frameshift mutations, however, the addition or deletion of a single base can cause large-scale changes in the amino acid composition of the polypeptide chain, and usually leads to a nonfunctional gene product. We will use a hemoglobin variant with an extended chain as a simple example of an altered gene product that results from a frameshift mutation. In this case, the frameshift occurs near the end of the gene and has a minimum impact on the function of the gene product.

In hemoglobin alpha, the mRNA codons for the last few amino acids are as follows:

Position number	138	139	140	141	TER
mRNA codon	UCC	AAA	UAC	CGU	UAA
Amino acid	ser	lys	tyr	arg	

In hemoglobin Wayne, a deletion in the last base of codon 139 produces a frameshift:

Position number	138	139	140	141	142
mRNA codon	UCC	AAU	ACC	GUU	AAG
Amino acid	ser	asn	thr	val	lys

The deletion of a single base causes a shift in the codon reading frame so that the normal termination codon UAA adjacent to codon 141 is split up into two codons, causing new amino acids to be added until another stop codon (generated by the deletion) is reached. The result is an alpha chain variant with 146 amino acid residues instead of 141.

Trinucleotide Repeats and Allelic Expansion

Trinucleotide repeats are a recently discovered class of insertion mutations associated with a number of genetic disorders. Trinucleotide repeats are a sequence of three nucleotides, repeated in tandem a variable number of times within a gene (Table 11.3). Mutations involving an increase in the number of repeats are responsible for several

Trinucleotide repeats
A form of mutation associated with the expansion in copy number of a nucleotide triplet in or near a gene.

TABLE 11.3

Mutations with Expanded Trinucleotide Repeats

GENE	TRIPLET REPEAT	NORMAL COPY #	COPY # IN DISEASE	MIM/OMIM NUMBER
Spinal and bulbar muscular atrophy	CAG	12–34	40–62	313200
Spinocerebellar ataxia type 1	CAG	6–39	41–81	164400
Huntington disease	CAG	6–37	35–121	143100
Haw-River syndrome	CAG	7–34	54–70	140340
Machado-Joseph disease	CAG	13–36	68–79	109150
Fragile X syndrome	CGG	5–52	230–72,000	309550
Myotonic dystrophy	CTG	5–37	50–72,000	160900
Friedreich ataxia	GAA	10–21	200–900	229300

Allelic expansion
Increase in gene size caused by an increase in the number of trinucleotide sequences.

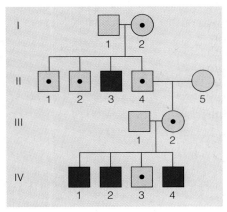

FIGURE 11.8

A pedigree illustrating the inheritance of fragile-X syndrome. Mothers (I-2) of phenotypically normal, but transmitting males (II-4) are phenotypically normal, but have some offspring with fragile-X syndrome (II-3). Daughters of transmitting males (III-2) are at high risk of having affected children. Allelic expansion of premutation alleles is more likely when inherited from a male. III-2 has inherited such an allele, which is likely to undergo expansion and affect her children.

genetic disorders. Usually this expansion involves only one of the two copies of a gene, and the phenomenon is called **allelic expansion.** The discovery of allelic expansion in fragile-X syndrome has explained some aspects of how this condition is inherited (see Chapter 6 for a review of fragile sites).

In fragile-X syndrome, the phenotype includes mental retardation. Up to 1% of all males institutionalized for mental retardation have this syndrome. Mothers of affected males are heterozygous carriers, and pass the fragile-X chromosome to 50% of their offspring. In some cases, the phenotype has a low degree of penetrance in males. These males, who inherit the mutant allele but have a normal phenotype, are called transmitter males. Carrier mothers of transmitter males are phenotypically normal and have a low risk of having children with fragile-X syndrome. Daughters of transmitter males, on the other hand, have a high risk of having affected children, leading to the type of pedigree shown in ▶ Figure 11.8.

The *FMR-1* gene at the fragile-X site has a repeated CGG sequence in the first exon. Normal individuals have 6 to 52 copies of this repeat, and those with more than 230 copies of this sequence have the clinical symptoms associated with the fragile-X syndrome. Those with an intermediate number of copies (ranging from 60–200) are unaffected carriers. *FMR-1* alleles that carry an intermediate number of copies are called premutation alleles; carriers of these alleles are themselves unaffected, but their children and grandchildren are at high risk for being affected.

When intermediate alleles are transmitted by males, the number of CGG repeats is more likely to remain constant or even decrease; when transmitted by females, the number of CGG repeats is likely to increase, abolishing expression of the *FMR-1* gene (▶ Figure 11.9) and resulting in fragile-X syndrome.

Other disorders caused by an increase in trinucleotide repeats are listed in Table 11.3. In myotonic dystrophy (DM), the mutation is caused by expansion of a CTG repeat adjacent to a structural gene. As with fragile-X syndrome, there is a progressive earlier onset of the disorder in succeeding generations, and a correlation with the size of the expanded repeat, the age of onset, and the severity of symptoms. In contrast to the situation in fragile-X syndrome, expansion of repeats in myotonic dystrophy and the onset of clinical symptoms is more likely with male transmission than with female transmission.

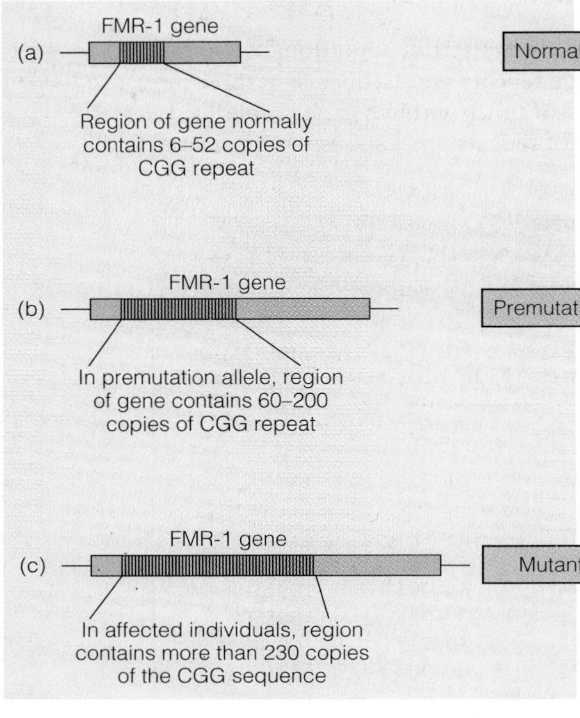

(a) FMR-1 gene

Region of gene normally contains 6–52 copies of CGG repeat

Normal allele

(b) FMR-1 gene

In premutation allele, region of gene contains 60–200 copies of CGG repeat

Premutation allele

(c) FMR-1 gene

In affected individuals, region contains more than 230 copies of the CGG sequence

Mutant allele

FIGURE 11.9

Allelic expansion in the *FMR-1* gene at the fragile-X locus. (a) The gene normally contains 6–52 copies of a CGG trinucleotide repeat. (b) In premutation alleles, this region expands to include 60-200 copies of this repeat. (c) Affected individuals have more than 230 copies of the repeat. How expansion occurs and how it brings about the altered phenotype are still unknown.

Allelic Expansion and Anticipation

Five disorders (the first five in Table 11.3) associated with expansion of trinucleotide repeats show several similarities. All are progressive neurodegenerative disorders inherited as autosomal dominant traits. All have expanded CAG repeats, and all show an inverse correlation between the size of the repeat and the age of onset.

The appearance of symptoms at earlier ages in succeeding generations is called **anticipation,** and was first noted for myotonic dystrophy early in this century. Although carefully documented by clinicians, the phenomenon of anticipation was discounted by geneticists because genes were regarded as highly stable entities, with only occasional mutations. The discovery of staged expansions of nucleotide repeats as the molecular basis of anticipation indicates that in these disorders, initial changes in the number of copies of a repeat sequence in or near a gene (generating intermediate numbers of repeats and premutation alleles) increases the chances that further changes in repeat number will occur, creating alleles with full mutations.

This finding means that the concept of mutation must now be modified to incorporate the existence of unstable genome regions that undergo these dynamic changes. In other words, when some regions of the genome (those containing trinucleotide repeats) undergo an expansion in number, this event enhances the chance that further expansions, with corresponding changes in phenotype, will occur. This also means that other disorders, especially those associated with nonclassical segregation patterns that have been traditionally described as incomplete penetrance or variable expression, may need to be reexamined to establish a possible relationship between expansion of trinucleotide repeats and the phenotype.

Anticipation
Onset of a genetic disorder at earlier ages and with increasing severity in successive generations.

DNA REPAIR MECHANISMS

Fortunately, not every mutation that occurs results in a permanent alteration of the genome. A number of genetically controlled systems repair damage to DNA. This repair function was first observed by cytologists, who noted that chromosome breaks, whether generated spontaneously or by exposure to chemicals or radiation, often rejoin with no apparent detrimental effects. At the molecular level, damage to DNA can be classified into two types: single nucleotide changes that alter the nucleotide sequence but do not change the physical structure of the DNA molecule, and structural alterations or distortions that can interfere with replication or transcription. Such changes include pairing between bases on the same strand or the introduction of nicks on one or the other strand.

Assessing Damage to DNA

Table 11.4 gives the estimated rate of damage to DNA in a typical mammalian cell at 37°C (body temperature). The rate of damage accumulation from background levels

TABLE 11.4	
Rates of DNA Damage in a Mammalian Cell	
DAMAGE	**EVENTS/HR**
Depurination	580
Depyrimidation	29
Deamination of cytosine	8
Single-stranded breaks	2300
Single-stranded breaks after depurination	580
Methylation of guanine	130
Pyrimidine (thymine) dimers in skin (noon Texas sun)	5×10^4
Single-stranded breaks from background ionizing radiation	10^{-4}

Thymine dimer
A molecular lesion in which chemical bonds form between a pair of adjacent thymine bases in a DNA molecule.

of radiation and chemicals is so high that within the normal life span of the cell, all of its DNA would be completely destroyed. Fortunately, humans (and other organisms) have a number of highly efficient DNA repair systems (Table 11.5). However, because the rate of background damage is so high, it is easy to overload the repair systems. One type of damage, the formation of **thymine dimers,** is thought to be a major cause of cell death, mutation, and transformation to a cancerous condition.

Repairing Damage to DNA

One type of repair system can correct errors made during DNA replication. Other systems recognize and repair damage or structural modifications to the DNA molecule that occur during other phases of the cell cycle. Exposure of DNA to ultraviolet light (from sunlight, tanning lamps, or other ultraviolet lamps) causes adjacent thymine molecules in the same DNA strand to pair with each other, forming thymine dimers (➡ Figure 11.10). These dimers cause a regional distortion of the DNA molecule and can interfere with normal replication processes. Their continued presence in DNA can cause the insertion of incorrect bases during replication. This problem can be corrected by DNA repair mechanisms. Several genetic disorders, including xeroderma pigmentosum and Cockayne syndrome (MIM/OMIM 216400), are caused by mutations in genes controlling DNA repair mechanisms.

✸ MUTATION, GENOTYPES, AND PHENOTYPES

One of the first genetic disorders to be analyzed at the molecular level was sickle cell anemia. In this disorder, the single nucleotide substitution in codon 6 changes the sixth amino acid in the beta globin polypeptide amino acid at position 6 and produces a distinctive set of clinical symptoms. All affected individuals and all heterozygotes have the same nucleotide substitution, which led geneticists to the conclusion that specific genetic disorders were caused by specific mutations.

As it turns out, sickle cell anemia is probably an exception rather than the rule. Molecular analysis of mutations in other genes reveals that more often, a spectrum of mutations is possible within a single gene (➡ Figure 11.11). As the molecular basis of mutations in a large number of genes becomes known, it is common to find that a genetic disorder can be caused by many different mutational events in a given gene.

DAMAGE	REPAIRS/ HR
Single-stranded breaks	2×10^5
Pyrimidine dimers	5×10^4
Guanine methylation	10^4–10^5

TABLE 11.5

Maximum DNA Repair Rates in a Human Cell

➡ **FIGURE 11.10**

Thymine dimers are produced when ultraviolet light crosslinks two adjacent thymine bases in the same strand of DNA. This structure causes a distortion in the DNA, and errors in replication are likely to occur unless corrected.

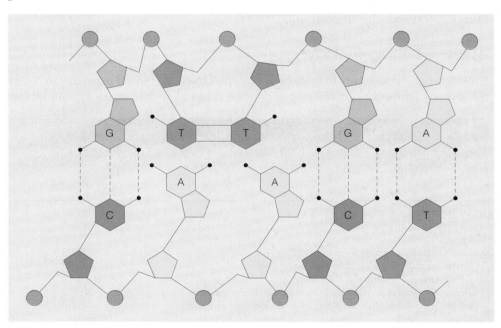

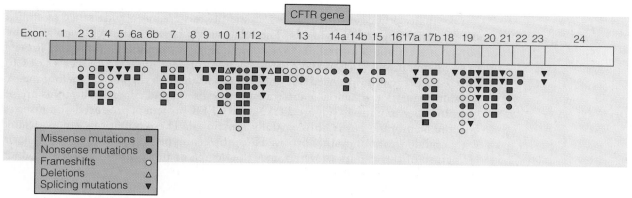

CFTR gene

Missense mutations ■
Nonsense mutations ●
Frameshifts ○
Deletions △
Splicing mutations ▼

FIGURE 11.11

Distribution of mutations in the exons of the cystic fibrosis gene, CFTR. More than 300 different mutations have now been discovered. The mutations shown here include nucleotide substitutions, deletions, frameshift mutations, and splicing mutants. Any of these mutations in the homozygous condition result in the phenotype of cystic fibrosis.

Mutation Can Cause a Range of Phenotypes

The situation where a genetic disorder is caused by a range of mutational events affecting a single gene is a form of *genetic heterogeneity*. In fact, as more becomes known about mutations at the molecular level, it seems generally true that most human genetic disorders are heterogeneous. Cystic fibrosis provides a clear example of the variable nature of mutations in a single gene. More than 300 different mutations have been identified in the cystic fibrosis gene. These include single nucleotide substitutions that change amino acids and cause premature termination of translation, deletions that affect single amino acids, and larger deletions that involve one or more exons. In addition, there are frameshift mutations and splice-site mutations. Mutations are distributed in all regions of the CF gene (Figure 11.12), strengthening the idea that any mutational event that interferes with expression of a gene will produce an abnormal phenotype.

FIGURE 11.12

Mutations in the CFTR gene differ in their phenotypic effects. When homozygous, mutations R117, R334, and R347 allow between 5% and 30% normal activity for the gene product and produce only mild symptoms. These nucleotide substitution mutations are not common: together they account for about 2% of all cases of cystic fibrosis. The most common mutation, ΔF508, causes an amino acid deletion in a cytoplasmic region of the protein and accounts for 70% of all mutations in the CF gene. This mutation inactivates the CFTR protein and is associated with severe symptoms.

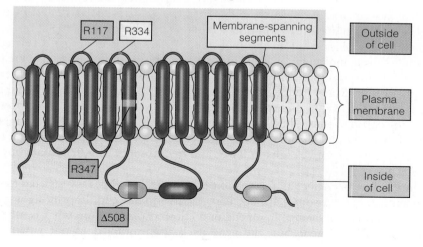

Like many other genetic disorders, cystic fibrosis creates a wide range of clinical symptoms in affected individuals. The relationship between the genotype and phenotype has been investigated for a number of specific mutations in the CFTR gene. In some mutations, such as the ΔF508 deletion (present in 70% of all cases of CF), the CFTR protein is produced but does not associate with the plasma membrane. As a result, regulation of chloride ion transport is absent, and clinical symptoms are severe. In other mutations (Figure 11.12), the CFTR protein is produced and inserted into the membrane but is only partially functional. These mutations are associated with a milder form of cystic fibrosis. Thus, the genotype (in the form of the molecular nature of the mutation) determines the degree of function of the gene product, which in turn determines the phenotype.

Genomic Imprinting: Reversible Alterations to the Genome

Humans carry two copies of each gene, one received from the mother, the other from the father. Normally there is no difference in the expression of the two copies. But in certain genetic disorders, expression of alleles may depend on whether they are inherited from the mother or the father. This differential expression is called **genomic imprinting.**

The first evidence for imprinting in mammals came from experimentally transplanting haploid germ cell nuclei in mice to produce zygotes containing two female or two male haploid genomes. Experimental mouse zygotes with a genome of male origin develop abnormal embryonic structures, but have normal placentas; zygotes with a female-derived genome develop normal embryonic structures and abnormal placentas. In the mouse, both conditions are lethal, leading to the conclusions that both a maternal and a paternal genome are required for normal development, and that different sets of genes are inactivated during the formation of eggs and sperm.

Genomic imprinting plays a role in several genetic disorders, including Prader-Willi syndrome (PWS) and Angelman syndrome (AS). Most cases of PWS, an autosomal recessive disorder characterized by obesity, uncontrolled appetite, and mental retardation, are associated with a small deletion in the long arm of chromosome 15 (see Figure 6.23). In about 40% of cases, however, no deletion can be detected. Using molecular markers, these nondeletion cases are found to have inherited two maternal copies of chromosome 15. This condition, where both copies of a given chromosome are inherited from a single parent, is called uniparental disomy. In this situation, the clinical symptoms of Prader-Willi syndrome are not caused by a mutation or deletion of a chromosome region, but by the presence of two maternal copies of chromosome 15. Interestingly, in cases of PWS that do involve a deletion, the deleted region is always from the paternal copy of the chromosome, leaving the individual with only a single, maternal copy of the region.

Angelman syndrome is characterized by severe mental retardation, uncontrollable puppet-like movements, and seizures of laughter. Cytogenetic analysis of affected individuals reveals that about 50% of affected individuals have a small deletion in the q11q13 region of the long arm of chromosome 15 (the same region that is deleted in PWS). Studies using molecular markers indicate that the deletion is carried in the maternal copy of chromosome 15, leaving the affected individual with only a paternal copy of the region. Many nondeletion cases of AS are associated with paternal disomy of chromosome 15. In these cases, AS is caused by the presence of two paternal copies of the chromosome. These findings indicate that both a paternal and maternal copy of this region of chromosome 15 are required for normal development, that absence of a paternal copy results in PWS, and that absence of a maternal copy results in AS.

Imprinting does not affect all regions of the genome, but appears restricted to certain segments of chromosomes 4p, 8q, 17p, 18p, 18q, and 22q. Imprinting is not a mutation or permanent change in a gene or a chromosome region; what is affected is the *expression* of a gene, not the gene itself. Imprinting does not violate the

Genomic imprinting
Phenomenon in which the expression of a gene depends on whether it is inherited from the mother or the father. Also known as genetic or parental imprinting.

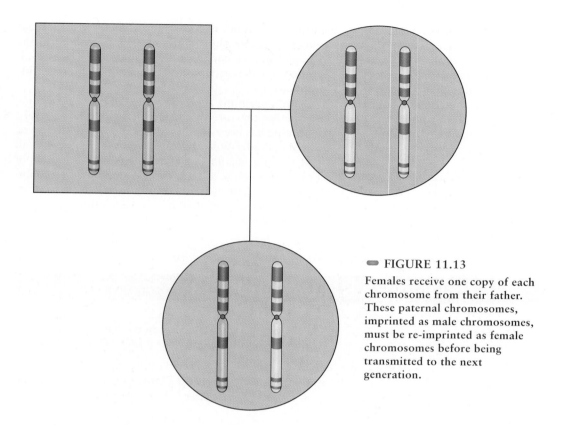

Females receive one copy of each chromosome from their father. These paternal chromosomes, imprinted as male chromosomes, must be re-imprinted as female chromosomes before being transmitted to the next generation.

Mendelian principles of segregation or independent assortment. Imprinting is not permanent; remember that a copy of a given chromosome received by a female from her father will be transmitted as a maternal chromosome in the next generation (▬ Figure 11.13). In each generation, the previous imprinting must be erased, and a new pattern of imprinting imposed, defining the newly imprinted region as either paternal or maternal for transmission to the next generation. Imprinting events are thought to take place during gamete formation and are transmitted to all tissues of the offspring. Although imprinting is not strictly a mutational event, it does involve chemical modification of DNA in paternally and maternally derived chromosomes. The precise mechanism of imprinting remains unknown, but the process may play an important role in gene expression and may be part of the molecular explanation of the phenomenon of incomplete penetrance.

SUMMARY

1. The study of mutations is an essential part of genetics. Mutation, the ultimate source of genetic variation, gives the geneticist a means of studying genetic phenomena. Without mutations it would be difficult to determine whether a trait is under genetic control at all and impossible to determine its mode of inheritance.

2. Mutations can be classified in a variety of ways using criteria such as morphology, biochemistry, and degrees of lethality. Somatic mutations may drastically affect an individual, but such mutations are not heritable. Only mutations in the germ cells or gametes are passed on to the next generation and are of genetic significance.

3. The detection of mutations in humans is more difficult than in experimental organisms such as bacteria and fruit flies. As a class, dominant mutations are the easiest to detect because they are expressed in the heterozygous condition. Accurate pedigree information can often identify the individual in whom the mutation arose.

4. It is more difficult to determine the origin of sex-linked recessive mutations, but an examination of the male progeny is often informative. If the mutation in question is an autosomal recessive, it is almost impossible to identify the original mutant individual.

5. Studies of mutation rates in a variety of dominant and sex-linked recessive traits indicate that mutations in the human genome are rare events, occurring about once in every 1 million copies of a gene. The cumulative effect of this rate generates between 6 and 7 million mutant genes in each generation. The impact of this mutational load is diminished by several factors, including the redundant nature of the genetic code, the recessive nature of most mutations, and the lowered reproductive rate or early death associated with many genetic diseases.

6. Studies on the molecular basis of mutation have provided evidence for a direct link between gene, protein, and phenotype. Mutations can arise spontaneously, as the result of an error in DNA replication, or as the result of atomic shifts in nucleotide bases. Environmental agents, including chemicals and radiation, also cause mutations. Frameshift mutations cause a change in the reading frame of codons, often resulting in dramatic alterations in the structure and function of polypeptide products.

7. Genomic imprinting alters expression of genes, depending on whether they are inherited maternally or paternally. Imprinting has been implicated in a number of disorders, including Prader-Willi and Angelman syndromes. Not all regions of the genome are affected, and only segments of chromosomes 4, 8, 17, 18, and 22 are known to be imprinted. Genes are not permanently altered by imprinting, and must be re-imprinted in each generation during gamete formation.

QUESTIONS AND PROBLEMS

1. Replication involves a period of time during which DNA is particularly susceptible to the introduction of mutations. If nucleotides can be incorporated into DNA at a rate of 20 nucleotides/second and the human genome contains 3 billion nucleotides, how long would replication take? How is this time reduced so that replication can take place in a few hours?

2. Achondroplasia is an autosomal dominant form of dwarfism caused by a single gene mutation. Calculate the mutation rate of this gene given the following data: 10 achondroplastic births to unaffected parents in 245,000 births.

3. Why is it almost impossible to measure directly the mutation rates in autosomal recessive alleles?

4. Distinguish between spontaneous and induced mutations.

5. Define the following terms:
   a. frameshift
   b. mutation rate
   c. somatic mutation

6. Define and compare the following types of nucleotide substitutions. Which is likely to cause the most dramatic mutant effect?
   a. missense mutation
   b. nonsense mutation
   c. sense mutation

7. Identify a chemical mutagen that induces:
   a. A-T to G-C substitutions
   b. G-C to A-T substitutions

8. What is a frameshift mutation and how can agents that insert themselves into the DNA molecule bring about these mutations?

9. If the coding region of a gene (the exons) contains 2100 base pairs of DNA, would a missense mutation cause a protein to be shorter, longer, or the same length as the normal 700 amino acid protein? What would be the effect of a nonsense mutation? A sense mutation?

10. In the gene coding sequence shown below, which of the following events will produce a frame shift after the last mutational site?

    normal mRNA: UCC AAA UAC CGU CGU UAA
                    ser lys tyr arg arg stop

    a. insertion of an A after the first codon
    b. deletion of the second codon (AAA)
    c. insertion of TA after the second codon and deletion of CG in the fourth codon
    d. deletion of AC in the third codon.

11. The cystic fibrosis gene encodes a chloride channel protein necessary for normal cellular functions. Let us assume that if at least 10% normal channels are present, the affected individual has mild symptoms of cystic fibrosis. Less than 10% normal channels produces severe symptoms. At least 50% of the channels must be expressed for the individual to be phenotypically normal. This gene has various mutant alleles:

allele	molecular defect	% functional channels	symptoms
CF508	deletion in exon	0%	severe
CF1	missense mutation in 5′ flanking region	25%	mild
CF2	nonsense mutation in exon	0%	severe
CF3	missense mutation in exon	5%	mild

Predict the percent of functional channels and severity of symptoms for the following genotypes:
a. heterozygous for CF508
b. homozygous for CF508
c. doubly heterozygous, with one copy of CF508 and one of CF3
d. doubly heterozygous, with one copy of CF1 and one copy of CF3

12. Familial retinoblastoma, a rare dominant autosomal defect, arose in a large family that had no prior history of the disease. Consider the following pedigree (the colored symbols represent individuals):

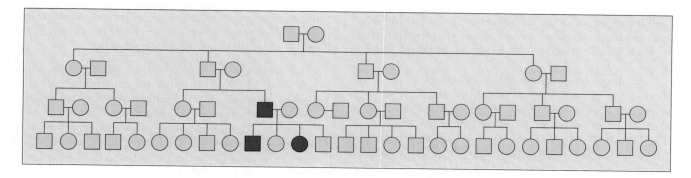

a. Circle the individual(s) in which the mutation most likely occurred.
b. Is this individual affected by the mutation? Justify your answer.
c. Assuming that the mutant allele is fully penetrant, what is the average percentage of an affected individual's offspring that will be affected?

13. Achondroplasia is a rare dominant autosomal defect resulting in dwarfism. The unaffected brother of an individual with achondroplasia is seeking counsel on the likelihood of his being a carrier of the mutant allele. What is the probability that the unaffected client is carrying the achondroplasia allele?

14. Tay-Sachs disease is a recessive autosomal disease. Since affected individuals do not often survive to reproductive age, why has Tay-Sachs disease persisted in human population?

15. You are conducting an Ames test on a series of suspected mutagens. The following results are obtained:

dish 1	no mutagen	20 colonies
dish 2	substance A	50 colonies
dish 3	substance B	100 colonies
dish 4	substance C	20 colonies

a. Describe the Ames test
b. describe the findings in dish 1
c. Rank the substances A, B, and C from most mutagenic to least mutagenic.

16. Our bodies are not defenseless against mutagens that alter our genomic DNA sequences. What mechanisms are used to repair DNA?

17. Even though it is well known that x-rays cause mutations, they are routinely used to diagnose medical problems including potential tumors, broken bones, or dental cavities. Why is this done? What precautions need to be taken?

SCIENCE AND SOCIETY

1. You are an expert witness called by the defense in a case where a former employee is suing an industrial company because his son was born with muscular dystrophy, an X-linked recessive disorder. The employee claims that he was exposed to mutagenic chemicals in the work place which caused his son's illness. His attorney argues that neither the employee, his wife or their parents have this genetic disorder, and therefore, the disease in the employee's son represents a new mutation.

   How would you analyze this case? What would you say to the jury to support or refute this man's case?

2. Bruce Ames and his colleagues have pointed out that while detailed toxicological analysis has been conducted on synthetic chemicals, almost no information is available about the mutagenic or carcinogenic effects of the toxins produced by plants as a natural defense against fungi, insects and animals predators. Tens of thousands of such compounds have been discovered, and he estimates that in the U.S. adults eat about 1.5 grams of these compounds each day, about 10,000 times higher than the levels of synthetic pesticides present in the diet. For example, cabbage contains 49 natural pesticides and metabolites, and only a few of these have been tested for their carcinogenic and mutagenic effects.

   With the introduction of new foods into the U.S. diet over the last two hundred years (mangoes, kiwi fruit, tomatoes, etc), has there been enough time for humans to have evolved resistance to the mutagenic effects of toxins present in these foods?

   Since the natural pesticides present in plants constitute more than 99% of the toxins we eat, should diet planning, especially for vegetarians, take into account the doses of toxins present in the diet?

INTERNET ACTIVITIES

The following activities use the resources of the World Wide Web to enhance the topics covered in this chapter. To investigate the topics described below, log on to the book's homepage at:

http://www.wadsworth.com/biology

1. Review the various types of mutations and their consequences by completing the Gene Action/Mutation worksheet found at the Access Excellence Activities Site.

2. The Human Gene Mutation Database at the Institute of Medical Genetics at Cardiff, Wales is a resource which contains information about the mutations identified in human genes, including nucleotide substitutions, missense and nonsense mutations, splicing mutations and small insertions and deletions. The data provided includes the name and symbol for the gene, its chromosomal location, the mutant sequence codon number, and a reference to the paper that identified the mutation.

Click on this site and find the entry for the breast cancer gene BRCA1. Scroll through the mutations, noting the type of mutation and its location. Are the mutations reported here scattered throughout the gene, or are they clustered in certain locations? Since this gene was identified only a few years ago, does this list seem comprehensive? How does this entry compare to the listing for the cystic fibrosis gene? What factors may account for these differences?

FOR FURTHER READING

Ames, B. 1974. Identifying environmental chemicals causing mutation and cancer. Science *204:* 587–593.

Ames, B., Profet, M., and Gold, L. S. 1990. Dietary pesticides (99.00% all natural). Proc. Nat. Acad. Sci. *87:* 7777–7781.

Ames, B., Profet, M., and Gold, L.S. 1990. Nature's chemicals and synthetic chemicals: Comparative toxicology. Proc. Nat. Acad. Sci. *87:* 7782–7786.

Barnes, D.E., Lindahl, T. and Sedgwick, B. 1993. DNA repair. Curr. Opin. Cell Biol. *5:* 424–433.

Brunner, H., Bruggenwirth, H., Nillesen, W., Jansen, G., Hamel, B., Hoppe, R., deDie, C., Howler, C., vanDost, B., Wieringa, B., Ropers, H., and Smeets, H. 1993. Influence of sex of the transmitting parent as well as of parental allele size on the CTG expansion in myotonic dystrophy (DM). Am. J. Hum. Genet. *53:* 1016–1023.

Cohen, M. M., and Levy, H. P. 1989. Chromosome instability syndromes. *Adv. Hum. Genet. 18:* 43–149, 365–371.

Deering, R. A. 1962. Ultraviolet radiation and nucleic acids. Sci. Am. (December) 207: 135–144.

Engel, E. 1993. Uniparental disomy revisited: the first twelve years. Am. J. Med. Genet. *46:* 670–674.

Hanawalt, P. C., and Haynes, R. H. 1967. The repair of DNA. *Sci. Am.* 216 (February): 36–43.

Harper, P., Harley, H., Reardon, W. and Shaw, D. 1992. Anticipation in myotonic dystrophy: new light on an old problem. Am. J. Hum. Genet. *51:* 10–16.

Huntington's Disease Collaborative Research Group. 1993. A novel gene containing a trinucleotide repeat that is expanded and unstable on Huntington's Disease chromosomes. Cell *72:* 971–983.

Issa, J.P. and Baylin, S.B. 1996. Epigenetics and human disease. Nat. Med. *2:* 281–282.

Ledbetter, D.H. and Engel, E. 1995. Uniparental disomy in humans: development of an imprinting map and its implications for prenatal diagnosis. Hum. Mol. Genet. 4 (Special No.) 1757–1764.

Muller, H. and Scott, R. 1992. Hereditary conditions in which the loss of heterozygosity may be important. Mutat. Res. *284:* 15–24.

McCann, J., Choi, E., Yamasaki, E. and Ames, B. 1975. Detection of carcinogens as mutagens in the Salmonella/microsome test: Assay of 300 chemicals. Proc. Nat. Acad. Sci. *72:* 5135–5139.

Moss, T. and Sills, D. 1981. The Three Mile Island nuclear accident: Lessons and implications. Ann. N.Y. Acad. Sci. *365:* entire issue.

Neel, J.V. 1995. New approaches to evaluating the genetic effects of the atomic bombs. Am. J. Hum. Genet. *57:* 1275–1282. A.A., Satoh,

Nicholls, R. 1993. Genomic imprinting and uniparental disomy in Angelman and Prader-Willi syndromes: a review. Am. J. Med. Genet. *46:* 16–25.

Orr, H., Chung, M., Banfi, S., Kwiatkowski, T., Servadio, A., Beaudet, A., McCall, A., Duvick, A., Rnaum, L., and Zoghbi, H. 1993. Expansion of an unstable trinucleotide repeat in spinocerebellar ataxia type 1. Nature Genetics *4:* 221–226.

Sapienza, C. 1995. Genome imprinting: an overview. Dev. Genet. *17:* 185–187.

Schwartz, E., and Surrey, S. 1986. Molecular biologic diagnosis of the hemoglobinopathies. *Hosp. Pract. 9:* 163–178.

Tsui, L-C. 1992. The spectrum of cystic fibrosis mutations. Trends Genet. *8:* 392–398.

Warren, S.T. 1996. The expanding world of trinucleotide repeats. Science *271:* 1423–1427.

Weeda, G., Hoeijmakers, J. and Bootsma, D. 1993. Genes controlling nucleotide excision repair in eukaryotic cells. Bioessays *15:* 249–258.

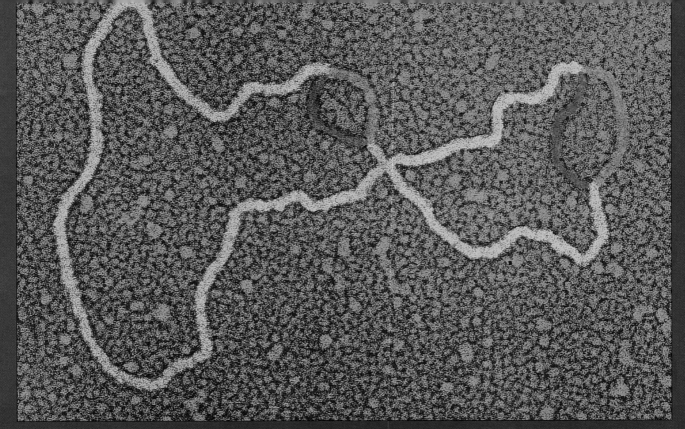

RECOMBINANT DNA TECHNOLOGY

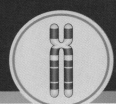

Chapter Outline

WHAT ARE CLONES?
Plants Can Be Cloned from Single Cells
Animals Can Be Cloned by Two Methods
CLONING GENES IS A MULTISTEP
  PROCESS
Restriction Enzymes Cut DNA at Specific
  Sites

Vectors Serve as Carriers of DNA
Steps in the Process of Cloning DNA
Cloned Libraries
Finding a Specific Clone in a Library
CONCEPTS AND CONTROVERSIES
  Asilomar: Scientists Get Involved
ANALYZING CLONED SEQUENCES

Southern Blotting
DNA Sequencing
THE POLYMERASE CHAIN REACTION
GUEST ESSAY   The Human Genome Project:
  Reading Our Own Genetic Blueprint

Chapter 12

OPENING IMAGE
*Plasmids are DNA molecules used as
vectors for recombinant DNA.*

T*he story begins simply enough. A boy of Ghanaian descent, born in
England and therefore a British citizen, moved to Ghana to live with
his father, leaving behind his mother, two sisters, and a brother.
Subsequently, he attempted to return to Britain to live with his mother and
siblings, and the story gets a little complicated. Immigration authorities
suspected that the returning boy was an imposter and was either an
unrelated child or possibly the nephew of the boy's mother. Acting on this
belief, the authorities denied him residence. The boy's family sought
assistance to help establish his identity and to allow him to live in the*

country of his birth. A series of medical tests was conducted, using genetic markers including ABO and other blood types and more sophisticated techniques such as HLA testing (for details, see Chapter 15). The results indicated that the boy was closely related to the woman he claimed was his mother, but the tests could not tell whether she was the mother or an aunt.

The family's legal counsel then turned to Alec Jeffreys at the University of Leicester to see if the DNA fingerprinting technique developed in Jeffreys' research laboratory could help. To complicate the situation even more, neither the mother's sisters nor the boy's father was available for testing, and the mother was not sure about the boy's paternity. Jeffreys began by taking blood samples from the boy, his reputed siblings, and the woman who claimed to be his mother. DNA was extracted from the white blood cells in each sample and was treated with enzymes that cut the DNA at specific base sequences; the resulting fragments were separated by size. The pattern of these fragments, known as a DNA fingerprint, was analyzed to determine the boy's paternity and maternity. The results show that the boy has the same father as the brother and sisters because they all share paternal DNA fragments (those not contributed by the mother) in common. The most important question was whether the boy and his "mother" were related.

Twenty-five fragments found in the woman's DNA fingerprint were also found in the boy's fingerprint, indicating that the two are very closely related and that in all probability the boy is the woman's child. (The chance that they are unrelated was calculated as 2×10^{-15}, or about one in a trillion.) Faced with this evidence, immigration authorities reversed their position and allowed the boy to take up residence with his family.

DNA fingerprinting is but one example of the array of new techniques developed in recent years as a product of the ongoing revolution in genetic technology. This revolution began with the discovery of how to combine DNA from different organisms in a specific and directed way to create recombinant DNA molecules. In this and the next chapter we will examine how this revolution began, how recombinant DNA molecules are constructed, and how this technology is being used in areas of human genetics, biology, medicine, and agriculture.

WHAT ARE CLONES?

In some cases a fertilized egg divides into two cells, and these cells separate to form identical twins. Because they are derived from a common ancestor (in this case a fertilized egg or zygote), such twins can be said to be **clones**. Clones are molecules, cells, or individuals derived from a single ancestor. Methods for producing cloned organisms are not new; horticultural techniques to produce clones of fruit trees were used in ancient times and are still used today. Techniques for the production of cloned cells, single-celled organisms, and some animals have all been developed in this century. More recently it has become possible to clone DNA molecules.

The development of methods to produce identical copies of DNA molecules in large quantities has had a profound effect on genetic research and has generated applications of this technology across many disciplines, ranging from archaeology to environmental conservation. This chapter reviews the methods by which cloned DNA molecules are prepared and used in genetic research, forensics, medicine, agriculture, and the repair of defective human genes. Before we consider the basic techniques of DNA cloning, we will look briefly at recent advances in the cloning of plants and animals.

Clones
Genetically identical organisms, cells, or molecules all derived from a common ancestor.

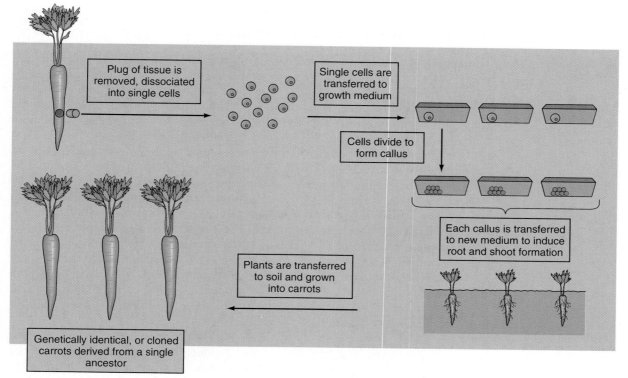

FIGURE 12.1

Carrots can be cloned by removing a plug of tissue which is dissociated into single cells. These cells are placed in growth medium, and divide to produce a mass of cells called a callus. Calluses are transferred to a new medium to induce the formation of roots and shoots. The developing plants are then transferred to soil, where they grow into genetically identical copies, or clones, of the original carrot.

Plants Can Be Cloned from Single Cells

Domesticated plants and animals have been genetically manipulated for thousands of years by selective breeding. Organisms with desirable characteristics were selected and bred together, and the offspring with the best combinations of these characteristics were used for breeding the next generation. While this method seems slow and unreliable, Charles Darwin noted that only a few generations of intense selection were required to produce many varieties of pigeons and minks.

In the 1950s Charles Steward demonstrated that individual carrot cells could be grown in culture, and that under the appropriate conditions the cells would divide to form a cell mass known as a callus (━ Figure 12.1). When transferred to a different medium, the calluses grew into mature plants (━ Figure 12.2). Using this method on a large scale, hundreds or thousands of clones could be produced from a single carrot. Variations on this method have been used to clone plants of several different species. One application of this method has been the development of a loblolly pine tree that is resistant to disease, grows rapidly, and has a high wood content. Cells from such a tree were grown individually until they formed a callus and were converted into thousands of copies of the original tree. Using these clones, it is possible to plant a forest of genetically identical trees that all mature at the same time, allowing the forest to be harvested for pulpwood on a predictable schedule. This method offers a new approach to timber farming.

FIGURE 12.2

This cloned plant was grown from single cells removed from a parental plant.

Animals Can Be Cloned by Two Methods

The cloning of domesticated animals such as cattle and sheep has moved from the research laboratory to the level of commercial enterprise in the last decade. Two methods are available for cloning animal embryos: embryo splitting and nuclear transfer. In embryo splitting, an egg is fertilized in a glass dish (*in vitro*) and allowed to develop into an embryo containing 8–16 cells. The embryo is then divided one or more times by micromanipulation, and the resulting individual cells form genetically identical embryos that can be implanted into a host uterus for development. This method mimics the way that identical twins or triplets are produced naturally, and can be used to clone any mammalian embryo, including human embryos.

Creating clones by nuclear transfer has the advantage of producing larger numbers of genetically identical embryos. The method uses eggs from which the nucleus has been removed with a fine glass pipette. These enucleated eggs are then fused with individual cells taken from a 16–32 cell embryo. In successful experiments, the fused cells begin dividing to produce a new embryo and are transplanted into the uterus of a foster mother. If the original embryo contains 16 or 32 cells, then 16 or 32 genetically identical offspring, or clones, can be produced (⬤ Figure 12.3). In this way it is possible to produce herds of cloned cattle or sheep with superior wool, milk, or meat production (⬤ Figure 12.4).

The development of methods for cloning plants and animals represents a significant advance in agricultural technology. When coupled with methods of molecular screening for defective genes, gene transfer, and the prospect of gene surgery, these techniques present us with the possibility of transferring genes between species—and even creating new forms of life by combining genetic information from plants and animals in a single organism that can be cloned into thousands of copies. With this background and these possibilities in mind, we will consider the methodology of genetic engineering and gene cloning.

Prize cow has embryo sired by prize bull

Donor cow is source of unfertilized eggs

Cells are removed from embryo

Nuclei are removed from donor eggs by microsurgery

Cell fusion is used to insert nucleus from embryo into egg

Eggs are implanted into surrogate mother

Eggs are frozen in liquid nitrogen for later use

After gestation, genetically identical calves are born

⬤ **FIGURE 12.3**

Several types of animals, ranging from frogs to cattle, have been cloned. In cattle, this process has two stages. First, unfertilized eggs are removed from a donor, and the nucleus is removed from each egg by microsurgery. Second, the embryo to be cloned is recovered, and separated into single cells. Embryo cells are fused with the donor eggs. Each egg then contains a genetically identical nucleus. These eggs can be frozen in liquid nitrogen for future use, or implanted into the uterus of a surrogate mother to develop. All offspring of these eggs would be genetically identical copies, or clones, of the original embryo.

FIGURE 12.4
These cattle were cloned using nuclei derived from a single embryo.

CLONING GENES IS A MULTISTEP PROCESS

Cloning DNA molecules or segments of DNA molecules (genes) produces a large number of identical DNA molecules, all with a common ancestor. In this sense cloning DNA is similar to cloning whole plants or animals. The methods for cloning DNA molecules depend on genetic and biochemical discoveries made in the late 1960s and early 1970s. Collectively these techniques are often referred to as **recombinant DNA technology.** A small number of techniques forms the basis of recombinant DNA technology. These methods are used to:

Recombinant DNA technology
A series of techniques in which DNA fragments are linked to self-replicating vectors to create recombinant DNA molecules, which are replicated in a host cell.

1. Produce DNA fragments using enzymes that cut DNA at specific base sequences.
2. Link these DNA fragments to self-replicating forms of DNA, called vectors, to create recombinant DNA molecules.
3. Replicate the recombinant DNA molecule in a host organism to create hundreds or thousands of exact copies (clones) of the DNA segment inserted into the vector.
4. Retrieve the cloned DNA insert in quantities large enough to allow further studies or modifications.
5. Produce and purify gene products encoded by the cloned DNA inserts.

Restriction Enzymes Cut DNA at Specific Sites

The story of how recombinant DNA technology was discovered is a good illustration of how basic research in one field often has an unexpected impact on unrelated areas. It might seem odd that the mapping the gene for cystic fibrosis and the commercial production of human insulin by bacteria are a direct outgrowth of basic research into how soil bacteria are able to resist infection by viruses; but often, this is how science progresses. The discovery of bacterial enzymes that inactivate invading viruses by cutting the viral DNA into fragments marks the beginning of genetic technology.

In the mid 1970s, Hamilton Smith and Daniel Nathans discovered a number of bacterial enzymes that attach to DNA molecules and cut both strands of DNA at sites of specific base sequences. These enzymes, known as **restriction enzymes,** are a key component in recombinant DNA technology. The recognition and cutting site for an enzyme isolated from *Escherichia coli,* a bacterium that lives in the human intestine,

Restriction enzymes
Enzymes that recognize a specific base sequence in a DNA molecule and cleave or nick the DNA at that site.

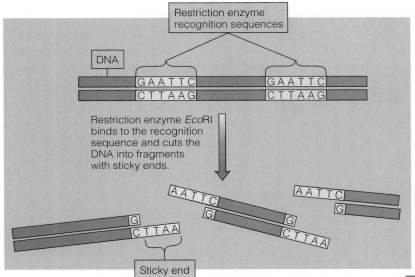

is shown in ⬤ Figure 12.5. This recognition and cutting sequence reads the same on either DNA strand (when read in the 5′ to 3′ direction). This recognition sequence is a **palindrome**, since it reads the same on either strand of the DNA. Words like *mom*, *pop*, and *radar* are palindromes, as are phrases such as "Todd erases a red dot" or "live not on evil." This recognition and cutting sequence is that of the enzyme *Eco*RI. Some restriction enzymes, like *Eco*RI, create single-stranded tails when they cut DNA. These sticky ends can reassociate with each other or with other DNA molecules having complementary tails to produce recombinant DNA molecules (⬤ Figure 12.6). Restriction enzymes allow

⬤ **FIGURE 12.5**

The recognition and cutting sites for the enzyme *Eco*RI.

Palindrome
A word, phrase, or sentence that reads the same in both directions. In DNA, a sequence of nucleotides that reads the same on both strands when read in the 5′ to 3′ direction.

⬤ **FIGURE 12.6**

Recombinant DNA molecules can be created using DNA from two different sources, a restriction enzyme, and DNA ligase. DNA from each source is cut with the restriction enzyme, and the resulting fragments are mixed. In the mixture, the complementary ends of the two types of DNA will associate by forming hydrogen bonds. These linked fragments can be covalently joined by treatment with DNA ligase, creating recombinant DNA molecules.

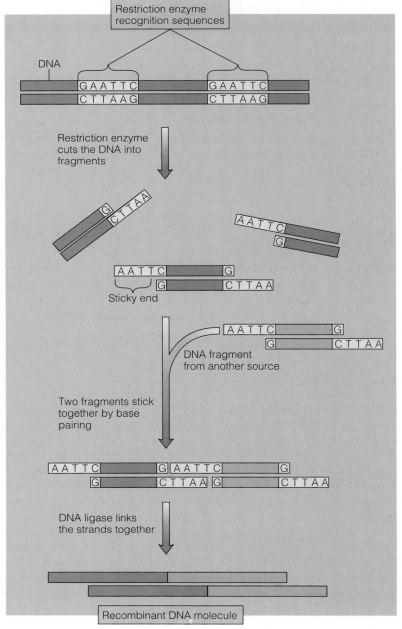

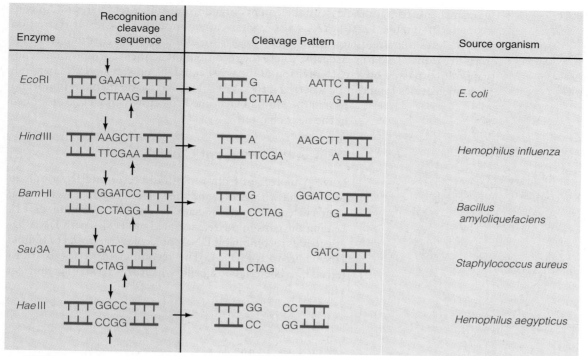

Enzyme	Recognition and cleavage sequence	Cleavage Pattern		Source organism
EcoRI	GAATTC / CTTAAG	G / CTTAA	AATTC / G	E. coli
HindIII	AAGCTT / TTCGAA	A / TTCGA	AAGCTT / A	Hemophilus influenza
BamHI	GGATCC / CCTAGG	G / CCTAG	GGATCC / G	Bacillus amyloliquefaciens
Sau3A	GATC / CTAG	CTAG	GATC	Staphylococcus aureus
HaeIII	GGCC / CCGG	GG / CC	CC / GG	Hemophilus aegypticus

FIGURE 12.7

Some common restriction enzymes and their cutting sites.

DNA fragments from different organisms to be joined together to form new combinations, called recombinant DNA molecules. The recognition and cutting sites for several restriction enzymes are shown in Figure 12.7.

Vectors Serve as Carriers of DNA

Vectors are used to carry DNA segments into cells for replication (cloning). Many of the vectors initially used in recombinant DNA work were derived from self-replicating, circular DNA molecules called **plasmids,** found in the cytoplasm of bacterial cells (Figure 12.8). One such plasmid, pBR322, is shown in Figure 12.9. The middle section of the diagram shows the position of sites recognized and cut by restriction enzymes that can be used for the insertion of DNA molecules to be cloned.

For cloning large DNA segments, **yeast artificial chromosomes (YACs)** are used as vectors. YACs are constructed from DNA segments assembled from a number of or-

Vector
A self-replicating DNA molecule that is used to transfer foreign DNA segments between host cells.

Plasmids
Extrachromosomal DNA molecules found naturally in bacterial cells. Modified plasmids are used as cloning vectors or vehicles.

Yeast artificial chromosome (YAC)
A cloning vector with telomeres and a centromere that can accommodate large DNA inserts, and that uses the eukaryote, yeast, as a host cell.

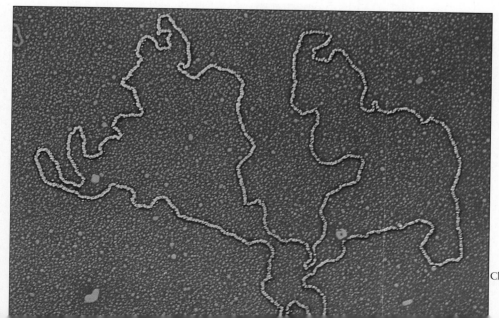

FIGURE 12.8

A plasmid isolated from a bacterial cell. Such plasmids can be used as vectors for cloning DNA.

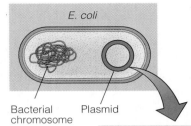

Bacterial chromosome   Plasmid

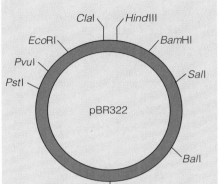

ClaI   HindIII

EcoRI

PvuI

PstI

BamHI

SalI

pBR322

BalI

SnaI

Cut with restriction enzyme *Bam*HI

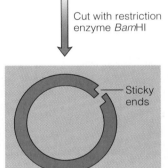

Sticky ends

FIGURE 12.9

Plasmids, such as pBR322, contain restriction sites that can be used to carry DNA inserts for cloning.

ganisms, and contain the essential elements of a chromosome: telomeres and a centromere (● Figure 12.10). YACs also contain a region with a cluster of restriction enzyme sites that are used to carry DNA inserts for cloning. YACs carrying DNA inserts are transferred to yeast cells, where the recombinant artifical chromosome replicates and is passed on at each division of the yeast cell. DNA inserts more than a million nucleotides long can be inserted into a YAC. This has made them an important tool in the Human Genome Project, which will be described in the next chapter.

Steps in the Process of Cloning DNA

If DNA molecules from a plasmid vector and from human cells are cut with *Eco*RI and then placed together in solution, their cut ends can reassociate, or anneal (● Figure 12.11). Sealing the gaps in the reassociated molecules with DNA ligase creates recombinant DNA molecules composed of human DNA and vector DNA. The recombinant vector is transferred into bacterial host cells, which are grown on a nutrient

● FIGURE 12.10

A yeast artificial chromosome used as a cloning vector. It contains two telomeres (structures at the end of all eukaryotic chromosomes), a centromere, and a region with restriction enzyme cutting sites that can be used to carry DNA inserts of more than one million (1Mb, a megabase) nucleotides.

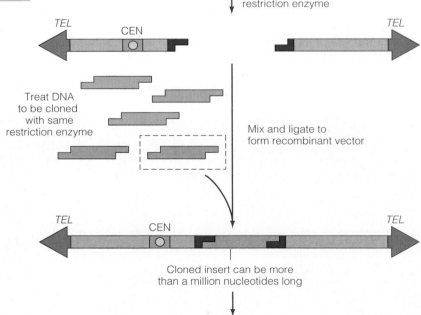

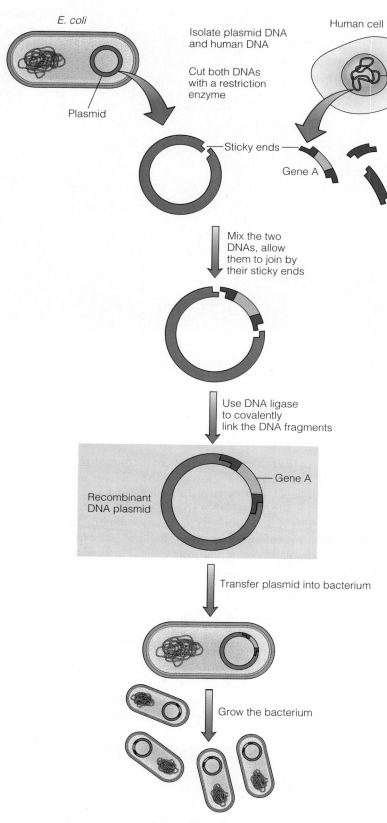

E. coli

Isolate plasmid DNA and human DNA

Human cell

Cut both DNAs with a restriction enzyme

DNA

Plasmid

Sticky ends

Gene A

Mix the two DNAs, allow them to join by their sticky ends

Use DNA ligase to covalently link the DNA fragments

Recombinant DNA plasmid

Gene A

Transfer plasmid into bacterium

Grow the bacterium

Bacteria carrying cloned copies of human gene A

◼ FIGURE 12.11

A summary of the cloning process. Two types of DNA are isolated: vector DNA in the form of a plasmid, and human DNA containing gene A. Both DNAs are cut with the same restriction enzyme. The cut DNAs are mixed and, after pairing, are covalently linked by DNA ligase. The recombinant plasmid DNA is inserted into a bacterial host cell. At each bacterial cell division the plasmid is replicated, producing many copies, or clones, of the DNA insert carrying the A gene.

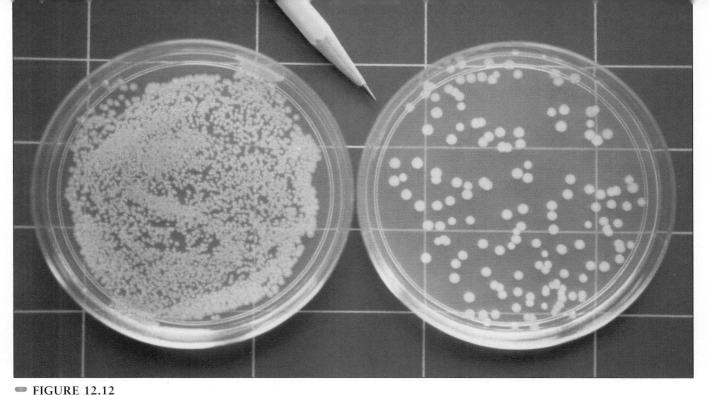

FIGURE 12.12

Colonies of bacteria on petri plates. Each colony is descended from a single cell; therefore, each colony is a clone.

plate, where they form colonies (● Figure 12.12). Since the cells in each colony are derived from a single ancestral cell, all cells in the colony, and the plasmids they contain, are clones. The colonies are screened to identify those that have taken up recombinant plasmids.

Several methods can be used to identify colonies that contain plasmids carrying DNA inserts. One method uses differential growth of the colonies in the presence of antibodies. The plasmid pBR322 carries two antibiotic resistance genes, one for tetracycline and one for ampicillin. If the DNA to be cloned is inserted into the gene for tetracycline resistance, this gene will be inactivated (● Figure 12.13). Colonies formed from a cell carrying this recombinant vector will not grow in the presence of tetracycline, but will grow on plates containing ampicillin. Host cells that have taken up a pBR322 vector with no insert will grow on plates containing ampicillin and on plates containing tetracycline. Thus, colonies that grow on ampicillin but not on tetracyline carry vectors with DNA inserts.

The steps involved in cloning DNA can be summarized as follows:

1. The DNA to be cloned is isolated and treated with restriction enzymes to produce segments ending in specific sequences.
2. These segments are linked to DNA molecules that serve as vectors, or carriers, producing a recombinant DNA molecule.
3. Plasmids carrying DNA to be cloned are transferred into bacterial cells, where the recombinant plasmids replicate, producing many copies, or clones, of the inserted DNA.
4. After growth, the bacterial cells can be broken open, and the recombinant plasmids extracted.

The inserted human DNA can be released from the plasmid with the same restriction enzyme used in cloning. Cloning using YACs follows a similar procedure, except that yeast cells are used as hosts.

The cloned human DNA can then be used in further experiments, or transferred to new vectors and host cells for synthesis of the protein encoded by the cloned human DNA.

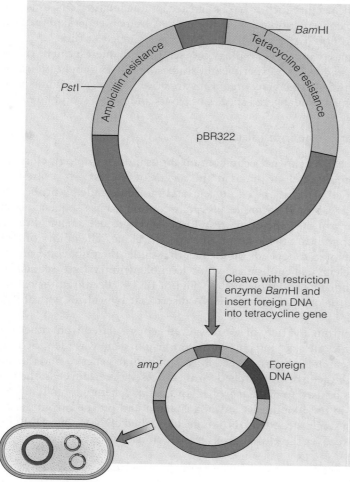

Cleave with restriction enzyme *Bam*HI and insert foreign DNA into tetracycline gene

amp^r

Foreign DNA

Transformed cells resistant to ampicillin, sensitive to tetracycline

■ FIGURE 12.13

The plasmid pBR322 carries two antibiotic resistance genes, one for tetracycline and one for ampicillin. If DNA is inserted into the tetracycline gene, bacterial host cells that take up this plasmid will be resistant to ampicillin, but not tetracycline. Cells that have not taken up a plasmid will be killed by either antibiotic.

Scientists working in the field of recombinant DNA technology were among the first to realize that there might be unrecognized dangers in the use and release of recombinant organisms. Accordingly, they called for a moratorium on all such work until issues relating to the safety of genetic engineering could be discussed (see "Concepts and Controversies," page 299). After years of discussion and experimentation, there is general agreement that such work poses little risk, but the episode demonstrates that scientists are concerned about the risks as well as the benefits of their work.

Cloned Libraries

Because each cloned fragment of human DNA is small, relative to the size of the genome, many separate clones must be created to include a significant portion of the entire human genome. A collection of clones that contains all the DNA sequences in the genome of an individual is known as a **genetic library.** Cloned libraries can represent the entire genome of an individual, the DNA from a single chromosome, or the set of genes that are actively transcribed in a single cell type. In a genomic library, the number of clones required to cover the entire genome depends, of course, on the size of the genome and the number of segments created by the restriction enzyme. A human library composed of cloned fragments 1700 base pairs (1.7 kilobases) in length would require about 8.1 million plasmids to contain the genetic information

Genetic library
In recombinant DNA terminology, a collection of clones that contains all the genetic information in an individual. Also known as a gene bank.

from one human cell. Vectors such as YACs can accept much larger DNA inserts and are now used in the construction of clone libraries. A human genetic library can be contained in about 3,000 YACs that can be stored in a single test tube.

Using the techniques of molecular biology, any sequence of interest can be recovered from such a library and used in experimental studies, in clinical applications, or for commercial use. Libraries from many organisms are now available, including bacteria, yeasts, crop plants, many endangered species of plants and animals, and humans.

Finding a Specific Clone in a Library

A library of cloned DNA sequences can contain thousands of different clones. One of the problems is finding a clone that contains a gene of interest. Most often, a specific clone is identified using a labeled nucleic acid molecule called a **probe.** Probes can be radioactive DNA or RNA molecules that contain a base sequence complementary to all or part of the gene of interest. Other methods use chemical reactions or color reactions to indicate the location of a specific clone. The ability of a probe to identify a gene of interest depends on the fact that under the right conditions, two single-stranded nucleic acid molecules with a complementary base sequence will form a double-stranded hybrid molecule (➡ Figure 12.14). Because the probe is labeled in some way, the clone carrying a DNA insert that hybridizes with the probe can be identified.

Probes can come from a variety of sources; even genes isolated from other species can be used. Once a clone carrying part of the rat insulin gene was identified, it was used as a probe to search through a cloned library of human genes to find the human insulin gene. Or, if the gene being searched for is expressed in certain cells, the mRNA from those cells can be used to make a probe. For example, hemoglobin is almost the only protein made in red blood cells. mRNA isolated and purified from these cells can be copied into a single-stranded DNA molecule, called cDNA. The cDNA can be used as a probe to recover the globin genes from a cloned library.

Probe
A labeled nucleic acid used to identify a complementary region in a clone or genome.

➡ **FIGURE 12.14**

A DNA probe is a single-stranded molecule labeled for identification in some way. Both chemical and radioactive labels are used. The single-stranded probe forms a double-stranded hybrid molecule with complementary regions of the DNA being studied.

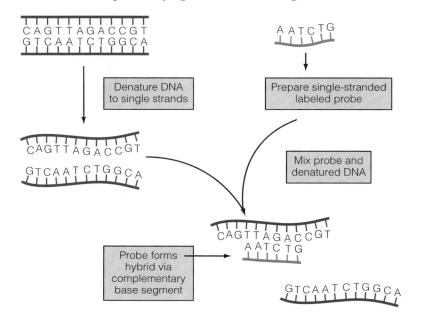

CONCEPTS AND CONTROVERSIES

Asilomar: Scientists Get Involved

The first steps in creating recombinant DNA molecules were taken in 1973 and 1974. Scientists immediately realized that modifying the genetic information in Escherichia coli, a bacterium that lives in the human gut, could be potentially dangerous. A group of scientists asked the National Academy of Sciences to appoint a panel to assess the risks and the need for control of recombinant DNA research. A second group published a letter in Science and in Nature, two leading scientific journals, calling for a moratorium on certain kinds of experiments until the potential hazards could be assessed.

Shortly afterwards, an international conference was held at Asilomar, California, to consider whether recombinant DNA technology posed any dangers, and whether this form of research should be regulated. In 1975, a set of guidelines resulting from this conference was published, under the direction of the National Institutes of Health (NIH), a government agency that sponsors biomedical research in the United States. In 1976, NIH published a new set of guidelines that prohibited certain kinds of experiments and dictated that other types of experiments were to be conducted only with appropriate containment that would prevent the release of bacterial cells carrying recombinant DNA molecules. NIH also called for research to accurately assess the risks, if any, associated with recombinant DNA techniques.

In the meantime, legislation was proposed in Congress and at the state and local levels to regulate or prohibit the use of recombinant DNA technology. The federal legislation was withdrawn after exhaustive sessions of testimony and reports. By 1978, research had demonstrated that the common K12 laboratory strain of E. coli was much safer for use as a host cell than originally thought. Several projects showed that K12 could not survive in the human gut or outside a laboratory setting. Other work showed that recombinant DNA was produced in nature, with no detectable serious effects. In 1982, NIH issued a new set of guidelines that eliminated most of the constraints on recombinant DNA research. No experiments are currently prohibited.

The most important lesson from these events is that the scientists who developed the methods were the first to call attention to the possible dangers of recombinant DNA research, and they did so based only on its potential for harm. There were no known cases of the release of recombinant DNA-carrying host cells being released into the environment. Scientists voluntarily shut down their research work until the situation could be properly and objectively assessed. Only when they reached a consensus that there was no danger did their work resume. Contrary to their portrayal in the popular media, scientists do care about the consequences of their work, and do get involved in issues of social importance.

ANALYZING CLONED SEQUENCES

Once a cloned sequence representing all or a portion of a gene has been identified and selected from a library, it can be used for many things: to find and study regulatory sequences on adjacent chromosome regions, to investigate the internal organization of the gene, and to study its expression in cells and tissues. For these studies, geneticists use several techniques, some of which will be outlined in the following sections.

Southern Blotting

The use of cloned DNA segments on filters separated by electrophoresis and screened by probes was developed by Edward Southern. Known as a **Southern blot**, this procedure has many applications. It is used to find differences in the organization of normal and mutant alleles, identify related genes in other genomes, and study the evolution of genes. To make a Southern blot, genomic DNA is extracted from

Southern blot
A method for transferring DNA fragments from a gel to a membrane filter, developed by Edward Southern for use in hybridization experiments.

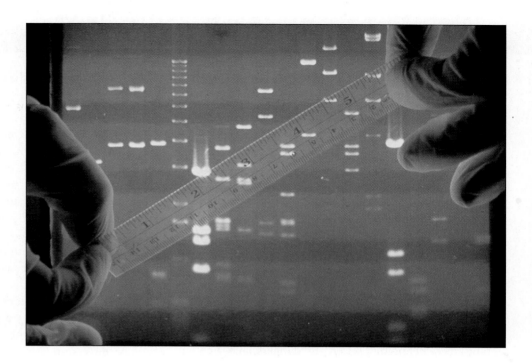

➡ **FIGURE 12.15**

A gel stained to show the separation of restriction fragments by electrophoresis.

the organism being studied, cut into fragments with one or more restriction enzymes, and placed in a gel made of agarose. The DNA fragments are then separated by gel electrophoresis, a technique in which an electric current is passed through the gel. DNA molecules are negatively charged, and the fragments migrate through the gel toward the positive pole. As they migrate through the gel, they separate by size, with the smaller fragments migrating faster. The gel is then stained and photographed (➡ Figure 12.15). The DNA in the gel is denatured into single-stranded fragments and transferred to a sheet of DNA-binding material, usually nitrocellulose or a nylon derivative. The transfer is made by placing the sheet of membrane on top of the gel and allowing buffer to flow through the gel and the nylon membrane by capillary action. Movement of the buffer transfers the DNA from the gel to the membrane.

This is done by placing the gel onto a thick sponge that acts as a wick. The sponge is partially immersed in a tray of buffer. A sheet of membrane filter is placed on top of the gel, and covered by stacks of paper towels and a weight (➡ Figure 12.16). Capillary action draws the buffer up through the sponge, gel, and DNA-binding membrane into the paper towels. As the buffer passes through the gel, DNA fragments are transferred from the gel to the membrane, where they stick.

The membrane is placed in a heat-sealed food storage bag with the labeled, single-stranded probe that corresponds to the gene of interest. Only those single-stranded DNA fragments imbedded in the membrane that are complementary to the base sequence of the probe will form hybrids. The unbound probe is washed away, and the hybridized fragments are visualized. For radioactive probes, a piece of x-ray film is placed next to the filter. The radioactivity in the probe exposes parts of the film. The film is developed, and a pattern of one or more bands is seen. These patterns are analyzed and compared with patterns from other experiments.

DNA Sequencing

DNA sequencing
A technique for determining the nucleotide sequence of a fragment of DNA.

It is possible to determine the exact order of nucleotides in a segment of DNA using **DNA sequencing** techniques. The most widely used method has been automated, and uses a different-colored fluorescent probe for each of the four bases in DNA. The re-

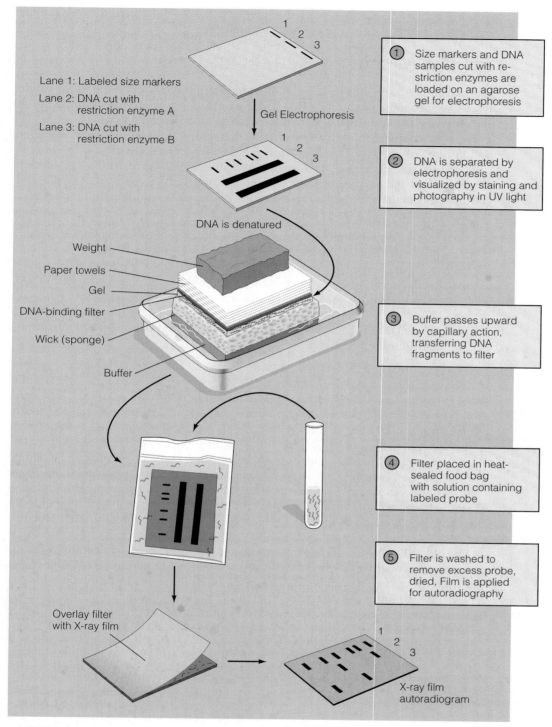

Lane 1: Labeled size markers

Lane 2: DNA cut with restriction enzyme A

Lane 3: DNA cut with restriction enzyme B

Gel Electrophoresis

DNA is denatured

Weight
Paper towels
Gel
DNA-binding filter
Wick (sponge)
Buffer

Overlay filter with X-ray film

X-ray film autoradiogram

① Size markers and DNA samples cut with restriction enzymes are loaded on an agarose gel for electrophoresis

② DNA is separated by electrophoresis and visualized by staining and photography in UV light

③ Buffer passes upward by capillary action, transferring DNA fragments to filter

④ Filter placed in heat-sealed food bag with solution containing labeled probe

⑤ Filter is washed to remove excess probe, dried, Film is applied for autoradiography

▬ FIGURE 12.16

The Southern blotting technique. DNA is cut with a restriction enzyme, and the fragments are separated by gel electrophoresis. The DNA in the gel is denatured to single strands, and the gel is placed on a sponge that is partially immersed in buffer. The gel is covered with a DNA-binding membrane, layers of paper towels, and a weight. Capillary action draws the buffer up through the sponge, gel, DNA-binding membrane, and paper towels. This transfers the pattern of DNA fragments from the gel to the membrane. The membrane is placed in a heat-sealed food bag with the probe and a small amount of buffer. After hybrids have been allowed to form, the excess probe is washed away, and the regions of hybrid formation are visualized by overlaying the membrane with a piece of x-ray film. After development, regions of hybrid formation appear as bands on the film.

sults are read by a scanner. Banks of sequencing machines are used in large-scale sequencing projects such as the Human Genome Project.

 ## THE POLYMERASE CHAIN REACTION

One advantage offered by the development of cloning techniques is the ability to produce large amounts of specific DNA sequences for a variety of uses. Cloning is not the only way to produce a large number of copies of a specific DNA sequence. The **polymerase chain reaction (PCR)** technique, invented in 1986, has revolutionized, and in some cases replaced methods of recombinant DNA research.

PCR uses single-stranded DNA as a template for the synthesis of a complementary strand by the enzyme DNA polymerase, in much the same way as DNA replication works in the cell nucleus. (See Chapter 8 for a discussion of DNA replication.) In the PCR reaction:

1. The DNA to be amplified is heated to break the hydrogen bonds joining the two polynucleotide strands, producing single strands (⬤ Figure 12.17).
2. Short nucleotide sequences that act as primers for DNA replication are added, and these primers bind to complementary regions on the single-stranded DNAs. Primers can be synthesized in the laboratory and are usually 20 to 30 nucleotides long.
3. The enzyme DNA polymerase begins at the primers and synthesizes a DNA strand complementary to the primer.

This set of three steps is known as a PCR cycle. The entire cycle can be repeated by heating the mixture and separating the double-stranded DNAs into single strands, each of which can serve as a template. The end result is that the amount of DNA present doubles with each cycle. After n cycles, there is a 2^n increase in the amount of double-stranded DNA (Table 12.1).

It is this power to amplify DNA that is one advantage of the PCR technique. The DNA to be amplified does not have to be purified and can be present in minute amounts; even a single DNA molecule can serve as a template. DNA from many sources has been used as starting material for the PCR technique, including dried blood, hides from extinct animals such as the quagga (a zebra-like African animal exterminated by hunting in the late 19th century), single hairs, mummified remains, and fossils.

The oldest DNA used in the PCR reaction to date has been extracted from insects preserved in amber for about 30 million years (⬤ Figure 12.18). The DNA amplified from these samples will be used to study the evolution of these insects.

The PCR technique is also used in clinical diagnosis, forensic applications, and other areas, including conservation. Some of these applications will be discussed in the next chapter.

Polymerase chain reaction (PCR) A method for amplifying DNA segments that uses cycles of denaturation, annealing to primers, and DNA-polymerase directed DNA synthesis.

TABLE 12.1

DNA Sequence Amplification by PCR

CYCLE	NUMBER OF COPIES
0	1
1	2
5	3
10	1024
15	32,768
20	1,048,576
25	33,544,432
30	1,073,741,820

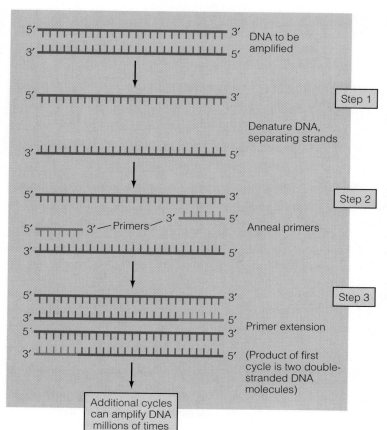

5′ |||||||||||||||||||||||||||||| 3′ DNA to be
3′ |||||||||||||||||||||||||||||| 5′ amplified

↓

5′ |||||||||||||||||||||||||||||| 3′ Step 1

Denature DNA,
separating strands

3′ |||||||||||||||||||||||||||||| 5′

↓

5′ |||||||||||||||||||||||||||||| 3′ Step 2
                          3′ ||||||| 5′
5′ ||||||| 3′—Primers—3′   Anneal primers

3′ |||||||||||||||||||||||||||||| 5′

↓

5′ |||||||||||||||||||||||||||||| 3′ Step 3
3′ |||||||||||||||||||||||||||||| 5′
5′ |||||||||||||||||||||||||||||| 3′ Primer extension

3′ |||||||||||||||||||||||||||||| 5′ (Product of first
                                      cycle is two double-
                                      stranded DNA
                                      molecules)

↓

Additional cycles
can amplify DNA
millions of times

● **FIGURE 12.17**

In step 1 of the polymerase chain reaction (PCR), the DNA to be amplified is denatured into single strands. In step 2, short single-stranded primers pair with the nucleotides adjacent to the region to be amplified. These primers are made synthetically, and are complementary to the nucleotide sequence flanking the region to be amplified. In step 3, enzymes and nucleotides for DNA synthesis are added and the primers are extended, forming a double-stranded DNA molecule, with the primers incorporated into the newly synthesized strand. This series of three steps is called a cycle. In the second cycle, the double-stranded molecules produced in the first cycle are denatured to form single strands, which serve as templates for binding of primers and another round of DNA synthesis. Repeated cycles can amplify the original DNA sequence by more than a million times.

● **FIGURE 12.18**

Insects embedded in amber are the oldest organisms from which DNA has been extracted.

The Human Genome Project: Reading Our Own Genetic Blueprint

FRANCIS SELLERS COLLINS

I developed an early love for mathematics and science and, after learning about the elegant features of the structure of the atom and the chemical bond in a high school chemistry class, I became convinced that I wanted to be a chemist. Accordingly, I majored in chemistry at the University of Virginia, and immediately after graduation went into a Ph.D. program in physical chemistry at Yale, never glancing around to notice what other exciting areas of science I might be missing. Almost by accident, however, I was introduced to molecular biology. To my surprise, I learned that all of my biases about biology being chaotic, intellectually unsatisfying, and devoid of the principles that I prized so much in the physical sciences were really quite unjustified. In fact, it was clear that biology was poised on the threshold of a remarkable revolution, as it became possible to analyze the information content of DNA and the nature of the genetic code.

After a somewhat prolonged and torturous route, including medical school, I resolved to pursue a career that combined clinical practice and research in medical genetics. I eventually got a "real job" as a junior faculty member at the University of Michigan, splitting my time between organizing a research program in human genetics and seeing patients with genetic diseases. Often frustrated by the lack of information available on the fundamental basis of many genetic diseases, I was particularly drawn to those disorders where the action of a single mutant gene caused a great deal of sickness and distress, but where the cell biology had not been worked out sufficiently to allow a direct identification of the responsible gene. Cystic fibrosis (CF) was a particularly puzzling and heart-breaking example of this situation. In collaboration with another researcher in Toronto, my research group began an intense effort to try to identify the CF gene by mapping it to the proper chromosome, and then narrowing down the region where the gene must be until finally the correct candidate was identified. This process, known as positional cloning, had never really succeeded for a problem of this complexity, so it was both gratifying and sobering to participate in such an effort. Many times we thought the problem was just too difficult and were tempted to give up. But finally the strategy worked, and the successful cloning of the cystic fibrosis gene in 1989 made better diagnosis available and opened new doors to the design of therapies, including gene therapy.

After this, similar efforts in which my research group participated yielded up the genes for other puzzling human genetic disorders, including neurofibromatosis (often erroneously referred to as the Elephant Man disease) and Huntington disease. At about the same time an international effort to map and sequence all of the human DNA, known as the Human Genome Project, was getting under way. This would make it possible to find *all* of the genes responsible for human disease, and so I was happy to have the chance to participate by setting up a Human Genome Center at the University of Michigan. When the first U.S. director of the Human Genome Project, Dr. James Watson (the same Watson who with Francis Crick discovered the structure of DNA in 1953) resigned, I was asked to take on this role. Since 1993 I have been director of the National Center for Human Genome Research of the National Institutes of Health, which is the lead agency in the United States responsible for this ambitious and historic effort to map and sequence all the human DNA by the year 2005. So far the project is doing very well—actually running ahead of schedule and under budget.

While my own career path was far from focused, I can now look back on all the experiences that I had in science and medicine and see how they have helped prepare me for overseeing this remarkable project.

FRANCIS SELLERS COLLINS *has been the director of the National Center for Human Genome Research of the National Institutes of Health since 1993. In addition to numerous honors and awards, certifications, and society memberships, he is an associate editor of a number of scientific journals in the area of genetics. He received a Ph.D. from Yale University and an M.D. with honors from the University of North Carolina School of Medicine, Chapel Hill.*

SUMMARY

1. Cloning is the production of identical copies of molecules, cells, or organisms from a single ancestor. The development and refinement of methods for cloning higher plants and animals represents a significant advance in genetic technology that will speed up the process of improving crops and the production of domestic animals.

2. These developments have been paralleled by the discovery of methods to clone segments of DNA molecules. This technology is founded on the discovery that a series of enzymes known as restriction endonucleases recognize and cut DNA at specific nucleotide sequences. Linking DNA segments produced by restriction enzyme treatment with vectors such as plasmids or engineered viral chromosomes produces recombinant DNA molecules.

3. Recombinant DNA molecules are transferred into host cells and cloned copies are produced as the host cells grow and divide. A variety of host cells can be used, but the most common is the bacterium, *E. coli*. The cloned DNA molecules can be recovered from the host cells and purified for further use.

4. A collection of cloned DNA sequences from one source is a library. The clones in the library serve as a resource for work on specific genes.

5. Clones for specific genes can be recovered from a library by using probes to screen the library.

6. Cloned sequences are characterized in several ways, including Southern blotting and DNA sequencing.

QUESTIONS AND PROBLEMS

1. Nuclear transfer to clone cattle is done by the following technique:
   a. an eight cell embryo is divided into 2 4-cell embryos and implanted into a surrogate mother
   b. a sixteen cell embryo is divided into sixteen separate cells and these cells are allowed to form new 16-cell embryos and directly implanted into surrogate mothers
   c. a 2-cell embryo is divided into 2 separate cells and implanted into a surrogate mother
   d. a sixteen cell embryo is divided into sixteen separate cells and fused with enucleated eggs. The fused eggs are then implanted into surrogate mothers
   e. none of the above

2. Restriction enzymes:
   a. recognize specific nucleotide sequences in DNA.
   b. cut both strands of DNA.
   c. often produce single-stranded tails.
   d. do all of the above.
   e. do none of the above.

3. What is meant by the term recombinant DNA?
   a. DNA from bacteria and viruses
   b. DNA from different sources that are not normally found together
   c. DNA from restriction enzyme digestions
   d. DNA that can make RNA and proteins
   e. none of the above

4. Which enzyme is responsible for covalently linking DNA strands together?
   a. DNA polymerase
   b. DNA ligase
   c. *Eco*RI
   d. restriction enzymes
   e. RNA polymerase

5. A cloned library of an entire genome contains:
   a. the expressed genes in an organism.
   b. all the genes of an organism.

   c. only a representative selection of genes.
   d. a large number of alleles of each gene.
   e. none of the above.

6. The DNA sequence below contains a 6-base palindromic sequence that acts as a recognition and cutting site for a restriction enzyme. What is this sequence? Which enzyme will cut this sequence? Consult Figure 12.7
   CCGAGTAAGCTTAC
   GGCTCATTCGAATG

7. Briefly describe how to clone a segment of DNA.

8. You are given the task of preparing a cloned library from a human tissue culture cell line. What type of vector would you select for this library and why?

9. When cloning human DNA, why is it necessary to insert the DNA into a vector such as a bacterial plasmid?

10. Assume restriction enzyme sites as follows: E = *Eco*RI, H = *Hind*III and P = *Pst*I. What size bands would be present when the DNA shown below is cut with
    a. *Eco*RI
    b. *Hind*III and *Pst*I
    c. all three enzymes

2 kb	5 kb	3 kb	3.5 kb	4 kb	6 kb

    ———————E———————H————————P————————E————————H———————

11. Name three of the many applications for Southern blotting.

12. You are running a PCR reaction to generate copies of a fragment of the cystic fibrosis (CF) gene. Beginning with two copies at the start, how much of an amplification of this fragment will be present after 6 cycles in the PCR machine? How can you be sure that you are amplifying only the CF gene, and not other DNA sequences?

13. A new gene has been isolated in mice that causes an inherited form of retinal degeneration. This disease leads to blindness in affected individuals. You are a researcher in a human vision lab and want to see if a similar gene exists in humans (genes with similar sequences usually

mean similar functions). With your knowledge of the Southern blot procedure, how would you go about doing this? Start with the isolation of human DNA.

14. A cystic fibrosis (CF) mutation in a certain family involves a change in a single nucleotide. This mutation destroys an *Eco*RI restriction site normally found in this position. What experiments would you perform so that you can use this information in counseling individuals in this family about the likelihood that they are carriers of CF? Be precise in your description of the experiments. Assume that you find that a woman in this family is a carrier, and it happens that she is married to a man who is also heterozygous for CF, but for a different mutation in this gene. How would you counsel this couple about their risks of having a child with cystic fibrosis.

15. The steps in the polymerase chain reaction (PCR) are:
    a. denaturation, annealing of primers, synthesis using DNA polymerase
    b. restriction cutting, annealing primers, synthesis using DNA polymerase
    c. ligating, restriction cutting and transforming into bacteria
    d. DNA sequencing and restriction cutting
    e. transcription and translation

16. DNA studies are conducted using samples from a large family with a certain late onset disorder inherited in an autosomal dominant fashion. A DNA sample from each family member is digested with the restriction enzyme TaqI and the fragments are separated by size on an agarose gel. A Southern blot is then performed and the results are shown below, aligned with the family pedigree.
    a. Is there a relationship between the disorder and a band pattern in this family, excluding individual II-? Is linkage shown? If so, what band pattern is linked to the disorder?
    b. How do you explain the genotype and phenotype of II-7?
    c. How would you use this information to counsel II-2, II-3 and II-6 about their risks of developing this disorder?

17. Southern blotting can be used to detect the allelic status of the beta globin gene, and detect the allele for sickle cell anemia. The base change (A to T) that causes sickle cell anemia destroys an *Mst*II restriction site that is present in the normal beta globin gene. This difference can be detected by Southern blotting. Using a labeled beta globin gene as a probe, what differences would you expect to see for a Southern blot of the normal beta globin gene and the mutant sickle cell gene?

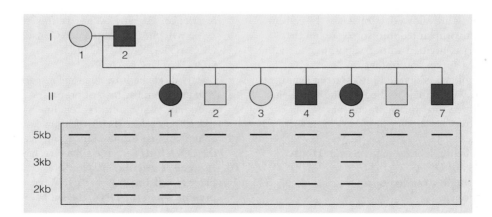

SCIENCE AND SOCIETY

1. Soon after the development of recombinant DNA techniques, one concern discussed at length was whether scientists themselves should write and enforce regulations controlling the use of recombinant DNA research or whether this should be done by others, such as local, state and federal governments. The federal government stepped in and with the help of scientists, wrote and enforced the regulations which cover this work at government-funded institutions. Today, concern has shifted to the production, release, sale and consumption of genetically altered plants and animals. Should decisions about the production, release into the environment and sale of genetically altered organisms and products be left to private industry? If not, who should oversee this activity? Should the public be involved in this process? How? Do you have any concerns about the safety of genetically altered organisms or products made by recombinant DNA technology? What are they? How can these issues be addressed?

INTERNET ACTIVITIES

The following activities use the resources of the World Wide Web to enhance the topics covered in this chapter. To investigate the topics described below, log on to the book's homepage at:

http://www.wadsworth.com/biology

1. The most recent developments concerning the Human Genome Project are regularly published in Human Genome News. This publication is sponsored by the Department of Energy, Office of Environmental Research. Find this site using the book's homepage and read the latest issue to update the information in the text about recombinant DNA. You can download the publication, or subscribe on-line to receive the publication by mail.

2. Public policy and laws concerning the use of genetic information are an important consideration as we acquire more knowledge of the human genome. Genetic discrimination in health insurance and employment is becoming a genuine concern for certain sectors of our society. Federal legislation is now being introduced to prevent misuse of this information. The National Center for Genome Resources has information available on genetic legislation on their home page.

Select one of the most recent pieces of legislation listed at this site and evaluate the bill. Do you think it has the ability to protect personal genetic information?

FOR FURTHER READING

Arnheim, N., White, T., and Rainey, W. E. 1990. The application of PCR: organismal and population biology. Bioscience 40: 174–182.

Drlica, K. 1992. Understanding DNA and gene cloning: A guide for the curious. 2nd edition. New York: Wiley.

Farello, A., Hillier, L. and Wilson, R. K. 1995. Genomic DNA sequencing methods. Methods Cell Biol. 48: 551–569.

Finch, J. L., Hope, R. M. and van Daal. A. 1996. Human sex determination using multiplex polymerase chain reaction. Sci. Justice 36: 93–95.

Heitman, J. 1993. On the origins, structure, and function of restriction-modification enzymes. Genet. Eng. 15: 57–108.

Hochmeister, M. M. 1995. DNA technology in forensic applications. Mol Aspects Med. 16: 315–437.

Gasser, C. S. and Fraley, R. T. 1989. Genetic engineering of plants for crop improvement. Science 244: 1293–1299.

Jaenisch, R. 1989. Transgenic animals. Science 240: 1468–1474.

Lawn, R. M. and Vehar, G. 1986. The molecular genetics of hemophilia. Sci. Amer. 253: 84–93.

Maniatis, T., Hardison, R., Lacy, E., Lauer, J., O'Connell, C., Quon, D., Sim, G., and Efstradiatis, A. 1978. The isolation of structural genes from libraries of eukaryotic DNA. Cell 15: 687–701.

Micklos, D. A. and Freyer, G. A. 1990. DNA science: A first course in recombinant DNA technology. Cold Springs Harbor New York: Cold Springs Harbor Press.

Mullis, K. B. 1990. The unusual origin of the polymerase chain reaction. Sci. Amer. 262: 56–65.

Nobel, D. 1995. Forensic PCR. Primed, amplified and ready for court. Anal. Chem. 67: 613A–615A.

Sader, H. S., Hollis, R. J., and Pfaller, M. A. 1995. The use of molecular techniques in the epidemiology and control of infectious disease. Clin. Lab. Med. 15: 407–431.

Smith, A. E. 1995. Viral vectors in gene therapy. Ann. Rev. Microbiol. 49: 807–838.

Southern, E. M. 1975. Detection of specific sequences among DNA fragments separated by gel electrophoresis. J. Mol. Biol. 98: 503–517.

Watson, J. D., Gilman, M., Witkowski, J, and Zoller, M. 1992. Recombinant DNA. 2nd edition. New York: Scientific American Books.

Zilinskas, R. A. and Zimmerman, B. K. 1986. The gene splicing wars: reflections on the recombinant DNA controversy. New York: Macmillan.

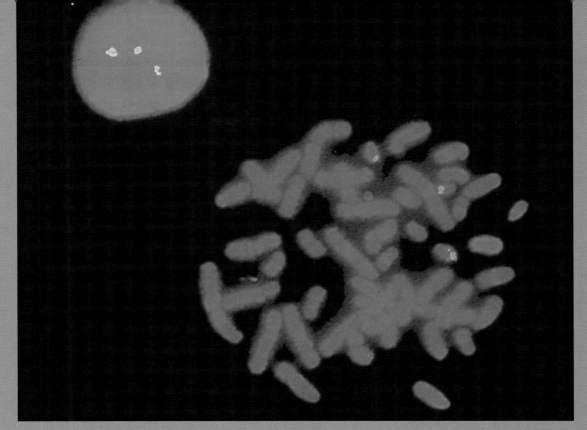

APPLICATIONS OF RECOMBINANT DNA TECHNOLOGY

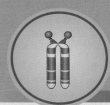

Chapter 13

Chapter Outline

RECOMBINANT DNA TECHNIQUES
   HAVE REVOLUTIONIZED GENETIC
   MAPPING
RFLPs Are Heritable Genetic Markers
Mapping Genes Using RFLPs and Positional
   Cloning
Mapping at the Chromosomal Level
DNA FINGERPRINTING
Analyzing DNA Fingerprints
Other Applications of DNA Fingerprinting

PRENATAL AND PRESYMPTOMATIC
   TESTING FOR GENETIC DISORDERS
CONCEPTS AND CONTROVERSIES   *Death of
   a Czar*
THE HUMAN GENOME PROJECT IS AN
   INTERNATIONAL EFFORT
Steps in the Project
The Human Genome Project: A Progress
   Report
Implications of the Human Genome Project

GENE TRANSFER TECHNOLOGY HAS
   MANY APPLICATIONS
Proteins Can Be Manufactured by
   Recombinant DNA Technology
Genetic Disorders Can Be Corrected by Gene
   Therapy
New Plants and Animals Can Be Created by
   Gene Transfer
ETHICAL QUESTIONS ABOUT
   RECOMBINANT DNA

OPENING IMAGE
*Trisomy 21 (Down syndrome), a
condition associated with three copies of
chromosome 21, can be diagnosed by
fluorescent* in situ *hybridization (FISH).*

S*ome 17–20 million years ago, a magnolia leaf fluttered into the cold water
of a lake in what is now Idaho. Magnolias and other plants found in
warm, humid, temperate climates flourished along the shores of the lake,
which was formed when volcanic lava flowed into the streambed of a valley.
The leaf sank into the cold, still water down to the oxygen-poor bottom and
quickly became covered with mud. Because of the lack of oxygen, the leaf did
not deteriorate; instead, over a period of millions of years, it formed a compression fossil as the mud turned to shale.*

On a day millions of years later, researchers in the 20th century split the shale layers. The exposed fossil was still green, although its color faded rapidly in the oxygen-containing atmosphere. The researchers scraped the fossilized leaf into a mortar and ground it with dry ice to form a fine powder. From this powder, the DNA of the fossil leaf was extracted and purified. Using a recombinant DNA technique, the researchers isolated a chloroplast gene from the fossil leaf. This gene encodes the information for an enzyme, which in turn controls the production of a sugar that is an intermediate in photosynthesis.

The researchers determined the nucleotide sequence of this fossil gene and compared it with that of similar genes from present-day species of magnolias. This analysis indicated that although there are some differences in the sequence between the fossil gene and the contemporary gene, there has been little overall change as this gene has travelled through the intervening generations. The differences in nucleotide sequence between the fossil magnolia and present-day species were used to establish its relationship to the species we know today. The results indicate that the fossil species is closely related to one of the species of Magnolia that grows in the eastern Unites States.

The ability to isolate and characterize a specific gene from a plant that lived some 17–20 million years ago and compare it to the gene from species alive today demonstrates the power of recombinant DNA technology. The data gathered in this experiment allow a direct measurement of the rate of mutation in an individual gene over evolutionary time, and assist in establishing the evolutionary relationship between present species and their fossil ancestors.

Recombinant DNA technology is having a dramatic impact on many other areas, including molecular biology, pharmaceutical manufacturing, agriculture, diagnosis and treatment of genetic disorders, and criminal investigations. This revolution is just beginning, and the impact of recombinant DNA technology and the accompanying biotechnology industry will continue to spread and profoundly change the lives of many individuals.

In this chapter, we will discuss some of the changes this technology has brought about in medicine, genetics, and agriculture.

RECOMBINANT DNA TECHNIQUES HAVE REVOLUTIONIZED GENETIC MAPPING

As discussed in Chapter 4, mapping human genes involves the detection of linkage between genes (genetic evidence that two or more genes are on the same chromosome) and the assignment of these linked genes to individual chromosomes. While genes can be assigned directly to the X chromosome by their unique pattern of inheritance, it is more difficult to map genes to individual autosomes. Mapping many genetic disorders is hampered because the nature of the mutant gene or its product is unknown. In some cases, the only information available is derived from family studies that have established the mode of inheritance as dominant or recessive and from population studies that estimate the frequency of the condition.

New methods of mapping human genes are now available. Mapping can now be done with no initial information about the nature of the mutant gene or the gene product. One method uses variations in the presence or absence of restriction enzyme cutting sites as genetic markers. These markers can be assigned to specific chromosomes, and genetic disorders can be mapped by showing linkage between these chromosome-specific markers and the disorder.

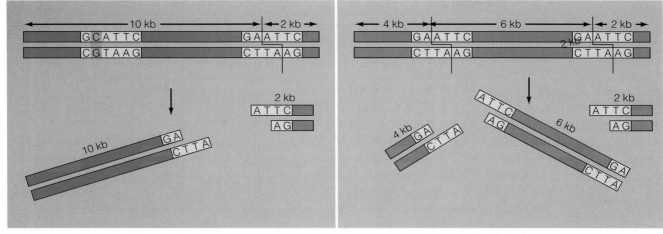

FIGURE 13.1

Restriction fragment length polymorphisms. The *A* and *B* alleles represent segments of DNA from homologous chromosomes. Arrows indicate recognition and cutting sites for restriction enzymes. Because of variation in nucleotide sequence (highlighted) in one region, a cutting site present in *B* is missing in *A*. This variation produces differences in the number and length of DNA fragments in *A* and *B* when they are cut with a restriction enzyme. In *A*, 2 fragments, one of 10 kb (10,000 base pairs) and one of 2 kb are produced. In *B*, three fragments are produced: one of 6 kb, one of 4 kb, and one of 2 kb. Because these variations in cutting sites are inherited in a codominant fashion, there are three possible genotypes: *AA*, *AB*, and *BB*. The allele combination carried by any individual can be determined by restriction digestion of genomic DNA, followed by separation of the fragments by gel electrophoresis. The band patterns for the three combinations are shown as they would appear on a Southern blot.

Restriction fragment length polymorphism (RFLP)
Variations in the length of DNA fragments generated by a restriction endonuclease. Inherited in a codominant fashion, RFLPs are used as markers for specific chromosomes or genes.

DNA restriction fragment
A segment of a longer DNA molecule produced by the action of a restriction endonuclease.

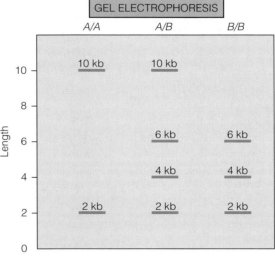

GENOTYPES		*RFLP* FRAGMENT SIZES
Homozygous	*A/A*	10 kb, 2 kb
Heterozygous	*A/B*	10 kb, 6 kb, 4 kb, 2 kb
Homozygous	*B/B*	6 kb, 4 kb, 2 kb

RFLPs Are Heritable Genetic Markers

Restriction enzymes work by recognizing specific nucleotide sequences in DNA and by cutting both strands of DNA at these sites. The nucleotide sequence in long stretches of DNA is subject to a small degree of variation. This variation is not associated with any deleterious phenotype, and occurs mostly in regions between genes. In some cases variation in nucleotide sequence creates or destroys a recognition/cutting site for a restriction enzyme, altering the pattern of cuts made in the DNA. This creates a heritable difference in the length and number of DNA fragments generated by a given restriction enzyme.

This difference is known as a **restriction fragment length polymorphism,** or **RFLP**. RFLPs are passed from generation to generation in a codominant fashion (review codominant inheritance in Chapter 3). In other words, RFLPs can serve as genetic markers, although the phenotype of an RFLP is not externally visible, as in albinism, or biochemically detectable, as with a blood type. Rather, the phenotype depends on the production of differently sized DNA fragments. Because of linkage, any genes near these markers are usually inherited along with the RFLP. Thousands of RFLPs have been mapped in humans, and many such markers have been assigned to each chromosome.

For RFLP analysis, a small blood sample (10 to 20 ml) is withdrawn, and the white blood cells (leukocytes) are separated from the red blood cells (erythrocytes). DNA is extracted from the white cells and treated with a restriction enzyme. As a result, the DNA is cut into **DNA restriction fragments.** These fragments are placed on an agarose gel and separated by size using electrophoresis. The separated fragments are then Southern blotted, using an RFLP probe (Figure 13.1).

If a mutational event has created or eliminated a restriction-enzyme cutting site, it can be detected as a change in the length of a DNA fragment, making it larger or smaller (see Figure 13.1). This variation in the cutting pattern is known as an RFLP. Using other methods, RFLPs can be mapped to specific chromosomes, and RFLP markers for each human chromosome are available.

Mapping Genes Using RFLPs and Positional Cloning

Two things are needed to assign a gene to a particular chromosome: a large, multi-generational family in which a genetic disorder is inherited and a collection of RFLPs (at least one for each human chromosome). First, a pedigree analysis is performed to determine the pattern of inheritance for the genetic disease and to identify affected individuals (➡ Figure 13.2). Then family members are tested to determine the pattern of inheritance for chromosome-specific RFLP markers. If the pattern of inheritance for the genetic defect matches the pattern of inheritance for a chromosome-specific RFLP marker, then both the genetic disorder and the RFLP must be on the same chromosome. In this case, the genetic defect can be assigned to the chromosome represented by the RFLP marker.

➡ **FIGURE 13.2**

Inheritance of an RFLP allele and a dominant trait. A family pedigree is positioned above a gel showing the distribution of alleles A and B in members of the family. Members affected by a genetic disorder are shown by filled symbols. The unaffected father (I-1) is homozygous for allele *B*, and the affected mother(I-2) is heterozygous *AB*. Examination of the pedigree and the Southern blot indicates that affected children have inherited a maternal chromosome carrying allele *A* (II-1, II-3, II-5, and II-6), while unaffected children (II-2 and II-4) have inherited a maternal chromosome carrying allele B. This pattern of inheritance means that the A allele for the RFLP is carried on the same chromosome as the mutant allele for the genetic disorder.

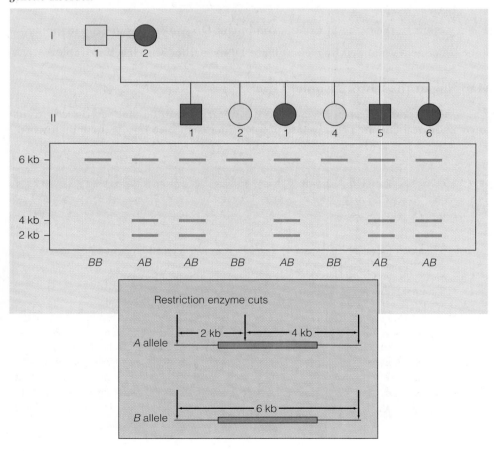

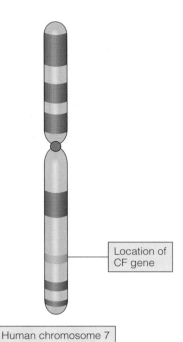

Human chromosome 7

FIGURE 13.3

The gene for cystic fibrosis was mapped to the long arm of chromosome 7 using RFLP analysis.

Positional cloning
Identification and cloning of a gene responsible for a genetic disorder that begins with no information about the gene or the function of the gene product.

The use of RFLPs in mapping human genes can be illustrated by considering the gene for cystic fibrosis (CF). Cystic fibrosis is an autosomal recessive condition with an incidence of 1 in 2000 births among those of Northern European ancestry. CF homozygotes develop obstructive lung disease and infections that lead to premature death. The mapping of the CF gene was accomplished in several steps.

Large families with a history of CF were studied to find linkage between CF and RFLP markers representing specific chromosomes. The result of these initial studies produced a list of chromosomes where the gene was *not* linked to a marker. This list is called an exclusion map, and indicates where the gene is *not* located. Using other RFLP markers, it was discovered that the CF allele was linked to markers on chromosome 7. Further work established that the CF gene is located in a region near the tip of the long arm (Figure 13.3). In the last stage, researchers cloned, recovered, and sequenced over 500,000 base pairs of DNA from the region, identifying the CF gene by finding a nucleotide sequence that encoded information for an unknown protein. From the nucleotide sequence, the amino acid sequence of the protein was predicted. Normal and mutant alleles of the gene were cloned, and the normal and mutant proteins were isolated. The protein, known as CFTCR, is inserted in the cell membrane and functions in the transport of ions. In CF, the protein is missing or is defective in function.

The mapping, identification, and cloning of the CF gene was accomplished in about 5 years, beginning with no knowledge of the nature of the gene product, the location of the gene, or the kind of mutational event that results in cystic fibrosis. This method of mapping and isolating human genes is known as **positional cloning.** The successful cloning of the CF gene has several consequences. Studies on the structure and function of the CFTCR protein have the following benefits:

- They can lead to new and effective therapies for CF.
- Heterozygotes can be detected in the population (4% of the Caucasian population), and those couples at risk for having a child with CF can be identified and counseled.
- They confirm the value of using recombinant DNA methods in gene mapping.

Some other genes mapped by recombinant DNA methods are listed in Table 13.1.

Mapping at the Chromosomal Level

If a cloned gene has been recovered from a library, it can be mapped directly to its chromosomal locus. In a metaphase preparation, each member of the human chro-

TABLE 13.1
Some of the Genes Identified by Positional Cloning

Chromosome 4	Chromosome 17
Huntington disease	Charcot-Marie-Tooth disease
Facioscapulohumeral dystrophy	Breast cancer
Chromosome 5	Neurofibromatosis
Familial polyposis (APC)	Chromosome 19
Chromosome 7	Myotonic dystrophy
Cystic fibrosis	Chromosome 21
Chromosome 11	Amyotrophic lateral sclerosis
Wilms tumor	X Chromosome
Ataxia - telangiectasia	Duchenne muscular dystrophy
Chromosome 13	Fragile-X syndrome
Retinoblastoma	Adrenoleukodystrophy
Chromosome 16	
Polycystic kidney disease	

mosome set has a distinctive set of banding patterns (Chapter 2). For mapping, the cloned gene is labeled and used as a probe. The most commonly used labels are radioactivity and fluorescent dyes. In **fluoresence *in situ* hybridization (FISH)**, the probe is labeled with a fluorescent dye and hybridized to a metaphase chromosome preparation that has been partially denatured. The probe forms a hybrid with complementary sequences on the chromosome, and is visualized as a bright fluorescent spot on a pair of homologous chromosomes under a microscope (Figure 13.4).

DNA FINGERPRINTING

The technique of RFLP analysis was developed in the mid-1970s as a method to study the organization of genes. In the intervening years, RFLP analysis has been used in mapping human genes and in many other applications, including forensics, ecology, archaeology, preservation of endangered species, and even dog breeding.

A version of RFLP mapping developed by Alec Jeffreys and his colleagues at the University of Leicester detects variations in the number of short, repeated DNA sequences present at specific chromosomal sites. These sequences are called minisatellites, and are sequences ranging from 14 to 100 nucleotides in length that are organized into clusters of tandem repeats. For example, the nucleotide sequence

CCTTCCCTTCCCTTCCCTTCCCTTCCCTTC

is made up of six tandem copies of a five-nucleotide sequence, CCTTC. Clusters of such repeats are scattered at many sites on all chromosomes. The number of repeats at each site is variable, ranging from 2 to more than 100, and each variation is an allele. These loci are called **variable-number tandem repeats (VNTRs)**. Because there are many different VNTR loci, and because many loci have dozens of alleles, heterozygosity is common. As a result, the pattern of bands produced when VNTR se-

 FIGURE 13.4
Genes mapped to homologous chromosomes by fluorescent *in situ* hybridization (FISH).

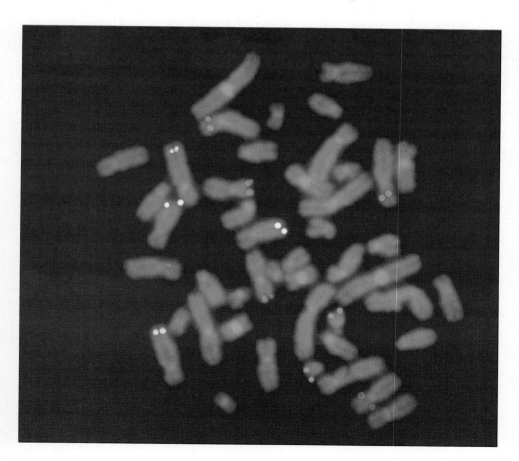

DNA fingerprint
A pattern of restriction fragments that is unique to an individual.

quences are cut with restriction enzymes and Southern blotted is unique to each person (except for identical twins), and the term **DNA fingerprint** is used to describe this pattern of DNA fragments (Figure 13.5).

In criminal cases, DNA is extracted from biological material left at a crime scene. This can include blood, tissue, hair, skin fragments, and semen. The DNA is cut with restriction enzymes, and the resulting pattern of fragments is analyzed and compared with the DNA fingerprints of the victim and any suspects in the case. DNA fingerprinting was first used in England to solve the rape and murder of two teenage girls. Over 4000 men were DNA fingerprinted during the investigation. The results freed an innocent man who had been jailed for the crime, and led to a confession from the killer. This case was described in the best-selling book, *The Blooding*, by Joseph Wambaugh. In the United States, DNA fingerprinting was first used in a criminal case in 1987. Since then it has been used in over a thousand similar cases. DNA fingerprinting came to widespread public attention in the murder trial of O. J. Simpson.

Analyzing DNA Fingerprints

The use of DNA fingerprints in legal cases requires care in the collection and handling of samples, accurate identification of bands in the gel, methods for determining when bands match, and reliable calculations for the probability of matching bands from the evidence with those from the defendant.

In the U.S., about 12 VNTR probes, located on different chromosomes, are used in forensic DNA testing. Most of these have been patented by biotechnology companies and are available for purchase by law enforcement agencies. Each probe can be used to determine a fingerprint pattern for a specific VNTR. In a criminal case, at least four different probes are typically used to develop a DNA fingerprint profile for a suspect. If the DNA fingerprint profile of the suspect does not match that of the evidence, then he or she can be excluded as the criminal. If the profile of the suspect matches that of the evidence, then there are two possibilities: The DNA fingerprint profiles came from the same person, or the DNA profile from the evidence came from someone else, who has the same pattern of DNA fingerprint bands. Most of the efforts to discredit DNA fingerprints in court cases centers around this last possibility, and not the DNA analysis itself.

Analysis of DNA fingerprints uses a combination of probability theory, statistics, and population genetics. These are used to estimate how frequently the profile of

FIGURE 13.5

DNA fingerprinting in a criminal case. DNA fingerprints for two suspects (S1 and S2) and a fingerprint from evidence [E(vs)] are shown. The profile of suspect 1 is different than that of the evidence, but the profile of suspect 2 matches that of the evidence band for band.

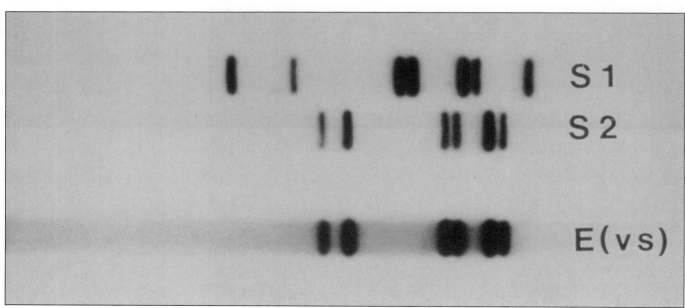

TABLE 13.2		
Calculating a DNA Fingerprint Profile Frequency		
ALLELE AT LOCUS	FREQUENCY IN POPULATION	COMBINED FREQUENCY
1	1 in 25 (0.040)	—
2	1 in 100 (0.010)	1 in 2500
3	1 in 320 (0.0031)	1 in 806,000
4	1 in 75 (0.0133)	1 in 60,600,000

VNTR fingerprints in question might be found in an individual who is a member of a given population group, or in the general population. This is done by first calculating the individual frequencies for each pair of VNTR alleles, using information from population studies. In a second step, the frequencies for each VNTR are multiplied together to produce the final estimate of frequency. The frequencies are multiplied together because the probes used represent VNTRs on different chromosomes, and are inherited by independent assortment.

Multiplication of the frequencies of each VNTR locus typically results in a rare frequency, even when the individual frequencies are fairly common. Table 13.2 shows how VNTR alleles that by themselves, are fairly common in the population, become rare when combined together. The allele detected at locus 1 has a frequency of 1 in 25 (4%) in the population, and the allele locus 2 has a frequency of 1 in 100 (1%). The combination of these two would be found in about 1 in every 2500 individuals. The combination of these two loci with loci 3 and 4 results in a frequency of 1 in about 60 million, that is only one person in a population of 60 million would be expected to have this particular combination of VNTR alleles. The frequency estimate does not prove the suspect is guilty, but is a factor that should be considered along with the other facts in the case.

Other Applications of DNA Fingerprinting

DNA fingerprints have been used in many other applications, including analyzing DNA recovered from an Egyptian mummy, settling a dispute over the bloodlines of a purebred dog and establishing the fate of the Romanov family (see "Concepts and Controversies," page 316). It has also been used to determine the degree of relatedness among members of endangered species, and on the frozen remains of a wooly mammoth recovered in Siberia to determine the evolutionary relationships between mammoths and modern-day elephants.

By far, the most common usage of DNA fingerprinting in the U.S. is in establishing paternity. Over 30% of the births in the U.S. are to single mothers, and over 130,000 paternity tests are performed each year, using DNA fingerprints. These tests are performed to establish legal responsibility for financial support, and efforts by local, state and federal governments result in support payments of over five billion dollars per year.

 ## PRENATAL AND PRESYMPTOMATIC TESTING FOR GENETIC DISORDERS

Using recombinant DNA techniques, it is possible to do both prenatal and presymptomatic genotypic analysis. **Prenatal testing** can detect the presence of a genetic disorder in an embryo or fetus. The use of recombinant DNA techniques extends the scope of amniocentesis and chorionic villus sampling (CVS) in prenatal testing (see Chapter

Prenatal testing
Testing to determine the presence of a genetic disorder in an embryo or fetus; commonly done by amniocentesis or chorionic villus sampling.

Death of a Czar

Czar Nicholas Romanov II of Russia was overthrown in the Bolshevik Revolution that began in 1917. He and the Empress Alexandra (grand-daughter of Queen Victoria), their daughters Olga, Tatiana, Marie, Anastasia, and their son, Alexei (who had hemophilia) were taken prisoners. In July, 1918, it was announced that the Czar had been executed, but for many years, the fate of his family was unknown. In the 1920s, a Russian investigator, Nikolai Solokof, reported that the Czar, his wife and children and four others were executed at Ekaterinburg, Russia on July 16, 1918, and their bodies were buried in a grave in the woods near the city. Other accounts indicated that at least one family member, Anastasia, escaped to live in Western Europe or the United States. Over the years, the mystery surrounding the family generated several books and movies.

In the late 1970s, two Russian amateur historians began investigating Sokolf's accounts, and after a painstaking search, nine skeletons were dug from a shallow grave at a site 20 miles from Ekaterinberg in July of 1991. All of the skeletons bore marks and bullet wounds indicating violent death. Forensic experts examined the remains, and using computer-assisted facial reconstructions and other evidence, concluded that the remains were those of the Czar, the Czarina, and three of their five children. The remains of two children were missing: the son, Alexei and one daughter. To confirm the findings, DNA analysis was used.

The investigators used a three-fold strategy in the DNA analysis. DNA was extracted from bone fragments and used for sex testing, for DNA typing to establish family relationships, and for mitochondrial DNA testing to trace maternal relationships. The sex testing used a six-base pair difference in a gene carried on both the X and Y chromosome. The results indicated that the skeletons were of four males and five females, confirming the results of physical analysis. The family relationship was tested using probes for five short tandem repeat (STR) sequences. These results indicate that skeletons 3-7 were a family group, with 4 and 7 as parents, and 3,5 and 6 as children. If the remains are those of the Romanovs, the combination of the sex tests and the STR tests establish that the remains of one of the princesses and the Tsarevitch, Alexei, are missing.

To determine whether the remains belonged to the Romanovs, mitochondrial DNA (mtDNA) testing was conducted. Since mtDNA is maternally inherited, living relatives of the Czarina, including Prince Philip, the husband of Queen Elizabeth of England were included in the tests. This analysis shows an exact match between the remains of the Czarina, the three children and living relatives. mtDNA from the Czar matched that of two living maternal relatives, confirming that the remains are those of the Czar, his wife and three of his children. The fate of Alexei and one daughter remains unknown, but historical accounts suggest that their bodies were burned or buried separately.

This study overcame several technical challenges, but clearly established the identity of the skeletons as those of the Romanovs. The results are a significant application of genetic technology in solving a mystery of world history. The intrigue, mystery, and science surrounding the search for the Romanovs is told by Robert Massie in his book *The Romanovs: The Final Chapter*.

FIGURE 13.6

Prenatal diagnosis for sickle cell anemia by Southern blot analysis. In sickle cell anemia, the mutation destroys a cutting site for a restriction enzyme. As a result, there is an alteration in the number and size of restriction enzyme fragments. Since the mutant allele has a distinctive band pattern, the genotypes of family members can be read directly from the blot. The parents (I-1, I-2) are heterozygotes. The first child (II-1) is a heterozygous carrier, the second child (II-2) is affected with sickle cell anemia, and the unborn child (II-3) is homozygous for the normal alleles, will be unaffected, and will not be a carrier.

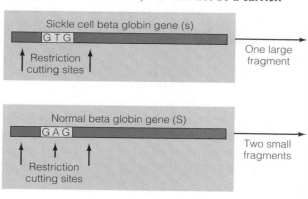

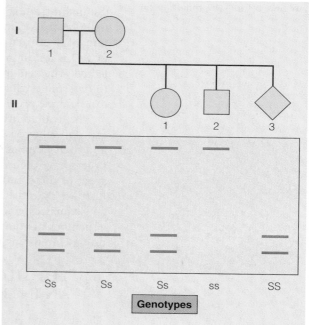

6 for a discussion of amniocentesis and CVS). Screening for sickle cell anemia can be used to illustrate the use of recombinant DNA methods in prenatal testing.

As described in Chapter 4, sickle cell anemia is a recessive trait found in families with ancestral origins in areas of West Africa and the lowland regions around the Mediterranean Sea. The defective gene product, beta globin, is not produced before birth, and so the condition cannot be prenatally diagnosed using conventional techniques.

The mutation that causes sickle cell anemia destroys a restriction enzyme cutting site, changing the length and number of DNA fragments generated by the enzyme (Figure 13.6). By analyzing the DNA restriction fragments from fetal cells collected by amniocentesis, the genotypes of normal homozygous, heterozygous, and affected homozygous individuals can be determined. Prenatal diagnosis can be performed by amniocentesis after the 15th week of development or by chorionic villus sampling in the 8th week of development.

In **preimplantation testing,** human eggs are fertilized *in vitro* and allowed to develop in a culture dish for 3 days. Then one of the 6 to 8 embryonic cells, called a blastomere, is removed by microdissection, and the DNA in this single cell is extracted and analyzed to test for a genetic disorder (Figure 13.7). DNA from the single cell is amplified by the polymerase chain reaction (PCR) and used to determine the genetic status of the embryo. To date, the method has been used successfully to test for the most common form of cystic fibrosis, muscular dystrophy, Lesch-Nyhan syndrome, and hemophilia. Embryos not affected with a genetic disorder are transplanted for pregnancy and delivery.

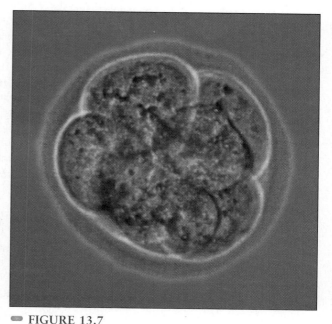

FIGURE 13.7

In blastomere testing a single cell is surgically removed from an early embryo, and the DNA from this cell is used to test for the presence of a genetic disease.

Preimplantation testing
Testing for a genetic disorder in an early embryo; testing is done by removing a single cell from the embryo.

Presymptomatic screening involves the detection of genetic disorders that only become apparent later in life, as in polycystic kidney disease (PCKD). The symptoms of PCKD develop between 35 and 50 years of age. This condition, inherited as a dominant trait, is characterized by the development of cysts in the kidney that gradually destroy kidney function. Treatment includes kidney dialysis and transplantation of a normal kidney, but many affected individuals die prematurely. Because PCKD is a dominant trait, anyone heterozygous or homozygous for the gene is affected. The gene for PCKD is located on chromosome 16, and markers can be used to determine which family members are most likely to develop PCKD. This testing can be done prenatally, or at any age before (or after) the condition appears.

The availability of presymptomatic testing for disorders such as PCKD raises social and ethical issues that are being addressed by the medical profession, patients and their families, and the public at large. Should parents in families with such disorders have their children tested? Should children be informed of their status with respect to these and other conditions? Questions and issues such as these serve to illustrate that the effects of the recombinant DNA revolution have far-reaching consequences, and may in fact affect decisions you make in your personal life or as a member of your community. The ethical consequences of recombinant DNA technology are discussed later in this chapter.

THE HUMAN GENOME PROJECT IS AN INTERNATIONAL EFFORT

The development of recombinant DNA technology and its application to gene mapping led to the establishment of the Human Genome Project, a large-scale coordinated effort to determine the location of the 50,000 to 100,000 genes in the human genome (a **genome** is the set of genes carried by an individual), and to analyze the nucleotide sequence of these genes. Originally established by the U.S. Congress, and now an international effort coordinated by the Human Genome Organization (HUGO), the project is scheduled to be completed by 2005 at a cost of about $3 billion dollars (about $1 per nucleotide). Although not reflected in the name, the Human Genome Project includes work on other organisms that are used in genetic studies. These include bacteria, yeast, roundworms, plants, fruit fly, and the mouse. The sequence of the 15 million nucleotides yeast genome was determined in 1996, and work on the genomes of several bacterial species has already been completed. The genomes of the roundworm (*Caenorhabditis elegans*), the plant (*Arabidposis thaliana*), the fruit fly (*Drosophila melanogaster*) should be completed sometime in 1998 or 1999. Because

TABLE 13.3		
Organisms Included in the Human Genome Project		
ORGANISM	**GENOME SIZE, (BP)**	**ESTIMATED NO. OF GENES**
Escherichia coli (bacteria)	4.2×10^6	4,000
Saccharomyces cerevisiae (yeast)	1.2×10^7	6,000
Caenorhabditis elegans (roundworm)	1.0×10^8	13,000
Arabidopsis thaliana (plant)	1.0×10^8	25,000
Drosophila melanogaster (fruit fly)	1.2×10^8	10,000
Mus musculus (mouse)	3×10^9	80,000
Homo sapiens (human)	3×10^9	80,000

of their size and complexity (Table 13.3), the sequences of the mouse and human genomes will not be completed for several years beyond those dates.

Steps in the Project

For the human genome, the major steps in the project are shown in ⬤ Figure 13.8. Although the work is shown as a series of separate projects, work is progressing more or less simultaneously on all phases of the project in laboratories around the world. Briefly, the objectives are

1. Developing high-resolution genetic maps for each human chromosome. Using the methods described earlier for making genetic maps, geneticists generated

⬤ **FIGURE 13.8**

The Human Genome Project is proceeding in four major steps. First, geneticists are producing genetic maps of each chromosome, with markers spaced about 1 million base pairs apart. Next, high-resolution physical maps, with markers assigned to chromosomal sites about every 100,000 base pairs are prepared. Following that, overlapping clones covering the regions between markers are being recovered. Finally, the nucleotide sequence of each clone is being determined, and the sequence covering the entire genome is being assembled.

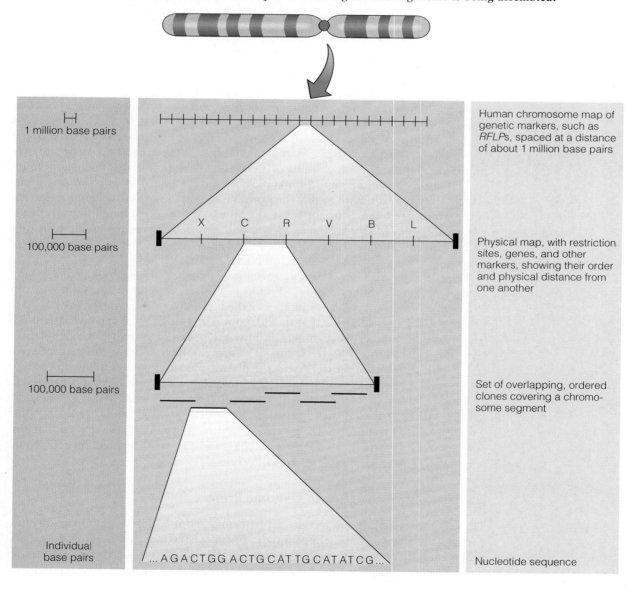

maps (using about 3000 genes, RFLPs, and other markers) with markers spaced evenly along each chromosome. High-resolution maps will make it easier to map new genes by testing for linkage to the markers spaced on the chromosomes. Maps for all chromosomes are now available, and this phase of the project is essentially complete.

2. Physical mapping of each chromosome. Physical maps show the order and distance between genes and markers, expressed in base pairs of DNA. The goal of this stage of the project is the production of physical maps of each chromosome with markers spaced every 1 million base pairs (Mb) of DNA.

3. Cloning each chromosome. In the third stage, overlapping clones covering the length of each chromosome will be developed. The problem is not in generating such clones, but in identifying and putting in order a collection of clones that overlap with each other and cover the entire chromosome. This will be done by dividing a chromosome into a number of segments and identifying clones that cover one segment at a time.

4. Sequencing the genome. The final stage will be determining the exact order of each nucleotide in each chromosome. This stage will use the overlapping clones from stage 3 as a starting point. The result will be a catalog of the over 3 billion base pairs in the human genome. This part of the Project will probably be time-consuming, and may require 5–7 years to complete.

The Human Genome Project: A Progress Report

By mid-1996, the Human Genome Project reached several of its goals. As mentioned above, genetic maps for all human chromosomes were completed in 1994. There are about 6,000 markers on the overall genetic map, but more work remains to be completed on the order and distance between many of these markers. Much progress has been made toward the completion of a physical map with markers spaced about every million base pairs. Such a map would require about 30,000 markers, and over 23,000 markers have been mapped to a chromosome or chromosome region. It appears that the rest of the physical mapping will be completed by late 1997 or sometime in 1998. The ultimate goal of the project is to determine the nucleotide sequence of the over three billion nucleotides in the human genome. Although improvements in the technology of DNA sequencing will probably be required to complete the project, sequencing of selected regions on several chromosomes (covering about 3% of the genome) has started, and should be completed by 1999.

What have we learned so far about the biology of the human genome? There have been many significant findings resulting from the genome project, including the discovery of a new mechanism of mutation, called trinucleotide expansion (discussed in Chapter 11), and the finding that the disruption of a single gene can give rise to different genetic disorders, depending on how the gene is affected. For example, the gene RET (MIM/OMIM 164761) encodes a protein that is a cell-surface receptor engaged in the transfer of signals across the plasma membrane. Depending on the type and location of mutations within this gene, four distinct genetic disorders can result, including two types of multiple endocrine neoplasia (MIM/OMIM 171400 and MIM/OMIM 162300), familial medullary thyroid carcinoma (MIM/OMIM 155240), and Hirschprung disease (MIM/OMIM 142623). These and similar discoveries have already had an impact on the diagnosis, treatment and genetic counseling in several groups of genetic disorders.

Implications of the Human Genome Project

The implications of the project are far-reaching, and it will have an impact on clinical medicine, genetic counseling, and treatment for the more than 4000 genetic disorders that affect humans. Information from the project is also expected to have an impact on the identification of genes for polygenic traits such as adult-onset diabetes,

some forms of cancer, mental illnesses such as manic depression and schizophrenia, high blood pressure, and conditions for which familial tendencies interact with one or more environmental factors.

The Human Genome Project has raised a number of related legal, ethical, and moral issues, including the use of and access to information about an individual's genetic status or predisposition. Within the project, a program has been established to identify and discuss such issues. This program, called ELSI (Ethical, Legal and Social Implications), draws on the expertise of scientists, lawyers, ethicists, philosophers, and others to consider how the information generated by the Human Genome Project affects individuals and society. It also examines the possible uses of information and techniques generated by the project, and develops public policy options to ensure that the information is used for the benefit of individuals and society.

◢ FIGURE 13.9

Transgenic sheep, carrying the human gene for alpha-1-antitrypsin, secrete the gene product into their milk. The protein can be extracted, purified, and used for treating emphysema.

GENE TRANSFER TECHNOLOGY HAS MANY APPLICATIONS

Recombinant DNA technology was originally used to transfer foreign genes into bacterial cells as a way of cloning large amounts of a specific gene for further study. Later, methods were developed for producing eukaryotic proteins in the host bacterial cells. Gene transfer is not limited to the use of bacteria as host cells; it is also possible to transfer genes between higher organisms. In this section, we will review some of the current applications of gene transfer technology.

Proteins Can Be Manufactured by Recombinant DNA Technology

One of the first commercial applications of recombinant DNA technology was the production of gene products (in the form of proteins) that could be used in the therapeutic treatment of human disease. Previously, such proteins were collected from animals, pooled blood samples, or even human cadavers. Most of these methods produce only a limited amount of therapeutic proteins, and specific risks are associated with the use of such products. For example, individuals afflicted with hemophilia, an X-linked recessive disorder, are unable to manufacture a clotting factor, and suffer episodes of uncontrollable bleeding. The missing clotting factor can be extracted from pooled blood samples; however, before blood testing for HIV became routine, many hemophiliacs treated with clotting factor prepared in this way were infected with the human immunodeficiency virus (HIV) associated with the development of AIDS (acquired immunodeficiency syndrome).

In humans, an enzyme deficiency is associated with heritable forms of emphysema, a progressive and fatal respiratory disorder. The defective enzyme is alpha-1-antitrypsin, and it can be produced for use in treating emphysema by gene transfer technology. The human alpha-1-antitrypsin gene has been cloned into a vector at a site adjacent to a DNA sequence that regulates expression of milk proteins. Vectors carrying this gene were microinjected into fertilized sheep eggs, and the eggs were implanted into female sheep (◢ Figure 13.9). The resulting transgenic sheep developed normally, and the females produce milk that contains up to 1/3 of a pound of alpha-1-antitrypsin per gallon of milk. This method is still under development, but it is not hard to imagine that a small herd of sheep could supply the world's need for this protein.

The use of recombinant DNA technology to manufacture specific proteins such as insulin, clotting factors, and alpha-1-antitrypsin ensures a controlled supply of a product free from contamination by disease-causing agents. Human insulin derived from a cloned gene inserted into bacteria was first marketed in 1982, and is used by many diabetics. When your cat is inoculated against feline leukemia virus, it receives a vaccine produced by recombinant DNA technology; farmers routinely use recombinant-DNA-derived vaccines to prevent diseases in hogs. Table 13.4 lists some genetically engineered products now available or in testing.

The use of such proteins is not without controversy, however. When introduced, there was considerable disagreement about the use of recombinant-DNA-derived bovine growth hormone to boost milk production in dairy cows. The use of this hormone was approved by the U.S. Food and Drug Administration in February 1994 and is now used on about 15% of the dairy cows in the United States. On the one hand, use of the hormone, known as BST, benefits farmers by increasing milk production by about 10%, and results in lowered fixed costs. On the other hand, opponents charge that the technology is unnecessary, that cows given this hormone are at greater risk of disease, and that the risks of long-term use of this protein are unknown. Nevertheless, it is estimated that by the year 2000, 70% of the nation's milk supply will be produced with BST.

Genetic Disorders Can Be Corrected by Gene Therapy

The use of genetically engineered proteins (such as insulin) for therapy is an indirect method of treating genetic disorders. The development of gene transfer techniques has made it possible to treat human genetic disorders by transferring normal copies of genes into cells carrying defective copies. A number of methods for transferring cloned genes into human cells are under investigation, including the use of viruses as vectors, chemical methods that aid transfer of DNA across the cell membrane, and physical methods such as microinjection or fusion of cells with vesicles carrying cloned DNA sequences.

The use of viral vectors, especially viruses known as retroviruses, is well advanced, and is currently used for human gene transfer experiments. In these experiments, some viral genes are removed, allowing a human gene to be inserted (● Figure 13.10). Gene therapy began in 1990, when a human gene for the enzyme adenosine deaminase (ADA) was inserted into a retrovirus and then transferred into the white

TABLE 13.4

Some Products Made By Recombinant DNA Technology

PRODUCT	USE
Atrial natriuetic factor	Treatment for hypertension, heart failure
Bovine growth hormone	Improve milk production in dairy cows
Cellulase	Break down cellulose in animal feed
Colony stimulating factor	Treatment for leukemia
Epidermal growth factor	Treatment of burns, improve survival of skin grafts
Erythropoieten	Treatment for anemia
Hepatitis B Vaccine	Prevent infection by hepatitis B virus
Human insulin	Treatment for diabetes
Human growth hormone	Treatment for some forms of dwarfism, other growth defects
Interferons (alpha, gamma)	Treatment for cancer, viral infections
Interleukin-2	Treatment for cancer
Superoxide dismutase	Improve survival of tissue transplants
Tissue plasminogen activator	Treatment of heart attacks

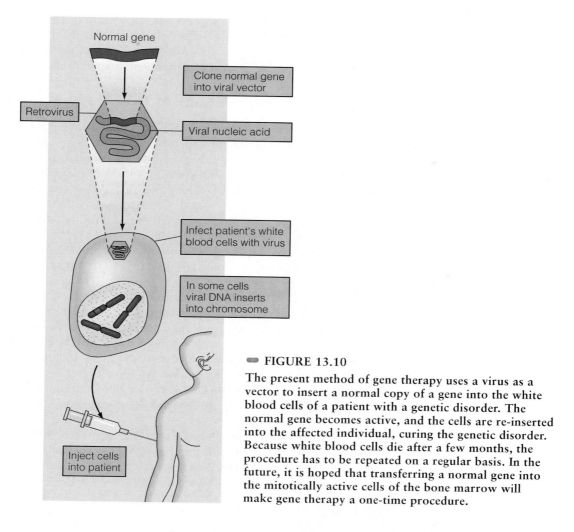

Normal gene

Retrovirus

Clone normal gene into viral vector

Viral nucleic acid

Infect patient's white blood cells with virus

In some cells viral DNA inserts into chromosome

Inject cells into patient

FIGURE 13.10

The present method of gene therapy uses a virus as a vector to insert a normal copy of a gene into the white blood cells of a patient with a genetic disorder. The normal gene becomes active, and the cells are re-inserted into the affected individual, curing the genetic disorder. Because white blood cells die after a few months, the procedure has to be repeated on a regular basis. In the future, it is hoped that transferring a normal gene into the mitotically active cells of the bone marrow will make gene therapy a one-time procedure.

blood cells of a young girl, who was suffering from a genetic disorder called severe combined immunodeficiency (SCID). Affected individuals have no functional immune system and are prone to infections, many of which can be fatal. The normal ADA gene, inserted into her blood cells, encodes an enzyme that allows cells of the immune system to mature properly. As a result, she now has a functional immune system and is leading a normal life.

Gene therapy is now being used in more than 100 clinical trials for a wide range of purposes, including the treatment of genetic disorders, cancer and HIV infection. In spite of the early success, gene therapy for the treatment of genetic disorders is still a developing technique with several obstacles to overcome. Among these are inconsistent results. After three years, the first child treated with gene therapy for SCID had a new ADA gene in more than 50% of her circulating white blood cells. A second child, who began treatment a short time later, has the normal gene in only 0.1% to 1% of her cells. In 11 trials for transfer of the cystic fibrosis (CF) gene into the epithelial cells of the respiratory system using an adenovirus as a vector, only about 5% of the target cells express the normal CF gene, and in many recipients, no expression can be detected. Most of these problems have been traced to inefficient vectors. Retroviral vectors can only insert genes into cells that are active in growth and division. In addition, there is no way to direct where the transferred gene inserts into the host cell DNA, and as a result, many transferred genes are not expressed. A new generation of viral vectors is now under development, and other methods of gene transfer are being investigated.

Gene replacement therapy eventually will become a standard method for treating certain genetic disorders. One form of diabetes is currently treated by daily injection of a gene product, insulin. In the future, treatment by transfer of the insulin gene itself would represent a one-time treatment to permanently correct this condition.

New Plants and Animals Can Be Created by Gene Transfer

Gene transfer technology is not only being used in trials on humans; it has been used for some time in agriculture as a way of improving crop plants and farm animals. Corn is a major cereal crop in the United States, with an annual market value of about $22 billion. Corn is used as an animal feed, a source of sweeteners for foods and beverages, and for the production of ethanol, which may grow in importance as an alternative to gasoline.

To transfer genes into corn, cloned genes for a desired trait are blasted into cultured cells with a "gene gun" that forces the genes into the cell (⬭ Figure 13.11). The cells are cultured to form a tissue mass that will grow into a corn plant. Corn plants that have been transformed with a gene for herbicide resistance have completed field trials and are now being marketed to farmers. Testing is underway for corn plants transformed with a gene for resistance to certain insects.

We are now entering a time when strains of corn that have been genetically modified using recombinant DNA techniques will be planted, harvested, and sold commercially. This first generation of genetically engineered corn will be resistant to herbicides. Future strains will be resistant to insect pests and plant diseases. The second generation of genetically engineered corn strains will have altered levels of protein, carbohydrate, and oils. Field testing of genetically modified strains of other crop plants—including potatoes, tomatoes, and cotton—are underway, and these will reach the market in a few years.

Genetically altered tomatoes, called Flavr-Savr tomatoes (⬭ Figure 13.12), are currently on the market in many areas of the United States. They have been genetically modified using recombinant DNA techniques to slow the softening that accompanies the ripening process. This allows tomatoes to be left on the vine longer, and makes refrigeration in shipping unnecessary. The result is a tomato with more flavor. Through genetic engineering, it is possible to customize the genetic makeup of crop plants (like the tomato) for specific purposes, such as delayed ripening,

⬭ **FIGURE 13.11**

(a) A gene gun is used to transfer genes into plant cells. (b) In the gene gun, a plastic bullet is used to drive DNA-coated pellets into cells.

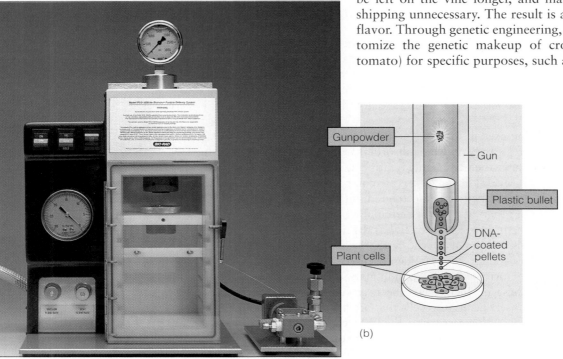

(a)

(b)

Transgenic tomatoes are now on the market. The tomato has been genetically altered to slow fruit softening and to improve flavor.

or the development of high-protein strains for food uses, high oil content for sweeteners, etc. Manipulating organisms by genetic engineering achieves the same goals as selective breeding, but is more efficient and faster than traditional methods.

Genetic engineering of crop plants is accompanied by parallel developments in genetic alterations of domestic animals. Gene transfer technology has been used to transfer human and cow growth hormone genes into pigs in an attempt to develop leaner, faster-growing hogs (■ Figure 13.13). The genes were transferred by injection into newly fertilized eggs that were implanted into a foster mother. Although the transgenic (carrying a transferred gene) pigs grow faster on a high-protein diet, they have a number of problems including ulcers, arthritis, sterility, and premature death resulting from excessive production of growth hormone in their tissues. Further work on the regulation of transferred genes will be necessary to eliminate these problems and pave the way for the appearance of genetically engineered pork in the meat case at the supermarket.

❀ ETHICAL QUESTIONS ABOUT RECOMBINANT DNA

The ability to transfer genes into human cells not only opens the way to a new method for treating genetic disorders but also raises the possibility that we can direct the evolution of our species by modifying the genetic makeup of individuals and their offspring. The gene therapy now being used involves the use of somatic cells as tar-

■ FIGURE 13.13
This transgenic pig carries human growth hormone genes.

gets for genes. Genes can also be transferred to germ cell, the parent cells of gametes. Transfer of genes into these cells will alter the genetic makeup of future generations. There is serious disagreement about whether germ-line therapy is ethical. A related question is whether it is ethical to create new forms of plants and animals to produce therapeutic proteins.

There is also the possibility that gene therapy will be used as a form of self-improvement rather than a treatment for a genetic disorder. Should children who are very short receive growth hormone or a growth hormone gene to allow them to be taller adults? If it is acceptable to treat abnormally short children, how about treating children of normal height to enhance their chances of becoming professional basketball or volleyball players?

The current guidelines of the U.S. Food and Drug Administration do not require identifying labels on food produced by recombinant DNA technology. Should such food be labeled, and if so, why? It can be argued that food products have been genetically manipulated for thousands of years, and that gene transfer is simply an extension of past practices. It can also be claimed that consumers have a need and a right to know that food products have been altered by gene transfer.

The legal, moral, and ethical implications of gene transfer technology need to be considered carefully. As outlined earlier, some of these issues are being addressed by the Human Genome Project; but in other areas, discussion, education, and policy formation lag far behind the technology.

SUMMARY

1. Recombinant DNA techniques can be used in a variety of applications, including gene mapping, forensic applications such as DNA fingerprinting, prenatal diagnosis, gene therapy, and the production of human gene products for therapeutic uses.

2. Gene mapping has been greatly enhanced using recombinant DNA techniques. Genes can be mapped by several techniques, including positional cloning and direct mapping to chromosomes.

3. An ever-growing list of genetic disorders can be diagnosed by RFLP analysis. Mutant genes and heterozygous carrier status can be detected in adults, children, fetuses, embryos, and even gametes.

4. The Human Genome Project uses recombinant DNA technology to map all of the estimated 50,000 to 100,000 genes carried in human cells. The goal of the project is to determine the sequence of the 3 billion base pairs of human DNA.

5. The first clinical trials involving the insertion of genes into humans have already started, and although some technical barriers remain, gene therapy will probably become a more common form of medical treatment within the next decade.

6. Genetic engineering is also being used to transfer genes into crop plants, conferring resistance to herbicides, insect pests, and plant diseases. Gene transfers to alter the protein, carbohydrate, and oil content of cereal crops will dramatically alter farming practices in the next century. Experiments to produce genetically altered farm animals used in meat and milk production are underway, and the products from these experiments should reach consumers within the next decade.

QUESTIONS AND PROBLEMS

1. RFLP sites are useful as genetic markers for linkage and mapping studies as well as disease diagnosis. Keeping in mind that RFLPs behave as genes, what factors are important in selecting RFLPs for use in such studies?

2. In the examples given in this chapter (Figure 13.2), the RFLP is always inherited with (linked to) the genetic disorder. In practice, however, it is sometimes observed that in some progeny the RFLP is not linked to the genetic disorder, reducing its effectiveness in detecting carrier heterozygotes. How do you explain this observation, and what circumstances are likely to affect the frequency with which this nonlinkage occurs?

3. In selecting target cells to receive a transferred gene in gene therapy, what factors must be taken into account?

4. VNTRs are:
   a. used for DNA fingerprinting
   b. repeated sequences present in the human genome
   c. highly variable in copy number
   d. all of the above
   e. none of the above
5. Gene therapy involves:
   a. the introduction of recombinant proteins into individuals
   b. cloning human genes into plants
   c. the introduction of a normal gene into an individual carrying a mutant copy
   d. DNA fingerprinting
   e. none of the above
6. Which of the following is not a goal of the Human Genome Project?
   a. construction of high resolution genetic maps
   b. sequencing the entire genome
   c. curing all genetic diseases
   d. generating a physical map of each chromosome
   e. obtaining a set of overlapping clones covering the genome
7. At what stages in life are prenatal testing, preimplantation testing and presymptomatic testing done?
8. A paternity test is conducted using PCR to analyze an RFLP that consistently produces a unique DNA fragment pattern from a single chromosome. Examining the results of the Southern blot below, which male(s) can be excluded as the father of the child? Which male(s) could be the father of the child?

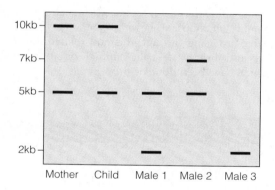

9. What are the steps involved in the procedures currently used for gene therapy?
10. Can you think of other uses for DNA fingerprinting than those mentioned in the text?

11. What are some of the potential dangers of recombinant DNA technology? How should these potential problems be investigated to determine if they are in fact dangers?
12. A crime is committed and the only piece of evidence the police are able to gather is a small bloodstain. The forensic scientist at the crime lab is able to extract DNA from the blood. The DNA is cut with a restriction enzyme and the fragments separated by electrophoresis. The DNA fragments on the gel are transferred to a membrane and probed with a piece of radioactive DNA (Probe 1) to visualize the pattern of bands. The forensic scientist compares the band pattern in the evidence (E) with the patterns from the suspects (S1, S2). The first probe is removed, and the membrane is hybridized using another probe (Probe 2), and the band patterns are compared. This process is repeated for Probe 3 and Probe 4.

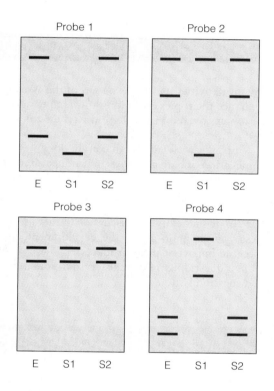

a. Based on the results of this testing, can either of the suspects be excluded as the one who committed the crime? If so, which one? Why?
b. Is the pattern from the evidence consistent with the band pattern of one of the suspects? Which one?

SCIENCE AND SOCIETY

1. The prospect of using gene therapy to alleviate genetic conditions is still a vision of the future. Gene therapy for adenosine deaminase deficiency has proven to be quite promising but many obstacles remain to be overcome. Currently, the correction of human genetic defects is done using retroviruses as vectors. For this purpose, viral genes are removed from the retroviral genome, creating a vector capable of transferring human structural genes into sites on human chromosomes within target tissue cells. Do you see any potential problems with inserting pieces of a retroviral genome into humans? If so, are there ways to combat or prevent these problems?

2. Genetic testing using DNA markers for specifically identified mutations allows the diagnosis of many adult onset disorders years or decades before symptoms appear. Presymptomatic testing to determine whether individuals are at risk for certain conditions such as familial hypercholesteremia, Huntington disease or cancer, raises many ethical, legal and social issues. What are the possible psychological and medical effects of a positive test for a condition that causes a premature death? Is it appropriate to offer such testing before we have effective measures to treat or cure the condition? Does this testing raise the possibility of discrimination against those who test positive for a fatal disorder? How? Should the law require that such individuals be given life and health insurance?

INTERNET ACTIVITIES

The following activities use the resources of the World Wide Web to enhance the topics covered in this chapter. To investigate the topics covered below, log on to the book's homepage at:

http://www.wadsworth.com/biology

1. The application of biotechnology to produce altered plant and animal products is somewhat controversial. Use the BIOSIS site to review currently available genetically engineered food products.
   a. Participate in the on-line discussion at this site and express your opinion about the development, use and potential impact of these products.
   b. Fill in a questionnaire or register your vote in the poll on disucssion issues.

2. Return to the Human Genome homepage used in the first activity in Chapter 12. Look for the articles about organ transplants across species (i.e, using baboon kidneys in humans).
   a. Write a summary of what you found. What are your thoughts and feelings about transpecific transplants (xenotransplants)? Is there reason to be concerned about transferring infections from the animal donor to the human recipient? If you had a spouse or a child whose life could be extended with such a transplant, would you choose to have it done?
   b. After browsing through this and related linked sites, list and briefly describe animal organ transplants which have been done or proposed.

FOR FURTHER READING

Anderson, W. F. 1992. Human gene therapy. *Science* **256**: 808–813.

Caskey, C. 1993. Presymptomatic diagnosis: a first step toward genetic health care. *Science* **262**: 48–49.

Collins, F. and Galas, D. 1993. A new five-year plan for the U.S. human genome project. *Science* **262**: 43–46.

Crystal, R. G. 1995. Transfer of genes to humans: early lessons and obstacles to success. *Science* **270**:404-410.

deWachter, M. 1993. Ethical aspects of human germ-line therapy. *Bioethics* **7**: 166–177.

Friedman, T. 1989. Progress toward human gene therapy. *Science* **244**: 1275–1281.

Gilbert, W., and Villa-Komaroff, L. 1980. Useful proteins from recombinant bacteria. *Sci. Am.* (April) **242**: 74–97.

Guyer, M., and Collins, F. S. 1995. How is the Human Genome Project Doing, and what have we learned so far? Proc. Nat. Acad. Sci. USA **92**:10841-10848.

Harris, J. 1992. *Wonderwoman and Superman: The ethics of human biotechnology.* New York: Oxford University Press.

Hubbard, R. and Wald, E. 1993. *Exploding the Gene Myth. Boston: Beacon Press.*

Kantoff, P. W., Freeman, S. M., and Anderson , W. F. 1988. Prospects for gene therapy for immuno-deficiency diseases. Ann. Rev. Immunol. **6**: 581–594.

Kevles, D. and Hood, L. 1992. *The Code of Codes: Scientific and Social Issues in the Human Genome Project.* Cambridge MA: Harvard University Press.

Kohn, D. B., Anderson, W. F., and Blaese, R. M. 1989. Gene therapy for genetic diseases. *Cancer Investig.* **7**: 179–192.

Lapham, E. V., Kozma, C., and Weiss, J. O. 1996. Genetic discrimination: perspectives of consumers. *Science* **274**:621-624.

Marshall, E. 1995. Gene therapy's growing pains. *Science* **269**:1050-1055.

Marshall, E. 1996. The genome program's conscience. *Science* **274**:488-490.

Marx, J. L. 1987. Assessing the risks of microbial release. *Science* **237**: 1413–1417.

Morsy, M., Mitani, K., and Clemens, P. 1993. Progress toward human gene therapy. JAMA **270**: 2338–40.

Neufeld, P. J., and Colman, N. 1990. When science takes the witness stand. *Sci. Am.* (May) **262**: 46–53.

Nichols, E. K. 1988. *Human Gene Therapy.* Cambridge, Mass: Harvard University Press.

Olson, M. V. 1993. The human genome project. Proc. Nat. Acad. Sci. **90**: 4338–4344.

Porteus, D. and Alton, E. 1993. Cystic fibrosis: prospects for therapy. Bioessays **15**: 485–486.

Pursel, V. G., Pinkert, C. A., Miller, K. F., Bolt, D. J., Campbell, R. G., Palmiter, R. D., Brinster, R. L., and Hammer, R. E. 1989. Genetic engineering of livestock. *Science* **244**: 1281–1288.

Roberts, L. 1989. Ethical questions haunt new genetic technologies. *Science* **243**: 1134–1135.

Watson, F. 1993. Human gene therapy—progress on all fronts. Trends in Biotechnol. **11**: 114–117.

Weatherall, D. J. 1989. Gene therapy: Getting there slowly. *Br. Med. J.* **298**: 691–693.

White, R., and Lalouel, J.-M. 1988. Chromosome mapping with DNA markers. *Sci. Am.* (February) **258**: 40–47.

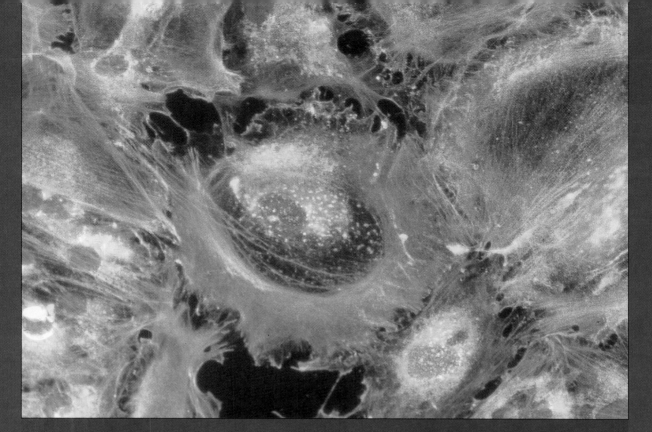

GENES AND CANCER

Chapter Outline

TUMORS AND CANCERS: WHAT ARE
   THEY?
GENES THAT PREDISPOSE TO CANCER
TUMOR SUPPRESSOR GENES AND THE
   CELL CYCLE
Retinoblastoma
The Search for Breast Cancer Genes
Colon Cancer Requires Multiple Mutations
Genetic Instability and Cancer

ONCOGENES AND CANCER
Rous Sarcoma Virus and Oncogenes
Oncogenes and Mutation
CHROMOSOMES AND CANCER
Chromosome Instability Syndromes
Chromosome Aberrations and Leukemia
CANCER AND THE ENVIRONMENT
Epidemiology and Links to Environmental
   Factors

Occupational Hazards and Cancer Risk
Environmental Factors and Cancer
CONCEPTS AND CONTROVERSIES
   Epidemiology, Asbestos, and Cancer
Genetic Models for Susceptibility
GUEST ESSAY   A Journey through Science

Chapter **14**

OPENING IMAGE
*Immunofluorescent-stained human
cancer cells.*

As you sit in a classroom, a crowded stadium, or a concert hall, look around. According to the American Cancer Society, about one in three of the people you see will develop cancer at some point in their life, and about one in four will die from cancer. Each year about 500,000 people die of cancer, a rate of about 1 death per minute, and almost 1.5 million new cases of cancer are diagnosed annually in the United States (Table 14.1). Currently over 10 million individuals are receiving medical treatment for cancer in U.S. hospitals and medical centers.

Cancer is a complex group of diseases that affect many different cells and tissues in the body. It is characterized by the uncontrolled growth and division of cells and by the ability of these cells to spread, or metastasize, to other sites within the body. Unchecked, the growth and metastasis result in death, making cancer a devastating and feared disease. Improvements in medical care have reduced deaths from infectious disease and have led to increases in life span, but these benefits have also helped make cancer a major cause of illness and death in our society. Because the risk of many cancers is age-related and because more Americans are living longer, they are at greater risk of developing cancer.

Although our society seems preoccupied with cancer, the idea that it is a disease of modern civilization is not accurate. Ancient Egyptian and Indian manuscripts reveal that cancer was recognized as a life-threatening disease over 3500 years ago. The Greek physician Galen (a.d. 131–201) provided clear descriptions of cancers and referred to them as karkinos or karkinomas, terms that translate into the Latin word cancer.

The link between cancer and mutation was forged early in this century by Theodore Boveri, who proposed that normal cells mutate into malignant ones because of changes in chromosome constitution. Four lines of evidence support the idea that cancer has a genetic origin:

1. More than 50 forms of cancer are known to be inherited to one degree or another.
2. The Ames test (Chapter 11) has shown that most carcinogens are also mutagens.
3. Some viruses carry mutant genes, known as oncogenes, that promote and maintain the growth of a tumor.
4. As Boveri proposed, specific chromosomal changes are found in particular forms of cancer, especially leukemia.

Mutation is a common feature of all cancers. In most cases, these mutational events take place in somatic tissue and the mutant alleles are not passed on to offspring. In other cases, the mutations take place in germ cells and are passed on to succeeding generations. Cancer, then, is a genetic disorder that acts at the cellular level.

Because mutation is the ultimate cause of cancer, and because there is always a background rate of spontaneous mutation, there will always be a baseline rate of cancer. The environment (ultraviolet light, chemicals and viruses) and behavior (diet, smoking) can also play a significant role in cancer risks by increasing the rate of mutation. In this chapter we will examine the relationship between genes and cancer, and describe the role of tumor suppressor genes and oncogenes in causing and

TABLE 14.1	
Estimated New Cases of Cancer in the United States, 1996	
SITE	**NUMBER OF NEW CASES**
Skin	>700,000
Lung	177,000
Colon-rectum	133,500
Breast (female)	184,300
Prostate	317,000
Urinary	83,500
Uterus	49,700
Pancreas	26,300
Ovary	26,700

supporting malignant transformation in cells. We will discuss the relationship between leukemia and chromosomal aberrations, and finally, we will analyze the interaction between cancer and the environment to explain how a multitude of factors may initiate the multistep process required for the development of malignant growth.

TUMORS AND CANCERS: WHAT ARE THEY?

Before we consider cancer, some distinction should be made between tumors and cancer. Tumors are abnormal growths of tissue. *Benign* tumors are self-contained, noncancerous growths that do not spread to other tissues (are not metastatic) and are not invasive. Benign tumors usually cause problems by growing and increasing in size until they interfere with the function of neighboring organs.

Cancers are malignant tumors. Such tumors have several distinguishing characteristics. Cancers are usually clonal in origin; they arise from a single cell (usually in somatic tissue). Cancers develop in a series of steps over time, and pass through a series of genetic alterations that result in more aggressive growth with each mutation. Third, cancers are invasive and become *metastatic*; cells can detach from the primary tumor and move to secondary sites where new malignant tumors are formed. The property of metastasis is conferred as a result of mutational changes in the cell.

GENES THAT PREDISPOSE TO CANCER

Families with high rates of specific cancers have been known for hundreds of years, but in most cases no clear-cut pattern of inheritance can be identified. How is it, then, that some families have a much higher than average rate of cancer? Many explanations have been offered, including multiple gene inheritance, environmental agents, or chance alone (Table 14.2).

Recent advances in cancer research have provided some clues about the relationship between mutant genes and the cellular events that lead to tumor formation. Cancer is now viewed as a disease that develops as a result of a small number of separate mutational events that can take place over long time intervals. While the exact number of steps varies for different cancers, experimental evidence suggests that two mutational events may be the minimum number needed to cause cancer (Figure 14.1). In the majority of cases, these mutational events accumulate randomly over a period of years, correlating with the age-related incidence of many cancers.

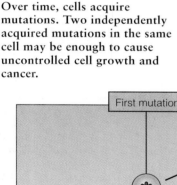

FIGURE 14.1

Over time, cells acquire mutations. Two independently acquired mutations in the same cell may be enough to cause uncontrolled cell growth and cancer.

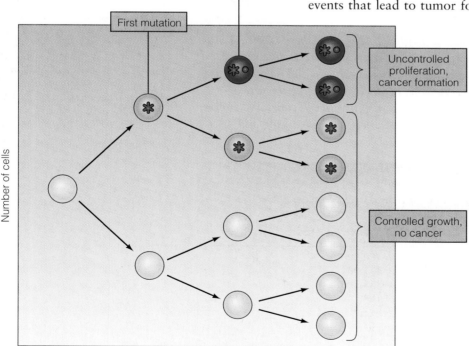

TABLE 14.2

Factors in Cancer

GENETIC	NONGENETIC
Single gene mutations	Environmental carcinogens
Chromosome aberrations	Abnormal hormone levels
	Diet
	Chance

TABLE 14.3

Heritable Predispositions to Cancer

DISORDER	CHROMOSOME	MIM/OMIM NUMBER
Early-onset familial breast cancer	17q	113705
Familial adenomatous polyposis	5q	175100
Hereditary nonpolyposis colorectal cancer	2p	120435
Li-Fraumeni syndrome	17p	151623
Multiple endocrine neoplasia type 1	11q	131100
Multiple endocrine neoplasia type 2	10	171400
Neurofibromatous type 1	17q	162200
Neurofibromatous type 2	22q	101000
Retinoblastoma	13	180200
Von Hippel-Lindau disease	3p	193300
Wilms tumor	11p	194070

In cancers with a heritable predisposition, the first mutation is present in the germ cells and is transmitted to offspring (Table 14.3). Additional mutations accumulate in somatic cells by spontaneous mutation or by exposure to environmental agents that cause genetic damage, and can result in cancer. In some cases, individuals who carry an allele predisposing them to cancer have a 100,000-fold increase in the risk of developing cancer. But not all individuals who inherit the first mutation will develop cancer. If a second mutational event does not occur, then no tumor will develop.

TUMOR SUPPRESSOR GENES AND THE CELL CYCLE

One of the basic properties of cancer cells is uncontrolled cell division; as a result, studies on the cell cycle have become an important part of cancer research. The events of interphase and mitosis make up the cell cycle (Figure 14.2). The cell cycle is regulated at two points: at the transition between G2 and M (the G2/M transition) and at a point in G1 just before cells enter S, known as the G1/S transition. Mutations in critical genes that regulate the cell cycle can lead to the formation of cancer.

Mitosis can be regulated in two ways: (1) by genes that suppress cell division, and (2) by genes that stimulate cell division.

 FIGURE 14.2

The cell cycle consists of two parts: interphase and mitosis. Interphase is divided into three stages G1, S, and G2. These stages make up the majority of the cycle. Mitosis involves the partitioning of replicated chromosomes and cytoplasm to daughter cells.

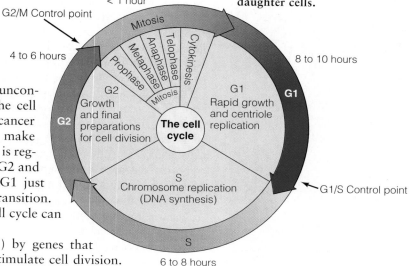

G2/M Control point
< 1 hour
Mitosis
4 to 6 hours
Prophase / Metaphase / Anaphase / Telophase / Cytokinesis
Mitosis
8 to 10 hours
G2
Growth and final preparations for cell division
G1
Rapid growth and centriole replication
G1
The cell cycle
G1/S Control point
S
Chromosome replication (DNA synthesis)
6 to 8 hours
S

Tumor suppressor gene
A gene that normally functions to suppress cell division.

Proto-oncogene
A gene that normally functions to control cell division and may become a cancer gene (oncogene) by mutation.

Oncogene
A gene that induces or continues uncontrolled cell proliferation.

Retinoblastoma
A malignant tumor of the eye that arises in the retinal cells, usually occurring in children. Associated with a deletion on the long arm of chromosome 13.

● **FIGURE 14.3**

A child with a retinoblastoma in one eye.

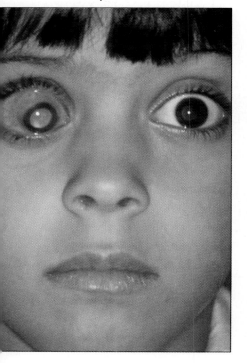

The first type are called **tumor suppressor genes.** These genes can act at either the G1/S or the G2/M control points to inhibit cell division. If these genes are lost or inactivated by mutation, control over cell division is removed, and cells divide in an uncontrolled fashion. The second class of regulatory genes, called **proto-oncogenes,** act to promote cell division. When these genes are active, cells undergo division. If these genes become permanently activated or overproduce their products, uncontrolled cell division results. Mutant forms of proto-oncogenes are called **oncogenes.**

The following examples will describe how mutations in a number of different tumor suppressor genes are involved in the development of cancer. A genetic model of colon cancer will integrate what is known about tumor suppressor genes and control of the cell cycle.

Retinoblastoma

Retinoblastoma (RB) (MIM/OMIM 180200) is a cancer of the eye, affecting the light-sensitive retinal cells. It occurs with a frequency of 1 in 14,000 to 1 in 20,000 births, and although it may be present in infancy, it is most often diagnosed between the ages of 1 and 3 years. Two forms of retinoblastoma can be distinguished. One form, *hereditary retinoblastoma* (accounting for 40% of all cases), a susceptibility is inherited as an autosomal dominant trait. In families in which the susceptibility is inherited, offspring have a 50% chance of receiving the mutant RB gene, and 90% of these individuals will develop retinoblastoma, usually in both eyes. In addition, those carrying the mutation are at high risk of developing other cancers, especially osteosarcoma and fibrosarcoma. The second form (60% of all cases), is *sporadic retinoblastoma.* Affected individuals usually develop tumors only in one eye and are not at high risk for other cancers (● Figure 14.3).

Alfred Knudson and his colleagues have proposed a two-step model for retinoblastoma that explains both forms of the disease. According to this model, retinoblastoma develops when two mutant copies of the RB gene are present in a single retinal cell. This model predicts that retinoblastoma can arise in two ways. If a child inherits a mutated RB allele, all cells of the body, including the retinal cells, will carry this mutation. If the normal RB gene in any retinal cell becomes mutated, the child will develop retinoblastoma (● Figure 14.4). Since the retinal cells already carry one mutant gene, this form of the disease is more likely to involve both eyes (bilateral cases) and to occur at an earlier age than the sporadic form.

If a child inherits two normal alleles of the RB gene, then two separate mutations must occur in a single retinal cell for a tumor to develop. Since the chance of having two RB mutations in the same cell is low, sporadic cases are more likely to involve only one eye (unilateral cases); and because of the time required to acquire two separate mutations, this form of retinoblastoma will arise later in life.

Surveys of patients with retinoblastoma have confirmed these predictions. Pedigree analysis indicates that most cases involving two eyes are inherited, while the vast majority of unilateral cases are sporadic and noninherited. In addition, most cases that involve only one eye occur at a later age than bilateral cases.

The RB gene is located on chromosome 13 at 13q14 (● Figure 14.5), and it encodes a protein (pRB) that is confined to the nucleus. The protein is found in cells of the retina and in almost all other cell types and tissues of the body. The pRB is present at all stages of the cell cycle, and its activity is regulated in synchrony with the cell cycle. The protein acts as a molecular switch, controlling progression through the cell cycle. During G1, if the protein is active, it acts to suppress passage from G1 into S, halting cell division. Conversely, if pRB is inactive, it allows cells to pass through the S phase, through G2, and on to mitosis. If both copies of the RB gene are deleted or become mutated in a retinal cell, the absent or defective pRB cannot regulate cell division, and the cell begins to divide in an uncontrolled fashion, forming a tumor.

What happens if both copies of the RB gene become mutated in a cell type other than retinal cells? In the case of bone cells, the result is a cancer known as osteosar-

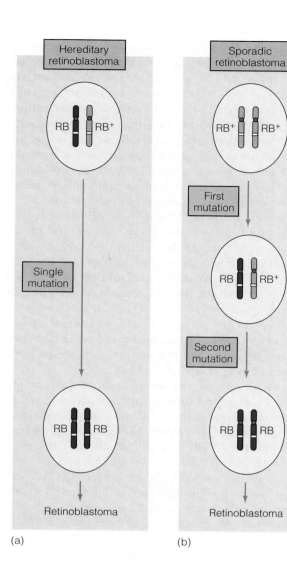

(a)   (b)

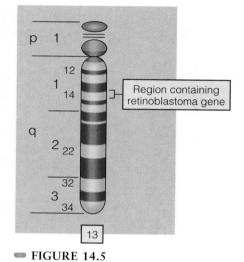

FIGURE 14.4

A model of retinoblastoma. In hereditary cases, one mutation is inherited. A single mutation in the normal allele of the RB gene will cause retinoblastoma. (b) Sporadic retinoblastoma requires two independent mutations in the RB gene in a single cell.

FIGURE 14.5

A diagram of chromosome 13, showing the locus of the retinoblastoma gene.

coma. In fact, cultured osteosarcoma cells have been used to provide evidence for the role of the RB gene in cancer. Analysis using recombinant DNA techniques indicates that osteosarcoma cells carry two mutant copies of the RB gene and produce no retinoblastoma protein. If a cloned copy of a normal RB gene is transferred into the osteosarcoma cells, pRB is produced, and cell division stops. This finding reinforces the idea that the retinoblastoma protein plays a central role in the regulation of the cell cycle.

The Search for Breast Cancer Genes

For women in the United States, the overall risk for breast cancer is 1 in 8. It is the most common form of cancer in women; more than 44,000 women die from breast cancer, and more than 180,000 new cases are diagnosed each year. Although environmental factors may be involved in breast cancer, geneticists struggled for years with the question: Is there a genetic predisposition to breast cancer? After more than 20 years of work, the answer is yes. Although it is involved in only about 5% of all cases, *BRCA1* (MIM/OMIM 113705), a gene located on the long arm of chromosome 17 at q21.1, has been identified. This gene is responsible for susceptibility to breast cancer that appears in women under 40 years of age. About 1 in 200 females inherit the mutant allele, and of these, about 90% will develop breast cancer.

The search for this gene began in the 1970s with the analysis of patterns of breast cancer by Mary Claire King and her colleagues. They looked for families with a clear history of breast cancer, and found that about 15% of the 1500 families surveyed had multiple cases of breast cancer. Genetic models based on this information suggested that about 5% of the breast cancers were related to an autosomal dominant pattern of inheritance. The models also predicted that two-thirds of the families with multiple cases had no genetic predisposition to breast cancer. This meant that it was impossible to distinguish multiple-case families with a genetic predisposition from the other multiple-case families with no genetic predisposition. King and her colleagues decided on a brute force approach. They began testing as many families as possible, looking for linkage between breast cancer and a genetic marker.

Using protein variants as markers, the search began by testing multiple-case families to find linkage between the markers and breast cancer. In the 1980s, as recombinant DNA techniques became widely used, King and her colleagues switched to DNA markers and the PCR technique for screening. Finally, in 1990, after testing hundreds of families with hundreds of markers, the 183rd marker to be used, an RFLP marker from chromosome 17 called D17S74, was tested on family members from 23 pedigrees with a history of breast cancer. This marker was clearly linked to breast cancer, and other laboratories quickly confirmed linkage using this marker. Linkage between the marker and ovarian cancer was also established.

The investigators formed an international consortium, and using DNA from members of 214 families with multiple cases of either breast or ovarian cancer, narrowed the search to a small segment of the long arm of chromosome 17 (▬ Figure 14.6). The *BRCA1* gene was identified and cloned in 1994. The mutant allele of this gene causes about half of all hereditary forms of breast cancer.

A second gene for a predisposition to breast cancer, *BRCA2*, was discovered in 1995; the mutant allele is inherited in an autosomal dominant fashion. It maps to region q12-13 on the long arm of chromosome 13 and may be responsible for the majority of inherited cases that are not caused by a mutation in *BRCA1*. Many questions remain unanswered about the normal function of both genes, and how mutations lead to breast cancer. All of the dominantly inherited cancer susceptibility genes identified to date are tumor suppressor genes, and preliminary evidence indicates that both these genes normally act to suppress cell division. Work on BRCA1 suggests that the function of the mutant allele in mammary epithelial cells is abnormal, but the role of the protein in controlling cell division is not yet known.

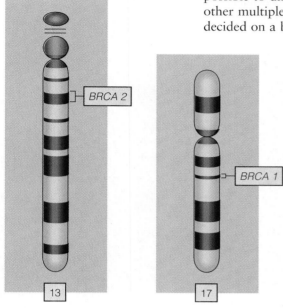

▬ **FIGURE 14.6**

The chromosome locations for *BRCA1* and *BRCA2*. Together these genes account for the majority of heritable cases of breast cancer.

Familial adenomatous polyposis (FAP)
A dominant condition associated with the development of growths known as polyps in the colon. These polyps often develop into malignant growths, causing cancer of the colon and/or rectum.

Hereditary nonpolyposis colon cancer
A form of colon cancer associated with genetic instability of microsatellites.

Polyp
A growth attached to the substrate by a small stalk. Commonly found in the nose, rectum, and uterus.

Colon Cancer Requires Multiple Mutations

Cancer of the colon and rectum is one of the most common forms of cancer in the United States (Table 14.4). There are two major forms of genetic predisposition to colon cancer: **familial adenomatous polyposis (FAP)** (MIM/OMIM 175100) and **hereditary nonpolyposis colon cancer** (MIM/OMIM 120435). The first accounts for only about 1% of all cases of colon cancer, but has been useful in deriving a genetic model for colon cancer that is described below. The second accounts for about 15% of all cases, and is associated with a form of genetic instability, described in the next section.

To clarify the role of inheritance in colorectal cancer, Randall Burt and his colleagues studied a large pedigree with more than 5000 members covering six generations. This family contains clusters of siblings and relatives with colon cancer. Like many other families, this one shows no definite pattern of inheritance for the cancer. However, as part of this study, about 200 family members were examined for the presence of intestinal growths (▬ Figure 14.7). These benign tumors, known as **polyps**, usually precede or accompany colon cancer and are regarded as precursors

TABLE 14.4		
Colon and Rectal Cancer in the United States		
Estimated new cases, 1996		
Colon		94,500
Rectum		39,000
Total		133,500
Mortality (estimated deaths, 1996)		
Colon		46,400
Rectum		8,500
Total		54,500
5-Year survival rate (early detection)		
Colon		91%
Rectum		85%

of the malignant condition. When the presence of intestinal growths and colon cancer are considered together as a single phenotype, an autosomal dominant pattern of inheritance is clear. The results also show that the dominant allele for these intestinal growths and cancer may have a relatively high frequency in the general population (3/1000).

RFLP analysis was used to localize the gene for these polyps to chromosome 5. The gene, called APC, is a tumor suppressor gene, so that in the normal homozygote no growth of polyps occurs. In the heterozygote, cell growth in the colon is not completely regulated, causing production of polyps (the FAP phenotype). Mutations in APC are not enough to cause cancer, and mutations in other genes are required to cause the transition from polyp to colon cancer. Most early polyps show only a single genetic change (the APC gene is mutated), while most colon cancers carry four or five mutations. Intermediate stages between polyp and colon cancer carry an intermediate number of mutations (➡ Figure 14.8). In general, deletions of chromosome 17p and 18q usually occur at later stages of tumor development, while deletions of 5p and mutations in 12p take place in early-stage polyps. For example, the loss of a segment of 17p is seen in more than 75% of colon cancers, but is seen infrequently in early polyps.

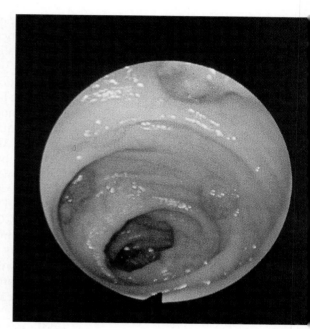

➡ **FIGURE 14.7**

Polyps in the colon (the round, orange-yellow growths) are a precursor to colon cancer. If a cell in one of these polyps acquires enough mutations, it will transform into a cancer cell and form a tumor.

➡ **FIGURE 14.8**

A model for colon cancer. In this multiple-step model, the first mutation occurs in the APC gene, leading to the formation of polyps. Subsequent mutations in genes on chromosomes 12, 17, and 18 cause the transformation of the polyp into a tumor. In this model, the sum of the changes is more important than the order in which the changes take place.

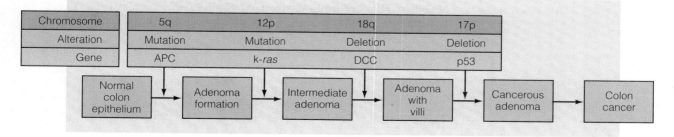

These findings have been incorporated into a genetic model of colon cancer (Figure 14.8). This model requires a series of mutations that accumulate over time in a colon cell. Each mutation confers a slight growth advantage on the cell, first allowing it to proliferate and form a polyp, then enlarging the polyp through a series of stages; eventually, one cell accumulates enough mutations to escape from cell cycle control and form a malignant tumor. Later, additional mutations allow the tumor cell to become metastatic and break away to form a tumor at a remote site. Although the model shows the mutations in a sequence, it is the sum of the accumulated changes that is critical to the development of colon cancer.

Recombinant DNA techniques have been used to identify cases in which tumor development involves a number of mutational events at specific chromosomal sites, often on different chromosomes (Table 14.5).

Genetic Instability and Cancer

Most cancers are caused by multiple mutations that accumulate over time. If one of these mutations is inherited, fewer mutations are required to cause cancer, resulting in a genetic predisposition to cancer. An unresolved question about the development of cancers is how and why the multiple mutations required for tumor formation accumulate. Recently, a second form of colon cancer has provided a partial answer to this question. Hereditary nonpolyposis colon cancer (HPNCC) is associated with a gene that has been mapped to chromosome 2. This gene, called FCC, is unique because a mutational event in this gene sets off a cascade of mutations in minisatellite DNA sequences (review minisatellite in Chapter 13) scattered throughout the genome. Analysis of colon cancers caused by FCC show mutations at many minisatellite loci. The mutant FCC gene may promote colon cancer by making parts of the genome unstable and prone to mutation, increasing the chance that a mutation will occur in the pathway to colon cancer. As many as 1 in 200 individuals may carry a mutant FCC gene, making it one of the most common causes of a genetic disease.

The FCC gene has not yet been identified or isolated, and its mechanism of action remains unknown. However, markers near the gene are available, making it possible to identify those who have inherited the mutant allele and are at high risk for colon cancer. Eventually, using this or other markers, it may be possible to do widespread population screening to identify those at risk, and eliminate some or all of the 46,000 annual deaths from colon cancer.

 ## ONCOGENES AND CANCER

Oncogenes are mutant alleles of genes that normally stimulate or maintain cell division. In mutant form, the genes induce or maintain uncontrolled cell division associated with cancer. The existence of oncogenes was first discovered by work on a virus that causes cancer in chickens.

TABLE 14.5		
Number of Mutations Associated with Specific Forms of Cancer		
CANCER	**CHROMOSOMAL SITES OF MUTATIONS**	**MINIMAL NUMBER OF MUTATIONS REQUIRED**
Retinoblastoma	13q14	2
Wilms tumor	11p13	2
Colon cancer	5q, 12p, 17p, 18q	4 to 5
Small-cell lung cancer	3p, 11p, 13q, 17p	10 to 15

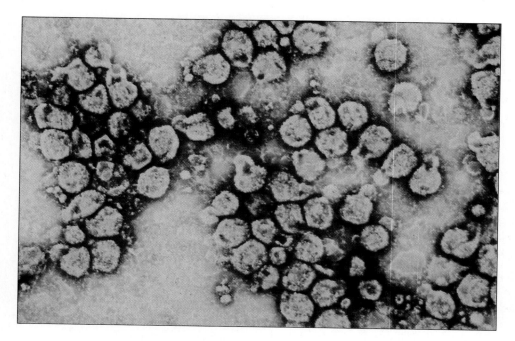

● FIGURE 14.9
The Rous sarcoma virus as seen in the transmission electron microscope.

Rous Sarcoma Virus and Oncogenes

The role of viruses in cancer began with the work of Peyton Rous on a malignant tumor, known as a **sarcoma,** found in chickens. In 1911 Rous found that cell-free extracts from these tumors would induce tumor formation when injected into healthy chickens. The agent in the extract was later identified as a virus, known as the Rous sarcoma virus (RSV) (● Figure 14.9). At the time, Rous's work was criticized by many of his colleagues, who claimed that his extract was not cell-free and that he was simply transferring cancer cells that grew in the injected chickens to form tumors. As a result, Rous gradually abandoned the project. Several decades later, RSV was identified as the cause of the tumors and became one of the most widely studied animal tumor viruses. In belated recognition of his pioneering work on viral tumors, Rous was awarded the Nobel Prize in 1966 (at the age of 85).

Viruses can be grouped into two classes: DNA viruses or RNA viruses, depending on the nature of the genetic material. Cancer-causing viruses are found in both groups (Table 14.6). The DNA tumor viruses include SV40 (simian virus 40), first identified in monkey tumors, and polyoma, a virus that produces tumors in several species of animals, including mice, hamsters, and rats. Some RNA viruses are known as **retroviruses** because the single-stranded RNA viral genome must return to the form of a double-stranded DNA molecule before it can replicate. Tumor-causing retroviruses have been found in the chicken, mouse, rat, hamster, and other species. The Rous sarcoma virus is an example of a tumor-producing retrovirus. The results of work with RSV and similar viruses have been important in understanding the origins of human cancer.

Sarcoma
A cancer of connective tissue. One type of sarcoma in chickens is associated with the retrovirus known as the Rous sarcoma virus.

Retrovirus
Viruses that use RNA as a genetic material. During virus life cycle, the RNA is transcribed into DNA. The name retrovirus symbolizes this backward order of transcription.

TABLE 14.6

Viruses and Cancer

DNA CANCER VIRUSES	RNA CANCER VIRUSES
SV40	Rous sarcoma virus
Polyoma	Mouse mammary tumor virus
Adenovirus	

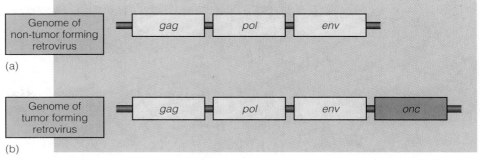

(a)

(b)

FIGURE 14.10

Organization of the genome in a non-transforming strain of Rous sarcoma virus. (a) The three genes carried by the virus enable the virus to infect cells and replicate itself, but not to cause tumors. (b) In a tumor-producing strain, the genome contains an extra gene, an oncogene. This gene is derived from the host cell in a previous infection, and confers upon the virus the ability to produce uncontrolled growth and tumor formation in another host cell.

The ability of the Rous sarcoma virus to cause tumor formation in chickens is due to the presence of a single gene (Figure 14.10). Since this gene is associated with the ability of the virus to induce tumors, it is an oncogene. The discovery of the oncogene in RSV was a central and important event in cancer research, because it indicated that cancer could be caused by changes in a small number of genes. Over the years other types of RNA tumor viruses have been discovered, and many forms of animal tumors, including mouse leukemia, cat leukemia, and mouse breast cancer, were shown to be caused by retroviruses. Like RSV, some of these RNA tumor viruses carry a single gene that causes cancer. These genes are of several different types, but all have the common property of being oncogenic. More than 20 different oncogenes have been identified by their presence in retroviruses, and more than 50 oncogenes have been identified (Table 14.7). Oncogenes are named for the virus in

TABLE 14.7

Retroviral Oncogenes and Human Proto-Oncogenes

VIRAL ONCOGENE	ASSOCIATED TUMOR	HUMAN PROTO-ONCOGENE	HUMAN CHROMOSOME
v-*src*	Sarcoma	c-*src*	20
v-*fps*/v-*fes*	Sarcoma	c-*fps*/c-*fes*	15
v-*yes*	Sarcoma	c-*yes*	?
v-*ros*	Sarcoma	?	?
v-*ski*	?	?	?
v-*myc*	Carcinoma, sarcoma, myelocytoma	c-*myc*	8
v-*erb*-A	?	c-*erb*-A	17
v-*erb*-B	Erythroleukemia, sarcoma	c-*erb*-B	7
v-*myb*	Myeloblastic leukemia	c-*myb*	6
v-*rel*	Lymphatic leukemia	?	?
v-*mos*	Sarcoma	c-*mos*	8
v-*abl*	B-cell lymphoma	c-*abl*	9
v-*fos*	Sarcoma	c-*fos*	14
v-*raf*	?	c-*raf*-1	3
v-H*aras*/v-*bas*	Sarcoma, erythroleukemia	c-Ha-*ras*-1	11
		c-Ha-*ras*-2	X
v-Ki-*ras*	Sarcoma, erythroleukemia	c-Ki-*ras*-1	6
		c-Ki-*ras*-2	12
v-*fms*	Sarcoma	c-*fms*	5
v-*sis*	Sarcoma	c-*sis*	22

TABLE 14.8

Cellular Localization of Oncogene (c-*onc* and v-*onc*) Gene Products

GENE	LOCATION OF C-ONC PROTEINS	LOCATION OF V-ONC PROTEINS
abl	nucleus	cytoplasm
erb-B	plasma membrane	plasma membrane and Golgi
fos	cytoplasm	cytoplasm and membranes
myc	nucleus	nucleus
ras	membranes	membranes
src	membranes	membranes

which they were discovered. In Rous sarcoma virus, the gene is known as v-*src;* the oncogene in avian erythroblastosis virus is known as v-*erb,* and so forth.

Since not all retroviruses carry oncogenes, where did such genes originate? Are they viral in origin, or might they represent genes captured by the virus from host animal cells? Research has clearly demonstrated that oncogenes carried by retroviruses are acquired from the host genome during viral infection. The normal version of these genes are called proto-oncogenes, or cellular oncogenes (c-*onc*). Proto-oncogenes are normal genes, present in all cells that have the potential to cause cancer if they are mutated or if their usual pattern of expression is altered.

But what is the usual function of such genes? For the most part, proto-oncogenes are associated with cell growth, cell division, and cell differentiation; and their gene products at many sites within the cell (Table 14.8). For example, the DNA sequence of the *sis* oncogene closely matches that of a proto-oncogene that encodes a growth factor called PDGF. Similarly, the DNA sequence of the oncogene *erb*-B is related to a proto-oncogene that encodes a cellular receptor for another growth factor. The majority of proto-oncogenes regulate cell growth and division, and mutations in these genes lead to uncontrolled proliferation and cancer.

Oncogenes and Mutation

The version of the oncogenes carried by retroviruses are called v-*onc* genes. Retroviruses that carry a v-*onc* gene are able to infect and transform a host cell into a malignant tumor cell. Although oncogenes were discovered in viruses, only a few rare human forms of cancer are caused by virally transmitted oncogenes. In most cases, the conversion from proto-oncogene to oncogene takes place in a somatic cell, without intervention by a virus.

What is the difference between a proto-oncogene in a normal cell and a mutant version of that gene (an oncogene) in a cancer cell? Many differences are possible, including mutations that produce an altered gene product and those that cause underproduction or overproduction of the normal gene product. In fact, all these kinds of mutants have been found in human oncogenes or in their adjacent regulatory regions.

The normal *ras* gene encodes a protein 189 amino acids long that is a receptor molecule in the plasma membrane. The *ras* protein receives and transfers growth-inhibiting signals across the cell membrane. Analysis of 12 different *ras* oncogenes isolated from human tumors reveals that in each case a single nucleotide change differentiates the mutant oncogene from the proto-oncogene found in normal cells. In all 12 tumors, a nucleotide substitution leads to an amino acid substitution in the gene product. The mutant gene and the mutant oncoprotein are found only in the tumor cells and *not* in the normal tissue of the patient. Somewhat surprisingly, the amino acid substitution in all 12 mutant genes occurred at either amino acid 12 or amino

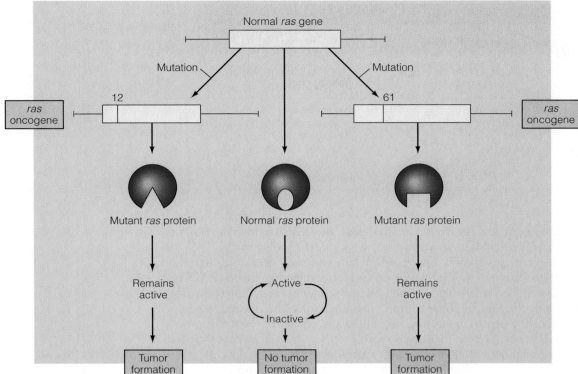

FIGURE 14.11

The *ras* proto-oncogene is a normal component of the genome, and encodes a gene product that receives and transduces signals needed for cell growth. Mutations at amino acid positions 12 or 61 cause the formation of an oncoprotein that promotes the formation of a cancer cell.

acid 61 (Figure 14.11). Work using x-ray analysis of protein crystals has shown that substitution of the glycine at position 12 with any other amino acid disrupts the structure of the protein and prevents its folding into the proper configuration. The altered protein is not able to function in signal transfer across the cell membrane, and the cell escapes from growth control, becoming cancerous.

Knowledge about the molecular organization of oncogenes and their products is being used to develop new methods for the diagnosis and treatment of cancer. If altered oncogene proteins are released into the blood, antibodies against these proteins can be used to detect cancer at a very early stage. Similar tests have already been developed for a protein released into the bloodstream by breast cancer cells. New strategies for treatment may also be derived from knowledge about oncogenes themselves. If multiple copies of oncogenes are present in lung cancer, breast cancer, or cervical cancer, aggressive treatment and therapy are indicated. Laboratory studies on cultured cells indicate that if an active oncogene is switched off, the cell becomes nonmalignant. Further work on the mechanism of gene switch-off may result in development of a new class of anticancer drugs directed against the regulatory regions of specific genes. Alternatively, since the protein products of oncogenes have been characterized, it may be possible to block or to reduce the action of such proteins, causing the cancer cell to become quiescent.

CHROMOSOMES AND CANCER

Changes in chromosome structure and number are a common feature of cancer cells. In some cases, the relationship between a single chromosome change and the development of cancer is not clear. For example, Down syndrome is caused by the presence of an extra copy of chromosome 21. This quantitative change in genetic information is not associated with any known gene mutation. In addition to defects in cardiac structure and in the immune system, children with Down syndrome are 18 to 20 times more likely to develop leukemia than children in the general population.

TABLE 14.9

Human Genetic Disorders Associated with Chromosome Instability and Cancer Susceptibility

DISORDER	INHERITANCE	CHROMOSOME DAMAGE	CANCER SUSCEPTIBILITY	HYPERSENSITIVITY
Ataxia telangiectasia	Autosomal recessive	Translocations on 7, 14	Lymphoid, others	X-rays
Bloom syndrome	Autosomal recessive	Breaks, translocations	Lymphoid, others	Sunlight
Fanconi anemia	Autosomal recessive	Breaks, translocations	Leukemia	X-rays
Xeroderma pigmentosum	Autosomal recessive	Breaks	Skin	Sunlight

How extra copies of genes on chromosome 21 predispose to cancer is not yet known, but may be an effect of increasing the dosage of some proto-oncogenes.

Chromosome Instability Syndromes

Several genetic disorders are associated with chromosomal instability and cancer. Bloom syndrome (MIM/OMIM 210900) and Fanconi anemia (MIM/OMIM 227650) are both autosomal recessive conditions that result in a large number of chromosome breaks, gaps, rearrangements, and translocations. Children with Bloom syndrome are characterized by low birth weight, short stature (dwarfism), and a variety of malignancies, including leukemia and intestinal cancer. Fanconi anemia is associated with a marked reduction in circulating blood cells, abnormal pigmentation of the skin, and greatly increased risks of leukemia.

Another autosomal recessive disorder, ataxia telangiectasia (AT), also causes chromosomal breaks; but in contrast to the preceding diseases, the breaks in this syndrome consistently involve chromosome 14 and, to a lesser extent, chromosome 7. Patients with ataxia telangiectasia (MIM/OMIM 208900) have increased rates of leukemia, skin cancer, and cancers of the lymphatic system such as Hodgkin disease (Table 14.9).

It is tempting to speculate that the common thread in all these chromosome instability syndromes is the inheritance of a germ-line mutation that predisposes to cancer by reducing the ability to repair damage to DNA; and that subsequent mutagenic events, such as exposure to environmental radiation from ultraviolet light or x-rays, causes the development of cancer. Until more is known about the molecular basis of these diseases, their relationship to the multistep theory of cancer will remain uncertain.

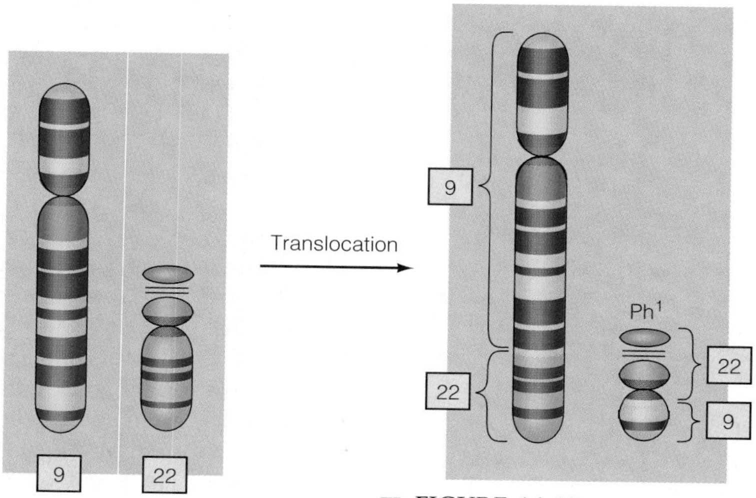

Chromosome Aberrations and Leukemia

The relationship between chromosomes and cancer was first proposed by Boveri in 1917. Since then chromosome aberrations have been found in the cells of many tumor types, including those experimentally induced by radiation or chemical carcinogens. For many years these aberrations were regarded as a by-product of the malignant condition. One such aberration found in chronic myelogenous leukemia was originally thought to involve a deletion of part of chromosome 22. The aberration was named the **Philadelphia chromosome**, after the city in which it was discovered. Later it was determined that the Philadelphia chromosome was actually a translocation between chromosomes 9 and 22 (● Figure 14.12). More importantly, this defect was consistently and specifically associated with this form of **leukemia**. This

● FIGURE 14.12

A reciprocal translocation between chromosomes 9 and 22 results in the formation of a chromosome involved in chronic myelogenous leukemia (CML).

Philadelphia chromosome
An abnormal chromosome produced by an exchange of portions of the long arms of chromosome 9 and 22.

Leukemia
A form of cancer associated with uncontrolled growth of leukocytes (white blood cells) or their precursors.

TABLE 14.10	
Chromosome Translocation Associated with Human Cancers	
CHROMOSOME TRANSLOCATION	**CANCER**
t(9;22)	Chronic myelogenous leukemia (Philadelphia chromosome)
t(15;17)	Acute promyelocytic leukemia
t(11;19)	Acute monocytic leukemia, acute myelomonocytic leukemia
t(1;9)	Pre-B-cell leukemia
t(8;14), t(8;22), t(2;8)	Burkitt lymphoma, acute lymphocytic leukemia of the B-cell type
t(8;21)	Acute myelogenous leukemia, acute myeloblastic leukemia
t(11;14)	Chronic lymphocytic leukemia, diffuse lymphoma, multiple myeloma
t(4;18)	Follicular lymphoma
t(4;11)	Acute lymphocytic leukemia
t(11;14)(p13;q13)	Acute lymphocytic leukemia

discovery by Janet Rowley of the University of Chicago was the first example of a chromosome translocation accompanying a human disease.

Other cancers are now known to be associated with specific translocations, including acute myeloblastic leukemia, Burkitt lymphoma, and multiple myeloma (Table 14.10). The chromosomal defects are usually deletions of a specific band, or a reciprocal exchange of chromosome parts between different chromosomes. The finding that certain forms of cancer are consistently associated with specific chromosome abnormalities suggests that these aberrations are related to the development of the cancer. There is strong evidence that chromosome rearrangements are not by-products of the malignant condition, but are important steps in the development of certain cancers. The genetic and molecular basis for this role is now becoming clear as the field of cancer cytogenetics merges with the molecular biology of oncogenes. As oncogenes became identified in human cells using the techniques of molecular biology, the chromosomal locations of the normal proto-oncogenes were systematically mapped by cytogeneticists. It soon became clear that many of these genes were located at or very near the break points of chromosomal translocations involved with specific cancers. In some cases, it has been shown that chromosome breaks alter the expression of proto-oncogenes and bring about the development of cancer.

Chronic myelogenous leukemia (CML) is associated with the fusion of two genes present at the breakpoints of the 9; 22 translocation characteristic of CML. The Abelson oncogene c-*abl* maps at the breakpoint on chromosome 9, and the *bcr* gene maps at the breakpoint on chromosome 22. The translocation produces a hybrid gene that has *bcr* sequences at the beginning of the gene, and most, but not all, of the normal c-*abl* sequences at the end of the gene (Figure 14.13). This hybrid gene is transcribed and the message is translated to produce a fusion protein in which the *bcr*-encoded amino acids activate the amino acids in the region encoded by the c-*abl* gene. The hybrid protein switches on cell division in the lymphoid cells, resulting in CML.

CANCER AND THE ENVIRONMENT

Research into the relationship between the environment and cancer has been conducted for over 50 years, but it is only in recent years, with the development of more sophisticated data gathering and analysis, that this work has provided solid evidence for the relationship between the environment and cancer. **Epidemiology** is the study of factors that control the presence or absence of a disease. It is an indirect and inferential science and provides correlations between factors and the existence of a dis-

Epidemiology
The study of the factors that control the presence, absence, or frequency of a disease.

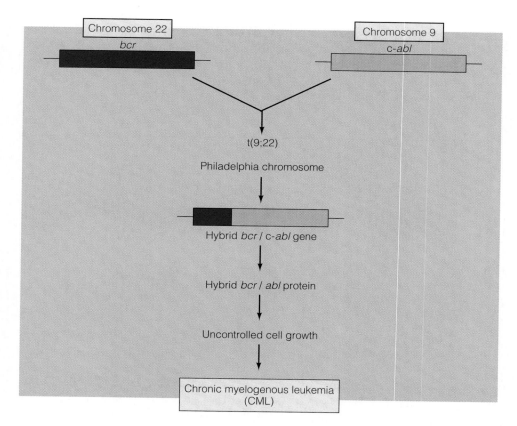

■ FIGURE 14.13
Gene fusion associated with the 9;22 translocation in chronic myelogenous leukemia (CML). The *bcr* gene on chromosome 22 is fused to the c-*abl* proto-oncogene on chromosome 9. The hybrid gene is transcribed, and the resulting fusion protein stimulates cell division in white blood cells. Overproduction of these cells results in CML.

ease such as cancer. These correlations provide working hypotheses that must be confirmed in laboratory experiments on animal models and then in carefully controlled clinical trials with humans (see "Concepts and Controversies," page 347).

Epidemiology and Links to Environmental Factors

Typically, epidemiology begins with a large-scale study on the incidence of cancer across a number of populations. If statistically significant differences are found, further studies seek to identify the factors that systematically correlate with these differences. The results of many such studies illustrate that there are widespread geographic variations in cancer cases and mortality that are presumably correlated with environmental factors (Table 14.11). Many cases of cancer in the United States are thought to be related to our physical surroundings, personal behavior, or both. Estimates indicate that at least 50% of all cancer can be attributed to environmental factors.

Occupational Hazards and Cancer Risk

The relationship between occupation and cancer was first noted in 1775 by the English physician Percival Potts, who recorded that London chimney sweeps had a high rate of scrotal cancer, presumably caused by exposure to soot and coal tars. Coal tars and more than 65,000 other chemicals are in commercial and industrial use in the United States. Fewer than 1% of these have been adequately tested for their ability to cause cancer. Occupational exposure to some chemicals is known to cause cancer, but because of the long lag between the time of exposure and the onset of cancer, identification of those at risk is often difficult. One study estimates that occupational exposure to only a few materials that are used in industrial processes may account for 18% to 38% of all cancer cases in the next few decades. Among these materials is vinyl chloride.

TABLE 14.11

Age-Adjusted Cancer Death Rates per 100,000 Population 1990-1993

| COUNTRY | ALL SITES | |
	MALE	FEMALE
United States	165.3 (27)*	111.1 (18)
Australia	158.5 (28)	100.2 (20)
Austria	171.6 (20)	105.6 (16)
Denmark	178.7 (17)	138.1 (1)
Germany	177.3 (18)	108.2 (11)
Hungary	258.7 (1)	135.2 (2)
Japan	149.8 (32)	75.2 (43)
Latvia	206.1 (6)	98.7 (23)
Mauritius	85.4 (47)	63.8 (46)
Mexico	81.6 (48)	77.6 (41)
Poland	204.2 (8)	107.6 (13)
Romania	140.2 (36)	84.5 (38)
Slovenia	203.9 (9)	108.0 (12)
Switzerland	167.2 (24)	96.5 (26)
Trinidad, Tobago	120.0 (42)	91.4 (31)
United Kingdom	179.1 (16)	124.6 (5)

*rank among 48 countries surveyed.

Vinyl chloride is a gas first discovered in 1837 and now used in the manufacture of many plastic items. Over 8 billion pounds is produced each year. Vinyl chloride is used to make polyvinyl chloride (PVC), which in turn is used to manufacture products as diverse as floor tile, bottles, food wrap, and insulation. In laboratory experiments, vinyl chloride causes a rare form of liver cancer in rats at doses as low as 50 parts per million (ppm). When these experiments were conducted in 1970, the permissible exposure to vinyl chloride workers was 500 ppm. Surveys of workers in U.S. vinyl chloride plants showed that several workers were diagnosed as having the same rare form of liver cancer as the rats exposed to vinyl chloride. In 1974, permissible exposure levels were reduced to 50 ppm and in 1975 to 1 ppm. The Food and Drug Administration also banned the use of PVC in beverage containers. Although workers in vinyl chloride plants receive the highest levels of exposure, finished plastics always contain entrapped vinyl chloride gas in amounts that can be significant, and the effects of this exposure on the population at large are yet to be assessed.

Environmental Factors and Cancer

The American Cancer Society estimates that 85% of the lung cancer cases among men and 75% of the cases among women are related to smoking. Smoking produces cancers of the oral cavity, larynx, esophagus, and lungs, and accounts for 30% of all cancer deaths. Most of these cancers have very low survival rates. Lung cancer, for example, has a 5-year survival rate of 13%. Cancer risks associated with tobacco are not limited to smoking; the use of snuff or chewing tobacco carries a 50-fold increased risk of oral cancer.

About 800,000 new cases of skin cancer are reported in the United States every year, almost all of them related to ultraviolet exposure from sunlight or tanning lamps. The incidence of skin cancer is increasing rapidly in the population, presumably as a result of an increase in outdoor recreation. Skin color is a trait controlled by several genes and is associated with a continuous variation in phenotype. In humans, traits controlled by several genes typically produce a wide range of phenotypes, and skin color is no exception. Epidemiologic studies have shown that lightly

CONCEPTS AND CONTROVERSIES

Epidemiology, Asbestos, and Cancer

Asbestos is a fibrous material known since ancient times. The emperor Charlemagne is said to have had a tablecloth made of asbestos that was thrown into the flames after meals, emerging from the flames unburned, to the amazement of his guests. In more modern times, asbestos has been widely used in manufactured goods and is present in our homes, schools, and automobiles. It has been used in brake linings, ceiling tiles, wallboard, textiles, ironing boards, and kitchen gloves. Almost everyone in the United States has been exposed to asbestos in one form or another. To determine the possible role of asbestos in cancer, an epidemiological study compared the cause of death in a group of asbestos workers with an age- and sex-matched group of individuals selected from the general population. Some data from this study are shown in the following table.

A total of 444 deaths were recorded in the asbestos workers, and 301 deaths were observed in the control group. In determining whether a disease such as cancer is linked to asbestos, the number of cancer deaths in asbestos workers is divided by the number of cancer deaths in the control population. If the number of deaths is the same, the ratio will be about 1.0. If the number of cancer deaths among asbestos workers is greater than the population at large, the ratio will be higher. The results show that the ratio of cancer deaths is 3.86, and the ratio of deaths from lung cancer is 7.62.

This circumstantial evidence was used in laboratory tests on rats and mice. Animals were exposed to various amounts of asbestos fibers and monitored for the development of cancer. A control group was not exposed to asbestos. Cancers in the control group were used as a baseline measurement of cancer rates among the experimental animals. These experiments supported the link between asbestos exposure and cancer, leading to government standards for maximum permissible exposure to asbestos fibers.

	NUMBER OF DEATHS 1943–1973		
CAUSE OF DEATH	Expected	Observed	Ration of Obs/Exp
Cancer, all sites	51	198	3.86
Lung cancer	12	89	7.62
Pleural mesothelioma	0	10	
Peritoneal mesothelioma	0	25	
Stomach cancer	5	18	3.53
Colon-rectal cancer	8	22	2.93
Asbestosis	0	37	
All other causes	249	209	0.84
Total deaths, all cases	301	444	1.48

SOURCE: *Seilcoff, I. J., and Hammond, E. C. (1975). Major risk factors in environmental cancer. In: Fraumeni, J. F., ed. Persons at High Risk of Cancer. New York: Academic Press, p. 467–483.*

pigmented individuals are at much higher risk for skin cancer than heavily pigmented individuals. This observation supports the idea that genetic characteristics can affect the susceptibility of individuals or subpopulations to environmental agents that cause a specific form of cancer.

Over the past decade, epidemiologic and laboratory studies have increasingly focused on the role of diet and nutrition in the development of cancer. Many investigators believe that 30% to 40% of all cancers are related to diet.

Colon cancer occurs with a much higher frequency in North America than in Asia, Africa, or other parts of the world. When people migrate from a low risk-area to a high risk area, their rate of colon cancer rises to that of the native residents, suggesting that environmental factors, including diet, may play a role in the development of colon cancer. The health of more than 88,000 registered nurses across the United States has been monitored since 1980. In one 6-year period, 150 cases of colon can-

A Journey through Science

BRUCE AMES

As a youngster, I was always interested in biology and chemistry, and read the books left lying around the house by my father, who was chairman of a high school chemistry department, and later supervisor of science for all the New York City public schools. During the summers, my sisters and I explored the natural world and collected animals at our family's summer cabin on a lake in Adirondack Mountains. Throughout my childhood, I read voraciously, and would come back from the library with a whole stack of books.

I attended the Bronx High School of Science, where I conducted my first scientific experiments, studying the effect of plant hormones on the growth of tomato root tips. Motivated by my experiences with research, I enrolled at Cornell University to study chemistry and biology. After graduating, I headed west to study at the California Institute of Technology. In the early 1950s, there was an exceptional group of faculty and students at Cal Tech, many of whom were learning about genes by studying biochemical genetics. I joined the laboratory of Herschel K. Mitchell, and began using mutant strains to work out the steps used by the bread mold *Neurospora* to make the amino acid histidine.

After completing my studies at Cal Tech, I moved to the National Institutes of Health at Bethesda, Maryland, to do research on gene regulation, using mutant strains of the bacterium *Salmonella*. By 1964, I was married and had two children, a daughter, Sofia, and a son, Matteo. Sometime in that same year, I happened to read the list of ingredients on a box of potato chips, and began to think about all the new synthetic chemicals being used, and wondered if they might cause genetic damage to human cells.

To test the ability of chemicals to cause mutation, I devised a simple test, using strains of *Salmonella*. Chemicals that cause mutations in bacteria may cause mutation in human genes. Using this test, over 80 percent of cancer-causing substances were shown to cause mutations. The *Salmonella* test, widely known as the Ames test, is now used by more than 3,000 laboratories as a first step in identifying chemicals that might cause cancer.

In 1968, I joined the faculty at the University of California at Berkeley, where my students and I developed genetically engineered bacterial strains that can be used to identify what types of DNA changes are caused by mutagens. My colleague Lois Gold and I have assembled a database on the results of animal cancer tests. I have also studied the mechanisms of aging and cancer.

The accumulated evidence indicates that there is no epidemic of cancer caused by synthetic chemicals. In fact, pollution appears to account for less than 1 percent of human cancer. Several factors, including tobacco and diet, have been identified as the major contributors to cancer in the U.S. The use of tobacco contributes to about one third of all cases of cancer, and the quarter of the population with the lowest dietary intake of fruits and vegetables compared to the highest quarter, have twice the cancer rate for most types of cancer. Hormonal factors contribute to most breast cancer cases. Decreases in physical activity and recreational exposure to the sun have also contributed importantly to increases in some cancers. These results strongly suggest that a large portion of cancer deaths can be avoided by using knowledge at hand to modify lifestyles.

BRUCE AMES *is a professor of biochemistry and molecular biology at the University of California, Berkeley. He has been the international leader in the field of mutagenesis and genetic toxicology for over 20 years. His work has had a major impact on, and changed the direction of, basic and applied research on mutation, cancer, and aging. He earned his B.A. from Cornell University and his Ph.D. from California Institute of Technology.*

cer were observed in this group. Analysis of dietary intake indicates that the risk of colon cancer is positively associated with the intake of animal fat. Nurses who ate beef, pork, or lamb on a daily basis had a 2.5-fold increased risk of colon cancer compared to those who ate such meals less than once a month. This correlation suggests that animal fat may be an environmental risk factor for colon cancer.

A correlation does not mean a cause-and-effect relationship. Other dietary factors, including total calories consumed, protein intake, and trace elements, might be associated with colon cancer. In the meantime, the National Academy of Sciences has issued cautionary diet guidelines. These include the reduction of fat intake to 20% or less of total calories, with increases in the intake of high-fiber foods such as whole grains and vegetables rich in vitamins A and C.

Most research indicates that behavior patterns contribute heavily to the burden of cancer cases and represent about 50% of all cancer deaths, nearly all of which could be eliminated by alterations in lifestyle.

Genetic Models for Susceptibility

Genetic factors may play several roles in determining individual susceptibility to environmental carcinogens. Disorders mentioned earlier in this chapter, including xeroderma pigmentosum (XP) and Fanconi anemia, represent examples of inherited conditions that exhibit hypersensitivity to environmental agents that promote cancer. Xeroderma patients develop skin cancer upon exposure to levels of ultraviolet light that have little or no effect on non-XP individuals, and Fanconi patients are hypersensitive to x-ray-induced cancers.

Evidence for the involvement of specific enzymes in cancer susceptibility comes from studies on smokers and lung cancer. In one study, smokers who smoked few cigarettes and yet developed lung cancer were compared with heavy smokers with no signs of lung cancer. Those patients who developed cancer had significantly elevated metabolism in a pathway that converts carcinogens in tobacco smoke into highly active chemicals that promote tumor formation. Heavy smokers without cancer had much lower levels of activity in this metabolic pathway. These findings suggest that genetic traits controlling the activity or efficiency of metabolic pathways can affect individual susceptibility to environmental cancer agents. The identification and study of such metabolic pathways may help to diagnose individuals at risk for certain cancers and represent a new area of investigation in cancer research.

SUMMARY

1. Although some cancers show hereditary tendencies, there is no single cancer that shows a consistent pattern of Mendelian inheritance. In several cases, such as retinoblastoma, a gene for cancer susceptibility is inherited, with at least one additional mutation required to bring about malignancy.

2. These diseases serve as the basis for a model in which cancer is a multistep process, requiring a minimum of two separate mutational events to occur within a cell to produce cancer. According to this model, cancer cells are clonal descendants from a single mutant cell.

3. The study of two classes of genes, tumor suppressor genes and oncogenes, has established the relationship between cancer, the regulation of cell growth and division, and the cell cycle.

4. The discovery of tumor suppressor genes that normally act to inhibit cell division has provided insight into the regulation of the cell cycle. These gene products act at control points in the cell cycle at G1/S or G2/M, and deletion or inactivation of these products causes cells to continuously divide.

5. The discovery of an oncogene in the Rous sarcoma virus led to the identification of almost 75 oncogenes and their normal cellular counterparts, proto-oncogenes. Proto-oncogenes may serve to regulate cell growth and are converted to oncogenes by alterations in activity or by mutations that produce a defective gene product. Human tumors express at least two oncogenes and occasionally up to seven such genes. Since all human tumors show alterations in oncogenes, it is possible that a limited

number of molecular pathways lead to the development of cancer.

6. Other human disorders, including Down syndrome, are associated with high rates of cancer, and this predisposition may result from the presence of an initial mutation or genetic imbalance that moves cells closer to a cancerous state.

7. It is now apparent that many cancers are environmentally induced. Occupational exposure to minerals and chemicals poses a cancer risk to workers in a number of industries, and the widespread dissemination of these materials poses an undefined but potentially large risk to the general population. Social behavior is responsible for about 40% of all cancer cases in the United States, the majority of which are preventable.

8. Evidence is accumulating that individuals have different susceptibilities to environmental agents that cause cancer, and that these differences have a genetic basis.

QUESTIONS AND PROBLEMS

1. Benign tumors:
   a. are non-cancerous growths that do not spread to other tissues
   b. do not contain mutations
   c. are malignant and clonal in origin
   d. metastasize to other tissues
   e. none of the above

2. Evidence that cancer has a genetic origin includes:
   a. most carcinogens are not mutagens
   b. the discovery of oncogenes, that promote tumor growth
   c. cancer does not spread to other tissues
   d. tumors become benign
   e. the environment plays no role in cancer

3. Cancer is now viewed as a disease that develops in stages. What are the stages that this statement is referring to?
   a. non-malignant tumors become malignant
   b. proto-oncogenes become tumor suppressor genes
   c. younger people get cancer more than older people
   d. small numbers of individual mutational events that can be separated by long periods of time
   e. none of the above

4. Metastasis refers to the process in which:
   a. tumor cells die
   b. tumor cells detach and move to secondary sites
   c. cancer does not spread to other tissues
   d. tumors become benign
   e. cancer can be cured

5. What can cause DNA mutations?
   a. mistakes made during DNA replication
   b. UV light from the sun
   c. smoking
   d. chemicals in our environment
   e. all of the above

6. It is often the case that a predisposition to certain forms of cancer is inherited. Examples are familial retinoblastoma and colon cancer. What does it mean to have inherited an increased probability to acquire a certain form of cancer? What subsequent event(s) must occur?

7. Describe the likelihood of developing bilateral (both eyes affected) retinoblastoma in the inherited versus the sporadic form of the disease.

8. Parents of a one-year old son are concerned that their son may be susceptible to retinoblastoma because the father's brother had bilateral retinoblastoma. Both parents are normal (no retinoblastoma). They have their son tested for the Rb gene, and find to their surprise that he has inherited a mutant allele. The father is then tested and also found to carry a mutant allele.
   a. Why didn't the father develop retinoblastoma?
   b. What is the chance that the couple will have another child carrying the mutant allele?
   c. Is there a benefit to knowing their son may develop retinoblastoma?

9. Describe how the following terms relate to cancer:
   a. benign tumors
   b. malignant tumors
   c. metastasis

10. A proto-oncogene is a gene that:
    a. normally causes cancer
    b. normally suppresses tumor formation
    c. normally functions to promote cell division
    d. is involved in forming only benign tumors
    e. is only expressed in blood cells

11. What are the normal functions of tumor suppressor genes and oncogenes?

12. Theodore Boveri predicted that malignancies would often be associated with chromosomal mutation. What lines of evidence substantiate this prediction?

13. Can you postulate a reason or reasons why children with Down syndrome are 20 times more likely to develop leukemia than children in the general population?

14. What is the difference between an oncogene and a proto-oncogene?

15. Viral oncogenes are often transduced copies of normal cellular genes—they become oncogenic when their gene product or its regulation is subtly altered. What is the role of cellular proto-oncogenes, and how is this role consistent with their implication in oncogenesis?

16. What oncogene has been implicated in Burkitt lymphoma? What mutational event is typically associated with this tumor?

17. What are some factors that epidemiologists have associated with a relatively high risk of developing cancer?

18. What is the probability that a phenotypically normal couple will have a child with retinoblastoma if one of the parents has a sibling with bilateral familial retinoblastoma?

19. Distinguish between dominant inheritance and recessive inheritance in retinoblastoma.

20. Which of the following mutations will result in cancer?
    a. homozygous recessive point mutations in a tumor suppressor gene coding for a non-functional protein
    b. dominant mutation in a tumor suppressor gene in which the protein product is overexpressed
    c. homozygous recessive mutation in which there is a deletion in the coding region of a proto-oncogene, leaving it non-functional
    d. dominant mutation in a proto-oncogene in which the protein product is over-expressed

21. Distinguish between a carcinogen and a mutagen.

22. Smoking cigarettes has been shown to be associated with the development of lung cancer. However, a direct correlation between how many cigarettes one smokes and the onset of lung cancer does not exist. A heavy smoker may not get lung cancer, while a light smoker may get the disease. Explain why this may be.

23. Discuss the relevance of epidemiologic and experimental evidence in recent governmental decisions to regulate exposure to asbestos in the environment.

24. The following is a description of a family that has a history of inherited breast cancer.

    Betty (grandmother) does not carry the gene. Don, her husband, does. Don's mother and sister had breast cancer. One of Betty and Don's daughters (Sarah) has breast cancer, the other (Karen) does not. Sarah's daughters are in their 30s. Dawn, 33, has breast cancer, Debbie, 31, does not. Debbie is wondering if she will get the disease because she looks like her mother. Dawn is wondering if her two-year old daughter (Nicole) will get the disease.
    a. Draw a pedigree, indicate affected individuals and identify all individuals.
    b. What is the most likely mode of inheritance of this trait?
    c. What is Don's genotype and phenotype?
    d. What is the genotype of the unaffected women (Betty and Karen)?

e. An RFLP marker has been found that maps very close to the gene. Given the following RFLP data for chromosomes 4 and 17, which chromosome does this gene map to?

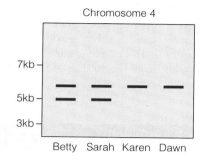

Chromosome 4

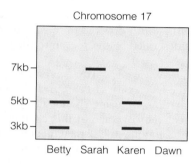

Chromosome 17

f. Using the same RFLP marker, Debbie and Nicole were tested. The results are shown below. Based on their genotypes, are either of them at increased risk for breast cancer?

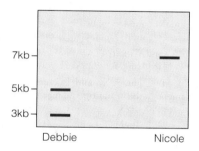

SCIENCE AND SOCIETY

1. Studies have shown that there are significant differences in cancer rates among different ethnic groups. For example, the Japanese have very high rates of colon cancer, but very low rates of breast cancer. It has also been demonstrated that members of low-risk ethnic groups move to high-risk areas, their cancer risks rise to that of the high-risk area.

For example, Japanese who live in the United States, where the risk of breast cancer is high, have higher rates of breast cancer than Japanese who live in Japan. What are some of the possible explanations for this interesting phenomenon? What factors may explain why the Japanese have higher rates of colon cancer than other ethnic groups?

INTERNET ACTIVITIES

The following activities use the resources of the World Wide Web to enhance the topics covered in this chapter. To investigate the topics described below, log on to the book's home page at:

http://www.wadsworth.com/biology

1. Oncolink is the University of Pennsylvania's resource for cancer information. By using the menus at this site you can supplement the coverage in this chapter on cancers with a genetic component. Use the Oncolink to access the most recent developments in cancer research.
2. Breast cancer screening followed by prophylactic mastectomy has now become an option for some women with

strong family histories of breast cancer. What would you do if you were found to carry the gene which would predispose you to this type of cancer? Access the Breast Cancer and Genetic Screening page of Lawrence Berkeley national Laboratory's ELSI project and read about breast cancer. Answer the questions under "What would you do?"
3. The MD Anderson Oncolog is a site maintained by the University of Texas M.D. Anderson Cancer Center. Use this site for information on cancer patient care, diagnostic advances and therapies.

FOR FURTHER READING

Alberts, D. S., Lipkin, M., and Levin, B. 1996. Genetic screening for colorectal cancer and intervention. Int. J. Cancer 69: 62–63.

Ames, B., Gold, L. S., and Willett, W. C. 1995. The causes and prevention of cancer. Proc. Nat. Acad. Sci. 92: 5258–5265.

Benedict, W. F., Xu, H. J., Hu, S. X., and Takahashi, R. 1990. Role of the retinoblastoma gene in the initiation and progression of human cancer. J. Clin. Invest. 85: 988–993.

Bodmer, W. F., Bailey, C. J., Bodmer, J., Bussey, H., Ellis, A., Gorman, P., Lucibello, F., Murday, V., Rider, S., Scambler, P., Sheer, D., Solomon, E., and Spurr, N. 1987. Localization of the gene for familial adenomatous polyposis on chromosome 5. Nature 328: 614–616.

Burt, R., Bishop, D. T., Cannon, L. A., Dowdle, M. A., Lee, R. G., and Skolnick, M. H. 1985. Dominant inheritance of adenomatous polyps and colorectal cancer. N. Engl. J. Med. 312: 1540–1544.

Call, K. M., Glaser, T., Ito, C. Y., Buckler, A. J., Pelletier, J., Haber, D. A., Rose, E. A., Kral, A., Yeger, H., Lewis, W. H., Jones, C., and Housman, D. E. 1990. Isolation and characterization of a zinc finger polypeptide gene at the human chromosome 11 Wilms tumor locus. Cell 61: 509–520.

Cancer Facts and Figures. 1996. New York: American Cancer Society.

Committee on Diet, Nutrition and Cancer, Assembly of Life Sciences, National Research Council. 1982. Diet, Nutrition, and Cancer. Washington, D.C.: National Academy Press.

Corbett, T. H. 1977. Cancer and Chemicals. Chicago: Nelson-Hall.

Croce, C., and Klein, G. 1985. Chromosome translocations and human cancer. Sci. Am. (March) 252: 54–60.

Fearon, E. R., and Vogelstein, B. 1990. A genetic model for colorectal tumorigenesis. Cell 61: 759–767.

Hamm, R. D. 1990. Occupational cancer in the oncogene era. Br. J. Indust. Med. 47: 217–220.

Lee, W-H., Bookstein, R., and Lee, E. 1988. Studies on the human retinoblastoma susceptibility gene. J. Cellular Biochem. 38: 213–227.

Maitland, N., Brown, K., Poirier, V., Shaw, A., and Williams, J. 1989. Molecular and cellular biology of Wilms tumor. Antican. Res. 9: 1417–1426.

Malkin, D. and Knoppers, B. M. 1996. Genetic predisposition to cancer - issues to consider. Semin. Cancer Biol. 7: 49–53.

Marshall, E. 1993. Search for a killer: Focus shifts from fat to hormones. Science 259: 618–621.

Perrera F. P. 1996. Molecular epidemiology: insights into cancer susceptibility, risk assessment and prevention. J. Natl. Cancer Inst. 88: 496–509.

Reddy, J. C. and Licht, J. D. 1996. The WT1 Wilms tumor suppressor gene: how much do we really know? Biochim. Biophys. Acta 1287: 1–28.

Rous, P. 1911. Transmission of a malignant new growth by means of a cell-free filtrate. J. Am. Med. Assoc. 56: 1981.

Ruoslahti, E. 1996. How cancer spreads. Sci. Am. 275: 72–77.

Stahl, A., Levy, N., Wadzynska, T., Sussan, J. M., Jourdan-Fonta, D. and Saracco, J. B. 1994. The genetics of retinoblastoma. Ann. Genet. 37: 172–178.

Sugimura, T. 1990. Cancer prevention: underlying principles and practical proposals. *Basic Life Sci. 52:* 225–232.

Vasen, H. F. 1994. What is hereditary nonpolyposis colon cancer (HNPCC)? Anticancer Res. 14(4B): 1613–1615.

Vogelstein, B., Fearson, E. R., Kern, S., Hamilton, S., Preisinger, A., Nakamura, Y., and White, R. 1989. Allelotypes of colorectal carcinomas. Science **244:** 207–211.

Weinberg, R. A. 1985. The action of oncogenes in the cytoplasm and nucleus. *Science 203:* 770–776.

Weinberg, R. A. 1996. How cancer arises. Sci. Am. 275: 62–70.

Yunis, J. J. 1983. The chromosomal basis of human neoplasia. Science **221:** 227–236.

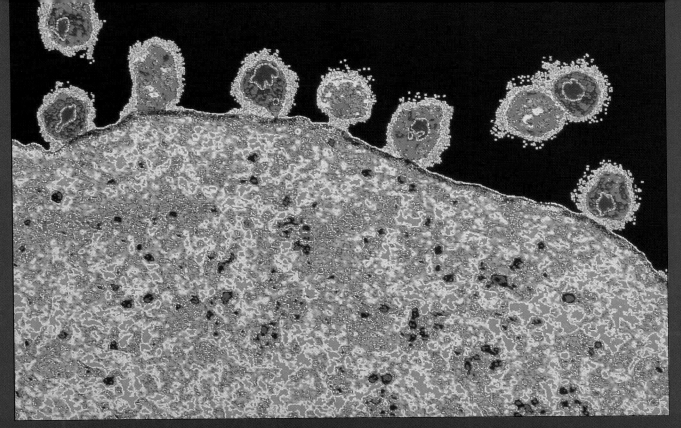

GENETICS OF THE IMMUNE SYSTEM

Chapter 15

Chapter Outline

THE IMMUNE SYSTEM DEFENDS THE BODY AGAINST INFECTION

THE INFLAMMATORY RESPONSE IS A GENERAL REACTION

Nonspecific Responses Are Activated by the Inflammatory Reaction

The Complement System Kills Microorganisms Directly

THE IMMUNE RESPONSE IS A SPECIFIC DEFENSE AGAINST INFECTION

An Overview of the Immune Response

Antibody-Mediated Immunity Uses Molecular Weapons

Antibodies Are Molecular Weapons against Antigens

Rearrangement in Antibody Genes

T Cells Mediate the Cellular Immune Response

The Immune System Has a Memory Function

BLOOD TYPES ARE DETERMINED BY CELL SURFACE ANTIGENS

ABO Blood Typing Allows Safe Blood Transfusions

Rh Blood Types Can Cause Immune Reactions between Mother and Fetus

ORGAN TRANSPLANTS MUST BE IMMUNOLOGICALLY MATCHED

Successful Transplants Depend on HLA Matching

SIDEBAR *Genetically Engineered Blood*

Animal-Human Transplants

The HLA System and Disease Associations

DISORDERS OF THE IMMUNE SYSTEM

Overreaction in the Immune System Causes Allergies

Autoimmune Reactions Cause the Immune System to Attack the Body

Genetic Disorders Impair the Immune System

CONCEPTS AND CONTROVERSIES *Why Bee Stings Can Be Fatal*

AIDS Attacks the Immune System

GUEST ESSAY *Medicine—A Scientific Safari*

OPENING IMAGE
Newly-produced particles of the human immunodeficiency virus (HIV) are shown budding off the surface of a white blood cell. Each of these HIV particles can infect other cells.

Approximately 2500 years ago, a mysterious plague swept through Athens, Greece, killing thousands of residents. The historian Thucydides wrote an account of the epidemic, and noted that those who recovered from the disease could care for the sick without becoming ill a second time. Physicians in ancient China observed that people who

contracted smallpox became resistant to the disease. Records from 8th-century China indicate that partially successful attempts were made to transfer resistance to uninfected individuals by injecting them with fluid obtained from smallpox victims.

The first safe and successful method of transferring resistance to a disease was developed about a thousand years later by Edward Jenner, an English physician. He noted that people who developed cowpox were resistant to smallpox infections. To see if he could transfer resistance to smallpox, he inoculated a boy with dried scrapings from a cowpox patient, and followed this a few weeks later with an injection from a smallpox patient. The boy did not develop smallpox, and the method, called vaccination (from vaccus, the Latin word for cow) became an effective tool in controlling this disease.

The World Health Organization led a worldwide vaccination campaign against smallpox and eradicated the disease by 1980. Since the virus that causes smallpox cannot reproduce outside the body of an infected individual, the disease has disappeared. The only remaining samples of the virus are stored in research facilities in the United States and Russia.

Vaccines are used to prevent a number of diseases, including diphtheria, whooping cough, measles, and hepatitis B. But the study of the body's resistance to disease is a young and developing science, and new diseases still arise to remind us of our limited knowledge. In the early 1970s, women began to develop a condition known as toxic shock syndrome. By 1980, several thousand cases and over 25 deaths had been reported. Careful investigation determined that certain brands of highly absorbent tampons led to vaginal infections with certain strains of Staphylococcus aureus. The bacteria secrete a toxin that produce the symptoms of fever, rash, low blood pressure, and in some cases, death.

Other new diseases remain a mystery. In 1981, an infectious disease known as acquired immunodeficiency syndrome (AIDS) appeared in the United States. Affected individuals exhibit rare forms of cancer, pneumonia, and other infections. In all cases, there is a complete and irreversible breakdown of the immune system, associated with infection by the human immunodeficiency virus (HIV). This breakdown allows the development of infections, one or more of which proves fatal. Because death eventually results from infection by any of a number of normally nonpathogenic agents, AIDS is known as a syndrome.

THE IMMUNE SYSTEM DEFENDS THE BODY AGAINST INFECTION

Vertebrates have evolved a series of defense mechanisms against the entry of foreign agents into their internal environment. Infections caused by viruses, bacteria, and fungi remain a health problem in industrialized nations, and are a major cause of death in Third World nations. The responses of the body to infection include a nonspecific response and a highly specific set of responses known as the immune reaction.

Nonspecific responses are designed to (1) block the entry of disease-causing agents into the body, and (2) block the spread of infectious agents if they are successful in gaining entry to the body. The immune system has two types of responses to invading agents: antibody-mediated immunity and cell-mediated immunity. Each of these is highly specific and consists of two stages, a primary response and a later-developing secondary response. The secondary response is characterized by a quick reaction after a second exposure to the same invading organism. In addition, the immune system is responsible for the success or failure of blood transfusions and organ

transplants. In this chapter, we will examine the cells of the immune system and how they are mobilized to mount an immune response.

We will also consider the role of the immune system in determining blood groups, mother-fetus incompatibility, how cell-surface markers are matched in organ transplants, and how these markers can be used in a predictive way to determine risk factors for a wide range of diseases. Finally, we will describe a number of disorders of the immune system, including how AIDS acts to cripple the immune response of infected individuals.

✸ THE INFLAMMATORY RESPONSE IS A GENERAL REACTION

The skin represents a passive barrier to infectious agents such as viruses and bacteria. Bacteria, fungi, and even mites populate the surface of the body, but are unable to penetrate the protective layers of dead skin cells to cause infection. The skin contains glands, which secrete acidic oils that inhibit bacterial growth; sweat, tears, and saliva contain enzymes that break down the outer walls of many bacteria.

The mucus membranes that line the respiratory, digestive, urinary, and reproductive tracts secrete mucus that forms a barrier against infection. The respiratory system has an additional barrier in the form of cilia that sweep out bacteria trapped in the mucus. These physical barriers form the first line of defense against infection with disease-causing agents.

Nonspecific Responses Are Activated by the Inflammatory Reaction

If microorganisms penetrate the skin or epithelial layers lining the respiratory, digestive, or urinary systems through a break or injury, a reaction called inflammation results (● Figure 15.1). Damaged cells release chemical

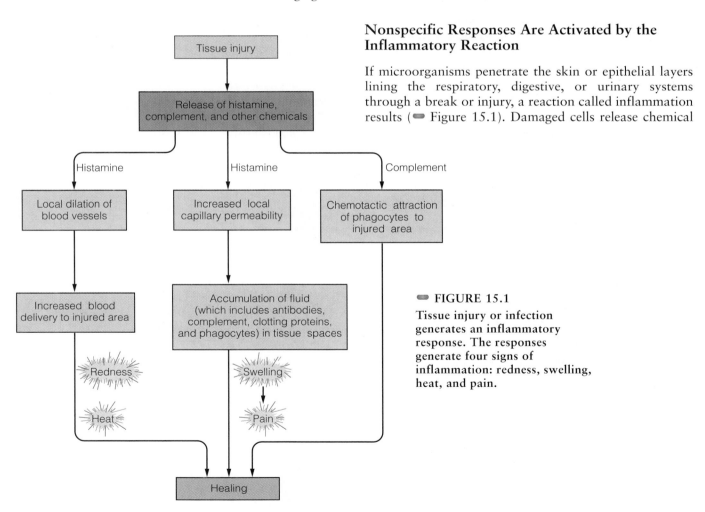

● **FIGURE 15.1**

Tissue injury or infection generates an inflammatory response. The responses generate four signs of inflammation: redness, swelling, heat, and pain.

signals including histamine. These chemicals increase capillary blood flow in the affected area (the action of these chemicals is responsible for the heat and redness that develops around a cut or scrape). The increased heat creates an unfavorable environment for the growth of microorganisms, causes an increase in the mobility of white blood cells, and raises the metabolic rate in nearby cells, promoting healing. In addition, macrophages and other phagocytes migrate to the area in response to the chemical signals and the increased capillary circulation, engulfing and destroying the invading microorganisms.

The capillary beds in the area become leaky, allowing plasma to flow into the injured tissue, often causing the affected area to become swollen. Clotting factors in the plasma trigger a cascade of small blood clots to seal off the injured area, preventing the escape of invading organisms. Finally, the area becomes the target for another type of white blood cell, the **monocytes**, which clean up dead viruses, bacteria, or fungi and dispose of dead cells and debris.

This chain of events, beginning with the release of chemical signals and ending with the clean-up by monocytes, makes up the **inflammatory response**. This response is an active defense mechanism employed by the body to resist infection. This localized and limited reaction is usually enough to stop the spread of infectious agents. If this system fails, another more powerful system—the immune response—is called into action.

The Complement System Kills Microorganisms Directly

The **complement system** is a chemical defense system that works to kill microorganisms directly, to supplement the inflammatory response, and to work with the immune response (➡ Figure 15.2). The name of the system is derived from the way it complements the action of the immune system. Complement proteins are synthesized in the liver and circulate in the bloodstream as inactive precursors. When activated, the first component (C1) activates the second (C2), and so forth, in a cascade of activation. The final five components (C5–C9) form a large, cylindrical multiprotein complex, called the membrane-attack complex (MAC). The MAC embeds itself in the

Monocytes
White blood cells that clean up viruses, bacteria, and fungi and dispose of dead cells and debris at the end of the inflammatory response.

Inflammatory response
Body's reaction to invading microorganisms.

Complement system
A chemical defense system that kills microorganisms directly, supplements the inflammatory response, and works with (complements) the immune system.

➡ **FIGURE 15.2**
The complement system has several actions, all associated with defending the body against infection.

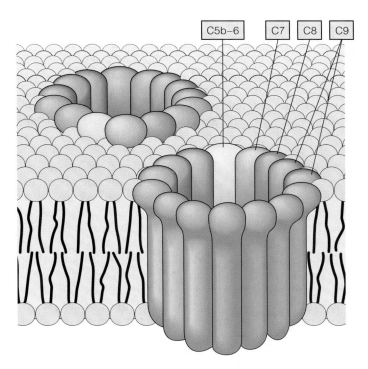

C5b–6   C7   C8   C9

FIGURE 15.3

The membrane attack complex (MAC). The complement proteins insert into the membrane of an invading microorganism. Water flows into the cell causes it to swell and burst.

Antibody
A class of proteins produced by B cells that bind to foreign molecules (antigens) and inactivate them.

Antigens
Molecules carried or produced by microorganisms that initiate antibody production.

Lymphocytes
White blood cells that arise in bone marrow and mediate the immune response.

Stem cells
Cells in bone marrow that produce lymphocytes by mitotic division.

T cells
A type of lymphocyte that undergoes maturation in the thymus and mediates cellular immunity.

B cells
A type of lymphocyte that undergoes maturation in the bone marrow and mediates antibody-directed immunity.

Antibody-mediated immunity
Immune reaction that protects primarily against invading viruses and bacteria by means of antibodies produced by plasma cells.

Cell-mediated immunity
Immune reaction mediated by T cells that is directed against body cells that have been infected by viruses or bacteria.

plasma membrane of an invading microorganism, creating a pore (Figure 15.3). Water flows through the pore in response to an osmotic gradient, bursting the cell.

In addition to directly destroying microorganisms, some of the complement proteins guide phagocytes to the site of microbial invasion. Other components aid the immune response by binding to the outer surface of microorganisms and marking them for phagocytosis.

THE IMMUNE RESPONSE IS A SPECIFIC DEFENSE AGAINST INFECTION

The immune system generates a response designed to neutralize and/or destroy specific agents including viruses, bacteria, fungi, and cancer cells. The immune system is more effective than the nonspecific defense system, and has a memory component that remembers previous encounters with infectious agents. Immunological memory allows a rapid, massive response to a second exposure to a foreign substance.

An Overview of the Immune Response

Immunity is a state of resistance brought about by the production of proteins called **antibodies.** Antibodies bind to foreign molecules and microorganisms and can inactivate them in several ways. Molecules carried by or produced by microorganisms that initiate antibody production are called **antigens** (*anti*body *gen*erators). Most antigens are themselves proteins or proteins combined with polysaccharides, but *any* molecule, regardless of its source, that causes antibody production is an antigen.

The immune response is mediated by white blood cells called **lymphocytes.** These cells arise in the bone marrow, by mitotic division of **stem cells** (Figure 15.4). One type of lymphocyte is formed when daughter cells migrate from the bone marrow to the thymus gland, where they are irreversibly programmed to become **T cells.** Mature T cells circulate in the blood and become associated with lymph nodes and the spleen. The **B cells** mature in the bone marrow and move directly to the circulatory system and the lymph system. B cells are genetically programmed to produce antibodies; each B cell produces only one type of antibody.

The immune system has two components, **antibody-mediated** immunity, regulated by B cells and antibody production, and **cell-mediated** immunity, controlled by T

TABLE 15.1

Comparison of Antibody-Mediated and Cell-Mediated Immunity

ANTIBODY-MEDIATED	CELL-MEDIATED
Principal cellular agent is the B cell. B cell responds to bacteria, bacterial toxins, and some viruses.	Principal cellular agent is the T cell. T cells respond to cancer cells, virus-infected cells, single-celled fungi, parasites and foreign cells in an organ transplant.
When activated, B cells form memory cells and plasma cells, which produce antibodies to these antigens.	When activated, T cells differentiate into memory cells, cytotoxic cells, suppressor cells, and helper cells; cytotoxic T cells attack the antigen directly.

Macrophages
Large white blood cells derived from monocytes that engulf antigens and present them to T cells, activating the immune response.

cells (Table 15.1). The primary task of antibody-mediated reactions is to defend the body against invading viruses and bacteria. Cell-mediated immunity is directed against cells of the body that have been infected by viruses and bacteria. T cells also protect against infection by parasites, fungi, and protozoans. One group of T cells can also kill cells of the body if they become cancerous.

Antibody-Mediated Immunity Uses Molecular Weapons

The antibody-mediated immune response involves several stages: antigen detection, activation of helper T cells, and antibody production by B cells. Each of these stages is directed by a specific cell type of the immune system.

White blood cells called **macrophages** continuously wander through the circulatory system and the interstitial spaces between cells searching for foreign (nonself) antigenic molecules, viruses, or microorganisms. When such an antigen is encountered, it is engulfed, ingested by the

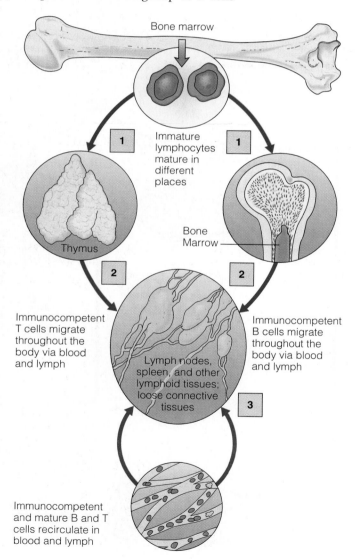

Bone marrow

1 Immature lymphocytes mature in different places 1

Thymus

Bone Marrow

2

2

Immunocompetent T cells migrate throughout the body via blood and lymph

Immunocompetent B cells migrate throughout the body via blood and lymph

Lymph nodes, spleen, and other lymphoid tissues; loose connective tissues

3

Immunocompetent and mature B and T cells recirculate in blood and lymph

● FIGURE 15.4

Immature lymphocytes (lymphoblasts) produced in bone marrow that travel to the thymus for maturation become T cells. Those that remain and mature in bone marrow become B cells. Once mature, T and B lymphocytes migrate through the body in the circulatory system as part of the immune system.

Helper T cells
A type of lymphocyte that stimulates the production of antibodies by B cells when an antigen is present.

Plasma cells
Cells produced by mitotic division of B cells that synthesize and secrete antibodies.

B-memory cells
Long-lived B cells produced after exposure to an antigen that play an important role in secondary immunity

● **FIGURE 15.5**

Macrophages engulf invading microorganisms and process their antigens for presentation to the helper T cells of the immune system. The activated T cell, in turn, stimulates division of the B cell, producing antibodies against the antigen presented by the macrophage. Daughter B cells become differentiated as plasma cells for the production of large quantities of antibody. Macrophages can also directly stimulate antibody production by interaction with a B cell.

macrophage (● Figure 15.5), and destroyed by enzymes. Small fragments of the antigen are displayed on the outer surface of the macrophage's plasma membrane, along with cell surface markers that identify the cell as a macrophage.

As the macrophage moves about, it may encounter a lymphocyte called a **helper T cell**. Surface receptors on the T cell make contact with the antigen on the macrophage, activating the T cell. The activated T cell in turn identifies and activates B cells, which manufacture an antibody against the antigen presented by the T cell to the B cell. The activated B cells divide, forming two types of daughter cells; one type is the **plasma cell**, which synthesizes and releases from 2,000 to 20,000 antibody molecules per *second* into the bloodstream during its lifespan of 4–5 days (● Figure 15.6). A smaller number of the second type of cells, called **B-memory cells,** are also produced at this time. These cells have a life span that extends for months and even years. They are part of the immune memory system, and will be described in a later section. This same cascade of events results when a macrophage presents an antigen directly to a B cell.

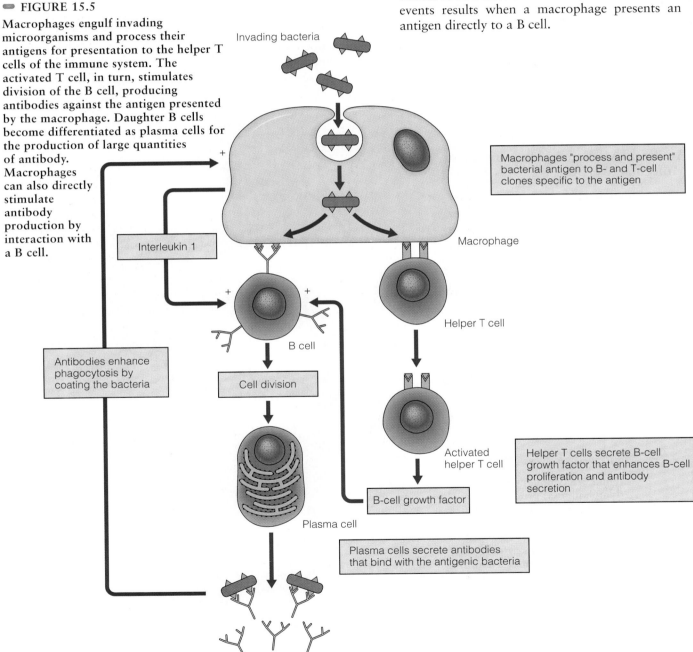

Invading bacteria

Macrophages "process and present" bacterial antigen to B- and T-cell clones specific to the antigen

Macrophage

Interleukin 1

Antibodies enhance phagocytosis by coating the bacteria

B cell

Helper T cell

Cell division

Activated helper T cell

Helper T cells secrete B-cell growth factor that enhances B-cell proliferation and antibody secretion

B-cell growth factor

Plasma cell

Plasma cells secrete antibodies that bind with the antigenic bacteria

Antibodies

Antibodies Are Molecular Weapons against Antigens

Antibodies are Y-shaped protein molecules that bind to specific antigens in a lock-and-key fashion to form an antigen-antibody complex (● Figure 15.7). They are secreted by plasma cells and circulate in the blood and lymph, or are attached to the surface of B cells. Antibodies belong to a class of proteins known as **immunoglobulins**.

There are five classes of immunoglobulins: IgG, IgA, IgM, IgD, and IgE. Each class has a unique structure, size, and function (Table 15.2). In general, antibody mole-

Immunoglobulins
The five classes of proteins to which antibodies belong.

TABLE 15.2

Types and Functions of the Immunoglobulins

CLASS	LOCATION AND FUNCTION
IgD	Present on surface of many B cells, but function uncertain; may be a surface receptor for B cells; plays a role in activation of B cells.
IgM	Found on surface of B cells and in plasma; acts as a B-cell surface receptor for antigen, secreted early in primary response; powerful agglutinating agent.
IgG	Most abundant immunoglobulin in the blood plasma; produced during primary and secondary response; can pass through the placenta, entering fetal bloodstream, thus providing protection to fetus.
IgA	Produced by plasma cells in the digestive, respiratory, and urinary systems, where it protects the surface linings by preventing attachment of bacteria to surfaces of epithelial cells; also present in tears and breast milk; protects lining of digestive, respiratory, and urinary systems.
IgE	Produced by plasma cells in skin, tonsils, and the digestive and respiratory systems, over-production is responsible for allergic reactions, including hay fever and asthma.

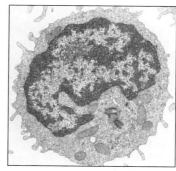

(a)

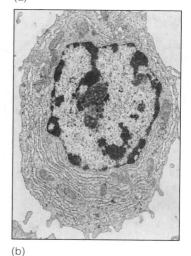

(b)

● FIGURE 15.6

Electron micrographs of (a) a mature, unactivated B cell, and (b) a differentiated plasma cell (an activated B cell).

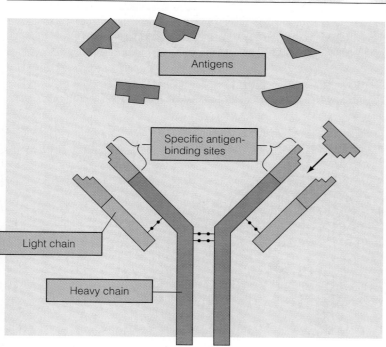

Antigens

Specific antigen-binding sites

Light chain

Heavy chain

● FIGURE 15.7

Antibody molecules are made up of two different proteins (an H chain and an L chain). The molecule is Y-shaped, forming a specific antigen-binding site at the ends.

cules are Y-shaped structures composed of two identical long polypeptides (H chains), and two identical short polypeptides (L chains). The chains are held together by chemical bonds.

The structure of antibodies is related to their functions: (1) recognize and bind to antigens, and (2) inactivate the antigen. At one end of the antibody, there is an antigen-combining site formed by the ends of the H and L chains. This unique antigen-combining site recognizes and binds to a site on the antigen, called the **antigenic determinant**. The formation of an antigen-antibody complex leads to the destruction of an antigen in several ways (● Figure 15.8).

Rearrangement in Antibody Genes

Humans can produce billions of different antibody molecules, each of which can bind to a different antigen. How is this diversity encoded within the genome? Since there are literally billions of combinations of H and L chains that produce antibodies, it seems unlikely that each combination is separately encoded in the genome.

Antigenic determinant
The site on an antigen to which an antibody binds, forming an antigen-antibody complex.

● **FIGURE 15.8**

After an antigen and antibody combine, several pathways lead to the destruction of the antigen.

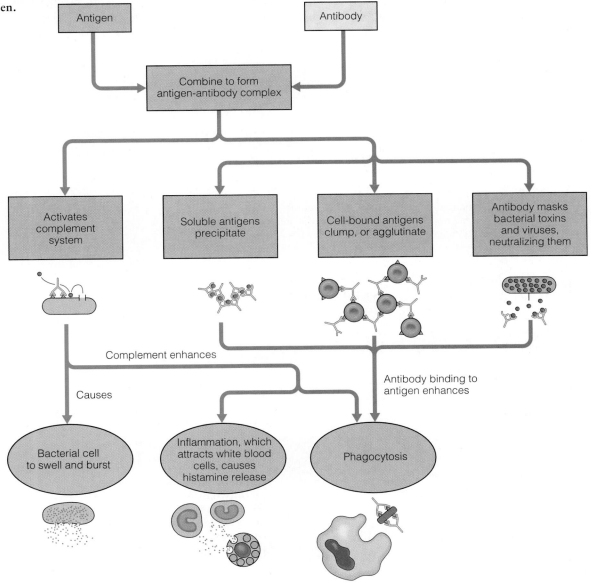

Several theories have been put forward to explain how antibody diversity can be genetically encoded, but the available evidence supports the **recombination theory.**

This model proposes that recombination events in antibody genes take place during B-cell maturation, before antibody genes are transcribed and antibody production begins. As an example, let us consider one class of light chain genes. These genes contain three regions: The V-L (variable-leader) region, the J (joining) region, and the C (constant) region (Figure 15.9). In the germ cells and B-cell precursors, each of these L genes is composed of 70 to 300 V-L regions, about 6 J regions, and 1 C region. These segments are located some distance apart on the chromosome.

As the B cell matures, one of the several hundred V-L regions is randomly joined to one of the J regions and the adjacent C region by a recombination event. The remaining regions are excised from the chromosome and destroyed. The fusion gene encodes a specific L chain. In a mature B cell, this gene is transcribed and translated to form an L chain that becomes part of an antibody molecule. This rearranged gene is stable, and is passed on to all daughter cells. Genes for the other class of light

Recombination theory
The idea that functional antibody genes are created by the recombination of DNA segments during B-cell maturation.

 FIGURE 15.9

In germ cells, light chain genes contain several hundred V-L regions, six J regions, and one C region. As B cells mature, random combinations of V-L and J regions are fused by recombination to a C region, generating a functional antibody L-chain gene.

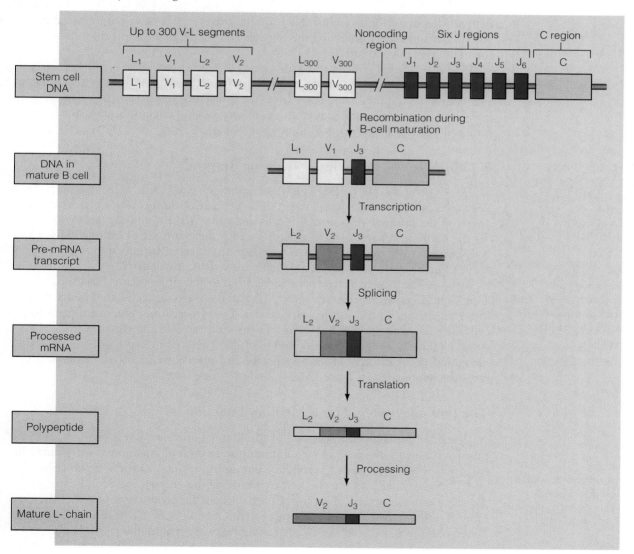

TABLE 15.3

Summary of T Cells

CELL TYPE	ACTION
Cytotoxic T cells	Destroy body cells infected by viruses, and attack and kill bacteria, fungi, parasites, and cancer cells.
Helper T cells	Produce a growth factor that stimulates B-cell proliferation and differentiation and also stimulates antibody production by plasma cells; enhance activity of cytotoxic T cells.
Suppressor T cells	May inhibit immune reaction by decreasing B- and T-cell activity and B- and T-cell division.
Memory T cells	Remain in body awaiting reintroduction of antigen, at which time they proliferate and differentiate into cytotoxic T cells, helper T cells, suppressor T cells, and additional memory cells.

chains and the genes for the heavy chains are also composed of regions that undergo recombination during B-cell maturation. Because these recombination events take place at random in each B cell during maturation, the result is the production of many different antibody chains. Each B cell, however, has been programmed by the recombination events involving the L genes and the H genes to produce only one of the many possible variants.

Antibody diversity is the result of genetic events that shuffle a number of basic components into a large number of combinations. In addition to the recombination events described, other events that take place during B-cell maturation expand antibody diversity, allowing production of billions of possible antibodies from several hundred basic gene segments in three gene classes.

T Cells Mediate the Cellular Immune Response

There are several types of T cells in the immune system (Table 15.3). Helper T cells, described earlier, activate B cells to produce antibodies. **Suppressor T cells** slow down and stop the immune response of B cells and other T cells, and act as the off switch for the immune system. A third type of T cell is the **cytotoxic or killer T cells**. These cells target and destroy cells of the body that are infected with a virus or with bacteria (● Figure 15.10). If a cell is infected with a virus, it will display viral antigens on its surface. The foreign antigens are recognized by receptors on the surface of a killer T cell. The T cell attaches to the infected cell and secretes a protein that punches holes in the plasma membrane of the infected cell. The cytoplasmic contents of the infected cell leak out through these holes, and the infected cell dies and is removed by phagocytes. Cytotoxic T cells will also bind to and kill cells of transplanted organs if they recognizes them as foreign. The nonspecific and specific reactions of the immune system are summarized in Table 15.4.

The Immune System Has a Memory Function

As described in the opening section of the chapter, ancient writers observed that exposure to certain diseases conferred immunity to second infections by the same disease. This resistance, called **secondary immunity**, results from the production of B and T memory cells during the first exposure to the antigen. A second exposure to the same antigen results in an immediate, large-scale production of antibodies and killer T cells. Because of the presence of the memory cells, the second reaction is faster, more massive, and lasts longer than the primary immune response.

Suppressor T cells
T cells that slow or stop the immune response of B cells and other T cells.

Cytotoxic or killer T cells
T cells that destroy body cells infected by viruses or bacteria. Can also directly attack viruses, bacteria, cancer cells, and cells of transplanted organs.

Secondary immunity
Resistance to an antigen the second time it appears, due to T and B memory cells. The second response is faster, larger, and lasts longer than the first.

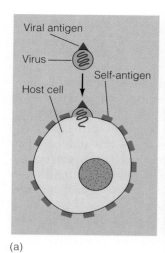

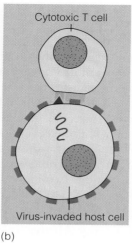

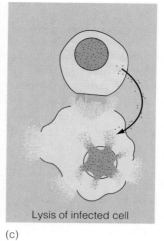

(a)

(b)

(c)

FIGURE 15.10

(a) Virus-infected cells display viral antigens on their surface. (b) Cytotoxic T cells can recognize virus-infected cells of the body. (c) These T cells can bind to the infected cell and release chemicals that lead to the destruction of the infected cell before the virus can begin to replicate.

The secondary immune responses is the basis for vaccination against infectious diseases. A **vaccine** is designed to stimulate the production of memory cells against a disease-causing agent. The disease-causing antigen is administered orally or by injection, and it provokes a primary immune response and the production of memory cells. Often, a second dose is administered to elicit another secondary response that raises or boosts the number of memory cells (which is why such shots are called booster shots).

Vaccines are made from killed pathogens, which are weakened strains that can stimulate the immune system but cannot produce life-threatening symptoms of the disease. Recombinant DNA techniques are now being used to prepare vaccines against a number of diseases that affect humans and farm animals. The irony is that while vaccination is a proven and effective means of controlling a wide range of infectious diseases, fewer and fewer people in the United States are being vaccinated.

Vaccine

A preparation containing dead or weakened pathogens that elicit an immune response when injected into the body.

TABLE 15.4
Nonspecific and Specific Immune Responses to Bacterial Invasion

NONSPECIFIC IMMUNE MECHANISMS	SPECIFIC IMMUNE MECHANISMS
INFLAMMATION Engulfment of invading bacteria by resident tissue macrophages Histamine-induced vascular responses to increase blood flow to area, bringing in additional immune cells Walling off of invaded area by fibrin clot Migration of neutrophils and monocytes/macrophages to the area, to engulf and destroy foreign invaders and to remove cellular debris Secretion by phagocytic cells of chemical mediators, which enhance both nonspecific and specific immune responses **NONSPECIFIC ACTIVATION OF THE COMPLEMENT SYSTEM** Formation of hole-punching membrane attack complex that lyses bacterial cells Enhancement of many steps of inflammation	Processing and presenting of bacterial antigen by macrophages Proliferation and differentiation of activated B-cell clone into plasma cells and memory cells Secretion by plasma cells of customized antibodies, which specifically bind to invading bacteria Enhancement by helper T cells, which have been activated by the same bacterial antigen processed and presented to them by macrophages Binding of antibodies to invading bacteria and activation of mechanisms that lead to their destruction Activation of lethal complement system Stimulation of killer cells, which directly lyse bacteria Persistence of memory cells capable of responding more rapidly and more forcefully should the same bacteria be encountered again

BLOOD TYPES ARE DETERMINED BY CELL SURFACE ANTIGENS

The presence or absence of certain antigens on the surface of blood cells is the basis of blood transfusions. Each of the 30 or more known antigens on blood cells constitutes a blood group or **blood type**. In transfusions, the critical blood types of the donor and recipient must be matched. If transfused red blood cells have a foreign antigen on their surface, the immune system of the recipient will already have, or will produce, antibodies to this antigen. These antibodies will cause the transfused cells to clump and block circulation in capillaries and other small blood vessels, with severe and often fatal results. Two blood groups are of major significance: the ABO system and the Rh blood group.

ABO Blood Typing Allows Safe Blood Transfusions

ABO blood types are determined by a gene I (for isoagglutinin) that encodes a cell surface protein. This gene has three alleles, I^A, I^B, and I^O, often written as A, B, and O. The A and B alleles each produce a slightly different version of the gene product, and O produces no gene product. Individuals with type A blood carry the A antigen on their red blood cells, so they will not make antibodies against this cell surface marker. But type A individuals have antibodies against the antigen encoded by the B allele (Table 15.5). Those with type B blood have B antigens on their red cells, and have antibodies against the A antigen. If you have type AB blood, both antigens are present on the surface of red cells, and no antibodies against A or B are made. In those with type O blood, neither antigen is present, but antibodies against *both* the A and B antigen are present in the blood.

In transfusions, AB individuals have no serum antibodies against A or B and can receive blood of any type. Type O individuals have neither red cell antigen and can donate blood to anyone, even though their plasma contains antibodies against A and B. After transfusion, the concentration of these antibodies is too low to cause problems.

When transfusions are made between incompatible blood types, several problems arise. 🔶 Figure 15.11 shows the cascade of reactions that follow transfusing someone who is type A with type B blood. Antibodies to the B antigen are in the blood of the recipient; these bind to the tranfused red blood cells, causing them to clump together and burst. The clumped cells restrict blood flow in capillaries, reducing oxygen delivery. Lysis of red blood cells releases large amounts of hemoglobin into the blood. In the kidneys, the hemoglobin crystallizes, blocking the tubules of the kidney and often causing kidney failure.

Rh Blood Types Can Cause Immune Reactions between Mother and Fetus

The Rh blood group (named for the rhesus monkey, in which it was discovered) consists of those who can make the Rh antigen (*Rh positive*, Rh+) and those who cannot make the antigen (*Rh negative*, Rh–).

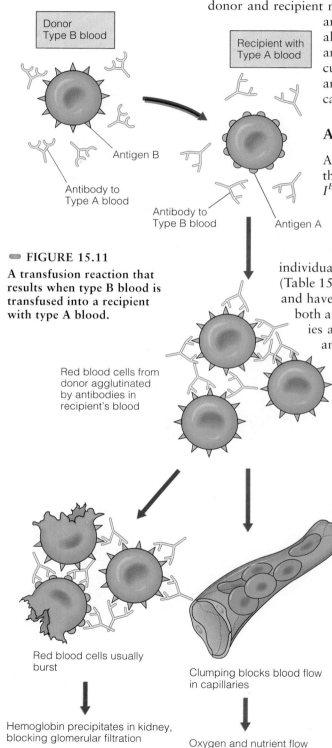

Donor Type B blood

Recipient with Type A blood

Antigen B

Antibody to Type A blood

Antibody to Type B blood

Antigen A

🔶 **FIGURE 15.11**

A transfusion reaction that results when type B blood is transfused into a recipient with type A blood.

Red blood cells from donor agglutinated by antibodies in recipient's blood

Red blood cells usually burst

Clumping blocks blood flow in capillaries

Hemoglobin precipitates in kidney, blocking glomerular filtration

Oxygen and nutrient flow to cells and tissues is reduced

	TABLE 15.5			
	Summary of ABO Blood Types			
BLOOD TYPE	ANTIGENS ON PLASMA MEMBRANES OF RBCS	ANTIBODIES IN BLOOD	SAFE TO TRANSFUSE TO	FROM
A	A	Anti-B	A, AB	A, O
B	B	Anti-A	B, AB	B, O
AB	A + B	none	AB	A, B, AB, O
O	—	Anti-A Anti-B	A, B, AB, O	

The Rh blood group is of major concern when it leads to immunological incompatibility between mother and fetus, a condition known as **hemolytic disease of the newborn** or **HDN**. This occurs when the mother is Rh⁻ and the fetus is Rh⁺ (⬭ Figure 15.12). If the mother is Rh⁻, and Rh⁺ blood from the fetus enters the

Hemolytic disease of the newborn (HDN)
A condition of immunological incompatibility between mother and fetus that occurs when the mother is Rh⁻ and the fetus is Rh⁺.

⬭ **FIGURE 15.12**

The Rh factor and pregnancy. (a) Rh-positive cells from the fetus can enter the maternal circulation at birth. If the mother is Rh-negative, she produces antibodies against the Rh factor. **(b)** In a subsequent pregnancy, if the fetus is Rh-positive, the maternal antibodies cross into the fetal circulation and destroy fetal red blood cells, producing hemolytic disease of the newborn (HDN).

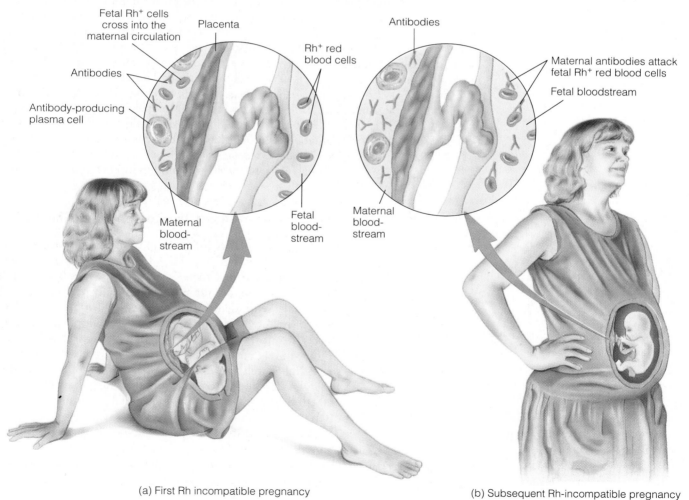

(a) First Rh incompatible pregnancy

(b) Subsequent Rh-incompatible pregnancy

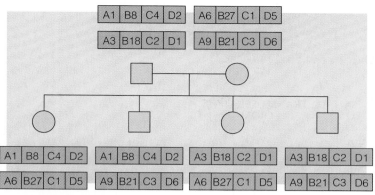

● FIGURE 15.13

The transmission of HLA haplotypes. Each haplotype contains four genes, each encoding a different antigen.

maternal circulation, antibodies against the Rh antigen will be made. This mixing most commonly occurs during the process of birth, so that the first Rh$^+$ positive child is often unaffected. But the maternal circulation now contains antibodies against the Rh antigen, and a subsequent Rh$^+$ fetus evokes a secondary response from the maternal immune system, producing massive amounts of antibodies that cross the placenta in late stages of the pregnancy and destroy the red blood cells of the fetus (Figure 15.12).

To prevent HDN, Rh$^-$ mothers are given an Rh-antibody preparation during the first pregnancy with an Rh$^+$ child and all subsequent Rh$^+$ children. These antibodies move through the maternal circulatory system and destroy any fetal cells that may have entered the mother's circulation. To be effective, this antibody must be administered before the maternal immune system can make its own antibodies against the Rh antigen.

❀ ORGAN TRANSPLANTS MUST BE IMMUNOLOGICALLY MATCHED

The success of organ transplants and skin grafts depends on matching histocompatibility antigens found on the surface of all cells in the body. In humans, antigens produced by a cluster of genes on chromosome 6 known as the HLA complex (human leucocyte antigen complex) play a critical role in the outcome of transplants. The HLA complex consists of four neighboring genes: HLA-A, HLA-B, HLA-C, and HLA-D. A large number of alleles have been identified for each of the HLA genes, making possible literally millions of allele combinations. The array of HLA alleles on a given copy of chromosome 6 is known as a **haplotype**. Since we each carry two copies of chromosome 6, we each have two HLA haplotypes (● Figure 15.13).

Because of the large number of alleles that are possible, it is rare that anyone will be genetically identical to anyone else for the HLA genes. In the example in Figure 15.13, a child receives one haplotype from each parent. The result is four new haplotype combinations represented in the children.

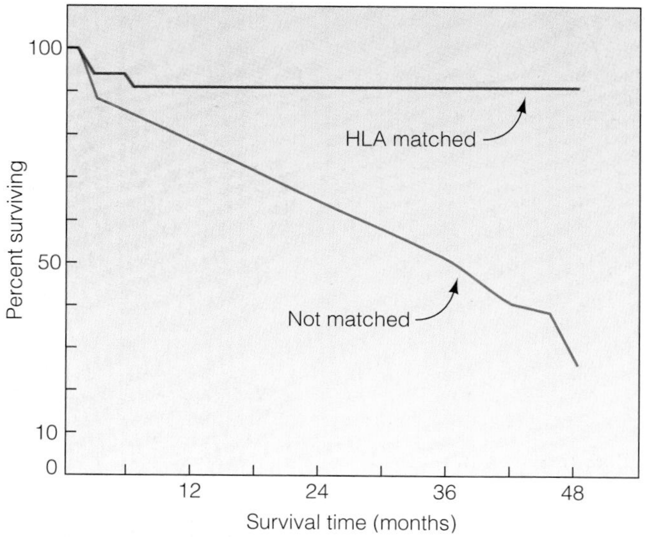

Haplotype
A cluster of closely linked genes or markers that are inherited together. In the immune system, the HLA alleles on chromosome 6 are a haplotype.

Successful Transplants Depend on HLA Matching

Successful transplantation of organs and tissues depends to a large extent on matching HLA haplotypes between donor and recipient. Because there is such a large number of HLA alleles, the best chance for a match is usually between related individuals, with identical twins having a 100% match. The order of preference for organ and tissue donors among relatives is identical twin > sibling > parent > unrelated donor. Among unrelated donors and recipients, the chances for a successful match are only 1 in 100,000 to 1 in 200,000. Because HLA allele frequency differs widely between racial and ethnic groups, matches across racial and ethnic lines are often more difficult.

When HLA types are matched, the survival of transplanted organs is dramatically improved. ● Figure 15.14 shows survival rates for matched and unmatched kidney transplants over a 4-year period.

● FIGURE 15.14

The outcome of kidney transplants with (upper curve) and without (lower curve) HLA matching.

Animal-Human Transplants

Each year about 18,000 organs are transplanted in the United States, but 40,000 qualified patients are on waiting lists. About 3000 people on the list die each year waiting for an organ transplant, and another 100,000 die before they are placed on the waiting list. While demand for organ transplants is rising, the number of organs donated has leveled off. If enough organs were available, over 50,000 lives would be saved each year. One proposed solution to this problem is the use of animal donors for organ transplants. In the last decade, animal-human transplants (called xenotransplants) have been attempted using baboon and pig organs, but with little success. Recently, there has been significant progress in xenograft technology, and animals may soon serve as organ donors.

If animal organs are to be used for human transplants, they will probably come from pigs rather than from baboons or other primates. Pigs are about the same size as humans, and pig organs are physiologically similar to those of humans. Baboons and related primates are difficult to raise in captivity, and are susceptible to viral infections that can be lethal in humans. In addition, there are ethical questions about using social primates as organ donors.

There are two serious biological problems with the use of animal organs in humans. First, the cell surface proteins (part of the HLA system) that act as antigens are very different across species. When an animal organ (say from a pig) is transplanted into a human, the cell surface proteins are so different that they trigger an immediate and massive immune response known as a hyperacute rejection. This reaction is triggered by the complement system. Usually within hours, the transplanted organ has been destroyed. The second problem is the same as in transplants between two humans: suppressing T-cell rejection of the transplant.

To overcome the first problem, several research groups have isolated and cloned human genes that suppress hyperacute rejection. These human genes were injected into fertilized pig eggs, and the transgenic pig offspring display human recognition antigens on their cell surfaces. It is hoped that pig organs carrying these antigens will be recognized as "self" by the complement system and the immune system. Transplants using transgenic animals are underway to test this theory, but the ultimate step will be an organ transplant from a transgenic pig to a human.

Even if the hyperacute rejection can be suppressed, transplanted pig organs will still face the problem found in human-to-human transplants: T-cell rejection. With pig organs, long-term T-cell rejection may be stronger, and the use of immunosuppressive drugs may not prevent rejection. To deal with this problem, it may be necessary to transplant bone marrow from the donor pig to the human recipient. The resulting dual immune system would recognize the pig organ as self and still retain normal human immunity. As far-fetched as this may sound, animal experiments using this approach have been successful in preventing rejection more than 2 years after transplantation, without the use of immunosuppressive drugs.

As recently as 1993, the possibility of animal-human organ transplants seemed remote, but advances since then make it likely that cross-species transplants will be attempted in the next 2 years. Although the final combination of transgenic donors, immunosuppressive drugs, and immune tolerance remains to be worked out, xenotransplants will probably be common in the near future.

The HLA System and Disease Associations

In studying the distribution of HLA alleles in the population, a relationship between certain HLA alleles and specific diseases has been discovered. For example, more than 90% of the individuals with the connective tissue disease **ankylosing spondylitis** (MIM/OMIM 106300) carry the HLA-B27 allele. This disease is a chronic inflammatory condition associated with joints and the spine, leading to fusion of the joints between vertebrae. The available evidence suggests that B27 class I antigens

Ankylosing spondylitis
An autoimmune disease that produces an arthritic condition of the spine; associated with HLA allele B27.

are involved in promoting the joint inflammation characteristic of this disease. Other diseases also show an association with certain HLA alleles, and some of these are listed in Table 15.6. Several hypotheses have been proposed to explain the relationship between HLA alleles and disease, but so far none has proven to be valid. It appears that most of these disorders result from a combination of HLA and non-HLA effects, with environmental activation, possibly by infection. For example, ankylosing spondylitis may be triggered in B27 patients by an infection, and the bacterium *Klebsiella* has been implicated in the onset of this disease.

DISORDERS OF THE IMMUNE SYSTEM

The immune system is vital in protecting the body against infectious disease. Unfortunately, failures in the immune system can result in abnormal or even absent immune responses. The consequences of these disorders can range from mild inconvenience to systemic failure and death. In this section, we will briefly catalog some of the ways in which the immune system can fail.

Overreaction in the Immune System Causes Allergies

Allergies are the result of immunological hypersensitivity to weak antigens that do not provoke an immune response in most people (Figure 15.15). These weak antigens are known as **allergens**, and include a wide range of substances: house dust, pollen, cat dander, certain foods, and even medicines such as penicillin. It is estimated that up to 10% of the U.S. population suffers from at least one allergy. Typically, allergic reactions develop after exposure to an allergen. When some people are exposed to an allergen, B cells make antibodies belonging to the IgE class of immunoglobulins, and memory cells are produced.

Subsequent exposure to the same antigen causes a secondary immune response, which releases a massive amount of IgE antibodies. These antibodies bind to **mast cells**, which are found most often in connective tissues surrounding blood vessels. In response to antibody binding, the mast cells release histamine, a chemical signal that starts an inflammatory response, resulting in fluid accumulation, tissue swelling, and mucus secretion.

In some individuals, the secondary reaction is severe, and histamine is released into the circulatory system, causing a life-threatening collapse in blood pressure and

Allergens
Antigens that provoke an immune response.

Mast cells
Cells that synthesize and release histamine during an allergic resposne, or during an inflammatory response.

		TABLE 15.6		
		HLA Alleles and Disease		
DISEASE	HLA ALLELE	FREQUENCY IN PATIENTS %	FREQUENCY IN GENERAL POPULATION %	RELATIVE RISK FACTOR
Ankylosing spondylitis	B27	>90	8	>100
Congenital adrenal hyperplasia	B47	9	0.6	15
Goodpasture syndrome	DR2	88	32	16
Juvenile rheumatoid arthritis	DR5	50	16	5
Multiple sclerosis	DR2	59	26	4
Pernicious anemia	DR5	25	6	5
Psoriasis	B17	38	8	6
Reiter's syndrome	B27	75	8	50
Rheumatoid arthritis	DR4	70	28	6
Systemic lupus erythematosus (SLE)	DR3	50	25	3

constriction of bronchioles in the lungs. This reaction, called **anaphylaxis** or anaphylactic shock, most often occurs on exposure to the antibiotic penicillin or to the venom in bee or wasp stings (see "Concepts and Controversies," page 373). Prompt

FIGURE 15.15
The steps in an allergic reaction.

Sensitization stage

Antigen (allergen) enters the body

Plasma cells synthesize and release large amounts of IgE antibodies

IgE antibodies bind to mast cells located in many body tissues

Subsequent (secondary) responses

More of same allergen enters body

Allergen combines with IgE on mast cells, triggering release of histamines from mast cell

Histamine stimulates dilation of blood vessels, causing fluid to leak out; stimulates release of copious amounts of mucus; and causes contraction of smooth muscle in bronchioles

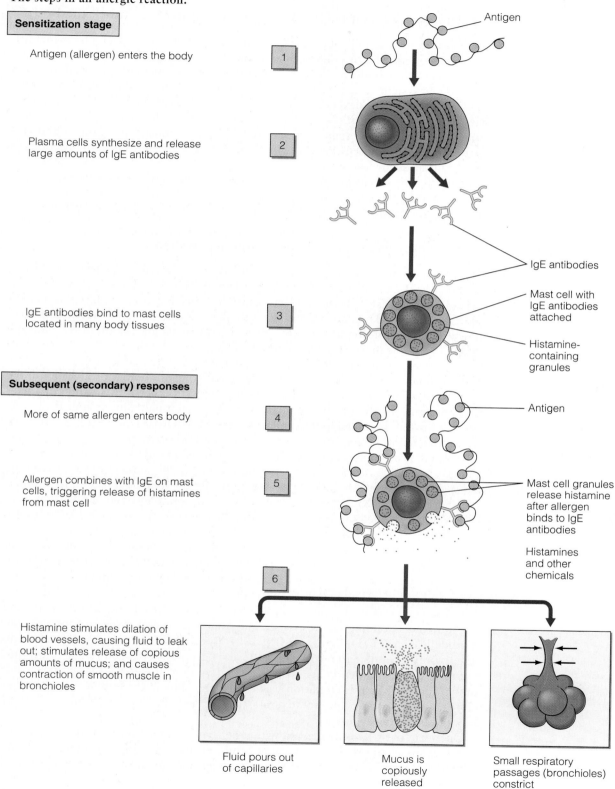

Antigen

IgE antibodies

Mast cell with IgE antibodies attached

Histamine-containing granules

Antigen

Mast cell granules release histamine after allergen binds to IgE antibodies

Histamines and other chemicals

Fluid pours out of capillaries

Mucus is copiously released

Small respiratory passages (bronchioles) constrict

TABLE 15.7

Some Autoimmune Diseases

Addison disease
Autoimmune
  hemolytic anemia
Diabetes mellitus—
  insulin-dependent
Graves' disease
Membranous
  glomerulonephritis
Multiple sclerosis
Myasthenia gravis
Polymyositis
Rheumatoid arthritis
Scleroderma
Sjögren's syndrome
Systemic lupus
  erythematosus

treatment of anaphylaxis with antihistamines, epinephrine, and steroids can reverse the reaction. As the name suggests, antihistamines block the action of histamine; epinephrine opens the airways and constricts blood vessels, raising blood pressure. Steroids such as prednisone inhibit the inflammatory response. Some people with a history of severe reaction to insect stings carry these drugs with them in a kit.

Autoimmune Reactions Cause the Immune System to Attack the Body

One of the most elegant properties of the immune system is its capacity to distinguish self from non-self. During development, the immune system "learns" not to react against cells of the body. In some disorders this immune tolerance breaks down, and the immune system attacks and kills cells and tissues in the body. Juvenile diabetes, also known as insulin-dependent diabetes (IDDM) (MIM/OMIM 222100), is an autoimmune disease. Clusters of cells in the pancreas normally produce insulin, a hormone that lowers blood sugar levels. In IDDM, the immune system attacks and kills the insulin-producing cells, resulting in diabetes and the need for insulin injections to control blood sugar levels.

Other forms of autoimmunity, such as systemic lupus erythematosus (SLE) (MIM/OMIM 152700), are directed against many of the major organ systems in the body, instead of just one cell type. Some autoimmune disorders are listed in Table 15.7.

Genetic Disorders Can Impair the Immune System

The first recognized immunodeficiency disease was described in 1952 by Ogden Bruton, a physician at Walter Reed Army Hospital. He examined a young boy who had suffered at least 20 serious infections in the preceding 5 years. Blood tests indicated that this child had no circulating antibodies. As other patients were discovered, they all had similar characteristics. Affected individuals are usually boys, who are highly susceptible to bacterial infections. In all these cases, either the B cells were completely absent, or immature B cells were unable to mature and produce antibodies. Without functional B cells, there can be no circulating antibodies produced. On the other hand, there are nearly normal levels of T cells. In other words, antibody-mediated immunity is absent, but cellular immunity is normal. This X-linked disease, called **X-linked agammaglobulinemia (XLA)** (MIM/OMIM 300300), usually appears 5 to 6 months after birth, when maternal antibodies transferred to the fetus during pregnancy disappear, and when the infant's B-cell population normally begins to produce antibodies. Patients with this syndrome are highly susceptible to pneumonia and streptococcal infections and pass from one life-threatening infection to another.

Individuals with XLA lack mature B cells, but they have normal populations of B-cell precursors, called pre-B cells, indicating that the defect is in the maturation of B cells. The XLA gene was mapped to Xq21.3–Xq22 and encodes an enzyme involved in transmitting signals into the cytoplasm from outside the cell. B-cell development depends on signals from other cell types, and it appears that the defective gene product in XLA plays a critical role in B-cell maturation. Understanding the role of this kinase in B-cell development may allow use of gene therapy to treat this disorder.

A rare genetic disorder causes a complete absence of both the cell-mediated and antibody-mediated immune response. This condition is called **severe combined immunodeficiency (SCID)** (MIM/OMIM 102700, 600802, and others). Affected individuals are susceptible to recurring and severe bacterial, viral, and fungal infections, and usually die at an early age from seemingly minor infections. One of the oldest known survivors of this condition was David, the "boy in the bubble," who died at 12 years of age after being isolated in a sterile plastic bubble for all but the last 15 days of his life (Figure 15.16).

One form of SCID is associated with a deficiency of an enzyme known as adenosine deaminase (ADA). A small group of children affected with ADA-deficient SCID (MIM/OMIM 102700) are currently undergoing gene therapy to give them a normal

X-linked agammaglobulinemia (XLA)
A rare, sex-linked, recessive trait characterized by the total absence of immunoglobulins and B cells.

Severe combined immunodeficiency disease (SCID)
A genetic disorder in which affected individuals have no immune response; both the cell-mediated and antibody-mediated responses are missing.

CONCEPTS AND CONTROVERSIES

Why Bee Stings Can Be Fatal

In most cases an allergy is an inconvenience, not a life-threatening condition. Typically, the response to contact with an allergen involves localized itching, swelling, and reddening of the skin, often in the form of hives. Inhaled allergens usually result in a localized response with itching and watery eyes, runny nose, and constricted bronchial tubes. The most common form of allergy involving inhaled allergens is hay fever; in the United States, upwards of 20 million people are affected.

In response to injected allergen such as venom from a bee sting, or certain drugs such as penicillin, the reaction can be systemic rather than localized, and results in anaphylactic shock. Anaphylaxis is usually a two-stage process. In the first stage, say a bee sting, the venom enters the body, and IgE antibodies are made in response, causing sensitization to future stings. It is not clear why some people become sensitized and others do not. If a person is sensitized, a second exposure to bee venom can provoke a life-threatening allergic reaction. When a sensitized individual is stung by a bee, the allergen in the venom enters the body and binds to immunoglobulin E antibodies made in response to a previous exposure. Within 1 to 15 minutes after exposure, the IgE antibodies activate mast cells. The stimulated mast cells release large amounts of histamines and chemotactic factors, which attract other white blood cells as part of the inflammatory response. In addition, the mast cells release prostaglandins and the slow-reacting substance of anaphylaxis (SRS-A). SRS-A is more than 100 times more powerful than histamine and prostaglandins in eliciting an allergic reaction, and intensifies the response to the allergen.

Release of SRS-A, histamine, and other factors into the bloodstream causes a systemic reaction. In response, the bronchial tubes constrict, closing the airways, and fluids pass from the tissues into the lungs, making breathing difficult. Blood vessels dilate, dropping blood pressure, and plasma escapes into the tissues, causing shock. Heart arrhythmias and cardiac shock can develop, and cause death within 1 to 2 minutes after the onset of symptoms. Immediate treatment with epinephrine, antihistamines, and steroids is effective in reversing the symptoms.

In the case of hypersensitivity to insect stings, desensitization can be used as a form of immunotherapy. This process consists of injecting small quantities of the allergen, with a gradual increase in the dose. It is thought that exposure over time to small doses of the allergen causes the production of IgG antibodies against the allergen, rather than IgE antibodies. When desensitization is complete, subsequent exposure to the allergen causes the more numerous IgG antibodies to bind to the mast cells, preventing the binding of IgE antibodies and the resulting anaphylatic reaction.

FIGURE 15.16
David, the "boy in the bubble," the oldest known survivor of severe combined immunodeficiency disease.

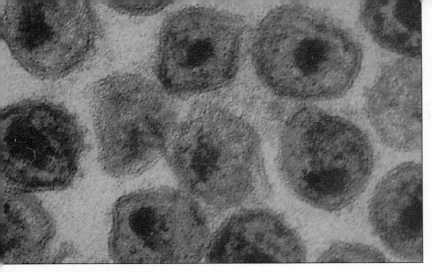

■ FIGURE 15.17
Particles of HIV.

Acquired immunodeficiency syndrome (AIDS)
A collection of disorders that develops as a result of infection with the human immunodeficiency virus (HIV).

copy of the gene. The genetically modified white blood cells are replaced into their circulatory systems by transfusion. Expression of the normal ADA gene stimulates the development of functional T and B cells, and at least partially restores a functional immune system. The recombinant DNA techniques used in gene therapy are reviewed in Chapter 13.

AIDS Attacks the Immune System

The immunodeficiency disorder that is currently receiving the most attention is **acquired immunodeficiency syndrome (AIDS)**. Acquired immunodeficiency syndrome is a collection of disorders that develop as a result of infection with a retrovirus known as the human immunodeficiency virus (HIV) (■ Figure 15.17). HIV consists of a protein coat enclosing an RNA molecule that serves as the genetic material and an enzyme called reverse transcriptase. The entire viral particle is enclosed in a coat derived from the plasma membrane of a T cell. The virus selectively infects and kills the T4 helper cells of the immune system. Inside the cell, the RNA is transcribed into a DNA molecule by reverse transcriptase, and the viral DNA is inserted into a human chromosome, where it can remain for months or years.

Later, when the infected T cell is called upon to participate in an immune response, the viral genes are activated. Viral RNA and proteins are made, and new viral particles are formed. These bud off the surface of the T cell, rupturing and killing the cell and setting off a new round of T-cell infection (■ Figure 15.18). Gradually, over the course of HIV infection, there is a decrease in the number of helper T4 cells. Recall that these cells act as the master "on" switch for the immune system. As the T4 cell population falls, there is a decrease in the ability to mount an immune response.

The result is increased susceptibility to infection, and increased risk of certain forms of cancer. The eventual outcome is premature death, brought about by any of a number of diseases that overwhelm the body and its compromised immune system.

■ FIGURE 15.18

A colorized electron micrograph showing particles of HIV (purple) on the outside of its principal target, a helper T-lymphocyte.

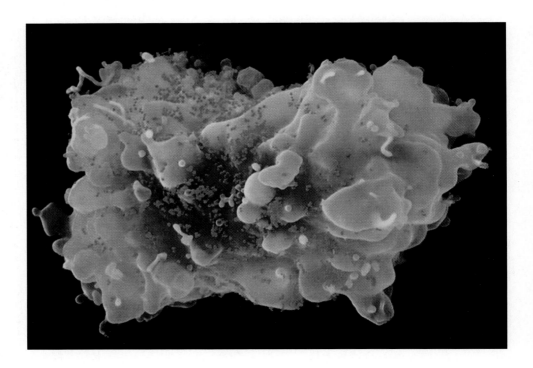

Medicine—A Scientific Safari

M. MICHAEL GLOVSKY

What is it that motivates a person to become a physician or a scientist? Chance and the desire for adventure and the opportunity to discover the unknown are important ingredients. Let me explain.

Growing up in a small town in central Massachusetts, I attended Tufts University. Chemistry was a favorite subject. I learned that it was possible to question why certain chemical reactions occurred and that several different approaches could be used to solve problems. The desire to work in a rewarding and stimulating profession was also important. I then entered Tufts Medical School. Most medical students are overwhelmed by the amount of knowledge that is available. I was not an exception. Yet, after the initial shock, coupled with long hours of study, I adapted to the need to absorb the most important information in anatomy, physiology, and biochemistry.

During my second year I became intrigued with the problems in immunology. How is the fetus able to tolerate the foreign environment of the mother's uterus? Why do habitual abortions occur? These were two questions I had an opportunity to explore in the laboratory of Dr. Wadi Bardawell, an obstetrical pathologist. In the final two years of medical school, patient contact and the reality of the consequences of disease were opportunities to integrate knowledge gained in the basic sciences.

After graduation from medical school, I spent almost four years learning about complement and immunoglobulins. I was fortunate to have as mentors Dr. Elmer Becker at the Walter Reed Army Institute of Research and Hugh Fudenberg, M.D., at the University of California, San Francisco. My initial research addressed what chemicals could block the inflammatory reactions in the skin when complement and immunoglobulins interact.

Because of my interest in immunology, I became an allergist. Can chemicals derived from the structure of IgE, the allergy antibody, interfere in the allergic response? We were fortunate to have as collaborators Drs. Bergitt Helm and Hannah Gould from King's College, London. They provided recombinant proteins synthesized from the known structure of the heavy chain regions of the IgE myeloma proteins. Together, we were able to show that the IgE recombinant fragment (301-376) was able to block ragweed allergens and grass allergen reactions in human skin and in blood basophils. Further studies were performed to pinpoint the binding site of the allergy antibody, IgE, binding to human basophils.

More recently we have studied substances in air pollution that are important in causing the nose to run and bronchial tubes to constrict. We are exploring whether latex, an ingredient in natural rubber, produces allergenic proteins that are important in asthma. Together with Dr. Ann Miguel and Dr. Glenn Cass at Caltech, we have demonstrated latex allergen in air samples and roadside dust samples. Latex allergen, present in natural rubber gloves, balloons, and tire dust, is one of the most potent allergens of the last 10 years. We are studying whether latex allergy is important in the increasing symptoms of asthma in the last decade.

Medical science has evolved to provide sophisticated tools, especially in molecular biology, to address important questions and seek relevant answers. Biologic science is a safari through the wilderness. Every path leads to adventure and exploration with both frustration and rewards. But the trail is always interesting and provocative.

M. MICHAEL GLOVSKY is director of the Asthma and Allergy Center at Huntington Memorial Hospital in Pasadena, California. He received a B.S. degree from Tufts University in 1957 and an M.D. degree from Tufts Medical School in 1962.

1. The immune system protects the body against infection by a graded series of responses that attack and inactivate foreign molecules and organisms. The lowest level involves a nonspecific, local, inflammatory response.

2. The immune system has two components, antibody-mediated immunity, regulated by B cells and antibody production, and cell-mediated immunity, controlled by T cells.

3. The primary task of antibody-mediated reactions is to defend the body against invading viruses and bacteria. Cell-mediated immunity is directed against cells of the body that have been infected by viruses and bacteria.

4. The presence or absence of certain antigens on the surface of blood cells is the basis of blood transfusions and blood types. Two blood groups are of major significance: the ABO system and the Rh blood group.

5. Matching blood types of the ABO group is important in blood transfusions. In some cases, mother-fetus incompatibility in the Rh system can cause maternal antigens to destroy red blood cells of the fetus, causing hemolytic disease of the newborn.

6. The success of organ transplants and skin grafts depends on matching histocompatibility antigens, found on the surface of all cells in the body. In humans, the antigens produced by a group of genes on chromosome 6 (known as the HLA complex) plays a critical role in the outcome of transplants.

7. Allergies are the result of immunological hypersensitivity to weak antigens that do not provoke an immune response in most people. These weak antigens are known as allergens, and include a wide range of substances: house dust, pollen, cat hair, certain foods, and even medicines such as penicillin.

8. Acquired immunodeficiency syndrome (AIDS) is a collection of disorders that develop as a result of infection with a retrovirus known as the human immunodeficiency virus (HIV). The virus selectively infects and kills the T4 helper cells of the immune system.

1. Define attenuation, and discuss its importance in combating immunological diseases.

2. Identify the components of cellular immunity, and define their roles in the immune response.

3. Compare the general inflammatory response, the complement system, and the specific immune response.

4. Compare the roles of the three types of T cells: helper cells, suppressor cells and cytotoxic cells.

5. What type of cell can signal T cells to assist in an immune response, and what chemical messenger does it use?

6. Distinguish between antibody-mediated and cell-mediated immunity. What components are involved in each?

7. Describe the rationale for vaccines as a form of preventative medicine.

8. Antibodies have long been a subject for study because of the staggering variety of antigens to which they are capable of responding. What other element of the immune system is equally adept at antigen recognition?

9. The molecular weight of IgG is 150,000 kd. What are the molecular weights of each individual subunit assuming that the two heavy chains are equivalent and the two light chains are equivalent? Also assume that the molecular weights of the light chains are half the molecular weight of the heavy chains.

10. Name the class of molecules that includes antibodies and the five groups which make up this class.

11. a. How is Rh incompatibility involved in hemolytic disease of the newborn? Is the mother Rh^+ or Rh^-? Is the fetus Rh^+ or Rh^-?

b. Why is a second child that is Rh^+ more susceptible to attack from the mother's immune system?

12. It is often helpful to draw a complicated pathway in the form of a flow chart in order to visualize the multiple steps and the ways in which the steps are connected to each other. Draw the antibody-mediated immune response pathway that acts in response to an invading virus.

13. AIDS is an immunodeficiency syndrome. In the flow chart you drew above, describe where AIDS sufferers are deficient. Why can't our immune systems fight off this disease?

14. Describe the genetic basis of antibody diversity.

15. Identify three chemical messengers involved in the immune response, and discuss their roles.

16. In the human HLA system there are 23 HLA-A alleles, 47 for HLA-B, 8 for HLA-C, 14 for HLA-DR, 3 for HLA-DQ, and 6 for HLA-DP. How many different human HLA genotypes are possible?

17. What mode of inheritance has been observed for the HLA system in humans?

18. Why can someone with blood type AB receive blood of any type? Why can a blood type O individual donate blood to anyone?

19. What is more important to match during blood transfusions: the antibodies of the donor or the antigens of the donor/recipient?

20. The following data were presented to a court during a paternity suit: (1) the infant is a universal donor for blood transfusions; (2) the mother bears antibodies

against the B antigen only; (3) the alleged father is a universal recipient in blood transfusions. Can you identify the ABO genotypes of the three individuals? Can the court draw any conclusions?

21. A man has the genotype $I^A I^A$ and his wife is $I^B I^B$. If their son needed an emergency blood transfusion, would either parent be able to be a donor? why or why not?

22. In cystic fibrosis gene therapy, scientists propose the use of viral vectors to deliver normal genes to cells in the lungs. What immunological risks are involved in this procedure?

23. A burn victim receives a skin graft from her brother; however, the graft is rejected by her body a few weeks later. The procedure is attempted again, but this time the graft is rejected in a few days. Explain why the graft was rejected the first time and why it was rejected faster the second time.

24. In the near future, pig organs may be used for organ transplants. How are researchers attempting to prevent rejection of the pig organs by human recipients?

25. An individual has an immunodeficiency that prevents helper T cells from recognizing the surface antigens presented by macrophages. As a result, the helper T cells are not activated, and they, in turn, fail to activate the appropriate B cells. At this point, is it certain that the viral infection will continue unchecked?

26. A couple have the following HLA genotypes:
Male A12, B36, C7, DR14, DQ2, DP5/A9, B27, C3, DR14, DQ3, DP1
Female A8, B15, C2, DR5, DQ2, DP3/A2, B20, C3, DR8, DQ1, DP3
What is the probability that an offspring will suffer from ankylosing spondylitis if:
a. The child is male and has HLA-A9?
b. The child is female and has HLA-A9?
c. The child is male and has HLA-DP1?
d. The child is male and has HLA-C7?

27. A patient of yours has just undergone shoulder surgery and is now experiencing kidney failure for no apparent reason. You check his chart and find that his blood is type B, but he has been mistakenly transfused with type A. Describe why he is experiencing kidney failure.

28. Assume the Rh character is controlled by a single gene having alleles that show complete dominance relationships at the phenotypic level. An Rh^+ father and an Rh^- mother have 8 boys and 8 girls, all Rh^+.
a. What are the Rh genotypes of the parents?
b. Should they have been concerned about hemolytic disease of the newborn?

29. Why are allergens called "weak" antigens?

30. Antihistamines are used as anti-allergy drugs. How do these drugs work to relieve allergy symptoms?

31. A young boy, who has suffered from over a dozen viral and bacterial infections in the past 2 years, comes to your office for an examination. You examine the boy and determine by testing that he has no circulating antibodies. What syndrome does he have and what are its characteristics? What component of the two-part immune system is nonfunctional?

32. Researchers have been having a difficult time developing a vaccine against a certain pathogenic virus due to the lack of an attenuated strain. They turn to you because of your wide knowledge of recombinant DNA technology and the immune system. How could you vaccinate someone against the virus using a cloned gene from the virus that encodes a cell-surface protein?

33. A couple has a young child who needs a bone marrow transplant. They propose that pre-implantation screening be done on several embryos fertilized *in vitro* to find a match for their child. What do they need to match in this transplant procedure? They propose that the matching embryo will be transplanted to the mother's uterus, and will serve as a bone marrow donor when old enough. What are the ethical issues involved in this proposal?

SCIENCE AND SOCIETY

1. After three years of intense debate and under much protest, New York state now requires that mothers of newborns be told if their child has tested positive for the HIV virus. Even though New York has required newborns to be tested for HIV status for the past ten years, the test results were only used for tracking AIDS statistics and were kept secret. Under this new agreement, parents will automatically be told of the results. The debate over this bill concerns issues of violation of constitutional rights of parents and individuals, the adverse health consequences of HIV transmission from mother to fetus, and forced testing of mothers without their permission.

Do you think the legislative leaders in New York by instituting this bill are helping or hurting AIDS research?

What do you think are the advantages and disadvantages to this bill?

Do you think it would be reasonable for every state to pass such a law? Why or why not?

Do you think that individuals carrying an infectious disease have the right to keep this information secret? What are the public health implications of allowing this? Do these concerns outweigh the right to privacy?

INTERNET ACTIVITIES

The following activities use the resources of the World Wide Web to enhance the topics covered in this chapter. To investigate the topics described below, log on to the book's home page at:

http://www.wadsworth.com/biology

1. For a good review on antibody structure, function and production, access the Microbiology 101 Internet text. This page also includes a discussion on Rh incompatibility and using antibodies to treat cancer.

2. The Journal of Immunology is available on-line, and includes a "Cutting Edge" section dealing with the latest advances in immunology. Browse this section for information on immunogenetics. You may also use this site as a personal resource by posting a question to be answered by immunologists, on any topic presented in this chapter or on something you read somewhere else.

FOR FURTHER READING

Allan, J. S. 1996. Xenotransplantation at a crossroads: prevention versus progress. Nat. Med. 2: 18–21.

Arnett, F. 1986. HLA genes and predisposition to rheumatic diseases. Hosp. Pract. 20: 89–100.

Bach, F. H., Winkler, H., Wrighton, C. J., Robson, S. C., Stuhlmeier, K., and Ferran. C. 1996. Xenotransplantation: a possible solution to the shortage of donor organs. Transplant. Proc. 28: 416–417.

Barre-Sinoussi, F. 1996. HIV as the cause of AIDS. Lancet 348: 31–35.

Bosma, M. J. 1989. The SCID mutation: Occurrence and effect. Curr. Topics Microbiol. Immunol. 152: 3–9.

Britton, C. 1993. HIV infection. Neurol. Clin. 11: 605–624.

Buckley, R. 1992. Immunodeficiency diseases. JAMA 268: 2797–2806.

Burrows, P. and Cooper, M. 1993. B-cell development in man. Curr. Opin. Immunol. 5: 201–206.

Dierich, M. P., Stoiber, H., and Clivio, A. 1996. A complement-ary AIDS vaccine. Nat. Med. 2: 153–155.

Hors, J., and Gony, J. 1986. HLA and disease. Adv. Nephrol. 15: 329–351.

Iseki, M. and Heiner, D. 1993. Immunodeficiency disorders. Pediatr. Rev. 14: 226–236.

Just, J. J. 1995. Genetic predisposition to HIV-1 infection and acquired immunodeficiency syndrome: a review of the literature examining association with HLA. Hum. Immunol. 44: 156–159.

Kotzin, B., Leung, D., Kappler, J., and Marrack, P. 1993. Superantigens and their potential role in human disease. Adv. Immunol. 54: 99–166.

Lokki, M. L., and Colten, H. R. 1995. Genetic deficiency of complement. Ann. Med. 27: 451–459.

McDivitt, H. 1986. The molecular basis of autoimmunity. Clin. Res. 34: 163–175.

Morgan, B. P. 1996. Intervention in the complement system: a therapeutic strategy in inflammation. Biochem. Soc. Trans. 24: 224–229.

Puck, J. 1993. X-linked immunodeficiencies. Adv. Hum. Genet. 21: 107–144.

Quinn, T. C. 1996. Global burden of the HIV pandemic. Lancet 348: 99–106.

Rapaport, F. T. 1995. Skin transplantation - experimental basis for the study of human histocompatibility. Transplant. Proc. 27: 2205–2210.

Tomlinson, I. P. and Bodmer, W. F. 1995. The HLA system and the analysis of multifactorial genetic disease. Trends Genet. 11: 493–498.

Tonegawa, S. 1985. The molecules of the immune system. Sci. Am. 253 (October): 123–131.

Vetri, D., Vorechovsky, I., Sideras, P., Holland, J., Davies, A., Flinter, F., Hammarstrom, L., Kinnon, C., et al., 1993. The gene involved in X-linked agammaglobulinaemia is a member of the src family of protein-tyrosine kinases. Nature 361: 226–233.

Vladutiu, A. 1993. The severe combined immunodeficient (SCID) mouse as a model for the study of auto-immune diseases. Clin. Exp. Immunol. 93: 1–8.

Yamamoto, F. 1995. Molecular genetics of the ABO histo-blood group system. Vox Sang. 69: 1–7.

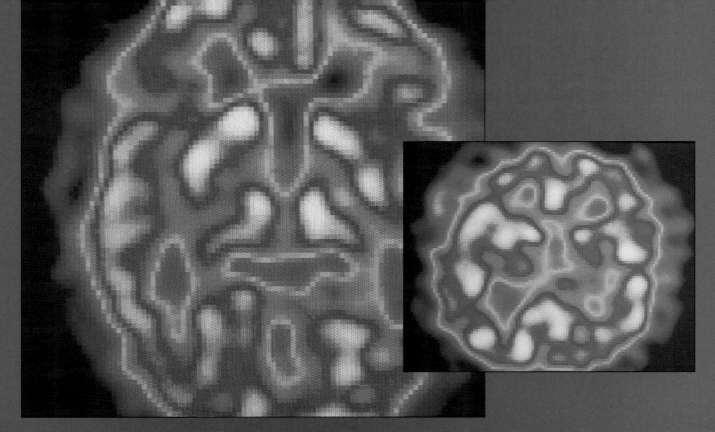

GENETICS OF BEHAVIOR

Chapter Outline

MODELS, METHODS, AND
  PHENOTYPES
Genetic Models of Inheritance and Behavior
CONCEPTS AND CONTROVERSIES   *Is Going
  to Medical School a Genetic Trait?*
Methods of Studying Behavior Genetics
Phenotypes: What Is Behavior?
ANIMAL MODELS: THE SEARCH FOR
  BEHAVIOR GENES
Open-Field Behavior
Learning in *Drosophila*
SINGLE-GENE EFFECTS ON HUMAN
  BEHAVIOR

Charcot-Marie-Tooth Syndrome
Friedreich Ataxia
Menkes Kinky-Hair Disease
Huntington Disease
AGGRESSIVE BEHAVIOR AND BRAIN
  METABOLISM
SIDEBAR   *A Genetic Link to a Personality
  Trait*
THE GENETICS OF MOOD DISORDERS
  AND SCHIZOPHRENIA
Mood Disorders: Unipolar and Bipolar
  Illnesses
Schizophrenia

CONCEPTS AND CONTROVERSIES   *The Link
  between Madness and Genius*
GENETICS AND SOCIAL BEHAVIOR
Tourette Syndrome
Alzheimer Disease
Alcoholism
Sexual Orientation
GUEST ESSAY   *Neurogenetics: From Mutants
  to Molecules*
SUMMING UP: THE CURRENT STATUS
  OF HUMAN BEHAVIOR GENETICS

Chapter 16

OPENING IMAGE
*On the left is a PET scan of a normal
human brain. On the right is a PET scan
from a brain of a schizophrenic, showing
altered metabolism.*

Sometime in the late 1850s, an 8-year-old boy and his father, a physician,
drove along a road through the woods on eastern Long Island. They
met two women walking along the road, and this chance encounter had a
profound effect on the young boy. Years later, he would recall that meeting:

> I recall it as vividly as though it had occurred but yesterday. It made a most
> enduring impression upon my boyish mind, an impression every detail of which

I recall today, an impression which was the very first impulse to my choosing chorea as my virgin contribution to medical lore. Driving with my father through a wooded road leading from East Hampton to Amagansett, we suddenly came upon two women, mother and daughter, both tall, thin, almost cadaverous, both bowing, twisting, grimacing. I stared in wonderment, almost in fear. What could it mean? My father paused to speak to them and we passed on.

The young boy, George Huntington, went on to study medicine at Columbia University. In 1872, a year after graduation, he published an account of this disorder, which became known as Huntington's chorea, or as it is called today, Huntington disease. In the paper, his summary of the condition is a model of brevity and clarity:

> *There are three characteristics of this disorder: 1. Its hereditary nature, 2. A tendency to insanity and suicide, 3. Its manifesting itself as a grave disease only in adult life.*

Huntington described the pattern of inheritance of the disorder in a way that is consistent with an autosomal dominant trait. Unfortunately, having described the condition, Huntington turned his attention in other directions, and little more was accomplished in the next 88 years until recombinant DNA techniques were used to map the locus for this disease to the short arm of chromosome 4.

In several ways, conditions such as Huntington disease (HD) seem to be an ideal model for genetic disorders that affect behavior. The pattern of autosomal dominant inheritance is well defined and clear cut. The gene for HD was one of the first to be mapped using restriction fragment length polymorphisms (RFLPs), demonstrating the power of molecular techniques in the analysis of human behavior. More recently, the gene was isolated by positional cloning, one of the newer genetic techniques of recombinant DNA technology. Lastly, the molecular basis of mutation in the HD gene represents a new class of mutations that affect the nervous system. From all of this, it would seem that by following the methods used in studying Huntington disease, researchers could identify, map, and isolate many genes affecting human behavior.

Unfortunately, searching for single genes (like the HD gene) that control behavior may have only limited success. One of the most difficult problems in human behavioral genetics is defining the phenotype. While Huntington disease has a well-defined phenotype and progression, many behavioral traits do not. In addition, the phenotype of some conditions, such as schizophrenia (well defined as a medical condition), can be genetically heterogeneous and may actually include several genetic disorders, each with a similar phenotype. Finally, many behavioral traits are multifactorial, with the phenotype determined by several genes and environmental interactions, with no single gene having a major effect.

To understand the issues in behavior genetics and how decisions about phenotypic definitions, genetic models of behavior, and the roles of methods influence both the speed and the outcome of this research, this chapter begins with a discussion of the genetic models and methods used in studying human behavior. Then we briefly consider animal models, for which single-gene effects on behavior have been well documented. We discuss single genes that affect human behavior through their effect on the nervous system, and then consider more complex traits, and those that have the greatest social impact. The chapter ends with a summary of the current state of human behavior genetics and the ethical, legal, and social implications of this research.

MODELS, METHODS, AND PHENOTYPES

The genetic control of behavior in humans has been clearly demonstrated. But observation and pedigree analysis indicate that not all behaviors are inherited as simple Mendelian traits, demonstrating the need for genetic models that can explain observed patterns of inheritance. To a large extent, the model of inheritance proposed for a trait determines the methods used to analyze its pattern of inheritance, and the techniques that can be pursued in mapping and isolating the gene or genes responsible for the trait's characteristic phenotype. This is true of all traits, behavioral and otherwise. In the case of behavior, however, many traits—especially those with social impact—have complex phenotypes and are not inherited as single-gene traits, making it necessary to consider first how such traits might be inherited.

Genetic Models of Inheritance and Behavior

Several models for genetic effects on behavior have been proposed (Table 16.1). The simplest model is a single gene, dominant or recessive, that affects a well-defined behavior. In fact, several human behavioral traits—including Huntington disease, Lesch-Nyhan syndrome, fragile-X syndrome, and others—can be described by such a model (Figure 16.1). Some multiple-gene models are also possible. The simplest of these is a polygenic additive model in

TABLE 16.1	
Models for Genetic Analysis of Behavior	
MODEL	**DESCRIPTION**
Single gene	One gene controls a defined behavior
Polygenic trait	Additive model, with two or more genes
	One or more major genes with other genes contributing to phenotype
Multiple genes	Interaction of alleles at different loci generates a unique phenotype

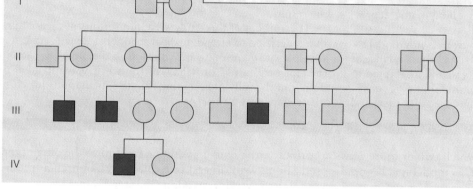

(a)

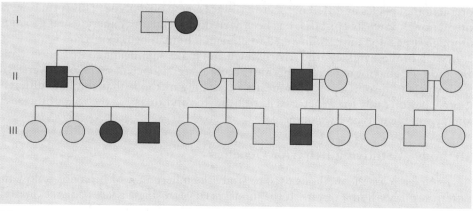

(b)

FIGURE 16.1

Many genetic disorders inherited as sex-linked recessive traits (a) or as autosomal dominant traits (b) have behavioral phenotypes.

Is Going to Medical School a Genetic Trait?

It is clear that many behavioral traits exhibit a familial pattern of inheritance. This observation, along with twin studies and adoption studies, indicates that there is a genetic component to many complex behavioral disorders such as manic depression and schizophrenia. In most cases, these phenotypes are not inherited as simple Mendelian traits. Researchers are then faced with selecting a model that will describe how a behavioral trait is inherited. Using this model, further choices select the methods used in genetic analysis of the trait. A common strategy is to find a family in which the behavior appears to be inherited as a recessive or an incompletely penetrant dominant trait controlled by a single gene. One or more molecular markers (such as RFLPs) are used in linkage analysis to identify the chromosome carrying the gene controlling the trait.

If researchers are looking for a single gene when the trait is controlled by two or more genes, or by genes interacting with environmental factors, then the work may produce negative results, even though preliminary findings can be encouraging. Reports of loci for manic depression on chromosome 11 and the X chromosome were based on single-gene models, and after initial successes, these reports were found to be flawed. Overall, regions on 14 chromosomes have been proposed as candidates for genes controlling manic depression, but none have been substantiated.

To illustrate some of the pitfalls associated with model selection in behavior genetics, one study selected attendance at medical school as a behavioral phenotype and attempted to determine if the distribution of this trait in families is consistent with a genetic model. This study surveyed 249 first- and second-year medical students. Thirteen percent of these students had first-degree relatives who had also attended medical school, as compared with 0.22% relatives of individuals selected from the general population. Thus, the overall risk factor among first-degree relatives for medical school attendance was 61 times higher than in the general population, indicating a strong familial pattern. To determine whether this trait was inherited in a Mendelian fashion, researchers used standard statistical analysis, which supported familial inheritance and rejected the model of no inheritance. Analysis of the pedigrees most strongly supported a simple recessive mode of inheritance, although other models including polygenic inheritance were not excluded. Using a further set of statistical tests, the researchers concluded that recessive mode of inheritance was just at the border of statistical acceptance.

Similar results are often found in studies of other behavioral traits, and it is usually argued that another, larger study would confirm the results; in this case, that attendance at medical school is a recessive Mendelian trait. While it is true that genetic factors may partly determine whether one will attend medical school, it is unlikely that this decision is controlled by a single recessive gene, although that conclusion *is* supported by this family study and segregation analysis of the results.

The authors of this study were not serious in their claims that a decision to attend medical school is a genetic trait, nor was it their intention to cast doubts on the methods used in the genetic analysis of behavior. Rather, it was intended to point out the folly of accepting simple explanations for complex behavioral traits.

which two or more genes contribute equally in an additive fashion to the phenotype. This model has been proposed (along with others) to explain schizophrenia (the inheritance of additive polygenic traits was considered in Chapter 5). In a variation of this model, one or more genes might have a major effect, with other genes making smaller contributions to the phenotype. Still another multigene model involves the interaction of alleles at different loci to produce a new phenotype. This form of gene interaction, known as epistasis, has been well documented in experimental genetics, although it has not yet been invoked to explain a human behavior trait.

In each of these models, the environment can make significant contributions, and the study of behavior must take this into account (see "Concepts and Controversies," on this page). In some cases, this means developing methods that combine different approaches to study the genetic basis of behavior and to assess the role of the environment in phenotype development.

Methods of Studying Behavior Genetics

For the most part, the methods used to study the inheritance of behavior follow the pattern for other human traits. If the model involves a single gene, pedigree analysis

and linkage and segregation studies, including the use of RFLP markers and other methods of recombinant DNA technology, are the most appropriate methods. However, because many behavior traits are polygenic, twin studies are a prominent part of human behavior genetics. Concordance and heritability values based on twin studies have established that there is a genetic component to mental illnesses such as manic depression and schizophrenia, and to behavioral traits such as sexual preference and alcoholism. The results of such studies should be interpreted with caution, since they are subject to the limitations inherent in interpreting heritability (see Chapter 5) and are often conducted on small sample sizes, where minor variations can have a disproportionately large effect on the outcome.

To overcome these problems, geneticists are extending and adapting twin studies as a genetic tool to study behavior. One innovation is the study of the children of twins. This second-generation research, using both concordant and discordant traits, can provide clues about the maternal effects on a phenotype and confirm the existence of genes predisposing to a certain behavior. Twin studies are also being coupled to recombinant DNA techniques to search for behavior genes, and this combination may prove to be a powerful method for identifying such genes.

Phenotypes: What Is Behavior?

As we mentioned earlier, a basic problem that limits progress in human behavior genetics is an accurate phenotypic description of a trait. The phenotypic definition must be precise enough to distinguish the behavior from other, similar behaviors and from the behavior of the control group, but not so narrow that it excludes variations of a behavior pattern. For some mental illnesses, clinical definitions are provided by guidelines such as the Diagnostic and Statistical Manual of Mental Disorders of the American Psychiatric Association. For other behaviors, the phenotypes are often poorly defined, and may be unrelated to the underlying biochemical and molecular basis of the behavior. For example, alcoholism can be defined as the development of characteristic deviant behaviors associated with excessive consumption of alcohol. Is this definition explicit enough to be useful as a phenotype in genetic analysis? Is there too much room for interpretation of what is deviant behavior, or of what is excessive consumption? As we will see, whether the behavioral phenotype is narrowly or broadly defined can affect the outcome of the genetic analysis, and even the model of inheritance for the trait.

ANIMAL MODELS: THE SEARCH FOR BEHAVIOR GENES

Several approaches have been used in experimental genetics to study behavior in animals. In one method, two closely related species or two strains of the same species are studied to detect variant behavior phenotypes. Genetic crosses are used to establish whether the behavior is inherited, and if so, to determine the pattern of inheritance. In another approach, individuals exhibiting variant behavior are isolated from a population and interbred to establish a strain with a distinct behavioral pattern. As mentioned earlier, genetic crosses can be used to establish the pattern of inheritance and the number of genes controlling the phenotype. More recently, the effects of single genes on animal behavior have been studied. In some cases, these studies have led to the isolation and cloning of genes that affect behavior. In the following sections, we describe some examples of behavior genetic studies on experimental organisms.

Open-Field Behavior

Beginning in the mid-1930s, the emotional and exploratory behaviors of mice were tested by studying open-field behavior. When mice are introduced into a brightly lit environment, some actively explore the environment while others are apprehensive,

do not move about, and have elevated rates of urination and defecation. This behavior pattern is under genetic control, since strains exhibiting both types of behavior have been established.

To test the genetic components of this behavior, beginning in the 1960s, studies used an enclosed, illuminated box with the floor marked into squares (Figure 16.2). Exploration is tested by counting the mouse's movements in different squares, and emotion quantified by counting the number of defecations. The BALB/cJ strain is homozygous for a recessive albino allele, shows low exploratory behavior, and is highly emotional. The C57BL/6j strain has normal pigmentation, is active in exploration, and shows low emotional behavior.

If these two strains are crossed, and the offspring interbred, each generation beyond the F_1 will contain both albino and normally pigmented mice. When tested for open-field behavior, pigmented mice behaved like the C57 parental line, showing active exploration and low emotional behavior; the albino mice behaved like the BALB parental line, with low exploratory activity and high emotional behavior, indicating that the albino gene affects behavior as well as pigmentation.

Tests for heritability indicate that the albino gene accounts for 12% of the genetic variance in exploratory activity and 26% of the variance in emotional activity. These results indicate that open-field behavior is a polygenic trait, with additive contributions by the controlling genes.

Learning in *Drosophila*

The fruit fly, *Drosophila*, offers several advantages for the study of behavior, including the ability for short-term learning (Table 16.2). To learn, flies are presented with a series of odors, one of which is accompanied by an electric shock. Flies learn to avoid the odor associated with the shock. Mutant screens have identified a number of genes that control this learning ability, including the mutants *dunce, turnip,* and *rutabaga.*

 FIGURE 16.2

An open-field trial. Movements are automatically recorded as the rat moves across the open field.

TABLE 16.2		
Some Behavior Mutants of *Drosophila*		
CATEGORY	MUTATION	PHENOTYPE
Learning	*dunce*	Cannot learn conditioned response.
	turnip	Impaired in learning conditioned response.
	rutabaga	Impaired in several types of learning and memory.
Sexual Behavior	*fruitless*	Males court each other.
	savoir-faire	Males unsuccessful in courtship.
	coitus-interruptus	Males stop copulation prematurely.
Motor Behavior	*flightless*	Lacks coordination for flying.
	sluggish	Moves slowly.
	wings up	Holds wings perpendicular to body.

These single-gene mutants exert their effect through an intracellular signal molecule called cyclic AMP (cAMP). Inside the cell, cAMP sets off a cascade of biochemical reactions that controls gene transcription, and in cells of the nervous system, the responses associated with learning. Cyclic AMP is produced by the enzyme adenyl cyclase (Figure 16.3); the *rutabaga* gene encodes this enzyme. In the mutant, there is no adenyl cyclase, and no production of cAMP. The *turnip* gene encodes a protein that activates adenyl cyclase, and the *dunce* gene controls the pathway by which adenyl cyclase is recycled. The clustering of these mutations in the cAMP pathways provides strong evidence for the involvement of cAMP in learning. Experiments in other organisms support this finding, and imply that some aspects of learning and memory in humans may be controlled by cyclic nucleotides.

SINGLE-GENE EFFECTS ON HUMAN BEHAVIOR

In Chapter 10, we discussed the role of genes in metabolism. Mutations that disrupt metabolic pathways or interfere with the synthesis of required gene products can influence the function of cells, and in turn, produce an altered phenotype. If the affected cells are part of the nervous system, alterations in behavior may be part of the phenotype. In fact, some genetic disorders do affect cells in the nervous system, in turn, affecting behavior. In PKU, for example, brain cells are damaged by excess levels of phenylalanine, preventing the uptake of other amino acids and causing mental retardation and other behavioral deficits.

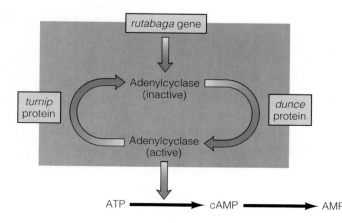

FIGURE 16.3

The metabolic pathway involving production of cyclic AMP (cAMP) is involved in learning. In this pathway, ATP is converted into cAMP by the enzyme adenyl cyclase. cAMP is active in signal transduction, and then is converted into AMP. In *Drosophila*, adenyl cyclase is encoded by the *rutabaga* gene. The enzyme is inactive when first produced, and is activated by the action of a protein encoded by the *turnip* gene. When no longer needed, the enzyme is inactivated by a gene product encoded by the *dunce* gene. When any of these genes are mutant in *Drosophila*, flies have difficulty in learning.

In this section we discuss several single-gene defects that have specific effects on the development, structure, and/or function of the nervous system, and that consequently, affect behavior. Following this we discuss more complex interactions between the genotype and behavior, where the number and action of genes are less well described, and where effects on the nervous system may be more subtle.

Charcot-Marie-Tooth Disease

Charcot-Marie-Tooth disease
A heritable form of progressive muscle weakness and atrophy. One form, CMT-I, can be produced by mutation at any of three loci.

This disorder of the peripheral nervous system is characterized by the onset of weakness and atrophy of lower leg muscles and may progress to involve arm muscles (teeth are not involved; H. H. Tooth described the condition in 1886). Loss of sensation in the feet and hands may also occur. Affected nerve fibers lose their myelin sheath (● Figure 16.4), and the speed of nerve impulse conduction is greatly reduced. One form of **Charcot-Marie-Tooth** (MIM/OMIM 118200) disease (CMT-1)

● FIGURE 16.4

(a) Myelinated nerve fibers are surrounded by a sheath at regular intervals. Each nonmylinated interval is called the node of Ranvier. (b) In the peripheral nervous system, the myelin sheath is formed by a Schwann cell wrapping itself around a single nerve fiber. In CMT-1, a gene called the peripheral myelin gene (PMP-22) is mutant, producing a defective myelin sheath that breaks down, slowing nerve impulses. (c) A transmission electron micrograph of a myelinated nerve fiber viewed in cross-section.

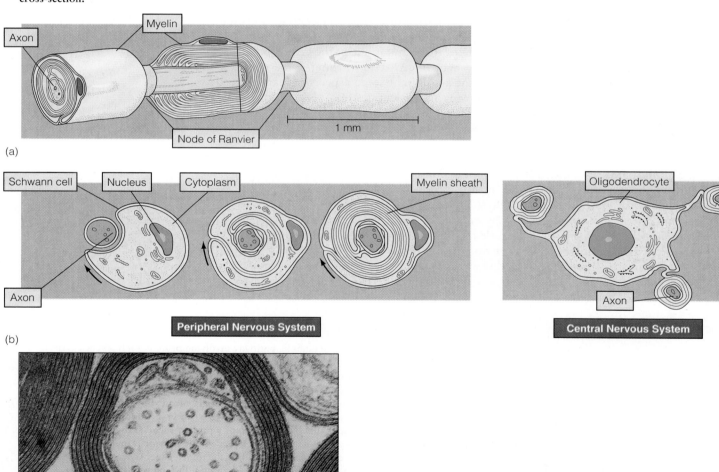

is inherited as an autosomal dominant disorder; mutations at any of three loci are associated with this form of CMT. One of these has been mapped to chromosome 17, one to chromosome 1, and a third locus is on an as yet unidentified autosome. Individuals with CMT-1 begin to show loss of control over foot movement during childhood, and develop muscle wasting and loss of sensation in the lower legs. Muscle atrophy and loss of sensation in hands appears later. Walking becomes difficult, and leg braces are often needed.

The CMT-1 locus on chromosome 17 encodes a membrane-associated protein, expressed in cells that form the myelin nerve sheath in the peripheral nervous system. Altered expression of this protein impairs peripheral nerve function, which in turn leads to muscle atrophy. The gene products encoded by the other two loci associated with CMT-1 have not been identified.

Friedreich Ataxia

This trait (MIM/OMIM 229300), inherited as an autosomal recessive condition, is a progressive neurodegenerative disorder that causes cell death in parts of the brain, including the cerebellum and brain stem. The spinal cord and some peripheral nerves also degenerate. Affected individuals show signs of unsteady gait and uncoordinated limb movements between the ages of 5 and 15 years. Structural degeneration of the brain and spinal cord follow, and death usually occurs in the third decade of life. The frequency of the disorder is about 1 in 22,000, although some populations have a higher frequency because of founder effects.

The gene for **Friedreich ataxia** (FRDA) maps to the long arm of chromosome 9, in the region 9q12-q13 (Figure 16.5). Recently, a gene from this region has been identified as a candidate for the FRDA locus. This gene encodes a protein expressed in the brain, but not in other tissues such as liver. The amino acid sequence of the protein has been deduced from the nucleotide sequence of the mRNA. This protein is not related to any known proteins, but does contain a membrane-spanning segment of amino acids, meaning that it is probably membrane-associated and may be involved in the reception or transduction of signals into and/or out of the cell. More work is needed to identify the function of the protein, and to establish the presence of mutant forms of the gene in those affected by FRDA.

Friedreich ataxia
An autosomal recessive disorder associated with progressive degeneration of the brain, spinal cord, and some peripheral nerves. Onset usually occurs in childhood and results in early death.

Menkes Kinky-Hair Disease

This X-linked recessive disorder (MIM/OMIM 309400), first described in 1962, is a disorder of copper metabolism. Copper is an element essential to life; in the body, it is normally bound to certain proteins that participate in metabolic reactions and that

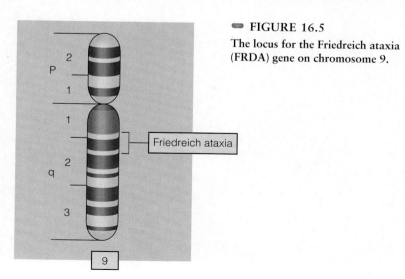

 FIGURE 16.5

The locus for the Friedreich ataxia (FRDA) gene on chromosome 9.

Menkes kinky-hair disease
An X-linked recessive disorder of copper metabolism causing neurological impairment, progressive failure of the nervous system, and death in early childhood.

form connective tissue. **Menkes kinky-hair** disease (MNK) is characterized by a postnatal failure to grow and by the appearance of severe neurological impairment by 1–2 months of age. No treatment is available, and death occurs from failure of the nervous system between 1 and 10 years of age, with most deaths occurring between the ages of 6 months and 3 years.

The hair of affected individuals is stubby, twisted, or kinky, and of varying diameter along the length of the hair shaft. This abnormality is caused by the defective formation of molecular links in keratin (a connective tissue protein) that is the main component of hair. The formation of these crosslinks during hair growth requires normal serum levels of copper, which is affected in this disorder.

The gene for MNK has been mapped to Xq12-q13, and encodes a copper-binding membrane protein involved in the transport of copper across cell membranes. In many cases, the mutation involves nucleotide deletions that completely inactivate the gene. The resulting abnormal transport of copper causes motor disorders, severe mental retardation, and degeneration of brain tissues.

Huntington Disease

Huntington disease
An autosomal dominant disorder associated with progressive neural degeneration and dementia. Adult onset is followed by death 10–15 years after symptoms appear.

This autosomal dominant disorder is usually first expressed in mid-adult life as involuntary muscular movements and jerky motions of the arms, legs, and torso. As **Huntington disease** (MIM/OMIM 143100) progresses, there are personality changes, agitated behavior, and dementia. Most affected individuals die within 10 to 15 years after onset of symptoms.

Brain autopsies of affected individuals show damage to several brain regions, including those involved with motor activity. In many cases, the cells in affected regions are altered in shape or destroyed (● Figure 16.6).

Although the gene has been isolated, the gene product has not yet been identified. Brains from affected individuals exhibit metabolic abnormalities, and accumulate excessive amounts of a neurotoxic chemical, quinolonic acid. The metabolite is derived from the amino acid tryptophan, and is produced by the enzyme 3-hydroxyanthranilate oxygenase, which is also elevated in the brains of affected individuals. In Huntington disease, it appears likely that abnormal metabolism leads to destruction of brain cells, which in turn affects behavior.

● **FIGURE 16.6**

At left is a slice from a normal brain. At right is a slice from a Huntington patient's brain. The central region (caudate nucleus) is missing.

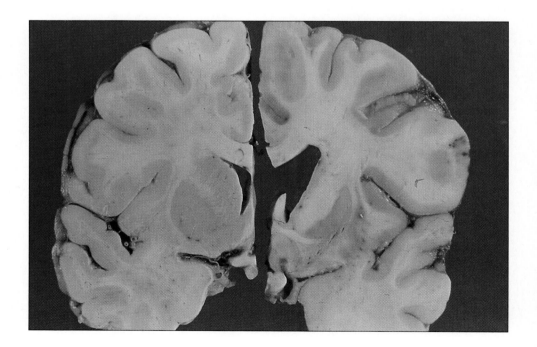

AGGRESSIVE BEHAVIOR AND BRAIN METABOLISM

Recently, preliminary studies have established a link between a mutant gene, abnormal brain metabolism, and forms of aggressive behavior. This finding grew out of a study of one form of X-linked mental retardation associated with behavioral abnormalities, and represents a condition for which a direct link between a single gene defect and a phenotype with aggressive and/or violent behavior has been established. A multigenerational family showed several males with a mild form of mental retardation (Figure 16.7). In particular, eight males with mild or borderline mental retardation showed a characteristic pattern of aggressive and often violent behavior triggered by anger, fear, or frustration. The behavior responses varied widely in levels of violence and time, but included acts of attempted rape, arson, stabbings, and exhibitionism.

Using three different molecular marker systems, the locus for this behavior was mapped to the short arm of the X chromosome in the region of Xp11.23-11.4. One of the structural genes in this region encodes an enzyme that breaks down a neurotransmitter (Table 16.3). Neurotransmitters are chemical signals that carry nerve impulses from cell to cell in the

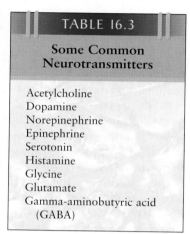

TABLE 16.3

Some Common Neurotransmitters

Acetylcholine
Dopamine
Norepinephrine
Epinephrine
Serotonin
Histamine
Glycine
Glutamate
Gamma-aminobutyric acid
(GABA)

SIDEBAR

A Genetic Link to a Personality Trait

Recently two research groups have found a link between an allele of a neurotransmitter receptor and a personality trait. The trait, novelty seeking, is cataloged by personality inventory tests. Some time ago, twin studies and animal studies indicated that there is a genetic component to this personality trait. The linked allele D4, encodes a receptor for the neurotransmitter dopamine. This allele has an expanded exon which is associated with novelty seeking. Those carrying this allele were much more likely to rate as quick-tempered, impulsive, curious and extravagant than others in the general population. The work of these two research groups is the first to establish a link between a normal personality trait and a gene. A relationship between dopamine and novelty-seeking was thought to exist because individuals with Parkinson's disease lose dopamine-producing cells, and are notable for their lack of novelty-seeking behavior. The next step will be to determine how the expanded allele changes the interaction between the brain and dopamine, producing the novelty-seeking personality.

 FIGURE 16.7

Co-segregation of mental retardation, aggressive behavior, and a mutation in the monoamine oxidase type A (MAOA) gene. Affected males are indicated by the filled symbols. Symbols marked with an asterisk represent males known to carry a mutation of the MAOA gene; those marked with a triangle are known to carry the normal allele. Symbols marked with a dot inside represent females known to be heterozygous carriers.

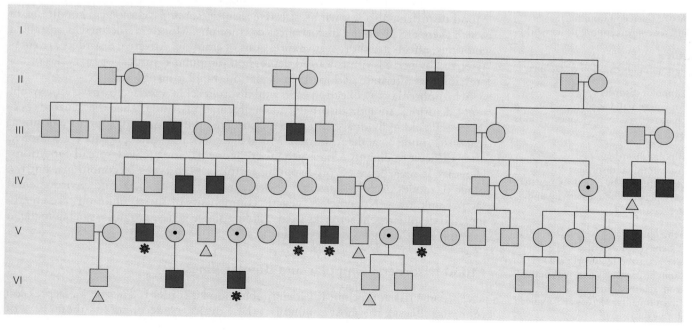

brain and nervous system (Figure 16.8). Urinalysis of the eight affected individuals indicated abnormal levels of several compounds normally metabolized by the enzyme monoamine oxidase type A (MAOA). The preliminary conclusion of this study was that the eight affected males studied may carry a mutation in the gene encoding this enzyme, and that lack of MAOA activity is associated with their behavior pattern.

A subsequent study of the MAOA gene (MIM/OMIM 309850) in five of the eight affected individuals shows that they all carry a mutation that changes a codon for glutamine into a termination codon, which produces a nonfunctional gene product. This mutation was found in two obligatory female heterozygotes, and is not present in the unaffected males in this pedigree. Lack of MAOA activity in affected males alters metabolism of certain neurotransmitters as reflected in altered urinary concentration of metabolites. Other studies in both humans and animals have concluded that altered metabolism of these same neurotransmitters is associated with aggressive and impulsive behavior.

Further work is needed to determine whether mutations of MAOA are associated with altered behavior in other pedigrees and in animal model systems. In addition, the interaction of MAOA with external factors such as diet, drugs, and environmental stress remain to be established. The identification of a specific metabolic defect associated with this behavior pattern suggests that biochemical or pharmacological treatment for this disorder may be possible.

While the use of recombinant DNA markers in linkage studies as a way of identifying single genes that affect behavior has been successful in the case of Huntington disease and the other disorders just described, in other cases, it has led to erroneous results. In a 1987 linkage study using DNA markers, a gene for manic depression was mapped to a region of chromosome 11. Later, individuals from the study group who did not carry the markers developed manic depression, indicating the lack of linkage between markers on chromosome 11 and the gene or genes for manic depression. Similarly, a report on the linkage between DNA markers on chromosome 5 and schizophrenia was found to be coincidental, or at best to apply only to a small, isolated population. These early failures to find single genes that control these disorders have led to the reevaluation of single-gene models for many behavior traits, and to the development of alternative models, as described in the next section.

THE GENETICS OF MOOD DISORDERS AND SCHIZOPHRENIA

Mood disorders, also known as affective disorders, are psychological conditions in which there are profound disturbances of emotions. **Moods** are defined as sustained emotions; **affects** are short-term expressions of emotion. Affective disorders are characterized by periods of prolonged depression (**unipolar disorder**) or by cycles of depression that alternate with periods of elation (**bipolar disorder**).

Schizophrenia is a collection of mental disorders characterized by psychotic symptoms, delusions, thought disorders, and hallucinations, often called the schizoid spectrum. Schizoid individuals suffer from disordered thinking, inappropriate emotional responses, and social deterioration. Mood disorders and schizophrenia are complex, often difficult to diagnose, have genetic components, and are widespread conditions. Heredity is regarded as a predisposing factor in both types of conditions, but the mode or modes of inheritance are unclear, and the role of social and environmental factors unknown. Nonetheless, genetic components of these conditions are emerging, and despite recent setbacks in identifying single genes, progress is being made in forming genetic models of these disorders.

Mood Disorders: Unipolar and Bipolar Illnesses

The lifetime risk for a clinically identifiable mood disorder is 8% to 9%. Depression (unipolar illness), the most common of these disorders, accounts for about 10% of

Mood disorders
A group of behavior disorders associated with manic and/or depressive syndromes.

Mood
A sustained emotion that influences perception of the world.

Affect
Pertaining to emotion or feelings.

Unipolar disorder
An emotional disorder characterized by prolonged periods of deep depression.

Bipolar disorder
An emotional disorder characterized by mood swings that vary between manic activity and depression.

Schizophrenia
A behavioral disorder characterized by disordered thought processes and withdrawal from reality. Genetic and environmental factors are involved in this disease.

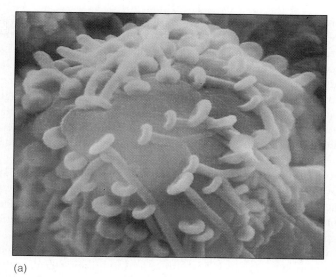

(a)

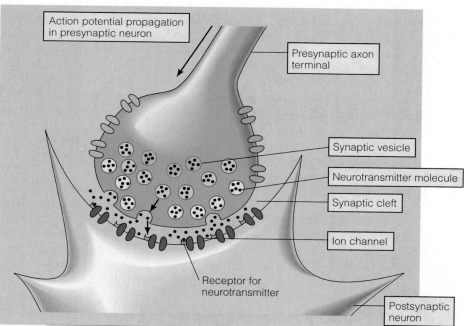

Action potential propagation in presynaptic neuron

Presynaptic axon terminal

Synaptic vesicle

Neurotransmitter molecule

Synaptic cleft

Ion channel

Receptor for neurotransmitter

Postsynaptic neuron

(b)

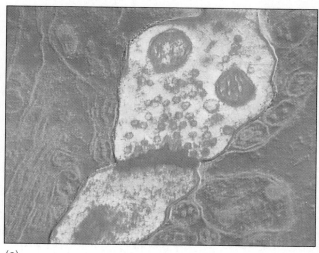

(c)

FIGURE 16.8

The synapse and synaptic transmission. (a) A scanning electron micrograph of the endings (called terminal boutons) of an axon in contact with another cell. (b) In this diagram, a nerve impulse arriving at the end of an axon triggers the release of a chemical neurotransmitter from storage in synaptic vesicles. The neurotransmitters diffuse across the synapse and bind to receptors on the membrane of the cell on the other side of the synapse (post-synaptic neuron), where they trigger another nerve impulse. (c) A transmission electron micrograph of a synapse. The cell above the synapse contains synaptic vesicles with stored neurotransmitters.

all patients seen in nonpsychiatric clinical settings. Depression is more common in females (about a 2:1 ratio), begins in the fourth or fifth decade of life, and is often a protracted or recurring condition. Depression has several characteristics, including weight loss, insomnia, poor concentration, irritability and anxiety, and lack of interest in surrounding events.

About 1% of the U.S. population suffers from bipolar illness. The age of onset is during adolescence or the second and third decades of life, and males and females are at equal risk for this condition. Manic activity is characterized by hyperactivity, acceleration of thought processes, low attention span, creativity, and feelings of elation or power.

The link between mood disorders and genetics is derived from twin studies, with concordance of 57% in monozygotic (MZ) twins and 14% in dizygotic (DZ) twins. In addition, the rates of mood disorders in adopted individuals and their biological parents support the role of genetic factors. The evidence for genetic factors is stronger for bipolar disorders than for unipolar disorders.

Several attempts have been made to map genes for bipolar illnesses using a single-gene model, but were unsuccessful. The failure to find linkage between genetic markers and single genes for manic depression does not undermine the role of genes in bipolar illness, but means that new strategies of linkage analysis are required to identify the genes involved. A new strategy, called an association study, is being used in a worldwide effort to screen all human chromosomes for genes controlling bipolar illness. Association studies use DNA markers, but follow the inheritance of the marker and the disorder (bipolar illness in this case) in unrelated individuals affected with the disorder rather than following the trait in large families. The idea is to identify portions of the genome that are more common in affected individuals than in those without the trait. Association studies have identified regions on chromosomes 6, 13, 15, and 18 as candidates that may contain genes for manic depression. Now that these regions have been identified, they are being closely studied to search for genes responsible for bipolar illness.

In addition to its elusive genetic nature, bipolar illness remains a fascinating behavioral disturbance because of its close association with creativity (see "Concepts and Controversies," page 394). Many great artists, authors, and poets have been afflicted with manic depressive illness (● Figure 16.9). Studies on the nature of creativity have shown that the thought patterns of the creative mind parallel those of the manic stage of bipolar illness. In her book, *Touched with Fire*, Kay Jamison explores the relationship among genetics, neuroscience, and the lives and temperaments of creative individuals including Byron, Van Gogh, Poe, and Virginia Woolf.

● **FIGURE 16.9**

Virginia Woolf, the author and poet, was affected by manic depression. Like others, she often commented on the relationship between creativity and her illness.

Schizophrenia

Schizophrenia is a relatively common mental illness, affecting about 1% of the population (about 2.5 million people in the United States are affected). The disorder usually appears in late adolescence or early adult life. Because of its prevalence, it has been estimated that half of all hospitalized mentally ill and mentally retarded individuals are schizophrenic.

Schizophrenia is a disorder of the thought processes rather than of mood. Diagnosis is often difficult, and there is notable disagreement on the definition of schizophrenia because it has no single distinguishing feature and causes no characteristic brain pathology. Some features of the disorder include

- Psychotic symptoms, including delusions of persecution
- Disorders of thought; loss of the ability to use logic in reasoning
- Perceptual disorders, including auditory hallucinations (hearing voices)
- Behavioral changes, ranging from mannerisms of gait and movement to violent attacks on others
- Withdrawal from reality and inability to participate in normal activities

Several models have been proposed for schizophrenia, and in general fall into two groups: models in which biological factors (including genetics) play a major role and environmental factors are secondary; and conversely, models in which environmental factors are primary and biological factors are secondary. Some evidence points to metabolic differences in the brains of schizophrenics compared to those of normal individuals (Figure 16.10), but it is unclear whether these differences are genetic. Overall, however, the best evidence supports the role of genetics as a primary factor in schizophrenia, with environmental factors needed for full expression.

 FIGURE 16.10

Brain metabolism in a set of monozygotic quadruplets, all of whom suffer from varying degrees of schizophrenia. These scans of glucose utilization by brain cells are visualized by positron emission tomography (PET scan). They show low metabolic rates in the frontal lobe (top of each scan) in comparison to non-schizophrenics (top left image). The frontal lobe is where cognitive ability resides.

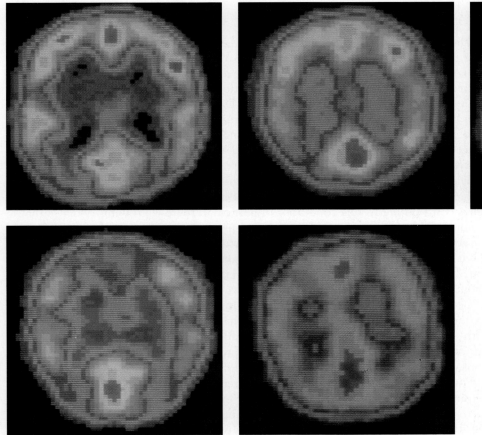

CONCEPTS AND CONTROVERSIES

The Link between Madness and Genius

As long ago as the 4th century BC, Aristotle observed that talented philosophers, poets, and artists tend to have mental problems. This idea has been incorporated into the popular wisdom of our culture, as illustrated by statements such as "There is a thin line between genius and madness." In recent years, a substantial amount of evidence has accumulated that distinguished artists, poets, authors, and composers suffer from mood disorders, particularly depression and manic depression, at rates 10 to 30 times more frequent than the general population. Based on these results, some researchers have proposed that there is a link between bipolar disorder and creativity. Several books, including *Touched with Fire*, (Kay Jamison), *The Price of Greatness* (Arnold Ludwig), and *The Broken Brain* (Nancy Andreasen) have explored this link.

The poet Alfred Lord Tennyson and members of his family were affected by mental instability, ranging from unstable moods to insanity. Alfred was affected by life-long bouts of depression, as were two of his brothers, his sister, father, two uncles, an aunt, and his grandfather. Along with this family temperament went a consuming passion for poetry and verse. Although Alfred is the best-known member of his family, his brothers published volumes of poetry and each won prestigious awards for translating ancient Greek poems and epics. Alfred's siblings and his aunt also wrote verse, and one of his nieces became a poet and playwright.

Brain imaging shows that different regions of the brain are affected in depression and in manic stages. Manic depressives have a characteristic pattern of metabolism and blood flow in the prefrontal cortex, the part of the brain associated with intellect. It is thought that connections in the nervous system ("wiring") may be different in certain regions of the brain in manic depressives, and that the transition from mania to depression may stimulate mental activity and creativity.

Family studies and twin studies strongly support a genetic component for manic depression, although no genes controlling this trait have been identified. When the genetic basis for this disorder is known, it may shed some light on the basis of artistic creativity.

The influence of genotype on schizophrenia can be seen by examining risk factors for relatives of schizophrenics (Figure 16.11). Overall, relatives of affected individuals have a 15% chance of developing the disorder (as opposed to 1% among unrelated individuals). Using a narrow definition of schizophrenia, the concordance value for MZ twins is 55% versus 10% for DZ twins. MZ twins raised apart show the same level of concordance as MZ twins raised together. If a broader definition is used, combining schizophrenia and borderline or schizoid personalities, the concordance for MZ twins approaches 100%, and the risk for siblings, parents, and offspring of schizophrenics is about 45%.

The mode of inheritance of schizophrenia is unknown. Pedigree and linkage studies have suggested loci on the X chromosome and a number of autosomes as sites of genes contributing to this condition. In particular, there is growing evidence that a region on chromosome 6 carries a gene for susceptibility to schizophrenia, although the gene has not yet been identified. Several studies indicate that this gene may be responsible for up to 25% of all cases. Although all the linkage studies have been contested and contradicted by other studies, several tentative conclusions can be drawn about the genetics of schizophrenia.

Genetic models indicate that a polygenic model with a single major gene making most of the contribution is consistent with the results from family studies as well as with other observations, including concordance in MZ twins and incidence of the disorder in the general population. Schizophrenia is probably genetically heterogenous, and several loci may be involved, even if there is a major gene effect.

For identifying genes related to schizophrenia, familial linkage studies appear to be more valuable than association studies. Some 18 research centers in Europe are currently screening for major genes controlling bipolar illness and schizophrenia using about 150 DNA markers from all regions of the genome. The recognition and de-

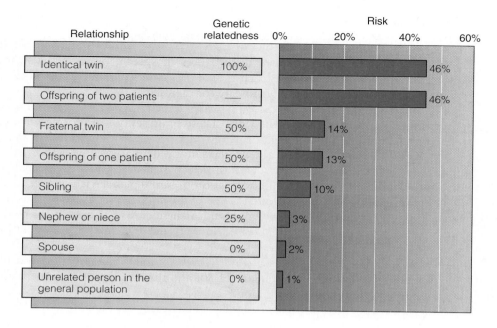

Relationship	Genetic relatedness	Risk
Identical twin	100%	46%
Offspring of two patients	—	46%
Fraternal twin	50%	14%
Offspring of one patient	50%	13%
Sibling	50%	10%
Nephew or niece	25%	3%
Spouse	0%	2%
Unrelated person in the general population	0%	1%

FIGURE 16.11

The lifetime risk for schizophrenia varies by degree of relationship to an affected individual. The observed risks are more compatible with a multifactorial mode of transmission than a single-gene or polygenic mode of inheritance.

finition of subphenotypes (also known as endophenotypes) of the disorder schizophrenia will also be needed to genetically analyze this puzzling condition.

 GENETICS AND SOCIAL BEHAVIOR

Although many genetic disorders with behavioral effects are controlled by single genes, these behavioral alterations are often secondary to a biochemical abnormality. Human geneticists have long been interested in aspects of human behavior that take place in a social context, that is, behavior that results from the interaction between and among individuals. This behavior is often complex in structure, and genetic evidence indicates that such behavior involves multifactorial inheritance. Several traits with different levels of social behavior are discussed in the following sections.

Tourette Syndrome

Tourette syndrome (GTS) (MIM/OMIM 137580) was first described as a familial disorder by a French physician, Georges Gille de la Tourette in 1885. This condition is characterized by both motor and behavioral disorders. About 10% of affected individuals have a family history of the condition; males are affected more frequently than females (3:1), and onset is usually between 2 and 14 years of age. The disorder is characterized by episodes of motor and vocal tics that can progress to more complex behaviors involving a series of grunts and barking noises. The vocal tics include outbursts of profane and vulgar language and parrot-like repetition of words spoken by others. Because of variable expression, the incidence of the condition is unknown, but it has been suggested that the disorder may be very common.

Family studies indicate that biological relatives of affected individuals are at significantly greater risk for GTS than relatives of unaffected controls. Linkage studies on over 1000 GTS families have been performed, and a recent review of these studies proposed that a model of autosomal dominant inheritance with incomplete penetrance and variable expression is most compatible with the linkage results. A worldwide collaborative effort using over 600 DNA markers to map a major gene associated with GTS has excluded over 85% of the genome as a site for the GTS gene. If a major gene for GTS exists, it should be identified in the next few years. However, as more of the genome is excluded in this search, it is possible that the genetic model of autosomal dominant inheritance will need to be reexamined.

Tourette syndrome
A behavioral disorder characterized by motor and vocal tics and inappropriate language. Genetic components are suggested by family studies showing increased risk for relatives of affected individuals.

Alzheimer Disease

Alzheimer disease
A heterogenous condition associated with the development of brain lesions, personality changes, and degeneration of intellect. Genetic forms are associated with loci on chromosomes 14, 19, and 21.

The behavioral symptoms of **Alzheimer disease** (AD) begin with loss of memory and a progressive dementia that involves disturbances of speech, motor activity, and recognition. There is an ongoing degeneration of personality and intellect, and eventually, affected individuals are unable to care for themselves.

Brain lesions (Figure 16.12) accompany these behavioral changes, and were first described by Alois Alzheimer in 1906. These brain lesions are formed from a protein fragment called amyloid beta-protein, which accumulates outside cells in aggregates known as senile plaques. The proteins and cells that become embedded in plaques cause the degeneration and death of nearby neurons, affecting selected regions of the brain (Figure 16.13). Formation of senile plaques is not specific to AD; almost everyone who lives beyond the age of 80 will have such lesions. The difference between normal aging of the brain and Alzheimer disease appears to be the number of such plaques (greatly increased in AD) and the time of accumulation (decades earlier in AD).

It is estimated that Alzheimer disease affects 10% of the U.S. population over the age of 65 and 50% of those over the age of 80, and that the cost of treatment and care for those affected is over $80 billion.

The genetics of Alzheimer disease is somewhat complex; less than 50% of all cases can be directly traced to genetic causes, indicating that the environment plays a significant role in this disorder. We will first examine the genetic evidence and then discuss some of the proposed environmental factors associated with this disorder. Studies of families with members affected with Alzheimer disease indicate that the familial incidence is 43%, with the age of onset ranging from 25 years to 85 years of age.

The gene encoding the beta protein (known as APP) is located on the long arm of chromosome 21, and mutations of this gene are responsible for an early-onset form of AD, which accounts for a small percentage of all cases. Mutations in APP are inherited as an autosomal dominant trait, and this form of the disorder is called Alzheimer-disease 1 (AD 1) (MIM/OMIM 104300).

Other individuals with early-onset Alzheimer disease and those with late-onset disease have mutant genes on other chromosomes, or a combination of genetic and environmental factors. A second form of early-onset AD, perhaps accounting for the majority of all early-onset cases, has been mapped to the long arm of chromosome

FIGURE 16.12

A lesion called a plaque in the brain of someone with Alzheimer disease. The deposit of protein is surrounded by a ring of degenerating nerve cells.

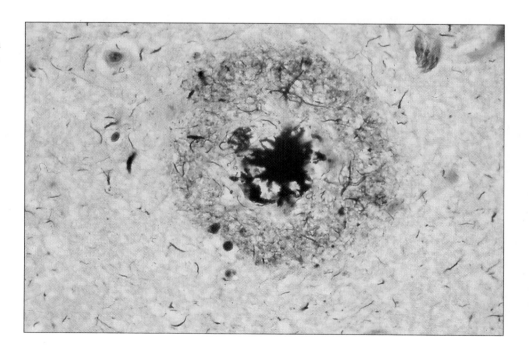

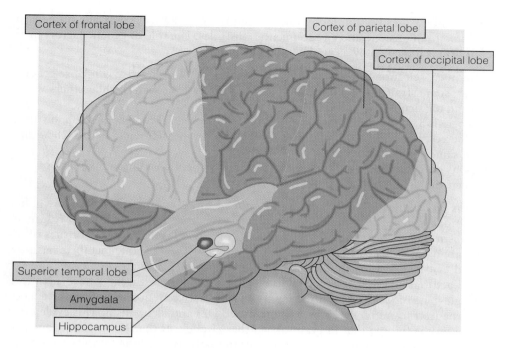

FIGURE 16.13

Location of brain lesions in Alzheimer disease. Plaques are most heavily concentrated in the amygdala and hippocampus. These brain regions are part of the limbic system, a region of the brain involved in controlling memory.

14. One form of late-onset Alzheimer disease (AD 2) (MIM/OMIM 104310) has been mapped to the long arm of chromosome 19, in the region 19q12-q13.2.

It is not clear whether all cases of AD have a genetic explanation, with other genes yet to be discovered, or whether environmental factors are important in the development of this behavioral disorder. In an analysis of 232 families in which AD is segregating, it was concluded that components of AD are multifactorial, indicating an important role for other genetic and nongenetic factors. Among the environmental factors that may play a role in the development of AD, two have received the most attention. Aluminum is found deposited in the brain lesions associated with AD; thus, it has been suggested that aluminum intake and differences in the uptake, transport, and metabolism of this metal may play a role in the development of AD.

One of the proteins present in the brain lesions of AD is similar to that found in infectious proteins called **prions** (MIM/OMIM 176640). Prions are known to cause neurodegenerative diseases in domesticated animals, including Mad-Cow disease, and are associated with several human neurological diseases including kuru and Creutzfeldt-Jakob disease (MIM/OMIM 123400). It has been proposed that exposure to prions and prion infection may be a factor in the development of AD.

It has already been established that AD is genetically heterogenous, and that mutations at any of several loci can produce the AD phenotype. In addition, the fact that many cases of AD cannot be traced to a genetic source may indicate that there is more than one cause for AD, and the role of nongenetic influences and their mechanisms should be considered to define all the risk factors for this debilitating condition.

Prion

An infectious protein that is not a virus, but is the cause of several disorders, including Creutzfeldt-Jakob syndrome.

Alcoholism

As a behavioral disorder, the excessive consumption of alcohol (MIM/OMIM 103780) has two important components. First, consumption of large amounts of alcohol can cause cell and tissue damage to the nervous system and other parts of the body. Over time, this results in altered behavior, hallucinations and delirium, and loss of recent memory. These effects are secondary to the behavior patterns that result in a decline in the ability to function in social settings, the workplace, and the home.

It is estimated that 75% of the adult U.S. population consumes alcohol; about 10% of these adults will be classified as alcoholics, with a male:female ratio of about

4:1. From the genetic standpoint, alcoholism is most likely a genetically influenced, multifactorial (genetic and environmental) disorder. The role of genetic factors in alcoholism is indicated by a number of findings:

- In mice, selection experiments indicate that alcohol preference can be selected for; some strains of mice will select 75% alcohol over water, while others will shun all alcohol.
- There is a 25% to 50% risk of alcoholism in sons and brothers of alcoholic men.
- There is a 55% concordance rate for alcoholism in MZ twins, with a 28% rate in same-sex DZ twins.
- Sons adopted by alcoholic men show a rate of alcoholism more like that of their biological father.

The biochemical pathways involved in the metabolism of alcohol are known, but mutations in genes controlling these pathways are unlikely to play a major role in alcoholism. The nature of the genetic influence on alcoholism and its site or sites of action are unknown; segregation analysis in families with alcoholic members has produced evidence against the Mendelian inheritance of a single major gene, and for multifactorial inheritance involving several genes. Other researchers have advanced a single-gene model and reported an association between an allele of a gene encoding a neurotransmitter receptor protein (called D2) and alcoholism. This evidence is based on the finding that in brain tissue, the A1 allele of the D2 gene was found in 69% of the samples from severe alcoholics but only 20% of the samples from nonalcoholics, implying that an impaired function of the A1 allele is involved in alcoholism.

Subsequent linkage and association studies on the A1 allele have produced conflicting results. In some studies, there was no statistical difference between the incidence of the A1 allele between alcoholics and nonalcoholics; in other studies there was a difference, although of borderline statistical significance. Taken together, however, the available studies have failed to show a link between the A1 allele and alcoholism. They have also failed to show any relationship between abnormal neurotransmitter metabolism or receptor function and alcoholic behavior.

The search for genetic factors in alcoholism illustrates the problem of selecting the proper genetic model for analysis of behavioral traits. Although segregation and linkage studies indicate there is no major gene for alcoholism, association studies have provided a weak correlation between the D2 gene and alcoholism. However, this single-gene model has produced no evidence for a cause-and-effect relationship between the gene and behavior. If a multifactorial model involving a number of genes, each with a small additive effect, is invoked, the problem becomes more complicated. How do you prove or disprove that a given gene contributes, say, 10% to the behavioral phenotype? At present, the only method would involve studying thousands of individuals to find such effects.

Sexual Orientation

In sexual behavior, most humans are heterosexual and show a preference for the opposite sex, but a fraction of the population is homosexual and has a preference for sexual activity with members of the same sex. These variations in sexual behavior have been recorded since ancient times, but biological models for these behaviors have been proposed only recently.

Among the biological models, the role of genetics in sexual orientation has been investigated by twin studies and adoption studies. In a twin study that employed 56 MZ twins, 54 DZ twins, and 57 genetically unrelated adopted brothers, concordance for homosexuality was 52% for MZ twins, 22% for DZ twins, and 11% for the unrelated adopted sibs. Using these values to calculate heritability assuming different numbers of genes involved, overall heritability was calculated to range from 31% to 74%. Another study investigating homosexual behavior in women employed 115

twin pairs and 32 genetically unrelated adopted sisters. In this study, heritability calculated from concordance values was found to range from 27% to 76%.

The results from these and other studies indicate that homosexual behavior has a strong genetic component. These studies have been challenged on the grounds that the results can be affected by the phrasing of the interview questions, by the methods used to recruit participants, and that the phenotype is self-described. But the average heritability estimates from these studies parallels those from the Minnesota Twin Project, a study of MZ twins separated at birth and reared apart. Further twin studies are needed to determine whether the heritability values are accurate. If confirmed, the studies to date indicate that homosexual behavior is a multifactorial trait involving several genes as well as unidentified environmental components.

Work using RFLP markers to study male homosexual behavior has found linkage between one subtype of homosexuality and markers on the long arm of the X chromosome (Figure 16.14). In this study, a two-step approach was employed. First, family histories were collected from 114 homosexual males. From 76 randomly selected individuals, pedigree analysis was performed, using interviews with male relatives to ascertain sexual preference. The results indicated that maternal uncles and sons of maternal aunts had a higher rate of homosexual orientation than paternally related individuals. This indicated the possibility of maternal inheritance (MIM/OMIM 306995).

A further pedigree analysis was conducted using 38 families in which there were two homosexual brothers, with the idea that this might show a stronger trend for maternally controlled inheritance. The results from this analysis do show a stronger trend toward maternal inheritance, and an absence of paternal transmission (Figure 16.15).

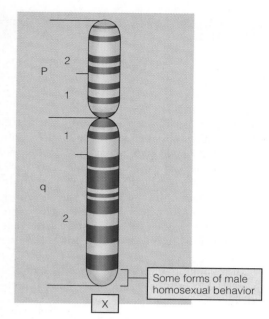

 FIGURE 16.14

Region of the X chromosome found by linkage analysis to be associated with one form of male homosexual behavior.

 FIGURE 16.15

Pedigree showing maternal transmission of male homosexuality. Affected males are indicated by the filled symbols.

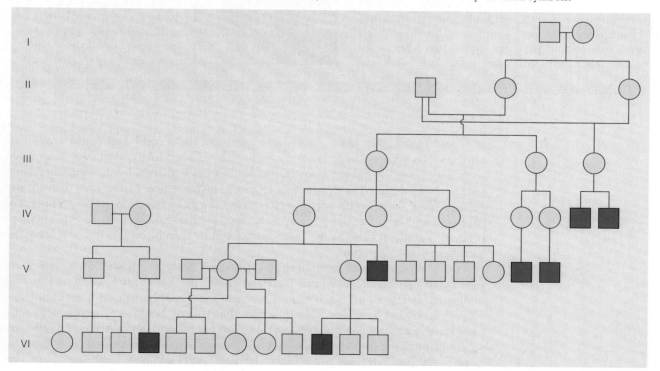

Neurogenetics: From Mutants to Molecules

BARRY S. GANETZKY

From the time I was young, I was fascinated by living things and enjoyed reading books on natural history. But I really had no idea how biologists earned a living. I just knew that I was about 100 years too late to become a naturalist. So I planned on studying chemistry, although it did not give me the same sheer pleasure as biology. In introductory biology I become interested in genetics and molecular biology, and realized that biology was what I wanted to immerse myself in. I have never regretted that choice.

In my junior year, I signed up to do an honor's research project. My mentor was a new young professor (a certain Michael R. Cummings) who at the time was studying egg development in *Drosophila* (fruit flies). This was my first exposure to research, and imagination to discover answers to some of nature's secrets was the most exciting thing I had ever done. Although my project was to last only 10 weeks, I remained for the next two years.

I pursued a Ph.D. in genetics at the University of Washington with the late Larry Sandler, who was so intellectually gifted that I knew instinctively no one could provide me with better graduate training.

As a postdoctoral fellow with Seymour Benzer, I was interested in the molecular basis of the signaling mechanisms in neurons. Ion channel proteins were known to play key roles in nerve impulses, but little was known about their molecular structure or how they worked. I isolated mutations that were defective in neuronal signaling to identify the genes encoding ion channels.

The trick was to find the right mutations. I began by screening for mutants that became paralyzed when exposed to elevated temperatures. In a stroke of luck, one of the first paralytic mutations I found caused a complete block of action potentials. This mutation led us to identify other mutants with neuronal defects. After taking a faculty position at the University of Wisconsin, my colleagues and I succeeded in cloning these genes. We now have the largest collection of mutations affecting ion channels in any organism, and they are providing us with new insights into the molecular basis of neuronal activity. One of the human genes we identified, because of its similarity to a *Drosophila* gene, turns out to be defective in a heritable form of cardiac arrhythmia. Identification of the affected gene opens the way to identifying individuals at risk. It is gratifying to know that work pursued primarily because it was interesting and fun is also important and useful.

BARRY S. GANETZKY received a B.S. in biology from the University of Illinois-Chicago and a Ph.D. in genetics from the University of Washington. He has been a faculty member in the Laboratory of Genetics at the University of Wisconsin, Madison, since 1979, where he is now the Steenbock Professor of Biological Sciences. After spending more than half his life working with fruit flies he still derives great pleasure from discovering new mutations with interesting and unusual phenotypes.

Using information from the pedigree analysis, the second part of the study employed DNA markers to determine whether an X-linked locus or loci was associated with male homosexual behavior in the 38 families with two homosexual brothers. Linkage was detected with markers from the distal region of the long arm, in the Xq28 region. This region was present in two-thirds of the 32 pairs of homosexual brothers, and in about one-fourth of the heterosexual brothers. More work will be needed to confirm the linkage relationship and to search the region for a locus affecting sexual orientation.

Two important factors related to this study need to be mentioned. First, seven sets of homosexual brothers did not coinherit all the markers in the Xq28 region, and about one fourth of all heterosexual brothers inherited the region, but did not display homosexual behavior. This indicates that genetic heterogeneity or nongenetic factors are significant in this behavioral variation. Second, if confirmed by other research groups, the study cannot estimate what fraction of homosexual behavior is related to the Xq28 region, nor whether lesbian sexual behavior is influenced by this

region. In spite of its preliminary nature, this work applies genome screening with molecular markers to study the role of genes in one type of male sexual behavior, and represents a model for future studies in this area of behavior genetics.

✻ SUMMING UP: THE CURRENT STATUS OF HUMAN BEHAVIOR GENETICS

In reviewing the current status of human behavior genetics, several elements are apparent. Almost all studies of complex human behavior have provided only indirect and correlative evidence for the role of specific genes. Segregation studies and heritability estimates indicate that these complex traits most likely involve multiple genes, either with a major gene effect or with several genes contributing in an additive way to the phenotype. Searches for single-gene effects have to date proven unsuccessful, and initial reports of single genes controlling bipolar illness, schizophrenia, and alcoholism have been retracted, unconfirmed, or at best limited to small isolates.

The multifactorial nature of these complex traits means that methods for the investigation of genes with small, incremental effects will have to be refined, and new combinations of the classical methods of twin studies and adoption studies with molecular methods will have to be devised. By their nature, twin studies and adoption studies involve small numbers of individuals. For example, less than 300 pairs of MZ twins raised apart have been identified worldwide. Where traits involve multiple genes, replication of results to confirm gene assignments can require detailed examination of thousands of individuals in hundreds of families. This process is necessarily slow and labor-intensive. Perhaps newer approaches such as association studies in combination with new and quantitative ways of defining phenotypes can be used to provide a meaningful way of dissecting the genetic components of a behavioral phenotype.

Even the limited evidence currently available indicates that the environment plays a significant role in the behavioral phenotype. As confirmation of the role of genes in behavior becomes available, investigations on the role of environmental factors cannot be neglected. The history of human behavior genetics in the eugenics movement of the early part of this century provides a lesson in the consequences of overemphasizing the role of genetics in behavior. Attempts to provide single-gene explanations for behavioral "traits" inhibited the growth of human genetics as a discipline.

The increasing evidence for the involvement of specific genes in controlling human behavior traits has implications outside the laboratory for society at large. As discussed in Chapter 13, the Human Genome Project has raised questions about how genetic information will be disseminated and used, who will have access to this information, and under what conditions. For genes affecting behavior, these same concerns need to be addressed. If genes for alcoholism or homosexuality can be identified, should this information be used to predict an individual's future behavior patterns? Will this information be used to discriminate in employment or insurance?

Many behavioral phenotypes such as Huntington or Alzheimer disease are clearly regarded as abnormal. Few would argue against the development of treatments for intervention and perhaps prevention of these conditions. When do behavior phenotypes move from being abnormal to being a variant? If there is a connection between bipolar illness and creativity, to what extent should this condition be treated? If genes that influence sexual orientation are identified, will this behavior be regarded as a variant, or as a condition that should be treated and/or prevented?

While research can provide information on the biological factors that play a role in determining human behavior, it cannot provide answers to questions of social policy. Those answers have to be formulated using information from research to develop social policy and laws.

1. Many forms of behavior represent complex phenotypes with multifactorial inheritance. Single genes that affect behavior do so as a consequence of their effect on the development, structure, and function of the nervous system.

2. The methods used to study inheritance of behavior encompass both classical methods of linkage and pedigree analysis, newer methods of recombinant DNA analysis, and new combinations of techniques such as twin studies combined with molecular methods. Refined definitions of behavior phenotypes are also being used in the genetic analysis of behavior.

3. Results from work on experimental animals indicate that behavior is under genetic control, and have provided estimates of heritability. The molecular basis of single-gene effects in some forms of behavior has been identified, and provides useful models to study gene action and behavior.

4. Several single-gene effects on human behavior are known; most of these affect the development, structure, or function of the nervous system and consequently affect behavior.

5. Bipolar illness and schizophrenia are common behavior disorders, each affecting about 1% of the population. General models of single-gene inheritance for these disorders have not been supported by extensive studies of affected families, and more complex forms of multifactorial inheritance seem likely.

6. Other multifactorial traits that affect behavior include Tourette syndrome, Alzheimer disease, alcoholism, and sexual orientation.

7. Twin studies in combination with the use of molecular markers have identified a region of the X chromosome that may affect one form of homosexual behavior. If this study can be confirmed, and the gene or genes identified, this combination of methods may be useful as a model for future work on identifying genes that affect behavior.

QUESTIONS AND PROBLEMS

1. When studying the genetics of behavior, what are the major differences in the methods used for single gene versus polygenic traits?

2. In human behavior genetics, why is it important for the trait under study to be defined accurately?

3. What are the advantages of using *Drosophila* for the study of behavior genetics? Can this organism serve as a model for human behavior genetics? Why or why not?

4. A premature stop codon leads to the altered expression of a membrane-associated protein found in cells that form the myelin sheath in the peripheral nervous system. What phenotype results and what disease is this phenotype linked to?

5. In a long-term study of over 100 pairs of MZ and DZ twins separated shortly after birth and reared apart, one of the conclusions was that "general intelligence or IQ is strongly affected by genetic factors." The study concluded that about 70% of the variation in IQ is due to genetic variability (review the concept of heritability in Chapter 5). Discuss this conclusion, and include in your answer the relationship between IQ and intelligence, and to what extent these conclusions can be generalized. In evaluating their conclusion, what would you like to know about the twins?

6. One of the models for behavioral traits in humans involves a form of interaction known as epistasis. In a simplified example involving two genes, the expression of one gene affects the expression of the other. How might this interaction work, and what patterns of inheritance might be shown?

7. Perfect pitch is the ability to name a note when it is sounded. In a study of this behavior, perfect pitch was found to predominate in females (24 out of 35 in one group). In one group of 7 families, 2 individuals had perfect pitch. In 2 of these families, the affected individuals included a parent and a child. In another group of 3 families, 3 or more members (up to 5) had perfect pitch, and in all 3 families, 2 generations were involved. Given this information, what if any conclusions can you draw as to whether this behavioral trait might be genetic? How would you test your conclusion? What further evidence would be needed to confirm your conclusion?

8. Opposite to perfect pitch is tune deafness, the inability to identify musical notes. In one study, a bimodal distribution in populations was found, with frequent segregation in families and sib pairs. The author of the study concluded that the trait might be dominant. In a family study, segregation analysis suggested an autosomal dominant inheritance of tune deafness with imperfect penetrance. One of the pedigrees is presented below. On the basis of the results, do you agree with this conclusion? Could perfect pitch and tune deafness be alleles of a gene for musical ability?

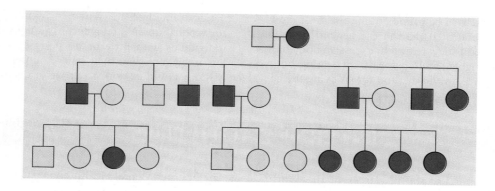

9. A woman diagnosed with Alzheimer disease wants to know the probability of her children inheriting this disorder. Explain to her the complications of determining heritability for this disease.

10. You are a researcher studying manic depression. Your RFLP data shows linkage between a marker on chromosome 7 and manic depression. Later in the study, you find that a number of individuals lack this RFLP marker, but still develop the disease. Does this mean that manic depression is not genetic?

11. A pedigree analysis was performed on the family of a man with schizophrenia. Based on the known concordance statistics, would his monozygotic twin be at high risk for the disease? Would the twin's risk decrease if he were raised in a different environment than his schizophrenic brother?

12. In schizophrenia, a region on chromosome 6 has been linked to this disease, but researchers have not yet found a gene. Explain this linkage and why linkage does not necessarily locate a gene.

13. If you discover a single-gene mutation that leads to an altered behavioral phenotype, what would you suspect about the nature of the mutant gene and the focus of its action?

14. The two main affective disorders are manic depression and schizophrenia. What are the essential differences and similarities between these disorders?

15. What evidence does not support the idea that alcoholism is genetic?
    a. some strains of mice select alcohol over water 75% of the time, while others shun alcohol
    b. the concordance value for MZ twins is 55% and for DZ twins it is 28%
    c. sons of adopted alcoholic men have a rate of alcoholism more like their adoptive fathers
    d. there is a 20–25% risk of alcoholism in sons of alcoholic men
    e. none of the above

16. There could be significant personal, social, and even legal effects if sexual orientation is proven to have genetic components. What are some of these implications?

SCIENCE AND SOCIETY

1. Research using rodents has shown that addictive drugs, such as alcohol and cocaine, stimulate the brain's pleasure center. Stimulation of this region of the brain, researchers believe, may be the cause of all drug addictions. Experiments in rats showed that these rodents could be trained to press a lever to stimulate their pleasure center. Some rats pressed the lever for hours, ignoring water, food, and sex. These animals continued this self-stimulation until they fell over with exhaustion. Upon waking, they immediately restarted this addictive behavior. Further experiments demonstrated that cocaine stimulates the release of large amounts of the neurotransmitter dopamine. Cocaine, ethanol, and nicotine cause increased dopamine concentrations in the brain. These levels, however, are much higher in the pleasure center. Is there a problem using rodents as a model for learning about disorders of the nervous system? If so, identify the specific problems. Is it possible to state that neurotransmitter abnormalities are responsible for all drug addictions? Why or why not? Could genetics be a factor in one's susceptibility to alcoholism or other addictive behaviors? How much influence does social, economic, and physical characteristics have on a person's addictive behavior? Is it reasonable to state that addictions are the result of habits rather than of a disease? Explain your reasoning. Do you think addictions have a psychological or biological basis?

2. In July of 1996, *The Independent*, a popular newspaper published in London, England reported a study conducted by Dr. Aikarakudy Alias, a psychiatrist, who has been working on the relationship between body hair and intelligence for 22 years. Dr. Alias told the 8th Congress of the Association of Europeans Psychiatrists that hairy

chests are more likely to be found among the most intelligent and highly educated than in the general population. According to this new research, excessive body hair could also mean higher intelligence. Is correlating body hair with intelligence a valid method for studying the genetics of intelligence? Why or why not? What other factors contribute to intelligence? Is it logical to assume that individuals with little or no body hair are consistently less intelligent than their hairy counterparts? What type of study could be done to prove or disprove this idea?

INTERNET ACTIVITIES

The following activities use the resources of the World Wide Web to enhance the topics covered in this chapter. To investigate the topics described below, log on to the book's home page at:

http://www.wadsworth.com/biology

1. The National Alliance for the Mentally Ill home page regularly posts articles updating research in the field of genetics and mental illness. Use this site to locate information concerning research on manic-depression or schizophrenia. You can find pertinent information by clicking on many of the headings in the column on the left. For instance, click on "Links" to find related Web sites for either illness. Read at least three articles or search through three different sites for your information.

   a. What recent updates did you find with information from genetics research? Are any promising gene therapies suggested?

   b. From what you have read, have your own views changed as to whether manic-depression or schizophrenia is strongly linked to an inherited genetic component versus environmental causes such as stress, abuse, etc.? Why or why not?

2. The Internet Mental Health homepage from Canada provides a wealth of information about various disorders and has over 1,000 other mental health Web sites linked to it. Click on "Mental Disorders" in the left column and choose three that are of interest to you.

   a. Which did you choose? Did you discover genetic research for any or all of the three through the topical links provided? What did you find? (Hint: for each disorder there is a link, "Research Re: Cause" that provides a summary of recent research articles).

   b. Alcohol dependence is a major problem in many societies today. Click on that disorder heading. What genetic links are described in the research articles? Read one or two magazine articles and try to discover any difference between the genetics of male and female alcoholism. (If not listed here, *The Harvard Mental Health Letter* of Nov. 1994 has an excellent article and it is at the Web site for that periodical) What did you discover? Is there a major difference between the sexes?

FOR FURTHER READING

Aldhous, P. 1992. The promise and pitfalls of molecular genetics. Science **257**: 164–165.

Aston, C. and Hill, S. 1990. Segregation analysis of alcoholism in families ascertained through a pair of male alcoholics. Am. J. Hum. Genet. **46**: 879–887.

Blum, K., Noble, E., Sheridan, P., Montgomery, A., Ritchie, T., Jagadeeswaran, P., Nogami, H., Briggs, A., and Cohn, J. 1990. Allelic association of human dopamine D(2) receptor gene in alcoholism. J.A.M.A. **263**: 2055–2060.

Bolos, A., Dean, M., Lucas-Derse, S., Ramsburg, M., Brown, G., and Goldman, D. 1990. Population and pedigree studies reveal a lack of association between the dopamine D(2) receptor gene and alcoholism. J.A.M.A. **264**: 3156–3160.

Brunner, H., Nelen, M., vanZandvoort, P., Abeling, N., van Gennip, A., Walters, E., Kulper, M., Ropers, H. and van Dost, B. 1993. X-linked borderline mental retardation with prominent behavioral disturbance: phenotype, genetic localization, and evidence for disturbed monoamine metabolism. Am. J. Hum. Genet. **52**: 1032–1039.

Brunner, H., Nelen, M., Breakfield, X., Ropers, H. and van Oost, B. 1993. Abnormal behavior associated with a point mutation in the structural gene for monoamine oxidase A. Science **262**: 578–580.

Coryell, W., Endicott, J., Keller, M., Andreasen, N., Grove, W., Hirschfield, R., and Scheftner, W. 1989. Bipolar affective disorder and high achievement: a familial association. Am. J. Psychiatry **146**: 983–988.

Devore, E., and Cloninger, C. 1989. The genetics of alcoholism. Ann. Rev. Genet. **23**: 19–36.

Duclos, F., Boschert, U., Sirugo, G., Mandel, J-L., Hen, R., and Koenig, M. 1993. Gene in the region of Friedreich ataxia locus encodes a putative transmembrane protein expressed in the nervous system. Proc. Nat. Acad. Sci. **90**: 109–113.

Freimer, N. B., Rens, V. I., Escamilla, M. A., McInnes, L. A., Spesny, M., Leon, P., Service, S. K., Smith, L. B., et al. 1996. Genetic mapping using haplotype, association and linkage methods suggest a locus for severe bipolar disorder (BPI) at 18q22-q23. Nat. Genet. **12**: 436–441.

Ginns, E. I., Ott, S., Egeland, J. A., Allen, C. ; R., Fann, C. S., Pauls, D. L., Weissenbachoff, J., Carulli, J. P. et al. 1996. A genome-wide search for chromosomal loci linked to bipolar affective disorder in the Old Order Amish. Nat. Genet. **12**: 431–435.

Haines, J. 1991. The genetics of Alzheimer disease—a teasing problem. *Am. J. Hum. Genet.* **48**: 1021–1025.

Hamer, D., Hu, S., Magnuson, V., Hu, N., and Pattatucci, A. 1993. A linkage between DNA markers on the X chromosome and male sexual orientation. *Science* **261**: 321–327.

Hu, S., Pattatucci, A. M., Patterson, C., Li, L., Fulker, D. W., Cherney, S. S., Krugylak, L., and Hamer, D. H. 1995. Linkage between sexual orientation and chromosome Xq28 in males but not in females. Nat. Genet. 11: 248–256.

Jamison, Kay. 1993. *Touched With Fire: Manic Depressive Illness and the Artistic Temperament.* New York: Free Press.

Kendler, K., Heath, A., Neale, M., Kessler, R., and Eaves, L. 1992. A population-based twin study of alcoholism in women. J.A.M.A. **268**: 1877–1882.

Lawrence, S., Keats, B., and Morton, N. 1992. The AD1 locus in familial Alzheimer disease. *Ann. Hum. Genet.* **56**: 295–301.

Levay, S. 1991. A difference in hypothalamic structure between heterosexual and homosexual men. *Science* 253: 1034–1037.

Moizes, H. W., Yang, L. Kristbjarnarson, H., Wiese, C., Byerley, W., Macciardi, F., Arott, V., Blackwood, D., et al. 1995. An international two-stage genome-wide search for schizophrenia susceptibility genes. Nat. Genet. 11: 321–324.

Patel, P., Roa, B., Welcher, A., Schoener-Scott, R., Trask, B., Pentao, L., Snipes, G., Garcia, C., Francke, U., Shooter, E., Lupski, J., and Suter, U. 1992. The gene for the peripheral myelin protein PMP-22 is a candidate for Charcot-Marie-Tooth disease type 1A. *Nature Genet.* **1**: 159–165.

Pericak-Vance, M., Bebout, J., Gaskell, P., Yamaoka, L., Hung, W-Y., Alberts, M., Walker, A., Bartlett, R., Haynes, C., Welsh, K., Earl, N.,

Heyman, A., Clark, C., and Roses, A. 1991. Linkage studies in familial Alzheimer disease: evidence for chromosome 19 linkage. *Am. J. Hum. Genet.* **48**: 1034–1050.

Powledge, T. 1993. The genetic fabric of human behavior. Bioscience **43**: 362–367.

Powledge, T. 1993. The inheritance of behavior in twins. BioScience **43**: 420–424.

Risch, N. and Botstein, D. 1996. A manic depressive history. Nat. Genet. 12: 351–353.

Schellenberg, G., Paijami, H., Wigsman, E., Orr, H., Goddard, K., Anderson, L. Nemens, E., White, J., Alonso, M., et al. 1993. Chromosome 14 and late-onset familial Alzheimer disease (FAD). Am. J. Hum. Genet. 53: 619–628.

Tivol, E. A., Shalish, C., Schuback, D. E., Hsu, Y. P., and Breakefield, V. O. 1996. Mutational analysis of the human MAOA gene. Am. J. Med. Genet. 67: 92–97.

Tumer, Z., Tommerup, N., Tonneson, T., Kreuder, J., Craig, I., and Horn, N. 1992. Mapping of the Menkes locus to Xq13.3 distal to the X-inactivation center by an intrachromosomal insertion of the segment Xq13.3-q21.2. *Hum. Genet.* **88**: 668–672.

van de Wetering, B., and Heutink, P. 1993. The genetics of the Gilles de la Tourette syndrome: a review. *J. Lab. Clin. Med.* **121**: 638–645.

Vulpe, C., Levinson, B., Whitney, S., Packman, S., and Gitschier, J. 1993. Isolation of a candidate gene for Menkes disease and evidence that it encodes a copper-transporting ATPase. *Nature Genet.* **3**: 7–13.

GENES IN POPULATIONS

Chapter Outline

THE POPULATION AS A GENETIC
  RESERVOIR
MEASURING ALLELE FREQUENCIES
Codominant Alleles
Recessive Allele Frequencies Cannot Be
  Measured Directly
THE HARDY-WEINBERG LAW
CONCEPTS AND CONTROVERSIES   *The
  Thrifty Genotype*

Assumptions for the Hardy-Weinberg Law
Calculating Allele Frequencies and Genotype
  Frequencies
Genetic Equilibrium
USING THE HARDY-WEINBURG LAW IN
  HUMAN GENETICS
Autosomal Codominant Alleles

Autosomal Dominant and Recessive Alleles
X-Linked Traits
Multiple Alleles
Estimating Heterozygote Frequency
ANTHROPOLOGY AND POPULATION
  STRUCTURE

Chapter 17

OPENING IMAGE
*The Samburu tribe of Kenya represents a
distinct human population.*

Arguments in which a father and son take opposite sides are neither
new nor even unusual. All offspring occasionally disagree with their
parents. It is rare, however, when such arguments result in ideas that are
regarded as controversial some 175 years later. One such disagreement,
between Thomas Malthus and his father, arose in the years following the
French Revolution. This event, like the American Revolution that preceded
it, was hailed by many (including the elder Malthus) as the beginning of a
new era for humanity. According to his view, throwing off the repressions
of monarchy presented an opportunity for unlimited progress in social,
political, and economic areas. The younger Malthus argued that to the

contrary, even if all social impediments were removed, there were immutable natural constraints that would limit progress. These limits would always result in the continuation of poverty and misery as part of the human condition. His essay on this subject was first published in 1798 as The Essay on the Principle of Population as It Affects the Future Improvement of Society. Later versions of this work were expanded and published as several editions of a book and also appeared in the 1824 supplement to the Encyclopedia Britannica.

In his essay, Malthus noted that populations grow geometrically, with the human population doubling in size every 25 years or so (Figure 17.1). Resources such as living space and food supply are more limited and grow slowly, if at all. This means that population size will rapidly outstrip the ability of the environment to support a continual increase in the birth rate. When this point is reached, constraints such as war, disease, and starvation begin to limit population growth by increasing the death rate. The use of voluntary constraints on population growth such as delayed marriage, celibacy, and birth control can help limit population growth and bring about a reduction in human suffering and an improvement in living conditions. But the existence of sexual passion and human nature cause most people to ignore such voluntary constraints. According to the younger Malthus, the result is a continuation of unrelieved poverty and marginal living conditions, even in the most prosperous of nations.

In the 19th century, the writings of Malthus were used to argue that social reform and welfare were useless, since poverty was the result of natural law and not social inequities. In the 20th century, the debate over Malthus continues. Beginning in the 1960s, population growth was again regarded as a global threat that would override technologic progress, leading to a lowered standard of living and an increase in poverty and social problems. Movements calling for zero population growth and universal policies of birth control arose in the United States and other Western countries. More recently, China instituted a policy of one couple; one child. Many developing nations regard such policies as attempts to limit their potential for growth and economic expansion and, in the extreme, as policies designed to result in extinction for smaller, poorer countries.

 FIGURE 17.1

Exponential growth of the human population. It took 1800 years to reach 1 billion, but only another 130 years to reach 2 billion, and another 45 years to reach 4 billion. Before the year 2000, the population will be 6 billion.

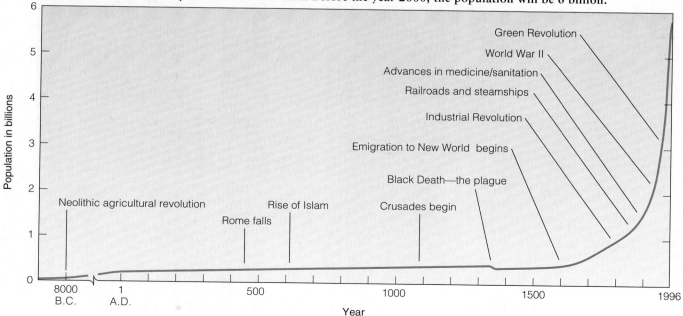

Malthus correctly foresaw the implications and dangers of uncontrolled population growth, and he was one of the first to deal with the dynamics of populations. His work on the relationship between a population and its environment influenced both Wallace and Darwin, who incorporated Malthus' ideas into the theory of natural selection. In considering the effects of limited resources on populations, Wallace and Darwin concentrated their attention on those that lived rather than those that perished. Both observed that individuals carrying advantageous hereditary variations were more likely to survive and to leave the greatest number of offspring. Neither Wallace nor Darwin had any knowledge of how this variation was generated, but they recognized its importance.

In the early part of this century, after Mendel's work was widely recognized, it became obvious that genes are the basis of phenotypic variation in populations, and that the genetic organization of populations is an essential part of the evolutionary process. Today the study of populations is closely tied to the study of evolution. Populations are regarded as collections of allele frequencies and evolution as the result of changes in allele frequencies.

In this chapter we will consider the population as a genetic unit and examine its organization, the methods of measuring allele frequencies, and the ways in which the genetic structure of the population directly affects the incidence of human genetic disease. We begin with a definition of populations, their subunits, and the concept of populations as reservoirs of genetic diversity. We will then consider how allele frequencies can be measured in populations, and how this information is used to answer practical questions about the frequency of disorders and heterozygotes in a population.

● FIGURE 17.2

Human population density. Humans are not randomly distributed across the land areas of the world, but are clustered into discrete populations.

 ## THE POPULATION AS A GENETIC RESERVOIR

Humans are distributed over a wide range of geographic areas that include most of the land surfaces of the Earth (● Figure 17.2). Because humans are clustered in

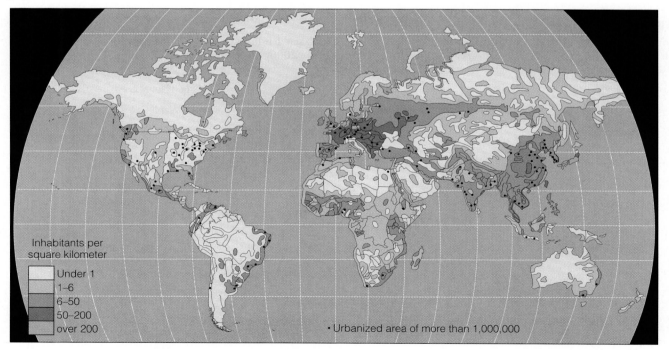

Inhabitants per square kilometer

Under 1
1–6
6–50
50–200
over 200

• Urbanized area of more than 1,000,000

many different regions, our species is subdivided into locally interbreeding units known as **populations,** or **demes.** Like individuals, populations are dynamic: They have a life history of birth, growth, and response to the environment, and they can reach senescence and eventually die. Populations can be described by parameters such as age structure (⬤ Figure 17.3), spatial distribution, birth and death rates, and allele frequencies.

Populations contain more genetic diversity than individuals. For example, no single individual can have blood types A, B, and O. Only a group of individuals has the genetic capacity to carry all three blood types. The set of genetic information carried by a population is known as its **gene pool.** For a given gene, such as the ABO locus, the pool includes all the *A, B,* and *O* alleles present in the population. Zygotes produced by one generation represent samples withdrawn from the gene pool to form the next generation. The gene pool of a new generation is descended from the parental pool but for a variety of reasons, including chance, may have different distributions of allele frequencies than those in the parental pool. Through alterations in allele frequency, a population can change and evolve while maintaining its existence over a period of time. The long-term effect of changes in the genetic structure of a population is evolutionary change.

Population
A local group of organisms belonging to a single species, sharing a common gene pool; also called a deme.

Gene pool
The set of genetic information carried by the members of a sexually reproducing population.

⬤ **FIGURE 17.3**

The rate of growth of a population is strongly influenced by its age. The population of Mexico (a) is pyramid-shaped, and has more individuals who have yet to reproduce. This type of population has the potential for explosive growth. (b) The population structure of the United States is tapered at the bottom, with more individuals who have already reproduced. (c) The population of Sweden is of roughly constant size across all age groups, and is a stable population.

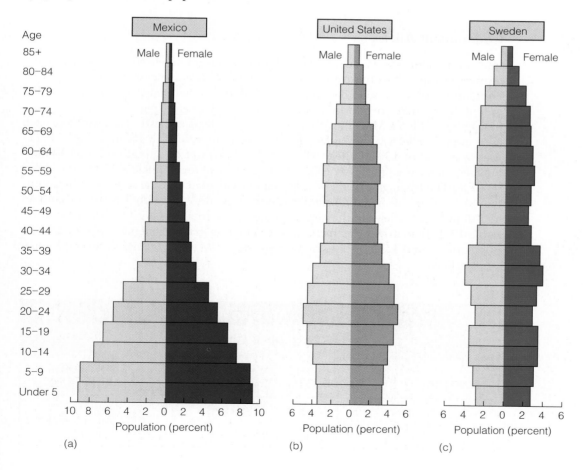

MEASURING ALLELE FREQUENCIES

Populations can undergo drastic changes in size through rapid expansion, or they may decline and have only a few or no survivors. Birth rates, disease, migration, and climate are among the factors that influence the size of a population. As these factors change, the genetic structure of a population can also change (see "Concepts and Controversies," page 412). The problem is how to measure the genetic structure of a population and how to tell when allele frequencies undergo change. One way to do this is to search for the appearance of new phenotypes. As we will see later, most often this is an inefficient method. If the trait is recessive, the new allele has probably spread to many members of the population in a heterozygous form before it appears as a new phenotype in a homozygous recessive individual.

The most direct way of monitoring the genetic structure of a population is to measure **allele frequencies**. In our discussion, the term *allele frequency* will mean the frequency with which alleles of a given genetic locus are present in the population. As several following examples will show, allele frequencies are not the same as genotype frequencies.

Allele frequencies cannot always be determined directly, because we most often observe phenotypes rather than genotypes. But if we consider codominant alleles, phenotypes are equivalent to genotypes, and we can determine allele frequencies in a direct manner. Earlier we examined the MN blood group in humans. In this case the gene L on chromosome 4 has two alleles, L^M and L^N, that control the M and N blood types, respectively. Each allele controls the synthesis and presence of an antigen on the surface of red blood cells, independent of the other allele. Thus individuals may be type M ($L^M L^M$), type N ($L^N L^N$), or type MN ($L^M L^N$). The genotypes, blood types, and immunologic cross-reactions of the MN blood groups are shown in Table 17.1.

Codominant Alleles

In a codominant system such as the MN blood group, allele frequency can be determined simply by counting how many copies of each allele are present in a given population. For example, in a population of 100 individuals, suppose that blood typing shows there are 54 *MM* homozygotes, 26 *MN* heterozygotes, and 20 *NN* homozygotes. The 54 *MM* individuals represent 108 *M* alleles (54 individuals, each carrying 2 *M* alleles). The 26 *MN* heterozygotes represent an additional 26 *M* alleles, for a total of 134 *M* alleles (108 + 26 = 134) out of a total of 200 (100 individuals, each with 2 alleles = 200). The frequency of the *M* allele is 134/200 = 0.67, or 67%. The frequency of the *N* allele can be calculated in the same way by counting 40 *N* alleles in the homozygotes (20 individuals, each with 2 *N* alleles) and an additional 26 *N* alleles in the heterozygotes, for a total of 66/200 = 0.33, or 33%. Table 17.2 summarizes this method of calculating gene frequencies in codominant populations, and Table 17.3 lists the frequency of *M* and *N* alleles in several human populations.

Allele frequency
The percentage of all alleles of a given gene that are represented by a specific allele.

TABLE 17.1

MN Blood Groups

GENOTYPE	BLOOD TYPE	ANTIGENS PRESENT	ANTIBODY REACTIONS
$L^M L^M$	M	M	Anti-M
$L^M L^N$	MN	M, N	Anti-M, Anti-N
$L^N L^N$	N	N	Anti-N

TABLE 17.2

Determining Allele Frequencies for Codominant Genes by Counting Alleles

GENOTYPE	MM	MN	NN	TOTAL
Number of individuals	54	26	20	100
Number of L^M alleles	108	26	0	134
Number of L^N alleles	0	26	40	66
Total	108	52	40	200

Frequency of L^M in population: 134/200 = 0.67 = 67%
Frequency of L^N in population: 66/200 = 0.33 = 33%

TABLE 17.3

Frequencies of L^M and L^N Alleles in Various Populations

POPULATION	GENOTYPE FREQUENCY (%)			ALLELE FREQUENCY	
	MM	*MN*	*NN*	L^M	L^N
U.S. Indians	60.00	35.12	4.88	0.776	0.224
U.S. blacks	28.42	49.64	21.94	0.532	0.468
U.S. whites	29.16	49.38	21.26	0.540	0.460
Eskimos (Greenland)	83.48	15.64	0.88	0.913	0.087

Recessive Allele Frequencies Cannot Be Measured Directly

The preceding example used a codominant gene system for measuring allele frequencies. But most human genes exhibit dominant or recessive phenotypes. If one allele is recessive, then the heterozygote and the homozygous dominant individuals have identical phenotypes. In this situation, it is not possible to determine allele frequencies by counting alleles, since we cannot determine how many heterozygotes are present in the population. However, a mathematical formula can be used to determine allele frequencies when one or more alleles is recessive and a number of conditions (described below) are met. This method, developed independently by Godfrey Hardy and Wilhelm Weinberg in 1908, is known today as the **Hardy-Weinberg Law**.

 THE HARDY-WEINBERG LAW

After Mendel's work became widely known, there was a great deal of debate about whether the principles of Mendelian inheritance applied to humans. One of the first Mendelian traits identified in humans was a dominant mutation known as brachydactyly (MIM/OMIM 112500). Since the phenotypic ratio of dominant traits is 3:1, it was thought that over time, most of the population should have brachydactyly. Since this was not the case, and only a small fraction of the population has brachydactyly, perhaps Mendelian inheritance was valid for plants and other animals, but did not explain inheritance in humans.

An English mathematician, Godfrey Hardy, and a German physician, Wilhelm Weinberg, independently recognized that this reasoning was false because it failed to distinguish between the *mode of inheritance* (in this case a dominant trait with a 3:1 ratio) and the *frequency* of the dominant and recessive alleles in the population. A simple mathematical model developed independently by Hardy and Weinberg provides a way of estimating the frequency of alleles in a population and describes how alleles combine to form genotypes.

Hardy-Weinberg Law
The statement that allele frequencies and genotype frequencies will remain constant from generation to generation when the population meets certain assumptions.

CONCEPTS AND CONTROVERSIES

The Thrifty Genotype

The Pima Indians of the American Southwest have one of the highest rates of adult diabetes of any population in the United States. Between 42% and 66% of the Pima over the age of 35 years are affected with diabetes. This disorder, accompanied by obesity developed in the Pima only in this century, became recognized as a serious health problem only after 1950. Diabetes is usually followed by blindness, kidney failure, and heart disease.

How is it that an inherited condition with so many deleterious effects can be present in a population with such a high frequency? James Neel of the University of Michigan speculated on this question. He observed that the frequency of diabetes is very low in hunter-gatherer societies, such as the Pima were before the 20th century. He also noted that females prone to diabetes become sexually mature at an earlier age. In addition, susceptible females give birth to larger-than-average babies (increased birth weight is linked to increased survival). He postulated that these characteristics might provide a reproductive advantage to diabetics, and account for the high frequency of this disorder.

In addition, Neel proposed that in the feast-or-famine diet of hunter-gatherers, the diabetic represents a "thrifty" genotype that is more efficient in converting food into energy. In diabetics, more insulin is released after each meal, and more glucose is metabolized. According to Neel, as the age of the individual increases, these repeated cascades of insulin release produce a counterreaction that releases an antagonist to stop insulin action. In the hunter-gatherer culture, this overloading occurs infrequently, and adult-onset diabetes does not fully develop.

We now know that there is no antagonist as envisioned by Neel; but as he reviewed the concept in 1982, he noted that "although incorrect in detail, it may have been correct in principle." It appears that adult-onset diabetics release more insulin after a meal than nondiabetics. This quick response prevents loss of blood glucose through the kidneys and is effective adaptation in hunter-gatherer societies. With the conversion of the Pima diet to one that is high in refined carbohydrates, the release of extra insulin occurs over and over again, eventually causing a reduction in the number of cell surface insulin receptors. As a result, although insulin is present in the blood, it is ineffective in mobilizing glucose, and the symptoms of diabetes appear.

The adult-onset diabetic genotype may represent one that was well adapted to the environment of the hunter-gatherer societies that prevailed for hundreds of thousands of years. In the case of the Pima Indians, environmental conditions changed dramatically in less than a century, and the genotype is now at a distinct disadvantage in an environment where carbohydrate-rich foods are freely available. This idea is an interesting one, and if confirmed would be an example of natural selection in action.

Assumptions for the Hardy-Weinberg Law

The mathematical model developed by Hardy and Weinberg is based on a number of assumptions:

- The population is large. In practical terms, this means that the population is large enough so that errors in measuring allele frequencies are negligible.
- There is no selective advantage for any genotype; that is, all genotypes are equal in ability to survive and reproduce.
- Mating within the population is random.
- Other factors such as mutation and migration are absent or rare events and can be ignored.

These assumptions make the Hardy-Weinberg method less exact than counting alleles directly, as in a codominant system. Since the assumptions of the Hardy-Weinberg method only rarely exist in natural situations, allele frequencies determined in this way are regarded as estimates.

Calculating Allele Frequencies and Genotype Frequencies

Let us illustrate how the model works by considering a population carrying an autosomal gene with two alleles, A and a. The frequency of the dominant allele A in

gametes is represented by *p,* and the frequency of the recessive allele *a* in gametes is represented by *q.* Because the sum of *p* and *q* represents 100% of the alleles for that gene in the population, then *p* + *q* = 1. A diagram can be used to represent the genotypes produced by the random combination of gametes carrying these alleles (Figure 17.4).

In the combination of gametes that produces the next generation, the chance that both the egg and sperm will carry the A allele is $p \times p = p^2$. The chance that the gametes will carry unlike alleles is $(p \times q) + (p \times q) = 2pq$. The chance that a homozygous recessive combination of alleles might result is $q \times q = q^2$. It is important to note that while the value p^2 is the chance that both gametes carried an A allele, p^2 is also a measure of the frequency of the homozygous *AA* genotype. Similarly, *2pq* is a measure of heterozygote frequency, and q^2 is the frequency of homozygous recessive (*aa*) individuals. In other words, the distribution of genotypes in the next generation can be expressed as:

$$p^2 + 2pq + q^2 = 1$$

where 1 means 100% of the genotypes present. This formula represents the Hardy-Weinberg Law, which states that both allele frequencies and genotype frequencies will remain constant from generation to generation in a large, interbreeding population where mating is at random and there is no selection, migration, or mutation.

The formula can be used to calculate the frequency of the *A* and the *a* allele or the frequency of the various genotypes in a population. To show how the model works, let's begin with a population for which we already know the frequency of the alleles. Suppose we have a large, randomly mating population in which the frequency of an autosomal dominant allele *A* is 60% and the frequency of the recessive allele *a* is 40%. This means that *p* = 0.6 and *q* = 0.4. Since *A* and *a* are the only two alleles, the sum of *p* + *q* equals 100% of the alleles:

$$p \ (0.6) + q \ (0.4) = 1$$

In the gametes of the population that will produce the next generation, 60% of the gametes carry the dominant allele *A,* and 40% carry the recessive allele *a.* The distribution of genotypes in the next generation is shown in Figure 17.5.

In the new generation, 36% ($p^2 = 0.6 \times 0.6$) of the offspring will have a homozygous dominant genotype *AA,* 48% (2 *pq* = 2[0.6 × 0.4]) will be heterozygous *Aa,* and 16% ($q^2 = 0.4 \times 0.4$) will have a homozygous recessive genotype, *aa.*

We can also use the Hardy-Weinberg equation to calculate the frequency of the *A* and *a* alleles in the new generation. The frequency of A is

$$p^2 + 1/2 \ (2pq)$$

$$0.36 + 1/2 \ (0.48)$$

$$0.36 + 0.24 = 0.60 = 60\%$$

For the recessive allele *a,* the frequency is

$$q^2 + 1/2 \ (2pq)$$

$$0.16 + 1/2 \ (0.48)$$

$$0.16 + 0.24 = 0.40 = 40\%$$

Because *p* + *q* = 1, we could have calculated the value for *a* by subtraction:

$$p + q = 1$$

$$q = 1 - p$$

$$q = 1 - 0.60$$

$$q = 0.40 = 40\%$$

	Sperm	
	A(*p*)	a(*q*)
A(*p*)	AA (p^2)	Aa (*pq*)
a(*q*)	Aa (*pq*)	aa (q^2)

(Eggs)

 FIGURE 17.4

The frequency of the dominant and recessive alleles in the gametes of the parental generation determines the frequency of the alleles and the genotypes of the next generation.

	Sperm	
	A(*p* = 0.6)	a(*q* = 0.4)
A (*p* = 0.6)	AA (p^2 = 0.36)	Aa (*pq* = 0.24)
a (*q* = 0.4)	Aa (*pq* = 0.24)	aa (q^2 = 0.16)

(Eggs)

 FIGURE 17.5

The frequency of alleles and genotypes where the alleles in the parental generation are present at 0.6 for the dominant allele (*A*) and 0.4 for the recessive allele (*a*).

Genetic Equilibrium

Genetic equilibrium
The situation when the frequency of alleles for a given gene remains constant from generation to generation.

The frequency of *A* and *a* in the new generation is the same as in the parental generation. Populations in which the allele frequency of a given gene remains constant from generation to generation are in **genetic equilibrium** for that gene. This does not mean that the population is in a state of equilibrium for *all* alleles. On the contrary, if forces such as mutation, selection, or migration are operating on other genotypes, then the other alleles will change in frequency from one generation to the next.

The presence of a Hardy-Weinberg equilibrium also illustrates why dominant alleles do not increase in frequency as new generations are produced. In the case of brachydactyly, if conditions for the Hardy-Weinberg Law are met, a genetic equilibrium will be established. Because allele and genotype frequencies determine phenotype frequencies, brachydactyly will not increase in the population and reach a 3:1 frequency, but instead will be maintained at an equilibrium frequency from generation to generation.

In addition, genetic equilibrium also helps to maintain genetic variability in the population. In the example above, at equilibrium we can count on 60% of the alleles for gene *A* being dominant (*A*) and 40% being recessive (*a*) in generation after generation. The presence and maintenance of genetic variability is important to the process of evolution.

USING THE HARDY-WEINBERG LAW IN HUMAN GENETICS

The Hardy-Weinberg Law is one of the foundations of population genetics and has many applications in human genetics and human evolution. We will consider only a few of its uses, primarily those that apply to the measurement of allele frequencies and genotype frequencies.

Autosomal Codominant Alleles

As outlined earlier, in the case of autosomal codominant traits, the allele frequency and genotype frequency can be determined directly from the phenotype, since each genotype gives rise to a distinctive phenotype, as in the MN blood groups. For this mode of inheritance, allele and genotype frequencies can be determined by counting individuals in the population. Further, there is no need to make assumptions about Hardy-Weinberg conditions.

Autosomal Dominant and Recessive Alleles

In the case of most autosomal traits, the homozygous dominant and heterozygous genotypes have the same phenotype. For recessive traits, the allele frequencies can be estimated from the number of homozygous recessive individuals in the population. For example, cystic fibrosis is an autosomal recessive trait, and homozygous recessive individuals can be identified by their distinctive phenotype. Suppose that in a population, 1 in 2500 individuals are affected with cystic fibrosis. These individuals have the recessive genotype *aa*. The frequency of this genotype in the population is given by q^2. Thus, the frequency of the *a* allele in this population is the square root of q^2:

$$q^2 = 1/2500 = 0.0004$$

$$q = \sqrt{0.0004}$$

$$q = 0.02 = 1/50$$

Once we know the frequency of the *a* allele is 0.02 (2%), we can calculate the frequency of the dominant allele *A*:

$$p + q = 1$$
$$p = 1 - q$$
$$p = 1 - 0.02$$
$$p = 0.98 = 98\%$$

In this population the distribution of the alleles for cystic fibrosis is 98% *A* and 2% *a*.

X-Linked Traits

In estimating the allele frequency for the autosomal recessive trait cystic fibrosis, one of our underlying assumptions was that the frequency of either the dominant *A* allele or the recessive allele *a* is the same in both sperm and eggs. In X-linked traits, this is not true. Human females carry two X chromosomes, and two copies of all genes on the X. Males, on the other hand, have only one X chromosome and are hemizygous for all loci on the X chromosome. This means that genes on the X chromosome are not distributed equally in the population: females carry two thirds of the total number, and males carry one third. However, because males are hemizygous for all traits on the X chromosome, the allele frequency for recessive X-linked traits in the population is simply the frequency of males with the mutant phenotype. For example, in the United States, about 8% of males are color blind. Therefore, the frequency of the allele for color blindness in the population is 0.08.

Because females have two copies of the X chromosome, genotypic frequencies for X-linked recessive traits in females can be calculated using the Hardy-Weinberg equation. If color blindness in males occurs with a frequency of 8% ($q = 0.08$), then we would expect color blindness to occur with a frequency of q^2, or 0.0064 (0.64%) in females. Given these allele frequencies, in a population of 10,000 males, 800 would be color blind, but in a population of 10,000 females, only 64 would be color blind. This example emphasizes again that males are at much higher risk for deleterious traits carried on the X chromosome. Table 17.4 lists values for the frequency of X-linked traits in males and females.

TABLE 17.4
Frequency of X-Linked Traits in Males and Females

MALES WITH TRAIT	FEMALES WITH TRAIT
1/10	1/100
1/100	1/10,000
1/1000	1/1,000,000
1/10,000	1/100,000,000

Multiple Alleles

Until now we have discussed allele frequencies in genes with only two alleles. For genes such as the ABO blood type, however, three alleles of the isoagglutinin locus (*I*) are present in the population. In this system, *A* and *B* are codominant, and both are dominant to O. This system has six possible genotypic combinations:

AA, AO, BB, BO, AB, OO

Homozygous *AA* individuals and *AO* individuals are phenotypically identical, as are *BB* and *BO* individuals. This results in four phenotypic combinations, known as blood types A, B, AB, and O.

The Hardy-Weinberg Law can be used to calculate both the allele frequencies and genotype frequencies for this three-allele system by the addition of another term to the equation. For the three blood group alleles:

$$p(A) + q(B) + r(O) = 1$$

In other words, the sum of the frequency of the *A*, *B*, and *O* alleles accounts for 100% of the alleles for this gene present in the population. The genotypic frequencies will be given by the equation:

$$(p + q + r)^2$$

The allele frequency values for *A*, *B*, and *O* can be estimated from the distribution of phenotypes in a population, if random mating is assumed.

If we know or have estimated the frequency of the A, B, and O alleles for a given population, we can then calculate the genotypic and phenotypic frequencies for all allelic combinations. The genotypic combinations can be calculated by an expansion of the equation:

$$p^2 \, (AA) + 2pq \, (AB) + 2pr \, (AO) + q^2 \, (BB) + 2qr \, (BO) + r^2 \, (OO) = 1$$

Table 17.5 lists the frequencies for the A, B, and O alleles in different populations in the world. Figure 17.7 shows the geographic distribution of ABO alleles. By using the equations shown above and the values in Table 17.5, we can calculate the genotypic and phenotypic frequencies for the populations shown in ⬬ Figure 17.6.

Estimating Heterozygote Frequency

An important application of the Hardy-Weinberg Law is the estimation of heterozygote frequency in a population. In the genetic structure of human populations, the majority of deleterious recessive genes are carried in the heterozygous condition. To calculate the frequency of heterozygous genotypes for recessive traits, we usually begin by counting the number of homozygous recessive individuals in the population. For example, earlier we calculated the frequency of the allele for cystic fibrosis, an autosomal recessive trait with a frequency of 1 in 2500 among white Americans. (The disease is much rarer among American blacks and Asians). Homozygous individuals can be distinguished from the rest of the population by clinical symptoms that indicate defects in the function of exocrine glands. (To review the symptoms, see Chapter 4.) The frequency of the homozygous recessive genotype is 1 in 2500, or 0.0004, and is represented by q^2. The frequency of the recessive allele q in the population can be calculated as

$$q = \sqrt{q^2}$$
$$q = \sqrt{0.0004}$$
$$q = 0.02 = 2\%$$

Since $p + q = 1$, we can calculate the frequency of p:

$$p = 1 - q$$
$$p = 1 - 0.02$$
$$p = 0.98 = 98\%$$

Knowing the allele frequencies, we can use the Hardy-Weinberg equation to calculate genotype frequencies. Recall that in the Hardy-Weinberg equation, the frequency of the heterozygous genotype is given by $2pq$. Using the values we have calculated for p and q, we can determine the frequency of heterozygotes:

TABLE 17.5

Genotype and Phenotype Frequencies in Multiple-Allele Systems

GENOTYPE	GENOTYPIC FREQUENCY	PHENOTYPE	PHENOTYPIC FREQUENCY
AA	$p^2 = (0.38)^2 = 0.14$	A	0.53
AO	$2pr = 2(0.38 \times 0.51) = 0.39$		
BB	$q^2 = (0.11)^2 = 0.01$	B	0.12
BO	$2qr = 2(0.11 \times 0.51) = 0.11$		
AB	$2pq = 2(0.38 \times 0.11) = 0.082$	AB	0.08
OO	$r^2 = (0.51)^2 = 0.26$	O	0.26

The distribution of alleles in the ABO system. (a) The distribution of the *A* allele in the indigenous population of the world. (b) Distribution of the *B* allele.

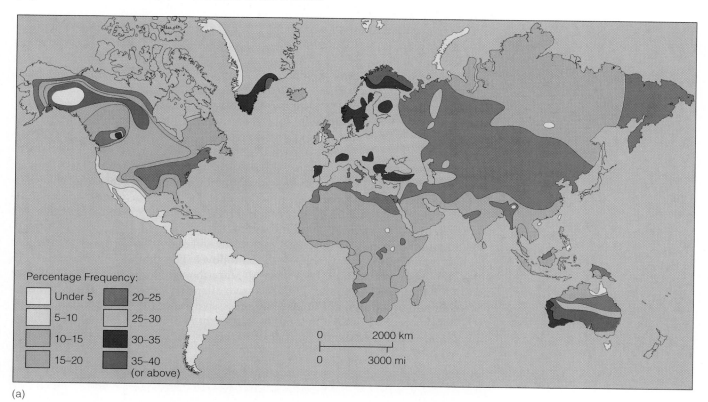

(a)

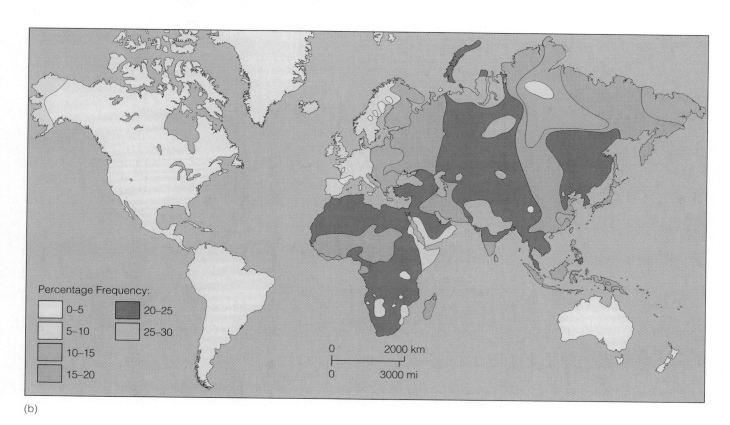

(b)

$$2pq = 2(0.98 \times 0.02)$$
$$2pq = 2(0.0196)$$
$$\text{Heterozygote frequency} = 0.039 = 3.9\%$$

This means that about 4%, or about 1 in 25, white Americans carry the gene for cystic fibrosis.

Sickle cell anemia is an autosomal recessive trait that affects 1 in 500 black Americans. Using the Hardy-Weinberg equation, we can calculate that 8.5% of black Americans, or 1 in every 12, are heterozygous carriers for this trait. Table 17.6 lists the frequencies of heterozygous carriers for recessive traits with frequencies ranging from 1 in 10 to 1 in 10,000,000. Table 17.7 lists the heterozygote frequencies for some common human autosomal recessive traits.

Many people are surprised to learn that heterozygotes for recessive traits are so common in the population. In most cases this is because they assume that if a trait is relatively rare (say 1 in 10,000 individuals), they assume that the number of heterozygotes must also be rather low. In fact, under these circumstances, 1 in 50 individuals is a heterozygote for a trait (Table 17.7), and there are about 200 times as many heterozygotes as there are homozygotes.

What are the chances that two heterozygotes will marry and produce an affected child? We can calculate how this occurs as follows: The chance that two heterozygotes will marry is $1/50 \times 1/50 = 1/2500$. Since they are heterozygotes, the chance that they will produce a homozygous recessive offspring is 1/4. The chance that they will marry and produce a child affected by a recessive trait is therefore $1/2500 \times 1/4 = 1/10,000$. In other words, for the trait to be present in 1 in every 10,000 individuals, 1 in 50 *must* be a heterozygous carrier of the recessive allele.

TABLE 17.6

Heterozygote Frequencies for Recessive Traits

FREQUENCY OF HOMOZYGOUS RECESSIVES (q^2)	FREQUENCY OF HETEROZYGOTES INDIVIDUALS ($2pq$)
1/100	1/5.5
1/500	1/12
1/1000	1/16
1/2500	1/25
1/5000	1/36
1/10,000	1/50
1/20,000	1/71
1/100,000	1/158
1/1,000,000	1/500
1/10,000,000	1/1582

TABLE 17.7

Heterozygote Frequency for Some Recessive Traits in the United States

TRAIT	HETEROZYGOTE FREQUENCY
Cystic fibrosis	1/22 whites; much lower in blacks, Asians
Sickle cell anemia	1/12 blacks; much lower in most whites and in Asians
Tay-Sachs disease	1/30 among descendants of Eastern European Jews; 1/350 among others of European descent
Phenylketonuria	1/55 among whites; much lower in blacks and those of Asian descent
Albinism	1/10,000 in Northern Ireland; 1/67,800 in British Columbia

Once the frequency of either allele is known, we can calculate the frequency of the homozygous genotypes as well as the heterozygotes. The frequency of the genotypes depends on the allele frequency. ▬ Figure 17.7 shows the relationship between allele frequency and genotype frequency. As the frequencies of *p* and *q* move away from zero, the percentage of heterozygotes in the population increases rapidly. This further illustrates that in traits such as cystic fibrosis or sickle cell anemia, the majority of the recessive alleles are carried by heterozygotes. For most deleterious conditions, the presence of a large number of heterozygotes helps reduce the impact of genetic disease on the population.

✿ ANTHROPOLOGY AND POPULATION STRUCTURE

In many situations, anthropologists use properties such as language, dress, social customs, taboos, and food sources to determine the relative distances between cultures and to determine the ancestral sources of contemporary population groups. The analysis of allele frequencies and genotypes has proven to be a valuable tool in these studies, and the application of population genetics to anthropology has given rise to a discipline known as **anthropological genetics.**

The relationship between linguistic or cultural differences and biological differentiation is illustrated by the population structure on Bougainville Island in Papua New Guinea (▬ Figure 17.8). Bougainville, which is roughly 130 miles long and 40 miles

▬ **FIGURE 17.7**

The relationship between allele frequency and genotype frequency in the Hardy Weinberg Law. As the frequency of the homozygous genotypes (p^2 and q^2) decline, the frequency of the heterozygote ($2pq$) rises.

Anthropological Genetics
The union of population genetics and anthropology to study the effects of culture on gene frequencies.

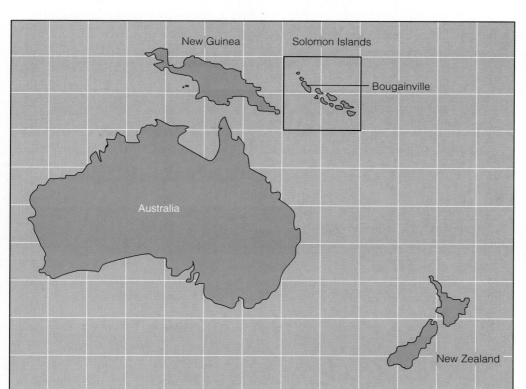

▬ **FIGURE 17.8**

Map of the southwest Pacific, showing the Solomon Islands and the location of Bougainville, which is part of Papua New Guinea.

at its maximum width, is home to 17 different languages (— Figure 17.9). Most of these languages are spoken over a range of only about 10 miles, and many are subdivided into distinct dialects or even sublanguages occupying much smaller ranges of only a mile or two. The populations on this island traditionally have little social or political contact with anyone outside their immediate area. The linguistic evidence and other aspects of their culture suggests that the local population groups are quite isolated from one another.

If these populations have little contact, there is a possibility that they are also genetically distinct from one another. To examine this possibility, blood-type phenotypes were determined in 18 villages representing eight of these language groups. Some of these data are presented in Table 17.8. There is a wide range in the observed frequencies of blood types in the 18 villages. As we will see in Chapter 18, if there were interbreeding between or among these populations, blood-type frequencies would be equalized within a generation or two. The differences in allele frequencies observed in these populations supports the idea that they are also genetically isolated.

— **FIGURE 17.9**

Language divisions on Bougainville. Villages included in the genetic study are numbered 1 through 18. Blood-type data for these groups are given in Table 17.8.

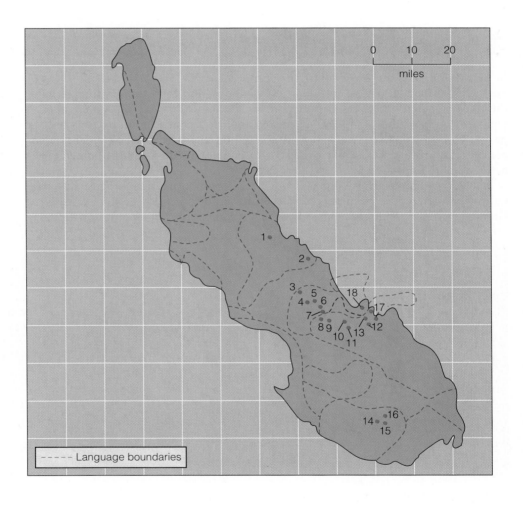

TABLE 17.8

Observed ABO Phenotypes in 18 Villages on Bougainville Island

GROUP	ABO PHENOTYPE (%)			
	A	O	B	AB
1	63.7	16.3	10.3	9.4
2	47.9	52.0	0.00	0.00
3	41.6	58.3	0.00	0.00
4	41.5	58.4	0.00	0.00
5	71.2	28.7	0.00	0.00
6	56.4	43.5	0.00	0.00
7	41.9	58.06	0.00	0.00
8	45.6	53.5	0.78	0.00
9	40.6	59.3	0.00	0.00
10	41.2	57.7	0.004	0.004
11	43.5	56.4	0.00	0.00
12	53.9	40.8	0.043	0.008
13	40.0	41.6	15.0	0.033
14	22.4	56.2	15.7	5.61
15	51.8	35.0	10.5	2.6
16	38.4	50.0	7.69	3.8
17	23.0	47.7	24.7	4.5
18	47.5	26.4	15.8	10.1

SUMMARY

1. The work of Charles Darwin and Alfred Russel Wallace on evolution and natural selection was influenced by Malthus's essay on population dynamics. Both Darwin and Wallace recognized that the struggle for existence favored those carrying variations that helped them adapt to the existing conditions, allowing them to leave more offspring.

2. In the early decades of this century, genes were recognized as the agents causing such variations, giving rise to the field of population genetics. After the mathematic and theoretic basis of this field was established, experimentalists began to study gene frequencies in populations rather than in the offspring of a single mating. This work has produced the basis for our understanding of genetic evolution.

3. The Hardy-Weinberg Law provides a means of measuring gene frequencies within populations and determining whether the population is in equilibrium.

4. The Hardy-Weinberg equation assumes that the population is large and randomly interbreeding and that factors such as mutation, migration, and selection are absent. The presence of equilibrium in a population explains why dominant traits do not replace their recessive alleles.

5. The Hardy-Weinberg Law can also be used to measure the frequency of heterozygotes in a population and to establish when gene frequencies are shifting in the population. The conditions leading to changing gene frequencies in a population are those that produce evolutionary change.

QUESTIONS AND PROBLEMS

1. Draw a graph showing the difference between a population that grows at a geometric rate and one that is only permitted to grow at a constant arithmetic rate. Be sure to label each axis.

2. What are some of the natural constraints referred to by Malthus that keep the size of human populations in check?

3. Define the following terms: population, gene pool, gene frequency, and genotype frequency.

4. Explain the connection between changes in population gene frequencies and evolution, and relate this to the observations made by Darwin and Wallace concerning natural selection.

5. Do you think populations can evolve without changes in gene frequencies?

6. Design an experiment to determine if a population is evolving.

7. Suppose you are monitoring the allelic and genotypic frequencies of the MN blood group locus in a small human population. You find that for 1-year-old children the genotypic frequencies are MM = 0.25, MN = 0.5, and NN = 0.25, while the genotypic frequencies for adults are MM = 0.3, MN = 0.4, and NN = 0.3.
   a. Compute the M and N allelic frequencies for the 1-year-olds and adults.
   b. Are the gene frequencies in equilibrium in this population?
   c. Are the genotypic frequencies in equilibrium?

8. Drawing on your newly acquired understanding of the Hardy-Weinberg equilibrium law, point out why the following statement is erroneous: "Since most of the people in Sweden have blond hair and blue eyes, the genes for blond hair and blue eyes must be dominant in that population."

9. In a population where the females have the allelic frequencies $A = 0.35$ and $a = 0.65$ and the frequencies for males are $A = 0.1$ and $a = 0.9$, how many generations will it take to reach Hardy-Weinberg equilibrium for both the allelic and genotypic frequencies? Assume random mating, and show the allelic and genotypic frequencies for each generation.

10. Explain why a population carries more genetic diversity than an individual.

11. If a trait determined by an autosomal recessive allele occurs at a frequency of 0.25 in a population, what are the allelic frequencies? Assume Hardy-Weinberg equilibrium, and use A and a to symbolize the dominant wild-type and recessive alleles, respectively.

12. Five percent of the males of a population express a sex-linked recessive trait.
   a. What are the frequencies of the dominant and recessive alleles?
   b. What are the genotypic frequencies for the males and females in the population?

13. In a given population, the frequencies of the 4 phenotypic classes of the ABO blood groups are found to be A = 0.33, B = 0.33, AB = 0.18, and O = 0.16. What is the frequency of the O allele?

14. In Table 17.3 which pairs of populations appear to be most closely related in terms of their allelic frequencies at the MN locus? What scenario would you propose to account for these relationships?

15. For each population in Table 17.3 use the given allelic frequencies to determine if the genotypic frequencies are in general agreement with the Hardy-Weinberg law.

16. Using Table 17.6, determine the frequencies of p and q that result in the greatest proportion of heterozygotes in a population.

SCIENCE AND SOCIETY

1. Eugenics is the term used for the selective breeding of humans to bring about improvements in the species. In the early part of the twentieth century, it was suggested that individuals suffering from serious genetic conditions should be prevented from reproducing (by forced sterilization) to reduce the frequency of the disorder in future generations. The legal sterilization of criminal males by vasectomy was first instituted in Indiana in 1907 and was shortly followed by 15 other states. These early laws were later found to violate constitutional rights and have since been reversed. Eugenics, however, may not be a thing of the past. For example, do you think that prenatal diagnosis, particularly when it is known that the woman will terminate the pregnancy if a defect is found, is a form of eugenics? Do you view predisposition testing for adult-onset conditions as a form of eugenics? How do you think the identification of all the genes in the human genome through the Human Genome Project will impact society and its views on eugenics?

2. The cloning of human embryos is a recent advance in genetic technology that offers the possibility of altering gene frequencies in offspring. Although this technology is new for humans, its use in livestock and other agricultural animals has been occurring for years. The mechanism behind natural twinning, when the embryo splits to form two genetically identical individuals, can now be duplicated in the laboratory for human embryos. What are the genetic consequences of cloning human embryos? Will this alternative reproductive technique have genetic consequences for the species? Will the frequency of deleterious recessive genes increase? What are some of the ethical dilemmas that need to be addressed before this method is practiced? Are there legal measures in place to ensure that embryo cloning is not abused?

INTERNET ACTIVITIES

The following activities use the resources of the World Wide Web to enhance the topics covered in this chapter. To investigate the topics described below, log on to the book's home page at:

http://www.wadsworth.com/biology

1. GenBank is the NIH's database of all known nucleotide and protein sequences coupled with supporting bibliographic and biological data. In the next two activities you will use two features of GenBank, the ENTREZ system to search for a DNA sequence and BLAST, to find similar sequences in GeneBank.

Begin this activity by searching the nucleotide data base of ENTREZ.

Enter the gene designation "glycosyltransferase" (an enzyme which places blood group antigens on red blood cell surfaces) in the query block. Select "retrieve" to find all data in GeneBank on this particular enzyme. Select one of the documents related to this gene in humans and then retrieve the sequence in FASTA format. Highlight a portion of the sequence (300-500 bases) and copy it to the clipboard.

In this activity you will search the GenBank database for sequence similarity between the sequence you highlighted and the sequence data of various species. Access BLAST.

Enter the sequence you copied to the clipboard by pasting it into the query box. Submit the query. How many different species have similar sequences to the one you selected? What percentage homology do these sequences have? Are there other human sequences which are identical or similar to the sequence you selected?

When used in the above manner, GenBank can be helpful in determining phylogenic relationships between species and also provide information about the evolution of a particular gene.

FOR FURTHER READING

Barrantes, R., Smouse, P. E., Mohrenweiser, H. W., Gershowitz, H., Azofeifa, J., Arias, T. D., and Neel, J. V. 1990. Microevolution in lower Central America: Genetic characterization of the Chibcha-speaking groups of Costa Rica and Panama, and a consensus taxonomy based on genetic and linguistic affinity. *Am. J. Hum. Genet.* **46:** 63–84.

Bodmer, W. F., and Cavelli-Sforza, L. L. 1976. *Genetics, Evolution and Man.* San Francisco: Freeman.

Chakraborty, R., Smouse, P. E., and Neel, J. V. 1988. Population amalgamation and genetic variation: Observations on artificially agglomerated tribal populations of Central and South America. *Am. J. Hum. Genet.* **43:** 709–725.

Constans, J. 1988. DNA and protein polymorphism: Application to anthropology and human genetics. *Anthropol. Anz.* **46:** 97–117.

Deevey, E. S., Jr. 1960. The human population. *Sci. Am.* (September) **203:** 194–205.

Feldman, M. W., and Christiansen, F. B. 1985. *Population Genetics.* Palo Alto, CA: Blackwell Scientific.

Friedlaender, J. S. 1975. *Patterns of Human Variation.*

Cambridge, Mass.: Harvard University Press.

Mettler, L. E., Gregg, T. G. and Schaffer, H. E. 1988. *Population Genetics and Evolution.* 2nd ed. Englewood Cliffs, N.J.: Prentice-Hall.

Neel, J. V. 1978. The population structure of an Amerindian tribe, the Yanomama. *Ann. Rev. Genet.* **12:** 365–413.

Relethford, J. H. 1985. Isolation by distance, linguistic similarity and the genetic structure on Bougainville Island. *Am. J. Physiol. Anthrop.* **66:** 317–326.

Romeo, G., Devoto, M., and Galietta, L. J. 1989. Why is the cystic fibrosis gene so frequent? *Hum. Genet.* **84:** 1–5.

Spiess, E. B. 1989. *Genes in Populations.* 2nd Ed. New York: Wiley.

Woo, S. L. 1989. Molecular basis and population genetics of phenylketonuria. *Biochem.* **28:** 1–7.

HUMAN DIVERSITY AND EVOLUTION

Chapter 18

Chapter Outline

GENETIC DIVERSITY IN HUMAN
  POPULATIONS
New Alleles Are Generated by Mutation
Genetic Drift
Natural Selection Acts on Variation in
  Populations
Selection and the Genetic History of a
  Population
NATURAL SELECTION AND THE
  FREQUENCY OF GENETIC
  DISORDERS
HUMAN ACTIVITY AS A FORCE IN
  CHANGING ALLELE FREQUENCIES

Migration
Mate Selection
Culture
ALLELE DIFFERENCES BETWEEN
  POPULATIONS
Tracking Gene Flow in Populations
Gene Flow between Populations
PRIMATE EVOLUTION AND HUMAN
  ORIGINS
Human-Like Hominids Appeared about 4
  Million Years Ago
The Genus *Homo* Appeared about Two
  Million Years Ago

Homo erectus Originated in Africa
THE APPEARANCE AND SPREAD OF
  HOMO SAPIENS
CONCEPTS AND CONTROVERSIES *Tool
  Time: Did* Homo erectus *Use Killer
  Frisbees?*
Two Theories Differ on How and Where
  Homo sapiens Originated
The Transition to Agriculture Is a Cultural
  Adaptation
SIDEBAR *Stone Age Fabrics*
Human Migration to the Americas Is a
  Recent Event

OPENING IMAGE

*The remains of a man who lived about
5,000 years ago may provide clues to our
genetic past.*

Ο*ne day, about three and a half million years ago, two human-like
  creatures, one larger, one smaller, walked across a muddy field of
volcanic ash in a region of what is now Tanzania, Africa. Then as now, the
region contained small lakes, patches of vegetation, and a volcano. The pair
passed through the area during or just after a rain, and shortly after an
eruption had covered the ground with a layer of volcanic ash. Along the*

way, the smaller one stopped, turned away to look at something, then resumed walking. This unremarkable event was later to provide important clues about several aspects of human evolution. Soon after these creatures passed, their footprints were covered by several new layers of volcanic ash.

After about three and a half million years, erosion by wind and rain partly exposed the fragile footprints, and they were discovered in 1978 by a team of fossil hunters led by Mary Leakey. Altogether, more than fifty prints covering a distance of about a hundred feet were recovered and preserved as casts.

These prints demonstrate that ancestral primates, known as known as hominids, had feet with well-developed arches, heels, and toes. More importantly, these prints reveal that one of the key events in human evolution, upright posture and walking, evolved more than three million years ago. Other evidence from fossil remains suggest that these small, primitive hominids had ape-like faces with receding foreheads and small brains. However, their pelvis and leg anatomy allowed them to stand upright and walk much like modern humans, freeing their hands for other tasks such as carrying food or young.

In this chapter, we will consider the evidence for how and where our species, Homo sapiens, arose from primate ancestors through a series of evolutionary adaptations over a period spanning millions of years. The broad outlines of this evolutionary process are now well established. New discoveries and interpretations of the evidence are constantly refining our knowledge of the nature and sequence of the events in the history of our own species. Although much of the evidence consists of bits of fossilized bones dug out of rocks, there is a direct and thrilling connection between us and our ancestors when viewing human-like footprints that have survived for over three million years.

The key to understanding the evolutionary history of the human species lies in identifying factors that generate genetic variation among members of a species, and how these variations are acted upon by natural selection. In the following sections, we will explore how genetic variation is produced, and the role of culture as a force in changing allele frequencies.

GENETIC DIVERSITY IN HUMAN POPULATIONS

Blood types, such as the ABO system, are ideal for studies on genetic diversity in populations. Blood types are carried by everyone and can be analyzed from a few drops of blood. As a result, detailed maps of the geographic distribution of blood-type alleles are available (● Figure 18.1 on page 426).

The ABO blood types are an example of genetic **polymorphisms,** because two or more distinct alleles of the gene are present in the population. If an allele is present in a frequency greater than 1%, that locus is regarded as polymorphic. The study of genetic polymorphisms provides information about the amount of genetic variability that is present in a population.

Polymorphism
The occurrence of two or more genotypes in a population in frequencies that cannot be accounted for by mutation alone.

New Alleles Are Generated by Mutation

In each generation the gene pool is reshuffled to produce the genotypes of the offspring. Under these circumstances, genetic variability is produced by recombination and Mendelian assortment alone. These processes can generate new combinations of alleles, but they do not produce any *new* alleles. Mutation is the ultimate source of all new alleles and is the origin of all genetic variability.

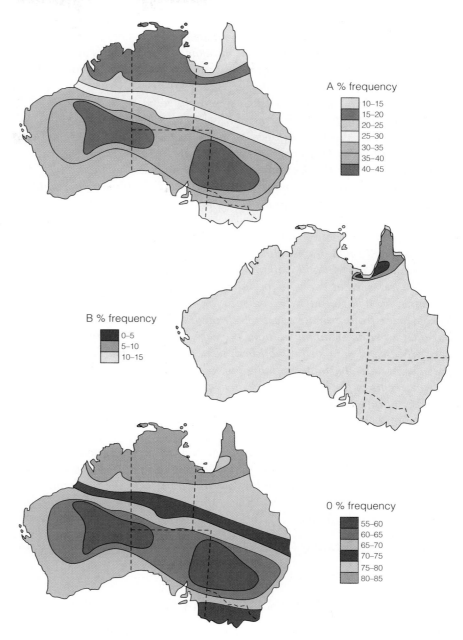

A % frequency

	10–15
	15–20
	20–25
	25–30
	30–35
	35–40
	40–45

B % frequency

	0–5
	5–10
	10–15

0 % frequency

	55–60
	60–65
	65–70
	70–75
	75–80
	80–85

⬛ FIGURE 18.1

A reconstruction of the geographic distribution of the ABO alleles in the prehistoric population of Australia.

The mechanisms and rates of mutation in humans were presented in Chapter 11. If the rate of mutation for a gene is known, we can use the Hardy-Weinberg Law to calculate the change in allele frequency that occurs in each generation as a result of mutation. As an example, we will consider the dominant trait, achondroplasia, a form of dwarfism. Evidence from statues and murals indicates that this condition has been known in Egyptian populations for over 2500 years, or about 125 generations (allowing 20 years per generation). If copies of the gene for achondroplasia were introduced into the gene pool only by mutation in each generation beginning 2500 years ago, how much has the frequency of achondroplasia changed over this period? Should we expect a higher frequency of achondroplasia among residents of an ancient city such as Cairo than among residents of a recently established city like Houston?

For this calculation we will assume that initially, only homozygous recessive individuals with the genotype *dd* (normal stature) were present in the population, and that mutation has added new mutant (*D*) alleles to each generation at the rate of 1 $\times$ 10^{-5}. ⬛ Figure 18.2 shows the change in allele frequency over time brought about by this rate of mutation. To change the frequency of the recessive allele (*d*)

from 1.0 to 0.5 with a mutation rate of 1×10^{-5}, some 70,000 generations, or 1.4 million years will be required. Thus the frequency of achondroplasia need not be any higher in Houston than in Cairo.

Even if exposure to radioactivity or chemical mutagens were to increase, the overall effect of mutations on allele frequency would be very small. Although mutation is the ultimate source of all genetic variation, mutation alone has a minimal impact on the genetic variability of a population. If, on the other hand, mutation is accompanied by other factors such as drift or selection, the impact on allele frequencies may be much greater.

Genetic Drift

In human population genetics, it is necessary to sample a large number of unrelated individuals to establish genotype frequencies and to apply the principles of the Hardy-Weinberg Law. Occasionally populations begin from a small group of individuals, known as founders. The allelic forms of genes carried by these founders, whether they are advantageous or detrimental, will become established in the new population. These events take place simply by chance and are known as **founder effects.**

Random changes in allele frequency that occur from generation to generation in small populations are examples of **genetic drift.** In addition to founder effects, genetic drift can occur in small, stable populations and by temporary but drastic reductions in population size. This effect, called a population bottleneck is often caused by natural disasters. In extreme cases, drift can lead to the elimination of one allele from all members of the population. Small interbreeding groups on isolated islands often provide examples of genetic drift.

The population history for one such isolated island, Tristan da Cuhna (Figure 18.3), is known in detail. Located in the southern Atlantic Ocean, it is one of the

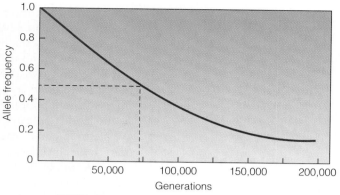

FIGURE 18.2

The rate of replacement of a recessive allele *a*, by the dominant allele *A* by mutation alone. Even though the initial rate of replacement is high, it will take about 70,000 generations or 1.4 million years to drive the frequency of *a* from 1.0 to 0.5.

Founder effects
Allele frequencies established by chance in a population that is started by a small number of individuals (perhaps only a fertilized female).

Genetic drift
The random fluctuations of allele frequencies from generation to generation that take place in small populations.

FIGURE 18.3

Location of the island of Tristan de Cuhna, first discovered by a Portuguese admiral in 1506.

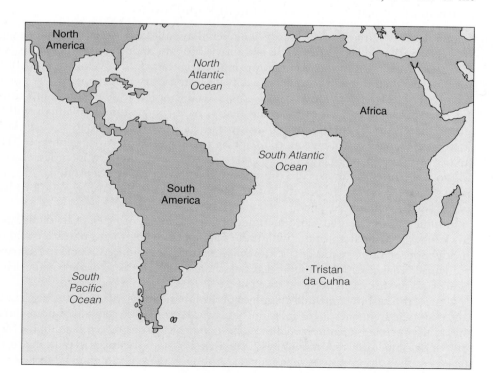

TABLE 18.1

Homozygous Markers among Tristan Residents

Transferrins
Phosphoglucomutase
6-phosphogluconate
   dehydrogenase
Adenylate kinase
Hemoglobin A variants
Carbonic anhydrase
   (2 forms)
Isocitrate dehydrogenase
Glutathione peroxide
Peptidase A, B, C, D

SOURCE: *Data from T. Jenkins, P. Beighton, & A. G. Steinberg, (1985) Ann. Hum. Biol., 12, 363–371,* **Table 2.**

Clinodactyly
An autosomal dominant trait that produces a bent finger.

Natural selection
The differential reproduction shown by some members of a population that is the result of differences in fitness.

Fitness
A measure of the relative survival and reproductive success of a given individual or genotype.

most remote locations on Earth. It is 2900 km (about 1800 mi) from Capetown, South Africa, and 3200 km (about 2000 mi) from Rio de Janeiro, Brazil. The island was occupied by the British in 1816 to prevent the rescue of Napoleon, who was in exile on the island of St. Helena. After Napoleon's death, Corporal William Glass, his wife, and two daughters received permission to remain after the British army withdrew. Others joined Glass at intervals, and the development of the isolated and highly inbred population that formed here can be traced with great accuracy.

In 1961 a volcanic eruption forced the removal of all 294 residents to England. While in England, the residents were tested for many genetic polymorphic traits to determine the effects of isolation and inbreeding on the structure of the island's gene pool. As might be expected, one effect of inbreeding is an increase in homozygosity for recessive traits. Table 18.1 lists genetic markers for which all the islanders tested are homozygous. In 1963 almost all the residents returned to the island, where they and their descendants remain.

Because of a founder effect, traits carried by one or a small number of early settlers are often found in a large fraction of the present population. On Tristan, a deformity of the fifth finger known as **clinodactyly** (MIM/OMIM 112700) is present at a high frequency. This autosomal dominant trait is especially prominent in members of the Glass family. Recall that the first permanent residents of the island were, in fact, William Glass, his wife, and two daughters. The high frequency of this trait in the present island population can be explained by its presence in one of the original colonists. An allele of the enzyme glucose-6-phosphate dehydrogenase (G6PD) that is now widely distributed among members of the present population, was brought to the island by Marie Williams, who arrived in 1827.

These examples illustrate how genetic drift can be responsible for changing allele frequencies in populations that are isolated, inbred, and stable for long periods of time. Most human populations, however, do not live on remote islands and are not subject to prolonged isolation and inbreeding. Yet there are many widespread differences in the distribution and frequency of alleles among populations, indicating that other factors must be at work. As we will see in the following section, the most powerful of these factors is **natural selection.**

Natural Selection Acts on Variation in Populations

In populations that follow the Hardy-Weinberg Law, allele frequencies do not change from generation to generation. This stability is brought about by several factors (see Chapter 17 for a list of the assumptions inherent in the Hardy-Weinberg model). In formulating their thoughts on evolution, Wallace and Darwin recognized that not all members of a given population can be equally viable or fertile, given the competition for limited resources such as food and mates. As a result, some individuals will be better adapted to the environment than others. These better-adapted individuals have increased chances of leaving more offspring than those with other genotypes. The ability of a given genotype to survive and to reproduce is known as its **fitness.** By definition, the fitter genotypes are those most able to survive and reproduce. As a result, they make a larger contribution to the gene pool of the next generation than other, less fit genotypes.

In time this differential reproduction of better-adapted, or fitter, individuals leads to changes in allele frequencies within the population. The process of differential reproduction of fitter genotypes is known as natural selection. Wallace and Darwin recognized that selection is the primary mechanism that leads to evolutionary divergence and the formation of new species.

One of the best documented examples of the interaction between natural selection and genotype frequency is the relationship between the sickle cell allele and malaria. Sickle cell anemia is an autosomal recessive condition associated with a mutant form of hemoglobin. Affected individuals have a wide range of clinical symptoms (for a review of the symptoms, see Chapter 11). Although there is a high childhood death

rate for untreated homozygotes, the allele is present in very high frequencies in certain populations. In some West African countries, 20% of the population may be heterozygous for this trait, and in regions along rivers, such as the Gambia, almost 40% of the population is heterozygous. In the absence of other factors, it is difficult to understand why this fatal disease has not been eliminated from the population.

The reason that the sickle cell allele is not eliminated in these West African countries and in certain regions of Europe and the Middle East is the presence of an infectious disease, malaria. Malaria is caused by a protozoan parasite, *Plasmodium falciparum*. The disease is transmitted to humans by infected mosquitoes, and affected individuals suffer recurring episodes of illness throughout life. Victims of malaria are more likely to contract other diseases, often with fatal results. Thus, malaria victims have a reduced fitness. To residents of some countries like the United States, malaria may seem like an exotic and rare disease, but more than 2 million people die from malaria each year, and more than 300 million individuals worldwide are infected with this disease. Because of population growth in the developing world, and the spread of drug-resistant strains of *Plasmodium*, malaria is actually increasing rather than decreasing.

The geographic distributions of malaria and sickle cell are shown in ➡ Figure 18.4. Research has shown that the sickle cell allele confers resistance to malaria, and experiments on human volunteers have confirmed this conclusion. In heterozygotes and in recessive homozygotes, sickle cell hemoglobin (Hb S) causes a physical alteration in the membrane of red blood cells and makes the cells resistant to infection by the malarial parasite. As a result, with respect to resistance to malaria, heterozygotes are fitter than those who carry the homozygous normal genotype. The homozygous sickle cell individual is also resistant to malaria but is less fit than heterozygotes, because homozygotes suffer from the clinical symptoms of sickle cell disease. In this case, selection favors the survival and differential reproduction of heterozygotes.

➡ **FIGURE 18.4**

(a) The distribution of sickle cell anemia in the Old World. (b) The distribution of malaria in the same region.

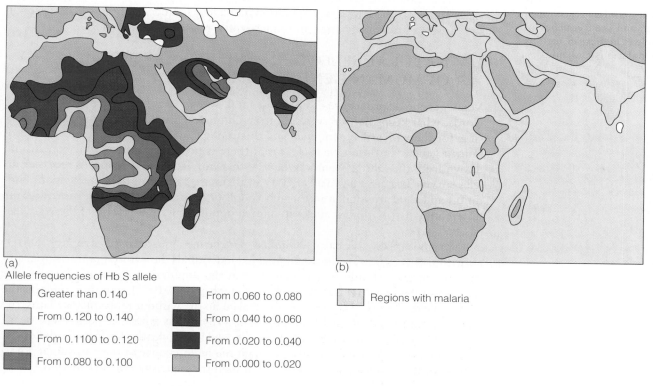

(a)

Allele frequencies of Hb S allele

Greater than 0.140		From 0.060 to 0.080	
From 0.120 to 0.140		From 0.040 to 0.060	
From 0.1100 to 0.120		From 0.020 to 0.040	
From 0.080 to 0.100		From 0.000 to 0.020	

(b)

Regions with malaria

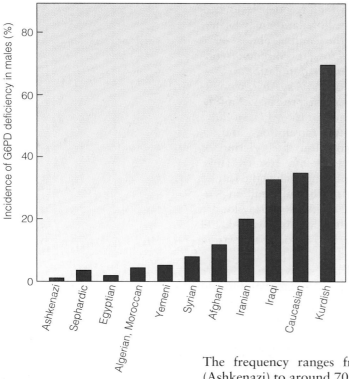

As a result of this increased fitness, heterozygotes make a larger contribution to the gene pool of the offspring than the other genotypes, and the Hb S allele is spread through the population and maintained at a high frequency. In contrast, if the selective force (malaria) is eliminated by mosquito control or by migration, the frequency of the allele should decline.

Selection and the Genetic History of a Population

The effects of selection on allele frequency can be seen by analyzing allele frequencies in subpopulations geographically separated from one another but all derived from one ancestral population. Several documented emigrations and dispersions of the Jewish people from ancient Israel have occurred over the last 2500 years. The dispersed populations took up residence in areas ranging across Europe, North Africa, the Middle East, and Asia. The frequency of the X-linked condition, glucose-6-phosphate dehydrogenase (G6PD) (MIM/OMIM 305900) deficiency, is now very different among the modern populations from these regions (Figure 18.5).

◗ **FIGURE 18.5**
Distribution of G6PD deficiency in various Jewish populations. Since intermarriage with native populations is rare, the differences in frequency are attributed to selection. G6PD deficiency confers resistance to malaria, and the frequency of the allele is highest in regions where malaria is endemic.

The frequency ranges from almost zero in populations from Central Europe (Ashkenazi) to around 70% in Kurdish Jews.

There are two likely contributors to such differences in allele frequency: founder effects and selection. The geographic distribution of G6PD deficiency is similar to that for malaria. This distribution and the fact that these dramatic differences in allele frequency arose in the short span of 100 to 125 generations indicate a role for selection. In this case the selective force once again is malaria. Malarial parasites reproduce well only in cells that contain the enzyme G6PD, offering protection against malaria to homozygous females and hemizygous males who are G6PD deficient. If we assume that the ancestral population had a low frequency of this allele, selection has caused a dramatic change in frequency in a relatively short time.

❀ NATURAL SELECTION AND THE FREQUENCY OF HUMAN GENETIC DISORDERS

Many genetic disorders are disabling or fatal, so why are they so common? In other words, what keeps natural selection from eliminating the deleterious alleles responsible for these disorders? In analyzing the frequency and population distribution of human genetic disorders, it is clear that there is no single answer. One conclusion, drawn from the Hardy-Weinberg Law, is that rare lethal or deleterious recessive alleles survive because the vast majority of them are carried in the heterozygous condition and thus are hidden in the gene pool. Other factors, however, can cause the differential distribution of alleles in human populations, and several of these are discussed below.

In some cases, such as X-linked Duchenne muscular dystrophy (DMD) (MIM/OMIM 310200), almost all affected individuals die without reproducing, and the mutant gene should be eliminated from the population. However, because the mutation rate for DMD is high (perhaps as high as 1×10^{-4}), mutation replaces the DMD alleles carried by affected individuals who die without reproducing. Thus, the frequency of the DMD allele in a population represents a balance between those alleles introduced by mutation and those removed by the death of affected individuals. Mutation rates can also be used to explain the maintenance of the autosomal dominant disease achondroplastic dwarfism at high frequencies in the population.

Detrimental alleles can spread through large, historically well established populations and become present at a high frequency by selection. We have already examined the classic case of heterozygote advantage in the relationship between malaria and sickle cell anemia. Untreated sickle cell homozygotes have a higher childhood death rate; the more numerous, surviving heterozygotes are resistant to malarial infection. There are similar advantages for carriers of thalassemias and glucose-6-phosphate dehydrogenase (G6PD) deficiency in areas where malaria is endemic.

For some other genetic diseases, if there is a selective advantage for heterozygotes, it is less obvious or perhaps no longer observable. Tay-Sachs (MIM/OMIM 272800) is an autosomal recessive disease that is fatal in early childhood. Although it is rare in most populations, there is a tenfold increase in Tay-Sachs disease in some populations of Ashkenazi Jews, and the frequency of heterozygotes can be as high as 11%. There is some indirect evidence to suggest that Tay-Sachs heterozygotes are more resistant to tuberculosis, a disease endemic to cities and towns, where most of the European Jews lived. As in sickle cell anemia, the death of homozygous Tay-Sachs individuals is the genetic price paid by the population that allows the higher fitness and survival of the more numerous heterozygotes.

The high incidence of cystic fibrosis (CF) (MIM/OMIM 219700) has been a more difficult case to explain. In European and European-derived populations, cystic fibrosis affects about 1 in 2000 births, and the frequency of heterozygotes is about 1 in 22. Until recently, this autosomal recessive disease has been lethal in early adulthood, and almost all cases have been the result of matings between heterozygotes. Several hypotheses have been advanced to explain the frequency of this disease, including a high mutation rate, higher fertility in heterozygotes, and genetic drift. None of these hypotheses has made a convincing case to explain the high frequency of this deleterious gene. In fact, recent evidence indicates that there is not a high mutation rate at this locus, that there is no higher fertility in heterozygotes, and that the probability of genetic drift is very low. At the physiologic level, CF impairs chloride ion transport in secretory cells, and heterozygotes have a reduced level of chloride transport. In many parts of the world, today as in the past, bacterial diarrhea contributes significantly to infant mortality. Because certain toxins produced in bacterial diarrhea cause an over-secretion of chloride ions, it has been postulated that infant CF heterozygotes are more likely to survive such illnesses that kill by electrolyte depletion and dehydration. Now that the CF gene has been cloned, it will be possible to examine this hypothesis in more detail.

Thus it appears that many different factors contribute to the frequency of genetic diseases in human populations, and that each deleterious gene must be analyzed individually. In some cases the frequency of genes that occupy long stretches of DNA or are at hypermutable sites is maintained by mutation. In other cases migration and founder effects can greatly increase the frequency of deleterious alleles. From an evolutionary perspective, natural selection favors certain heterozygote carriers of fatal genetic disorders, while affected homozygotes bear the burden associated with conferring advantages on other genotypes.

HUMAN ACTIVITY AS A FORCE IN CHANGING ALLELE FREQUENCIES

In addition to the force of natural selection, human activities can also influence the frequency and distribution of genes and their alleles. Activities such as discovery and invention are collectively known as culture. Social customs and rules are powerful constraints that dictate and shape human mating patterns. Culture and custom are social forces that are effective in changing allele frequencies. The invention of technology for long-distance travel in the 16th century led to widespread movement of populations, causing a redistribution of alleles over a wide area of the New World. Social constraints that limit mate selection to those with some common bonds (language, religion, and economic status) prevent random mating, and can change allele

and genotype frequencies. In this section we consider how two human activities, migration and mate selection, bring about such changes.

Migration

As an evolutionary force, migration breaks down genetic differences between populations. In one way migration is similar to mutation, because it can introduce new alleles into a population. Because migration rates are usually much higher than mutation rates, migration is usually more effective in changing allele frequencies than is mutation.

A large-scale genetic effect of migration can be seen by mapping the distribution of the *B* allele of the ABO blood type ( Figure 18.6). The highest frequency of the *B* allele in indigenous populations is in Central Asia. Waves of migration from Central Asia into Europe have distributed this allele in a gradient from east to west, with the highest frequencies in Eastern Europe, and the lowest in Southwest Europe.

Other studies have uncovered genetic relics of previous patterns of human migration. A large-scale study of 19 loci and 63 alleles carried out at over 3000 locations in Europe has resulted in the identification of 33 boundaries that represent regions of sharp genetic changes (Figure 18.7). Across a boundary, there is an abrupt shift in genotype combinations and allele frequencies, suggesting that little mixing of the

FIGURE 18.6

The gradient of the *B* allele of the ABO locus is due to waves of migration from Asia into Europe.

populations has occurred. Of the 33 boundaries, 22 are physical boundaries (mountains or ocean) over which there is little genetic exchange. But the other 11 genetic boundaries are not associated with physical barriers; instead, they represent linguistic barriers separating populations. (Some of the 22 physical boundaries also have linguistic barriers.)

The results of these studies suggest that the genetic structure of the populations in Europe is not caused only by adaptation to local environmental conditions, but reflects the diverse origins of populations that came into contact through migrations. The results further indicate that language is an effective barrier to gene flow, acting as a selective force to establish and maintain genetic differences between populations. Although European populations have been in contact for hundreds or thousands of years, there has been little breakdown of allelic differences in some regions. With the persistence of language barriers, there is little likelihood that these genetic boundaries will disappear in the near future.

Mate Selection

In a population at genetic equilibrium, one assumption of the Hardy-Weinberg Law is that mating is at random. This ideal condition rarely occurs in human populations, partly as a result of geographic proximity and partly as a result of social structure and cultural limitations. One form of nonrandom mating is called **assortative mat-**

Assortative mating
Reproduction in which mate selection is not at random but instead is based on physical, cultural, or religious grounds.

◉ FIGURE 18.7

Genetic/linguistic barriers in Europe. Thirty-three genetic barriers have been discovered, each representing an abrupt shift in allele frequencies. Of these, 31 correspond to modern linguistic boundaries. The two that do not match are #1 and #32. The correlation between language and allele frequency suggests that culture in the form of language may play a major role in establishing and maintaining genetic boundaries.

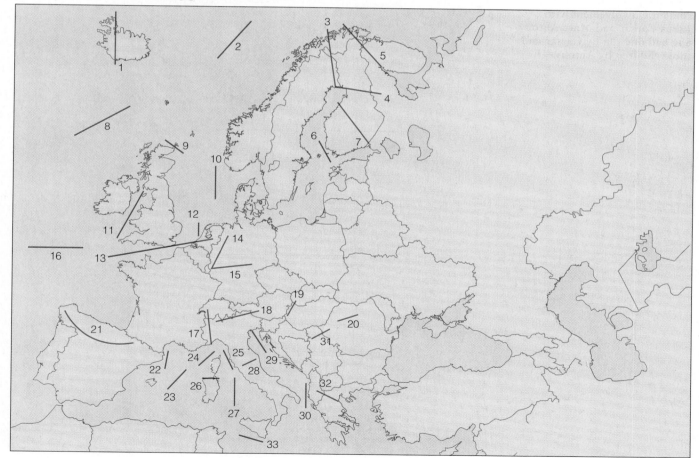

Inbreeding
Production of offspring by related parents.

Incest
Sexual relations between parents and children or between brothers and sisters.

Consanguineous matings
Matings between two individuals who share a common ancestor in the preceding two or three generations.

ing. Among humans, cultural factors such as common language, physical characteristics, economic status, and religion are often important in mate selection. To the extent that these factors are partially genetically controlled, mating is nonrandom and can influence allele frequency.

Inbreeding is another form of nonrandom mating that involves mating between related individuals sharing common genes. In humans the most extreme form of inbreeding is **incest,** mating between parents and children or between siblings. In almost all societies, strictures against incest are common. In some societies, however, incest or mating with close relatives was common among royalty. In the Ptolemaic dynasties of Egypt, such matings were frequent (Figure 18.8). The genetic effect of such mating is an increase in homozygosity and a decrease in heterozygosity. Table 18.2 shows the frequency of some autosomal recessive conditions among the offspring of **consanguineous matings.**

In modern times, consanguineous matings involving cousins were common in many cultures during the 19th and early 20th centuries, including those of Western Europe (Figure 18.9a). But, as population mobility has increased, the incidence of such matings has decreased, contributing to a more random system of matings (Figure 18.9b). In the United States, many states have laws regulating the degree of

 FIGURE 18.8
Pedigree of the Ptolemaic dynasty of Egypt. Incest and consanguineous matings (indicated by the double horizontal lines) were common. Cleopatra VII, the great Cleopatra, is known for her romantic involvement with Julius Caesar and Marc Antony. She had one son by Caesar and three children by Antony.

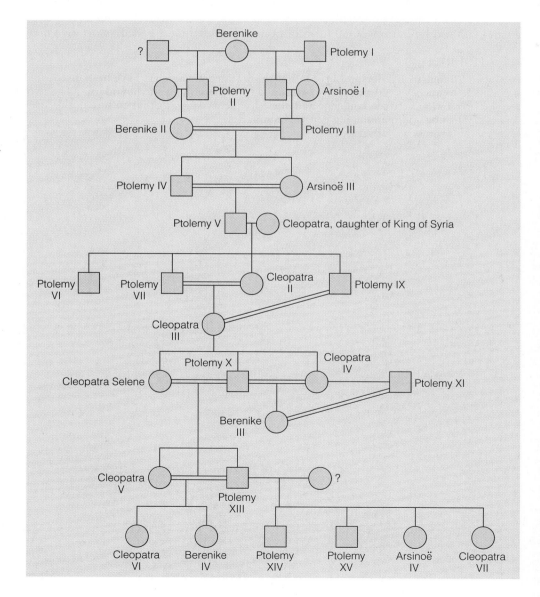

TABLE 18.2

Percentage of First Cousin Parents in Children with Recessive Genetic Diseases

DISEASE	% OF FIRST-COUSIN PARENTS	MIM/OMIM NUMBER
Albinism	10	203100
PKU	10	261600
Xeroderma pigmentosum	26	278700
Alkaptonuria	33	203500
Ichthyosis congenita	40	242300
Microcephaly	54	215200

SOURCE: S. Reed (1980) Counseling in medical genetics (3rd Ed.). New York: Alan Liss, p. 77, Table 10.1.

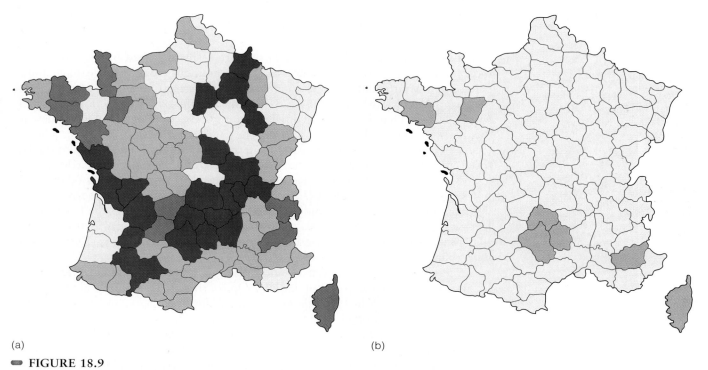

(a)

(b)

▬ FIGURE 18.9

(a) Relative levels of consanguinity in France between 1926 and 1930. Darker shades represent higher levels of inbreeding. (b) Relative levels of consanguinity in France between 1956 and 1958.

consanguinity that is permitted in marriages, but these laws are based on social or religious customs rather than on genetics.

Culture

Collective human activity, in the form of cultural practices, can act as a selective force to alter the frequency of genotypes and alleles. The introduction of slash-and-burn agricultural practices in Africa has been linked to the spread of malaria and a parallel increase in the frequency of the allele for sickle cell anemia. Another example of culture as a selective force in human populations is the evolution of the ability of adults to digest and utilize dietary lactose.

Lactose is the principal sugar in milk (human milk is 7% lactose) and serves as a ready energy source. In the small intestine of infants, the enzyme lactase converts lac-

TABLE 18.3

Lactose Absorption in Various Populations

POPULATION	PERCENT LACTOSE ABSORBERS (LA)
Eskimos—Greenland	15
!Kung—Africa	2.5
Tuareg—Africa	85
Bantu—Africa	0
Arabs—Saudi Arabia	86
Sephardic Jews—North Africa	38
Danes—Europe	98
Czechs—Europe	100
U.S.—Asians	3
Aborigines	15
U.S.—Blacks	25

tose into glucose and galactose, sugars that are easily absorbed by the intestine. In most humans the production of lactase declines at about the time of weaning, and as children grow into adults they are unable to absorb lactose—they are termed lactose malabsorbers (LM) (MIM/OMIM 223100). Such adults exhibit a reaction to the presence of lactose, characterized by flatulence, cramps, diarrhea, and nausea. In these individuals, undigested lactose passes from the small intestine into the colon, where it exerts an osmotic effect to draw water from the surrounding tissues. In the colon, lactose is digested by coliform bacteria, producing gas and the resulting diarrhea.

In some human populations, lactase is produced throughout adulthood; these individuals are lactose absorbers (LA). Population surveys of lactose absorption ranging from hunter-gatherers to industrialized urban areas show that the frequency of lactose absorption varies from 0.0 to 100% (Table 18.3). Genetic evidence indicates that adult lactose absorption (and the adult production of lactase) is inherited as an autosomal dominant trait.

Several hypotheses have been advanced to explain the wide-ranging differences in lactose absorption in various populations. One of these relies on cultural practices to explain the spread of the LA allele. According to this hypothesis, human populations originally resembled other land mammals and were lactose intolerant as adults. As the practice of dairy herding developed in some groups, adults carrying the LA allele had the selective advantage of being able to derive nutrition from milk. This improved their chances of survival and success in leaving offspring. As a result, the cultural practice of maintaining dairy herds provided the selective factor that conferred an increased advantage on the LA genotype.

Surveys of populations provide a strong correlation between a cultural history of dairying and the frequency of lactase persistence. For example, the Tuareg of North Africa are nomadic herders who have been in the Central Sahara for 2000 to 3000 years (● Figure 18.10). Other food is often unavailable, and adult consumption of several liters of milk per day is common. In this population, there is a high frequency of the LA allele. In fact, in all populations with high LA frequencies (60% to 100%), there is a history of dairying often traced back for over 1000 years. In contrast, among populations such as those in the tropical forest belt of Africa—where sleeping sickness, carried by the tsetse fly, inhibits herding—the frequency of lactose absorption is low (0% to 20%). Taken together, the evidence from genetics, anthropology, and geography supports the idea that the variation in frequency of lactose absorption found in present human populations is derived from cultural practices acting as a selective force on allele frequencies. The presence of this mode of selection makes humans unique among land mammals in having populations with a high frequency of adult lactose absorbers.

FIGURE 18.10

The Tuareg people of Africa inhabit the central region and the southern edge of the Sahara desert.

ALLELE DIFFERENCES BETWEEN POPULATIONS

In this chapter and in other parts of the book we have come across many human traits that are polymorphic. The evidence indicates that a great deal of genetic variation is present in the human genome. All this variation has been introduced by the process of mutation. To be detectable as a polymorphism in a substantial fraction of the population, the mutant allele must somehow spread through the population, since the rate of mutation is too low to account for the observed levels of gene frequencies. Natural selection and drift are the primary mechanisms by which alleles spread through local population groups.

Tracking Gene Flow in Populations

One of the ways to monitor the spread of alleles through a population is to study polymorphisms that exhibit a geographical gradient. This distribution may result from migration patterns, selection, or a combination of factors. An example of such a distribution is the gradient of blond or tawny hair among Australian aborigines (Figure 18.11). This allele apparently

FIGURE 18.11

An Australian aborigine near Kolomburu in Western Australia, with a polymorphic hair color.

originated in the west-central desert region (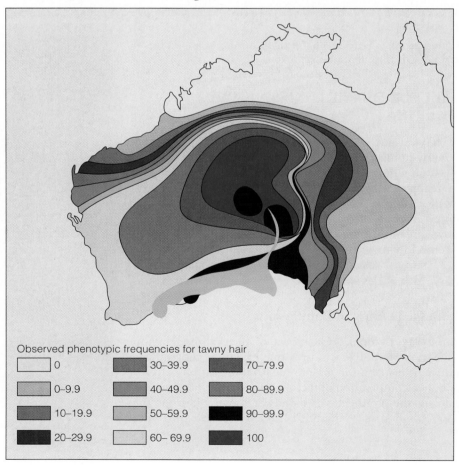Figure 18.12) and spread from there to much of the west coast. The trait is inherited in a codominant fashion.

It is difficult to imagine what selective forces might act directly on a hair-color allele to enable it to spread through much of the aborigine population of western Australia. It is possible that tawny hair is only a phenotypic by-product of a gene that controls a biochemical trait with more direct selective significance. The aborigines live in a harsh desert environment, and perhaps this allele contributes to an increase in fitness or interacts with other genes to increase fitness, or perhaps those with tawny hair are more often selected as mates.

Gene Flow between Populations

There has been a long-standing interest in both anthropology and human genetics in estimating gene flow among divergent populations as a means of studying and reconstructing the origin and history of hybrid populations formed when European and non-European populations come into contact. The best documented and now classic example is the gene flow into the American black population from Europeans, but other populations have been studied as well.

Most of the black population in the United States originated in West Africa, and the majority of the white population arrived from Europe. In African populations,

FIGURE 18.12

The frequency of tawny hair color in Australian aborigines forms a gradient, from a center in the west-central desert region.

Observed phenotypic frequencies for tawny hair

0	30–39.9	70–79.9
0–9.9	40–49.9	80–89.9
10–19.9	50–59.9	90–99.9
20–29.9	60–69.9	100

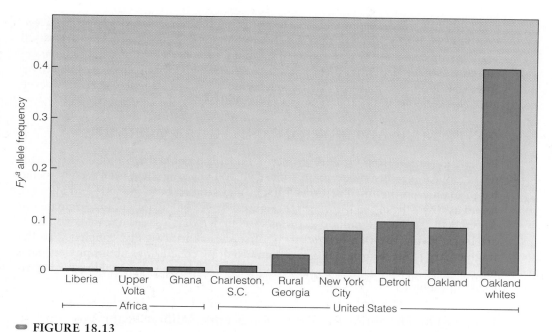

FIGURE 18.13

Distribution of the Fy^a allele among African and American black populations.

the frequency of the Duffy blood group allele Fy^o (MIM/OMIM 110700) is close to 100%, while in Europeans this allele has a frequency close to zero. Europeans are almost all Fy^a or Fy^b, and these alleles have very low frequencies in native African populations. By measuring the frequency of the Fy^a and Fy^b alleles in the U.S. black population, we can obtain an estimate of how much genetic mixing has occurred over the last 300 years. ● Figure 18.13 shows the frequency of Fy^a among black populations in West Africa and in several locations in the United States. Using this as an average gene, we can calculate that in some Northern cities about 20% of the genes in the black population are derived from Europeans.

Other studies give similar results. The frequency of PKU (phenylketonuria) (MIM/OMIM 261600) in U.S. blacks has been estimated to be 1 in 50,000, about one-third that of the U.S. white population. Using analysis of the PKU gene and molecular markers such as RFLP sites, the origin of the PKU mutation and the phenylalanine hydroxylase (PAH) gene in U.S. blacks has been studied. Results suggest that about 20% of the PAH genes in U.S. blacks originated from a Caucasian population, while the rest are likely to be of West African origin.

A more comprehensive study using 15 polymorphic loci studied 52 alleles in U.S. blacks from the Pittsburgh region, including 18 unique alleles of African origin, and found that the proportion of European genes in this black population is about 25%. Another approach to the study of gene flow between Caucasian and U.S. black populations employed both nuclear genes (ABO, MN, Rh, etc.) and mitochondrial markers to examine gene flow. Since mitochondrial markers are maternally inherited, they can be used to estimate the maternal contribution to the population under study. In this work, the results from nuclear alleles also indicate that about 25% of the genes in the black population studied (60 U.S. blacks) originate from Caucasians.

However, not all contact between genetically distinct populations leads to a reduction in genetic differences. Using a combination of genetics and historical demography, researchers have investigated the origin and extent of European-American admixture in the Gila River American Indian community of central Arizona. Results from the genetic study indicate a European admixture of 0.054

(5.4%), while the demographic data indicate an admixture of 0.059. The first contact between Europeans and the Gila River community occurred in 1694. Using 20 years as the estimate for one generation, about 15 generations of contact have occurred, with the gene flow being about 0.4% year, indicating that the Gila River American Indian community has retained almost 95% of its native gene pool, even after close contact with other gene pools for 300 years.

PRIMATE EVOLUTION AND HUMAN ORIGINS

Primate evolution from the early Miocene Epoch, some 20 to 25 million years ago, to the appearance of modern man some 100,000 years ago has been reconstructed based mainly on the fossil record. Primates ancestral to both humans and apes are found as fossils from the Miocene (Figure 18.14). These **hominoids** originated in Africa between 4 and 8 million years ago and underwent a series of rapid evolutionary steps, giving rise to a diverse array of species. This diversity, coupled with the fragmentary fossil record, makes it difficult to draw conclusions about phylogenetic relationships among the early hominoids and to identify the ancestral line leading to modern **hominids**.

Human-like Hominids Appeared about Four Million Years Ago

The earliest human fossils (hominids) are from a species called *Australopithecus afarensis* which first appeared 3.6–4.0 million years ago. This species, which lived in East Africa, had a combination of ape-like and human-like characteristics. Members of this species used bipedal locomotion (they were the creatures described in the opening vignette of the chapter), but the body proportions were ape-like, with short legs and relatively long arms (Figure 18.15). The arm bones of australopithecines are long and curved like those of chimpanzees, but have human-like elbows that could not support body weight while knuckle-walking (which is how chimpanzees and gorillas move around). This combination of features is well suited for a species that spends time climbing in trees, but walks on two legs across the ground. The skulls of australopithecines (Figure 18.16) are ape-like and have a small brain, receding face and large, canine teeth. Perhaps the most famous specimen of *Australopithecus* is a 40% complete skeleton recovered in the 1970s and known as Lucy—named after the Beatles song, "Lucy in the Sky with Diamonds"

Hominoid
A member of the primate superfamily *Hominoidea*, including the gibbons, great apes, and humans.

Hominid
A member of the family *Hominidae*, which includes bipedal primates such as *Homo sapiens*.

 FIGURE 18.14
Hominid fossil sites from the Miocene (22.5 to 5 million years ago).

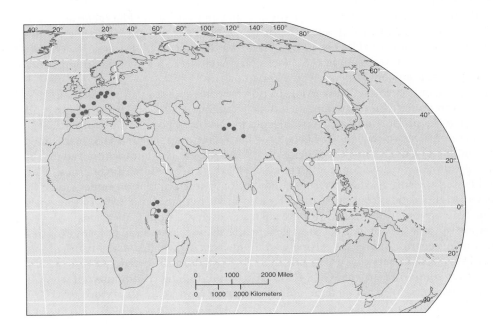

FIGURE 18.15

A reconstruction of a group of *Australopithecus afarensis* gathering and eating fruits and seeds.

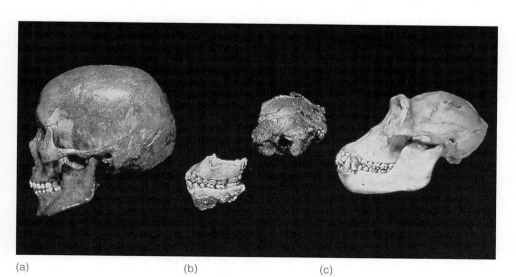

(a)   (b)   (c)

FIGURE 18.16

Comparison of the skulls of (a) modern humans, (b) *Australopithecus* fragments, and (c) chimpanzee.

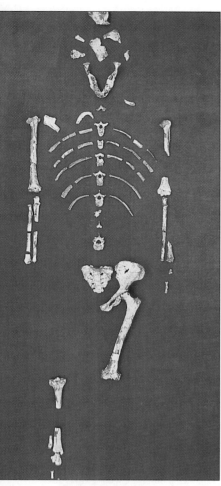

FIGURE 18.17

The skeleton of Lucy, a 3.5 million-year-old female *Australopithecus afarensis*.

(◉ Figure 18.17). A new set of fossils, older and anatomically more ape-like than Lucy, has recently been discovered in East African rock layers dating to 4.4 million years ago. This species has been named *Australopithecus ramidus,* and its relationship to *A. afarensis* remains to be established.

There is general, though not universal, agreement that *Australopithecus afarensis* is the ancestral stock from which all other known hominid species are derived (◉ Figure 18.18). For over a million years after they appeared in the fossil record, this species was remarkably stable. About 2 million years ago, however, there was a burst of evolutionary change—probably related to climatic changes that accompanied the advancing glaciers in Europe. The fossil record indicates that at least three and perhaps as many as six or more species of hominids occupied different or overlapping habitats at this time. These hominid species can be placed into two groups. One was composed of several species of more graceful (gracile), small-brained forms including *Australopithecus africanus,* as well as heavier, more robust species including *Australopithecus robustus.* This group gradually died out, with the last species surviving until about 1 million years ago.

The other group was characterized by relatively large brains, a smaller facial structure, and reduced teeth. These relatively large-brained, less robust species are grouped in the genus *Homo,* the genus to which our species belongs.

While the fossil record is incomplete, it is commonly recognized that the australopithecines are ancestral to the later hominids. By examining the fossils of the australopithecines as well as earlier hominoids, it is clear that the evolutionary adaptations in primates developed at different rates, showing a pattern described as *mosaic evolution.* Skeletal changes leading to walking and dental changes leading to diet diversification were early adaptations. Later changes include an increase in brain size accompanied by the development of tools, the use of fire, and the origins of language.

The Genus *Homo* Appeared about Two Million Years Ago

The earliest humans classified as members of the genus *Homo* probably appeared in a cluster of hominid species that developed about 2–2.5 million years ago. This group contains several species, including one classified as *Homo habilis* (some scientists now think that this classification should actually be split into two or more species). Members of this species or species cluster, which arose about 2 million years ago, had

FIGURE 18.18

About three million years ago, the *A. afarensis* line split, with one line leading to several other species of australopithecines, and the other line leading to *Homo sapiens.*

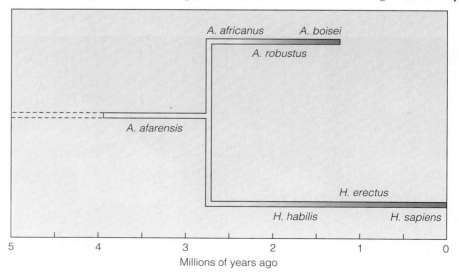

Millions of years ago

a brain size about 20% larger than that of the australopithecines. They also had a differently shaped skull, and teeth distinct from those of australopithecines. At least one and probably several species of the genus *Homo* lived alongside the robust australopithecines in East Africa for about a million years, while other members of the genus *Homo* lived in South Africa at the same time. After this period, the australopithecines became extinct. Sometime during this period, a species that became our immediate ancestor arose within the *Homo* line. This hominid, *Homo erectus* (Figure 18.19) represents an important turning point in human evolution (see "Concepts and Controversies," page 441).

Homo erectus Originated in Africa

African fossils of *Homo erectus* date to about 1.8 million years ago, but the species may actually be much older. Although *H. erectus* originated in Africa, members of this species migrated into Asia and Europe soon after its origins. Fossils of *H. erectus* have been recovered from Indonesia (Java Man) and China (Peking Man) as well as sites in North Africa. The recent dating of Indonesian fossils of *H. erectus* to about 1.8 million years ago indicates that as a species, *H. erectus* is probably older than 2 million years.

Physically *Homo erectus* is different from *Homo habilis* in several respects; increased brain size, a flatter face, and prominent brow ridges. There are physical similarities between *Homo erectus* and modern humans, including height and walking patterns, but there are also some significant differences. In some populations of *Homo erectus*, the skull is pointed in the back, not dome-shaped as in *Homo sapiens* (Figure 18.20). In addition, *H. erectus* had a receding chin, a prominent brow ridge, and some differences in teeth.

 ## THE APPEARANCE AND SPREAD OF *HOMO SAPIENS*

Tracing the origins of our species has become a multidisciplinary task, using the tools and methods of anthropology, paleontology, archeology—and more recently, satellite mapping from space—and the techniques of genetics and recombinant DNA technology. These methods are being used to reconstruct the origins and ancestry of populations of *Homo sapiens*, and to answer questions about how and when our species originated and became dispersed across the globe.

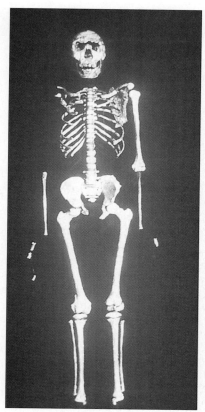

 FIGURE 18.19

A skeleton of *Homo erectus*. This is the most complete skeleton of *H. erectus* found to date, and is of a boy who lived some 1.6 million years ago.

 FIGURE 18.20

Skulls of (a) *Homo erectus* and (b) *Homo sapiens*. The skull of *H. erectus* is low and pointed in the rear, while the *H. sapiens* skull is high and dome-shaped.

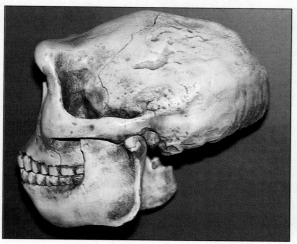

(a)

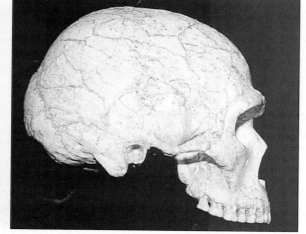

(b)

CONCEPTS AND CONTROVERSIES

Tool Time: Did *Homo erectus* Use Killer Frisbees?

The appearance of *Homo erectus* about two million years ago represents a turning point in human evolution. Studies of tooth wear patterns indicate that meat became an important component in the diet of *Homo erectus*. This species was also the first hominid to move out of Africa into Europe and Asia, exploiting new habitats as resources. Evidence indicates that these and other changes were accompanied by technological innovation in the form of new tools. The use of tools predates *Homo erectus* by about a million years, but these early tools (called Oldowan tools) were small, were used mainly for chopping, and remained unchanged over a span covering a million years.

The tools of *Homo erectus* (called Acheulian tools) were large, with two cutting faces, and included hand axes, cleavers, and picks (see art). The typical tool kit also included scrapers as well as trimmers for producing and sharpening new tools. Over time, Acheulian tools were gradually refined, but changed little in the million years they were used. Few new tools were added to the basic tool kit. These tools disappeared about 200,000 years ago, at a time when tool making entered a period of technological innovation and refinement that marks the Middle Paleolithic (Middle Stone Age).

Of all the tools in the kit of *Homo erectus*, the possible uses of the hand ax have remained a subject of speculation. Modern-day anthropologists have learned how to make such tools and have used them as small axes for chopping, or as heavy-duty knives for slicing animal hides or skinning carcasses. Examination of fossil hand axes by electron microscopy indicates that these tools may have had a range of uses on many materials including hide, meat, bone, and even wood. One form of the hand ax is ovoid, with a pointed end (art). Their size and shape has led to the suggestion that they may have been thrown like a frisbee into a herd of small animals, stunning or wounding one, which could then be overtaken and killed. Flight tests of fossils and replicas support the idea of killer frisbees, but this use is not widely accepted by anthropologists and remains among the most speculative proposals for the function of hand axes.

Whatever their uses, the tools of *Homo erectus* were associated with dramatic changes in behavior, including diet, migration, systematic hunting, the use of fire, and the establishment of home bases or camps. The role of new technology in promoting or supporting these new behaviors remains an area of intense investigation in paleoanthropology.

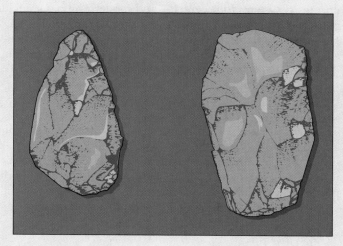

Acheulian hand-axe   **Acheulian cleaver**

Two Theories Differ on How and Where *Homo sapiens* Originated

From the evidence provided by fossils and artifacts, there is consensus that groups of *H. erectus* moved out of Africa 1–2 million years ago and spread through parts of Europe and Asia. What currently divides paleoanthropologists is the question of how and where *Homo sapiens* originated. In a general sense, there are two opposing views about the origin of modern humans. One idea (often called the out-of-Africa hypothesis) argues that after *H. erectus* moved out of Africa, populations that remained behind continued to evolve, and gave rise to *H. sapiens* about 200,000 years ago. From this single source somewhere in Africa, modern humans migrated to all parts of the world, displacing the lineages descended from *H. erectus*, which then became extinct. According to this model, modern human populations are all derived from a single speciation event that took place in a restricted region within Africa, and should show a relatively high degree of genetic relatedness.

This model of human evolution is based on evidence that African populations show the greatest amount of genetic diversity as measured by differences in mitochondrial DNA (based on differences in nucleotide sequence) from thousands of individuals tested worldwide. The underlying assumption in this study is that mutational changes in mitochondrial DNA accumulate at a constant rate, providing a "molecular clock" that can be calibrated by studying the fossil record. Studies on mitochondrial DNA show that African populations show the greatest amount of diversity in mitochondrial DNA. Phylogenetic trees constructed from differences in mitochondrial DNA lead back to a single ancestral mitochondrial lineage for our species, originating in Africa. Calculations using the rate at which new mutational changes occur indicates that our species began to branch about 200,000 years ago from an African population that could have consisted of as few as 10,000 individuals.

The second idea about the origin of *H. sapiens* postulates that after *H. erectus* spread from Africa over most of Europe and Asia, modern humans arose at multiple sites as part of an interbreeding network of lineages descended from the original colonizing populations of *H. erectus*. The evidence to support this model (often called the regional continuity hypothesis) derives from a combination of genetic and fossil evidence that shows a gradual transition from archaic to modern humans. This evidence indicates that this transition took place at multiple sites outside of Africa, and that *H. erectus* became gradually transformed into *H. sapiens*.

The two opposing ideas have been hotly debated, and have received a great deal of attention in the press and other media. These alternate explanations for the appearance of modern humans show that scientists can reach different conclusions about the same problem.

Although the accuracy of the molecular clock and the method used to construct mitochondrial phylogenetic trees has been called into question, work using nuclear genes supports a single point of origin and a time scale consistent with the out-of-Africa hypothesis. Recent work using RFLPs on the Y chromosome (which is passed from father to sons) indicates that our species developed at a single site about 200,000 to 270,000 years ago. Two genetic polymorphisms at a locus on chromosome 12 studied in 42 diverse populations also support an African origin for *Homo sapiens*, about 100,000 to 300,000 years ago.

The issue over the origins of *Homo sapiens* has not been resolved. Although we have considered only two possible origins for our species, further work may produce additional ideas. Each will have to be evaluated by using the available information as well as new information, and perhaps by applying new techniques.

The Transition to Agriculture Is a Cultural Adaptation

Since the appearance of *H. sapiens,* the most recent transitions in human evolution involve cultural adaptations, rather than physical changes such as methods of locomotion or brain size. One of the most important, starting about 10,000 years ago, is known as the Neolithic transition. It involved a change from hunter-gatherer cultures to those based on agriculture and animal breeding. Evidence suggests that this transition began in several regions of the world, but probably arose first in the Middle East (= Figure 18.21). How this cultural

FIGURE 18.21

The Fertile Crescent in the Middle East, where agriculture is thought to have originated, spreading from there to other regions.

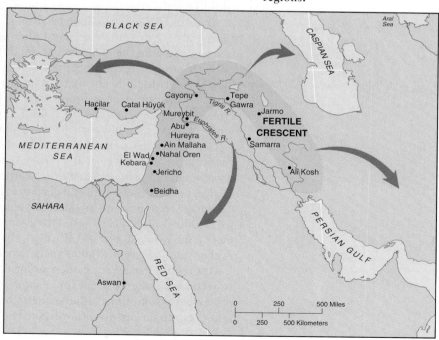

Stone Age Fabrics

When did human begin weaving fabrics? This is a difficult question to answer because materials made of plant fibers decay and leave little in the way for archaeologists to discover. Twisted fibers found in Israel that date to about 19,000 years ago are the earliest indications that humans used cord or fibers. Recently, pottery excavated from a site in the Czech republic between 1952 and 1972 has provided evidence that textile production in Central Europe was well developed some 27,000 years ago.

Examining pottery fragments from the site, researchers spotted imprints of fabric, pressed into the clay of the vessel while it was still wet. These impressions were made by loosely woven cloth or flexible basketry. The texture of the material suggests that it might have been made using a loom. Because of the sophisticated weave of the material, archaeologists suggest that weaving and fabric use had a beginning much earlier than 27,000 years ago and must have been used in cultures before the development of agriculture.

transition spread to other parts of the world is not yet understood. Was the spread of farming only cultural (the technique spread from region to region, but people essentially stayed in place), or was the technique spread by groups of migrating people who moved from the site of origin through existing populations?

While these events took place before recorded history, the genetic structure of present-day populations provides a clue to how the transition to farming spread from its center of origin. If farming spread by the movement of farmers through existing populations, such migrations would tend to blur the genetic differences between populations, and might provide some clues about the direction of migrations. Maps of genetic variability correlate well with maps of the spread of agriculture, constructed from archeological data, indicating that agriculture probably moved from its origin by the migration of farmers through hunter-gatherer cultures.

Human Migration to the Americas Is a Recent Event

The origins, migrations, and interrelationships of the original inhabitants of the Americas have been the subject of much controversy. It is generally agreed that North America—and in turn, Central and South America—were populated by migrations from Asia during the last period of glaciation. But there has been a great deal of disagreement about the number of migrations and their timing. The dispute centers around whether the earliest migrations into North America occurred around 30,000–35,000 years ago, or whether humans first arrived on this continent about 15,000 years ago. Techniques of archeology, anthropology, linguistics, and genetics have been used to study the prehistory of the Americas, but the origins of the first Americans are still obscure.

A land bridge called Berengia connected Asia and North America between 15,000 and 25,000 years ago, allowing passage between the continents along the shoreline or over land (Figure 18.22). This land bridge existed for thousands of years, allowing time for the passage of different groups of Asians at different times into North America.

Using linguistics and anthropology, scientists have identified at least three groups of American Indians: (1) the Amerinds, representing tribes spread across North and South America, (2) the Na-Denes, a cluster of tribes found in the northwestern region of North America, and (3) the Eskaleuts, composed of the Eskimos and Aleuts, who live across the far northern regions of North America.

Analysis of genetic differences using mitochondrial DNA (mtDNA) and nuclear genes indicate that all American Indian groups share a common lineage with populations in Siberia, the presumed origin of migrants who populated the Americas. The mtDNA studies reveal the presence of four mtDNA lineages among American Indians. Results indicate that the present-day Amerinds are derived from two or more population groups founded at different times; the oldest of these may have crossed from Siberia 21,000–42,000 years ago. The Na-Denes and Eskaleuts are of more recent origin, having arrived in North America some 8,500–12,000 years ago.

Genetic studies point to several waves of migration beginning more than 20,000 years ago. This work provides strong support for previously controversial classifications based on linguistics and other anthropological standards. The archeological evidence, on the other hand, still generates disputes. There is agreement that sites based on skeletal remains and artifacts are able to trace human habitation in the Americas to 13,000–15,000 years ago. Other sites indicating much earlier settlement are the most controversial; but if confirmed, they would indicate that humans were present in the Americas some 20,000 years ago.

At present, the genetic evidence, although incomplete in some regards, can be used to reconstruct the flow of *Homo sapiens* into the Americas. A genetic model (based on several assumptions) approximates how the genetic variation, population density, and geographic distribution of Native Americans could have been generated. The

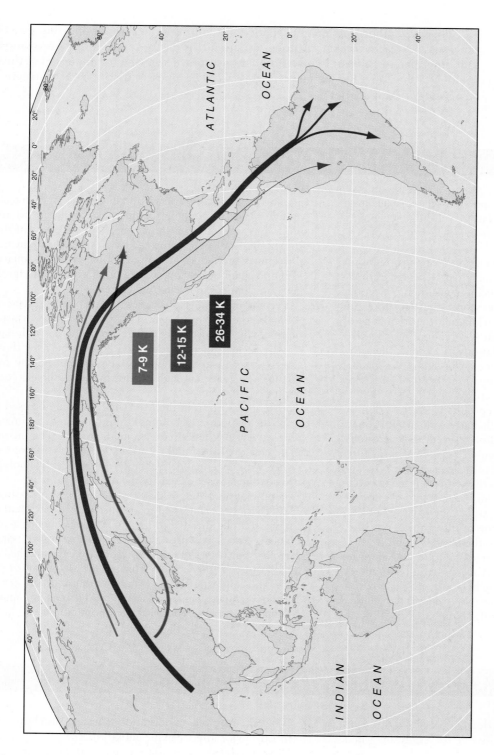

FIGURE 18.22

A land bridge that temporarily connected Asia and North America may have allowed waves of migration.

model assumes that several waves of migration crossed from Siberia, and that the migrants were in bands of no more than 500 individuals. If the bands reproduced and split off into new bands, doubling in size every 25 years, and migrated on average 5 miles each year, then North, Central, and South America could have been occupied in a few thousand years. Once established, neighboring populations underwent numerous fusions and splits, allowing gene flow to spread new alleles across geographic regions.

While this model remains speculative, it reinforces the earlier point that genetic analysis of present-day populations can provide evidence for the origin, migration, and interrelationships of human populations. Joined with the techniques of anthropology, archeology, and linguistics, genetics can be a powerful tool in reconstructing the history of our species.

SUMMARY

1. Studies indicate that human populations carry a large amount of genetic diversity. Natural selection acts on genetic diversity in populations to drive the process of evolution.

2. All genetic variants originate by mutation, but mutation is an insignificant force in bringing about changes in allele frequency. Other forces, including drift and selection, act on the genetic variation present in the gene pool and are primarily responsible for changing the frequency of alleles in the population. Drift is a random process that acts in small, isolated populations to change allele frequency from generation to generation. Examples include island populations or those separated from general population by socio-religious practices.

3. Selection acts to increase the reproductive success of fitter genotypes. As these individuals make a disproportionate contribution to the gene pool of succeeding generations, genotypes change. The differential reproduction of fitter genotypes is known as natural selection. Darwin and Wallace identified selection as the primary force in evolution, leading to evolutionary divergence and the formation of new species. The high frequency of genetic disorders in some populations is the result of selection, often conferring increased fitness on the heterozygote.

4. Humans have developed a set of adaptive mechanisms collectively known as culture. Culture has a profound effect on the interaction of the gene pool with the environment and can also act as a force that brings about changes in allele frequencies. While both plant and animal species employ strategies of dispersal and migration, human technology makes it possible for humans to migrate to any place on earth within a short time. The net effect of this short migratory time is the reduction of allele frequency differences among populations. In some instances, migration into small, relatively isolated populations can rapidly generate changes in allele frequencies.

5. Patterns of culture also influence mating patterns, tending to make them nonrandom. This process of assortative mating can also change allele frequencies, although slowly. Food choices, coupled with selection over thousands of years, are thought to have influenced the frequency of a gene that enables adults to use milk as a food source.

6. The fossil record from the Miocene Epoch can be used to trace the evolution of hominoids and hominids, primates that gave rise to the present human species. The incomplete nature of the fossil record makes it difficult to construct a phylogeny, but techniques of molecular biology are now being used to clarify the origin of humans.

7. A combination of linguistics, archaeology, anthropology, and genetics is being used to reconstruct the dispersal of human populations across the globe. The evidence available suggests that North and South America were populated by four waves of migration sometime during the last 12,000 to 75,000 years. In Europe, the alignment of genetic and linguistic barriers suggests that culture, in the form of language, can be a force in establishing and maintaining genetic differences between populations.

QUESTIONS AND PROBLEMS

1. Distinguish between mutations and polymorphisms. How are polymorphisms used in the study of genetic variation?

2. Why is it that mutation, acting alone, has little effect on gene frequency?

3. What is the relationship between founder effects and genetic drift?

4. The theory of natural selection has been popularly summarized as "survival of the fittest." Is this an accurate description of natural selection? Why or why not?

5. What are examples of nonrandom mating, and how does this behavior affect genetic equilibrium?

6. How do you think the development of culture affected the process of human evolution? Is our pre-sent culture affecting selection? Can you give specific examples?

7. Do the differences we see in the ABO blood group polymorphisms represent adaptive changes, or do they reflect some other process, not important to fitness of populations in which they occur?

8. How would a drastic reduction in a population's size affect the population?

9. How are genetic polymorphisms maintained in a population?

10. Will a recessive allele that is lethal in the homozygous condition ever be removed from a large population as a result of natural selection?

11. A specific mutation in the *BRCA1* gene has been estimated to be present in about 1% of Ashekenazi Jewish women of Eastern European descent. This specifc alteration, 185delAG, is found about three times more often in this ethnic group than the combined frequency of the other 125 mutations found to date. It is believed that the mutation is the result of a founder effect from many centuries ago. Explain the founder principle.

12. Successful adaptation is defined by:
    a. evolving new traits
    b. producing many offspring
    c. an increase in fitness
    d. moving to a new location

13. The major factor causing deviations from Hardy-Weinberg equilibrium is:
    a. selection
    b. nonrandom mating
    c. mutation
    d. migration
    e. early death

SCIENCE AND SOCIETY

1. Darwin's book, *The Origin of Species,* described the evolution of species through the action of natural selection. In the late nineteenth and early twentieth centuries, some observers thought that civilization had progressed to the point where it was inhibiting the action of natural selection on the human species. To reinstate the effects of natural selection in society, these individuals advocated eugenics, an idea first described by Darwin's cousin, Sir Francis Galton, who proposed that reproduction should be encouraged among the gifted members of society (positive eugenics) and discouraged among the inferior members (negative eugenics) of society. In this way, the evolution of our species could be guided by conscious effort. In the United States, eugenic ideas were influential in passing laws regarding immigration, marriage and sterilization of mentally handicapped individuals. With the rise of Nazism in the 1930s, eugenics fell into disfavor. However, the development of methods to transfer genes into humans and other genetic technologies has kindled new interest in eugenics.

Do you think that our species is still evolving, or are we shielded from natural selection by civilization?
Is it possible that misapplications of technology will end up exposing our species to more rather than less natural selection (consider the history of antibiotics)?

Is gene transfer a form of eugenics? Is it advantageous to use gene transfer to eliminate some genetic disorders? Can this and other technology be used to influence the evolution of our species? Should there be guidelines for the use of genetic technology to control its application to human evolution? Who should create and enforce these guidelines?

INTERNET ACTIVITIES

The following activities use the resources of the World Wide Web to enhance the topics covered in this chapter. To investigate the topics described below, log on to the book's home page at:

http://www.wadsworth.com/biology

1. For a good overview of hominid evolution, descriptions and photographs of the important fossil finds which currently shape our ideas on hominid evolution, and rebuttals of creationists attacks on evolution theory, study the Web site by Jim Foley at the Talk Origins page.
   a. Compare and contrast the scientific evidence and hypotheses with the creationists views for the Australopithocenes, *Homo erectus* and the Neanderthals. You should read the Overview article of Creationists Arguments, also. For more sites on either side of the issues, click on Links. Finally, look at the Hominid Fossils page for each of these. Briefly summarize the differences between the creationists and evolutionists. Which arguments do you find more persuasive, the evolutionists or the creationists? Do you feel the "debate" has merit?
   b. Click on Illustrations at the bottom of the page, and, once there, find the reference to "Far Side" cartoons and Gary Larson. Click and, hopefully, be amused.

Ayala, F. 1984. Molecular polymorphism: How much is there, and why is there so much? *Dev. Genet.* **4:** 379–391.

Bahn, P. 1993. 50,000 year old Americans of Pedra Furada. Nature 362: 114–115.

Barbujani G. and Sokol, R. 1990. Zones of sharp genetic change in Europe are also linguistic boundaries. Proc. Nat. Acad. Sci. 87: 1816–1819.

Bodmer, W. F., and Cavelli-Sforza, L. L. 1976. *Genetics, Evolution and Man.* San Francisco: Freeman.

Cavalli-Sforza, L., Menzonni, P., and Piazza, A. 1993. Demic expansion and human evolution. Science **259:** 639–646.

Durham, W. 1991. *Coevolution: Genes, Culture and Human Diversity.* Stanford: Stanford University Press.

Gould, S. J. 1982. Darwinism and the expansion of evolutionary theory. Science **216:** 380–387.

Gyllensten, U. B., and Erlich, H. A. 1989. Ancient roots for polymorphism at the HLA-DQ alpha locus in primates. *Proc. Nat. Acad. Sci.* **86:** 9986–9990.

Kennedy, K. 1976. *Human Variation in Space and Time.* Dubuque, Iowa: Brown.

Lewontin, R. 1974. *The Genetic Basis of Evolutionary Change.* New York: Columbia University Press.

Little, B. B., and Malina, R. M. 1989. Genetic drift and natural selection in an isolated Zapotec-speaking community in the valley of Oaxaca, Southern Mexico. *Hum. Hered.* **39:** 99–106.

Mayr, E. 1963. *Animal Species and Evolution.* Cambridge, Mass.: Harvard University Press.

Molnar, S. 1983. *Human Variation.* Englewood Cliffs, N.J.: Prentice-Hall.

Relethford, J. H. 1988. Heterogeneity of long-distance migration in studies of genetic structure. *Ann. Hum. Biol.* **15:** 55–63.

Roberts, D. F. 1988. Migration and genetic change. Raymond Pearl lecture 1987. *Hum. Biol.* **60:** 521–539.

Romero, G., Devoto, M., and Galietta, L. J. 1989. Why is the cystic fibrosis gene so frequent? *Hum. Genet.* **84:** 1–5.

Schanfield, M. 1992. Immunoglobulin allotypes (GM and KM) indicate multiple founding populations of native Americans: evidence of at least four migrations to the New World. Human Biol. **64:** 381–402.

Semino, O., Torrino, A., Scozzari, R., Brega, A., De Benedictis, G., and Santachiara-Benerecetti, A. S. 1989. Mitochondrial DNA polymorphisms in Italy: III. Population data from Sicily: A possible quantitation of maternal African ancestry. *Ann. Hum. Genet.* **53:** 193–202.

Shields, G., Schmiechen, A., Frazier, B., Redd, A., Voevoda, M., Reed, J., and Ward, R. 1993. mtDNA sequences suggest a recent evolutionary divergence for Beringian and northern North American populations. Am. J. Hum. Genet. 53: 549–562.

Smith, J. M. (Ed.). 1982. *Evolution Now: A Century after Darwin.* San Francisco: Freeman.

Stanton, W. 1960. *The Leopard's Spots.* Chicago: University of Chicago Press.

Torroni, A., Schurr, T., Cabell, M., Brown, M., Neel, J., Larsen, M., Smith, D., Vullo, C., and Wallace, D. 1993. Asian affinities and continental radiation of the four founding native American mtDNAs. Am. J. Hum. Genet. **53:** 563–590.

Torroni, A., Sukernik, R., Schurr, T., Starikovskaya, Y., Cabell, M., Crawford, M., Comuzzie, A., and Wallace, D. 1993. mtDNA variation of aboriginal Siberians reveals distinct genetic affinities with native Americans. Am. J. Hum. Genet. **53:** 591–608.

Towne, B., and Hulse, F. S. 1990. Generational changes in skin color variation among Habbani Yemeni Jews. *Hum. Biol.* **62:** 85–100.

Wallace, D. and Torroni, A. 1992. American Indian prehistory as written in the mitochondrial DNA: a review. Human Biol. **64:** 403–416.

Yunis, J. J., and Prakash, O. 1982. The origin of man: A chromosomal pictoral legacy. *Science 215:* 1525–1530.

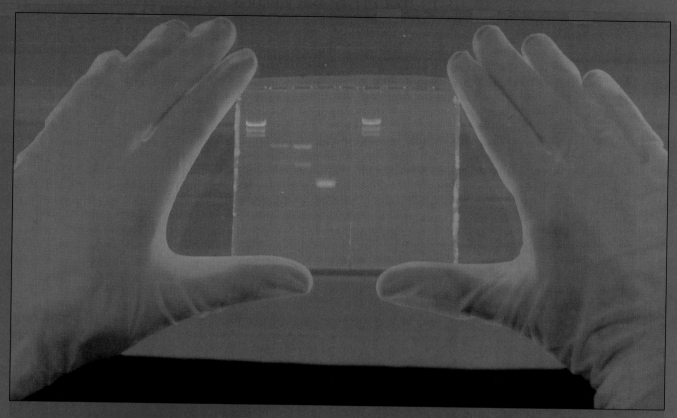

GENETIC SCREENING AND GENETIC COUNSELING

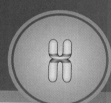

Chapter Outline

GENETIC SCREENING
Newborn and Carrier Screening
Occupational Screening
Reproductive Screening
Cost-Benefit Analysis in Genetic Screening
PRENATAL TESTING
Ultrasonography
Fetoscopy

Testing Embryonic Blastomeres
Risks and Problems Associated with Prenatal
  Testing
GENETIC COUNSELING
Who Are Genetic Counselors?
CONCEPTS AND CONTROVERSIES   *The*
  Business of Making Babies
Reasons to Seek Counseling

How Does Counseling Work?
Future Directions
THE IMPACT OF GENETIC TESTING
  AND GENETIC SCREENING
Personal Consequences
Social Consequences
Legal Implications

Chapter 19

OPENING IMAGE
*Genetic screening can be done using
recombinant DNA techniques.*

Huntington disease is inherited as an autosomal dominant trait, and is associated with the gradual loss of motor coordination, degenerative personality changes, and progressive dementia. The disease develops slowly and leads to death within 15 years after its onset. Most affected individuals develop symptoms of the disease around the age of 40, beginning with involuntary limb tremors and behavior changes. Through a combination of pedigree analysis and molecular biology, the gene controlling the disease has been mapped to chromosome 4. The gene has been cloned, and genetic markers within and near the gene are used in genetic testing to identify those at risk for developing Huntington disease.

Suppose that your uncle, age 49, has recently been diagnosed with Huntington disease. His physician calls you to inform you of the diagnosis and indicates that you have a 25% chance of developing the disease. You are 25 years old, married, and have one child. Should you undergo testing to determine whether you are at risk? Can you live with the outcome if the results indicate that you will develop the disease? Do you want your children to be informed of your condition? Do you want them to be tested? Do you want them to know if they will develop the disease? Should you have any more children? What if your child was tested and found to have the Huntington disease gene? You are the only parent who could have transmitted the mutant allele. You now have information about your genotype that you may not have wanted. Does this mean you can prevent your child from being tested?

This scenario and the questions it raises are not hypothetical. Although Huntington disease affects only a small fraction of the population (3 or 4 out of 100,000), it is now possible to identify those who will develop this devastating disease. Helping individuals to understand the implications of genetic screening and to make informed decisions about actions to be taken are goals of genetic counseling.

In this chapter we will survey the field of genetic screening, exploring the rationale, methods, and economics of testing and the potential for its use and misuse. We will also consider the role of the genetic counselor in informing and educating those who undergo genetic screening. With the growth in genetic technology, these fields will have a great impact on our own lives and personal decisions and on those of our family members and friends.

GENETIC SCREENING

Genetic screening and, as defined in the margin note:

> **Genetic screening**
> The systematic search for individuals of certain genotypes.

Genetic screening can be defined as the systematic and organized search for individuals of certain genotypes. Traditionally the term *genetic screening* has meant the detection of persons who have or may carry a genetic disease or who are at risk of producing a genetically defective child. More recently the term has been expanded to include the search for those who may have a genetic susceptibility to environmental agents. Genetic screening is conduct for a variety of reasons. Prenatal screening is often used as the basis for selective abortion; newborn screening is conducted to diagnose and treat a range of metabolic disorders. Adult screening for carrier status is of use in genetic counseling and family planning. Adult screening is also used for occupational screening to detect individuals who may have an inherited susceptibility to materials or conditions in the workplace.

Population screening to detect those exposed to an infectious disease such as tuberculosis is a well-established and effective means of controlling such diseases. New testing programs for acquired immunodeficiency syndrome (AIDS) are being implemented, and more inclusive testing programs for AIDS are being proposed. Unlike public health screening, genetic screening has several unique aspects that need to be recognized. First, identification of an individual with, or at risk for, a genetic disorder often leads to the discovery of other affected or at-risk individuals within the same family. Second, screening often identifies individuals who will develop genetic disorders later in adult life. When the genetic defect diagnosed is a traumatic and fatal one, such as Huntington disease, this knowledge often has serious personal and social effects. Third, the results of genetic screening often have a direct impact on the offspring of the screened individual.

Newborn and Carrier Screening

The autosomal recessive condition phenylketonuria (PKU) was the first genetic disease to be screened in newborns. Newborn screening for PKU is now mandatory in all states and in 20 foreign countries. Over 100 million children have been screened for this disease, and more than 10,000 affected individuals have been identified and treated (● Figure 19.1). Although PKU is a relatively rare disorder (1 in 12,000), it is severe, imposes a large personal and financial burden, and can be easily screened using an inexpensive test. In addition, the discovery that the effects of the disease can be controlled by dietary treatment was instrumental in establishing mandatory screening programs. PKU is the model disease in newborn screening programs, and most of the other diseases screened in newborns are metabolic deficiencies. Some of the other metabolic diseases included in newborn screening programs are listed in Table 19.1.

Carrier screening is the identification of phenotypically normal individuals who are heterozygous for an autosomal recessive or X-linked recessive disease. Screening for carriers of two genetic conditions has been carried out on a large scale: Tay-Sachs disease and sickle cell anemia. The development of screening programs for these two diseases has been made possible by three factors:

- The diseases occur mainly in defined populations. Tay-Sachs carriers are found most frequently among Jews of East European origin, and sickle cell carriers are most common in U.S. blacks of West African origin.
- Carrier detection for these disorders is inexpensive and rapid.
- The existence of prenatal testing gives couples at risk the option of having only unaffected children.

Tay-Sachs Disease Tay-Sachs disease is inherited as an autosomal recessive trait with an incidence in the general population of 1 in 360,000. In Ashkenazi Jews, the rate is almost 100 times higher (1 in 4800 births). In the 1970s, carrier screening programs were undertaken to identify heterozygotes in the United States and other countries. In the first 10 years of screening, over 300,000 individuals were tested. Of these, 268 couples were identified in which both members were carriers and had not yet had an affected child. The programs were coupled with counseling sessions that provided education about the risks of having an affected child, the availability of prenatal screening, and reproductive options. None of these screening programs is mandatory, although some states have laws that require couples to be informed that screening for Tay-Sachs disease is available. In 1970 there were 50 to 100 Tay-Sachs births annually in the United States. Because of screening programs, there are now fewer than 10 such births each year.

Sickle Cell Trait Sickle cell anemia is an autosomal recessive condition that differentially affects black Americans and whites whose family origins are in the lowlands of the Mediterranean Sea, including Sicily, Italy, Greece, Lebanon, and Israel.

TABLE 19.1

Genetic Sreening in Newborns (as of 1994)

GENETIC DISORDER	NUMBER OF STATES (PLUS DISTRICT OF COLUMBIA) SCREENING FOR
Phenylketonuria	51
Congenital hypothyroidism	51
Galactosemia	44
Hemoglobinopathies (sickle cell, thalassemias)	42
Maple syrup urine disease	25
Homocystinuria	22
Biotinidase deficiency	16
Congenital adrenal hyperplasia	13
Tyrosenemia	6
Cystic fibrosis	1

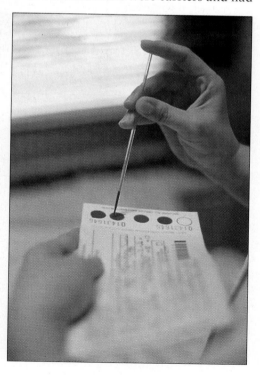

● FIGURE 19.1

In a Guthrie test for PKU, paper disks containing a drop of blood are placed on the surface of a bacterial culture that will grow only in the presence of phenylalanine. If an infant has PKU, rapid growth will occur around the disk and will be visible as a halo.

Sickle cell trait
The symptoms shown by those
heterozygous for sickle cell anemia.

Several blood tests were developed in the 1960s that can differentiate individuals who are carrier heterozygotes and affected homozygotes. In 1971 Connecticut instituted a program of screening black schoolchildren in grades 7–12, with parental consent, for **sickle cell trait,** a term used to designate heterozygous carriers. In 1972 federal funding was used to establish the National Sickle Cell Anemia Control Act, part of which was designed to establish carrier screening programs. As a result of this federal legislation, screening programs to detect carriers of the sickle cell trait were set up nationwide. Some of the programs were compulsory, requiring black children to be screened before attending school; others required screening before obtaining a marriage license. Professional football players were screened, as were cadets at the Air Force Academy in Colorado Springs, where heterozygotes were excluded from enrollment. The assumption was that heterozygotes might undergo sickling of red blood cells at high altitudes under reduced oxygen concentrations. This policy was reversed under threat of lawsuit in 1981. Other individuals who tested as positive heterozygotes were reportedly turned down for insurance and employment, even though carriers do not have any inherent health problems.

Some of these screening programs were criticized for laxity in confidentiality of records and the failure to provide counseling to those identified as heterozygotes. In the late 1970s, many of the sickle cell screening programs were cut back or reorganized, and currently only 10 states offer sickle cell screening.

Cystic Fibrosis Against the background of an uneven record of previous carrier screening programs, a debate is emerging about universal screening to detect carriers for cystic fibrosis (CF). Cystic fibrosis (see Chapter 4 for a detailed discussion) is an autosomal recessive condition that occurs in all ethnic groups, although at different rates (Table 19.2). About 30,000 individuals in the United States are affected by CF, and 8 million others are heterozygous carriers.

The questions surrounding CF screening are legal, ethical, and economic. Part of the reason for the debate is that CF screening is one of the first recombinant DNA-based tests to become available, and decisions about its implementation and avail-

TABLE 19.2	
Cystic Fibrosis among Live Births in the United States	
POPULATION	INCIDENCE AT BIRTH
Caucasian	1 in 2,500
Hispanic	1 in 9,600
African American	1 in 18,000
Asian American	1 in 90,000
Note. From Office of Technology Assessment, 1992.	

ability will set precedents for the scores of DNA-based tests that will be available in the next few years. With respect to CF screening, it appears that the question is not if there should be screening, but when and how such screening should be implemented. In 1992, approximately 63,000 individuals were screened to determine their genetic status for CF. This represented a sevenfold increase over 1991 but was still far short of the millions of pregnancies per year for which CF screening can be performed.

The concerns surrounding CF screening itself, and CF screening as a model for other forms of genetic testing, resolve into a number of issues:

- **Standards of care.** Should screening be offered to everyone, or only those with a family history?
- **Confidentiality and discrimination.** Who will have access to test results? Will identification as a carrier result in exclusion from health insurance coverage or employment?
- **Quality and reliability of tests.** How accurate are the tests? How often do false positive or false negative results occur?
- **Cost effectiveness.** What proportion of the population must participate in screening for it to be cost effective? How can participation be encouraged?

Still to be resolved are questions about who is qualified to do genetic testing and screening, how the costs of screening will be recovered, and how the public can be educated about the procedures and evaluation of risk.

Occupational Screening

Two classes of genetic tests are used for genetic screening in the workplace: tests to screen workers for genetically determined susceptibility to specific environmental agents that cause disease, and tests to monitor the amount of genetic damage actually produced in susceptible workers. We will consider only the first class of tests. Genetically determined sensitivity to certain environmental agents is well documented; in other cases the relationship between genetic factors and environmental agents is uncertain or is based on inadequate information.

Approximately 50 different genetic traits have been related to susceptibility to environmental agents. Some of these are listed in Table 19.3. In many of these cases the traits are rare, testing for carriers is difficult, or the relationship to a specific environmental agent is based on inadequate data. To justify use in occupational screening, the traits must be present in a sufficient fraction of the workforce, and the trait should be associated with a clear risk to carriers. Most often the trait must be present in at least 1% of the workforce, and exposure should result in serious illness or

TABLE 19.3

Some Genetic Factors Affecting Susceptibility to Environmental Agents

TRAIT	AGENTS
G6PD deficiency	Oxidants such as ozone and nitrogen dioxide
Sickle cell trait	Carbon monoxide, cyanide
Thalassemias	Lead, benzene
Erythrocyte porphyria	Lead, drugs including sulfanilomide and barbiturates
Gout	Lead
Sulfite oxidase deficiency	Sulfite, bisulfite, sulfur dioxide
Wilson disease	Copper, vanadium
Pseudocholinesterase variants	Carbamate insecticides, muscle relaxants
Cystinuria	Heavy metals

TABLE 19.4

Genetic Traits Associated with Workplace Hazards

TRAIT	ENVIRONMENTAL AGENT	STATUS OF INTERACTION
Glucose-6-phosphate dehydrogenase (G6PD) deficiency	Primaquine, fava beans	Definite
Methemoglobin reductase deficiency	Nitrates, acetanilide, amines, sulfanomides	Definite
N-Acetyl transferase deficiency	Isoniazid hydrochloride, dapsone, hydralazine	Definite
PTC nontaster	Thiouria, related compounds	Possible
Slow alcohol metabolism	Ethanol toxicity	Possible
Sickle cell trait (heterozygotes)	Low oxygen concentration	Inconclusive

risk of death for inclusion in a program of screening. Table 19.4 contains a list of traits that fulfill many of these requirements.

The current status of genetic testing in the workplace is difficult to evaluate. Originally, five genetic conditions were identified as suitable for occupational screening: serum alpha-1-antitrypsin deficiency, glucose-6-phosphate dehydrogenase deficiency, carbon disulfide sensitivity, hypersensitivity to organic isocyantes, and sickle cell trait (heterozygotes). Recommendations for these as candidates for testing were made because these conditions met "the prerequisites for industrial applications of bettering job assignment, improving coverage of industrial air limits, and hence reducing risk to worker health." Unfortunately, the recommendations for screening were not entirely based on a firm scientific foundation.

In 1983 the federal Office of Technology Assessment (OTA) conducted a thorough review of genetic screening in the workplace. The report, entitled *The Role of Genetic Testing in the Prevention of Occupational Disease,* indicates that there are clear-cut and well-known relationships between some genetic traits and agents present in the workplace. For example, G6PD deficiency hemizygotes or homozygotes may develop severe anemia when exposed to chemical oxidizing agents. Most of these relationships are based on *in vitro* exposure of cells from G6PD-deficient individuals to these chemicals. While many of these same chemicals can be encountered in industrial settings, the report calls for studies that directly assess whether exposure to these chemicals in the workplace actually poses any hazards to G6PD-deficient individuals. The report concludes that in the absence of direct evidence of harm to workers actually in contact with such agents, there is no justification for occupational screening programs of any kind. Critics of this report argue that sufficient information exists from laboratory studies on cells and tissues to show direct harm to certain genotypes upon exposure, and that little or no research is being done on workers in the workplace. In effect, they charge, workers are being used as guinea pigs, and testing will start only after workers with susceptible genotypes have been seriously affected.

In spite of this controversy, the OTA report found that 17 of the nation's largest firms had instituted genetic screening programs, and that 59 others planned to initiate occupational screening tests in the following 5 years. These tests will presumably be used to exclude some individuals from employment and to determine job assignments for others. Clearly, the issue of occupational screening will be of increasing im-

portance in the coming years. Unfortunately, the rush to install screening programs for AIDS and illegal drugs may set a precedent that will lead directly to the use of genetic screening in the workplace before the scientific and legal basis for such testing has been thoroughly considered.

Reproductive Screening

Artificial insemination by a donor (AID) is often used in cases in which male fertility is low or, more rarely, to avoid genetic risks to the offspring by the transmission of a genetic defect. Some 172,000 women are artificially inseminated each year, resulting in 65,000 births. Of these, 30,000 births are the result of insemination with anonymously donated sperm obtained through physicians or sperm banks. In all cases, care must be taken to prevent genetic defects from being transmitted through the donor sperm. Since everyone carries some deleterious mutations, genetic defects in the donors cannot be eliminated. The problem is to ensure that no genetic disorders are transmitted by the donor sperm and at the same time not to eliminate too many donors. In one study of over 600 potential semen donors, 6% were excluded as donors based on a detailed screening procedure. Of these, 2.6% were excluded for cytogenetic reasons and 3.4% for genetic reasons. The chromosomal abnormalities detected included breaks, translocations, partial aneuploidy, and the presence of fragile sites. Table 19.5 lists some of the genetic traits uncovered in family histories of the prospective donors. They include single-gene traits and polygenic or familial traits such as epilepsy.

In another study, the OTA surveyed 15 sperm banks and 367 physicians to determine whether sperm donors had been screened for infectious diseases, genetic defects, or both. According to the report, published in 1987, 14 sperm banks tested all donors for presence of the human immunodeficiency virus (HIV), while the other tested only men from high-risk groups. Twelve of the sperm banks screened for transmissible diseases; 13 screened for genetic diseases. Interestingly, only 44% of the physicians tested for HIV, and fewer than 30% tested for transmissible diseases such as syphilis or hepatitis. Moreover, only 48% screened for any genetic defects.

The most disturbing aspect of the report indicates that physician screening of sperm donors for genetic diseases is unreliable. Twenty-five percent of the physicians said they would accept sperm from a healthy donor with a family history of Huntington disease. Huntington disease is an autosomal dominant disorder that does not appear until the individual is over 40 years of age, while most sperm donors are under 30 years of age. On the other hand, 49% of physicians would reject a healthy sperm donor with a family history of hemophilia. Recall that hemophilia is an X-linked trait expressed from birth. Unaffected males do not carry the trait and are incapable of passing it on to their offspring. The report has sparked calls for the Food and Drug Administration (FDA) to require physicians and sperm banks to screen sperm samples for HIV and to use fresh sperm only when the donor is known to the recipient. In the meantime, the results from these surveys indicate some degree of genetic risk associated with artificial insemination.

Cost-Benefit Analysis in Genetic Screening

There are a number of genetic disorders, like PKU, for which corrective treatment is available, but they must be diagnosed early (even before symptoms appear) for treatment to be effective. Other genetic disorders, like Tay-Sachs disease or Down syndrome, cannot be treated but can be diagnosed by amniocentesis early enough for elective abortion. In instituting genetic screening programs, policy-makers must give some consideration to the question of cost. While the family of a PKU child might think that newborn screening programs should be continued at any cost, public administrators usually consider whether money expended in such programs benefits the state in terms of dollars and cents.

TABLE 19.5

Some Traits Uncovered in Screening 676 Potential Sperm Donors

TRAIT	NUMBER
Polyposis coli (predisposes to cancer)	3
Ankylosing spondylitis	2
Epilepsy	3
Manic-depressive psychosis	2
Dominant renal disease (not defined)	1
Severe hip dislocation	3

Note. From J. Selva, C. Leonard, M. Albert, J. Auger, & G. David, (1986). Genetic screening for artificial insemination by donor (AID). Clin. Genet., 29, 389–396.

TABLE 19.6

Cost-Benefit Analysis of Quebec's Network of Genetic Medicine

YEAR	COST (THOUSANDS OF DOLLARS)	BENEFITS	NET DIFFERENCE
1980	33,685	36,182	2,497
1981	36,020	39,929	3,909
1982	38,222	43,481	5,259
1983	40,301	46,483	6,542
1984	42,262	50,007	7,745
1985	44,111	52,981	8,870
1990	51,885	64,944	13,059
2000	61,962	78,125	16,163

Note. From D. Dagenais, L. Courville, & M. Dagenais. (1985). *A cost-benefit analysis for the Quebec Network of Genetic Medicine. Soc. Sci. Med., 20,* 601–607.

The actual calculation of costs and benefits is complex and includes not only the direct cost of the program but also the contributions made to the state by a treated PKU patient and the increase in the well-being of a patient and the family. To perform a simpler analysis, we will presume that the cost of analysis for PKU is $1.50 per test, including overhead and salaries. Assuming complete coverage of births in the United States, 4 million births per year will be screened at a total cost of $6 million. If the incidence of PKU is 1 in 12,500, about 320 PKU births will occur in the total of 4 million. Dietary treatment will cost about $5000 per year and will be maintained for an average of 10 years. Thus the cost of treatment for the 320 PKU births that occur annually is 320 x $5000 x 10, or $16 million. Since the total cost must include both testing and treatment, the cost for the PKU program is $22 million ($6 million for testing and $16 million for treatment). From the point of view of the state, the alternative to screening and treatment is placement of the untreated, retarded individual in a state institution. Placing the cost of maintaining severely retarded individuals at a *very* conservative $40,000 per year, and estimating the life expectancy of institutionalized PKU patients at 30 years, the cost to the state of housing the 320 affected individuals produced in a year is 320 × $40,000 × 30, or $384 million. Clearly, the screening and treatment program is 17 times less expensive than institutionalizing untreated, afflicted individuals. This method of computing costs and benefits does not include the human costs to patient and family and other intangibles that derive from having treated children function as normal members of society.

Quebec established a Network of Genetic Medicine in 1969 to screen, treat (where possible), and provide follow-up services for a variety of genetic diseases. The goal of the network is to offer all pregnant women in the province prenatal and newborn screening and effective treatment where possible. The network was subject to a cost-benefit analysis for the years 1969–1985. This analysis incorporated the actual costs of the operation and attempted to quantify many of the tangible, major benefits. Table 19.6 summarizes the information for 1980 to 1985 and makes projections through the year 2000. Clearly the social and economic benefits of the program far outweigh the costs incurred, even when benefits have been conservatively estimated.

PRENATAL TESTING

Prenatal testing
The use of fetal cells or amniotic fluid to determine whether a fetus is at risk for a genetic disorder.

Genetic testing is defined as the use of specific assays to determine the genetic status of individuals already suspected to be at high risk for a particular inherited condition. **Prenatal testing** is used to detect genetic diseases and birth defects in the fetus. Over 200 single-gene disorders can be diagnosed in the prenatal condition (Table 19.7). In most cases the conditions are rare, and genetic testing is done only when

TABLE 19.7

Some Metabolic Diseases and Birth Defects That Can Be Diagnosed by Prenatal Testing

Acatalasemia	Mannosidosis
Adrenogenital syndrome	Maple syrup urine disease
Chédiak-Higashi syndrome	marfan syndrome
Citrullinemia	Muscular dystrophy, X-linked
Cystathioninuria	Niemann-Pick disease
Cystic fibrosis	Oroticaciduria
Fabry disease	Progeria
Fucosidosis	Sandhoff disease
Galactosemia	Spina bifida
Gaucher disease	Tay-Sachs disease
G6PD deficiency	Thalassemia
Homocystinuria	Werner syndrome
I-cell disease	Xeroderma pigmentosum
Lesch-Nyhan syndrome	

there is a family history of the disease. For some conditions, such as Tay-Sachs disease or sickle cell anemia, biochemical tests can be conducted on the parents to determine if either is a carrier. If the tests for both parents are positive, the fetus has a 25% chance of being affected. In such cases prenatal testing can determine whether the fetus is a recessive homozygote afflicted with the disease. Similarly, if the mother is known to be a carrier for certain deleterious, X-linked genetic disorders, testing is indicated.

For other genetic conditions such as Down syndrome, which is caused by an extra copy of chromosome 21, cytogenetic examination of the fetus' chromosomes is the most direct way to determine whether the fetus is affected. In this case testing is not carried out because of a familial history of genetic disease or detection of heterozygotes in the parents, but usually because of advanced maternal age. Since the risk of Down syndrome increases dramatically with maternal age (see Chapter 6), cytogenetic testing is recommended for all pregnant females who are older than 34 years of age.

In addition to genetic disorders, some birth defects associated with abnormal embryonic development can be diagnosed prenatally. Among these are some associated with defects in the formation of the neural tube, a structure that arises in the first 2 months of development. One such defect, spina bifida, is a condition in which the spinal column is open or partially open. Neural tube defects can be diagnosed accurately by testing the amniotic fluid for elevated levels of alpha-fetoprotein. In about 80% of cases, alpha-fetoprotein levels in the maternal blood serum are also elevated. A test using maternal blood can identify mothers for whom further tests, such as amniocentesis, are recommended.

Samples or images for prenatal testing can be obtained in several ways. These include amniocentesis, chorionic villus biopsy, ultrasonography, and fetoscopy. The fluids and cells obtained for testing can be analyzed with several techniques, including cytogenetics, biochemistry, and recombinant DNA technology. Images obtained by ultrasonography can be used to diagnose conditions such as neural tube defects, cardiac abnormalities, and malformations of the limbs associated with chromosomal aberrations.

Because recombinant DNA technology is able to analyze the genome directly, it is the most specific and sensitive method currently available. The accuracy, sensitivity, and ease with which recombinant DNA technology can be used to assemble a profile of the genetic diseases and susceptibilities carried by an individual have raised a number of legal and ethical issues that have yet to be resolved.

We previously discussed two methods of obtaining samples for genetic testing (amniocentesis and chorionic villus biopsy; see Chapter 6). In this section, we examine some other methods of obtaining information about the fetus, including ultrasonography, fetoscopy, and blastomere isolation. We will also examine the consequences and potential problems associated with such tests. The process of genetic counseling, discussed later in this chapter, often uses these methods to determine whether a fetus is affected with a genetic disorder.

Ultrasonography

Ultrasonography is a technique based on sonar technology, which was developed for military use during World War II. For prenatal diagnosis, a transducer is placed on the abdominal surface, over the enlarged uterus (● Figure 19.2). The probe emits pulses of ultrasonic energy, and as the ultrasound strikes the surface of the fetus, some of the sonic waves bounce off the fetus and return to the transducer. These reflected waves are electronically converted to images and displayed on a screen (● Figure 19.3).

Ultrasound can be used to diagnose multiple pregnancy; determine fetal sex; and identify neural tube defects and skeletal disorders, limb malformations, other central nervous system defects, and congenital heart defects. Some practitioners claim they can diagnose Down syndrome by ultrasonography based on the posture and limb position of the fetus.

Fetoscopy

Fetoscopy is the direct visualization of the fetus by means of a fiber-optic device known as an endoscope. In this procedure a hollow needle is inserted through the abdominal wall into the amniotic cavity, and the fiber-optic cable is threaded through the needle. The image is transmitted to a video screen and can be viewed and recorded from the screen (● Figure 19.4). The technique is most useful when a disorder cannot be diagnosed by cytogenetic or biochemical methods. Fetoscopy can also be used to obtain samples of fetal blood, allowing diagnosis of some genetic dis-

● **FIGURE 19.2**

A pregnant woman undergoing an ultrasound examination.

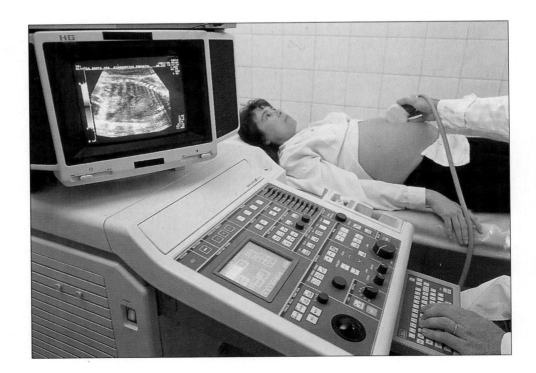

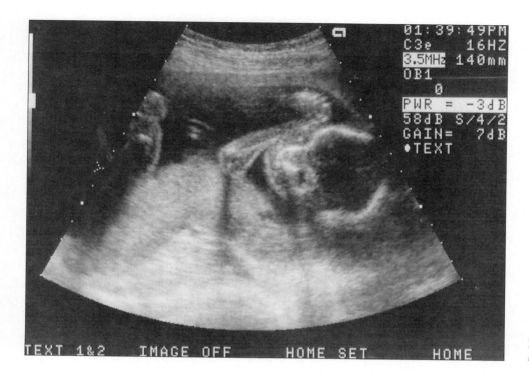

eases such as hemophilia and certain forms of thalassemia. Fetoscopy poses a danger to the fetus, however, and there is a 2% to 5% chance of spontaneous abortion with the use of this method.

Testing Embryonic Blastomeres

A new method of prenatal genetic screening, combining microsurgery and recombinant DNA technology, is being used for genetic testing of human preimplantation embryos at the 6- to 10-cell stage of development (see the discussion of this topic in Chapter 13). In this procedure embryos derived from *in vitro* fertilization are incubated until they reach a multicellular stage of development. Then, using a micromanipulator, a hole is made in the area surrounding the embryo (zona pellucida), and a single cell is removed for analysis. The DNA from this single cell, called a blastomere, is screened using the polymerase chain reaction (PCR) to detect the presence of mutant genes such as those for muscular dystrophy or hemophilia. Operated embryos continue to develop *in vitro* and after uterine transfer develop to full term. (see "Concepts and Controversies," page 463.)

FIGURE 19.4

The hand and face of a nine-week-old fetus as seen by fetoscopy.

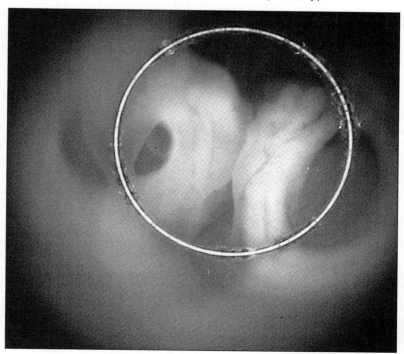

Risks and Problems Associated with Prenatal Testing

Although many genetic disorders and birth defects can be detected with prenatal testing, the technique has some limitations. These include measurable risks to the mother and fetus, including infection, hemorrhage, fetal injury, and spontaneous abortion. Conventional strategies for the use of prenatal testing will not always detect the majority of certain defects. In Down syndrome, for example, amniocentesis is recommended for all mothers over the age of 35 years. (In reality, only a small percentage of pregnancies to women over 35 are tested by amniocentesis.) However, some 65% of all Down syndrome births occur to mothers under the age of 35. The differential distribution of Down syndrome births reflects discrepancies in the number of pregnancies to women under and over the age of 35. Younger mothers may have 65% of the Down syndrome children, but they also have 93% of all births. Older women have about 7% of all children but 20% of the Down syndrome births, emphasizing once again the relationship between maternal age and increased risk of Down syndrome.

In the case of neural tube defects, some 90% of all affected infants are born to parents with no family history of such conditions. Thus, testing couples who have had an affected child will have little effect on the overall rate of prenatal detection for this birth defect. On the other hand, screening of all pregnant females is not cost-effective or possible, given the limited number of prenatal screening clinics.

GENETIC COUNSELING

Genetic counseling

A process of communication that deals with the occurrence or risk of occurrence of a genetic disorder in a family.

Genetic counseling is a process of communication that deals with the occurrence, or risk of occurrence, for a genetic disorder in a family. This process involves one or more appropriately trained persons helping an individual or family to understand:

- The medical facts, including the diagnosis, probable course of the disorder, and the available treatment and management
- The way heredity contributes to the disorder and the risk of recurrence
- The alternatives for dealing with the risk of recurrence
- How to adjust to the disorder in an affected family member, or to the risk of recurrence

The genetic counseling community attempts to achieve these goals in a nondirective way. That is, genetic counselors feel it is their obligation to provide all of the information available to and desired by an individual or family, so that the person or family can make the decisions most suitable to them based on their own cultural, religious, and moral beliefs. The National Society of Genetic Counselors has developed guidelines used by counselors in this process. These guidelines include respect for the autonomy and privacy of the individual, observing the need for confidentiality and informed consent, and providing information to the patient in a nondirective way. Genetic counselors also provide supportive counseling for families, serve as patient advocates, and refer individuals and families to community and state support services. They serve as educators and resource people for other health care professionals and for the general public. Some genetic counselors work in administrative positions, and others engage in research activities related to the field of medical genetics and counseling.

Who Are Genetic Counselors?

Genetic counselors are health care professionals with specialized graduate training and experience in the areas of medical genetics, psychology, and counseling. They usually work as members of a multidisciplinary health care team, offering information and support to families who have relatives with genetic conditions and to families who may be at risk for a variety of inherited conditions. Genetic counselors iden-

The Business of Making Babies

Recombinant DNA methods are revolutionizing the fields of genetic testing and genetic counseling. New technology has also made the business of human fertilization a part of private enterprise. One in six couples in the United States (over three million couples of childbearing age) are classified as infertile, and most of these couples want to have children. The first successful in vitro fertilization (IVF) was accomplished in 1981 at the Medical College of Virginia at Norfolk. Since then, over 150 hospitals and clinics using these and other techniques have opened. Many of these clinics are associated with university medical centers, but others are operated as free-standing businesses. Some are public companies that have sold stock to raise start-up money or to cover operating costs. It is estimated that a capitalization of about $1 million is required to start an IVF clinic, and that 50–60 fertilization attempts per month are necessary for the venture to be profitable. Each IVF attempt costs between $5,000 and $10,000, and several attempts (four to six) are usually required for success. Since these costs are not usually covered by insurance, IVF is a major expense for couples wanting to have children.

In IVF, egg maturation is induced with drugs, and the mature eggs are recovered by laparascopy (a small incision is made in the abdominal wall, and a fiber-optic device is used to recover the eggs). In an alternate procedure, an ultrasonically guided needle is inserted into the vagina and moved up to the ovary to remove the eggs. The eggs are fertilized in a dish (*in vitro* means, literally, "in glass"). After the fertilized egg begins development, it is implanted into the woman's uterus.

If extra eggs are recovered, they are fertilized and the resulting embryos frozen in liquid nitrogen. This eliminates the need to retrieve eggs every month for fertilization. If fertilization is successful, the extra embryos can remain in storage for implantation at a later time, or they can be donated to another couple.

Several companies, such as IVF Australia, are open in several locations in the United States. With the high start-up costs and expertise required, it is possible that the field will be dominated by a small number of companies through franchising agreements. Some investment analysts predict that IVF will grow into a $6 billion annual business. In parallel, a genetic testing and screening industry is beginning to emerge, offering tests in the areas of prenatal diagnosis, newborn screening, carrier screening, adult-onset screening, and forensic testing.

---

tify families at risk, investigate the problem present in the family, interpret information about the disorder, analyze inheritance patterns and risk of recurrence, and review available options with the family (Figure 19.5).

 FIGURE 19.5

In a genetic counseling session, the counselor uses the information from pedigree construction, medical records, and genetic testing to educate and inform a couple about their risks for genetic disorders.

Typically, genetic counselors are graduates of a 2-year master of science (MS) degree program. There are currently 22 genetic counseling programs in the United States; approximately 4–7 students are accepted into each program each year. Students in these programs are trained in biology, genetics, molecular biology, biochemistry, clinical work, and laboratory methods. They also receive training in ethical, social, and legal issues related to genetic disorders. A certification examination for counselors is offered every 3 years by the American Board of Genetic Counseling. Most counselors work in university medical centers or at large hospitals in metropolitan areas. As genetic testing and screening methods proliferate, it is hoped that genetic counseling services will become available to an increasing number of those who request genetic testing.

Reasons to Seek Genetic Counseling

There are many reasons why someone should seek genetic counseling services. The most typical case is an individual/family with questions about his or her reproductive future. For example, individuals with a family history of a genetic disorder, birth defect, developmental disability, or an affected child may have concerns about the risk of recurrence in future offspring. Women over 35 years of age and individuals from specific ethnic groups in which particular genetic conditions are seen more frequently will learn of their increased risk for genetic or chromosomal disorders and the diagnostic testing that is available. Other reasons for referral include multiple miscarriages, maternal diseases such as diabetes or lupus, known carrier status for a genetic disorder, parental anxiety, and environmental exposures such as drugs or infections. Fetal anomalies suspected as a result of a maternal screening test or an ultrasonogram may also lead a couple to genetic counseling. Anyone who has unanswered questions about diseases or traits in their family should consider genetic counseling. People who might be especially interested include

- Women who are pregnant or planning to be after age 35
- Couples who already have a child with mental retardation, an inherited disorder or a birth defect
- Couples who would like testing or more information about genetic defects that occur more frequently in their ethnic group
- Couples who are first cousins or other close blood relatives
- People concerned that their jobs, life-style, or medical history may pose a risk to a pregnancy, including exposure to radiation, medications, chemicals, infection, or drugs
- Women who have had two or more miscarriages or babies who died in infancy
- Couples whose infant has a genetic disease diagnosed by routine newborn screening
- Those who have, or are concerned that they might have, an inherited disorder or birth defect
- Pregnant women who, based on ultrasound tests or blood tests for alpha-fetoprotein, have been told their pregnancy may be at increased risk for complications or birth defects

How Does Genetic Counseling Work?

Most individuals are referred to genetic counseling services after a prenatal test or after the birth of a child with a genetic condition. In either case, the couple is concerned about the risks to the fetus in the current pregnancy or to future pregnancies based on this abnormal result. The counselor usually begins by constructing a detailed family and medical history, or pedigree. For prenatal or preconceptual counseling, all birth defects, causes of deaths, ages at death, and other health conditions are noted for each person in the family for at least three generations. It is also important to note

the occurrence of any pregnancy losses and the stage (first, second, or third trimester) when the pregnancy was lost. This information gives the counselors clues about certain genetic conditions that appear only in one sex, or conditions that are associated with repeated miscarriages.

Prenatal screening, cytogenetic, or biochemical tests performed on the expectant couple or on the developing fetus can be used along with the pedigree to help determine risk of occurrence or recurrence. The counselor uses as much information as possible to establish whether the trait is genetically determined.

Before pregnancy, genetic counseling can only offer probabilities that a specific birth defect may occur. The general population risk of having a child born with a serious genetic problem is about 2–5%. This is considered the background risk for every couple, regardless of family or medical history. This risk can increase if a genetic condition is in the family, but can never decrease. During pregnancy, chromosomal errors, many genetic disorders, and other conditions that may not have a genetic basis (such as heart defects) can be ruled out through prenatal tests.

If a condition in a family is found to be genetically determined, the counselor constructs a risk assessment for the couple. In this process, the counselor uses all the information available to explain the risk of having another child affected with the condition, or to explain the risk that the individual who is being counseled will be affected with the condition. Conditions that are considered high risk include dominant conditions (50% risk if one parent is heterozygous), simple autosomal recessive (25% when both parents are heterozygotes), and certain chromosomal translocations. Often conditions are difficult to assess because they involve polygenic traits or conditions with high mutation rates (like neurofibromatosis). Effectively communicating risk estimates so those being counseled can clearly understand can be a difficult task for the genetic counselor. Telling a couple that they have a one in four chance of having a child affected with a genetic condition may sound straightforward, but several barriers may exist that prevent accurate understanding of this risk. Many individuals lack a fundamental understanding of elementary probability. Some couples believe that if they have had one child affected with the condition, then the next three children will not be affected, so their risk of recurrence drops to zero. This is not the case. The one in four or 25% risk, is independent of the number of pregnancies that a couple has. To put it another way, this is the risk for each pregnancy (Table 19.8).

Learning about abnormal test results or a genetic disorder in the family can be devastating news for individuals. A genetic counselor offers emotional support and understanding during what can be a very difficult time. Intense emotions expressed by an individual or a couple during a counseling session can inhibit effective understanding of recurrence risks or the details of the condition. Emotional strife can influence decisions that may need to be made about a pregnancy, the care of a child, having more children, or the ability of the family to cope with ongoing problems. When necessary, counselors refer patients to parent organizations that deal with a

TABLE 19.8

Some Risk Factors in Families with One Affected Child

TRAIT	RISK OF MORE AFFECTED CHILDREN
Autosomal recessive	25%
Autosomal dominant	50%
Rare, sex-linked recessive	0% females, 50% males
Chromosome abnormality	<1% to 100%
Genetic anomaly; not a simple mode of inheritance	Generally <10%
Nongenetic malformation	2%

specific genetic condition, or to medical specialists, education specialists, or family support groups.

Genetic counselors explain basic concepts of biology and inheritance to all couples. This helps them understand how genes, proteins, or cell-surface antigens are related to the defects seen in their child or family. The counselor provides information that allows informed decision making about future reproductive choices. Reproductive alternatives such as adoption, artificial insemination, in situ fertilization, egg donation, and surrogate motherhood are options that the counselor presents to the couple.

Future Directions

As more and more genetic defects can be detected by heterozygote and prenatal screening, and as these techniques become more available, the role of the genetic counselor will become more important. The Human Genome Project is changing the focus of genetic counseling from reproductive risks to adult-onset conditions, such as polycystic kidney disease and Huntington disease. While counseling sessions address reproductive risks for these conditions, the primary focus is on the individual being counseled. The areas addressed include the risk of inheriting the gene, the potential severity of the condition, and the age of onset.

Advances in recombinant DNA technology are elucidating the genetic basis for conditions such as coronary artery disease, diabetes, and cancer. DNA tests for susceptibility to these adult-onset, common conditions are now being developed. Ultimately, it may be possible to treat these conditions following presymptomatic diagnosis. Presymptomatic genetic tests are already available for some forms of cancer, including breast and ovarian cancer. Genetic counseling has expanded its focus from reproductive risks to include common adult disease.

THE IMPACT OF GENETIC TESTING AND GENETIC SCREENING

The development of genetic screening and counseling programs has provided many benefits to individuals and society at large. But it has also created a number of associated problems, raising serious questions about whether screening should be mandatory, who is to have access to the results of screening, and whether individuals identified as carriers of genetic defects are socially stigmatized. In this section, we briefly examine several aspects of these problems.

Personal Consequences

The information that one is a carrier of a genetic disease often has a devastating psychological effect. Many identified carriers suffer a loss of self-image and regard themselves as worthless. This feeling is often reinforced by the feelings of family members toward carriers. For example, in some parts of rural Greece, marriages are arranged by parents and relatives. In one village in which screening for sickle cell was conducted, carriers were regarded as unsuitable marriage partners for anyone, not just other carriers.

To counter these effects, screening programs must be coupled with effective counseling programs for carriers, their families, and the general public. The education process must stress that carriers are not at risk for the disease, nor should they be prevented from marrying other carriers. Options for matings between heterozygotes should be carefully distinguished, including adoption, artificial insemination, and prenatal diagnosis coupled with selective abortion.

The effect of genetic testing on childbearing decisions has been documented in a number of studies. In one such study, couples at risk for having children afflicted with a severe form of beta thalassemia were counseled about the availability of prenatal diagnosis. Before such services were available, couples known to be at risk (through

birth of an affected child or carrier screening) had stopped having children altogether, and almost all pregnancies that occurred were reported as accidental. Of these pregnancies, 70% were terminated for fear of having a child with beta thalassemia. The availability of prenatal diagnosis brought about a significant change in childbearing decisions in such couples. In fact, reproductive patterns returned to almost normal levels, and less than 30% of all pregnancies were terminated because of thalassemia. Other surveys have reported similar findings, emphasizing the impact of genetic testing on individual lives.

Predictive genetic testing for autosomal dominant fatal genetic disorders that first appear in middle age (Huntington disease, polycystic kidney disease) has been evaluated to determine its psychological and social impact. Recently, the Canadian Collaborative Study of Predictive Testing reported on the psychological consequences of predictive testing for Huntington disease (HD). This form differs from other genetic testing because it requires other family members to be tested to produce informative results. Consequently, a request for testing affects the other members and forces them to consider whether they wish to be tested. In the study reported by the Canadian group, 200 individuals with an affected parent were followed after HD testing. They were separated into three groups: those with increased risk, those with no change in risk (mostly from uninformative test results), and those identified as having a decreased risk. The results suggest that testing has positive benefits for many participants. Clearly, those in the low-risk group showed an increase in well-being and psychological health. But those in the increased-risk group did not show a negative response to their condition. In fact, they reported less depression and an increased sense of well-being 12 months after testing. It appears that knowledge of status, whether for increased or decreased risk, has psychological value, while those with uncertain status remain susceptible to depression and have a lowered sense of well-being. Further tests and follow-up will be required to determine whether positive psychological effects are a hallmark of predictive genetic testing.

Social Consequences

At the broader level, we can compare the response of the Jewish community to screening for Tay-Sachs disease with some of the responses in the black community to sickle cell screening. In Tay-Sachs disease screening, the program was voluntary and welcomed by the community, which was involved in its planning and implementation. An adequate educational and counseling program accompanied the screening. In contrast, screening for sickle cell disease (homozygous recessive individuals afflicted with the disease) and sickle cell trait (heterozygous individuals unaffected by the disease) was largely mandated by law, and prominent members of the black community were not involved in the planning and initiation of screening. The origin of the program from outside the community coupled with sporadic problems (lack of confidentiality and inadequate education and counseling) generated suspicion and resentment about the screening program.

Many of these problems could have been avoided by better planning and implementation of this large-scale screening program. Voluntary rather than mandatory participation, coupled with adequate education and counseling and community involvement, would undoubtedly have eased many fears and suspicions. Perhaps it would be better to offer testing and counseling to those who request it rather than screening large groups to identify and label individuals as "carriers." Others argue that only mandatory screening programs can be effective. If, say, only 10% of those at risk take advantage of screening programs, the program is ineffective, and the cost-benefit ratio would not justify the existence of the program.

The lessons from earlier attempts at sickle cell screening are particularly important in light of new discoveries about sickle cell disease. A recent study has revealed that children with sickle cell disease who are under 3 years of age have poor resistance to bacterial infections, particularly those caused by *Streptococcus*. Children

with sickle cell anemia have a 15% chance of dying from a bacterial infection during the first 3 years of life. The study also demonstrated that doses of the antibiotic penicillin were highly effective in preventing illness and death.

These findings have prompted a National Institutes of Health (NIH) panel to recommend that sickle cell screening be made available to all newborns, whether or not they are members of high-risk ethnic groups. This recommendation has been made because it would avoid errors in classifying individuals as members of certain ethnic groups, and because screening is easy and inexpensive. Sickle cell screening can be done using a small blood sample and materials costing $0.22 per test. According to the panel, the expenditure of approximately $880,000 per year (4 million births x $0.22 per test) would produce a 15% reduction in the mortality rate among small children with sickle cell anemia. Recently, a panel convened by the U.S. Public Health Service has recommended that a program to screen all newborns in the U.S. for sickle cell anemia be implemented. If this recommendation is accepted, newborn screening will begin in the next few years.

It remains to be seen whether sickle cell screening programs will be adopted in any of the 40 states that do not currently test for this condition. This recommendation by the NIH panel also raises the questions whether such screening should be mandatory or voluntary, and whether the states should screen all newborns or only those in high-risk groups. These issues are certain to be debated once again by community groups and state legislatures in the near future.

Legal Implications

Genetic screening has raised a number of legal issues, many of which have not yet been resolved. Here, we will consider several questions about genetic screening to illustrate that genetic methodology and practice are several steps ahead of legislation, legal decisions, and social consensus.

If a child is born with a genetic defect that can be diagnosed prenatally, can the physician be held responsible for not informing the parents that prenatal screening for this defect is available? If an insurance company pays for a genetic screening test, does it have the right to know the results of the test? Can health or life insurance companies require genetic testing as a condition for obtaining insurance? Should individuals who test positive for Huntington disease or other genetic disorders be denied health or life insurance?

The Occupational Safety and Health Administration has categorized 24 chemicals that may be associated with reproductive hazards and excludes all fertile women from jobs that involve exposure to these chemicals. Is this protection or a form of sexual discrimination? Does knowing that these rules may apply to 20 million jobs change your answer?

These questions illustrate that many problems involving the development and use of genetic screening need to be resolved. These issues involve science as well as sociology, law, and ethics. In decisions about genetic screening, the rights of individuals must be considered and balanced against the rights of employers and society. Health policy is an area in which all citizens need to be educated and informed. As the constellation of genetic screening tests grows, these problems must be faced and solved.

SUMMARY

1. Genetic screening is the search for individuals of a particular genotype. In prenatal and newborn screening, several considerations are of importance. Treatable diseases are favorable for screening even when they are rare in the population. These include PKU, galactosemia, and maple syrup urine disease.

2. Carrier screening is the search for heterozygotes who may be at risk of producing a defective child. An increasing number of autosomal recessive diseases can be screened by molecular probes, including sickle cell anemia, Huntington disease, cystic fibrosis, and Duchenne muscular dystrophy. Large-scale carrier screening has been conducted for two autosomal recessive diseases that affect discrete population segments: Tay-Sachs disease and sickle cell anemia. The programs have been technically successful but were accepted somewhat differently in the affected segments of the population. A study of their implementation and the community reaction to them will be valuable in the design and planning of other carrier screening programs.

3. Occupational screening is used to detect individuals who are genetically susceptible to agents in the workplace that can cause the development of disease. While a number of agents that can cause adverse reactions have been identified and a number of diseases can be screened, no large-scale studies have been conducted to establish that such chemicals are harmful to sensitive individuals in the workplace. Because occupational screening can be used to exclude individuals from employment, its implementation should be restricted to those genetic conditions in which a danger has been clearly demonstrated.

4. The rapid development of methodology for genetic screening has generated a number of problems, including whether screening should be voluntary or mandatory and whether the results of screening tests can be used to deny services such as insurance or health care coverage. These issues will undoubtedly be the subject of much debate and a fair amount of legislation in the next few years.

5. Prenatal screening can also detect chromosome abnormalities, such as Down syndrome, and birth defects, such as spina bifida, that may have a genetic component. One of the considerations in prenatal screening is the identification of the risk group to be screened. The frequency of Down syndrome increases rapidly as maternal age increases over 35 years, and it is easy to see that screening should be made available to all pregnant females over the age of 35. Yet most Down syndrome births occur to younger mothers, because they have many more children than older mothers. Should screening be made available to all mothers for Down syndrome? Given the limited resources available now for such screening, is this cost effective? Several techniques are used in prenatal diagnosis, and each carries a risk to both the mother and the fetus. Less invasive methods such as the detection of fetal cells in the maternal circulation are under development, making prenatal screening for some diseases safer and more economical.

6. Genetic counseling is a service that undertakes the accurate assessment of a family history to determine the risk of genetic disease in subsequent children. In most cases this is done after the birth of a child affected with a genetic disorder, but in other cases counseling is entirely retrospective. Decisions about whether to have additional children or to undergo abortion or even to marry are always left to those being counseled.

QUESTIONS AND PROBLEMS

1. List the types of genetic screening covered in this chapter, and briefly summarize the unique characteristics of each type.

2. The measurement of αga-fetoprotein levels is used to diagnose neural tube defects. For every 1000 such tests, approximately 50 positive cases will be detected. However, up to 20 (40%) of these cases may be false positives. In a false positive, the αga-fetoprotein level is elevated, but the child has no neural tube defect. Your patient has undergone testing of the maternal blood for αga-fetoprotein, and the results are positive. She wants to abort a defective child but not a normal one. What are your recommendations?

3. Would you support a tax increase in your state to institute a genetic program similar to the Quebec Network of Genetic Medicine? State your answer from an economic and social viewpoint.

4. The reaction to screening for Tay-Sachs disease and sickle cell anemia offers an interesting contrast in the institution and administration of genetic screening programs. Cystic fibrosis is an autosomal disease that mainly affects the white population, and 1 in 20 whites are heterozygotes. Now that the gene has been mapped to chromosome 7, assume that RFLP markers are available to diagnose heterozygotes. Should a genetic screening program for cystic fibrosis be instituted? Should this be funded by the federal government? Should the program be voluntary or mandatory, and why?

5. As a genetic counselor, you are visited by a couple who wish to have children. There is a history of a deleterious,

recessive trait in males in the woman's family but not in the man's family. The couple are convinced that because his family shows no history of this genetic disease, they are at no risk of having affected children. What steps would you take to assess this situation and educate this couple?

6. A couple have had a child born with neurofibromatosis. They come to your genetic counseling office for help. After taking an extensive family history, you determine that there is no history of this disease on either side of the family. The couple want to have another child and want to be advised about risks of another child with neurofibromatosis. What advice do you give them?

7. The initial step in the process of genetic counseling is to construct a family pedigree and analyze it for inheritance pattens. In pedigree analysis, what are the major differences between autosomal recessive and autosomal dominant conditions?

8. An interesting polymorphism in the human population has to do with the ability to roll one's tongue (curl up the sides of the tongue to make a trough). Some people can do this trick, and others cannot. Hence it is an example of a dimorphism. Its significance is a mystery. In one family, a boy was unable to roll his tongue, but to his great dismay his sister could. Furthermore, both his parents were rollers, and so were both grandfathers and one paternal uncle and one paternal aunt. One paternal aunt, one paternal uncle , and one maternal uncle could not. Draw the pedigree for this family, clearly defining your symbols and deduce the genotypes of as many individuals as possible.

9. Phenylketonuria (PKU) is a human hereditary disease that prevents the body from processing the amino acid phenylalanine, which is contained in dietary protein. Symptoms of PKU present in early infancy and, if it remains untreated, leads to severe mental retardation. PKU is caused by a recessive allele with simple Mendelian inheritance. A couple intends to have children but seeks genetic counseling because the woman has a sister with PKU and the man has a brother with PKU. There are no other known cases in their families. They ask you, the genetic counselor, to determine the probabilities that their first child will have PKU. What is this probability?

SCIENCE AND SOCIETY

1. You are a genetic counselor and have been asked to review a proposal to screen local high school students for cystic fibrosis (CF) carrier status. The investigator's protocol states that the test will be done by extracting cells from inside the mouth with a cotton swab from all Caucasian students. Prior to testing, students will be given a booklet about CF and about the test and asked to sign a consent form. Results will be distributed to students in sealed envelopes with a toll-free number to call if they have questions about the test results. Of the various objections that you might raise with this screening protocol, the **LEAST** compelling of the following is that. . .
   a. non-Caucasian students will not be able to be tested, if they wish to be
   b. the method of informing the students of results does not adequately protect privacy or provide for appropriate follow-up counseling
   c. offering the screening in the classroom may unduly pressure students into being tested or stigmatize them
   d. the students' parents must be involved in providing consent
   e. the students are too young to benefit from the information

2. You are a genetic counselor and your patient has asked to be tested to determine if she carries a gene that predisposes her to early onset cancer. If your patient has this gene there is a 50:50 chance that all of her siblings inherited this gene and there is also a 50:50 chance that it will be passed on to their offspring. Your patient is very concerned about confidentiality and does not want anyone in her family to know she is being tested, including her identical twin sister. Your patient is tested and found to carry an altered gene that gives her an 85% lifetime risk of developing breast cancer and a 60% lifetime risk of developing ovarian cancer. At the result disclosure session, she once again reiterates that she does not want anyone in her family to know her test results. Knowing that a familial mutation is occurring in this family, what would be your next course of action in this case? Is it your duty to contact members of this family despite the request of you patient? Where do your obligations lie. . .with your patient or with the patient's family? Would it be inappropriate to try and convince the patient to share her results with her family members? What other problems can you foresee with this case?

3. A young woman (proband) and her partner are referred for prenatal genetic counseling because the woman has a family history of sickle cell anemia. The proband has sickle cell trait (Ss) and her partner does not have trait nor does he have sickle cell anemia (SS). Prenatal testing indicates that the fetus is affected with sickle cell anemia (ss). The results of this and other tests indicate that the only way the fetus could have sickle cell disease is if the woman's partner is not the father of the fetus. The couple is at the appointment seeking their test results. How would you handle this scenario? Should you have contacted the proband beforehand to explain the results and the implications of these results? Is it appropriate to keep this information from the partner since he believes he is the father of the baby? What other problems do you see with this case?

INTERNET ACTIVITIES

The following activities use the resources of the World Wide Web to enhance the topics covered in this chapter. To investigate the topics described below, log on to the book's home page at:

http://www.wadsworth.com/biology

1. Human Genome Project Information for the U.S. Dept. of Energy is a very valuable web site. Access it and then click on Ethical, Legal and Social Issues. Once there, scroll down to The Genetic Privacy Act and Commentary under the heading Products of ELSI Research. Click and read through Parts A and B under the heading Commentary.
   a. Do you think adequate safeguards have been established to protect individuals' genetic information?
   b. We are often curious about dead celebrities or major political figures. If a person, such as Abraham Lincoln, has been dead over one hundred years, should the public have the right through court approval to test a sample of hair or other body substance to determine if he carried any of the genetic markers for conditions such as Marfan syndrome or manic-depression? Why or why not? What rules would you propose to protect their descendants?
   c. If you were counseling a patient whose family history had evidence that a genetic disease like Huntington disease, a genetic condition that is damaging to the nervous system and can lead to an early death, would you advise that patient to have the genetic test done?

If you were the patient, would you want to know if you had the genetic marker for Huntington disease? Give some pros and cons for both positions.

2. On the ELSI home page there is an entry for the 1993 Insurance Task Force. Click on that title and read the brief report and its recommendations.
   a. Should insurance companies be denied all genetic information about applicants who want health or life insurance? Why or why not?
   b. If research has shown that women with specific identifiable genes have a 95% chance of developing an often fatal type of breast cancer, should the insurance companies be able to have that information? Give three reasons why they should have that information available and three other reasons why they shouldn't.

3. NOAH (The New York Online Access to Health) has an excellent home page for genetic counseling. Access it through the address provided. There should be brief scenarios provided as an introduction.
   a. Click and read the entry Is Genetic Counseling for You? Think about yourself or your family members. Are there any possible genetic conditions you may be concerned about? If so, there is useful information here about what genetic counselors can do for you and information on how to contact a counselor in your geographic area.

FOR FURTHER READING

Agency for Health Care Policy and Research. Sickle Cell Disease Panel. Sickle cell disease: comprehensive screening and management in newborns and infants. Rockville, MD, Public Health Service, Department of Health and Human Services, April, 1993.

Billings, P. and Beckwith, J. 1992. Genetic testing in the workplace: a view from the USA. *Trends in Genet.* 8: 198–202.

Calabrese, E. J. 1986. Ecogenetics: Historical foundation and current status. *J. Occup. Med.* 28: 1096–1102.

Dagenais, D., Courville, L., and Dagenais, M. 1985. A cost-benefit analysis for the Quebec Network of Genetic Medicine. *Soc. Sci. Med.* 20: 601–607.

Draper, E. 1991. *Risky Business: Genetic testing and exclusionary practices in the hazardous workplace.* New York: Cambridge University Press.

Emery, A. E. H., and Pullen, I. 1984. *Psychological Aspects of Genetic Counseling.* New York: Academic.

Fuhrmann, W., and Vogel, F. 1983. *Genetic Counseling.* 3rd ed. New York: Springer-Verlag.

Gibbs, R. A., and Caskey, C. T. 1989. The application of recombinant DNA technology for genetic probing in epidemiology. *Ann. Rev. Pub. Health* 10: 27–48.

Hodgson, S. V., and Bobrow, M. 1989. Carrier detection and prenatal diagnosis in Duchenne and Becker muscular dystrophy. *Br. Med. Bull.* 45: 719–744.

Jinks, D. C., Minter, M., Tarver, D. A., Vanderford, M., Hejtmancik, J. F., and McCabe, E. R. B. 1989. Molecular genetic diagnosis of sickle cell disease using dried blood specimens on blotters used for newborn screening. *Hum. Genet.* 81: 363–366.

Johnson, A., and Godmilow, L. 1988. Genetic amniocentesis at 14 weeks or less. *Clin. Obstet. Gynecol.* 31: 345–352.

Kolata, G. 1986. Genetic screening raises questions for employers and insurers. *Science* 232: 317–319.

Modell, B., and Kuliev, A. 1993. A scientific basis for cost-benefit analysis of genetics services. *Trends in Genet.* 9: 46–52.

Murray, R. F. 1986. Tests of so-called genetic susceptibility. *J. Occup. Med.* 28: 1103–1107.

Reed, S. 1980. *Counseling in Medical Genetics.* 3rd ed. New York: Liss.

Rowley, P. 1984. Genetic screening: Marvel or menace? *Science* 225: 138–144.

Sandovnick, A., and Baird, P. 1985. Reproductive counseling for sclerosis patients. *Am. J. Med. Genet.* 20: 349–354.

Selva, J., Leonard, C., Albert, M., Auger, J., and David, G. 1986. Genetic screening for artificial insemination by donor (AID). Clin. Genet. **29:** 389–396.

Sommer, S. S., Cassady, J. D., Sobell, J. L., and Bottema, C. D. 1989. A novel method for detecting point mutations or polymorphisms and its application to population screening for carriers of phenylketonuria. Mayo Clin. Proc. **64:** 1361–1372.

U.S. Congress, Office of Technology Assessment, *Cystic Fibrosis and DNA Tests: Implications of Carrier Screening,* OTA-BA-532. Washington, D.C.: U.S. Government Printing Office, August, 1992.

Uzych, L. 1986. Genetic testing and exclusionary practices in the workplace. *J. Public Health Policy* Spring 1986: 37–57.

Wapner, R. J., and Jackson, L. 1988. Chorionic villus sampling. Clin. Obstet. Gynecol. **31:** 328–344.

Williams, C., Weber, L., Williamson, R., and Hjelm, M. 1988. Guthrie spots for DNA-based carrier testing in cystic fibrosis. Lancet ii: 693.

APPENDIX A

Probability

Mendel's use of mathematics to analyze the results of his experiments is frequently overlooked as an important contribution to biology. His application of mathematical reasoning to the analysis of data helped transform an observational and descriptive science into a quantitative and experimental one. When Mendel carried out his experiments, statistics and statistical methods were not highly developed. In analyzing the results of his crosses, Mendel converted the numbers of individuals with particular genotypes or phenotypes into ratios. From these ratios, he was able to deduce the mechanisms of inheritance.

As we now know, the ratios Mendel observed are the result of random segregation and assortment of genes into gametes during meiosis and their union at fertilization in random combinations. This randomness provides an element of chance in the outcome, and prevents us from making exact predictions. In counting pea seeds in the F_2, we may expect three fourths of the seeds to be yellow, but we cannot be absolutely certain that the first seed in an unopened pod will be yellow. The rules of probability can, however, help us guess how often such an event will take place.

DEFINING PROBABILITY

Most people have an innate sense of probability that seems part of common sense. For example, almost everyone would agree with the idea that a January snowfall is more probable in Minneapolis than in Miami. Other aspects of probability also seem obvious. When a coin is flipped, the probable outcomes are heads or tails. In the birth of a child, we expect the outcome to be a boy or a girl.

Unfortunately, the use of intuition alone in matters of probability is not always reliable. For example, what would you say is the probability that in a crowd of 20 people, two individuals share the same birth date? Considering that there are 365 days in the year (excluding leap year), intuition may say that it is not very likely. In fact, in a group of 20, there is almost an even chance that two people share the same birthday. The probability of a shared birthday for groups of various sizes is as follows: for a group of 23, the probability is 51%; for a group of 30, it is 71%; for 40, it is 89%; and for 50, there is a 97% chance that two people will share the same birthday. We will not explore the mathematical reasoning behind this probability, but it is based on the fact that if one person can have any of the 365 days for his or her birthday, the second person can have any of the remaining 364 days, the third person can have any of the remaining 363 days, and so on.

From the preceding example, it should be clear that in order to be useful in genetics and in science, probability needs to be expressed in more quantitative terms. The use of a quantitative approach to probability allows us to assign a numerical value to the probability that a given event will occur, and prevents us from leaping to conclusions about the possible outcome of genetic crosses.

QUANTIFYING PROBABILITY

In quantifying probability, let us begin at the limits. If an event is certain to occur, it has a probability of 1; if the event is certain not to occur, then the probability is 0. In genetics as in most other areas, we usually deal with events that are a mixture of de-

grees of certainty. While it is certain that we will all die (a probability of 1), when we die is less certain and therefore must be assigned a probability somewhere between 0 and 1. Insurance companies spend a great deal of time and effort in attempting to determine such probabilities, although we may prefer not to think about them.

In general terms, we can express the probability (p) of an event as the proportion of times that such an event occurs (r) out of the number of times that the event can occur (n):

$$p = r/n$$

In other words, if an event occurs r times in n trials, the probability that the event will take place is r/n. This probability is somewhere between the limits of 0 and 1. If we toss a coin, it may land with heads up or tails up. The probability that it will land with heads up is

$$p = r/n = 1/2$$

Likewise, the probability of a child being a boy or a girl is 1/2. Other events have different probabilities. In a pair of dice, each die has six faces. When a die is thrown, the probability of any of the faces being up is

$$p = r/n = 1/6$$

In a deck of 52 cards, the probability of drawing any given card (the ace of spades for example) is

$$p = r/n = 1/52$$

In roulette, the wheel contains the numbers 1–36 plus 0 and 00. The probability of the ball landing on any number is therefore

$$p = r/n = 1/38$$

In a monohybrid cross, the probability that an offspring of the self-fertilized F_1 pea plant will have a dominant phenotype is

$$p = 3/4$$

In considering probability, we must consider not only the probability of one type of outcome but also the probability of other outcomes. If an event has a probability of p, the probability of an alternative outcome is $q = 1-p$. In other words, the sum of the probability of p and q equals 1. In the preceding examples, the probability of drawing an ace of spades is 1/52; the probability of drawing another card is 51/52, which when added to 1/52 equals 1. In the monohybrid cross, the probability of a dominant phenotype is 3/4, and the probability of a recessive phenotype is 1/4. Since we are certain that the F_2 will have either a dominant or recessive phenotype, adding the probabilities of both phenotypes (3/4 + 1/4 = 1) covers all the possible phenotypic combinations.

COMBINING PROBABILITIES

Two rules of probability are useful in analyzing genetics problems. The first, called the *product rule,* is used when we wish to calculate the probability of two or more independent events occurring at the same time. The second, called the *sum rule,* is used when two or more events are mutually exclusive, or are alternative events.

In the product rule, we are asking what is the probability that event A and event B will occur together. This rule can be summarized as follows: The probability that independent events will occur together is the product of their independent probabilities.

When a coin is tossed, the probability that it will be heads is 1/2, and the chance that it will be tails is 1/2. If we toss a coin four times, and it turns up heads each time, the probability that it will turn up tails on the fifth try is still 1/2. In other words,

chance has no memory. The probability that two heterozygotes will have a child with cystic fibrosis is 1/4. This does not mean that if their first child has cystic fibrosis, they can be assured of having three unaffected children. It means that for each child, there is a 1 in 4 chance that it will have cystic fibrosis, no matter whether they have 1 child or 20 children. If they have four unaffected children, the chance that their fifth child will have cystic fibrosis is still 1/4.

If, on the other hand, we want to ask what is the probability that we can toss a coin four times and get heads each time, we use the product rule. Since each coin toss is an independent event, the probability of getting heads four times out of four is $1/2 \times 1/2 \times 1/2 \times 1/2 = (1/2)^4 = 1/16$. Similarly, the probability that heterozygous parents will have four children affected with cystic fibrosis is $1/4 \times 1/4 \times 1/4 \times 1/4 = 1/256$.

In using the sum rule, we are asking how often one *or* the other of two mutually exclusive events can occur. For example, in rolling a die, what is the probability of a three or a five coming up? Since on a single throw only one number can come up, it is impossible to get both numbers on a single throw. The probability of a three is 1/6, and the probability of a five is 1/6. If we want to know what is the probability of either a three or a five coming up on a single throw, we add the individual probabilities.

$$1/6 + 16 = 2/6 = 1/3$$

In considering the possible genotypic combinations in children of parents heterozygous for cystic fibrosis, what is the probability that a child will have either one or two copies of the dominant allele? The probability of being homozygous dominant (two copies) is 1/4, and the probability of being heterozygous (one copy) is 1/2. Therefore, the probability of being either heterozygous or homozygous dominant is $1/2 + 1/4 = 3/4$. This is in fact the proportion of individuals with the dominant phenotype seen in the F_2 of a monohybrid cross.

In applying probability to the analysis of genetic problems, first determine whether you want to know the probabilities of event A *and* event B, or the probability of event A *or* event B. If you want A and B, use the product rule and multiply the probabilities of A and B. If you want the probability of A or B, use the sum rule, and add the probability of event A to the probability of event B. For example, the frequency of albinism is about 1/10,000, and the frequency of cystic fibrosis is about 1/2000. If we want to know the probability of having both albinism *and* cystic fibrosis, we multiply the probabilities:

$$1/10,000 \times 1/2000 = 1/20,000,000$$

If we want to know the probability of having either albinism or cystic fibrosis, we add the probabilities:

$$1/10,000 + 1/2000 = 6/10,000 = 1/1666$$

As you can see, the probabilities are very different and reflect whether we are asking that both events occur, or that one or the other event will occur.

APPENDIX B

Answers to Questions and Problems

Chapter 2 Answers

1. a. Chemical and physical cell barrier; controls flow of molecules
   b. Generation of metabolic energy sources
   c. Maintenance and allocation of genetic material
   d. Protein synthesis
2. a. Cytological structure identified as the gene repository
   b. The complex of DNA, RNA, histones and nonhistone proteins that make up the chromosomes.
   c. One of the two side-by-side constituents of a replicated chromosome, connected to its sister through the undivided centromere
3. d.
4. a. Chemical treatment of chromosomes resulting in unique banding patterns
   b. Q banding with quinacrine and G banding with giemsa
5. Allows the visualization of chromosomes. The sex of a fetus can be determined based on chromosomal content. The detection of chromosomal abnormalities is also possible.
6. Homologous chromosomes are similar in that they contain alleles of the same gene at the same position along the length of the chromosome. One member of the pair is maternally derived and the other is paternally derived. The homologs may or may not carry the same allele of a gene.
7. A sister chromatid is an exact copy of DNA synthesized from its partner (the other sister). A sister chromatid gets replicated in the S phase of the cell cycle in preparation for cell division. Replication of the sister chromatid should occur in a very precise manner ensuring that the sister is genetically identical to the original chromosome.
8. 21, chromosome number; q, long arm; 1, region; 3, band
9. The G1 stage of cell cycle. The cell will not need to enter the S phase (the phase following G1) to duplicate its DNA if it is not going to divide.
10. Prophase: chromosome condensation, spindle formation, centriole migration, nucleolar disintegration, nuclear membrane dissolution; metaphase: alignment of chromosomes on the equatorial plate, attachment of centromeres to spindles; anaphase: centromere division, daughter chromosomes migrate to opposite cell poles; telophase: cytoplasmic division, reformation of nuclear membrane and nucleoli, disintegration of the spindle apparatus.

11. Cell furrowing involves the constriction of the cell membrane which causes the cell to eventually divide. It is associated with the process of cytokinesis, cytoplasmic division of the cell. If cytokinesis does not occur in mitosis, the cell will be left with a $2 \times 2n$ the number of chromosomes or $4n$ (tetraploid).
12. d.
13. e. c. b. d.
14. Both daughter cells have the normal diploid complement of all chromosomes except for 7. Therefore, one cell has three copies of chromosome 7 for a total chromosome number of 47. The other cell has only one copy of chromosome 7 for a total chromosome number of 45.
15. Anaphase, telophase of mitosis, and G1 of interphase. These are the steps where one chromatid equals one chromosome. Sister chromatids have separated (in anaphase) and are then distributed into two daughter cells (in telophase). In the G1 phase, the two daughter cells are synthesizing cellular components and have not yet duplicated their DNA. During the S phase, chromosomes duplicate their genetic material creating a sister chromatid. Starting with the S phase and ending with metaphase of mitosis, one chromosome equals two chromatids.
16. Faithful chromosome replication during S phase; independent alignment of chromosomes on the equatorial plate during metaphase; centromere division and chromosome migration during anaphase.
17. Cells undergo a cycle of events where cells grow, replicate their DNA, and divide. The new cells produced will then undergo the same cycle of events leading to the production of more cells that are genetically identical. DNA replication (the making of a sister chromatid) happens during the S (synthesis) phase of the cell cycle. Mitosis happens at the M phase of the cell cycle. Mitosis involves the steps prophase, metaphase, anaphase, telophase resulting in cell division.
18. Meiosis involves the production of haploid gametes. These gametes do not undergo further cell division and therefore do not "cycle."
19. Meiosis II, the division responsible for separation of sister chromatids would no longer be required. Meiosis I, wherein homologs segregate, would still be necessary.

20. a.

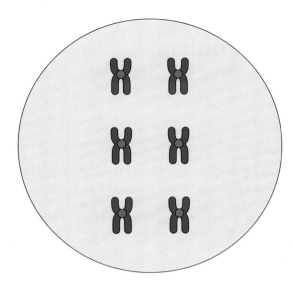

b.

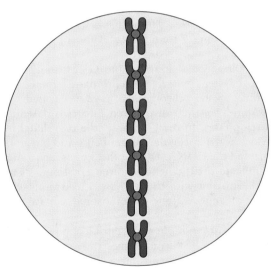

c. 3
d. 3
e. 6
f. 3

21. a. mitosis
    b. meiosis I
    c. meiosis II

22. 2 chromosomes, 4 chromatids, and 2 centromeres should be present.

23. Chiasma (chiasmata)

24. Meiotic anaphase I: no centromere division, chromosomes consisting of 2 sister chromatids are migrating; meiotic anaphase II: centromere division, the separating sister chromatids are migrating. Meiotic anaphase II more closely resembles mitotic anaphase by the two criteria cited above.

25. Males: 4 morphologically indistinguishable haploid spermatids (sperm when mature). All 4 sperm are capable of fertilizing an ovum. Females: 3 relatively small, infertile, haploid polar bodies are produced. The relatively large and fertile secondary oocyte will not complete meiosis until after fertilization, and is therefore only arguably regarded as haploid. The size difference between the 4 products is the result of asymmetric cytokinesis.

26. During gamete formation, the 23 pairs of human chromosomes *independently assort* creating gametes that are genetically different. For example, one gamete may have 10 paternally derived chromosomes and 13 maternally derived chromosomes. Another may have, 8 paternally derived chromosomes and 15 maternally derived chromosomes. After gamete formation, *fertilization*, the union of sperm and egg, creates more genetic diversity depending on which sperm fertilized which egg. Diversity in increased even more if *crossing over* occurs where new combinations of genetic information are produced along chromosomes.

27. Meiosis begins before birth of the parent and is completed shortly after fertilization. The time taken was therefore approximate. Shortest time: (July 1, 1994—Jan. 1, 1950) 0.95 = 42.3 years; longest time: (July 2, 1994—April 1, 1949) 1.05 = 45.4 years.

Chapter 3 Answers

1. a. A gene is the fundamental unit of heredity. The gene encodes a specific gene product (i.e. a pigment involved in determining eye color). Alleles are alternate forms of a gene that may cause various phenotypic effects. For example, there may be a blue eye color allele, a brown eye color allele, and a green eye color allele of a gene. The brown eye color allele may be the dominant allele where the blue and green alleles may be recessive. In many cases, such as with disease causing genes, the term "normal" allele (which gives the normal phenotype) is used in contrast to "mutant" allele (the allele that causes the disease). There may be several types of mutant alleles causing variable phenotypic effects associated with the disease.

   b. Genotype refers to the genetic constitution of the individual (AaBb or aabb). Notice that the genotype always includes at least two letters, each representing one allele of a gene pair in a diploid organism. A gamete would contain only one allele of each gene due to its haploid state (Ab or ab). Phenotype refers to an observable trait. For example, Aa (the genotype) will cause a normal pigmentation (the phenotype) in an individual where aa will cause albinism. Similarly Bb or bb (the genotypes) would give rise to brown hair versus blonde hair (the phenotypes) respectively.

   Phenotypes can refer to properties that are not observable to the naked eye. For example, in sickle cell

anemia, heterozygotes do not "look" sick however, their red blood cells are abnormal in shape (slightly sickled) causing an abnormal cellular phenotype. This cellular phenotype is seen only with the use of a microscope.

c. Dominance refers to a trait that is expressed in the heterozygous condition. Therefore, only one copy of a dominant allele needs to be present to express the phenotype. Recessiveness refers to a trait that is not expressed in the heterozygous condition. It is masked by the dominant allele. To express a recessive trait, two copies of the recessive allele must be present in the individual.

d. Complete dominance occurs when a dominant allele completely masks the expression of a recessive allele. For example, in pea plants, yellow seed color is dominant to green. In a heterozygous state, the phenotype of the seeds is yellow. This is the same phenotype seen in seeds homozygous for the yellow allele.

Incomplete dominance occurs when the phenotype of the heterozygote is intermediate between the two homozygotes. For example, in *Mirabilis*, a red flower crossed with a white flower will give a pink flower.

Codominance refers to a state where both alleles in a heterozygous individual are fully expressed. Therefore, the heterozygote shows the phenotype of both homozygotes. This is seen clearly in the ABO blood system in humans.

2. *AB* − 50% and *Ab* − 50%

3. The genotypic ratio is 1*AABb*:1*AaBb*:1*AAbb*:1*Aabb*
The phenotypic ratio is 1:1

4. Four, in equal proportions. If the genes are *AaBb*, the gametes are: *AB, Ab, aB* and *ab*.

5. a. Bb × Bb
   b. Bb × bb

6. ⅓

7. a. Homologous chromosomes are segregating, or gene pairs are segregating (*a* from *a*, *D* from *d*).
   b. Members of the *aa* gene pair are segregating independently from members of the *Dd* gene pair.
   c. 8
   d. 2
   e. *aaDd*
   f. albino, but not deaf
   g. metaphase of meiosis I
   h. 2 chromatids, 2 chromosomes

8. *Punnett Square:*

	AB	Ab	aB	ab
AB	AABB	AABb	AaBB	AaBb
Ab	AABb	AAbb	AaBb	Aabb
aB	AaBB	AaBb	aaBB	aaBb
ab	AaBb	Aabb	aaBb	aabb

phenotypes:

A_B_	⁹⁄₁₆
A_bb	³⁄₁₆
aaB_	³⁄₁₆
aabb	¹⁄₁₆

genotypes

AABB	¹⁄₁₆
AABb	²⁄₁₆
AAbb	¹⁄₁₆
AaBB	²⁄₁₆
AaBb	⁴⁄₁₆
Aabb	²⁄₁₆
aaBB	¹⁄₁₆
aaBb	²⁄₁₆
aabb	¹⁄₁₆

Fork-line:
phenotypes:

¾ A ⟨ ¾ B → ⁹⁄₁₆ A_B_
       ¼ b → ³⁄₁₆ A_bb

¼ a ⟨ ¾ B → ³⁄₁₆ aaB_
       ¼ b → ¹⁄₁₆ aabb

genotypes:

¼ AA ⟨ ¼ BB → ¹⁄₁₆ AABB
        ¾ Bb → ²⁄₁₆ AABb
        ¼ bb → ¹⁄₁₆ AAbb

¾ Aa ⟨ ¼ BB → ²⁄₁₆ AaBB
        ¾ Bb → ⁴⁄₁₆ AaBb
        ¼ bb → ²⁄₁₆ Aabb

¼ aa ⟨ ¼ Bb → ¹⁄₁₆ aaBB
        ¾ Bb → ²⁄₁₆ aaBb
        ¼ bb → ¹⁄₁₆ aabb

9. a. Both are 3:1
   b. 9:3:3:1
   c. Swollen is dominant to pinched, yellow is dominant to green.
   d. let *P* = swollen, and *p* = pinched; *C* = yellow and *c* = green. Then: P₁ = *PPcc* × *ppCC* or *PPCC* × *ppcc* F₁ = *PpCc*

10. a. Each affected parent is homozygous recessive (*aa*). Since the unaffected parent has no family history of sickle cell anemia, each is probably homozygous dominant (*AA*). Each member of the couple planning to marry is therefore heterozygous (*Aa*) for sickle cell anemia. There is a 25% chance that any children this couple has will be affected by sickle cell anemia.
    b. If the man is affected, he is homozygous recessive (*aa*), and the unaffected woman with no family history is probably homozygous dominant (*AA*). None of their children will be affected by sickle cell anemia, but all will be heterozygous (*Aa*) for the trait.

11. Let *S* = smooth, and *s* = wrinkled and *Y* = yellow and *y* = green. The parents are: *SSYY* × *ssyy*. The F₁ offspring are: *SsYy*.

12. Using the symbols from the problem above, the parents are: *SsYy* × *SsYy*. The genotypes of the F₁ are: *SsYy, Ssyy, ssYy* and *ssyy*.

13. a. All F$_1$ plants will be long-stemmed.
   b. Let S = long-stemmed and s = short-stemmed. The long-stemmed P$_1$ genotype is SS, the short-stemmed P$_1$ genotype is ss. The long-stemmed F$_1$ genotype is: Ss.
   c. Approximately 225 long-stemmed and 75 short-stemmed.
   d. The expected genotypic ratio is: 1 SS:2 Ss: 1 ss

14. The genotypic ratio in the offspring is: 1 AABB:2 AABb:1 AAbb:2 AaBB:4 AaBb:2 Aabb:1 aaBB:2 aaBb:1 aabb.

15. The P$_1$ generation is: $FF \times ff$. The F$_1$ generation is: Ff. The mode of inheritance is incomplete dominance.

16. ¼ straight, round, ¼ straight, wrinkled, ¼ gnarled, round, ¼ gnarled, wrinkled.

17. The 1:2:1 phenotypic ratio is suggestive of either incomplete dominance or codominance. The apparent contribution of both red and yellow to the orange phenotype suggests codominance as the mode of inheritance.

18. Possible genotypes of parents:
   a. BbHH × BbHH   BbH_ × BbH_
   b. BbHh × BbHH
   c. BbHH × Bbhh

19. ½ × ¼ × ¼ × ½ × ¼ = ¹⁄₂₅₆
    (Aa) (BB) (cc) (Dd) (ee)

20. ¾ for A × ½ for b × 1 for C = ⅜ for A, b, C

21. a. All plants will bear round seeds.
   b. The F$_1$ cross would be: $Ssss \times Ssss$.
      The male gametes produced would be: S (25%) and s (75%)
      The female gametes produced would be: Sss (75%) and sss (25%).
      From fertilizations in all combinations, ¹³⁄₁₆ or 325 of the offspring will bear round seeds and ³⁄₁₆ or 75 of the offspring will bear wrinkled seeds.

22. 9 of the 64 possible genotypic combinations will produce a phenotype of long, purple and wrinkled. Among 2048 progeny, 288 (⁹⁄₆₄ of 2048) would be expected to show this phenotype.

23. All progeny were yellow, therefore the parental plant was homozygous for seed color. Examination of pod shape among the progeny reveals a 3:1 ratio of swollen to pinched. This suggests that the parent was heterozygous for pod shape. If we let P = swollen and p = wrinkled, and C = yellow, then the genotype of the self-crossed plant is: $CCPp$.

24. Since neither species produces progeny resembling a parent, simple dominance is ruled out. The species producing pink-flowered progeny from red and white (or very pale yellow) suggests incomplete dominance as a mode of inheritance. However, in the second species, the production of orange-colored progeny cannot be explained in this fashion. Orange would result from an equal production of red and yellow; instead in this case, codominance is suggested, with one parent producing bright red flowers and the other producing pale yellow flowers.

25. The hair color of the albino parent is white (lack of pigment). The albino parent's genotype for hair color is homozygous recessive for red hair (rr). The genotype of the brown-haired parent is heterozygous (Rr). The genotype

of the brown-haired parent for skin color is heterozygous (Aa). The genotype of the first child with respect to hair color is heterozygous (Rr), and heterozygous for skin pigmentation (Aa). The possible genotypes of the second child for hair color are Rr or rr. The phenotype of the second child for hair color is white (lack of pigmentation). The production of hair color depends on the synthesis and deposition of pigment in the hair. Even though the second child carries the genetic information for brown or red hair, this gene is not expressed because the gene for albinism prevents pigment formation. This is a form of gene interaction.

26. During meiotic prophase I, the replicated chromosomes synapse or pair with their homologues. These paired chromosomes align themselves on the equatorial plate during metaphase I. During anaphase I it is the homologues (each containing two chromatids) that separate from each other. There is no preordained orientation for this process—it is equally likely that a maternal or a paternal homologue will migrate to a given pole. This provides the basis for the law of random segregation. Independent assortment results from the fact that the migrational polarity of one set of homologues has absolutely no influence on the orientation of a second set of homologues. For example, if the maternal homologue of chromosome 1 migrated to a certain pole, it will have no bearing on whether the maternal or paternal homologue of chromosome 2 migrates to that same pole.

27. No conclusion can be reached, since no information is available on how handedness is inherited.

Chapter 4 Answers

1. To generate an easily readable and standardized form of family history.
2. d.
3. a. Female
   b. Male
   c. Consanguineous mating
   d. Heterozygous male
   e. Identical twins, both female
4. Autosomal dominant with incomplete penetrance
5. Autosomal dominant
6. An autosomal dominant mode of inheritance is suggested by the pedigree. If the trait is highly penetrant, then the individual in question should show the trait.
7. a.

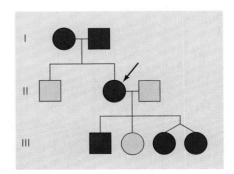

b. The mode of inheritance is consistent with an autosomal dominant trait. Both of the proband's parents are affected. If this trait were recessive, all of their children would have to be affected (*aa* × *aa* can only produce aa offspring). As we see in this pedigree, the brother of the proband is not affected indicating that this is a dominant trait. His genotype is *aa*, the proband's genotype is *AA* or *Aa* and both parents' genotype is most likely *Aa*.

c. Since the proband's husband is unaffected, he is *aa*

8. Autosomal dominant because, as with most autosomal dominant traits, every affected individual should have at least one affected parent. Here both parents are affected. Also, in autosomal dominant inheritance, two affected individuals can have an unaffected child. If this were an autosomal recessive disease, the unaffected female in generation II could not be produced. Two affected individuals with a recessive disease would be *aa* × *aa*. They can only produce affected children.

9. The pedigree is consistent with an autosomal dominant mode of inheritance, but with incomplete penetrance. Specifically, the proband must carry a dominant allele but does not exhibit the trait.

10. a. This pedigree is consistent with autosomal recessive inheritance.

b. If inheritance is autosomal recessive, the individual in question is heterozygous.

11. a. I

b. III

c. II

12. a. Marfan syndrome—individuals are usually tall and thin with long arms and legs. They encounter skeletal, visual and cardiovascular problems.

Huntington disease—progressive degeneration of the nervous system leading to dementia and early death.

b. Cystic fibrosis—characterized by salty sweat, mucus in the lungs, and blocked ducts leading to improper food digestion. This disease is disabling and usually fatal by early adulthood.

Sickle cell anemia—red blood cells are sickle in shape due to an abnormal type of hemoglobin. The deformed blood cells rupture easily and can also clog small blood vessels.

13. Autosomal. There will be two copies of the gene in all individuals

14. a. Maternal grandfather

b. No

c. No

15. c. X-linked dominant

16. d. Sex-linked recessive

17. Penetrance is a population parameter measuring the extent to which a phenotype that should be expressed is expressed. This is an all-or-none measure for any individual. Expressivity reflects the degree to which a phenotype is expressed in an individual.

18. $^{15}/_{19}$ = 79% penetrance.

19. 20% of 90 = 18

20. One cannot carry out crosses or control human matings. Human geneticists must base their analyses on matings that have already taken place. Sometimes the data regarding the phenotype of the individuals in these matings have not been carefully documented making the genetic analysis difficult. Also, humans produce too few offspring for accurate genetic analyses. Several families usually have to be used to study the inheritance of a certain trait.

21.

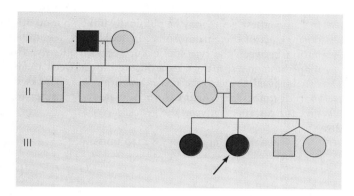

22. a. NF is caused by an autosomal dominant allele. Due to the relative rarity of the disease, it is most likely that Sam's dad is heterozygous. This would give Sam a 50% chance of contracting the disease, since the mother is homozygous recessive. However, there is a chance that Sam's dad is homozygous. Although unlikely, this would ensure that Sam would contract the disease.

b. Either at least one of Sam's paternal grandparents must suffer from the disease, or Sam's father represents a new mutation. Because the mutation rate for NF is high, we cannot say anything for sure about the grandparents.

23.

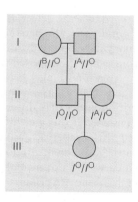

24. a. Seven phenotypes are possible: A, B, C, D, AB, AC, BC

b. Ten genotypes are possible: a/a, b/b, c/c, d/d, a/d, b/d, c/d, a/b, a/c, b/c

25. Due to the rarity of the disease, we assume the maternal grandfather is heterozygous for the gene responsible for

Huntington disease. His daughter has a ½ chance of possessing the deleterious allele. In turn, should the woman have the HD allele, her child would have a ½ chance of inheriting it. Therefore, at present, the child has a ½ × ½ = ¼ chance of having inherited the HD allele.

26. Such alleles can survive due to a number of factors, including low penetrance and adult onset of symptoms.

27. Technically no. A recombination frequency over 50% means that the two genes are independently assorting, indicating that the genes are not on the same chromosome. In reality, these genes may be physically linked but on opposite ends of the chromosome. In such cases, recombination between the two loci occurs very frequently. To map these genes, a third gene located in between them can be used to generate recombination data. The two map distances generated can then be added together to give the distance between the genes.

28.

```
        4 map units        8 map units
C ───────────────── A ───────────────── B
```

Chapter 5 Answers

1. Continuous variation is due to polygenic inheritance. As organisms have become evolutionary more advanced, complex phenotypes have developed which are controlled by multiple genes rather than a single gene. Human traits such as height, weight, skin color and intelligence may be controlled by polygenes.

2. a. Height in pea plants is determined by a single pair of genes with dominance and recessiveness. Height in humans is determined by polygenes.
   b. For traits determined by polygenes, the offspring of matings between extremes in the population show a tendency to regress toward the mean expression of the trait in the population.

3. Liability is caused by a number of genes acting in an additive fashion to produce the defect. If exposed to certain environmental conditions, the person above the threshold will most likely develop the disorder. The person below the threshold is not predisposed to the disorder and will most likely remain normal.

4. Differences in height may have reflected differences in the level of nutrition rather than differences in the genetic makeup of individuals. If this was the case, many of the crosses ordered by Frederick William would have amounted to little more than random breeding in the population, which would not increase the genetic components for height in the offspring.

5. Yes. Within some of the families it is likely that greater height was determined by genetic differences rather than by better nutrition. In these cases, brother-sister marriages would effectively cause the alleles for greater height in the offspring and subsequent generations to become homozygous, leading eventually to taller individuals.

6. a. F_1 genotype = A′AB′B, phenotype = height of 6 ft.
   b.
   $$A'AB'B \times A'AB'B$$
   ↓

Genotypes	Phenotypes
A′A′B′B′	7 ft
A′A′B′B	6 ft 6 in.
A′A′BB	6 ft
A′AB′B′	6 ft 6 in.
A′AB′B	6 ft
A′ABB	5 ft 6 in.
AAB′B′	6 ft
AAB′B	5 ft 6 in.
AABB	5 ft

7. In the case of polygenes, the expression of the trait depends on the interactions of many genes, each of which contributes a small effect to the expression of the trait. Thus, the differences between genotypes often are not clearly distinguishable. In the case of monogenic determination of a trait, the alleles of a single locus have major effects on the expression of the trait, and the differences between genotypes is usually easily discerned.

8. Genetic variance is the variation in phenotype exhibited by a population that is due to differences in the genotypes of the individuals of the population.

9. Environmental variance is any variation that occurs between individuals of the same genotype in a population.

10. Heritability is a measure of the proportion of variability in a population that is caused by genetic variance.

11. Relatives are used because the proportion of genes held in common by relatives is known.

12. b.

13. Intelligence is determined not only by multiple genes but also environment (age, birth order, nutrition, culture, etc.). How much of an impact the environment has on intelligence cannot be quantified. Also, it is difficult to accurately measure intelligence in an unbiased manner. A test would have to measure intelligence regardless of race, sex, etc.

14. In this particular case, the individuals are genetically identical so any differences in the expression of a trait must be due to differences in their environments.

15. This suggests that environmental factors play a major role in the expression of the trait. However, since there is a significant concordance difference between MZ and DZ twins, this trait is also shown to be genetic.

16. In this case, it is likely that the similarities in the expression of a trait between adopted and natural children are due to the sharing of a similar environment.

17. It suggests that heritability value, H = 1.

18. Heritability (H), would be zero.

19. mental age: 11
    chronological age: 9
    ¹¹⁄₉ = 1.2 × 100 = 120

20. The heritability difference observed between the racial groups for this trait cannot be compared because heritability measures variation within one population at the

time of the study. Heritability cannot be used to estimate genetic variation between populations.

Chapter 6 Answers

1. a. Trisomy 18, Edwards syndrome
   b. Karyotypic analysis
2. Condition 2 is most likely lethal. This condition involves a chromosomal aberration, trisomy. This has the potential for interfering with the action of all genes on the trisomic chromosome. Condition 1 involves an autosomal dominant lesion to a single gene, which is more likely to be tolerated by the organism.
3. a. Trisomy: 3 copies of a single chromosome; triploidy: 3 copies of the entire chromosomal complement
   b. Aneuploidy: a change in chromosome number involving less than an entire chromosome set; euploidy: one condition of having integral multiples of the haploid chromosome set (n, $2n$, $3n$ etc.).
   c. Euploidy: see b.; polyploidy: a case of euploidy where $n > 2$.
4. Triploidy
5. c.
6. a. The cells were haploid
   b. The cells were meiotic cells or gametes
7. Two or three possibilities should be considered. The child could be monosomic for the relevant chromosome. The child has the paternal copy carrying the allele for albinism (father is heterozygous) and a nondisjunction event resulted in failure to receive a chromosomal copy from the homozygous mother. The second possibility is that the maternal chromosome carries a small deletion, allowing the albinism to be expressed. The third possibility is that the child represents a new mutation, inheriting the albino allele and having the other by mutation. Since monosomy is lethal, either the second or third possibility seems likely.
8. In theory, the chances are ⅓.
9. Humans exhibit aneuploidy at levels 10 times that found in other mammals. A change in chromosome number is usually associated with a greatly reduced fitness and lowered reproductive success.
10. A mitotic, and not meiotic error—most likely the failure of a cell to undergo cytokinesis. However, inhibition of centromere division could also produce this condition. The error would have to occur in cells that are precursors to liver cells.
11. The sperm is produced from a tetraploid spermatogonial cell and is therefore diploid. Fertilization results in a triploid embryo.
12. The embryo will be tetraploid. Inhibition of centromere division results in nondisjunction of an entire chromosome set. After cytoplasmic division, some cytoplasm is lost in an inviable product lacking genetic material and the embryo develops from the tetraploid product.
13. Nondisjunction is the failure of homologous chromosomes or sister chromatids to properly separate during meiosis or mitosis. Separation of chromosomes or chromatids occurs in anaphase of meiosis or mitosis.
14. Nondisjunction during mitosis after twinning.
15. Failure of chromosomes or chromatids to segregate during either meiosis or mitosis. The result is that both homologues (or sister chromatids) migrate to the same pole during anaphase.
16.

	GENETIC BASIS	PHENOTYPE
Edwards syndrome	47,+18	clenched fists, second and fifth fingers overlapping, rocker bottom feet with protruding heels, heart malformations
Patau syndrome	47,+13	cleft lip and palate, eye defects, polydactyly, essentially lethal,
Kleinfelter syndrome	47, XXY	poor sexual development, low fertility, some breast development
Down syndrome	47,+21	mental retardation, epicanthic fold, heart defects,

17. Primary oocytes begin meiosis I before birth and do not complete meiosis until fertilization. Thus, these germ cells are exposed to years of environmental mutagens. In contrast, meiosis in males takes 48 days. Spermatogonial cells that suffer a mutation may never undergo meiosis.
18. Relaxed maternal selection allows older women to have more aneuploid children. In young women, the woman's body recognizes an abnormal fetus and will spontaneously abort an aneuploid child. This is the process of "maternal selection." As the woman ages, this selection process becomes less effective and an aneuploid child may be allowed to develop to term.
19. Turner syndrome (45,X) is monosomy for the X chromosome. A paternal nondisjunction event could contribute a gamete lacking a sex chromosome to result in Turner syndrome. The complementary gamete would contain both X and Y chromosomes. This gamete would contribute to Klinefelter syndrome (47,XXY).
20.

	Answers:
loss of a chromosome segment	deletion
extra copies of a chromosome segment	duplication
segment moved to another chromosome	translocation
reversal in the order of a chromosome segment	inversion

21. Amniocentesis and chorionic villus sampling (CVS). CVS can be performed earlier (8–10 weeks of gesta-

tion) than amniocentesis (16th week of gestation). If termination of pregnancy is desired, risks to the mother are lower at an earlier stage in the pregnancy. Also, earlier diagnosis would allow earlier treatment if one is available.

22. Advanced maternal age, previous aneuploid child, presence of a chromosomal rearrangement, presence of a known genetic disorder in the family history

Chapter 7 Answers

1. Males get an X chromosome from their mother and a Y chromosome from their father. The XY is the *genetic sex* of the individual. In XY males, the SRY gene (also called the TDF gene) on the Y chromosome causes the undifferentiated gonads to become testes. The formation of testes establishes the *gonadal sex* as male. The testis makes two hormones, testosterone and MIH. Testosterone causes the development of the Wolffian duct and MIH causes the degeneration of the Mullerian duct. Testosterone is converted to DHT which causes the external male genitalia to develop. The male ducts and external genitalia refer to the *phenotypic sex*.

2. Testicular feminization. This individual is XY but cannot respond to the hormone testosterone. Individual develops testes and makes testosterone and MIH but she is phenotypically female. The lack of the testosterone response causes the degeneration of the Wolffian duct and no male external genitalia are developed. The presence of MIH leads to the degeneration of the Mullerian duct so no internal female sexual organs are present either. The external phenotype is female. This person is sterile.

3. The female pathway. We would all be female if it wasn't for the SRY gene on the Y chromosome. The master gene causes the developmental switch to the male pathway.

4. d.

5. A mutation causing the loss of the SRY, testosterone, or testosterone receptor gene function. Also a defect in the conversion from testosterone to DHT can cause the female external phenotype until puberty

6. a. XY, homozygous for a recessive mutation in the testosterone gene, which renders the gene non-functional

    answer: gonadally male, no ducts, externally female, sterile. The Y chromosomes present in this individual contains the normal SRY gene which causes the formation of testes. The testes should produce testosterone and MIH but the mutation only allow the production of MIH. Therefore, the lack of testosterone leads to the degeneration of the Wolffian duct and the presence of MIH leads to the degeneration of the Mullerian duct. The lack of functional testosterone also leads to the female external genitalia.

    b. XX, heterozygous for a dominant mutation in the testosterone gene, which causes continuous production of testosterone

answer: gonadally female, both ducts, externally male and sterile. The lack of the SRY gene on the Y chromosome leads to the formation of ovaries from the undifferentiated gonads. The presence of testosterone leads to the stimulation of the Wolffian duct and the lack of MIH leads to the development of the Mullerian duct. Testosterone causes the male genitalia to develop externally.

   c. XY, heterozygous for a recessive mutation in the MIH gene

answer: This individual will be a normal fertile male. The mutation is recessive and is present in only one copy. Therefore, the dominant normal allele will mask the defect.

   d. XY, homozygous for a recessive mutation in the TDF gene

answer: gonadally female, Mullerian duct present, female external genitalia, fertile. The master switch for the male pathway is missing. The default female pathway will ensue.

   e. XY, homozygous for a recessive mutation in the MIH gene

answer: gonadally male, both ducts present, externally male, may be fertile

7. Presently unknown, but perhaps an XY chromosome constitution is necessary from conception to allow normal male development.

8. Different sex hormones are present in different concentrations in the two sexes, so different genes are turned on and off in males and females. These genes are the ones that control or code for the sex-limited and sex-influenced traits.

9. Female

10. Calico cats are heterozygous females where one allele encodes black fur color and the other allele encodes orange/yellow fur color. These alleles are X-linked. In these heterozygous females, one of the X chromosomes gets inactivated early in development leaving only one X-linked allele active in any patch of cells. Therefore, some patches of the cat are black and some are orange/yellow. This illustrates the fact that female mammals are mosaics. X-inactivation occurs in the homozygous females also.

11. a. normal male   __0__
    b. normal female   __1__
    c. Kleinfelter male __1__
    d. Turner female   __0__

12. Random inactivation in females, so the genes from both X chromosomes are active in the body as a whole

13. The Olympic committee previously used the Barr body test to look for an inactivated X chromosome in cheek cells. Normal males do not show the Barr body and normal females show one Barr body. This method would eliminate XY females who are androgen insensitive (as in testicular feminization). These females would not show a Barr body because they have only one X chromosome but they are female because they do not respond to testosterone.

In 1992, the SRY DNA test was used. Normal males have the SRY gene and normal females do not. This is because the SRY gene is located on the Y chromosome. This method would still eliminate XY females where the SRY gene is present but the body cannot make or respond to the hormone testosterone. A more accurate test would be the direct measurement of testosterone to determine "maleness".

Chapter 8 Answers

1. c.
2. Proteins are found in the nucleus. Proteins are complex molecules composed of 20 different amino acids, nucleic acids are composed of only four different nucleotides. Cells contain hundreds or thousands of different proteins, only two main types of nucleic acids.
3. c.
4. Protease destroyed any small amounts of protein contaminants in the transforming extract. Similarly, treatment with RNAse destroyed any RNA present in the mixture.
5. DNA.
6. The process is transformation, discovered by Frederick Griffith. The P bacteria contain genetic information that is still functional even though the cell has been heat-killed. However, it needs a live recipient host cell to accept its genetic information. When heat killed P and live D bacteria are injected together, the dead P bacteria can transfer its genetic information into the live D bacteria. The D bacteria are then "transformed" into P bacteria and can now cause polkadots.
7. pyrimidines: cytosine and thymine
   purines: adenine and guanine
   base pairs: A pairs with T; G pairs with C
8. Chargaff's Rule: A = T and C = G
   If A = 27%, then T must equal 27%
   If G = 23%, then C must equal 23%
   Base composition:
   A = 27%
   T = 27%
   C = 23%
   G = 23%
       100%
9. b.
10. b. and e.
11. b.
12. Hydrogen bonds hold the two stands of DNA together by linking the base pairs, A to T and C to G. Hydrogen bonds are formed between hydrogen atoms and oxygen or nitrogen atoms in DNA.
13. c.
14. Two polynucleotide chains running in opposite directions, within each chain, bases are interior and sugar-phosphate groups are exterior. Bases in opposite chains are bonded to each other by hydrogen bonds. In forming such bonds, A always pairs with T, and C with G.
15. d.

16.

17. d.
18. c.
19. a.
20. template: 5' P   – AGGCTCG – OH 3'
    new strand: 3' HO – TCCGAGC – P 5'
                                        ←

    Number of H-bonds: 19
    5 – GC pairs × 3 H bonds = 15
    2 – AT pairs × 2 H bonds = 4
                                  19
21. One G – C base pair

22.

		DNA	RNA
a.	Number of chains:	2	1
b.	bases used:	A,C,G,T	A,C,G,U
c.	sugar used:	deoxyribose	ribose
d.	function:	blueprint of genetic information	transfer of genetic information from nucleus to cytoplasm

23. Nucleotides are the building blocks of DNA. DNA is structured as a double chained helical molecule that wraps around a core of histone proteins. Each core of histones wrapped in DNA is a unit called a nucleosome. Nucleosomes are the building blocks of chromatin.

Chapter 9 Answers

1. Nucleotides in the DNA code for amino acids in proteins. A change in the nucleotide causes a change in the amino acid which changes the protein.
2. b.
3. rRNA   structural and functional part of a ribosome
   tRNA   transports amino acids to translation machinery. Contains an anticodon (nucleotide triplet) that recognizes the codon (its complement) on the mRNA
   mRNA intermediate between DNA and proteins. carries genetic information from the nucleus to the cytoplasm where translation occurs
4. 1. removal of introns: to generate a contiguous coding sequence that can make an amino acid chain

2. addition of the 5' cap: ribosome binding
3. addition of the 3' poly
   A tail   mRNA stability

5. a. exon. The problem is most likely a point mutation in an exon that makes a normal length protein but the protein is nonfunctional due to the alteration of an important domain.
   b. ribosome binding site. The mRNA cannot bind to the ribosome possibly due to a faulty 5' cap. Therefore, no translation of this protein occurs.
   c. exon. A premature stop codon was introduced in one of the exons so that the protein made is shorter than normal. The short protein is not functional probably because important domains are missing. Even if the important domains were present, the protein probably cannot fold properly due to the missing amino acids. The short protein is not due to the improper removal of an intron which may contain a stop codon. We know this because the mRNA was normal in length.
   d. intron. In this case, the longer mRNA is due to the improper removal of one or more introns. If the DNA sequence at the junctions between the exons and introns is altered, the intron may not be removed at all. The intron will now be translated along with the exons and the protein made will be longer in length. Whenever the primary sequence of a protein is altered significantly (such as the inclusion of an intron that should have been spliced out), the protein will probably not fold correctly and therefore loses its function.
   e. 5' flanking. This region is responsible for the binding of RNA polymerase to carry out transcription. If the RNA polymerase binding site is mutated, the enzyme may not be able to bind to the 5' flanking region of the gene and the gene will not be transcribed.
   f. cap and tail. The 3' poly A tail provides stability to the mRNA. If the tail is absent. The mRNA is rapidly degraded by the cell.

6. d.

7. Answer: 25%   Total length: 10kb
                          Coding region: 2.5kb

8. The transcription unit covers 3kb. This will encode 1000 amino acids.

9. pre-mRNA:
GCUAAAUGGCAaaauugccggaugacGCACAUUGACUCGGaaucgaGGUCAGAUGC
mRNA:
GCUAAAUGGCAGCACAUUGACUCGGGGUCAGUAUGC

10. tRNA   UAC UCU CGA GGC
mRNA: AUG AGA GCU CCG
DNA: TAC TCT CGA GGC-sense strand
protein: met arg ala   gly
Hydrogen bonds present in the DNA: 31
                7 GC pairs × 3 = 21
                5 AT pairs × 2 = 10

11. DNA: 5' CCGC ATG TTC AGT GGG CGT AAA CAC TGA 3'-missense
               3' GGCG TAC AAG TCA CCC GCA TTT GTG ACT 5'-sense
  mRNA: 5' CCGC AUG UUC AGU GGG CGU AAA CAC UGA 3'
  protein: met phe ser gly arg lys hrs (stop)
  tRNA: UAC AAG UCA CCC GCA UUU GUG (no tRNA for stop codon)

12. a. DNA: TAC ACC ATA GCA CCA GGA TGT
   mRNA: AUG UGG UAU CGU GGU CCU ACA
   b. Change the third base in the trp codon to U or C producing a termination codon
   c. Delete a G from the trp codon
   d. Change the first nucleotide in the gly codon to U
   e. Insert a fragment of DNA

13. mRNA: AUGCUUGUCACAGCCAAUGGGUAA
   Polypeptide: met-leu-val-thr-ala-asn-gly

14. d.

15. If the second mutation causes a change in the anticodon of tRNA, it can suppress the first mutation.

16. Tripeptide composed of glycine:

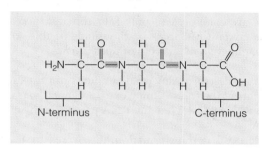

17. a. Mutation in the rRNA or the proteins in the small subunit
   b. Mutation in the rRNA or the proteins in the large subunit
   c. Same as a.

18. a. UAC
   b. ACC
   c. UC(A/G) or AG(A/C/U/G)
   d. GA(U/C/A/G) or AA(U/C)

19. Transcription: DNA, TATA box, RNA polymerase, nucleotides, pre-mRNA, enhancer. Translation: ribosomes, tRNA, amino acyl synthetase, A site, anticodon, amino acids

20. a. Less or no compound B
   b. No compound B

21. a. No
   b. Yes

22. Biochemical processes control the phenotype. Each biochemical process is a series of individual interconnected reactions. Each reaction is due to a single enzyme. Genes control the production specificity and function of enzymes. If a gene is mutated the protein it codes for changes as does the protein's ability to carry out the biochemical reaction. (This idea can be extended to nonenzymatic proteins that function in the cell.)

Chapter 10 Answers

1. The mother's metabolism can compensate for the defect.

2. Hemoglobin has a complex quaternary structure in that it is composed of 4 polypeptide chains: 2 alpha and 2 beta chains. These chains are each associated with a heme group. Alpha and beta polypeptides are encoded by different genes located on different chromosomes.

3. Accumulation of one or more precursors may be detrimental. Overuse of an alternative minor pathway may result in the accumulation of toxic intermediates. Deficiency of an important product may occur. Other reactions may be blocked.

4. Beta thalassemia—caused by a defect in the conversion of pre-mRNA into a mature RNA molecule.

   As in $\beta°$ thalassemia, a mutation in one or more of the introns could have interfered with normal mRNA splicing events, resulting in very low levels of functional mRNA and low level of beta globin

5. Let H = the mutant allele for hypercholesterolemia
   Let h = the normal allele

	answer
HH	heart attack as early as the age of 2, definite heart disease by age 20, death in most cases by 30. No functional LDL receptors produced.
Hh	heart attack in early 30's. Half the number of functional receptors are present and twice the normal levels of LDL.
hh	normal. Both copies of the gene are normal and can produce functional LDL receptors.

6. Gene therapy could be used, in which the normal gene is inserted into a vector and delivered to the cells of the liver of a HH or Hh individual. If the gene gets into the liver cells, it may express the normal receptor protein on the cell surface and remove LDL from the circulatory system. Biotechnology (the production of the human LDL receptor and injection into individuals) cannot be used. The LDL receptor has to be embedded in the cell membrane and therefore has to essentially be "inside cells". A human protein circulating in the blood cannot spontaneously insert itself in the membrane of liver cells.

7. The observation that some genes have multiple, seemingly unrelated effects does not contradict the one-gene-one enzyme hypothesis. In Marfan syndrome, a defect in a connective tissue protein has pleiotropic effects, with the aorta, the lens of the eye and the joints being affected. In sickle cell anemia, a defect in an oxygen transport protein (β-globin) has several pleiotropic effects.

8. The disease: phenylketonuria (PKU), a deficiency of the enzyme phenylalanine hydroxylase. This enzyme is used to convert the substrate phenylalanine to the product tyrosine.

phenotype: enhanced reflexes, convulsive seizures and mental retardation; also, they have lighter hair and skin color than siblings and other family members

9. There was a failure in a biochemical reaction in the pathway prior to this step; therefore, there was no substrate for the enzyme to work on.

10. It would add an amino acid to the protein. Most likely, the protein would lose some or all of its functional capacity because the addition of an amino acid early in the sequence of the protein would alter the three-dimensional shape of the protein.

11. The enzyme, RNA polymerase fails to correctly position at the promoter, causing greatly reduced transcription of the XP-A gene. XP-A is a zinc-finger protein. Its normal role is to transcriptionally regulate other genes. The mutation in the promoter would cause a large decrease in the amount of XP-A protein in the cell. As a result, the affected individual cannot repair DNA damage that was caused by ultraviolet light. The autosomal recessive disorder is xeroderma pigmentosum (XP), characterized by sensitivity to sunlight and the development of ultraviolet-light-induced skin cancer.

12. No. Essential amino acids are amino acids that the body cannot produce. Therefore, these amino acids must be included in the diet. PKU sufferers can limit their phenylalanine intake and prevent much of the mental retardation that would normally occur. If phenylalanine was not an essential amino acid, the body would be able to produce it but would not be able to convert it to tyrosine. This would lead to mental retardation. Therefore, a diet with low phenylalanine levels would not have a significant effect.

13. Normal. Phenylketonuria and alkaptonuria are caused by mutations in *different* genes affecting different enzymes. The children will be normal in phenotype because they will carry one normal copy of the PKU gene, the phenylalanine hydroxylase gene, from the AKU parent. Similarly, the children will have one normal copy of the AKU gene, the homogentisic acid oxidase gene, from the PKU parent.

    Let the mutant PKU gene be "p" and the normal gene be "P". Let the mutant AKU gene be "a" and the normal gene be "A". Both diseases are autosomal recessive.

    parental genotypes: ppAA   ×   PPaa
    .   (PKU parent)   (AKU parent)
    The genotypes of the children will be: PpAa
    .   (normal)

14. Disorder: testicular feminization.
    Without the ability to bind the hormone testosterone, a complete change in the sexual phenotype results, causing a genotypic male (XY) to develop into a phenotypic female

15. No, because individuals who are G^D/G^D show 50% activity. The g allele reduces activity by 50% so heterozygotes appear normal. It is not until the level of activity falls below 50% that the mutant phenotype is observed.

16. Yes. If you mutate gene X, the protein will be nonfunctional and this will cause the mutant phenotype. If you mutate the transcriptional regulator gene, the protein will be nonfunctional and will not allow the transcription of gene X. In both cases, no normal gene X protein is present and the mutant phenotype would be manifested.

17.

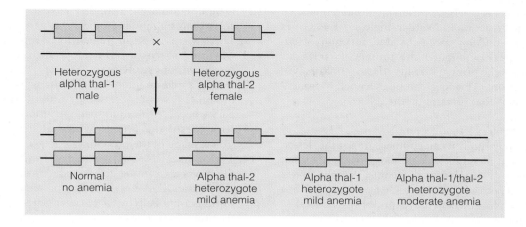

Heterozygous alpha thal-1 male × Heterozygous alpha thal-2 female

Normal no anemia | Alpha thal-2 heterozygote mild anemia | Alpha thal-1 heterozygote mild anemia | Alpha thal-1/thal-2 heterozygote moderate anemia

18. a. Let i = severe combined immunodeficiency, Let I = normal allele; Let n = Lesch Nyhan syndrome, let N = normal allele. Both disease are X-linked recessive

$X^{I,N}X^{i,n}$ X $X^{I,N}Y$
(woman carrier)   (normal man)
offspring: $X^{I,N}X^{I,N}$ ½ daughters are normal
          $X^{i,n}X^{I,N}$ ½ daughters are normal but carriers
          $X^{I,N}Y$ ½ sons are normal
          $X^{i,n}Y$ ½ sons have severe combined immunodeficiency and Lesch-Nyhan syndrome

b. $X^{I,n}X^{i,N}$ X $X^{I,N}Y$
offspring: $X^{I,n}X^{I,N}$ ½ daughters are normal but carriers for Lesch Nyhan syndrome
          $X^{i,N}X^{I,N}$ ½ daughters are normal but carriers for severe combined immunodeficiency
          $X^{I,n}Y$ ½ sons have Lesch Nyhan syndrome
          $X^{i,N}Y$ ½ sons have severe combined immunodeficiency

19. a. Buildup of substance A, no substance C
b. Buildup of substance B, no substance C
c. Buildup of substance B, as long as A is not limiting factor
d. ½ the amount of C

20. a. yes. each will carry the normal gene for the other enzyme (individual 1 will be mutant for enzyme 1 but normal for enzyme 2. This is because enzyme 1 and 2 are encoded by two different genes)
b. Let D = dominant mutation in enzyme 1, let normal allele = d
Let A = dominant mutation in enzyme 2, let normal allele = a
Ddaa   X   ddAa
offspring: DdAa   mutation in enzyme 1 and 2, A buildup, no C
        Ddaa   mutation in enzyme 1, A buildup, no C

ddAa   mutation in enzyme 2, B buildup, no C
ddaa   no mutation, normal

Ratio would be 1:2:1 for substance B buildup, no C: substance A buildup, no C: normal

21. Alleles for enzyme 1: *A* (dominant, 50% activity); *a* (recessive, 0% activity). Alleles for enzyme 2: *B* (dominant, 50% activity); *b* (recessive, 0% activity).

	Enzyme 1	Enzyme 2	Compound		
			A	B	C
1*AABB*	100	100	N	N	N
2*AaBB*	50	100	N	N	N
4*AaBb*	50	50	N	N	N
2*AABb*	100	50	N	N	N
1*AAbb*	100	0	N	B	L
2*Aabb*	50	0	N	B	L
1*aaBB*	0	100	B	L	L
2*aaBb*	0	50	B	L	L
1*aabb*	0	50	B	L	L

N, normal; B, buildup; L, less.

22. Drugs usually act on proteins. Different people have different forms of proteins. Different proteins are inherited as different alleles of a gene.

23. a. 1 and 6; 2 and 7, 3 and 8. We know this because when 1 and 6 are mixed, they cannot produce protein E because they contain defects in the same gene. The same is true for 2 and 7, 3 and 8. However, when 1 and 5 are combined, for example, protein E can be made because 1 and 5 contain mutations in different genes.
b. yes, individual 2 has a mutation in a different gene than individual 3.
c. no, individual 1 has a mutation in the same gene as individual 6.

24. 5, because the data shows that there are 5 groups of mutations (1 and 6, 2 and 7, 3 and 8, 4, 5) meaning that there are 5 different genes that are mutated corresponding to 5 steps in the pathway.

25. and **26.**

substrate → A → B → C → D → E
block for individuals: 5   2,7   1,6   3,8   4

An explanation of cells 2 and 7 will be used as an example of how to interpret this data:

In cell 2 or 7, adding substrate A has no effect, E cannot be made as indicated by the (−). The enzyme to convert A to B is mutant in this case. Therefore, substrate A cannot be converted to substrate B and the pathway stops. Adding substrate B bypasses the need for that enzyme and the pathway can continue to produce E. Similarly, addition of substrates C, D, or E, would produce the same effect as adding substrate B since they are all subsequent steps in the pathway.

27. a. ¼ normal, ¾ retarded
    b. Of the children who could not produce E (and are retarded), ⅔ would build up A, ⅓ would build up D. Of all children from this mating, ¼ would be normal, ½ will be retarded and accumulate A, ¼ will be retarded and accumulate D.

Chapter 11 Answers

1. $(3 \times 10^9 \text{ nt/sec})/(20 \text{ nt/sec}) = 1.5 \times 10^8 \text{ sec} = 4.7 \text{ years}$. To shorten the time one could postulate more than one site of replication proceeding simultaneously.

2. 245,000 births represent 490,000 copies of the achondroplasia gene, since each child carries two copies of the gene. The mutation rate is therefore $^{10}/_{490,000}$ or 2×10^{-5} per generation.

3. It is not possible to measure mutations in homozygous dominant individuals. If a dominant allele mutates to a recessive allele, the recessive phenotype will never be seen due to the second allele that is still dominant. It is highly unlikely that both dominant alleles will mutate in the same cell to show the recessive phenotype.

4. Spontaneous mutations are those mutations arising without any intentional intervention. Induced mutations are those mutations arising from intervention involving the application of a mutagen—regardless of whether or not the mutagen has been shown to be responsible for the mutation.

5. a. A mutation caused by the addition or deletion of nucleotide residues from a coding portion of a gene destroys the triplet reading frame (any additions or deletions that alter the frame except multiples of 3 bp).
   b. A measure of the occurrence of mutations per individual per generation.

c. Mutations that arise in somatic (non-germline) cells and are not inherited.

6. a. A *missense* mutation is a mutation where one amino acid is substituted for another. This protein will be normal in length.
   b. A *nonsense* mutation is a mutation that introduces a stop codon in place of a codon that specifies an amino acid. This kind of mutation causes premature translation termination and results in a shorter amino acid sequence.
   c. A *sense* mutation is a mutation that changes the stop codon into one that codes for an amino acid. The result is a longer than normal amino acid sequence.

The nonsense mutation generally causes the most dramatic effect especially if a large region of the protein is missing. A sense mutation may produce deleterious effects because the extra amino acids may cause improper folding or transport of the protein. A missense mutation is likely to have the least dramatic effect because only one amino acid is changed. If the one amino acid changed is at a critical position in the protein (for example a binding site for a substrate), it could completely destroy the function of the protein. However, most amino acid substitutions result in only minor effects on the normal function of the protein.

7. a. 5-Bromouracil
   b. Nitrous acid

8. A frameshift mutation is the addition or loss of nucleotide pairs such that the normal translocational reading frame is dislodged. Intercalating agents interpose themselves between adjacent nucleotide pairs and this spatial distortion can lead to the misincorporation of "extra" nucleotides during replication or repair.

9. missense—same
   nonsense–shorter
   sense—longer

10. a. and d.

11. a. 50% channels, normal
    b. 0% channels, severe symptoms
    c. 2.5% channels, severe symptoms
    d. 12.5% channels, mild symptoms

12. a. See pedigree below
    b. No, because there is no family history.
    c. 50%

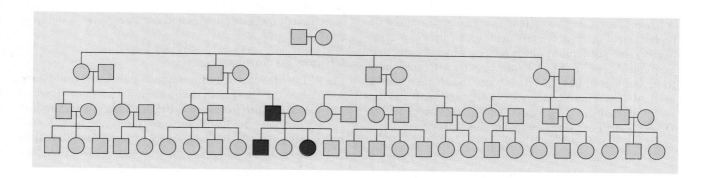

13. Achondroplasia is a dominant disorder with high pene- trance, thus an unaffected person does not carry the achondroplasia haplotype. Dominant germline muta- tions will occur in this individual, presumably at the av- erage rate of 4×10^{-5} per generation.

14. The disorder is recessive, therefore the genetic defect re- sponsible for the disease may be maintained in a het- erozygous state in the gene pool of a population.

15. a. The Ames test uses bacterial cells that are his$^-$. These cells are exposed to a potential mutagen and then plated on medium lacking the amino acid, histidine. If a mutation occurs causing the bacteria to become his$^+$, a bacterial colony will grow on the petri plate. The number of colonies determines the mutagenic ca- pability of that substance.

    b. dish 1 is the control experiment. Colonies in dish 1 are produced from spontaneous mutation and are not due to any mutagen.

    c. substance B is most mutagenic, then substance A. Substance C is not mutagenic at all. Dish 4 with sub- stance C has the same number of colonies as dish 1, the control dish.

16. Our bodies can correct basepairing errors made during DNA replication. We can also repair UV damaged DNA after thymine dimers form.

17. X-rays can cause mutations. Medical professionals need to be aware of the dose of X-rays that a patient receives. The benefits of the X-ray method need to outweigh the risks.

Chapter 12 Answers

1. d.
2. d.
3. b.
4. b.
5. b.
6. The sequence is: AAGCTT The enzyme *Hin*dIII will cut this sequence.
7. DNA may be cloned by inserting it into a plasmid or phage vector that can replicate in a host cell. DNA is pre- pared for cloning by using a restriction enzyme to cleave it into fragments with sticky ends. DNA can be joined to the cloning vector by using DNA ligase.
8. Because of the large size of the human genome, it would be best to select a vector with the capacity to accept large fragments of DNA, such as a virus or a yeast artificial chromosome.
9. A linear DNA segment, such as a human gene, cannot be replicated in a host cell and passed to progeny cells. Vectors are self replicating molecules which means that they contain specific DNA sequences that will cause them to be duplicated before cell division and then passed to progeny cells. Therefore, any DNA segment ligated to the vector will also be duplicated and many copies of the DNA segment can be generated in this manner.

10. *Eco*R1: 2kb, 11.5 kb, 10 kb
    *Hin*dIII/*Pst*1: 7 kb, 3 kb, 7.5 kb, 6 kb
    *Eco*R1/*Hin*dIII/*Pst*1: 2 kb, 5 kb, 3 kb, 3.5 kb, 4 kb, 6 kb

11. 1) Identify related genes in other genomes
    2) Study the evolution of genes
    3) Study differences between normal and mutant genes

12. 2^6 number of DNA fragments of the cystic fibrosis gene fragment will be present after 6 cycles. You can specifi- cally amplify this fragment because you have primers that pair only with this gene. The regions in between the primers will be amplified in the PCR reaction and not any other DNA sequences.

13. Isolate human DNA from blood. Separate the human DNA by size using gel electrophoresis. Transfer the DNA to a nylon sheet (this is the blot) and probe the blot us- ing the mouse gene that has been isolated. If the mouse gene forms a hybrid with one of the human genes, then you know that a similar gene exists in humans. You can now clone with gene from a library and start studying its role in human blindness.

14. The missing *Eco*RI restriction site can be assayed for all members of the family. DNA isolated form blood of each individual would be cut with *Eco*RI, electrophoresed, transferred by Southern blot, and then probed. If the re- striction site is missing within an individual, that person would then know that he or she carries the allele for cystic fibrosis. Those who have the restriction site could be re- lieved that they do not carry the allele. The two individuals carry two different mutations within the same gene that lead to cystic fibrosis. Because the presence of two copies of a cystic fibrosis gene, whether or not the defect is exactly the same, leads to expression of the disorder, 25% of the children from this mating would have cystic fibrosis.

15. a.

16. a. The last affected son represents a crossover between the gene in question and the locus of the probe.

    b. The 2-kb and 3-kb bands are closely linked to the dominant (mutant) allele. Their presence in an indi- vidual would indicate a high risk of developing the disorder, while their absence would indicate a low risk of developing the disorder.

    c. Exact risk cannot be stated until the map units be- tween the two bands and the gene in question are de- termined.

17. DNA derived from individuals with sickle cell anemia will lack one fragment contained in the DNA from nor- mal individuals, and in addition, there will be a large (un- cleaved) fragment not seen in normal DNA.

Chapter 13 Answers

1. RFLPs are inherited as codominant alleles. Useful RFLPs have at least two, but not too many alleles, some of which should be fairly common in the population being studied. For linkage, the RFLP not only should be on the same chromosome as the gene being studied, but should be close enough to the gene so that crossovers are infrequent.

2. When the RFLP marker and the gene in question are located relatively far apart, there is opportunity for crossing over, allowing the marker and the gene to be separated. In addition, the mutant gene may have arisen on a chromosome with a common RFLP marker, meaning that only a subset of the population has the marker linked to the mutant gene.

3. The target cells must be available for gene transfer. Cells that can be removed from the body, such as blood cells or liver cells, are examples. Gene transfer into other cells, such as brain cells, that cannot be removed and re-implanted and are separated from the rest of the body by the blood-brain barrier are difficult targets. Other factors include the average life-span of the target cells, their ability to produce enough of the gene product, and whether the target cells can divide to perpetuate themselves.

4. d.

5. c.

6. c.

7. Prenatal testing: detection of a genetic disorder in the embryo or fetus already in the womb.

Preimplantation testing: detection of a genetic disorder in an 8-cell embryo *in vitro*. The embryo has not yet been implanted in the mother.

Presymtomatic: genetic testing of newborns, children or adults.

8. The first two males cannot be excluded as the father of this child, but male #3 does not have an allele in common with the child, and is homozygous for an allele not present in the child. Male #3 can be excluded as the child's father.

9. In some current experiments, cells from the blood or bone marrow are removed from the patient and grown in the laboratory under conditions that stimulate them to multiply. Then the desired gene is inserted into the cells with the help of a vector, and the successfully altered cells are selected, grown under laboratory conditions, and returned to the patient's body.

10. a. DNA fingerprinting is used to diagnose inherited disorders in both prenatal and newborn babies in hospitals around the world. These disorders may include cystic fibrosis, hemophilia, Huntington disease, familial Alzheimer disease, sickle cell anemia, thalassemia, and many others. Genetic counselors can use DNA fingerprint information to help prospective parents understand the risk of having an affected child.

b. Developing cures for inherited disorders depends on researchers' ability to map inherited disorders to chromosomes. By studying the DNA fingerprints of relatives who have a history of some particular disorder, or by comparing large groups of people with and without the disorder, it is possible to identify DNA patterns associated with the disease in question.

c. Since every organ or tissue of an individual contains the same DNA fingerprint, the U.S. armed services started a program to collect DNA fingerprints from all personnel for use later, in case they are needed to identify casualties or persons missing in action.

d. Another important use of DNA fingerprints in the court system is to establish paternity in custody and child support litigation.

11. Potential dangers could include the escape of genetically altered organisms, and undesirable side effects of gene therapy. Gene therapy, as one form of recombinant DNA technology raises a number of ethical questions about germ-line therapy, in which altered genomes are transmitted to offspring, and use of gene therapy for cosmetic reasons, such as altering height.

Some of these potential dangers can be reduced or eliminated by research, while others require public policy decisions.

12. Conclusion: Evidence excludes suspect #1 and includes suspect #2. If Suspect #1 has a different DNA pattern than the evidence, the suspect is excluded from having committed the crime. But that evidence sample of DNA cannot possibly be Suspect #1's. Suspect #2's DNA corresponds perfectly at each of the four places of variation on the human chromosomes examined.

Chapter 14 Answers

1. a.

2. b.

3. d.

4. b.

5. e.

6. Carcinogenesis is often thought of as a multistep process—generally two or more distinct mutational events must occur. Genetic predisposition to acquire a particular form of tumor is often due to the genetic transmission of one or more of the mutant alleles through the germ line. Subsequently, individual somatic cells undergo secondary mutations to produce cancerous tissue.

7. Retinoblastoma is a recessive disease in that it requires two mutated copies of the Rb gene. In the inherited form of retinoblastoma, one mutant copy is passed from the previous generation. Therefore, every cell in the new individual will have one normal and one mutant copy of the gene. It only takes one mutation in the normal copy of the Rb gene, in any cell in the eye, to produce the eye cancer. Thus, bilateral retinoblastoma is common in the inherited form of the disease. In the sporadic form, individuals carry two normal copies of the Rb gene. The two genes must be mutated in the same eye cell for cancer to result. It is unlikely that both Rb genes would be mutated in the same cell given the millions of cells in the eye and therefore, sporadic cases are more likely to involve only one eye.

8. a. The father did not acquire a second mutation in the Rb gene in any of his eye cells. He remained heterozygous and therefore no cancer resulted.

b. 50%

c. Their son can be tested frequently for eye tumors. Early detection and treatment means that their son may be able to retain normal eyesight.

9. a. Benign tumors are not involved in cancer. They are self-contained growths that do not spread to other tissues

b. Malignant tumors are cancerous. Cells can detach from the primary malignant tumor and invade other tissues creating additional tumors at secondary sites.

c. The ability of cancers to invade other tissue is known as metastasis.

10. c.

11. Tumor suppressor genes—suppresses cell division
Oncogenes—promotes cell division

12. (1) The existence of inherited predisposition toward certain forms of cancer implies the existence of Mendelian (chromosomal) mutations responsible for these diseases. (2) Mutagens known to act on DNA have been shown to be carcinogens as well. (3) Viral oncogenes have been identified as a causal agent in the transmission of some cancers (RSV, MMTV, HTLV-I); the active viral genes are often transduced cellular genes that have altered patterns of gene expression. (4) Gross chromosomal aberrations have been linked to certain forms of cancer (Wilms tumor and chronic myelogenous leukemia).

13. There are genes on chromosome 21 that promote cell division in leukocytes (white blood cells). Somehow, three copies of the gene(s), make Down children more susceptible to leukemia.

14. A proto-oncogene is a gene normally found in the human genome that promotes cell division. An oncogene is a mutated proto-oncogene that promotes uncontrolled cell division that leads to cancer.

15. Proto-oncogenes are thought to be involved in the regulation of cellular differentiation and growth. Deregulation of these processes results in uncontrolled proliferation of mutant (oncogenic) cells.

16. c-*myc* lies at the breakpoint of a translocation involving chromosome 8 and either chromosome 14, 22, or 2. The translocation places the *myc* gene in altered chromosomal milieu and thus disrupts its normal expression. Altered expression of c-myc is thought to be necessary for the production of Burkitt's lymphoma.

17. Cigarette smoking, dietary fat vs. dietary fiber, asbestos, vinyl chloride, etc.

18. One of the parents has the mutant gene responsible for dominant familial retinoblastoma in his/her lineage. When present, there is a 90% chance that the gene is expressed in the form of retinoblastoma. Since both parents are phenotypically normal, there is a maximum 10% chance that one parent carries the defect. If carried, there is a 50% chance that the defective allele will be passed on to any particular child. If passed to a particular child, there is a 90% chance that the defect will be expressed. Therefore, the total probability of this couple having a child with retinoblastoma is (0.1)(0.5)(0.9) = 0.045 (4.5%).

19. The inheritance is dominant because only one mutant allele causes the predisposition to retinoblastoma. However, the second allele must also be mutated in at least one eye cell to produce the disease. Therefore, the expression of retinoblastoma is recessive

20. Conditions a and d would produce cancer. The loss of function of a tumor suppressor gene would allow cell growth to go unchecked. The overexpression of a proto-oncogene would promote more cell division than normal.

21. Carcinogens cause cancer. Mutagens cause base changes in the DNA sequence. Most carcinogens are also mutagens. Carcinogens mutate genes that are involved in cancer. However, a mutagen is not always a carcinogen. Mutagens can cause any change in DNA that can lead to any type of human disease, not just cancer.

22. The light smoker may have a genetic pre-disposition to develop lung cancer such as the debrisoquine pathway. This individual may not have the ability to metabolize the carcinogen in tobacco smoke as well as the heavy smoker.

23. Large-scale epidemiological studies were used to demonstrate a circumstantial association between individuals exposed to high levels of asbestos and the occurrence of certain forms of cancer, notably cancer of the lung and digestive tract. Laboratory experiments were then used to test the effect of asbestos exposure on animals under controlled conditions. The coupling of the two approaches allows researchers to define potentially hazardous environmental factors by statistical analysis of large populations and then directly test the carcinogenic potential of these factors in a controlled laboratory environment.

24. a.

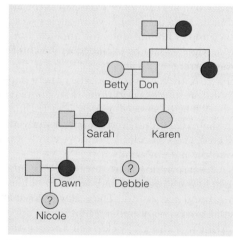

(a)

b. dominant

c. Bb − normal, men do not get this form of breast cancer

d. bb

e. Chromosome H

f. Debbie is not susceptible, but Nicole is.

Chapter 15 Answers

1. Attenuation is the loss of viability of an infectious agent—usually a virus or bacterium. Active immunization requires exposure to the antigens of the infectious agent. This is most readily achieved by exposure to the

agent itself. Since exposing people to viable infectious agents causes the disease one is trying to prevent, nonviable or attenuated agents are useful in this role.

2. *Phagocytes (macrophages and neutrophils):* recognize nonself organisms and cellular debris and engulf it. They then enzymatically degrade the materials, present antigens on the cell surface, and signal other elements of the immune system, alerting them to an infection. *T cells:* Helper T cells are involved in switching on the immune response and are crucial for signal transduction: killer T cells and natural killer cells recognize and destroy cells of the body harboring invading viruses and destroy cancer cells; suppressor T cells are involved in switching off the immune response. B cells produce antibodies but are more properly considered a part of humoral immunity.

3. Inflammatory response—cells damaged by microorganisms release a chemical signal. Blood carrying macrophages, and other phagocytes migrate to the area and engulf microorganisms.

    Complement—multiprotein complex creates a pore in the microorganism membrane. Water flows in that bursts cell.

    Specific immune response—antibody-mediated and cell-mediated immunity that include immunological memory

4. helper T cells—activate B cells to produce antibodies
    supressor T cells—stops the immune response of B and T cells
    cytotoxic T cells—targets and destroys infected cells

5. Macrophages (phagocytes) can activate T cells by releasing interleukin 1.

6. Antibody-mediated immunity involves the production of circulating antibodies from B cells and the recognition of antigens by T cells. This system is directed against invading viruses and bacteria. Cell-mediated immunity involves cytotoxic T cells that can detect and destroy cells that are infected with viruses or bacteria.

7. Vaccines aim to inject antigens to induce a primary immune response and the production of memory cells. A second injection (booster) of antigens then creates a secondary response to increase the number of memory cells. The antigen is often a killed or weakened strain of the microorganism. Vaccination using a weakened strain may cause some symptoms of illness but the antigen will not cause a life threatening disease.

8. The T-cell receptor

9. IgG molecules are monomers composed of two light chains and two heavy chains; therefore four polypeptide chains are required. Therefore, the molecular weights are:
    Light chain: 25,000
    Heavy chain: 50,000

10. Immunoglobulins: IgG, IgA, IgM, IgD, IgE

11. a. The mother is Rh$^-$. She will produce antibodies against the Rh antigen if her fetus is Rh$^+$. This happens when blood from the fetus enters the maternal circulation.

    b. the mother already has circulating antibodies against the Rh protein from her first Rh+ child. She can mount a greater immune response against the second Rh+ child by generating a large number of antibodies.

12. macrophages engulf virus
↓
macrophage displays viral antigens on its cell surface
↓
helper T cell recognizes this and binds the viral antigen via the T cell receptor
↓
helper T cell becomes activated   helper T cell divides to produce memory T cells
↓
activates B cells
↓
B cells divide several times
↓

plasma cells   memory cells—can respond
secretes antibodies that can   rapidly if antigen is encountered
recognize antigen, have   again—life span is months to years
4–5 day life span
↓
antibodies bind antigen on virus
which marks it for destruction
by phagocytes

13. The AIDS virus infects and kills helper T4 cells, the very cells that normally trigger the antibody-mediated immune response. Therefore, as the infection progresses, the immune system gets weaker and weaker as more T cells are killed. The AIDS sufferer is then susceptible to various infections and certain forms of cancer.

14. For any antibody class, the genes encoding the single heavy chain and the two light chains are complex. There are several hundred V or variable region gene segments, a few (5–10) J or joining region gene segments, and a single segment encoding the C or constant region. Recombination results in the juxtaposition of V, J, and C gene segments to form a functional gene. This process of recombination can therefore result in a large variety of functional antibody genes within the body's population of B cells.

15. (1) Migration inhibitory factor is released by T cells upon contact with a foreign antigen and, when received by macrophages, causes them to remain in the region of the infection. (2) Interleukin 1 is released by macrophages encountering an infection and activates T cells. (3) Interleukin 2 is released by activated T cells and stimulates more T cells to participate in the immune response.

16. $23 \times 47 \times 8 \times 14 \times 3 \times 6 = 2.2 \times 10^6$ haplotypes are possible. Since humans are diploid, there are $(2.2 \times 10^6)^2 = 4.84 \times 10^{12}$ possible genotypes.

17. Autosomal codominant inheritance

18. AB individual has no antibodies against the A or B antigen. Any blood given to this person will be accepted. The type O individual does not have the A or B antigen and therefore can be given to anyone. It doesn't matter what circulating antibodies are in the recipient since no A or B antigens are present in the donor blood cells.

19. The *antigens* of the donor/recipient are more important. The antigen of the donor will be rejected if the recipient does not have the same antigen. The antigen of the recipient determines which antibodies can be produced. For example, a blood type A individual will make B antibodies if exposed to the B.

20. The infant can only be type O and the genotype is therefore I^O/I^O. The man on trial can only be type AB and his genotype must therefore be I^A/I^B. The mother must be type A since she only possesses antibodies to type B blood. Since there is no question of maternity involved here, she contributed an I^O allele to the infant. Therefore the mother's genotype is I^A/I^O. The court can dismiss the suit because the father of the infant had to possess an I^O allele, and the man on trial doesn't carry one.

21. The son would be able to receive blood from both his parents. His genotype would be I^A/I^B and therefore he would express both the A and the B antigens. Therefore, he would not have the antibodies against the A or the B antigen.

22. Introducing a recombinant virus into the body can cause an immune response by the host. Since the body regards the virus as "non-self", it may activate the system that will destroy the virus and also the therapeutic gene it is carrying. If the virus manages to infect a cell, the cell may be targeted for destruction also since it will be displaying viral antigens on its cell surface.

23. The graft tissue acts as an antigen to the recipient's immune system. The cells of the graft tissue displays antigens (such as the HLA complex) on its surface. These proteins are not the same proteins found in the host and they are seen as "foreign". The recognition of the graft tissue as non-self mobilizes cytotoxic T cells to cause graft rejection. The graft also stimulates the development of immunological memory. Therefore, the second graft is rejected in a shorter amount of time because memory T cells, memory B cells, and antibodies specific to the graft tissue are already circulating in the blood.

24. Clone the human gene that suppresses hyperacute rejection and inject it into pig embryos. The hope is that the pig's cells will express this human protein on the cell surface. The transplanted organ may then be recognized by the human recipient as "self". In addition, transplants of bone marrow from donor pigs into human recipients may

help in preventing rejection mediated by T cells. This dual bone marrow system will recognize the pig's organ as "self" but will retain the normal human immunity.

25. No. Natural killer cells do not have to be activated by helper T cells to destroy virally infected cells.

26. 20% of all individuals carrying the HLA-B27 allele have ankylosing spondylitis. Also, males are affected 9:1 over females. Therefore, of 100 individuals who have B27, regardless of sex, twenty will be affected. Of these 100, half should be males, half should be females. If x is the rate in males, and y is the rate in females, $x = 9y$. In a group of 100 individuals with B27, $50x + 50y = 20$, or $450y + 50y = 20$; $y = 0.04$ and $x = 0.36$. This means that 36% of males with B27 will be affected, and 4% of females with B27 will be affected.
    a. This boy has the B27 allele, therefore the probability is 0.36.
    b. This girl has the B27 allele and the probability is therefore 0.04
    c. This boy also possesses the B27 allele and the probability is thus 0.36
    d. This boy doesn't have the B27 allele. His probability of having ankylosing spondylitis is equal to the percentage of the population who lack B27 and have ankylosing spondylitis.

27. Blood type B individuals do not make the A antigen. Therefore, the patient will generate antibodies against the A antigen because it is "foreign". The antibodies will bind to the transfused red blood cells that contain the A antigen causing them to clump and burst. Thus, hemoglobin, the major protein in the red blood cells, is released into the blood which crystallizes in the kidney. This can cause kidney failure.

28. a. Mother: Rh^-/Rh^-. Father: Almost certainly Rh^+/Rh^+ with a small chance that he contributed the Rh^+ allele 16 straight times but is genotypically Rh^+/Rh^-
    b. Yes. An Rh^+ offspring presents the antigen to the mother at birth. Lacking the Rh antigen, the mother would produce antibodies to combat it. These antibodies could then enter the infant's bloodstream at birth and cause massive hemagglutination. Therefore all children except perhaps the eldest were at considerable risk.

29. They do not produce an immune response in most people.

30. Antihistamines will block the production or action of histamine. The allergen causes a release of IgE antibodies which bind to mast cells. These cells release histamine which causes fluid accumulation, tissue swelling (such as swollen airways or eyes), and mucus secretion (such as a runny nose).

31. He has X-linked agammaglobulinemia (XLA) Affected individuals tend to be boys who are highly susceptible to bacterial infections. The antibody-mediated immunity is not functioning. B cells may be absent or immature B cells may be unable to mature and produce antibodies. The cell-mediated immunity is normal.

32. Express the cloned gene to make the protein product, isolate the protein and inject it into humans. The immune system should make antibodies to that protein. When the actual live virus is encountered, the immune system will have circulating antibodies and T cells that will recognize the protein (antigen) on the surface of the virus.

33. They need to test one cell of each 8-cell embryo for an ABO and Rh blood type match and also a HLA complex match. If a match exists, they will implant the embryo(s) into the mother and hope that pregnancy occurs. When the baby is born, bone marrow will be taken and transplanted into the existing child.

    Ethically, it is difficult to imagine having a child for the primary purpose of being a bone marrow donor. It may demean the value of the life of the new child. Also, what happens to the embryos that are not a match to the couple's existing child? These embryos are completely healthy; they simply have the wrong blood type and histocompatibility complex. On the other hand, if the couple will love and provide for this new child, it may be a wonderful experience that the new child has the opportunity to save the life of his/her sibling.

Chapter 16 Answers

1. If the case involves a single gene, pedigree analysis and linkage and segregation studies, including the use of RFLP markers and other recombinant DNA technologies are the most appropriate methods. In polygenic cases, twin studies to determine concordance and heritability are common. Recently, geneticists have studied the offspring of twins to overcome certain problems such as the limitations of small ample sizes. Also, recombinant DNA studies have begun with twins to locate polygenic genes.

2. The definition must be precise enough to distinguish the behavior from other, similar behaviors and from the behavior of the control group. The definition of the behavior can significantly affect the results of the genetic analysis, and even the mode of inheritance of the trait.

3. *Drosophila* has many advantages for the study of behavior. Mutagenesis and screening for behavior mutants allows the recovery of mutations that affect many forms of behavior. The ability to perform genetic crosses and recover large numbers of progeny over a short period of time also enhances the genetic analysis of behavior. This organism can serve as a model for human behavior, because cells of the nervous system in both *Drosophila* and humans use similar mechanisms to transmit impulses and store information.

4. The mutated protein impairs peripheral nerve function which leads to muscle atrophy in the lower leg and arm. This is one phenotypic characteristic of Charcot-Marie-Tooth disease.

5. As stated, the study shows that IQ is a strongly heritable trait. The relationship between IQ and intelligence is uncertain and questionable. Strictly speaking, the conclusions cannot be generalized, since conclusions about heritability are valid only for the group under study, and valid for this group only at the time of the study. In eval-

uating the conclusions of this study, additional information would be useful. This would include the family and economic conditions under which the twins were raised, whether the twins had contact with each other, and the IQs of the birth parents.

6. Epistasis is a form of nonreciprocal gene interaction, where one gene masks the expression of another. For example, if *A* masks the expression of *B* or *b*, the result is an increase in one phenotypic class (12:3:1 instead of 9:3:3:1), making one phenotype more common. If a recessive allele *a* masks the expression of *B* or *b*, the result is the appearance of a new phenotype in the offspring, in high frequency (9:3:3:4 instead of 9:3:3:1).

7. From a single study, perfect pitch (MIM/OMIM 159300) can be classified as a familial trait; its pattern of inheritance strongly suggests that it is an autosomal dominant trait. To confirm this, more studies covering several generations in families with perfect pitch would be desirable, or other supporting studies should be available (see answer to next question).

8. The pedigree presented is consistent with autosomal dominant inheritance associated with imperfect penetrance. In a study published in 1995, researchers using magnetic resonance and positron emission tomography (PET) scans found differences in brain structure between musicians with perfect pitch and those without perfect pitch. The difference between perfect pitch and tone deafness could be due to a single allele, but more work is necessary to confirm this.

9. The heritability of Alzheimer disease, a multifactorial disorder, cannot be established due to interactions between genetic and environmental factors. Less than 50% of Alzheimer cases can be attributed to genetic causes, indicating that the environment plays a large role in the development of this disease. Other non-genetic factors may involve aluminum and prions.

10. No, it means that there are probably other genes involved or the environment plays a significant role. The linkage to chromosome 7 is still valid and the next goal would be to find the gene on chromosome 7 that causes manic depression. Also, finding the other genes involved is important. A researcher may find that a subset of manic depressive individuals have a defect in the gene on chromosome 7 and another subset in a gene on chromosome 12. Both defects can cause the same disease.

11. His monozygotic twin is at high risk for the disease. Studies show that there is a 46% concordance where identical twins both develop schizophrenia. Studies also indicate that MZ twins raised apart display the same level of concordance as those raised together.

12. RFLP mapping uses known markers on chromosomes. The goal is to find a marker that segregates in a pattern that is similar to the disease. For example, in one case, the presence of the marker may indicate the presence of the disease causing allele. However, the marker may be hundreds of kilobases away from the actual gene itself. Therefore, the marker identifies a region on a chromosome that is involved. The researcher still needs to look

through that region, which may include hundreds of genes, to find the one gene that causes the disease. This is a time consuming and labor intensive task.

13. Most single gene mutations that affect behavior act on the brain and/or the nervous system to alter a cellular function.

14. Manic depression is a mood disorder, characterized by cycles of depression that alternate with periods of elation. Schizophrenia is a collection of disorders that affect the thought processes themselves, rather than mood. Both disorders that have strong genetic components, and both affect the ability of affected individuals to function in work and social settings.

15. c.

16. Twin studies indicated that this is the case. Also, genetic linkage has been shown to a region on the X chromosome. If a specific gene is found on the X, then there would be much greater support for the role of genetics in homosexuality. After the gene is cloned, a comparison between normal and homosexual individuals can be done to see if there is a specific DNA change in the gene that can be attributed to homosexuality. This data would not diminish the fact that the environment plays a major role in sexual orientation. It simply states that there is also a genetic cause of homosexuality in some individuals.

Chapter 17 Answers

1.

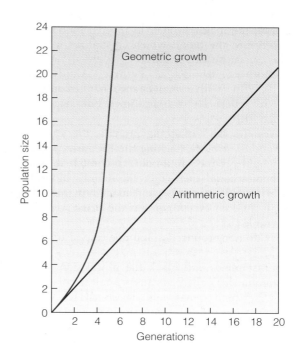

2. War, famine and disease
3. Population: Local groups of individuals occupying a given space at a given time.

   Gene pool: The set of genetic information carried by a population.

Allele frequency: The frequency of occurrence of particular alleles in the gene pool of a population.

Genotype frequency: The frequency of occurrence of particular genotypes among the individuals of a population.

4. Evolution is the change over time of heritable characteristics of a population. Since characteristics that are heritable are determined by genes (by definition), evolution constitutes the change of gene frequencies in a population over time. Darwin and Wallace observed that those individuals in a population possessing favored characteristics (phenotypes) were responsible for a greater proportion of the surviving offspring in future generations than individuals with less favored characteristics. Since the favored characters are determined by genes, Darwin and Wallace were observing that natural selection tends to change the frequency of specific genes over the course of time.

5. no

6. The simplest experiment consists of monitoring the frequencies of various alleles over a number of generations to determine if the allele frequencies are changing or are in equilibrium. If they are in equilibrium, then the population is not evolving.

7. a. Children: M = 0.5, N = 0.5. Adults: M = 0.5, N = 0.5.
   b. Yes, allelic frequencies are unchanged.
   c. No. The genotypic frequencies are changing within each generation.

8. The frequency of an allele in a population has no relationship to its mode of inheritance. For example, a dominant allele may exist at a very low frequency in a population, and cannot ultimately overtake a recessive allele in frequency.

9. It will take one generation for the allelic frequencies to reach Hardy-Weinberg equilibrium, and two generations for the genotypic frequencies to reach equilibrium. After the first generation of random mating: $A = 0.225$, $a = 0.775$. $AA = 0.035$, $Aa = .38$, $aa = 0.585$. After the second generation of random mating: $A = 0.225$, $a = 0.775$. $AA = 0.050625$, $Aa = .34875$, $aa = 0.600625$.

10. In the case of multiple alleles, such as the ABO blood system, the greatest number of alleles that can be carried by an individual is two. A population, however, has the capacity to carry many different alleles for any given locus.

11. $A = 0.5$, $a = 0.5$

12. a. $A = 0.95$, $a = 0.05$. Has to be X-linked.
    b. Genotypes of males: $A/Y = 0.95$, $a/Y = 0.05$. Genotypes of females: $AA = 0.9025$, $Aa = 0.095$, $aa = 0.0025$.

13. $O = 0.04$

14. U.S. Indians and Eskimos, and U.S. Blacks and Whites. The Indians and Eskimos are known to be derived from the same ancestral populations in Asia. Their allelic frequencies show some divergence. This is probably due to recent isolation of the two populations after their migrations to North America and Greenland. The similarity of the allelic frequencies in the U.S. Black and White populations may be due to genetic exchange between the populations after their arrival in North America.

15. All the populations are in agreement with the Hardy-Weinberg law.

16. $p = 0.5$, $q = 0.5$.

Chapter 18 Answers

1. All polymorphisms are mutations. When a mutation resulting in a particular allele is present in at least 1% of the population, it is termed a polymorphism. This percentage is chosen because it is clearly higher than can be accounted for by mutation alone. Because such genetic variations cannot be accounted for by mutation alone, other forces such as natural selection must be active. The study of such variation is important in understanding the process of evolution.

2. Mutation itself is a rare event, and as such, has little direct effect on allele frequency.

3. A founder effect is one example of genetic drift. Genetic drift is a chance event that alters gene frequencies. It acts through small populations, and founder effects involve a small number of individuals making a large contribution to the genes of the next generation.

4. No it is not an accurate description. Natural selection depends on fitness, the ability of a given genotype to survive and reproduce. It is the differential reproduction of some individuals that is the essence of natural selection.

5. Social customs and pressures have helped shape nonrandom mating patterns among humans, called assortative matings. Other forms of nonrandom matings include incest and consanguineous marriages. Such nonrandom matings lead to an increase in homozygouity and a decrease in genetic diversity. This produces a nonequilibrium situation.

6. Culture represents one form of adaptation, and is itself an evolutionary process. Culture tends to buffer populations from some forms of selection, and so alters the process of natural selection. Our present culture is affecting selection by permitting the survival and reproduction of genotypes that would otherwise not reproduce. Over the long run, this can lead to an increase in frequency of these genes.

7. Some scientists argue that differences in ABO frequency observed in populations may have adaptive value. They cite several pieces of evidence, including the fact that among white males, those with type O blood have the longest life expectancy, while those with type B blood have the shortest life expectancy. In addition, individuals with type A blood are more likely than others to get stomach cancer.

8. A drastic decrease in the size of a population for whatever reason, makes that population vulnerable to genetic drift. Such a reduction in size can also lead to inbreeding among the relatively small number of survivors. Under these circumstances, those alleles which are still present will tend to express themselves phenotypically, even if they are recessive. The limited variability that is characteristic of small populations plays a role in species extinction.

9. Genetic polymorphisms can be maintained in populations for several reasons: they can make different contributions

to the fitness of the organisms in which they occur, they are maintained in different frequencies in different parts of a subdivided population by natural selection, or they are in Hardy-Weinberg equilibrium.

10. No, it is difficult to eliminate deleterious recessive alleles from the gene pool of a large population by natural selection. These alleles survive in populations because the majority of them are carried in the heterozygous condition and are not expressed phenotypically. As a result, natural selection cannot act on these alleles, and they remain hidden in the gene pool.

11. In populations that are derived from a small number of individuals, one or a few individuals may carry alleles that are rare in the original population. Differences in allele frequency between the original population and the new population are due to the founder effect.

12. c.

13. a.

Chapter 19 Answers

1. Prenatal screening: used to diagnose genetic defects and birth defects in the unborn.
   Newborn screening: used to diagnose genetic defects in neonatal and early infants stages of life.
   Carrier screening: used to identify phenotypically normal individuals who carry deleterious recessive traits.
   Occupational screening: used to identify those who are genetically susceptible to agents found in the workplace.
   Reproductive screening: used for identification of gamete donors carrying genetic or chromosomal defects.

2. The first recommendation would be for another α-fetoprotein test to determine whether the first test may have been a false positive. If the second test is positive, amniocentesis is recommended. If the results from this procedure are ambiguous, fetoscopy may be considered, balancing the risks of this procedure against the benefits.

3. The essay answer depends on your point of view.

4. The essay answer depends on your point of view.

5. First, construct a pedigree to determine whether the trait is inherited as a sex-linked or an autosomal recessive trait, and whether the female could be or is a carrier. The second step is to educate the couple about the risks, if any, that their children may be affected.

6. Since NF is a dominant trait, and there is no evidence of this trait on either side of the family, the birth of the NF child is probably the result of a spontaneous mutation. However, because the phenotype of NF is so variable and some cases may escape detection, members of the immediate family should be examined by a specialist to rule out familial transmission. If it is confirmed that there is no family history, the recurrence risk is low.

7. Simple Mendelian inheritance of a recessive disorder is revealed by the appearance of the phenotype in the male and female progeny of unaffected individuals. The major clues for identifying an autosomal dominant disorder with Mendelian inheritance are that the phenotype tends to appear in every generation of the pedigree and that affected fathers and mothers transmit the phenotype to both sons and daughters.

8.

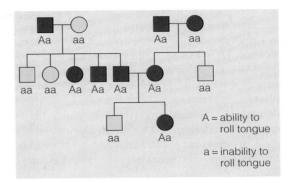

9. If we let the allele causing PKU be p and the normal allele be P, then the sister and the brother of the woman and the man, respectively must have been pp. In order to produce these affected individuals, all four grandparents must have been heterozygous normal. The pedigree can be summarized as:

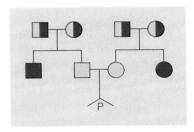

The only way the man and woman can have a PKU child is if both of them are heterozygotes, since they do not have the disease. Both the grandparental matings are simple Mendelian monohybrid crosses expected to produce progeny in the following proportions:

¼ - PP - Normal
½ - Pp - Normal
¼ - pp - PKU

We know that the man and the woman are normal, so the probability of either being a heterozygote is ⅔, because within the P− classes, ⅔ are Pp and ⅓ are PP. The probability of both the man and the woman being heterozygotes is ⅔ × ⅔ = ⁴⁄₉. If they are both heterozygous, then one-quarter of their children would have PKU, so the probability that their first child will have PKU is ¼, and the total probability of their being heterozygous and of their first child having PKU is ⁴⁄₉ × ¼ = ⁴⁄₃₆ or ⅑.

5' flanking region A nucleotide region adjacent to the 5' end of a gene that contains regulatory sequences.

ABO groups Three alleles of a gene on human chromosome 9 that specify the presence and/or identity of certain molecules on the surface of red blood cells.

Acquired immunodeficiency syndrome (AIDS) An infectious disease characterized by infection with human immunodeficiency virus (HIV) and the loss of T4 helper lymphocytes, causing an inability to mount an immune response.

Acrocentric A chromosome with the centromere placed very close to, but not at, one end.

Adenine and guanine Purine nitrogenous bases found in nucleic acids.

Affect Pertaining to mood or feelings.

Alkaptonuria A relatively benign autosomal recessive genetic disorder associated with the excretion of high levels of homogentisic acid.

Allele One of the possible alternative forms of a gene, usually distinguished from other alleles by its phenotypic effects.

Allele expansion Increase in gene size caused by an increase in the number of trinucleotide sequences.

Allele frequency The percentage of all alleles of a given gene that are represented by a specific allele.

Allergens Antigens that provoke an immune response.

Alpha thalassemia Genetic disorder associated with an imbalance in the ratio of alpha and beta globin caused by reduced or absent synthesis of alpha globin.

Alzheimer disease A heterogeneous condition associated with the development of brain lesions, personality changes, and degeneration of intellect. Genetic forms are associated with loci on chromosomes 14, 19, and 21.

Ames test A bioassay developed by Bruce Ames and his colleagues for identifying mutagenic compounds.

Amino group A chemical group (NH_2) found in amino acids and at one end of a polypeptide chain.

Amniocentesis A method of sampling the fluid surrounding the developing fetus by inserting a hollow needle and withdrawing suspended fetal cells and fluid. Used in diagnosing fetal genetic and developmental disorders; usually performed in the 16th week of pregnancy.

Anaphase A stage in mitosis during which the centromeres split and the daughter chromosomes begin to separate.

Anaphylaxis A severe allergic response in which histamine is released into the circulatory system.

Aneuploidy A chromosome number that is not an exact multiple of the haploid set.

Ankylosing spondylitis An autoimmune disease that produces an arthritic condition of the spine; associated with the HLA allele B27.

Anthropological genetics The union of population genetics and anthropology to study the effects of culture on gene frequencies.

Antibody A class of proteins produced by plasma cells that couple or bind specifically to the class of proteins that stimulate the immune response.

Antibody-mediated immunity Immune reaction that protects primarily against invading viruses and bacteria by means of antibodies produced by plasma cells.

Anticipation Onset of a genetic disorder at earlier ages and with increasing severity in successive generations.

Anticodon loop The region of a tRNA molecule that contains the three-base sequence (known as the anticodon) that pairs with a complementary sequence (known as a codon) in an mRNA molecule.

Antigen A foreign molecule or cell that stimulates the production of antibodies.

Antigenic determinant The site on an antigen to which an antibody binds, forming an antigen-antibody complex.

Assortative mating Reproduction in which mate selection is not at random but instead is based on physical, cultural, or religious grounds.

Assortment The random distribution of members of homologous chromosome pairs during meiosis.

Autosomes Chromosomes other than the sex chromosomes. In humans, chromosomes 1-22 are autosomes.

B cells White blood cells that originate in bone marrow and mature in the bone marrow.

Bacteriophage A virus that infects bacterial cells. Genetically modified bacteriophages are used as cloning vectors.

Beta thalassemia Genetic disorder associated with an imbalance in the ratio of alpha and beta globin caused by reduced or absent synthesis of beta globin.

Biometrics The application of statistical methods to problems in biological sciences.

Bipolar disorder An emotional disorder characterized by mood swings that vary between manic activity and depression.

Blastocyst The developmental stage at which the embryo implants into the uterine wall.

Blood type One of the classes into which blood can be separated based on the presence or absence of certain antigens.

B-memory cells Long-lived B cells produced after exposure to an antigen that play an important role in secondary immunity.

Camptodactyly A dominant human genetic trait that is expressed as immobile, bent little fingers.

Cap A modified base (guanine nucleotide) that is attached to the 5′ end of eukaryotic mRNA molecules.

Carboxyl group A chemical group (COOH) found in amino acids and at one end of a polypeptide chain.

Cell cycle The sequence of events that takes place between successive mitotic divisions.

Cell furrow A constriction of the cell membrane that forms at the point of cytoplasmic cleavage during cell division.

Cell-mediated immunity Immune reaction mediated by T cells that is directed against body cells that have been infected by viruses or bacteria.

Centromere A region of a chromosome to which fibers attach during cell division. Location of a centromere gives a chromosome its characteristic shape.

Charcot-Marie-Tooth disease A heritable form of progressive muscle weakness and atrophy. One form, CMT-1, can be produced by mutation at any of three loci.

Chiasmata (singular: chiasma) The crossing of nonsister chromatid strands seen in the first meiotic prophase. Chiasmata represent the structural evidence for crossing over.

Chorion A membrane outside and surrounding the amnion, from which projections known as villi extend to the uterine wall, forming the placenta.

Chorionic villus sampling (CVS) A method of sampling fetal chorionic cells by inserting a catheter through the vagina or abdominal wall into the uterus. Used in diagnosing biochemical and cytogenetic defects in the embryo. Usually performed in the 8th or 9th week of pregnancy.

Chromatid One of the strands of a longitudinally divided chromosome, joined by a single centromere to its sister chromatid.

Chromatin The component material of chromosomes, visible as clumps or threads in the nuclei examined under a microscope.

Chromosome theory of inheritance The theory that genes are carried on chromosomes and that the behavior of chromosomes during meiosis is the physical explanation for Mendel's observations on the segregation and independent assortment of genes.

Chromosomes The thread-like structures in the nucleus that carry genetic information.

Clinodactyly An autosomal dominant trait that produces a bent finger.

Clones Genetically identical organisms, cells, or molecules all derived from a single ancestor. Cloning is the method used to produce such clones.

Codominance Full phenotypic expression of both members of a gene pair in the heterozygous condition.

Codon A triplet of bases in messenger RNA that encodes the information for the insertion of a specific amino acid in a protein.

Color blindness Defective color vision caused by reduction or absence of visual pigments. There are three forms: red, green, and blue blindness.

Complement system A chemical defense system that kills microorganisms directly, supplements the inflammatory response, and works with (complements) the immune system.

Concordance Agreement between traits exhibited by both members of a twin pair.

Consanguineous matings Matings between two individuals who share a common ancestor in the preceding two or three generations.

Conservative replication An early model of DNA replication that results in one daughter molecule consisting of old strands, and one consisting of newly synthesized strands.

Constant region (c) The region of an H or L chain closer to the C-terminus that is invariant within a given class of antibody.

Continuous variation A distribution of phenotypic characters from one extreme to another in an overlapping, or continuous, fashion.

Correlation coefficient A measure of the degree to which variables vary together.

Covalent bond A chemical bond that results from electron sharing between atoms. Covalent bonds are formed and broken during chemical reactions.

Cri-du-chat syndrome A deletion of the short arm of chromosome 5 associated with an array of congenital malformations, the most characteristic of which is an infant cry that resembles a mewing cat.

Crossing over The process of exchanging parts between homologous chromosomes during meiosis; produces new combinations of genetic information.

C-terminus The end of a polypeptide or protein that has a free carboxyl group.

Cystic fibrosis A fatal recessive genetic disorder, common in the U.S. white population, associated with abnormal secretions of the exocrine glands.

Cytokinesis The process of cytoplasmic division that accompanies cell division.

Cytosine, thymine, and uracil Pyrimidine nitrogenous bases found in nucleic acids.

Cytoskeleton A system of protein microfilaments and microtubules that allows a cell to have a characteristic shape.

Cytotoxic or killer T cells T cells that destroy body cells infected by viruses or bacteria. Can also directly attack viruses, bacteria, cancer cells, and cells of transplanted organs.

Deletion A chromosomal aberration in which a segment of a chromosome is deleted or missing.

Deoxyribonucleic acid (DNA) A molecule consisting of antiparallel strands of polynucleotides that is the primary carrier of genetic information.

Deoxyribose and ribose Pentose sugars found in nucleic acids. Deoxyribose is found in DNA, ribose in RNA.

Dermatoglyphics The study of the skin ridges on the fingers, palms, toes, and soles.

Dihybrid cross A mating between two individuals who are heterozygous at two loci (e.g., BbCc × BbCc).

Diploid The condition in which each chromosome is represented twice, as a member of a homologous pair.

Discontinuous variation Phenotypes that fall into two or more distinct, nonoverlapping classes.

Dispermy Fertilization of a haploid egg by two haploid sperm, forming a triploid zygote.

Dizygotic (DZ) twins Twins derived from two separate and nearly simultaneous fertilization events, each involving one egg and one sperm. Such twins share, on average, 50% of their genes.

DNA polymerase An enzyme that catalyzes the synthesis of DNA using a template DNA strand and nucleotides.

DNA replication The process of DNA synthesis.

DNA restriction fragment A segment of a longer DNA molecule produced by the action of a restriction endonuclease.

DNA sequencing A technique for determining the nucleotide sequence of a fragment of DNA.

Dominant The trait expressed in the F_1 (or heterozygous) condition.

Dosage compensation A mechanism that regulates the expression of sex-linked gene products.

Duplication A chromosomal aberration in which a segment of a chromosome is repeated and therefore is present in more than one copy within the chromosome.

Endoplasmic reticulum (ER) A system of cytoplasmic membranes arranged into sheets and channels that functions in transport of gene products.

Environmental variance The phenotypic variance of a trait in a population that is attributed to exposure to differences in the environment by members of the population.

Epidemiology The study of the factors that control the presence, absence, or frequency of a disease.

Epigenesis The idea that an organism develops by the appearance and growth of new structures. Opposed to preformationism, which holds that development is the growth of structures already present in the egg.

Essential amino acids Amino acids that cannot be synthesized in the body and must be supplied in the diet.

Eugenics The attempt to improve the human species by selective breeding.

Eukaryote An organism composed of one or more cells that contain membrane-bound nuclei and that undergo mitosis and meiosis.

Evolution The appearance of new plant and animal species from pre-existing species.

Exons DNA sequences that are transcribed and joined to other exons during mRNA processing, and are translated into the amino acid sequence of a protein.

Expressivity The range of phenotypes resulting from a given genotype.

Familial adenomatus polyposis (FAP) An autosomal dominant condition associated with the development of growths known as polyps in the colon. These polyps often develop into malignant growths, causing cancer of the colon and/or rectum.

Familial hypercholesterolemia An autosomal dominant genetic condition associated with defective or absent LDL receptors, which function in cholesterol metabolism. Affected individuals are at increased risk for cardiovascular disease.

Fertilization The fusion of two gametes to produce a zygote.

Fetal alcohol syndrome A constellation of birth defects caused by maternal drinking during pregnancy.

Fitness A measure of the relative survival and reproductive success of a given individual or genotype.

Fluorescent *in situ* hybridization (FISH) A method of mapping DNA sequences to metaphase chromosomes using probes labeled with fluorescent dyes.

Founder effects Gene frequencies established by chance in a population that is started by a small number of individuals (perhaps only a fertilized female).

Fragile X An X chromosome that carries a nonstaining gap, or break, at band q27. Associated with mental retardation in hemizygous males.

Frameshift mutations Mutational events in which one to three bases are added to or removed from DNA, causing a shift in the codon reading frame.

Free radical An unstable and highly reactive molecule resulting from the interaction of ionizing radiation with water.

Friedreich ataxia An autosomal recessive disorder associated with progressive degeneration of the brain, spinal cord, and some peripheral nerves. Onset usually occurs in childhood and results in early death.

Fructosuria An autosomal recessive condition associated with the inability to metabolize the sugar fructose, which accumulates in the blood and urine.

Galactosemia An autosomal recessive trait associated with the inability to metabolize the sugar galactose. Left untreated, high levels of galactose-1-phosphate accumulate, causing cataracts and mental retardation.

Gamete A haploid reproductive cell, such as the egg or sperm.

Gene The fundamental unit of heredity.

Gene pool The set of genetic information carried by the members of a sexually reproducing organism.

Genetic counseling Process by which genetic counselors analyze the genetic risk within families and present the family with available options to avoid or reduce risks.

Genetic drift The random fluctuations of gene frequencies from generation to generation that take place in small populations.

Genetic equilibrium The situation when the frequency of alleles for a given gene remain constant from generation to generation.

Genetic goitrous cretinism A hereditary disorder in which the failure to synthesize a needed hormone produces physical and mental abnormalities.

Genetic library In recombinant DNA technology, a collection of clones that contains all the genetic information in an individual. Also known as a gene bank.

Genetic map The arrangement and distance between genes on a chromosome, deduced from studies of genetic recombination.

Genetics The scientific study of heredity.

Genetic screening The systematic search for individuals of certain genotypes.

Genetic variance The phenotypic variance of a trait in a population that is attributed to genotypic differences.

Genome The set of genes carried by an individual.

Genomic imprinting Phenomenon in which the expression of a gene depends on whether it is inherited from the mother or the father. Also known as genetic or parental imprinting.

Genotype The specific genetic constitution of an organism.

Golgi apparatus Membranous organelles composed of a series of flattened sacs. They sort, modify, and package proteins synthesized in the ER.

Gonads The male and female reproductive organs that produce gametes.

Haploid The condition in which each chromosome is represented once, in an unpaired condition.

Haplotype A set of closely linked genes that tend to be inherited together, as with the HLA complex.

Hardy-Weinberg Law The statement that allele frequencies and genotype frequencies will remain constant from generation to generation when the population meets certain assumptions.

Helper T cells A type of lymphocyte that stimulates the production of antibodies by B cells when an antigen is present.

Hemizygous A gene present in a single dose on the X chromosome that is expressed in males in both the recessive and dominant condition.

Hemoglobinopathies Disorders of hemoglobin synthesis and function.

Hemoglobin variants Alpha and beta globins with variant amino acid sequences.

Hemolytic disease of the newborn (HDN) A condition that results from Rh incompatibility and is characterized by jaundice, anemia, and an enlarged liver and spleen. Also known as erythroblastosis fetalis.

Hereditarianism The idea that all human traits are determined solely by the genotype, ignoring the contribution of the environment.

Hereditary nonpolyposis colon cancer A form of colon cancer associated with genetic instability of microsatellites.

Heritability An expression of how much of the observed variation in a phenotype is due to differences in genotype.

Heterogametic The production of gametes that contain different kinds of sex chromosomes. In humans, males produce gametes that contain X or Y chromosomes.

Heterozygous Carrying two different alleles for one or more genes.

Histones Small DNA-binding proteins that function in the coiling of DNA to produce the structure of chromosomes.

Hominid A member of the family *Hominidae*, which includes bipedal primates such as *Homo sapiens*.

Hominoid A member of the primate superfamily *Hominoidea*, including the gibbons, great apes, and humans.

Homogametic The production of gametes that contain only one kind of sex chromosome. In humans, all gametes produced by females contain only an X chromosome.

Homologues Members of a chromosome pair.

Homozygous Having identical alleles for one or more genes.

Homunculus The preformed, miniature individual imagined by preformationists to be contained in the sperm or egg.

Huntington disease An autosomal dominant genetic disorder characterized by involuntary movements of the limbs, mental deterioration, and death within 15 years of onset. Symptoms appear between 30 and 50 years of age.

Hydrogen bond A weak chemical bonding force that holds polynucleotide chains together in DNA.

Hypophosphatemia An X-linked dominant disorder. Those affected have low phosphate levels in blood, and skeletal deformaties.

Immunoglobulins The five classes of proteins to which antibodies belong.

Inborn error of metabolism The concept advanced by Archibald Garrod that many genetic traits are the result of alterations in biochemical pathways.

Inbreeding Production of offspring by related parents.

Incest Sexual relations between parents and children or between brothers and sisters.

Incomplete dominance Failure of a dominant phenotype to be expressed in the heterozygous condition. Such heterozygotes have a phenotype that is intermediate between those of the homozygous forms.

Independent assortment The random distribution of genes into gametes during meiosis.

Inflammatory response The body's reaction to invading microorganisms.

Inner cell mass A cluster of cells in the blastocyst that gives rise to the body of the embryo.

Intelligence quotient (IQ) A score derived from standardized tests that is calculated by dividing the individual's mental age (determined by the test) by his or her chronological age, and multiplying the quotient by 100.

Interphase The period of time in the cell cycle between mitotic divisions.

Introns Sequences present in some genes that are transcribed, but removed during processing, and therefore are not present in mRNA.

Inversion A chromosomal aberration in which the order of a chromosome segment has been rotated 180 degrees from its usual orientation.

***In vitro* fertilization (IVF)** A procedure in which gametes are fertilized in a dish in the laboratory, and the resulting zygote is implanted in the uterus for development.

Karyotype The chromosome complement of a cell line or a person, photographed at metaphase and arranged in a standard sequence.

Klinefelter syndrome Aneuploidy of the sex chromosomes resulting in a male with an XXY chromosome constitution.

Leptin A hormone produced by fat cells that signals the brain and ovary.

Lesch-Nyhan syndrome An X-linked recessive condition associated with a defect in purine metabolism that causes an overproduction of uric acid.

Leukemia A form of cancer associated with uncontrolled growth of leukocytes (white blood cells) or their precursors.

Linkage A condition in which two or more genes do not show independent assortment; rather, they tend to be inherited together. Such genes are located on the same chromosome. By measuring the degree of recombination between such genes, the distance between them can be determined.

Lipoproteins Particles with protein and phospholipid coats that transport cholesterol and other lipids in the bloodstream.

Locus The position occupied by a gene on a chromosome.

Lod (log of the odds) method A probability technique used to determine whether genes are linked.

Lymphocytes White blood cells that arise in bone marrow and mediate the immune response.

Lyon hypothesis The proposal that dosage compensation in mammalian females is accomplished by the random inactivation of one of the two X chromosomes.

Lysosomes Membrane-enclosed organelles containing digestive enzymes.

Macrophages Large, white blood cells that are phagocytic and involved in mounting an immune response.

Marfan syndrome An autosomal dominant genetic disorder that affects the skeletal system, the cardiovascular system, and the eyes.

Mast cells Cells that synthesize and release histamine during an allergic response, or during an inflammatory response.

Meiosis The process of cell division during which one cycle of chromosome replication is followed by two successive cell divisions to produce four haploid cells.

Menkes kinky-hair disease An X-linked recessive disorder of copper metabolism causing neurological impairment, progressive failure of the nervous system, and death in early childhood.

Messenger RNA (mRNA) A single-stranded complementary copy of the base sequence in a DNA molecule that constitutes a gene.

Metabolism The sum of all biochemical reactions by which living organisms generate and use energy.

Metacentric A chromosome with a centrally placed centromere.

Metaphase A stage in mitosis during which the chromosomes move and arrange themselves near the middle of the cell.

Metaphase plate The cluster of chromosomes aligned at the equator of the cell during mitosis.

Missense mutation A mutation that causes the substitution of one amino acid for another in a protein.

Mitochondria (singular: mitochondrion) Membrane-bound organelles present in the cytoplasm of all eukaryotic cells. They are the sites of energy production within cells.

Mitosis Form of cell division that produces two cells, each with the same complement of chromosomes as the parent cell.

Molecule A structure composed of two or more atoms held together by chemical bonds.

Monocytes White blood cells that clean up viruses, bacteria, and fungi and dispose of dead cells and debris at the end of the inflammatory response.

Monohybrid cross A mating between individuals who are each heterozygous at a given locus (e.g., Bb × Bb).

Monosomy A condition in which one member of a chromosome pair is missing; having one less than the diploid number $(2n - 1)$.

Monozygotic (MZ) twins Twins derived from a single fertilization event involving one egg and one sperm; such twins are genetically identical.

Mood A sustained emotion that influences perception of the world.

Mood disorders A group of behavior disorders associated with manic and/or depressive syndromes.

Mosaic An individual composed of two or more cell types of different genetic or chromosomal constitution. In this case, both cell lines originate from the same zygote.

Müllerian inhibiting hormone (MIH) A hormone produced by the developing testis that causes the breakdown of the Müllerian ducts in the embryo.

Multifactorial traits Traits that result from the interaction of one or more environmental factors and two or more genes.

Multiple alleles Genes with more than two alleles have multiple alleles.

Muscular dystrophy A group of genetic diseases associated with progressive degeneration of muscles. Two of these, Duchenne and Becker muscular dystrophy, are inherited as X-linked, allelic, recessive traits.

Mutation rate The number of events producing mutated alleles per locus/per generation.

Natural selection The differential reproduction shown by some members of a population that is the result of differences in fitness.

Nitrogen-containing base A purine or pyrimidine that is a component of nucleotides.

Nondisjunction The failure of homologous chromosomes to properly separate during meiosis or mitosis.

Nonhistone proteins The array of proteins other than histones that are complexed with DNA in chromosomes.

Nonsense mutation A mutation that changes an amino-acid-specifying codon to one of the three termination codons.

N-terminus The end of a polypeptide or protein that has a free amino group.

Nucleolus (plural: nucleoli) A nuclear region that functions in the synthesis and assembly of ribosomes.

Nucleosome A bead-like structure composed of histones wrapped by DNA.

Nucleotides The basic building blocks of DNA and RNA. Each nucleotide consists of a base, a phosphate, and a sugar.

Nucleotide substitutions Mutations that involve substitutions, insertions, or deletions of one or more nucleotides in a DNA molecule.

Nucleus The membrane-bounded organelle present in most eukaryotic cells; contains the chromosomes.

Oncogene A gene that induces or continues uncontrolled cell proliferation.

One gene-one enzyme hypothesis The idea that individual genes control the synthesis and therefore the activity of a single enzyme. This idea provides the link between the gene and the phenotype.

One gene-one polypeptide hypothesis A refinement of the one gene-one enzyme hypothesis made necessary by the discovery that some proteins are composed of subunits encoded by different genes.

Oogonia Mitotically active cells that produce primary oocytes.

Ootid The haploid cell produced by meiosis that will become the functional gamete.

Organelle A cytoplasmic structure having a specialized function.

Ovaries The female gonads; they produce ova and female hormones.

Ovulation The release of an egg (ova) from the ovary.

Palindrome A word, phrase, or sentence that reads the same in both directions. Applied to a sequence of base pairs in DNA that reads the same in the 5′ to 3′ direction on complementary strands of DNA. Many recognition sites for restriction enzymes are palindromic sequences.

Pangenesis A discarded theory of heredity that postulated the existence of pangenes, small particles from all parts of the body that concentrated in the gametes, passing traits from generation to generation and blending the traits of the parents in the offspring.

Pedigree analysis Use of family history to determine how a trait is inherited, and to determine risk factors for family members.

Pedigree chart A diagram listing the members and ancestral relationships in a family; used in the study of human heredity.

Penetrance The probability that a disease phenotype will appear when a disease-related genotype is present.

Pentose sugar A five-carbon sugar molecule found in nucleic acids.

Pentosuria A relatively benign genetic disorder of sugar metabolism characterized by the accumulation of xylulose in the blood and urine.

Peptide bond A chemical link between the carboxyl group of one amino acid and the amino group of another amino acid.

Phenotype The genetically controlled, observable properties of an organism.

Phenylketonuria (PKU) An autosomal recessive disorder of amino acid metabolism that results in mental retardation if untreated.

Philadelphia chromosome An abnormal chromosome produced by an exchange of portions of the long arms of chromosome 9 and 22.

Plasma cells Cells produced by mitotic division of B cells that synthesize and secrete antibodies.

Plasmids Extrachromosomal DNA molecules found naturally in bacterial cells. Modified plasmids are used as cloning vectors or vehicles.

Pleiotropy The appearance of several apparently unrelated phenotypic effects caused by a single gene.

Polar body A cell produced in the first or second division in female meiosis that contains little cytoplasm and will not function as a gamete.

Polygenic trait A phenotype resulting from the action of two or more genes.

Polymerase chain reaction (PCR) A method for amplifying DNA segments that uses cycles of denaturation, annealing to primers, and DNA-polymerase directed DNA synthesis.

Polymorphism The occurrence of two or more genotypes in a population in frequencies that cannot be accounted for by mutation alone.

Polypeptide A polymer made of amino acids joined together by peptide bonds.

Polyploidy A chromosome number that is a multiple of the normal diploid chromosome set.

Polyps Growths attached to the substrate by small stalks. Commonly found in the nose, rectum, and uterus.

Population A local group of organisms belonging to a single species, sharing a common gene pool; also called a deme.

Porphyria A genetic disorder inherited as a dominant trait that leads to intermittent attacks of pain and dementia, with symptoms first appearing in adulthood.

Positional cloning Identification and cloning of a gene responsible for a genetic disorder that begins with no information about the gene or the function of the gene product.

Prader-Willi syndrome A deletion of a small segment of the long arm of chromosome 15 that produces a syndrome characterized by uncontrolled eating and obesity.

Preformationism The idea that an organism develops by the growth of structures already present in the egg; in other words, the egg (or sperm) already contains a completely formed organism (the homunculus) that merely grows larger in the course of development.

Preimplantation testing Testing for a genetic disorder in an early embryo; testing is done by removing a single cell from the embryo.

Pre-mRNA The original transcript from a DNA strand, converted to messenger RNA (mRNA) molecules by removal of certain sequences, and addition of others.

Prenatal testing Testing to determine the presence of a genetic disorder in an embryo or fetus; commonly done by amniocentesis or chorionic villus sampling.

Presymptomatic testing Genetic testing for adult-onset disorders; testing can be done at any time before symptoms appear.

Primary oocytes Cells in the ovary that undergo meiosis.

Primary spermatocytes Cells in the testis that undergo meiosis.

Primary structure The amino acid sequence in a polypeptide chain.

Prion An infectious protein that is the cause of several disorders, including Creutzfeldt-Jakob syndrome and mad-cow disease.

Proband First affected family member seeking medical attention.

Probe A labeled nucleic acid used to identify a complementary region in a clone or genome.

Product The specific chemical compound that is the result of enzyme action. In biochemical pathways, a compound can serve as the product of one reaction and the substrate for the next reaction.

Progeria A rare autosomal recessive genetic trait in humans, associated with premature aging and early death.

Prokaryote An organism whose cells lack membrane-bound nuclei with true chromosomes. Cell division is usually by binary fission.

Promoter A region of a DNA molecule to which RNA polymerase binds and initiates transcription.

Promutagen A nonmutagenic compound that is a metabolic precursor to a mutagen.

Prophase A stage in mitosis during which the chromosomes become visible and split longitudinally except at the centromere.

Proto-oncogene A gene that normally controls cell division and may become a cancer gene (oncogene) by mutation.

Pseudogene A gene that closely resembles a gene at another locus, but is nonfunctional because of changes in its base sequences that prevent transcription or translation.

Pseudohermaphroditism An autosomal recessive genetic condition that causes XY individuals to develop the phenotypic sex of females, but change to a male phenotype at puberty.

Purine A class of double-ringed organic bases found in nucleic acids.

Pyrimidines A class of single-ringed organic bases found in nucleic acids.

Quaternary structure Structure formed by the interaction of two or more polypeptide chains in a protein.

R group A term used to indicate the position of an unspecified group in a chemical structure.

Radiation The process by which electromagnetic energy travels through space or a medium such as air.

Recessive The trait unexpressed in the F_1 but reexpressed in some members of the F_2 generation.

Reciprocal translocation A chromosomal aberration resulting in a positional change of a chromosome segment. This changes the arrangement of genes, but not the number of genes.

Recombinant DNA technology Technique for joining DNA from two or more different organisms to produce hybrid, or recombined, DNA molecules.

Recombination theory The idea that functional antibody genes are created by the recombination of DNA segments during B-cell maturation.

Regression to the mean In a polygenic system, the tendency of offspring of parents with extreme differences in phenotype to exhibit a phenotype that is the average of the two parental phenotypes.

Restriction enzymes Enzymes that recognize a specific base sequence in a DNA molecule and cleave or nick the DNA at that site.

Restriction fragment length polymorphism (RFLP) Variations in the length of DNA fragments generated by a restriction endonuclease. Inherited in a codominant fashion, RFLPs are used as markers for specific chromosomes or genes.

Retinoblastoma A malignant tumor of the eye that arises in the retinal cells, usually occurring in children, with a frequency of 1 in 20,000. Associated with a deletion on the long arm of chromosome 13.

Retrovirus Viruses that use RNA as a genetic material. During the virus life cycle, the RNA is transcribed into DNA. The name retrovirus symbolizes this backward order of transcription.

Ribonucleic acid (RNA) A nucleic acid molecule that contains the pyrimidine uracil and the sugar ribose. The several forms of RNA function in gene expression.

Ribosomal RNA (rRNA) A component of the cellular organelles known as ribosomes.

Ribosomes Cytoplasmic particles composed of two subunits that are the site of gene product synthesis.

RNA polymerase An enzyme that catalyzes the formation of an RNA polynucleotide chain using a template DNA strand and ribonucleotides.

Robertsonian translocation Breakage in the short arms of acrocentric chromosomes followed by fusion of the long parts into a single chromosome.

Sarcoma A cancer of connective tissue. One type of sarcoma in chickens is associated with the retrovirus known as the Rous sarcoma virus.

Schizophrenia A behavioral disorder characterized by disordered thought processes and withdrawal from reality. Genetic and environmental factors are involved in this disease.

Secondary immunity Resistance to an antigen the second time it appears, due to T and B memory cells. The second response is faster, larger, and lasts longer than the first.

Secondary oocyte The haploid cell produced by meiosis that will become a functional gamete.

Secondary structure The pleated or helical structure in a protein molecule that is brought about by the formation of bonds between amino acids.

Segregation The separation of members of a gene pair from each other during gamete formation.

Semen A mixture of sperm and various glandular secretions.

Semiconservative replication A model of DNA replication that results in each daughter molecule containing one old strand and one newly synthesized strand. DNA replicates in this fashion.

Sense mutation A mutation that changes a termination codon into one that codes for an amino acid. Such mutations produce elongated proteins.

Severe combined immunodeficiency disease (SCID) A disease characterized by the complete lack of ability to mount an immune response; inherited as an X-linked recessive and in another form as an autosomal recessive trait.

Sex chromosomes The chromosomes involved in sex determination. In humans, the X and Y chromosomes are the sex chromosomes.

Sex-influenced genes Loci that produce a phenotype that is conditioned by the sex of the individual.

Sex-limited genes Loci that produce a phenotype that is produced in only one sex.

Sex ratio The relative proportion of males and females belonging to a specific age group in a population.

Sexual dimorphism The presence of morphological traits that characterize males and females.

Sickle cell anemia A recessive genetic disorder associated with an abnormal type of hemoglobin, a blood transport protein.

Sickle cell trait The symptoms shown by those heterozygous for sickle cell anemia.

Sister chromatids Two chromatids joined by a common centromere. Each chromatid carries identical genetic information.

Southern blot A method for transferring DNA fragments from a gel to a membrane filter, developed by Edward Southern for use in hybridization experiments.

Sperm Male haploid gametes produced by morphological transformation of spermatids.

Spermatids The four haploid cells produced by meiotic division of a primary spermatocyte.

Spermatogenesis The process of sperm production, including meiosis and the cellular events of sperm formation.

Spermatogonia Mitotically active cells in the gonads of males that give rise to primary spermatocytes.

SRY A gene called the sex-determining region of the Y, located near the end of the short arm of the Y chromosome, that plays a major role in causing the undifferentiated gonad to develop into a testis.

Start codon or initiator codon A codon present in mRNA that signals the location for translation to begin. The codon AUG functions as an initiator codon.

Stem cells Cells in bone marrow that produce lymphocytes by mitotic division.

Stop codons Codons present in mRNA that signal the end of a growing polypeptide chain. UAA, UGA, and UAG function as stop codons.

Submetacentric A chromosome with a centromere placed closer to one end than the other.

Substrate The specific chemical compound that is acted upon by an enzyme.

Suppressor T cells T cells that slow or stop the immune response of B cells and other T cells.

Synapsis The pairing of homologous chromosomes during prophase I of meiosis.

T cells White blood cells that originate in bone marrow and undergo maturation in the thymus gland.

Telocentric A chromosome with the centromere located at one end.

Telophase The last stage of mitosis, during which division of the cytoplasm occurs, the chromosomes of the daughter cells disperse, and the nucleus reforms.

Template The single-stranded DNA that serves to specify the nucleotide sequence of a newly synthesized polynucleotide strand.

Teratogen Any physical or chemical agent that brings about an increase in congenital malformations.

Tertiary structure The three-dimensional structure of a protein molecule brought about by folding on itself.

Testes The male gonads; they produce sperm and male hormones.

Testicular feminization An X-linked genetic trait that causes XY individuals to develop into phenotypic females.

Testosterone A steroid hormone produced by the testis; the male sex hormone.

Tetraploidy A chromosome number that is four times the haploid number, having four copies of all autosomes and four sex chromosomes.

Thymine dimer A molecular lesion in which chemical bonds form between a pair of adjacent thymine bases in a DNA molecule.

Tourette syndrome An autosomal dominant behavioral disorder characterized by motor and vocal tics and inappropriate language. Genetic components are suggested by family studies showing increased risk for relatives of affected individuals.

Transcription Transfer of genetic information from the base sequence of DNA to the base sequence of RNA brought about by RNA synthesis.

Transfer RNA (tRNA) A small RNA molecule that contains a binding site for a specific type of amino acid and a three-base segment known as an anticodon that recognizes a specific base sequence in messenger RNA.

Transformation The process of transferring genetic information between cells by means of DNA molecules.

Transforming factor The molecular agent of transformation: DNA.

Translation The process of converting the base sequence in an RNA molecule into the linear sequence of amino acids in a protein.

Translocation A chromosomal aberration in which a chromosome segment is transferred to another, nonhomologous chromosome.

Trinucleotide repeats A form of mutation associated with the expansion in copy number of a nucleotide triplet in or near a gene.

Triploidy A chromosome number that is three times the haploid number, having three copies of all autosomes and three sex chromosomes.

Trisomy A condition in which one chromosome is present in three copies while all others are diploid; having one more than the diploid number ($2n + 1$).

Trisomy 13 The presence of an extra copy of chromosome 13 that produces a distinct set of congenital abnormalities resulting in Patau syndrome.

Trisomy 18 The presence of an extra copy of chromosome 18 that results in a clinically distinct set of invariably lethal abnormalities known as Edwards syndrome.

Trisomy 21 An aneuploidy involving the presence of an extra copy of chromosome 21, resulting in Down syndrome.

Trophoblast The outer layer of cells in the blastocyst that gives rise to the membranes surrounding the embryo.

Tubal ligation A contraceptive procedure in women in which the oviducts are cut, preventing ova from reaching the uterus.

Tumor suppressor gene A gene that normally functions to suppress cell division.

Turner syndrome A monosomy of the X chromosome (45,X) that results in female sterility.

Uniparental disomy A condition in which both copies of a chromosome are inherited from a single parent.

Unipolar disorder An emotional disorder characterized by prolonged periods of deep depression.

Vaccine A preparation containing dead or weakened pathogens that elicit an immune response when injected into the body.

Variable-number tandem repeats (VNTRs) Short nucleotide sequences, repeated in tandem, that are clustered at many sites in the genome. The number of repeats at homologous loci is variable.

Vasectomy A contraceptive procedure in men in which the vas deferens is cut and sealed to prevent the transport of sperm.

Vector A self-replicating DNA molecule used to transfer foreign DNA segments between host cells.

Werner syndrome A genetic trait in humans that causes aging to accelerate in adolescence, leading to death by about age 50.

X-linkage The pattern of inheritance that results from genes located on the X chromosome.

X-linked agammaglobulinemia (XLA) A rare, sex-linked, recessive trait characterized by the total absence of immunoglobulins and B cells.

XYY karyotype Aneuploidy of the sex chromosomes resulting in a male with an XYY chromosome constitution. Such males are disproportionately represented in penal institutions.

Yeast artificial chromosome (YAC) A cloning vector with telomeres and a centromere that can accommodate large DNA inserts, and that uses the eukaryote, yeast, as a host cell.

Y-linked Genes located only on the Y chromosome.

Zygote The diploid cell resulting from the union of a male haploid gamete and a female haploid gamete.

INDEX

A

Abelson oncogene *c-abl*, 344
ABO blood types, 64–65, 366, 409, 415–417, 421, 425–426, 432
Aborigines, 436–438
Abortions, chromosome abnormalities in spontaneous, 158–159
Acatalasemia, 459
Acheulian tools, 444
Achondroplasia, 87, 426–427
　frequency of, 427
　mutation rates for, 270
Acquired immunodeficiency syndrome (AIDS), 92, 321. *See also* Human immunodeficiency virus (HIV)
　attack of, on immune system, 355–356, 374
　screening programs for, 452, 457
Acrocentric chromosomes, 22–23
Acrosome, 173
Actin, 232
Active site, 232
Active transport, 17
Acute myeloblastic leukemia, 344
Additive model for polygenic inheritance, 114–115
Adenine, 203
Adenosine deaminase (ADA), 322, 372
　gene therapy for deficiency in, 328
Adenylate kinase, 428
Adoption studies, 401. *See also* Twin studies in behavior genetics, 382
Adrenogenital syndrome, 459
Adrenoleukodystrophy, 92, 312
Adult polycystic kidney disease (*See under* polycystic. . .), 87
Adult screening, 452
Aeschylus, 3
Affective disorders, 390
Affects, 390
Age
　and gene expression, 97–99
　maternal
　　as recommendation for amniocentesis, 141
　　as risk factor for trisomy, 148–149, 164
　paternal, as risk factor for trisomy, 149
Aggressive behavior and brain metabolism, 389–390
Agriculture, transition to, 445–446
AIDS. *See* Acquired immunodeficiency syndrome (AIDS); Human immunodeficiency virus (HIV)
Albinism, 66–67, 79–80, 264, 418, 435
Alcohol consumption during pregnancy, 180–181

Alcoholism, 397–398
　genetic influence on, 398
Alexei (Russia), 94, 316
Alias, Aikarakudy, 403–404
Alkapton, 217
Alkaptonuria, 218, 240, 243, 435
Alleles, 57, 63
　codominant, 65
　differences between populations, 437–440
　expansion of, 278
　　and anticipation, 279
　frequencies, 410
　　calculating, 412–413
　　　Hardy-Weinberg Law to calculate, 426
　　　human activity as force in changing, 431–436
　　measuring, 410–411
　generation of new, by, 425–427
　multiple, 64
Allergens, 370
Allergies, 370–372
　and bee stings, 373
Alpha-1-antitrypsin, 321–322
　cloning of, 321
Alpha globin genes, 252
Alpha thalassemia, 256
Alpha thalassemia-1, 256
Alpha thalassemia-2, 256
Alzheimer, Alois, 396
Alzheimer disease, 235, 396–397
　and behavior genetics, 401
America, human migration to, 446–448
American Board of Genetic Counseling, 464
American Breeder's Association, 6, 8
Amerinds, 446
Ames, Bruce, 273, 285, 348
Ames test, 273–275, 331, 348
Amino acids
　and composition of protein, 222–223
　essential, 241
　phenylketonuria as defect in metabolism of, 241–243
Amino group, 222
Amniocentesis, 140–141, 315, 317, 459–460, 462
Amyloid beta-protein, 396
Amylopectinosis, 245
Amyotrophic lateral sclerosis, 312
Anaphase, 29–30
Anaphase I, 38
Anaphylaxis, 371–373
Andersen disease, 245
Andreasen, Nancy, 394
Anemia
　Fanconi, 80, 343, 349
　sickle cell, 15, 80, 84–85, 142, 253–254, 266–267, 275–276, 280

Aneuploidy, 143–145
　consequences of, 158–159
　of sex chromosomes, 149–152
Angelman syndrome, 160, 282
Angiotensinogen (AGT), 126
Animal-human transplant, 369
Animals
　cloning methods for, 290
　domestication of, 1–2
　gene transfer in creating new, 324–325
　as models in searching for behavior genes, 383–385
　sex determination in, 181
Aniridia, mutation rates for, 270
Ankylosing spondylitis, 369–370, 457
Ant3 ADP/ATP translocase, 96
Anthropological genetics, 419–420
Anthropology and population structure, 419–420
Antibiotics and protein synthesis, 227
Antibodies, 358
　as molecular weapons against antigens, 361–362
Antibody genes, rearrangement in, 362–364
Antibody-mediated immunity, 355–356, 359–360
Anticipation, 279
Anticodon loop, 224
Anticodon, 224
Antigenic determinant, 362
Antigens, 358
　antibodies as molecular weapons against, 361–362
Antihistamines, 371–372
APC gene, mutations in, 337
Arabs, 436
Aradopsis thaliana, 318
Aristotle, 3, 394
Arteries, cross-section of, 127
Artificial fertilization, 2
Artificial insemination, 178
　and embryo transfer, 179
Artificial insemination by a donor (AID), 457
Asbestos, role of, in cancer, 347
Asians, U.S., 436
Asilomar Conference, 299
Association studies, 392
　in alcoholism, 398
　in schizophrenia, 394
Assortative mating, 433–434
Assortment, 40
Assurnasirpal II, 3
Ataxia telangiectasia (AT), 80, 248, 312, 343
Atherosclerosis, 126, 128
Atherosclerotic plaque, 250
Athrosclerosis susceptibility, 128

Atrial natriuetic factor, 322
Australian aborigines, 437–438
Australopithecus afarensis, 440–442
Australopithecus ramidus, 442
Australopithecus robustus, 442
Autoimmune reactions, 372
Autosomal codominant alleles, 414
Autosomal dominant traits, 85–88
  achondroplasia, 87, 270, 426–427
  adult polycystic kidney disease, 87
  brachydactyly, 66, 87, 411, 414
  camptodactyly, 87, 99
  Crouzon syndrome, 87
  Ehlers-Danlos syndrome, 78, 87
  familial hypercholesterolemia, 87, 128,
    248–250
  Huntington disease, 37, 87, 97, 270, 277,
    304, 312, 381, 388, 401,
    451–452,457, 464, 466, 468
  hypercalcemia, 87
  Marfan syndrome, 75–76, 87–88, 100,
    142, 270
  Nail-patella syndrome, 87, 100–101
  neurofibromatosis, 270–271, 304
  pattern of inheritance in, 85–86
  pedigrees for, 86
  porphyria, 78, 87, 97–99
  and recessive alleles, 414–415
Autosomal recessive traits, 79–85
  albinism, 66–67, 79–80
  ataxia telangiectasia (AT), 80, 248, 312,
    343
  Bloom syndrome, 80, 343
  cystic fibrosis (CF), 19, 80–83, 281, 304,
    312, 317, 323, 416, 418, 431,
    454–455
  Fanconi anemia, 80, 343, 349
  Galactosemia, 80, 243, 245–246, 453, 459
  pedigree for, 81
  phenylketonuria (PKU), 80, 180, 238,
    242–243, 264, 385, 439, 453, 458
  sickle cell anemia, 15, 80, 84–85, 142,
    253–254, 266–267, 275–276, 280,
    317, 418, 428–429, 431,
    435,453–454
  Tay-Sachs disease, 20, 80, 431, 453
  Thalassemia, 80, 255–257, 455, 459
  Xeroderma pigmentosum (XP), 80, 248,
    260–261, 280, 343, 349, 459
Autosomes, 31
Avery, Oswald, 198, 200

B

Background radiation, 272
Bacteria
  nonspecific and specific immune responses
    to invasions by, 365
  transfer of genetic traits in, 198
Bacterial viruses, reproduction in, 199–201
Bacteriophages, 199
BALB/cJ strain, 384
Baldness, pattern, 192
Bantu, 436
Baptiste-Lamarck, Jean, 4
Bardawell, Wadi, 375
Barr, Murray, 190

Barr bodies, 184
  testing for, 184
  and X inactivation, 189–190
Base pairing, 206
  in DNA replication, 211–212
Bateson, William, 6
B cells, 358–359, 361
bcr sequences, 344
Beadle, George, 218, 238
Becker, Elmer, 375
Becker muscular dystrophy, 95, 271
Bee stings, 373
Behavior. *See also* Human behavior
  aggressive, and brain metabolism,
    389–390
  social, and genetics, 395–401
Behavior genetics. *See also* Genetics; Human
    genetics
  aggressiveness and brain metabolism,
    389–390
  animal models in, 383–385
  current status of, 401
  genetic models in, 381–382
  methods of studying, 382–383
  and mood disorders, 390–392
  phenotypes in, 383
  and schizophrenia, 393–395
  single gene effects in, 385–388
  and social behavior, 395–401
Benign tumors, 332
Benzer, Seymour, 400
Berengia, 446
Bergson, Henri, 238–239
Beta globin genes, 252
Beta thalassemia, 256–257, 466–467
Binet, Alfred, 130
Biochemical pathways, 239–240
Bioethics. *See* Ethics
Biology, new theories on, 4
Biometrics, 6
Biotechnology, developments in, 12–13
Biotinidase deficiency, 453
Bipolar disorder, 390–392
Birth, 177
Birth control, 177–178
Birth control pills, 177
Birth defects, 12. *See also* Prenatal testing;
    specific defect
  and chromosome abnormalities, 159
  congenital, 116
  prenatal testing for, 459
Blastocyst, 172, 174
Blastomere, 317
  testing embryonic, 317, 461
Blood, using fetal cells from mother, 142
Blood pressure, 127
Blood pressure cuff, 127
Blood transfusion, 366
Blood types
  ABO, 64–65, 366, 409, 415–417,
    425–426, 432
  cell surface analysis in determining,
    366–368
  MN, 410
  Rh, 366–368
Bloom syndrome, 80, 343
Blue color blindness, 90

B-memory cells, 360
Body mass index (BMI), 123
Bombyx mori, 217
Bond
  covalent, 202
  hydrogen, 202
Boone, Aaron, 118
Boone, Bob, 118
Boone, Bret, 118
Boone, Ray, 118
Booster shots, 365
Boruwalski, Count, 238
Bougainville Island, ABO blood groups on,
    419–421
Boveri, Theodore, 62–63, 197, 331
Bovine growth hormone, recombinant-DNA-
    derived, 322
Brachydactyly, 66, 87, 411, 414
Brain lesions, 395
Brain metabolism and aggressive behavior,
    389–390
BRCA1 gene, 336
BRCA2 gene, 336
Breast cancer, 312, 352
  search for genes in, 335–336
Breeding, selective, 2
Brenner, Sidney, 228
Brown, Louise, 166–167
BST, 322
Buck v. *Bell*, 8–9
Bulbourethral glands, 170
Burkitt's lymphoma, 139, 344
Burt, Randall, 336
Byron, Lord, 392

C

C57BL/6j strain, 384
Caenorhabditis elegans, 318
Callistus, Pope, 189
Callus, 289
Camptodactyly, 87, 99
Canadian Collaborative Study of Predictive
    Testing, 467
Cancer, 330–331
  Ames test in, 348
  breast, 352
    search for genes in, 335–336
  characteristics of, 48
  and chromosomes, 342–344
  colon, 337, 347, 352
    multiple mutation in, 336–338
  development of, in somatic cells, 159
  diet in development of, 347, 349
  electromagnetic fields in, 48
  environment as factor in, 344–349
    and asbestos, 347
    epidemiology in, 345
    genetic models for susceptibility, 349
    occupational hazards, 345–346
  ethnic factor in, 352
  and fragile sites, 162
  genes that predispose to, 332–333
  and genetic instability, 338
  link between mutations and, 331–332, 338
  lung, 162, 346
  and oncogenes, 338–342

research into familial medullary thyroid, 320

role of viruses in, 339–341

skin, 346

and tumor suppressor genes, 333–338

Cap, 222

Carbohydrate metabolism, defects in, 244–246

Carbon disulfide sensitivity, 456

Carbonic anhydrase, 428

Carboxyl group, 222

Cardiovascular disease, genetic and environmental components of, 126–128

Cardiovascular system, effects of Marfan syndrome on, 87–88

Carrier screening, 453

Cass, Glenn, 375

C-banding, 138

cDNA, 298

Cellar, Emanuel, 7

Cellar Act (1965), 7

Cell cycle, 23–29

and tumor suppressor genes, 333–338

Cell division

by meiosis, 33, 36–45

by mitosis, 25

and spinal cord injuries, 24

Cell furrow, 29

Cell-mediated immunity, 355–356, 358–359

Cell membranes, exploring, 98

Cells

cloning of plants from single, 289

diploid, 22

eukaryotic, 15–16

haploid, 22, 38–39

HeLa, 25

life history of, 23–29

metastatic, 332

prokaryotic, 15

sizes of, 16

structures and functions of, 15–21

surface antigens in determining blood types, 366–368

theory of, 4

Cell theory, 50–51

Cellular immune response, T cells in mediating, 364

Cellulase, 322

Centimorgan (cM), 100

Centromere, 22, 210

Cervix, 170, 177

Charcot-Marie-Tooth disease, 312, 386–387

Chargaff, Erwin, 204–206

Chase, Martha, 200

Chédiak-Higashi syndrome, 459

Chemical mutagens, 272–274, 278

Chiasmata, 38

Chi-square test, 60–61

Chloramphenicol, 227

Cholesterol, 126, 128, 249–250

Chorion, 174

Chorionic villus biopsy, 459–460

Chorionic villus sampling (CVS), 140–142, 158, 174, 315

Chromatids, 28

sister, 28

Chromatin, 20, 209

Chromosomal sex, 183

Chromosome banding methods, 137–138

Chromosome instability syndromes, 343

Chromosome painting, 138–139

Chromosomes, 15, 20–21, 25

aberrations in, 139, 156, 267

Burkitt's lymphoma, 139, 344

chronic myelogenous leukemia (CML), 139, 344

leukemia, 343–344

previous child with, as indication for amniocentesis, 141

WAGR syndrome, 139

Wolf-Hirschhorn syndrome, 139

abnormalities in, 158–159

fragile sites, 161–162, 165

uniparental disomy, 159–160

analyzing, 34–35, 137–142

and cancer, 342–344

coiling of DNA with proteins in formation of, 208–210

deletions of

cri du chat syndrome, 154

Prader-Willi syndrome, 12, 154–155, 160, 282

retinoblastoma, 154, 312, 334–335

Wilms tumor, 154, 312

getting cells for studies on, 140–141

human set of, 31–33

identification and classification of, 22

metaphase, 137–138

mitochondrial, 208–209

nuclear, 209–210

presence of balanced rearrangement, as indication for amniocentesis, 141

sex, 31

aneuploidy of, 149–152

structural alterations within, 153–155, 157–158

translocations of, 155–158

variations in number of, 142–148

Chromosome structure, model of, 210

Chromosome theory of inheritance, 62–63, 217

Chronic myelogenous leukemia (CML), 139, 344

Citrullinemia, 459

Cleft lip, 117

Clinodactyly, 428

Cloned libraries, 297–298

finding specific clone in, 298

Cloned sequences, analyzing, 299–302

Clones, definition of, 288

Cloning

of animals, 290

by embryo splitting, 290

by nuclear transfer, 290

of DNA, 294–297

of genes as multistep process, 291–298

of human embryos, 422

of plants from single cells, 289

positional, 312

Club foot, 117

Cockayne syndrome, 280

Codominance, 65

Codominant alleles, 65, 410

Codons, 220, 228, 275

Collagen, 232

structure and function of, 258–259

Collins, Francis, 82, 304

Colon cancer, 337, 347, 352

multiple mutations in, 336–338

Colony stimulating factor, 322

Color blindness, 90–93, 192, 415

pedigree analysis for, 92

Collies, 232

Complement system, 357–358

Compression fossil, 308–309

c-onc, 341

Concordance in twin studies, 121

Condoms, 178

Congenital adrenal hyperplasia, 453

Congenital birth defects, 116

Congenital hip dislocation, 117

Congenital hypothyroidism, 453

Congenital pyloric stenosis, 117

Conjoined twins, 120

Connective tissue, inherited disorders of, 258–260

Consanguineous matings, 68, 434–435

Continuous variation, 110–112

Contraceptive sponges, 178

Coolidge, Calvin, 7

Copper metabolism and Menkes kinky-hair disease, 387–388

Cori disease, 245

Correlation coefficients, 118

Cost-benefit analysis in genetic screening, 457–458

Covalent bond, 202

Craniometry, 130

Cretinism, genetic goitrous, 243

Creutzfeldt-Jakob disease, 235, 397

Crick, Francis, 11, 204, 206, 219, 228, 267, 304

Cri du chat syndrome, 154

Crossing over, 38, 40–43, 101

Crouzon syndrome, 87

CSF2RA, 96

C-terminus, 224

Culture, 435–436

transition to, as adaptation, 445–446

Cummings, Michael R., 400

Cyclic AMP (cAMP), 385

Cyrillic (computer program), 77–78

Cystathioninuria, 459

Cystic fibrosis (CF), 312, 453, 459

allele frequency in, 416, 418

causes of, 19, 80–83, 281

diagnosis of, 19

and gene therapy, 323

and natural selection, 431

mapping by positional cloning, 312

newborn and carrier screening for, 454–455

preimplantation testing in, 317

research in, 304

restriction fragment length polymorphism in mapping genes in, 312

Cystic fibrosis transmembrane conductance regulator (CFTR), 82–83

Cystinuria, 455

Cytogenetic analysis, 138–139

Cytogenetics, 136–162

in analyzing chromosomes and karyotypes, 137–142

and aneuploidy of the sex chromosomes,
149–152
and chromosome abnormalities, 159–162
and consequences of aneuploidy, 158–159
and risks for autosomal trisomy, 148–149
and structural alterations within chromosomes, 153–158
and variations in chromosome number, 142–148
Cytokinesis, 24, 29, 38, 143
Cytoplasm, 17–18
Cytosine, 203
Cytoskeleton, 18
Cytotoxic T cells, 364
Czechs, 436

D

D17S74, 336
Danes, 436
Darwin, Charles, 1, 4, 6, 37, 49–50, 62, 120, 289, 408, 428, 449
Davenport, Charles, 6, 128–129
Davenport, Gertrude, 128–129
Deafness, hereditary, 67
Defective receptors, heritable traits associated with, 250
Defective T-cell immunity, 248
Deletions, 138, 154, 276–277
Del for deletion, 138
Demes, definition of, 409
Deoxyribonucleic acid (DNA), 197. *See also* Recombinant DNA
assessing damage to, 279–280
base pairing in replication of, 211–212
as carrier of genetic information, 197–201
as commercial product, 201
as double helix, 204–207
fingerprinting, 288, 313–315
and flow of genetic information, 220–228
in forming chromosomes, 208–210
mitochondrial, 445
as mutation target, 274–279
polymerase, 211
and polypeptide product of translation, 229–232
and repair mechanisms, 279–280
replication, 211–212
restriction fragments, 310
sequencing, 300, 302
steps in process of cloning, 294–297
storage of genetic information in, 219
structure of, 11, 202–208, 267
vectors as carriers of, 293–294
viruses, 339
Watson-Crick model of, 202, 206–207, 217, 219
Deoxyribose, 204
Depression, 390, 392
Dermal ridges, 119
Dermatoglyphics, 119
Desensitization, 373
Diabetes
gene therapy for, 324
in the Pima Indians, 412
Diabetes insipidus, 250
Diaphragms, 178

Diet. *See also* Food
in control of PKU, 242–243
in development of cancer, 347, 349
and metabolic disorders, 243
Diffusion
facilitated, 17
simple, 17
Dihybrid cross, 57
Dihydroxytestosterone (DHT), 185, 187
Dionne quintuplets, 123
Dipeptide, 224
Diploid cells, 22
Disaccharides, 244–245
Discontinuous variation, 110–111
Disperm, 144
Dizygotic (DZ) (fraternal) twins, 120–121
DNA. *See* Deoxyribonucleic acid (DNA); Recombinant DNA
DNA fingerprinting, 288, 313–315
analysis of, 314–315
applications of, 315
DNA markers, use of, in association studies, 392
Domestication of plants and animals, 1–2
Dominance, 66
incomplete, 65–66
Dominant renal disease, 457
Dominant traits, 54. *See also* autosomal dominant traits
Dosage compensation and X chromosome, 189–192
Double helix structure of DNA, 202
Down, John Langdon, 136–137, 147
Down syndrome (Trisomy 21), 9, 136–137, 145, 147–148, 156–158, 457
and leukemia, 148, 342–343
and maternal age, 148–149, 164
prenatal testing for, 459, 462
Drosophila, learning in, 384–385
Drosophila melanogaster, 207, 318
Duarte allele, 246
Duchenne muscular dystrophy (DMD), 94–95, 107, 271, 312, 430–431
mutation rates for, 270
Duffy blood group, 439
Dup for duplication, 138
Duplication, 138
Dwarfism, 238, 264
Dystrophin, 95

E

*Eco*RI, 292
Edwards, John, 147
Edwards, Robert, 167
Edwards syndrome, 147
Ehlers-Danlos syndrome, 78, 87, 258
Ejaculation, 172
Electromagnetic fields and cancer, 48
Electromagnetic radiation, 271–272
Elephant Man disease, research into, 304
Elizabeth (Queen of England), 316
ELSI, 321
Embryogenesis, 137
events in, 183
Embryo splitting, 123
cloning of animals by, 290

Emphysema, 321
Endocytosis, 17
Endometrium, 170, 174
Endoplasmic reticulum, 18–19, 229
Endoreduplication, 143
Environment
and cancer, 344–349
estimating interaction between genotype and, 117
Environmental variance, 117
Enzymes, 218, 232
and genes, 218–219
Epicanthic fold, 147–148
Epidemiology, 344–345
and links to environmental factors, 345
Epidermal growth factor, 322
Epididymis, 167, 169–170
Epigenesis, 3–4
Epilepsy, 457
Erythrocyte porphyria, 455
Erythropoietin, 322
Escherichia coli, 199, 207, 291–292, 299
Eskaleuts, 446
Eskimos, 436
Essay on the Principle of Population as It Affects the Future Improvement of Society (Malthus), 407
Essential amino acids, 241
Ethical, Legal and Social Implications (ELSI), Human Genome Project and, 321
Ethics. *See also* Legal implications
and genetic testing, 328
and recombinant DNA, 325–326
Eugenics, 6–9, 128, 134, 422, 449
and immigration laws, 7
and Nazi movement, 8–9
and reproductive rights, 8–9
Eugenics Record Office, 6
Eukaryotic cells, 15–16
Events in embryogenesis, 183
Evolution, 37
definition of, 4
mosaic, 442
primate, 440–443
Exocytosis, 17
Exons, 221–222
Expressivity and penetrance, 99
Eye
and colorblindness, 90–93
retinoblastoma in, 334–335

F

Fabrics, Stone Age, 446
Fabry disease, 92, 459
Facilitated diffusion, 17
Facioscapulohumeral dystrophy (FSHD), 312
Familial adenomatous polyposis (FAP), 336–338
Familial hypercholesterolemia, 87, 128, 248–250
Familial medullary thyroid carcinoma, research into, 320
Familial pattern of inheritance, 382
Familial polyposis, 312
Family studies in mood disorders, 394
Fanconi anemia, 80, 343, 349

Fatal hemolytic anemia, 140
FCC gene, 338
Feline leukemia virus, 322
Female athletes and leptin, 126
Female reproductive system, anatomy of, 170–172
Fertilization, 172–173
    artificial, 2
Fetal alcohol syndrome, 180–181
Fetal anomalies, 464
Fetal cells in prenatal diagnosis, 142
Fetoscopy, 459–461
Fetus, 176–177
    teratogens as risk to, 179–181
FHIT gene, 162
Fibroblasts, 140
Fingerprints
    DNA, 288, 313–315
    in estimating heritability, 119–120
First trimester pregnancy, 175–176
Fitness, 428
5′ Flanking region, 222
Flavr-Savr tomatoes, 324–325
Fluorescence *in situ* hybridization (FISH), 313
FMR-1 gene, 278
Fölling, Asbjorn, 238, 264
Food. *See also* Diet
    irradiated, 274
    mutagenic effects of toxins, 285
Food and Drug Administration (FDA)
    banning of PVC in beverage containers, 346
    and food labels, 326
    and irradiated food, 274
    and reproductive screening, 457
Foot blistering, 268
Forbes disease, 245
Ford, Charles, 150
Fossil, compression, 308–309
Founder effects, 427
    and allele frequency, 430
Fragile sites, 161–162
    and cancer, 162
Fragile-X syndrome, 165, 271, 277–278, 312, 381
    and mental retardation, 161–162
Frameshift mutations, 273, 276
Franklin, Rosalind, 204, 206–207
Fraternal twins, 120–121
Frederick the Great, 110
Frederick William I (King of Prussia), 109–110
Free radicals, 272
Friedreich ataxia, 277, 387
Fructosuria, 246
Fucosidosis, 459
Fudenberg, Hugh, 375
Fy alleles, Duffy blood group, 439

G

G1 stage of interphase, 24
G2 phase of interphase, 24
Galactose, 245
Galactosemia, 80, 243, 245–246, 453, 459

Galen, 331
Galileo, 54
Galton, Francis, 6–9, 49–50, 118, 120, 449
Gametes, 144
    definition of, 33
    formation of, 43–44
Ganetzky, Barry S., 400
Garrod, Archibald, 218, 240
Gartler, Stanley, 25
Gaucher disease, 459
G-banding, 137–138
Gemmules, 50
Gene expression, 216–232
    and flow of genetic information, 220–228
    penetrance and expressivity in, 99
    and polypeptide product of translation, 229–232
    proteins in, 217–219
    and sexual phenotype, 188
    and storage of genetic information in DNA, 219
    and temperature, 96–97
    variations in, 96–100
Gene flow
    between populations, 438–440
    tracking in populations, 437–438
Gene gun, 324
Gene pool, 409
Genes, 5, 57, 197, 381
    cloning of, as multistep process, 291–298
    in controlling traits, 110
    effect of, on phenotype, 53
    effect of single, on human behavior, 385–388
    and enzymes, 218–219
    expression of, on X chromosome, 189
    globin, 250–258
    internal organization of, 221–222
    and metabolism, 218
    multiple, 381
    pleiotropic, 100
    predisposal of, to cancer, 332–333
    and proteins, 217–219
    sex-influenced, 192
    sex-limited, 192
    single, 381
    X-linked, 190–192
Gene-specific mutation rates, 269–270
Gene switching, hemoglobin, 257
Genest, Paul, 156
Genetech, 214
Gene therapy, 11
    for adenosine deaminase deficiency, 328
    for genetic disorders, 322–324
    for hemoglobin disorders, 257–258
Genetic clues to obesity, 125–126
Genetic code, 228–229
Genetic barriers, 433
Genetic control of sexual differentiation, 186–188
Genetic counseling, 70, 462–464, 470–471
    function of, 464–466
    reasons for seeking, 464
Genetic crosses, 383–385
Genetic diseases, 15
    alkaptonuria, 218, 240, 243
    Angelman syndrome, 160, 282

catalog of Mendelian, 78–79
cri du chat syndrome, 154
cystic fibrosis, 19, 80–83, 281, 304, 312, 317, 323, 431, 454–455
Down syndrome, 136–137, 145, 147–148, 156–158
Edwards syndrome, 147
Ehlers-Danlos syndrome, 78, 87
familial hypercholesterolemia, 87, 128, 248–250
fructosuria, 246
galactosemia, 80, 243, 245–246
gene therapy in correcting, 322–324
genetic goitrous cretinism, 243
Grieg syndrome, 260
homocystinuria, 243
Huntington disease, 37, 87, 97, 270, 277, 304, 381, 388, 401, 454–452, 466
hypophosphatemia, 89
impact on immune system, 372, 374
Klinefelter syndrome, 151
Lesch-Nyhan syndrome, 92, 246–248, 317, 381
maple syrup urine disease, 243
Marfan syndrome, 75–76, 87–88, 100, 142, 270
and metabolic pathways, 239–248
muscular dystrophy, 92, 94–95, 317
nail-patella syndrome, 87, 100–101
natural selection in frequency of, 430–431
osteogenesis imperfecta, 259–260, 270
Patau syndrome, 146
pentosuria, 246
phenylketonuria, 80, 180, 238, 241–243, 385, 439, 453
Pompe's disease, 20, 245
porphyria, 78, 87, 97–99
Prader-Willi syndrome, 154–155, 160, 282
prenatal and presymptomatic testing for, 315, 317–321
progeria, 31, 37
Roberts syndrome, 29
sickle cell anemia, 15, 80, 84–85, 142, 253–254, 266–267, 275–276, 280
in society, history, and art, 12
Tay-Sachs disease, 20, 80, 431, 453
thalassemias, 80, 255–257
and transcription factors, 260
Turner syndrome, 149–151, 264
tyrosenemia, 243
uniparental disomy, 159–160, 282
Werner syndrome, 31
xeroderma pigmentosum, 80, 248, 260–261, 280, 349
XXX syndrome, 152
XYY syndrome, 151–152
Genetic diversity in human populations, 425–430
Genetic drift, 427–428
Genetic engineering of crop plants, 325
Genetic equilibrium, 414
Genetic goitrous cretinism, 243
Genetic heterogeneity, 281
Genetic information
    deoxyribonucleic acid (DNA) as carrier of, 197–201, 219
    flow of, 220–228

Genetic instability and cancer, 338
Genetic library, 297
Genetic mapping
    impact of recombinant deoxyribonucleic
        acid techniques on, 309–313
    and linkage, 100–102
Genetic models
    of inheritance and behavior, 381–382
    for susceptibility, 349
Genetic Privacy Act, 471
Genetic reservoir, population as, 408–409
Genetics, 6, 62. *See also* Behavior genetics;
        Heredity; Human genetics
    ancient concepts about, 2–3
    current status of, 401
    definition of, 6
    future of, 11–13
    Hardy-Weinberg law in, 414–419
    importance of nucleus in, 21
    pedigree analysis in, 67–68, 70–71
    and social behavior, 395–401
    solving problems in, 69
Genetic screening, 452, 466–468
    carrier, 453–455
    cost-benefit analysis in, 457–458
    ethics in, 328
    impact of, 466–468
    legal implications of, 467
    newborn, 453–455
    occupational, 455–457
    reproductive, 457
Genetic variance, 117
Gene transfer technology, 449
    applications of, 321–325
    creation of new plants and animals by,
        324–325
    legal issues in, 326
Genius and mental illness, 394
Genome, 318
    reversible alterations to, 282–283
    size in various organisms, 207
Genomic imprinting, reversible alterations to
        genome, 282–283
Genomic library, 297
Genomic research, 10
Genotype, 55
    estimating interaction between environ-
        ment and, 117
    frequencies, 412–413
    heterozygous, 57
    homozygous, 57
George III (King of England), 94, 98–99
George IV (King of England), 99
German shepherds, 232
Giemsa staining, 138
Gila River American Indian community,
        European-American admixture in,
        439–440
Glass, William, 428
Globin genes, 250–258
Glovsky, M. Michael, 375
GLP-1 (glucagon-like protein-1), 125
Glucose-6-phosphate dehydrogenase (G6PD),
        191, 428, 430
    deficiency of, 92, 430, 455–456, 459
Glutathiome peroxidase, 428
Glycogen storage disease, 245

Golgi apparatus, 18–20
Golgi complex, relationship between lyso-
        somes and, 20
Gonads, 167
Gould, Hannah, 375
Gout, 455
Greenblatt, R. B., 189
Green blindness, 90, 92
Grieg syndrome, 260
Griffith, Frederick, 198
Guanine, 203
Guthrie test for PKU, 453

H

Hammurabi, 2
Handedness, 135
Haploid cells, 22, 38–39
Haplotype, 368
Hardy, Godfrey, 411
Hardy-Weinberg Law, 411–414
    assumptions for, 412
    and calculating allele frequencies and
        genotype frequencies, 412–413, 426
    and genetic drift, 427
    and genetic equilibrium, 414
    in human genetics, 414–419
        autosomal codominant alleles, 414
        autosomal dominant and recessive alle-
            les, 414–415
        estimating heterozygote frequency, 416,
            418–419
        multiple alleles, 415–416
        X-linked traits, 415
    mate selection in, 433
    and natural selection, 428
Haw-River syndrome, 277
Hayflick limit, 30
Hb C, 254
Hb Makassar, 276
H chains, 361–362
HeLa cells, 25
Helm, Bergitt, 375
Helper T cells, 360, 364
Heme, 251
Hemizygous, 89
Hemoglobin, 232, 250–251
Hemoglobin C, 276
Hemoglobin disorders, gene switching in
        treating, 257–258
Hemoglobin variants, 253, 428
Hemoglobinopathies, 453
Hemolytic disease of newborn (HDN),
        367–368
Hemophilia, 92, 94, 316, 321
    preimplantation testing in, 317
    X-linked form of, 268
Hemophilia A, 92, 189
Hemophilia B, 92
Herbicide resistance, 324
Hepatitis B vaccine, 322
Hereditarianism, 6
Hereditary xanthinuria, 248
Heredity. *See also* Behavior genetics;
        Genetics; Human genetics
    changes in ideas on, 3–6
    description of, 50–51

independent assortment in, 57–62, 283
    parsimony in, 54
    retinoblastoma, 334
    segregation in, 52–57, 283
Heredity deafness, 67
Heredity nonpolyposis colon cancer, 336
Heritability
    fingerprints in estimating, 119–120
    in measuring phenotypic variations,
        117–126
Heritability studies, 132
Hermaphrodites, 187
Herpes virus II, 180
Hershey, Alfred, 200
Heterogametic sex, 182
Heterozygotes, 85
    estimating frequency of, 416, 418–419
Heterozygous genotype, 57
High-density lipoproteins (HDL), 128
Himalayan rabbits, 96–97
Hip dysplasia, German shepherds, 232
Hirschprung disease, research into, 320
Histidine, 241–242
Histones, 201, 209, 232
Hitler, Adolf, 8
HIV. *See* Acquired immunodeficiency syn-
        drome (AIDS); Human immunodeficien-
        cy virus (HIV)
HLA-B27 allele, 369–370
HLA complex (human leucocyte antigen
        complex), 368
HLA matching in organ transplants, 368
HLA system and disease associations,
        369–370
HLA testing, 288
Hodgkin disease, 343
Holmes, Oliver Wendell, 8
Hominids, 440–442
Hominoids, 440
Homocystinuria, 243, 453, 459
Homo erectus, 443–444
Homogametic, 182
Homogentisic acid, 217
Homo habilis, 442–443
Homologues, 22
Homo sapiens, 207, 318, 425
    appearance and spread of, 443–448
Homosexuality, 398–399
Homozygous genotype, 57
Homunculus, 4
Human behavior. *See also* Behavior
    as force in changing allele frequencies,
        431–436
    single-gene effects on, 385–388
Human chorionic gonadotropin (hCG), 174
Human chromosome set, 31–33
Human embryos, cloning of, 422
Human genetics, 76–77
    emergence of, as distinct branch of genet-
        ics, 9–11
    future of, 11–13
    pedigree analysis in, 75–103
Human Genome Project, 12, 304, 318, 466
    DNA sequencing in, 302
    ethical, legal and social implications of,
        321, 401
    future of, 466

goal of, 214
implications of, 320–321
as international effort, 10–11, 102, 318–319
linkage analysis in, 102–103
organisms included in, 318
progress report into, 320
steps in, 319–320
yeast artificial chromosomes (YACs) in, 294
Human growth hormone, 322
Human immunodeficiency virus (HIV), 92, 355, 374, 457. *See also* Acquired immunodeficiency syndrome (AIDS)
detection of, in blood, 321
legislation regarding, 377
Human insulin, 322
Human leucocyte antigen complex, 368
Human populations. *See* Populations
Humans
genetic diversity in, 425–430
and Mendelian inheritance, 66–68, 70–71
migration to America, 446–448
origins of, 440–443
reproduction of
female anatomy, 170–172
male anatomy, 167–170
sex determination in, 181–182
spread of, 443–448
as subject for genetics, 76–77
Huntington, George, 379–380
Huntington disease, 87, 107, 206, 312, 388, 451–452, 457, 464, 468
age as factor in, 97
and behavior genetics, 401
genetic models in describing, 381
mutation in, 37, 270, 277
research into, 304, 388, 466
Huntington's chorea, 379–380. *See also* Huntington disease
H-Y antigen, 96
3-Hydroxyanthranilate oxygenase, 388
Hydrogen bond, 202
Hydroxyurea in treating hemoglobin disorders, 257
Hyperacute rejection, 369
Hypercalcemia, 87
Hypercholesterolemia, 128
Hypersensitivity
to insect stings, 373
to organic isocyanates, 456
Hypertension, 126
Hypophosphatemia, 89
Hypoxanthine-guanine phosphoribosyltransferase (HGPRT), 247

I

I-cell disease, 459
Ichthyosis, 92, 107, 435
Identical twins, 120–121
Immigration Act (1924), 7
Immigration laws and eugenics, 7
Immune response as specific defense against infection, 358–365
Immune system, 355–356
AIDS attack on, 374

disorders of, 370–372, 374
memory function of, 364
protein antibodies in, 232
Immunity
antibody-mediated, 355–356, 358–360
cell-mediated, 355–356, 358–359
Immunodeficiency diseases, 372
Immunoglobulins, 361–362
IgA, 361
IgD, 361
IgE, 361, 373
IgG, 361, 373
IgM, 361
Immunosuppressive drugs, 369
Inborn error of metabolism, 240
Inbreeding, 434
Incest, 434
Incomplete dominance, 65–66
Independent assortment, 57–62, 283
Infertility, 178
Inflammation results, 356–357
Inflammatory response, 356–357
as general reaction, 356–358
Ingram, Vernon, 254, 267
Inheritance
chromosome theory of, 62–63, 217
in colorectal cancer, 336–337
familial pattern of, 382
genetic models of, 381–382
Mendelian, 5–6, 112, 411
mitochondrial, 95–96
pattern of, 85–86
polygenic, 112
quantitative, 112
sex-linked, 88–95
of single trait, 56–57
Y-linked, 88, 95
Initiator codon, 225
Inner cell mass, 174
Insertions, 276–277
Institute of Genomic Research, 235
Insulin, 264
Insulin-dependent diabetes (IDDM), 372
Intelligence, 130–133
correlation of body hair with, 403–404
Intelligence quotient (IQ), 130–133
and race, 132–133
Interferons, 322
Interleukin-2, 322
International Amateur Athletic Federation (IAAF), 184
International athletics, sex testing in, 184
International Olympic Committee (IOC), 184
Interphase, 30
stages in, 24–25
Introns, 221
Inversions, 153
In vitro fertilization (IVF), 166–167, 178–179, 242, 463
Ion channel proteins, 400
IQ and intelligence, 130–133
Irradiated food, 274
Isocitrate dehydrogenase, 428
Isoleucine, 241–242
Itano, Harvey, 266–267
IVF Australia, 453

J

Jacobs, Patricia, 151
Jamison, Kay, 392, 394
Japan, cancer in, 352
Java Man, 443
Jeffreys, Alec, 288, 313
Jenner, Edward, 355
Joan of Arc, 189

K

Kaplan, Nathan O., 10
Karyogram, 32
Karyotypes, 31–33
analyzing, 137–142
making, 34–35
Kearns-Sayre syndrome, 97
Keratin, 232
Killer T cells, 364
King, Mary Claire, 336
Klinefelter syndrome, 151
Knudson, Alfred, 334
Kölreuter, Josef, 111
!Kung, 436
Kunkle, Louis, 95
Kuru, 397

L

Labrador retrievers, 232
Lacks, Henrietta, 25
Lactase, 232
Lactose, 232, 245, 435–436
Lactose absorption, 436
Lamarck, Jean-Baptiste, 37
L chains, 361–362
LDL receptors, 249–250
Leakey, Mary, 425
Leber optic atrophy, 97
Legal implications. *See also* Ethics
of DNA fingerprints, 314–315
of genetic screening, 468
Lejeune, Jérôme, 136–137, 148
Leptin, 125–126
and female athletes, 126
Lesch, M., 246–247
Lesch-Nyhan syndrome, 92, 246–248, 381, 459
preimplantation testing in, 317
Leucine, 241–242
Leukemia
acute myeloblastic, 344
and chromosome aberrations, 343–344
chronic myelogenous, 139, 344
and Down syndrome, 148, 342–343
Levan, A., 9
Lincoln, Abraham, 75–76, 88, 471
Link, 394
Linkage analysis
of alcoholism, 398
and genetic maps, 100–102
and lod scores, 102–103
LINKMAP, 102
Lipid bilayers, 98
Lipoproteins, 128
Locus, 63

Lod method, 102
   and linkage analysis, 102–103
Longevity, 135
Lou Gehrig's disease, 235
Low-density lipoproteins (LDL), 128, 249
Lucy, 440, 442
Ludwig, Arnold, 394
Lumen, 19
Lung cancer, 162
Lymphocytes, 140, 358
Lyon, Mary, 189–190
Lyon hypothesis, 189–190
Lysine, 241
Lysosomes, 18–20
   relationship between Golgi complex and,
      20

M

Machado-Joseph disease, 277
MacLeod, Colin, 198
Macrophages, 359–360
Mad cow disease, 235, 397
Malaria, relationship between sickle cell ane-
      mia and, 84–85, 134, 428–429, 431,
      435
Male reproductive system, anatomy of,
      167–170
Malthus, Thomas, 406–408
Manic-depressive psychosis, 457
Mannosidosis, 459
Maple syrup urine disease, 243, 453, 459
Marfan, A. B., 87
Marfan syndrome, 75–76, 87–88, 100, 142,
      459, 471
   mutation rates for, 270
Martin-Bell syndrome, 161–162
Massie, Robert, 316
Mast cells, 370
Maternal selection, 149
Mate selection, 433–435
Matings
   assortative, 433–434
   consanguineous, 68, 434–435
McCarty, Maclyn, 198
McKees Rock, 276
McKusick, Victor, 79
Measles virus, 180
Meiosis, 15, 40–43
   cell division by, 33, 36–45
   definition of, 33
   and Mendelian inheritance, 62–63
Meiosis I, 36–39
Meiosis II, 38–39
Melanin, 241
MELAS syndrome, 97
Membrane-attack complex (MAC), 357–358
Memory function of immune system, 364
Memory T cells, 364
Mendel, Gregor, 6, 37, 50, 408
   experimental approach of, 51–52
   and independent assortment, 57–62, 283
   and principle of segregation, 52–57, 283
   and test anxiety, 50
Mendelian inheritance, 112, 411
   in humans, 66–68, 70–71
   and meiosis, 62–63

Menkes kinky-hair disease, 387–388
Mental illness and genius, 394
Mental retardation
   and fragile-X syndrome, 161–162, 165
   X-linked, 389
MERRF syndrome, 97
Metabolic disorders, 237–261
   alkaptonuria, 218, 240, 243
   amylopectinosis, 245
   Andersen disease, 245
   ataxia telangiectasia (AT), 80, 248, 312,
      343
   Cori disease, 245
   defective T-cell immunity, 248
   and dietary management, 243
   Ehlers-Danlos syndrome, 78, 87, 258
   familial hypercholesterolemia, 87, 128,
      248–250
   Forbes disease, 245
   fructosuria, 246
   galactosemia, 80, 243, 245–246, 453, 459
   genetic goitrous cretinism, 243
   and globin genes, 250–258
   glycogen storage disease, 245
   Grieg syndrome, 260
   hereditary xanthinuria, 248
   Lesch-Nyhan syndrome, 92, 246–248,
      381, 459
   metabolic pathways and genetic disorders
      in, 239–248
   and mutations in receptor proteins,
      248–250
   orotic aciduria, 248
   osteogenesis imperfecta (OI), 258–260
   pentosuria, 246
   phenylketonuria (PKU), 80, 180, 238,
      242–243, 264, 385, 439, 453, 458
   Pompe's disease, 20, 245
   role of proteins in, 238–239
   severe combined immunodeficiency
      (SCID), 248, 323, 372–374
   and structural proteins, 258–260
   transcription factors in, 260–261
   Xeroderma pigmentosum (XP), 80, 248,
      260–261, 280, 343, 349, 459
Metabolic pathways, 218
   and genetic disorders, 239–248
Metabolism, 240
   brain, and aggressive behavior, 389–390
   of copper, and Menkes kinky-hair disease,
      387–388
   defects in carbohydrate, 244–246
   and genes, 218
   inborn error of, 240
   inherited diseases of nucleic acid, 246–248
   phenylketonuria as defect in amino acids,
      241–243
   slow alcohol, 456
Metacentric chromosomes, 22
Metaphase, 28, 30
   chromosomes in, 137–138
Metaphase I, 38
Metaphase plate, 28
Metastatic cells, 332
Methemoglobin reductase deficiency, 456
Methionine, 241–242
MIC2, 96

Microcephaly, 435
Microdissection, 317
Micromanipulation in dividing embryos,
      290
Miescher, Frederick, 196–197
Migration
   as evolutionary force, 432–433
   human, 446–448
Miguel, Ann, 375
Minisatellites, 313
Minnesota Twin Project, 399
Miocene, 440
Missense mutations, 275–276
Mitchell, Herschel K., 348
Mitochondria, 18, 20
Mitochondrial chromosome, 208–209
Mitochondrial DNA, 445
   analysis of genetic differences using, 446
   testing for, 316
Mitochondrial inheritance, 95–96
Mitochondrial traits, 97
   Kearns-Sayre syndrome, 97
   Leber optic atrophy, 97
   MELAS syndrome, 97
   MERRF syndrome, 97
   oncocytoma, 97
Mitochondrion, 21
Mitosis, 15, 24
   cell division by, 25
   regulation of, 333–334
   significance of, 30–31
MN blood groups, 410
Molecular level, mutation at, 274–279
Molecules, 18
Mongolism, 147
Monoamine oxidase type A (MAOA), 390
Monocytes, 356
Monohybrid cross, 52
Monosaccharides, 244–245
Monosomy, 143, 146, 149, 158
Monozygotic (MZ) (identical) twins,
      120–121
Mood disorders, 390–392
Moods, 390
Morula, 174
Mosaic evolution, 442
Mosaics, 190–192
mRNA, 220, 298
Müllerian duct system, 183–185
Müllerian inhibiting hormone (MIH),
      184–185, 187
Multifactorial threshold traits
   cleft lip, 117
   club foot, 117
   congenital hip dislocation, 117
   congenital pyloric stenosis, 117
Multifactorial traits, 110, 116–117,
      126–133, 135
   handedness, 135
   longevity, 135
   and twin studies, 120
Multiple alleles, 64, 415–416
Multiple endocrine neoplasia, research into,
      320
Multiple genes, 381
Multiple myeloma, 344
Multiple sclerosis, 235

Mus musculus, 207, 318
Muscular dystrophy, 92, 94–95, 107, 285
  Becker, 95, 271
  Duchenne, 94–95, 107, 270–271, 312, 430–431
  preimplantation testing in, 317
  X-linked, 459
Mutagens
  chemical, 272–274, 285
  radiation as, 271–272
Mutations, 240, 266–283
  definition of, 267
  detecting, 267–269
  and DNA repair mechanisms, 279–280
  factors that influence rate of, 271–274
  frameshift, 273, 276
  link between cancer and, 331–332, 338
  link to genotypes and phenotypes, 280–283
  measuring rates of, 269–271
  missense, 275–276
  at molecular level, 274–279
  nonsense, 276
  and oncogenes, 341–342
  in receptor proteins, 248–250
  sense, 276
Myosin, 232
Myotonic dystrophy (MD), 277–278, 312

N

N-acetyl transferase deficiency, 456
Na-Denes, 446
Nail-patella syndrome, 87, 100–101
Nathans, Daniel, 291
National Institute of Child Health and Human Development, 142
National Organization for Albinism and Hypopigmentation (NOAH), 264
National Sickle Cell Anemia Control Act (1972), 454
National Society of Genetic Counselors, 462
Natural Inheritance (Galton), 6
Natural Science Society, 62
Natural selection, 6, 37, 428–430
  and frequency of human genetic disorders, 430–431
  theory of, 4
Nazi movement and eugenics, 8–9
Neel, James, 9, 267, 412
Nelson-Rees, Walter, 25
Neolithic transition, 445–446
Network of Genetic Medicine, 458
Neurofibromatosis, 270–271
  mutation rates for, 270
  research into, 304
Neurogenetics, 400
Neurospora, 218–219
Neurotransmitters, 389
Newborn screening, 452
  for PKU, 453–455
Nicholas II (Czar of Russia), 94
  DNA analysis into death of, 315–316
Niemann-Pick disease, 459
Nitrous acid, 272
NOAH (New York Online Access to Health), 471

Nondisjunction, 144–145, 149
Nonhistone proteins, 209
Nonsense mutations, 276
Norplant, 177
Novelty seeking, 389
N-terminus, 224
Nuclear chromosomes, 209–210
Nuclear transfer, cloning of animals by, 290
Nucleic acid metabolism, inherited diseases of, 246–248
Nuclein, 197
Nucleolus, 18
Nucleosomes, 209
Nucleotides, 203–204
Nucleotide substitutions, 274–276
Nucleus, 15, 18, 20–21
Nyhan, W. L., 246–247

O

Obesity
  genetic clues to, 125–126
  twins in studying, 122–124
Occupational hazards and cancer risk, 345–346
Occupational Safety and Health Administration, and genetic screening, 468
Occupational screening, 452, 455–457
Ockham's razor, 54
Office of Technology Assessment (OTA) and occupational screening, 456–457
Oldowan tools, 444
Oncocytoma, 97
Oncogenes, 331, 334, 339–341
  and cancer, 338–342
  and mutation, 341–342
Oncolink, 352
One gene-one enzyme hypothesis, 218–219
One gene-one polypeptide hypothesis, 219
Online Mendelian Inheritance in Man (OMIM), 79, 107
Oocytes
  primary, 44–45, 149, 170
  secondary, 44, 170, 172
Oogenesis, 43–45
Oogonia, 44
Ootid, 44
Open-field behavior, 383–385
Opsins, 90–93
Organelles, 15, 18–21
Organ transplant, 368–370
Origin of Species, The (Darwin), 6, 449
Orotic aciduria, 248, 459
Osmosis, 17
Osteogenesis imperfecta (OI), 258–260
  mutation rates for, 270
Osteosarcoma, 334–335
Out-of-Africa hypothesis, 444–445
Ovaries, 167, 170, 172
Oviduct, 170, 172
Ovulation, 170

P

Palindrome, 292
Pangenes, 2

Pangenesis, 2, 4, 50
Parathormone, 250
Parkinson's disease, 235
Parsimony, principle of, 54
Patau syndrome, 146
Paternity, DNA fingerprinting in establishing, 315
Pattern baldness, 192
Pauling, Linus, 9, 251, 254, 266–267
Pearson, Karl, 60, 112
Pedigree, 7
Pedigree analysis, 73–74, 77–78, 382–383
  of color blindness, 92
  and homosexuality, 399–400
  in human genetics, 67–68, 70–71, 75–103
  in schizophrenia, 394
Pedigree chart, 68, 71
  symbols used on, 70
Peking Man, 443
Penetrance and expressivity, 99
Penis, 168–170
Penrose, Lionel, 148
Pentose sugar, 203
Pentosuria, 246
Pepsin, 197
Peptidase, 428
Peptide bond, 224
Personality traits, genetic link to, 389
Phages, 200
Phenotypes, 55, 65
  averaging out, 115–116
  heritability in measuring, 117–126
  mutations in causing, 281–282
  polygenes and variation in, 111–116
Phenotypic sex, 183, 187
Phenylalanine, 232, 238, 241, 385
Phenylalanine hydroxylase, 232
Phenylalanine pathway, metabolic disorders in, 242–243
Phenylketonuria (PKU), 80, 180, 238, 242–243, 264, 385, 439, 453, 458
  diet in controlling, 242–243
  frequency of, 439
  newborn screening for, 453
  and reproduction, 242
  teratogens in, 180
Phenylpyruvic acid, 238
Philadelphia chromosome, 343
Philip (Prince of England), 316
Phosphoglucomutase, 428
Phrenology, 130
Phytohemagglutinin, 34
Pima Indians, 412
Placenta, 177
Plague, 354–355
Plants
  cloning of, from single cell, 289
  domestication of, 1–2
  gene transfer in creating new, 324–325
Plaques, 395
Plasma cell, 360
Plasma membrane, 17–18
Plasmid pBR322, 296
Plasmids, definition of, 293
Pleiotropy, 100
Pneumonia, 198
Poe, Edgar Allan, 392

Polani, Paul, 149–150
Polar bodies, 44
Polycystic kidney disease (PCKD) (or under adult), 87, 312, 318, 464, 466
  mutation rates for, 270
Polydactyly, 146
Polygenes
  and environment, 116–117
  and variation in phenotype, 111–116
Polygenic inheritance, 112
  additive model for, 114–115
Polygenic traits, 110, 381
  skin color as, 128–130
Polymerase chain reaction (PCR), 302–303, 461
  in commercial production of DNA, 201
Polymorphism, 425, 437
Polynucleotides, 204
Polypeptide, 224
  product of translation, 229–232
Polyploidy, 143–144
Polyposis coli, 457
Polyps, 336–337
Polysaccharides, 244
Polyvinyl chloride (PVC), 346
Pompe's disease, 20, 245
Population bottleneck, 427
Populations
  allele differences between, 437–440
  attempts to control growth of, 407–408
  definition of, 409
  density of, 408
  gene flow between, 438–440
  genetic diversity in human, 425–430
  as genetic reservoir, 408–409
  and Hardy-Weinberg law, 411–414
  measuring allele frequencies in, 410–411
  selection and genetic history of, 430
  structure and anthropology, 419–420
  tracking gene flow in, 437–438
Population screening, 452
Porphyria, 78, 87, 97–99
Positional cloning, 311–312
Potsdam Grenadier Guards, 110, 115–116
Potts, Percival, 345
Prader-Willi syndrome, 12, 154–155, 160, 282
Precocious puberty, 192
Predisposition testing, 422
Preformationism, 3–4
Pregnancy
  alcohol consumption during, 180–181
  first trimester of, 175–176
  Rh factor in, 367–368
  second trimester of, 176
  third trimester of, 177, 181
Preimplantation testing in genetic disorders, 317
Premature heart disease, 128
Prenatal testing, 315, 317–321, 452, 458–460
  amniocentesis, 140–141, 459, 462
  chorionic villus sampling (CVS), 140–142, 158, 174, 315
  embryonic blastomeres, 461
  fetoscopy, 459–461
  future directions of, 466

risks and problems associated with, 140–142, 462
  ultrasonography, 459–461
Presymptomatic screening, 318
  in genetic disorders, 315, 317–318
Primary oocytes, 44–45, 149, 170
Primary sex ratio, 182
Primary spermatocytes, 43
Primary structure of proteins, 230
Primate evolution, 440–443
Prions, 235, 397
Proband, 68
Probe, 298
Procollagen, 259
Products, 239–240
Progeria, 30–31, 37, 459
Prokaryotic cells, 15
Promoter, 220
Promutagens, 272
Prophase, 28, 30
Prostate gland, 170
Proteins, 217
  antibiotics and synthesis of, 227
  biological functions of, 230
  coiling of, with DNA in forming chromosomes, 208–210
  defects in transport, 250–258
  DNA technology in manufacture of recombinant, 321–322
  functions of, 230, 232
  and genes, 217–219
  ion channel, 400
  levels of structure in, 230
  mutations in receptor, 248–250
  nonhistone, 209
  processing, sorting, 229
  role of, 238–239
  structural, 258–260
  trans-membrane, 98
  zinc-finger, 260
Proto-oncogene gene products, cellular localization of, 341
Proto-oncogenes, 334, 341
Pseudoalpha-1, 252
Pseudocholinesterase variants, 455
Pseudogenes, 252
Pseudohermaphroditism, 188
Pseudohypoparathyroidism, 250
Pseudozeta, 252
PTC nontaster, 456
Puberty, precocious, 192
Public health screening, 452
Punnett, R. C., 56
Punnett square, 56, 59, 62, 115
Purine, 203
Puromycin, 227
Pyrimidine, 203

Q

Q-banding, 138
Quadruplets, 123
Quantitative inheritance, 112
Quantitative trait loci (QTLs), 135
Quaternary structure of proteins, 230
Quinolonic acid, 388
Quintuplets, 123

R

Race, and IQ, 132–133
Radiation as mutagen, 271–272
ras protein, 341
Rasputin, 94
R-banding, 138
Receptor proteins, mutations in, 248–250
Recessive allele frequencies, measurement of, 411
Recessiveness, 66
Recessive traits, 54. See also Autosomal recessive traits
Reciprocal translocations, 155, 157–158
Recombinant DNA molecules, 293
Recombinant DNA technology, 201. See also Deoxyribonucleic acid (DNA)
  applications of
    in cancer research, 335–336
    in cytogenetics, 149
    in DNA fingerprinting, 313–314
    in genetic research, 88
    in genetic testing and genetic counseling, 463, 466
    in gene transfer technology, 321–325
    in growth hormone manufacturer, 264
    in Human Genome Project, 318–321
    in insulin manufacturer, 264
    in in-vitro fertilization, 167
    in obesity research, 125–126
    in prenatal testing, 315, 317–318, 459
    in preparing vaccines, 365
    in sex testing, 184
  Asilomar conference on, 299
  assessing risks and need for control in research, 299
  definition of, 291
  ethical questions about, 325–326
  and polymerase chain reaction, 302–303
  products made by, 322
  in protein manufacture, 321–322
  techniques, 10–11, 336
    impact on genetic mapping, 309–313
    in preparing vaccines, 365
Recombinant vector, 294, 296
Recombination, 40
Recombination theory, 363
Rectal cancer, 337
Red blindness, 90, 92
Red blood cells, 84–85, 140
  lysis of, 366
Red-green blindness, 90–91
Regional continuity hypothesis, 445
Regression to the mean, 115–116
Reproduction and development, 166–192
  and dosage compensation and the X chromosome, 189–192
  in humans, 167–177
  and sex determination, 181–183
  and sex differentiation, 183–188
  and sex-influenced and sex-limited traits, 192
  and technology, 177–179
  teratogens in, 179–181
Reproductive rights and eugenics, 8–9
Reproductive screening, 457
Respiratory system in immune response, 356

Restriction enzymes, 291–293
Restriction fragment length polymorphism (RFLP), 310–311
  in behavior analysis, 382–383, 399
  in diagnosing colon cancer, 337
  in mapping genes, 311–312
    at chromosomal level, 312–313
    on Y chromosome, 445
RET gene, 320
Retina, 91
Retinoblastoma, 154, 312, 334–335
  mutation rates for, 270
Retroviruses, 339
  in gene therapy, 322–323
Reverse transcriptase, 374
R group, 222–223
Rh blood types, 366–368
Ribonucleic acid (RNA), 224
  messenger, 222, 224, 228
  polymerase, 220
  ribosomal, 224
  structure of, 207–208
  transfer, 224–228
Ribonucleic acid (RNA) viruses, 339
Ribose, 204
Ribosomes, 18–19
RNA transcript, 220
Robertsonian translocations, 155, 157–158
Roberts syndrome, 29
Role of Genetic Testing in the Prevention of Occupational Disease, The, 456–457
Romanov, Nicholas. See Nicholas II
Rose, Michael, 37
Rote, Neal, 98
Rous, Peyton, 339
Rous sarcoma, 339–341
Rowley, Janet, 344
RU-486, 178

S

6-phosphogluconate dehydrogenase, 428
Saccharomyces cerevisiae, 207, 318
Sandhoff disease, 459
Sarcoma, 339
Satellited Y, 156
Schizophrenia, 390, 393–395
  lifetime risk for, 395
Schleiden, 4
Schwann, 4
Scrotum, 170
Secondary oocytes, 44–45, 170, 172
Secondary sex ratio, 182
Secondary structure of proteins, 230
Second trimester pregnancy, 176
Secretory vesicles, 18
Seegmiller, J. E., 247
Segregation, principle of, 52–57, 283
Segregation studies, 401
Selection and allele frequency, 430
Selective breeding, 1–2, 134, 232, 289
Self-fertilization, 51
Semen, 170
Semiconservative replication, 211
Seminal vesicles, 170
Seminiferous tubules, 167–168
Sense mutations, 276

Sephardic Jews, 436
Serum alpha-1-antitrypsin deficiency, 456
Severe combined immunodeficiency (SCID), 248, 323, 372–374
Severe hip dislocation, 457
Sex accessory glands, 170
Sex chromosomes, 31, 181–182
Sex determination
  in animals, 181
  in humans, 181–182
  sex differentiation following, 183–186
Sex-determining region of Y, 184
Sex differentiation following sex determination, 183–186
Sex-influenced genes, 192
Sex-limited genes, 192
Sex-linked inheritance, 88–95
Sex ratio, 182–183
Sex testing in international athletics, 184
Sexual differentiation, genetic control of, 186–188
Sexual dimorphism, 181
Sexually transmitted diseases, 178
Sexual orientation, 398–401
  role of genetics in, 398
Sexual phenotype and gene expression, 188
Shock, anaphylactic, 371–373
Siamese cats, 96–97
Siamese twins, 120
Siberia, migration from, 446
Sickle cell anemia, 9, 80, 100, 253–254, 266–267
  as autosomal recessive trait, 418
  mutation in, 15, 142, 275–276, 280
  prenatal diagnosis for, 317
  relationship between malaria and, 84–85, 134, 428–429, 431, 435
  screening for, 467–468
Sickle cell trait, 267, 454–456
  newborn and carrier screening for, 453–454
Silk, as a gene product, 216–217
  fibroin, 219
Simple diffusion, 17
Sister chromatids, 28
Skin color as polygenic trait, 128–130
Skin grafts, 368
Slow alcohol metabolism, 456
Smallpox, 355
Smith, Hamilton, 291
Social behavior and genetics, 395–401
Solokof, Nicolai, 316
Southern, Edward, 299
Southern blotting technique, 299–301, 310
  in prenatal diagnosis for sickle cell anemia, 317
Sperm, 43, 167, 169–170, 172
Spermatids, 43
Spermatocytes, 167
  primary, 43
Spermatogenesis, 43–44
Spermatogonia, 43
Spermicide, 178
Spina bifida, 459
Spinal and bulbar muscular atrophy, 277
Spinal cord injuries and cell division, 24
Spinneret, 216

Spinocerebellar ataxia type 1, 277
Sporadic retinoblastoma, 334
SRY, role in sex determination, 184–186
S (synthesis) phase of interphase, 24
Stanford-Binet intelligence tests, 130
Staphylococcus aureus in toxic shock syndrome, 355
Start codon, 225
Stem cells, 358
Steptoe, Patrick, 167
Sterilization laws, 8–9
Stern, Wilhelm, 130–131
Steward, Charles, 289
Stop codon, 225
Streptococcus pneumoniae, 198
Streptomycin, 227
Structural proteins, 258–260
Sturtevant, Alfred, 100
Submetacentric chromosomes, 22
Substance abuse, and genetics, 403
Substrates, 239–240
Sulfite oxidase deficiency, 455
Sumner, James, 239
Superoxide dismutase, 322
Suppressor T cells, 364
Surrogate motherhood, 178, 242
Susceptibility, genetic models for, 349
Sutton, Walter, 62–63, 197
SV40 (simian virus 40), 339
Synapse, 391
Synapsis, 37
Synaptic transmission, 391
Syndactyly, 144
Systemic lupus erythematosus (SLE), 372

T

Tatum, Edward, 218, 238
Tawny hair, in aborigines, 427–438
Tay-Sachs disease, 20, 80, 431, 457, 459
  screening for, 453, 467
T cells, 358–359
  cytotoxic, 364
  helper, 360, 364
  in mediating cellular immune response, 364
  memory, 364
  rejection of, 369
  suppressor, 364
TDF/SRY, 96, 184–186
Telocentric chromosomes, 22
Telophase, 29–30
Telophase I, 38
Temperature and gene expression, 96–97
Template, 211
Tennyson, Alfred Lord, 394
Teratogens, 179–181
Tertiary structure of proteins, 230
Test anxiety and Gregor Mendel, 50
Testerone, 185
Testes, 167–168, 170
Testicular feminization, 187, 189, 250
Testis-determining factor (TDF), 95
Testosterone, 184
Tetracyclines, 227
Tetraploid, 143
Tetraploidy, 144
T for translocation, 138

Thalassemia, 80, 255–257, 455, 459
Thalassemias, 253
Thalidomide, 179–181
Third trimester pregnancy, 177, 181
Threonine, 241
Threshold effects, 116–117
Thucydides, 354
Thymine, 203
Thymine dimers, 280
Tijo, J. H., 9
Tissue plasminogen activator, 322
Tobacco plant, 207
Tooth, H. H., 386
Tortoiseshell cat, 191
Tourette, Georges Gille de la, 395
Tourette syndrome, 395
Toxic shock syndrome, 355
Traits
    dominant, 54
        autosomal, 85–88
    gene control of, 110
    inheritance of single, 56–57
    multifactorial, 110, 116–117, 126–133
    polygenic, 110, 128–130, 381
    recessive, 54
        autosomal, 79–85
Transcription, 220–221
    factors and genetic disorders, 260
Transfer RNAs (tRNAs), 224
Transferrins, 428
Transformation, 198
Transforming factor, 198
Transforming principle, 198
Transgenic organisms
    and animal-human transplants, 369
    corn, 324
    pigs, 324–325
    sheep, 321
    tomatoes, 324–325
Translation, 220, 222, 220–228
    polypeptide product of, 229–232
Translocation chromosome, 156
Translocations, 155
    reciprocal, 155, 157–158
    Robertsonian, 155, 157–158
Trans-membrane proteins, 98
Transport proteins, defects in, 250–258
Trinucleotide repeats, 277–278
Tripeptide, 224
Triplets, 123
Triploid, 143
Triploidy, 144, 158
Trisomy, 143, 146–149
    risks for autosomal, 148–149
Trisomy 13, 146
Trisomy 16, 158–159
Trisomy 18, 147
Trisomy 21, 147–148, 156, 159. *See also*
    Down syndrome
Tristan da Cuhna, population history for,
    427–428
tRNA, 227
Trophoblast, 174
Tryptophan, 241–242
Tsui, Lap-Chee, 82
Tuareg people, 436–437
Tubal ligation, 177

Tumors, 332. *See also* Cancer
    benign, 332
Tumor suppressor genes and cell cycle,
    333–338
Turner, Henry, 150
Turner syndrome, 149–151, 264
Twins, 120–121
    and concordance, 121
    conjoined, 120
    dizygotic (DZ) (fraternal), 68, 120–121
    monozygotic (MZ) (identical), 68,
        120–121, 123
Twin studies, 401
    in behavior genetics, 382–383
    on intelligence quotient, 131–132
    on mood disorders, 392, 394
    and multifactorial traits, 120
    on obesity, 122–124
    on schizophrenia, 394
    on sexual orientation, 398–399
Tyrosenemia, 243
Tyrosine, 232, 241–242

U

Ultrasonography, 459–461
Uniparental disomy, 159–160, 282
Unipolar disorder, 390–392
Uracil, 203, 272
Urease, 239
Urethra, 169–170, 172
Uterine tubes, 172
Uterus, 172, 174

V

Vaccines
    DNA-derrived, 322
    recombinant DNA techniques in prepar-
        ing, 365
Vagina, 170, 172
Valine, 241–242
Van Gogh, Vincent, 392
Variable number tandem repeats (VNTRs)
    in analyzing DNA fingerprints, 314–315
Variable-number tandem repeats (VNTRs),
    313–314
Variance
    environmental, 117
    genetic, 117
Variation
    continuous, 110–112
    discontinuous, 110–111
Vas deferens, 169–170
Vasectomy, 177
Vasopressin receptor, 250
Vectors, 291, 298
    as carriers of DNA, 293–294
    definition of, 293
    recombinant, 294, 296
Venter, J. Craig, 10
v-erb, 341
Victoria (Queen of England), 94, 268–269,
    316
Vinyl chloride, 346
Viruses
    in cancer, 339–341

deoxyribonucleic acid (DNA), 339
reproduction in bacterial, 199–201
ribonucleic acid (RNA), 339
Rous sarcoma, 339–340
Vogelstein, Bert, 10
v-onc genes, 341
Von-Gierke disease, 245
Von Hippel-Landau syndrome, mutation
    rates for, 270
v-src, 341

W

WAGR syndrome, 139
Wallace, Alfred Russel, 4, 408, 428
Walter, Anne, 98
Wambaugh, Joseph, 314
Watson, James, 11, 202, 204, 206, 219, 267,
    304
Watson-Crick model of deoxyribonucleic
    acid, 202, 206–207, 217, 219
Weinberg, Wilhelm, 411
Weismann, August, 197
Werner syndrome, 31, 459
White blood cells, 140, 196, 359
Wilkins, Maurice, 204, 206
William of Ockham, 54
Williams, Marie, 428
Willstätter, R., 239
Wilms tumor, 154, 312
Wilson disease, 455
Wolffian duct system, 183, 185, 187
Wolf-Hirschhorn syndrome, 139
Women, breast cancer in, 335–336
Woolf, Virginia, 392
World Health Organization (WHO), world-
    wide vaccination campaign of, 355

X

X chromosomes, 88, 167, 182
    and dosage compensation, 189–192
    expression of genes on, 189
Xenotransplants, 369
Xeroderma pigmentosum (XP), 80, 248,
    260–261, 280, 343, 349, 435, 459
X inactivation and Barr bodies, 189–190
X-linkage, 88–89, 190–192, 415
X-linked agammaglobulinemia (XLA), 372
X-linked disorders, 141
    Duchenne muscular dystrophy (DMD),
        430–431
X-linked dominant traits, 89–90
    hypophosphatemia, 89
    pedigree for, 90
X-linked mental retardation, 389
X-linked muscular dystrophy, 459
X-linked recessive traits, 90–93
    adrenoleukodystrophy, 92, 312
    color blindness, 90–93, 192
    Fabry disease, 92, 459
    glucose-6-phosphate dehydrogenase
        (G6PD) deficiency, 92, 455–456, 459
    hemophilia, 268, 321
    Hemophilia A, 92, 189
    Hemophilia B, 92
    ichthyosis, 92

Lesch-Nyhan syndrome, 92, 246–248,
    381, 459
muscular dystrophy, 92, 94–95, 317
pedigrees for, 93
X-ray crystallography in DNA analysis,
    204–205
XXX syndrome, 152
Xylitol dehydrogenase, 246
XYY syndrome, 151–152

Y

Y chromosome, 88, 182
Yeast artificial chromosomes (YACs),
    293–294, 298
  in cloning DNA, 296
Y-linked inheritance, 88, 95

Z

Zero population growth, 407–408
Zeta gene, 252
ZFY, 96
Zinc-finger proteins, 260
Zygote, 15, 22, 172, 174

CREDITS

Chapter 1

Opener	©Bios (D. Escartin)/Peter Arnold, Inc.
Figure 1.1	Giraudon/Art Resource, NY
Figure 1.2a	The Metropolitan Museum of Art, Gift of John D. Rockefeller, Jr., 1932
Figure 1.2b	©John D. Cunningham/Visuals Unlimited
Figure 1.3	Nat'l Library of Medicine Essay de dioptrique, Paris 1694, p.230
Figure 1.5	Bettmann Archive
Figure 1.7	Photo courtesy of American Philosophical Association
Figure 1.8	©1990 Custom Medical Stock Photo
Figure 1.9	©UCSFBOR/Science VU
Figure 1.10	©Petit Format/Nestle/Science Source/Photo Researchers, Inc.

Chapter 2

Opener	©Dr. Gopal Murti/Science Photo Library/Photo Researchers, Inc.
Figure 2.4b	©K.G. Murti/Visuals Unlimited
Figure 2.6b	©Bill Longcore/Photo Researchers, Inc.
Figure 2.7a	©Biophoto Associates/Science Source/Photo Researchers, Inc.
Figure 2.7b	©Don W. Fawcett/Visuals Unlimited
Figure 2.7c	©Don W. Fawcett/Visuals Unlimited
Figure 2.8	©Biophoto Associates/Science Source/Photo Researchers, Inc.
Figure 2.11	Photo courtesy of Dr. Andrew S. Bajer, University of Oregon
Figure 2.12b	©Science VU/Visuals Unlimited
Figure 2.14	©Photo R.M.N. Musee du-Louvre, Paris, France
Figure 2.15a	©David M. Phillips/Visuals Unlimited
Figure 2.15b	©David M. Phillips/Visuals Unlimited
Figure 2.16	Printed with permission of Dr. W. Ted Brown and Karen and Ken Sawyer
Figure 2.17	Courtesy of Cytogenetics Laboratory, Loyola University Medical Center, Maywood, Illinois
Figure 2.24a	©Cabisco/Visuals Unlimited

Chapter 3

Opener	©Yoav Levy/Phototake
Figure 3.1a	©James W. Richardson/Visuals Unlimited
Figure 3.1b	©David Sieren/Visuals Unlimited
Figure 3.1c	©R. Calentine/Visuals Unlimited
Figure 3.2	Photo by K. Libal. From Moravske Museum, Bruno
Figure 3.14a-c	©E.R. Degginger/Photo Researchers, Inc.
Figure 3.15	©John Watney/Science Source/Photo Researchers, Inc.

Chapter 4

Opener	©Yoav Levy/Phototake
Figure 4.3	©1991 Patricia Barber, RBP/Custom Medical Stock Photo
Figure 4.7	©Jeff Greenberg/Visuals Unlimited
Figure 4.11a-b	©Stanley Flegler/Visuals Unlimited
Figure 4.13	©Steven E. Sutton/DUOMO
Figure 4.15	©Biophoto Associates/Photo Researchers, Inc.
Figure 4.18a-b	Photo courtesy of Yvonne Alsip
Figure 4.24	©Renee Lynn/Photo Researchers, Inc.
Figure 4.25	Corbis-Bettmann

Chapter 5

Opener	©Mark Burnett/David R. Frazier Photolibrary, Inc.
Figure 5.3a	©Joe McDonald/Visuals Unlimited
Figure 5.3b	©Tim Hauf/Visuals Unlimited
Figure 5.3c	©M. Long/Visuals Unlimited
Figure 5.3d	©Marek Litman/Visuals Unlimited
Figure 5.3e	©Mark D. Cunningham/Visuals Unlimited
Figure 5.12	©Mark E. Gibson/Visuals Unlimited
Figure 5.14	©1996 Wedgworth/Custom Medical Stock Photo
Figure 5.15	John Sholtis, The Rockefeller University, New York, NY
Figure 5.18a	©Cabisco/Visuals Unlimited
Figure 5.18b	©W. Ober/Visuals Unlimited
Figure 5.23	©Science VU/Visuals Unlimited

Chapter 6

Opener	©M. Coleman/Visuals Unlimited
Figure 6.1	Courtesy of Oncor, Inc., Gaithersburg, MD and Dr. Huntington F. Willard, Stanford University, Stanford, CA
Figure 6.4	©SIU/Visuals Unlimited
Figure 6.7	Courtesy of Cytogenetics Laboratory, Loyola University Medical Center, Maywood, Illinois
Figure 6.8	Reproduced by permission of *Pediatrics* Vol. 74, p. 296, copyright 1984. Falix et al. 1984. *Pediatrics* 74: 296-299.
Figure 6.11	Courtesy of Dr. Ira Rosenthal, Dept. of Pediatrics, University of Illinois at Chicago
Figure 6.12a	Courtesy of Cytogenetics Laboratory, Loyola University Medical Center, Maywood, Illinois
Figure 6.12b	Courtesy of Dr. Ira Rosenthal, Dept. of Pediatrics, University of Illinois at Chicago
Figure 6.13a	©Bernd Wittich/Visuals Unlimited
Figure 6.13b	Photo courtesy of Dr. Irene Uchida, Genetic Services, Oshawa General Hospital, Hamilton, Ontario, Canada
Figure 6.16a	Courtesy of Dr. Ira Rosenthal, Dept. of Pediatrics, University of Illinois at Chicago
Figure 6.16b	Photo courtesy of Dr. Irene Uchida, Genetic Services, Oshawa General Hospital, Hamilton, Ontario, Canada
Figure 6.17	From: Weiss, et al., 1982. Monozygotic twins discordant for Ulrich-Turner Syndrome. *A.J. Med. Genet.* 13: 389-399.
Figure 6.18a	©Martin M. Rotker
Figure 6.18b	Photo courtesy of Dr. Irene Uchida, Genetic Services, Oshawa General Hospital, Hamilton, Ontario, Canada

Figure 16.8a	©Science VU/E.R. Lewis, T.E. Everhart, and Y.Y. Zeevi, University of California/Visuals Unlimited
Figure 16.8c	©T. Reese and D.W Fawcett/Visuals Unlimited
Figure 16.9	Photo courtesy of Bettmann Archives

Chapter 17

Opener	©Tim Davis/Tony Stone Images

Chapter 18

Opener	©Paul Hanny/The Gamma Liaison Network
Figure 18.10	©Olivier Martel/Photo Researchers, Inc.
Figure 18.11	Photo courtesy of Peter Weigand
Figure 18.16	Institute of Human Origins
Figure 18.17	Photo courtesy of the Cleveland Museum of Natural History

Figure 18.19	©National Museum of Kenya/Visuals Unlimited
Figure 18.20a	© John D. Cunningham/Visuals Unlimited
Figure 18.20b	Photo courtesy of David Frayer

Chapter 19

Opener	©Louise Lockley/CSIRO/Science Photo Library/Photo Researchers, Inc.
Figure 19.1	©1991 Custom Medical Stock Photo
Figure 19.2	©Carlos Goldin/Science Photo Library/Photo Researchers, Inc.
Figure 19.3	Photo courtesy of Terry and Kerry Lavery
Figure 19.4	©Alexander Tsiarus/Science Source/Photo Researchers, Inc.
Figure 19.5	Photo courtesy of Shelly Cummings